THEORY OF FUNCTIONS
OF A
COMPLEX VARIABLE

THEORY OF FUNCTIONS OF A COMPLEX VARIABLE

SHANTI NARAYAN

*Formerly, Dean of Colleges, Delhi University, Delhi
and Principal, Hans Raj College, Delhi*

Revised by

Dr. P.K. MITTAL
M.Sc., Ph.D.
*Formerly, Head of Mathematics Department
Govt. Post Graduate College
Rishikesh (Uttarakhand)*

S. CHAND
PUBLISHING
empowering minds

S. CHAND & COMPANY PVT. LTD.
(AN ISO 9001 : 2008 COMPANY)
RAM NAGAR, NEW DELHI - 110 055

S. CHAND & COMPANY PVT. LTD.

(An ISO 9001 : 2008 Company)

Head Office: 7361, RAM NAGAR, NEW DELHI - 110 055
Phone: 23672080-81-82, 9899107446, 9911310888 Fax: 91-11-23677446
www.schandpublishing.com; e-mail: helpdesk@schandpublishing.com

Branches

Ahmedabad	:	Ph: 27541965, 27542369, ahmedabad@schandpublishing.com
Bengaluru	:	Ph: 22268048, 22354008, bangalore@schandpublishing.com
Bhopal	:	Ph: 4274723, 4209587, bhopal@schandpublishing.com
Chandigarh	:	Ph: 2725443, 2725446, chandigarh@schandpublishing.com
Chennai	:	Ph. 28410027, 28410058, chennai@schandpublishing.com
Coimbatore	:	Ph: 2323620, 4217136, coimbatore@schandpublishing.com (Marketing Office)
Cuttack	:	Ph: 2332580; 2332581, cuttack@schandpublishing.com
Dehradun	:	Ph: 2711101, 2710861, dehradun@schandpublishing.com
Guwahati	:	Ph: 2738811, 2735640, guwahati@schandpublishing.com
Hyderabad	:	Ph: 27550194, 27550195, hyderabad@schandpublishing.com
Jaipur	:	Ph: 2219175, 2219176, jaipur@schandpublishing.com
Jalandhar	:	Ph: 2401630, 5000630, jalandhar@schandpublishing.com
Kochi	:	Ph: 2378740, 2378207-08, cochin@schandpublishing.com
Kolkata	:	Ph: 22367459, 22373914, kolkata@schandpublishing.com
Lucknow	:	Ph: 4026791, 4065646 lucknow@schandpublishing.com
Mumbai	:	Ph: 22690881, 22610885, mumbai@schandpublishing.com
Nagpur	:	Ph: 6451311, 2720523, 2777666, nagpur@schandpublishing.com
Patna	:	Ph: 2300489, 2302100, patna@schandpublishing.com
Pune	:	Ph: 64017298, pune@schandpublishing.com
Raipur	:	Ph: 2443142, raipur@schandpublishing.com (Marketing Office)
Ranchi	:	Ph: 2361178, ranchi@schandpublishing.com
Siliguri	:	Ph: 2520750, siliguri@schandpublishing.com (Marketing Office)
Visakhapatnam	:	Ph: 2782609 visakhapatnam@schandpublishing.com (Marketing Office)

First Edition 1956
Subsequent Editions and Reprints 1959, 62, 66, 69, 73, 78, 79, 82, 84, 86, 87, 92, 94, 95, 97, 2001, 2005, 2008, 2009; Revised and Enlarged Edition 2010; Reprint 2011, 2012, 2014
Reprint 2016 (Twice)

ISBN : 978-81-219-0639-5   **Code :** 1014C 104

PRINTED IN INDIA
By Nirja Publishers & Printers Pvt. Ltd., 54/3/2, Jindal Paddy Compound, Kashipur Road, Rudrapur-263153, Uttarakhand and published by S. Chand & Company Pvt. Ltd., 7361, Ram Nagar, New Delhi -110 055.

स्नेहमयी

माँ

की स्फूर्तिदायिनी स्मृति में

—शान्ति

PREFACE TO THE NINTH REVISED EDITION

Encouraged by the good response all over to the earlier edition, it is indeed a great pleasure and proud for me to present this revised, enlarged and updated ninth edition of the book after so many reprints. The special feature of this edition is that a large number of new topics have been added' and all the existing chapters have been thoroughly revised to meet the requirements of students and teachers. The feedback received has been incorporated to the extent possible in the present edition.

If the substantial fraction of users of this book feels that it helped them to overcome the difficulties of understanding the subject, my purpose of bringing this edition will be fulfilled.

For taking all pains and interest in the publication of this book, I owe my special gratitude to Mrs. Nirmala Gupta, CMD, M/s. S. Chand & Company Ltd. I would like to express heart felt gratitude to my friend Mr. Naveen Joshi, V.P. (Publishing), without whose continuous encouragement and persuation the present edition may have not reached to your hands. My thanks and admiration go to the talented editorial and production people, under the leadership of Mr. Shishir Bhatnagar, who have done a wonderful job to bring out the book in such a fabulous form. The final tribute and greatest appreciation, however, is reserved for my wife Prabha, without whose persuation the present book may have not reached to your hands.

An all out meticulous care was taken to make the presentation as free of errors as possible but as reviser of the book I owe the entire responsibility for any residual errors of omission or commission that may still be lingering in the text. I heartily welcome any suggestion or criticism from the readers towards the improvement of the text. These will be gratefully acknowledged.

269, Sai Vihar, Veerbhadra Road
Rishikesh (Uttarakhand)

Dr. P. K. Mittal

PREFACE TO THE FIRST EDITION

The book is an outcome of the lectures which the author has given in the University of Delhi during the last several years. It may also be thought of as a companion volume to the author's 'A course of Mathematical Analysis' which deals with functions of Real Variable and which appeared a few years ago.

Taking the aggregate of real numbers, as the basis, Ch. 1 introduces the Algebra and Ch. IV the Usual Topology of the aggregate of complex numbers. Ch. II is concerned with the representation of the aggregate of complex numbers by the Euclidean plane and by a sphere excluding one point thereof. Ch. III has been devoted to a consideration of Bilinear transformations with special emphasis an various invariants for the same, *i.e.,* of properties which remain preserved. Also it is shown how it is advantageously possible to represent the aggregate of complex numbers augmented by an additional number called infinity by a complete sphere or the Euclidean plane to which has been adjoined a *single* point at infinity. Thus this latter plane is different from the projective plane with a Euclidean metric.

Non-linear conformal mappings defined in terms of Elementary Transcendental functions have been studies in Ch. VIII preceded by a systematic development of the Theory of such functions in Ch. VI. The subject of Infinite Series and Power Series has also been developed in Ch. VI to the extent to which it is necessary for the purpose of a rigorous theory of these functions. The concept of an analystic function in a domain in terms of the property of Differentiability has been discussed in Ch. V.

The notion and some of the properties of complex integration have been introduced in Ch. VIII followed by Cauchy theory in Ch. IX . A study of isolated singular points has been made in Ch. X and the same chapter includes also application to the theory of Algebraic equations. The important concepts of Analytic continuation and of the Analytic function *in the large* have also been briefly discussed in this chapter.

Ch. XI is devoted to the application of the Calculus of Residues to the evaluation of real definite integrals and summation of certain types of series. The last Ch. XII is concerned with infinite products, uniform convergence, Mittag-Leffler's theorem on the partial decomposition of Meromorphic functions and Weierstrass's factorisation theorem of Integral functions.

The chief aim of the author has throughout been to present a clear and rigorous account of the subject.

It is very much hoped that, as a result of a careful study of the book, the reader would come to acquire a good appreciation of the important notion of Analytic function in terms of the Power Series approach, Differentiability approach and the Geometric approach and perceive them all as unified

The author takes this opportunity of thanking his friends Dr. M.L. Madan and Dr. Rajinder Singh of the Panjab University who went through a considerable part of the manuscript and helped him to remove a number of slips and obscurities.

The author would gratefully welcome suggestions for improvements and notices of errors.

Hans Raj College, Delhi   **THE AUTHOR**
Nov., 1956

CONTENTS

(xix)

COMPLEX NUMBERS

1.1. Introduction. The concept of imaginary numbers has had its origin in the fact that the solution of the quadratic equation

$$ax^2 + bx + c = 0,$$

leads to the expression

$$\frac{-b \pm \sqrt{(b^2 - 4ac)}}{2a}$$

which is not meaningful when

$$(b^2 - 4ac) < 0,$$

in that the square of no number which had hitherto fore been developed could be negative. In this context, Euler (1707 – 1783) was the first mathematician who introduced the *symbol*, *i*, for $\sqrt{-1}$ with the property, $i^2 = -1$, and accordingly, a root of the equation $x^2 + 1 = 0$. He also called the symbol, *i*, *imaginary*. In contradiction to this, the numbers developed before the advent of the symbol i, came to be called *Real*. Also, a symbol of the form $a + ib$ where a, b are any real numbers is called a *complex number*. The symbol, $i = \sqrt{-1}$ was, however, adjoined to the system of real numbers only naively and for a long time no attempt was made to put the system of complex numbers on a sound logical basis. The only justification for the introduction and continuation of the use of the symbol i, with the property $i^2 = -1$ lay in the fact that a systematic use of the same led to quite a number of interesting results. Also, it was noticed that very often results which were stated in terms of real numbers and which were also demonstrable in terms of the same could as well be comparatively more conveniently established with the use of the symbol i.

As against this, it is also a fact, that an injudicious use of this symbol i often lead to mutually contradictory, and absurd conclusions. In the beginning, however, it was not realised that the imaginary numbers could be introduced in a logically satisfactory manner so as to render, i, a legitimate possession of mathematics and mathematicians and thus rule out the possibilities of contradictions which may otherwise arise. It may also be remembered that the use of the word *imaginary* for $\sqrt{-1}$ only reflects the attitude (relatively to the absence of any logical approach) towards the same at the time it was first introduced. The logically sound basis was only later on provided by Hamilton (1805 – 1865) whose approach was arithmetical and by Gauss (1777 – 1855) whose approach was geometrical. As soon as the system of complex numbers was endowed by Gauss with a geometrical meaning, the system of complex numbers was accepted without any reservation.

In the following parts of the chapter, we shall, *starting with the set of real numbers as known*, define the set of complex numbers and the four fundamental algebraic operations and also establish the basic laws of these operations and thus equip the set of complex numbers with what is known as an *Algebraic Structure*.

1

It will be seen that the motivation for the particular definition of complex numbers and of the algebraic operations is provided by the symbol $a + ib$ and the usual manner in which these symbols were subjected to algebraic manipulation.

1.1.1. Symbols for One Way and Two Way Implications

In the following, as in all mathematics, we shall come across pairs of statements such that if one statement is true then the other is also true. Thus we shall be concerned with pairs of statements P, Q such that the truth of the statement P implies the truth of the statement Q. The fact that the truth of the statement P implies the truth of the statement Q is symbolically expressed as :

$$P \Rightarrow Q.$$

The symbol

$$\text{`}\Rightarrow\text{'}$$

is to be read as

$$\textit{`Implies'}.$$

Sometimes the statements P, Q are such that we have

$$P \Rightarrow Q,$$

as well as

$$Q \Rightarrow P,$$

i.e., the truth of either of the statements P and Q implies the truth of the other.

In this case, we write

$$P \Leftrightarrow Q,$$

so that the symbol

$$\text{`}\Leftrightarrow\text{'}$$

stands for

$$\textit{`Implies and is implied bv'}.$$

For example, we have

ABCD is a parallelogram $\Rightarrow$ AB = CD.

ABCD is a parallelogram $\Leftrightarrow$ AB = CD and BC = AD.

Some set-theoretic consideration. Symbols for the relations 'Belongs to' and 'Is contained in'. A collection is called a set and is said to be defined if there is given a rule such that it is possible, in terms of the rule, to say whether any given object is or is not a member of the set.

If any member a is a member of a set S, we write

$$a \in S$$

and say that a belongs to S.

Also if S_1, S_2 are two sets such that every member of S_1 is also a member of S_2, we write

$$S_1 \subset S_2$$

and say that S_1 is contained in S_2 or that S_1 is a subset of S_2.

1.1.2. Union, Intersection and Complementation of Sets

Union of two sets. If S_1, S_2 are two sets, then the set S will be called the union of S_1 and S_2 if it is defined by the rule that any given object is a member of S if and only if it is a member of the set S_1 or of the set S_2 or of both. This relationship is expressed as

$$S = S_1 \cup S_2.$$

The set S is said to be the union of the sets S_1 and S_2.

Intersection of two sets. A set S is called the intersection of the two sets S_1 and S_2 if it is defined by the rule that a given object belongs to the set S if and only if it belongs to S_1 as well as to S_2. In symbols, we exhibit this relationship as

$$S = S_1 \cap S_2.$$

Also, we say that the set S is the intersection of the sets S_1 and S_2.

In case the sets S_1 and S_2 have no member in common, then their intersection is empty. We find it convenient to have a symbol for a set having no member and the symbol often employed to denote a set having no member is ϕ.

The set ϕ is called **Null** or **Void**.

Thus, if the sets S_1 and S_2 have no common member, we write

$$S_1 \cap S_2 = \phi.$$

The fact of two sets S_1, S_2 having no common member is also expressed by saying that they are disjoint sets.

Complement of a set. Let S be any set and let A be a subset of S. Then, a set is called the complement of the set A relatively to the set S if it is defined by the rule that it consists of those of the members of S which do not belong to A. This complement will be denoted by A'.

Thus, we have

$$S = A \cup A', \phi = A \cap A'.$$

Symbols for 'For all' and 'There exists'. We shall adopt the symbols

$$\forall, \exists$$

to denote

'For all', 'There exists'

respectively.

Functions. Let S and T be two given sets and let f be a rule which associates to each member of S, a member of T. If x denotes a member of S, then the member of T which the rule f associates to x is denoted as $f(x)$.

The rule f is called a function from the set S into the set T and the member $f(x)$ of T is called the *f-image* of x or the *f-value* of x.

Also the set S is called the **domain** of the function f and the set of all those members of T which f associates to different members of S is called the **Range** of the function.

Thus, the range of f is the set $\{f(x) : x \in S\}$.

Surely, the range of the function f is a subset of the set T.

We say that the function f is from the set S **onto** the set T if the range of the function is actually the set T.

Also, we say that the function f is one-one *if it associates different members of the set T to two different members of the set S*. Thus, the function f is one-one if

$$x_1 \neq x_2 \Rightarrow f(x_1) \neq f(x_2).$$

Composites of functions. Let S, T, U be three sets and f, g be two functions such that

$$f \text{ is a function from S into T}$$

and

$$g \text{ is a function from T into U.}$$

We then have a function from S into U denoted by

$$g \circ f$$

and called the **Composite** or the **Resultant** of the function f and g and defined as follows :

$$(g \circ f)(x) = g \{f(x)\} \quad \forall \ x \in S.$$

A Property of Composites

Let f, g, h

be three functions from

$$S \ into \ T, \ T \ into \ U \ and \ U \ into \ V$$

respectively.

We then have the following equality of functions

$$h \circ (g \circ f) = (h \circ g) \circ f,$$

so that we have to show that

$$\{h \circ (g \circ f)\}(x) = \{(h \circ g) \circ f\}(x) \quad \forall \ x \in S.$$

We have

$$\{h \circ (g \circ f)\}(x) = h \{(g \circ f)(x)\}$$
$$= h[g\{f(x)\}]$$
$$\{(h \circ g) \circ f\}(x) = (h \circ g)f(x)$$
$$= h[g\{f(x)\}]$$

Thus, we have

$$\{h \circ (g \circ f)\}(x) = \{(h \circ g) \circ f\}(x) \quad \forall \ x \in S$$
$$\Rightarrow \qquad h \circ (g \circ f) = (h \circ g) \circ f.$$

Note. Whereas the notations for *Function* and the *Function value* we have described above, are the correct ones, it has been conventional to call $f(x)$ itself as a function.

Note. Complex valued functions of a complex variable

In this book, we shall be mostly concerned with functions whose domains and ranges are subsets of the set of complex numbers, *i.e.*, with what may be called *complex valued functions of a complex variable*.

In the following, we shall define complex numbers and also set up their Algebra.

1.2. Complex Numbers. Def. *An ordered pair of real numbers a, b to be written as (a, b) is called a complex number.*

We may write

$$\alpha = (a, b).$$

The set of all ordered pairs of real numbers is the set of complex numbers denoted by the symbol **C**.

Equality of two complex numbers. By definition, we have

$$(a, b) = (c, d) \quad \Leftrightarrow \quad a = c, b = d.$$

1.3. Sum of two complex numbers. The addition composition in the set of complex numbers.

Let

$$\alpha = (a, b), \beta = (c, d)$$

be two complex numbers.

By definition, we have

$$\alpha + \beta = (a, b) + (c, d) = (a + c, b + d).$$

We now state and prove the four fundamental properties of the addition composition in the set of complex numbers.

A.1. *The addition composition is commutative, i.e.,*

$$\alpha + \beta = \beta + \alpha \quad \forall \quad \alpha, \beta \in \mathbf{C}.$$

Let

$$\alpha = (a, b), \beta = (c, d).$$

We have

$$\alpha + \beta = (a, b) + (c, d)$$
$$= (a + c, b + d) = (c + a, d + b)$$
$$= (c, d) + (a, b) = \beta + \alpha.$$

A.2. *The addition composition is associative, i.e.,*

$$\alpha + (\beta + \gamma) = (\alpha + \beta) + \gamma \quad \forall \quad \alpha, \beta, \gamma \in \mathbf{C}$$

Let

$$\alpha = (a, b), \beta = (c, d), \gamma = (e, f).$$

We have

$$(\alpha + \beta) + \gamma = [(a, b) + (c, d)] + (e, f)$$
$$= (a + c, b + d) + (e, f)$$
$$= [(a + c) + e, (b + d) + f]$$
$$= [(a + (c + e), b + (d + f)]$$
$$= (a, b) + (c + e, d + f)$$
$$= (a, b) + [(c, d) + (e, f)] = \alpha + (\beta + \gamma).$$

A.3. *The addition composition is identity element admitting.*

We may easily see that $(0, 0)$ is the identity element for the addition composition in **C** in that

$$(a, b) + (0, 0) = (a, b) \quad \forall \quad (a, b) \in \mathbf{C}.$$

The complex number $(0, 0)$ is called the complex number zero.

A.4. *Every complex number is additively invertible.*

In fact $(-a, -b)$ is the additive inverse of (a, b) in as much as

$$(a, b) + (-a, -b) = (0, 0).$$

Note. Because of the four properties of the addition composition in the set of complex numbers we see that the *set* **C** *of complex number is a commutative group for the Addition Composition.*

Def. If α, β be two complex numbers, we write

$$\alpha - \beta = \alpha + (-\beta).$$

Thus,

$$\alpha = (a, b), \beta = (c, d)$$
$$\Leftrightarrow \quad \alpha - \beta = \alpha + (-\beta)$$
$$= (a, b) + (-c, -d)$$
$$= [a + (-c), b + (-d)]$$
$$= (a - c, b - d).$$

1.4. Product of two complex numbers. The multiplication composition in C.

Let α and β be two complex numbers.

For a logical development of the system of real numbers, the reader is advised to refer to the book *'Number Systems'* by the author.

Let
$$\alpha = (a, b), \quad \beta = (c, d).$$

By definition
$$\alpha\beta = (a, b)(c, d) = (ac - bd, \, ad + bc).$$

We now consider the fundamental laws of the multiplication composition in **C**.

M.1. *The multiplication composition is commutative, i.e.,*
$$\alpha\beta = \beta\alpha \quad \forall \; \alpha, \beta \in \mathbf{C}.$$

Let
$$\alpha = (a, b), \quad \beta = (c, d).$$

We have
$$\begin{aligned}
\alpha\beta &= (a, b)(c, d) \\
&= (ac - bd, \, ad + bc) \\
&= (ca - db, \, cb + da) \\
&= (c, d)(a, b) = \beta\alpha.
\end{aligned}$$

M.2. *The multiplication composition is associative, i.e.,*
$$(\alpha\beta)\,\gamma = \alpha\,(\beta\gamma) \quad \forall \; \alpha, \beta, \gamma \in \mathbf{C}.$$

Let
$$\alpha = (a, b), \quad \beta = (c, d), \quad \gamma = (e, f).$$

We have
$$\begin{aligned}
(\alpha\beta)\,\gamma &= [(a, b)(c, d)]\,(e, f) \\
&= (ac - bd, \, ad + bc)\,(e, f) \\
&= [(ac - bd)\,e - (ad + bc)\,f, \; (ac - bd)\,f + (ad + bc)\,e] \\
&= [a\,(ce - df) - b\,(cf + de), \; a\,(cf + de) + b\,(ce - df)] \\
&= (a, b)\,(ce - df, \, cf + de) \\
&= (a, b)\,[(c, d)(e, f)] = \alpha\,(\beta\gamma).
\end{aligned}$$

M.3. *The multiplication composition is identity element admitting.*

We may easily see that the complex number $(1, 0)$ is the identity element for the multiplication composition.

In fact, we have
$$(a, b)(1, 0) = (a, b) \; \forall \; (a, b) \in \mathbf{C}.$$

The complex number $(1, 0)$ is called the complex number unity.

M.4. *Every non-zero complex number is multiplicatively invertible.*

Let
$$\alpha = (a, b)$$

be a given complex number.

We shall now examine the existence of a complex number (u, v) such that
$$(a, b)(u, v) = (1, 0).$$

Now
$$(a, b)(u, v) = (1, 0)$$
$$\Leftrightarrow \quad (au - bv, \, av + bu) = (1, 0)$$

$$\Leftrightarrow \quad \begin{cases} au - bv = 1, \\ av + bu = 0. \end{cases}$$

$$\Leftrightarrow \quad u = \frac{a}{a^2 + b^2}, \ v = -\frac{b}{a^2 + b^2}, \text{ if } a^2 + b^2 \neq 0.$$

We notice that

$$(a^2 + b^2) \neq 0 \ \Leftrightarrow \ (a, b) \neq (0, 0).$$

Thus, we see that every non-zero complex number possesses a unique multiplicative inverse, usually called only *Inverse*. The multiplicative inverse of the non-zero complex number (a, b) is the complex number

$$\left(\frac{a}{a^2 + b^2}, \ -\frac{b}{a^2 + b^2} \right).$$

The inverse of the non-zero complex number α is usually denoted by α^{-1} and called the multiplicative inverse of α.

We have seen that

$$(a, b)^{-1} = \left(\frac{a}{a^2 + b^2}, \ -\frac{b}{a^2 + b^2} \right); \ (a, b) \neq (0, 0).$$

1.4.1. Division composition. If α, β be two complex numbers and β is non-zero, then, by definition

$$\alpha \div \beta = \alpha (\beta)^{-1}.$$

Also we write

$$\alpha \div \beta = \frac{\alpha}{\beta} \text{ or } \alpha / \beta.$$

A.M. *The multiplication distributes the addition, i.e.,*

$$\alpha (\beta + \gamma) = \alpha\beta + \alpha\gamma \ \forall \ \alpha, \beta, \gamma \in \mathbf{C}.$$

Let

$$\alpha = (a, b), \beta = (c, d), \gamma = (e, f).$$

We have

$$\begin{aligned} \alpha (\beta + \gamma) &= (a, b) [(c, d) + (e, f)] \\ &= (a, b) (c + e, d + f) \\ &= [a (c + e) - b (d + f), a (d + f) + b (c + e)] \\ &= (ac - bd, ad + bc) + (ae - bf, af + be) \\ &= (a, b) (c, d) + (a, b) (e, f) = \alpha\beta + \alpha\gamma. \end{aligned}$$

1.5. Usual notation for complex numbers. We shall, in this section, see how a complex number can be denoted by the usual symbol $a + ib$.

Consider the correspondence

$$a \to (a, 0),$$

which associates to a real number, a, the complex number whose first member is a, and the second member is 0. This correspondence is preserved through addition and multiplication, for

$$a + b \to (a + b, 0) = (a, 0) + (b, 0),$$

$$ab \to (ab, 0) = (a, 0) (b, 0).$$

This preservation of the correspondence through addition and multiplication means that if in any relation involving addition and multiplication of real numbers, we replace each real number, by the corresponding complex number then the relation would remain valid in terms of complex numbers and conversely. In view of this fact, we find it is possible to economise our notation by writing a for $(a, 0)$.

This will not cause any confusion for the relations must remain true whichever interpretation may be given to the symbols a, b, c, etc.

Further we shall write

$$(0, 1) = i,$$

as is justified by the fact that

$$i^2 = (0, 1) (0, 1)$$
$$= (-1, 0)$$
$$= -1, \text{ employing the above convention.}$$

Now,

$$(a, b) = (a, 0) + (0, b)$$
$$= (a, 0) + (b, 0) (0, 1)$$
$$= a + bi$$
$$= a + ib.$$

Thus, we see that in terms of the convention adopted above, every complex number is expressible in the usual form $a + ib$.

We have thus obtained a complete logical justification of the manner in which we denote complex numbers and algebraically manipulate with the same.

1.6. Summary of the fundamental laws of the addition and multiplication compositions. In the following α, β and γ denote any complex numbers whatsoever. Also, the symbols 0 and 1 will respectively denote the complex numbers zero, and unity respectively. Thus, the symbols 0, 1 might stand for the real numbers or for complex numbers but the context would always, without ambiguity, suggest as to what they actually stand for.

We shall now summarise the fundamental laws of the addition and multiplication of complex numbers as have already been established in the preceding sections. The reader must have already noticed that these laws are the same as those for real numbers.

(A.1) $\alpha + \beta = \beta + \alpha$ $\forall\ \alpha, \beta \in \mathbf{C}$

(A.2) $\alpha + (\beta + \gamma) = (\alpha + \beta) + \gamma$ $\forall\ \alpha, \beta, \gamma \in \mathbf{C}$

(A.3) $\alpha + 0 = \alpha$ $\forall\ \alpha \in \mathbf{C}$

(A.4) To each α, there corresponds another denoted by, $-\alpha$, such that

$$\alpha + (-\alpha) = 0.$$

(M.1) $\alpha \beta = \beta \alpha,$ $\forall\ \alpha, \beta \in \mathbf{C}$

(M.2) $\alpha (\beta\gamma) = (\alpha\beta)\ \gamma,$ $\forall\ \alpha, \beta, \gamma \in \mathbf{C}$

(M.3) $\alpha\ 1 = \alpha$ $\forall\ \alpha \in \mathbf{C}$

(M.4) To each $\alpha \neq 0$, there corresponds another complex numbers denoted by α^{-1} such that

$$\alpha\alpha^{-1} = 1.$$

(A.M.) $\alpha\ (\beta + \gamma) = \alpha\beta + \alpha\gamma$ $\forall\ \alpha, \beta, \gamma \in \mathbf{C}$

Regarding subtraction and division, we have

$$\alpha - \beta = \alpha + (-\beta),$$

$$\alpha \div \beta = \alpha \, (\beta)^{-1}, \text{ where } \beta \neq 0.$$

1.7. Some divided laws. In the preceding sections, we have, after defining the compositions of addition and multiplication, also obtained the fundamental laws of the same directly from the definition. Now, there are some other laws also which these operations obey and which are constantly made use of in our dealings with complex numbers. These laws can be deduced from the fundamental laws listed in the preceding section or directly from the definitions of the operations. Some of these laws are the following:

$$\alpha \, 0 = 0 \, \alpha = 0 \qquad\qquad\qquad \forall \; \alpha \in C$$

$$\alpha\beta = 0 \;\Leftrightarrow\; \alpha = 0 \text{ or } \beta = 0$$

$$\alpha \, (-\beta) = -(\alpha\beta) \qquad\qquad \forall \; \alpha, \beta \in C$$

$$(-\alpha)(-\beta) = \alpha\beta \qquad\qquad\quad \forall \; \alpha, \beta \in C$$

$$\alpha \, (\beta - \gamma) = \alpha\beta - \alpha\gamma \qquad\quad \forall \; \alpha, \beta, \gamma \in C$$

It is being left as an exercise for the reader to prove these laws directly from the definitions as also from the fundamental laws listed above.

1.8. Real and imaginary parts of a complex number. Conjugate complex numbers.

(Rohilkhand 2003)

If $\alpha = a + ib$ be a complex number, then a and b are respectively called the *Real* and *Imaginary* parts of α and we write

$$a = R \, (\alpha) \text{ and } b = I \, (\alpha).$$

A complex number, α, is said to be real if its imaginary part is zero and imaginary if its real part is zero.

The truth of the following statements may be easily seen:

$$R \, (\alpha \pm \beta) = R \, (\alpha) \pm R \, (\beta) \text{ and } I \, (\alpha \pm \beta) = I \, (\alpha) \pm I \, (\beta).$$

In general, however,

$$R \, (\alpha\beta) \neq R \, (\alpha) \, R \, (\beta) \text{ and } I \, (\alpha\beta) \neq I \, (\alpha) \, I \, (\beta).$$

Again, the complex number, $a - ib$ is called the conjugate of the complex numbers $\alpha = a + ib$ and is denoted by $\overline{\alpha}$. Thus, we write

$$\overline{\alpha} = a - ib \;\Leftrightarrow\; \alpha = a + ib.$$

Clearly, α is also conjugate of $\overline{\alpha}$ and accordingly we say that α and $\overline{\alpha}$ are conjugate complex numbers.

The following important relations may be easily verified:

$$\overline{(\alpha \pm \beta)} = \overline{\alpha} \pm \overline{\beta},$$

$$\overline{\alpha\beta} = \overline{\alpha} \, \overline{\beta},$$

$$\overline{(\alpha \div \beta)} = \overline{\alpha} \div \overline{\beta}, \; \beta \neq 0.$$

These relations show that the mapping

$$\alpha \rightarrow \overline{\alpha}$$

is preserved through the four algebraic compositions of addition, subtraction, multiplication and division, *i.e.*, the conjugate complex of the sum (difference, product and quotient) of two complex numbers is equal to the sum (difference, product and quotient) of their conjugate complexes.

It is also important to note that the sum and product of any two conjugate complex numbers are both real. Thus if $\alpha = a + ib$ so that $\bar{\alpha} = a - ib$, we have

$$\alpha + \bar{\alpha} = 2a = 2\,\text{R}\,(\alpha) \quad \Leftrightarrow \quad \text{R}\,(\alpha) = \frac{1}{2}\,(\alpha + \bar{\alpha})$$

$$\alpha\bar{\alpha} = a^2 + b^2 = [\text{R}\,(\alpha)]^2 + [\text{I}\,(\alpha)]^2.$$

Also, we have

$$\alpha - \bar{\alpha} = 2ib = 2i\,\text{I}\,(\alpha) \quad \text{or} \quad \text{I}\,(\alpha) = (\alpha - \bar{\alpha})\,/\,2i.$$

1.9. Modulus and the Amplitude of a Complex Number.

Let $\alpha = a + ib$ be any complex number. We find a non-negative real number, r, and a real number, θ, such that

$$a = r \cos\theta \text{ and } b = r \sin\theta.$$

These give

$$r = +\sqrt{(a^2 + b^2)}.$$

It will be seen that unless $\alpha = 0$, *i.e.*, a and b are both zero, θ can be chosen in an infinite number of ways and any two values of the same differ by a multiple of 2π.

The number, r, which is the non-negative square root of $a^2 + b^2$ is called the **Modulus of** α and is denoted by $|\alpha|$.

Thus,

$$\alpha = a + ib$$

$$\Rightarrow \qquad |\alpha| = |a + ib| = +\sqrt{(a^2 + b^2)}.$$

In this connection, it is useful to notice that

$$\alpha\bar{\alpha} = (a + ib)(a - ib) = a^2 + b^2 \quad \Rightarrow \quad |\alpha|^2 = \alpha\bar{\alpha}.$$

Also, θ is called an **Amplitude** or **Argument** of α and we write

$$\theta = \arg(\alpha) \text{ or } \text{amp}(\alpha).$$

We see that every non-zero complex number admits of an infinite number of arguments and of all these arguments there is one and only one argument θ such that $-\pi < \theta \le \pi$.

This argument is called the **principal** value.

We note that two complex numbers are equal if and only if their moduli and the principal arguments are equal.

We shall consider the basic properties of the moduli and the arguments of complex numbers in the following.

Note. It will be seen that relatively to the notion of limit and other allied notions, the concept of the modulus of complex number plays the same role in the Theory of a Complex Variable as that of the modulus of a real number in the Theory of Real Variables.

1.9.1. Some properties of the modulus. We prove that

I. $|\alpha| = 0 \quad \Leftrightarrow \quad \alpha = 0$

II. $|\alpha\beta| = |\alpha|\,|\beta| \quad \forall \ \alpha, \beta \in \mathbf{C}$

III. $\left|\dfrac{\alpha}{\beta}\right| = \dfrac{|\alpha|}{|\beta|}, \ \forall \ \alpha \in \mathbf{C}$ and $\forall$ non-zero $\beta \in \mathbf{C}$

IV. $|\alpha + \beta| \le |\alpha| + |\beta| \quad \forall \ \alpha, \beta \in \mathbf{C}$

i.e., the modulus of the sum of two complex numbers is less than or equal to the sum of their moduli.

Proof : I. Now,

$$0 = |\alpha|$$
$$= \sqrt{(a^2 + b^2)},$$
$$\Leftrightarrow \qquad a = 0, b = 0,$$
$$\Leftrightarrow \qquad \alpha = 0.$$

II. As,

$$|\alpha\beta|^2 = (\alpha\beta)(\overline{\alpha\beta})$$
$$= (\alpha\beta)(\overline{\alpha}\,\overline{\beta})$$
$$= (\alpha\overline{\alpha})(\beta\overline{\beta})$$
$$= |\alpha|^2 |\beta|^2,$$
$$\Leftrightarrow \qquad |\alpha\beta| = |\alpha||\beta|.$$

III. We have

$$|\alpha + \beta|^2 = (\alpha + \beta)(\overline{\alpha + \beta})$$
$$= (\alpha + \beta)(\overline{\alpha} + \overline{\beta})$$
$$= \alpha\overline{\alpha} + \beta\overline{\beta} + (\alpha\overline{\beta} + \overline{\alpha}\beta).$$
$$= |\alpha|^2 + |\beta|^2 + \alpha\overline{\beta} + \overline{\alpha}\beta \qquad \ldots(1)$$

As $\overline{\alpha}\beta$ is the conjugate complex of $\alpha\overline{\beta}$, we see that $\alpha\overline{\beta} + \overline{\alpha}\beta$ is real and $\alpha\overline{\beta} - \overline{\alpha}\beta$ is imaginary.

$$\left.\begin{array}{l} \alpha\overline{\beta} + \overline{\alpha}\beta \text{ is real } \Rightarrow (\alpha\overline{\beta} + \overline{\alpha}\beta)^2 \geq 0 \\ \alpha\overline{\beta} - \overline{\alpha}\beta \text{ is imaginary } \Rightarrow (\alpha\overline{\beta} - \overline{\alpha}\beta)^2 \leq 0 \end{array}\right\} \qquad \ldots(2)$$

Also

$$(\overline{\alpha}\beta^{-2}) - (\alpha\overline{\beta} - \overline{\alpha}\beta)^2 = 4\alpha\overline{\alpha}\beta\overline{\beta} = 4|\alpha|^2 |\beta|^2 \qquad \ldots(3)$$

From (2) and (3), we deduce that

$$(\alpha\overline{\beta} + \overline{\alpha}\beta)^2 \leq 4|\alpha|^2 |\beta|^2 \qquad \ldots(4)$$

From (1) and (4), we have

$$|\alpha + \beta|^2 \leq |\alpha|^2 + |\beta|^2 + 2|\alpha||\beta|$$
$$= [|\alpha| + |\beta|]^2,$$
$$\Rightarrow \qquad |\alpha + \beta| \leq |\alpha| + |\beta|.$$

Cor. From the preceding result, we can deduce that

$$|\alpha + \beta| \geq \big||\alpha| - |\beta|\big|. \qquad\qquad\qquad (Kumaon\ 2004)$$

In fact, we have

$$\alpha = \alpha - \beta + \beta$$
$$\Rightarrow \qquad |\alpha| = |\alpha - \beta + \beta|$$

$$\leq |\alpha - \beta| + |\beta|$$

$\Rightarrow$ $\qquad |\alpha| - |\beta| \leq |\alpha - \beta|$ $\qquad\qquad\qquad\qquad\qquad\qquad\qquad$ ...(5)

Interchanging α and β, we obtain

$$|\beta| - |\alpha| \leq |\beta - \alpha|,$$ $\qquad\qquad\qquad\qquad\qquad\qquad\qquad$ ...(6)

$\Rightarrow$ $\qquad -[|\alpha| - |\beta|] \leq |\alpha - \beta|.$

From (5) and (6), we deduce that

$$|\alpha - \beta| \geq ||\alpha| - |\beta||.$$ $\qquad\qquad\qquad\qquad$ (*Calicut 2004*)

1.9.2. Properties of the arguments. We shall now prove that

I. *The argument of the product of two complex numbers is equal to the sum of their arguments.*

II. *The argument of the quotient of two complex numbers is equal to the difference of their arguments.*

Let α and β be two complex numbers and let

$$\alpha = r_1 (\cos \theta_1 + i \sin \theta_1), \quad \beta = r_2 (\cos \theta_2 + i \sin \theta_2)$$

so that θ_1 and θ_2 are arguments of α and β respectively. We obtain, making use of the various laws of algebraic manipulation,

$$\alpha\beta = r_1 r_2 [\cos (\theta_1 + \theta_2) + i \sin (\theta_1 + \theta_2)],$$

so that $\theta_1 + \theta_2$ is an argument of the product $\alpha\beta$. This also shows that

$$|\alpha\beta| = r_1 r_2 |\alpha| |\beta|.$$ $\qquad\qquad\qquad$ [Refer II, § 1.9.1]

We should carefully understand the precise meaning of the equality

$$\arg (\alpha\beta) = \arg (\alpha) + \arg (\beta),$$ $\qquad\qquad\qquad\qquad\qquad$ ...(7)

in view of the multi-valuedness of the argument of a complex number. In fact, the equality (7) implies that *each value of L.H.S. is same value of the R.H.S. and vice-versa.*

The equality (7) may *not* be true for principal values.

Again, we have

$$\frac{1}{\beta} = \frac{1}{r_2 (\cos \theta_2 + i \sin \theta_2)}$$

$$= \frac{\cos \theta_2 - i \sin \theta_2}{r_2}$$

$$= \frac{1}{r_2} [\cos (-\theta_2) + i \sin (-\theta_2)]$$

$\Leftrightarrow$ $\qquad\dfrac{\alpha}{\beta} = \dfrac{r_1}{r_2} [\cos (\theta_1 - \theta_2) + i \sin (\theta_1 - \theta_2)],$

so that we obtain the corresponding result for quotient.

Note. It may be useful to remember that the principal argument of a real number is 0 or π according as the same is positive or negative and the principal value of the argument of an imaginary number is $+\dfrac{1}{2}\pi$ or $-\dfrac{1}{2}\pi$ according as the imaginary part of the same is positive or negative.

1.10. Roots of unity. Let z, denotes the nth root of unity so that, we have

$$z^n = 1$$ $\qquad\qquad\qquad\qquad\qquad\qquad\qquad\qquad\qquad$ ...(1)

We write

$$z = r (\cos \theta + i \sin \theta), \quad 1 = \cos 0 + i \sin 0,$$

$\Rightarrow$ $$z^n = r^n (\cos n\theta + i \sin n\theta) = \cos 2s\pi + i \sin 2s\pi$$
$$r^n = 1, \; n\theta = 0 + 2s\pi \; ; \; s \text{ being some integers.}$$

As, r is necessarily non-negative, we have
$$r = 1, \; \theta = 2s\pi/n.$$

Thus

$$z = \cos \frac{2s\pi}{n} + i \sin \frac{2s\pi}{n} \qquad \qquad ...(2)$$

It is easy to see that the nth power of the expression (2) is 1, whatever integer, s, may be.

Further, we may see that the expression (2) has only, n, different values obtained by giving values

$$0, 1, 2, \ldots, n - 1$$

to s.

Thus, we see that the *unity has, n, nth roots given by*

$$\cos \frac{2s\pi}{n} + i \sin \frac{2s\pi}{n}$$

where s takes the values 0, 1, 2...., ..., n – 1.

Meaning of z^n; n being any rational number.

By definition z^n denotes the product of z with itself iterated n times if n is a *positive integer.* Thus

$$z^n = z \cdot z \cdot z \cdot \ldots \ldots z \ldots, \; n \text{ times,}$$

when n is a positive integer.

If n is a *negative integer*, so that $-n$ is a positive integer and $z \neq 0$ we have, by definition
$$z^n = 1/z^{-n}.$$

As a consequence of the results proved in § 1.9, we may see that
$$r (\cos \theta + i \sin \theta)]^n = r^n (\cos n\theta + i \sin n\theta),$$

when n is any integer.

Again, if q is a positive integer, then by definition, $z^{1/q}$ denotes a complex number Z such that

$$Z^q = z.$$

Thus, $z^{1/q}$ denotes what is often called the *qth root* of z. It can be shown that $z^{1/q}$ has q different values. Let

$$z = r (\cos \theta + i \sin \theta), \; Z = \rho (\cos \phi + i \sin \phi).$$

Then, we have

$$Z^q = z$$

$\Rightarrow$ $$\rho^q (\cos q\phi + i \sin q\phi) = r (\cos \theta + i \sin \theta)$$

$\Rightarrow$ $$\rho^q = r, \; q\phi = \theta + 2s\pi,$$

where s, is some integer.

Thus

$$\rho = r^{1/q},$$

where $r^{1/q}$ denotes the positive qth root of the positive real number.

Thus $Z = z^{1/q} = r^{1/q} \left[\cos\left(\dfrac{\theta + 2s\pi}{q} \right) + i \sin\left(\dfrac{\theta + 2s\pi}{q} \right) \right].$

It may be shown that $z^{1/q}$ assumes q different values when s varies from 0 to $q - 1$.

Finally,

$$z^{p/q} = (z^{1/q})^p,$$

so that $z^{p/q}$ has also q values.

Thus, we have considered the meaning of z^n, when n is any rational number. The extension to the case when n is any arbitrary complex number will be given later on in Chapter 7.

EXAMPLES

1. *If the sum and the product of two complex numbers are both real then the two numbers must either be real or conjugate.*

Solution. $\qquad\qquad z_1 = x_1 + iy_1,\ z_2 = x_2 + iy_2$

$\therefore \qquad\qquad z_1 + z_2 = (x_1 + x_2) + i\,(y_1 + y_2)$

is real if $\qquad y_1 + y_2 = 0$ ...(i)

$\qquad\qquad\qquad z_1 z_2 = (x_1 x_2 - y_1 y_2) + i\,(x_1 y_2 + x_2 y_1)$

is real if $\qquad x_1 y_2 + x_2 y_1 = 0$ ...(ii)

From (ii), $\qquad \dfrac{x_1}{x_2} = -\dfrac{y_1}{y_2} = 1 \ \Rightarrow\ x_2 = x_1,\ y_2 = -y_1$

$\therefore \qquad\qquad z_2 = x_2 + iy_2 = x_1 - iy_1 = \bar{z}_1.$

2. *If z_1 and z_2 are two complex numbers such that $|z_1| < 1 < |z_2|$, then prove that*

$\left| \dfrac{1 - z_1 \bar{z}_2}{z_1 - z_2} \right| < 1.$

Solution. To prove $|1 - z_1 \bar{z}_2| < |z_1 - z_2|$

$\Leftrightarrow \quad (1 - z_1 \bar{z}_2)(1 - \bar{z}_1 z_2) < (z_1 - z_2)(\bar{z}_1 - \bar{z}_2)$

$\Leftrightarrow \quad 1 - z_1 \bar{z}_2 - \bar{z}_1 z_2 + |z_1|^2 |z_2|^2 < |z_1|^2 - z_2 \bar{z}_1 - z_1 \bar{z}_2 + |z_2|^2$

$\Leftrightarrow \quad (1 - |z_1|^2) - |z_2|^2 (1 - |z_1|^2) < 0$

$\Leftrightarrow \quad (1 - |z_2|^2)(1 - |z_1|^2) < 0$

which is obvious as $|z_1| < 1 < |z_2|$.

3. *If $iz^2 - \bar{z} = 0$, where $i = \sqrt{-1}$ and $\bar{z}$ is the complex conjugate of z, find values of $|z|$.*

Solution. $iz^2 - \bar{z} = 0 \ \Rightarrow\ iz^2 = \bar{z}$

Taking modulus on both sides, we get

$\qquad |iz^2| = |\bar{z}| \qquad\qquad \Rightarrow\ |i||z^2| = |z|$

$\Rightarrow |z|^2 = |z| \qquad\qquad \Rightarrow\ |z|^2 - |z| = 0$

$\Rightarrow |z|(|z| - 1) = 0 \ \Rightarrow\ |z| = 0,\ 1.$

4. *Show that $\arg z + \arg \bar{z} = 2n\pi$.*

Solution. Let $z = x + iy$, then $\bar{z} = x - iy$.

Now, $\arg z + \arg \overline{z} = \arg \overline{z}z$

$$= \arg (x - iy)(x + iy)$$

$$= \arg (x^2 + y^2) = \arg a, \text{ where } a = x^2 + y^2.$$

Clearly, a is positive and real. Let $a = r \cos \theta$, $0 = r \sin \theta$, so that $r = a$ and $\cos \theta = 1$. $\sin \theta = 0$.

Therefore, the general value of $\theta = 2n\pi$, when n is an integer or zero.

5. *For complex numbers z and w, prove that $|z|^2 w - |w|^2 z = z - w$ if and only if $z = w$ or $z\overline{w} = 1$.*

Solution. Given $|z|^2 w - |w|^2 z = z - w$

$\Rightarrow$ $\qquad |z|^2 w + w = z + |w|^2 z$

$\Rightarrow$ $\qquad w(1 + |z|^2) = z(1 + |w|^2)$

$\Rightarrow$ $\qquad \dfrac{w}{z} = \dfrac{1 + |w|^2}{1 + |z|^2}$, a real number.

$\Rightarrow$ $\qquad \dfrac{w}{z} = \lambda$ (say)

$\Rightarrow$ $\qquad w = \lambda z \Rightarrow w\overline{z} = \lambda z\overline{z}$ $\qquad\qquad\qquad$ ...(i)

Also, $\qquad w = \lambda z \Rightarrow \overline{w} = \lambda \overline{z}$

$\Rightarrow$ $\qquad \overline{w} \cdot z = \lambda \overline{z} \cdot z$ $\qquad\qquad\qquad\qquad\qquad$ ...(ii)

From (i) and (ii)

$$w\overline{z} = \overline{w}z \qquad\qquad\qquad ...(iii)$$

$\because$ $\qquad z \cdot \overline{z} = |z|^2$ and $w \cdot \overline{w} = |w|^2$

$\therefore$ $\quad |z|^2 w - |w|^2 z = z - w$

$\Rightarrow$ $\qquad z\overline{z}w - w\overline{w}z = z - w$

$\Rightarrow$ $\quad z\overline{z}w - w\overline{w}z - z + w = 0$

$\Rightarrow$ $\quad z(\overline{w}z - 1) - w(\overline{w}z - 1) = 0$

$\Rightarrow$ $\qquad (z - w)(\overline{w}z - 1) = 0$

$\Rightarrow$ $\qquad\qquad z = w \text{ or } \overline{w}z = 1.$

6. *For every real number $c \geq 0$, find all complex numbers z which satisfy the equation $|z|^2 - 2iz + 2c(1 + i) = 0$.*

Solution. By putting $z = x + iy$, we have

$\Rightarrow$ $\quad 2\ x\ =\ 1\ +\ y^2\ = 0$

$\Rightarrow$ $\quad (x^2 + y^2 + 2y + 2c) + 2i(c - x) = 0$

$\Rightarrow$ $\quad x^2 + y^2 + 2y + 2c = 0, \ 2c - 2x = 0$

$\Rightarrow$ $\quad x = c \text{ or } y^2 + 2y + c^2 + 2c = 0$ $\qquad\qquad$ ...(i)

For real values of y, the discriminant of (i) must be non-negative,

i.e., $4 - 4(c^2 + 2c) \geq 0 \Rightarrow 1 - c^2 - 2c \geq 0.$

For these values of c,

$$y = \frac{-2 \pm \sqrt{[4(1 - c^2 - 2c)]}}{2} = -1 \pm \sqrt{(1 - c^2 - 2c)}.$$

Hence, for $\Delta \geq 0$, the original equation has two roots

$$z_1 = c + [-1 + \sqrt{(1 - c^2 - 2c)}] \, i$$

and

$$z_2 = c + [-1 - \sqrt{(1 - c^2 - 2c)}] \, i.$$

For $\Delta = 0$, $z_1 = z_2 \Rightarrow$ there is only one solution. For $\Delta < 0$, the equation has no roots. Since $c \geq 0$, then c must satisfy the inequality

$$1 - c^2 - 2c \geq 0 \qquad \Rightarrow (c + 1)^2 - 2 \leq 0$$

$$\Rightarrow \quad -\sqrt{2} \leq c + 1 \leq \sqrt{2} \qquad \Rightarrow -1 - \sqrt{2} \leq c \leq -1 + \sqrt{2}$$

Now, choosing the numbers $c \geq 0$ from this interval, we obtain

$$0 \leq c \leq -1 + \sqrt{2}.$$

Thus, we have

(i) For $0 \leq c < -1 + \sqrt{2}$, there are two roots given by

$$z_{1, 2} = c + [-1 \pm \sqrt{(1 - c^2 - 2c)}] \, i.$$

(ii) For $c = -1 + \sqrt{2}$,

$$z = -1 + \sqrt{2} - i.$$

(iii) For $c > -1 + \sqrt{2}$, there is no solution.

7. *If $\theta_i \in [0, \pi/6]$, $i = 1, 2, 3, 4, 5$ and $\sin \theta_1 z^4 + \sin \theta_2 z^3 + \sin \theta_3 z^2 + \sin \theta_4 z$*

$+ \sin \theta_5 = 2$, then show that $|z| > \dfrac{3}{4}$.

Solution. Given that

$$\sin \theta_1 z^4 + \sin \theta_2 z^3 + \sin \theta_3 z^2 + \sin \theta_4 z + \sin \theta_5 = 2$$

or

$$2 = |\sin \theta_1 z^4 + \sin \theta_2 z^3 + \sin \theta_3 z^2 + \sin \theta_4 z + \sin \theta_5|$$

or

$$2 \leq |\sin \theta_1 z^4| + |\sin \theta_2 z^3| + |\sin \theta_3 z^2| + |\sin \theta_4 z| + |\sin \theta_5|$$

or

$$2 \leq |\sin \theta_1| |z^4| + |\sin \theta_2| |z^3| + |\sin \theta_3| |z^2| + |\sin \theta_4| |z| + |\sin \theta_5| \quad ...(i)$$

But given

$$\theta_i \in \left[0, \frac{\pi}{6}\right]$$

$$\therefore \qquad \sin \theta_i \in \left[0, \frac{1}{2}\right]$$

i.e.,

$$0 \leq \sin \theta_i \leq \frac{1}{2}.$$

$\therefore$ Inequality (i) becomes

$$2 \le \frac{1}{2}|z|^4 + \frac{1}{2}|z|^3 + \frac{1}{2}|z|^2 + \frac{1}{2}|z| + \frac{1}{2}$$

$\Rightarrow \qquad 3 \le |z|^4 + |z|^3 + |z|^2 + |z|$

$\Rightarrow \qquad 3 \le |z| + |z|^2 + |z|^3 + |z|^4$

$$< |z| + |z|^2 + |z|^3 + |z|^4 + ...\infty$$

$\Rightarrow \qquad 3 < \dfrac{|z|}{1-|z|}$

$\Rightarrow \qquad 3 - 3|z| < |z|$

$\Rightarrow \qquad |z| > \dfrac{3}{4}.$

8. *If $|z - 2 + i| \le 2$, then find the greatest and least value of $|z|$.*

Solution. Given that

$$|z - 2 + i| \le 2 \qquad \qquad ...(i)$$

$\therefore \qquad |z - 2 + i| \ge ||z| - |2 - i||$

$\therefore \qquad |z - 2 + i| \le ||z| - \sqrt{5}| \qquad \qquad ...(ii)$

From (i) and (ii)

$$||z| - \sqrt{5}| \le |z - 2 + i| \le 2$$

$\therefore \qquad ||z| - \sqrt{5}| \le 2$

$\Rightarrow \qquad -2 \le |z| - \sqrt{5} \le 2$

$\Rightarrow \qquad \sqrt{5} - 2 \le |z| \le \sqrt{5} + 2$

Hence, greatest value of $|z|$ is $\sqrt{5} + 2$ and least value of $|z|$ is $\sqrt{5} - 2$.

9. *Let $z_1 = 10 + 6i, z_2 = 4 + 6i$. If z is a complex number such that the argument of $(z - z_1)/(z - z_2)$ is $\pi/4$, then prove that $|z - 7 - 9i| = 3\sqrt{2}$.*

Solution. We have

$$\arg\left(\frac{z - z_1}{z - z_2}\right) = \pi/4$$

$\Rightarrow \qquad \arg(z - z_1) - \arg(z - z_2) = \pi/4$

Let $\qquad\qquad\qquad\qquad z = x + iy$

$\therefore \arg((x - 10) + i(y - 6)) - \arg((x - 4) + i(y - 6)) = \dfrac{\pi}{4}$

$\Rightarrow \qquad \tan^{-1}\left(\dfrac{y - 6}{x - 10}\right) - \tan^{-1}\left(\dfrac{y - 6}{x - 4}\right) = \dfrac{\pi}{4}$

$$\Rightarrow \qquad \tan^{-1}\left[\dfrac{\dfrac{y-6}{x-10} - \dfrac{y-6}{x-4}}{1 + \dfrac{(y-6)\,(y-6)}{(x-10)\,(x-4)}}\right] = \dfrac{\pi}{4}$$

$$\Rightarrow \qquad \dfrac{6\,(y-6)}{x^2 + y^2 - 14x - 12y + 76} = \tan\dfrac{\pi}{4}$$

$$\Rightarrow \qquad \dfrac{6\,(y-6)}{x^2 + y^2 - 14x - 12y + 76} = 1$$

$$\Rightarrow \qquad x^2 + y^2 - 14x - 18y + 112 = 0$$

$$\Rightarrow \qquad (x-7)^2 + (y-9)^2 = 18$$

$$\Rightarrow \qquad (x-7)^2 + (y-9)^2 = (3\sqrt{2})^2$$

$$\Rightarrow \qquad |(x-7) + i(y-9)| = 3\sqrt{2}$$

$$\Rightarrow \qquad |z - 7 - 9i| = 3\sqrt{2}.$$

10. *If* $\arg(z^{1/3}) = \dfrac{1}{2}\arg(z^2 + \bar{z}\,z^{1/3})$, *then find the value of* $|z|$.

Solution. We have

$$\arg(z^{1/3}) = \dfrac{1}{2}\arg(z^2 + \bar{z}\,z^{1/3})$$

$$\Rightarrow \qquad 2\arg(z^{1/3}) = \arg(z^2 + \bar{z}\,z^{1/3})$$

$$\Rightarrow \qquad \arg(z^{2/3}) = \arg(z^2 + \bar{z}\,z^{1/3})$$

$$\Rightarrow \qquad \arg\left(\dfrac{z^2 + \bar{z}\,z^{1/3}}{z^{2/3}}\right) = 0$$

$$\Rightarrow \qquad \arg\left(z^{4/3} + \dfrac{\bar{z}}{z^{1/3}}\right) = 0$$

$$\Rightarrow \qquad \text{Im}\left(z^{4/3} + \dfrac{\bar{z}}{z^{1/3}}\right) = 0$$

$$\Rightarrow \qquad \dfrac{\left(z^{4/3} + \dfrac{\bar{z}}{z^{1/3}}\right) - \overline{\left(z^{4/3} + \dfrac{\bar{z}}{z^{1/3}}\right)}}{2i} = 0$$

$$\Rightarrow \qquad z^{4/3} + \dfrac{\bar{z}}{z^{1/3}} = (\bar{z})^{4/3} + \dfrac{(\bar{\bar{z}})}{(\bar{z})^{1/3}}$$

$$\Rightarrow \qquad z^{4/3} + \dfrac{(\bar{z})(\bar{z})^{1/3}}{|z|^{2/3}} = (\bar{z})^{4/3} + \dfrac{z(z)^{1/3}}{|z|^{2/3}}$$

$$\Rightarrow \qquad z^{4/3} - (\bar{z})^{4/3} = \dfrac{1}{|z|^{2/3}}\{(z)^{4/3} - (\bar{z})^{4/3}\}$$

$$\therefore \qquad |z|^{2/3} = 1 \qquad\qquad (\because z \neq \bar{z})$$

$$\therefore \qquad |z| = 1$$

11. *If z_1 and z_2 both satisfy the relation $z + \bar{z} = 2\,|z - 1|$ and arg $(z_1 - z_2) = \pi/4$, then find the imaginary part of $(z_1 + z_2)$.*

Solution. Let $z = x + iy$, then $\dfrac{z + \bar{z}}{2} = x$

$\therefore$ from given relation

$$\frac{z + \bar{z}}{2} = |z - 1|$$

$$\Rightarrow \qquad x = |x + iy - 1|$$

$$\Rightarrow \qquad x^2 = (x - 1)^2 + y^2 \Rightarrow 2x = 1 + y^2$$

If $z_1 = x_1 + iy_1$ and $z_2 = x_2 + iy_2$

then

$$2x_1 = 1 + y_1^2$$

and

$$2x_2 = 1 + y_2^2$$

$$\Rightarrow \qquad 2(x_1 - x_2) = y_1^2 - y_2^2$$

$$\Rightarrow \qquad 2(x_1 - x_2) = (y_1 + y_2)(y_1 - y_2) \qquad\qquad (i)$$

But given that arg $(z_1 - z_2) = \pi/4$

i.e., $\qquad \tan^{-1} \dfrac{y_1 - y_2}{x_1 - x_2} = \pi/4$

$$\Rightarrow \qquad \frac{y_1 - y_2}{x_1 - x_2} = 1$$

or $\qquad y_1 - y_2 = x_1 - x_2$

Hence, from (i), we get

$$y_1 + y_2 = 2$$

or $\qquad \text{Im}\,(z_1 + z_2) = 2.$

12. *Prove that if z_1, z_2 are two complex numbers and $c > 0$, then*

$$|z_1 + z_2|^2 \leq (1 + c)\ |z_1|^2 + \left(1 + \frac{1}{c}\right)|z_2|^2$$

Solution. We know that $\text{Re}\,(z_1\bar{z}_2) \leq |z_1\bar{z}_2|$

$\therefore\ |z_1|^2 + |z_2|^2 + 2\,\text{Re}\,(z_1\bar{z}_2)|$

$$\leq |z_1|^2 + |z_2|^2 + 2|\,z_1\bar{z}_2\,|$$

$$\Rightarrow \qquad |z_1 + z_2|^2 \leq |z_1|^2 + |z_2|^2 + 2|z_1||z_2| \qquad\qquad ...(i)$$

Also A.M. $\geq$ G.M.

$$\therefore \qquad \frac{(\sqrt{c}\,|z_1|)^2 + \left(\dfrac{1}{\sqrt{c}}\,|z_2|\right)^2}{2} \geq \left\{ c\,|z_1|^2 \cdot \frac{1}{c}\,|z_2|^2 \right\}^{1/2} \qquad (\because c > 0)$$

$$\Rightarrow \qquad c\,|z_1|^2 + \frac{1}{c}\,|z_2|^2 \geq 2\,|z_1|\,|z_2|$$

$$\therefore \qquad |z_1|^2 + |z_2|^2 + 2\,|z_1|\,|z_2| \leq |z_1|^2 + |z_2|^2 + c\,|z_1|^2 + \frac{1}{c}\,|z_2|^2$$

$$\Rightarrow \qquad |z_1|^2 + |z_2|^2 + 2\,|z_1|\,|z_2| \leq (1+c)\,|z_1|^2 + (1+c^{-1})\,(|z_2|^2) \qquad \ldots(ii)$$

From (i) and (ii)

$$|z_1 + z_2|^2 \leq (1+c)\,|z_1|^2 + (1+c^{-1})\,|z_2|^2$$

13. *If z_1, z_2 and z_3 are three complex numbers, then prove that*
$z_1\,\mathrm{Im}\,(\bar{z}_2 z_3) + z_2\,\mathrm{Im}\,(\bar{z}_3\,z_1) + z_3\,\mathrm{Im}\,(\bar{z}_1 z_2) = 0.$

Solution. Let $z_1 = a_1 + ib_1, z_2 = a_2 + ib_2$ and $z_3 = a_3 + ib_3$, then

$$\bar{z}_2\,z_3 = (a_2 - ib_2)\,(a_3 + ib_3)$$

$$= (a_2 a_3 + b_2 b_3) + i\,(a_2 b_3 - a_3 b_2)$$

$$\Rightarrow \qquad \mathrm{Im}\,(\bar{z}_2\,z_3) = a_2 b_3 - a_3 b_2$$

Now, $\qquad z_1\,\mathrm{Im}\,(\bar{z}_2\,z_3) = (a_1 + ib_1)\,(a_2 b_3 - a_3 b_2)$

$$= (a_1 a_2 b_3 - a_3 a_1 b_2) + i\,(a_2 b_1 b_3 - a_3 b_1 b_2) \qquad \ldots(i)$$

Similarly, $\qquad z_2\,\mathrm{Im}\,(\bar{z}_3\,z_1) = (a_2 a_3 b_1 - a_2 a_1 b_3)$

$$+ i\,(b_2 a_3 b_1 - b_2 a_1 b_3) \qquad \ldots(ii)$$

and $\qquad z_3\,\mathrm{Im}\,(\bar{z}_1\,z_2) = (a_3\,a_1\,b_2 - a_3\,a_2\,b_1)$

$$+ i\,(b_3\,a_1\,b_2 - b_3\,a_2\,b_1) \qquad \ldots(iii)$$

Adding (i), (ii) and (iii) we get the required answer.

14. *Let z_1, z_2 be any two complex numbers and a, b are two real numbers such that $a^2 + b^2 \neq 0$. Prove that*

$$|z_1|^2 + |z_2|^2 - |z_1^2 + z_2^2| \leq \frac{2\,|az_1 + bz_2|^2}{a^2 + b^2}$$

$$\leq |z_1|^2 + |z_2|^2 + |z_1^2 + z_2^2|$$

Solution. Let $z_1 = r_1(\cos\theta_1 + i\sin\theta_1),\;\; z_2 = r_2(\cos\theta_2 + i\sin\theta_2),\;\; a = r\cos\alpha$ and $b = r\sin\alpha$, then $|z_1| = r_1, |z_2| = r_2$ and $a^2 + b^2 = r^2$ $\qquad \ldots(i)$

Now, $\qquad |az_1 + bz_2|^2 = (az_1 + bz_2)\,(a\bar{z}_1 + b\bar{z}_2)$

$$= a^2 z_1\bar{z}_1 + ab\,z_1\bar{z}_2 + ab\,z_2\bar{z}_1 + b^2\,z_2\bar{z}_2$$

$$= a^2\,|z_1|^2 + b^2\,|z_2|^2 + ab\,(z_1\bar{z}_2 + \bar{z}_1 z_2)$$

$$= a^2\,|z_1|^2 + b^2\,|z_2|^2 + 2ab\,\mathrm{Re}\,(z_1\,\bar{z}_2)$$

$$= r^2 r_1^2\cos^2\alpha + r^2 r_2^2\sin^2\alpha \ + 2r^2\cos\alpha\sin\alpha\,r_1\,r_2\cos(\theta_1 - \theta_2)$$

$$= r^2\,[r_1^2\cos^2\alpha + r_2^2\sin^2\alpha + 2r_1 r_2\,\cos\alpha\sin\alpha\cos(\theta_1 - \theta_2)]$$

$$= \frac{r^2}{2}[r_1^2(1 + \cos 2\alpha) + r_2^2(1 - \cos 2\alpha) + 2r_1 r_2\sin 2\alpha\cos(\theta_1 - \theta_2)]$$

$$= \frac{r^2}{2}[A + B\cos 2\alpha + C\sin 2\alpha]$$

where, $A = r_1^2 + r_2^2$, $B = r_1^2 - r_2^2$ and $C = 2r_1 r_2\cos(\theta_1 - \theta_2)$

$$\therefore \qquad \frac{2\,|az_1 + bz_2|^2}{r^2} = A + B\cos 2\alpha + C\sin 2\alpha$$

$$\Rightarrow \qquad \frac{2\,|az_1 + bz_2|^2}{(a^2 + b^2)} = A + \sqrt{(B^2 + C^2)}\left\{\frac{B}{\sqrt{B^2 + C^2}}\cos 2\alpha + \frac{C}{\sqrt{B^2 + C^2}}\sin 2\alpha\right\}$$

Now, let $B = R\sin\phi$ and $C = R\cos\phi$

$$\therefore \qquad \frac{2\,|az_1 + bz_2|^2}{a^2 + b^2} = A + R\sin(2\alpha + \phi)$$

Hence, maximum and minimum values of $\dfrac{2\,|az_1 + bz_2|^2}{(a^2 + b^2)}$ are $A + R$ and $A - R$ respectively.

$$\therefore \qquad\qquad A - R \le \frac{2\,|az_1 + bz_2|^2}{a^2 + b^2} \le A + R \qquad\qquad\qquad (ii)$$

Now, $$\qquad\qquad R = \sqrt{B^2 + C^2} = \sqrt{(r_1^2 - r_2^2) + 4r_1^2 r_2^2\cos^2(\theta_1 - \theta_2)}$$

$$= \sqrt{r_1^4 + r_2^4 + 2r_1^2 r_2^2\cos(2\theta_1 - 2\theta_2)}$$

and $$\quad |z_1^2 + z_2^2| = |r_1^2(\cos 2\theta_1 + i\sin 2\theta_1)| + r_2^2(\cos 2\theta_2 + i\sin 2\theta_2)2$$

$$= \sqrt{(r_1^2\cos 2\theta_1 + r_2^2\cos 2\theta_2)^2 + (r_1^2\sin 2\theta_1 + r_2^2\sin 2\theta_2)^2}$$

$$= \sqrt{r_1^4 + r_2^4 + 2r_1^2 r_2^2\cos(2\theta_1 - 2\theta_2)}$$

Thus, $$\qquad\qquad |z_1^2 + z_2^2| = \sqrt{B^2 + C^2} = R$$

Therefore, (ii) can be written as

$$|z_1|^2 + |z_2|^2 - |z_1^2 + z_2^2| \le \frac{2\,|az_1 + bz_2|^2}{a^2 + b^2}$$

$$\le |z_1|^2 + |z_2|^2 + |z_1^2 + z_2^2|$$

15. *A relation R on the set of complex numbers is defined by $z_1\,R\,z_2 \Leftrightarrow \dfrac{z_1 - z_2}{z_1 + z_2}$ is real. Show that R is an equivalence relation.*

Solution. R is

(*i*) reflexive $z_1 R z_1$, for $\dfrac{z_1 - z_2}{z_1 + z_1} = 0 = $ real

(*ii*) symmetric $z_1 R z_2 \Rightarrow z_2 R z_1$

For $z_1 R z_2 \Rightarrow \dfrac{z_1 - z_2}{z_1 + z_2} = $ real $\Rightarrow \dfrac{z_2 - z_1}{z_2 + z_1} = -$ real $= $ real

$\Rightarrow z_2 R z_1$

(*iii*) transitive $z_1 R z_2, z_2 R z_3 \Rightarrow z_1 R z_3$

For $\qquad z_1 R z_2, z_2 R z_3 \quad \Rightarrow \dfrac{z_1 - z_2}{z_1 + z_2} = $ real $\qquad\qquad$ (*i*)

and $\qquad\qquad \dfrac{z_2 - z_3}{z_2 + z_3} = $ real $\qquad\qquad$ (*ii*)

(*i*) $\Rightarrow$ $\qquad\qquad \dfrac{(x_1 - x_2) + i(y_1 - y_2)}{(x_1 + x_2) + i(y_1 + y_2)} = $ real

$\Rightarrow \dfrac{[(x_1 - x_2) + i(y_1 - y_2)][(x_1 + x_2) - i(y_1 + y_2)]}{(x_1 + x_2)^2 + (y_1 + y_2)^2} = $ real

$\Rightarrow \qquad\qquad -(x_1 - x_2)(y_1 + y_2) + (y_1 - y_2)(x_1 + x_2) = 0$

$\Rightarrow \qquad\qquad\qquad\qquad 2(x_2 y_1 - x_1 y_2) = 0$

$\Rightarrow \qquad\qquad\qquad\qquad x_2 y_1 = x_1 y_2$

$\Rightarrow \qquad\qquad\qquad\qquad \dfrac{x_1}{x_2} = \dfrac{y_1}{y_2} = k$ (real), say

$\Rightarrow \qquad\qquad\qquad z_1 = x_1 + iy_1 = k(x_2 + iy_2)$

$\Rightarrow \qquad\qquad\qquad\qquad z_1 = kz_2$

Similarly, (*ii*) $\Rightarrow z_2 = az_3$, where a is real

Now, $z_1 R z_3$ is true if $\dfrac{z_1 - z_3}{z_1 + z_3} = $ real

Now, $\qquad \dfrac{z_1 - z_3}{z_1 + z_3} = \dfrac{kz_2 - (z_2 / a)}{kz_2 + (z_2 / a)} = \dfrac{ka - 1}{ka + 1} = $ real

$\therefore\ z_1 R z_3$ is true.

Consequently, R is on equivalence relation.

EXERCISES

1. If $f(z) = a_0 z^n + a_1 z^{n-1} + \ldots + a_n$, is a polynomial with real coefficients $a_0, a_1, \ldots, a_n$, show that $\overline{f(z)} = f(\bar{z})$.

2. If $\phi(z) = f(z)/F(z)$ is a rational function such that the coefficients of the polynomials $f(z)$ and $F(z)$ are real, show that $\overline{\phi(z)} = \phi(\bar{z})$.

3. Find the real and imaginary parts, moduli and arguments of the following complex numbers:

(a) $\dfrac{1-i}{1+i}$ (GNDU 2004)　　　　　(b) $\left(\dfrac{2+i}{3-i}\right)^2$　　　(c) $\dfrac{1+2i}{1-(1-i)^2}$

(d) $-3i$　　　　　(e) -8　　　　　(f) 5　　　　　(g) $\dfrac{2+i}{4i+(1+i)^2}$

(h) $\dfrac{1-i}{3+i} - 2i$　　　(i) $\dfrac{3-i}{2+i} + \dfrac{3+i}{2-i}$.

[**Ans.** (a) $0, -1, 1, -\dfrac{1}{2}\pi$　　　　　(b) $0, \dfrac{1}{2}, \dfrac{1}{2}, \dfrac{1}{2}\pi$　　　(c) $1, 0, 1, 0$

(d) $0, -3, 3, -\dfrac{1}{2}\pi$　(e) $-8, 0, 8, \pi$　　　(f) $5, 0, 5, 0$

(g) $\dfrac{1}{6}, -\dfrac{1}{3}, \dfrac{\sqrt{5}}{6}, \tan^{-1}(2)$　　　　　(h) $\dfrac{1}{5}, -\dfrac{12}{5}, \dfrac{\sqrt{145}}{5}, -\tan^{-1}(12)$

(i) $2, 0, 2, 0$

4. The sum and the product of two complex numbers are both real; show that the two numbers are either both real or complex conjugates.

5. Show that the correspondence $a + ib \rightarrow \begin{bmatrix} a & b \\ -b & a \end{bmatrix}$, between the set of complex numbers and

the set of two-rowed square matrices of the form $\begin{bmatrix} a & b \\ -b & a \end{bmatrix}$, with real elements is one-one

and is preserved through both addition and multiplication.

[**Note.** *This gives another method of setting up the set of complex numbers.*]

6. Show that $|\alpha + \beta|^2 + |\alpha - \beta|^2 = 2\{|\alpha|^2 + |\beta|^2\}$; α and β being any complex numbers.

(*Kumaon 2003; Meerut 2003*)

7. Show that

$$|a + \sqrt{a^2 - b^2}| + |a - \sqrt{a^2 + b^2}| = |a + b| + |a - b|.$$

8. Solve the equation $z^2 + \alpha z + \beta = 0$, ($\alpha, \beta$ non-real) and show that it will have a real root if $(\overline{\alpha} - \alpha)(\alpha\overline{\beta} - \overline{\alpha}\beta) = (\beta - \overline{\beta})^2$.

Find also the condition for the equation to have an imaginary root.

[**Ans.** $(\alpha + \overline{\alpha})(\alpha\overline{\beta} + \overline{\alpha}\beta) + (\beta - \overline{\beta})^2 = 0$]

9. Show that if the equation $z^2 + \alpha z + \beta = 0$, has a pair of conjugate complex roots, then α and β are both real and $\alpha^2 < 4\beta$.

10. Find the condition for the equation $z^2 + 3\alpha z + \beta = 0$, ($\alpha, \beta$ non-real) to have

(i) a real root;

(ii) an imaginary root.

[**Ans.** (i) $(\overline{\beta} - \beta)^3 + 27\alpha(\overline{\beta} - \beta)(\alpha - \overline{\alpha})^2 + 27\beta(\alpha - \overline{\alpha})^3 = 0$

(ii) $(\overline{\beta} + \beta)^3 + 27\alpha(\overline{\beta} + \beta)(\alpha - \overline{\alpha})^2 + 27\beta(\alpha - \overline{\alpha})^3 = 0$]

11. Find the real and imaginary parts of the different values of the numbers $1^{1/5}$, $(-1)^{1/6}$, $(i)^{1/7}$, $(-i)^{1/8}$.

$$\left[\text{Ans. } \cos\frac{2n\pi}{5}, \sin\frac{2n\pi}{5}; n = 0, 1, ..., 4 \qquad \cos\frac{(2n+1)\pi}{6}, \sin\frac{(2n+1)\pi}{6}; n = 0, 1, ..., 5\right.$$

$$\left.\cos\frac{(4n+1)\pi}{14}, \sin\frac{(4n+1)\pi}{14}; n = 0, 1, ..., 6 \quad \cos\frac{(4n-1)\pi}{16}, \sin\frac{(4n-1)\pi}{16}; n = 0, 1, ..., 7\right]$$

12. Find the values of the following numbers in the form $a + ib$, a, b being real

$$\sqrt[3]{1}, \quad \sqrt[3]{-1}, \quad \sqrt[4]{-1}, \quad \sqrt[4]{1}.$$

$$\left[\text{Ans. } 1, -\frac{1}{2}\pm\frac{\sqrt{3}}{2}i, -1; \frac{1}{2}\pm\frac{\sqrt{3}}{2}i; \frac{1}{\sqrt{2}}\pm\frac{1}{\sqrt{2}}i, -\frac{1}{\sqrt{2}}\pm\frac{1}{\sqrt{2}}i; \pm 1, \pm i\right]$$

13. z_1 and z_2 are two complex numbers such that $\dfrac{z_1 - 2z_2}{2 - z_1\overline{z}_2}$ is unimodular, while z_2 is not

unimodular. Find $|z_1|$.

[Ans. 2]

14. Given that $|z - 1| = 1$, where z is a point on the Argand plane. Show that

$$\frac{z-2}{z} = i\tan(\arg z) \cdot$$

15. Show that if a and b are real, the principal value of arg a is 0 or π according as a is positive or negative and that of bi is $\pi/2$ or $-\pi/2$ accordingly as b is positive or negative.

16. If $iz^3 + z^2 - z + i = 0$, then show that $|z| = 1$.

17. If $|z| = 1$, then prove that arg $(z^2 + \overline{z}) = \dfrac{1}{2}\arg(z)$.

18. Prove that

$$|1 - \overline{z}_1 z_2|^2 - |z_1 - z_2|^2 = (1 - |z_1|^2)(1 - |z_2|^2) \cdot$$

19. Prove that $\left|\dfrac{a-b}{1-\overline{a}b}\right| < 1$ if $|a| < 1$ and $|b| < 1$

20. If z_1, z_2 are the roots of $\alpha z^2 + 2\beta z + \gamma = 0$.

Prove that

$$|z_1| + |z_2| = \frac{1}{|\alpha|} \cdot \{|-\beta + \sqrt{(\alpha\gamma)}| + |-\beta - \sqrt{(\alpha\gamma)}|\}$$

21. Prove that

$$|z_1| + |z_2| = \left|\frac{1}{2}(z_1 + z_2) + \sqrt{z_1 z_2}\right| + \left|\frac{1}{2}(z_1 + z_2) - \sqrt{z_1 z_2}\right|$$

22. If the equation $ax^2 + bx + c = 0$, $(0 < a < b < c)$ has non-real complex roots z_1 and z_2, show that $|z_1| > 1$, $|z_2| > 1$.

23. Find the value of x such that

$$\frac{(x+\alpha)^n - (x+\beta)^n}{\alpha - \beta} = \frac{\sin n\theta}{\sin^n \theta},$$

when α and β are the roots of $t^2 - 2t + 2 = 0$.

[**Ans.** $x = \cot \theta - 1$]

24. Find all complex numbers z for which

$$\arg\left[\frac{3z - 6 - 3i}{2z - 8 - 6i}\right] = \frac{\pi}{4} \text{ and } |z - 3 + i| = 3.$$

[**Ans.** $\left(4 - \frac{4}{\sqrt{5}}\right) + i\left(1 + \frac{2}{\sqrt{5}}\right)$ and $\left(4 + \frac{4}{\sqrt{5}}\right) + i\left(1 - \frac{2}{\sqrt{5}}\right)$]

25. Find all non-zero complex numbers z satisfying $\bar{z} = iz^2$.

$$\left[\textbf{Ans. } \frac{\sqrt{3}}{2} - \frac{i}{2}; -\frac{\sqrt{3}}{2} - \frac{i}{2}, i\right]$$

26. In a certain test, there are n questions. In this test, 2^{n-r} students gave wrong answers to at least r questions $(i \le r \le n)$. If total number of wrong answers given were 31, show that the greatest value of $|z|$ for which $|z - \frac{4}{z}| = 2$ is $1 + \sqrt{n}$.

27. If $m^2 + n^2 - mn - m - n + 1 \le 0$, where $m, n \in R$ and z_1, z_2 be the complex numbers such that $|z_1| \le m, |z_2| \le n$ and $a > (|z_1| - |z_2|)^2 + (\arg z_1 - \arg z_2)^2 - |z_1 - z_2|^2$.

$$f(x) = ax^2 + bx + c > 0 \text{ for all } x,$$

show that $f(x) + f'(x) + f''(x) > 0$ for all real x.

OBJECTIVE QUESTIONS

For each of the following questions, four alternatives are given for the answer. Only one of them is correct. Choose the correct alternative.

1. The argument of the complex number $z = \frac{(1 + i\sqrt{3})^2}{4i(1 - i\sqrt{3})}$ is :

    (a) $\pi/6$ (b) $\pi/4$ (c) $\pi/2$ (d) None of these.

2. The amplitude of $\frac{1 + i\sqrt{3}}{\sqrt{3} + 1}$ is :

    (a) $\pi/6$ (b) $\pi/4$ (c) $\pi/3$ (d) None of these.

3. If $z = 1 + i\sqrt{3}$, then $|\arg z| + |\arg \bar{z}|$ equals :

    (a) $\pi/3$ (b) $2\pi/3$ (c) 0   (d) $\pi/2$.

4. If $z \ne 0$ and $z' \ne 0$ be any two complex numbers such that

$$|z| = |z'| = 1 \text{ and } \arg z = -\arg z',$$

then zz' is equal to:

(a) 1   (b) -1 (c) 2   (d) None of these.

5. For any two complex numbers, z_1 and z_2 and $a, b \in R$,

$$|az_1 + bz_2|^2 + |bz_1 - az_2|^2 \text{ is equal to :}$$

(a) $|z_1|^2 + |z_2|^2$ (b) $(a^2 + b^2)(|z_1|^2 + |z_2|^2)$

(c) $(a^2 - b^2)(|z_1|^2 + |z_2|^2)$ (d) $|z_1| + |z_2|$.

6. In a geometrical progression the first term and the common ratio are both $\dfrac{1}{2}(\sqrt{3} + i)$. Then the absolute value of the nth term of the progression is:

(a) 2^n (b) 4^n (c) 1   (d) None of these.

7. Let z and w be two non-zero complex numbers such that $|z| = |w|$ and arg z + arg $w = \pi$. Then z equals:

(a) w (b) $-w$ (c) $\overline{w}$ (d) $-\overline{w}$.

8. The complex number z satisfying $|z - 1| = |z - 3| = |z - i|$ is:

(a) $2 + i$ (b) $\dfrac{3}{2} + \dfrac{1}{2}i$ (c) $2 + 2i$ (d) None of these.

9. Let z and w be two complex numbers such that $|z| \le |w| \le 1$ and $|z + iw| = |z - iw| = 2$. Then z equals:

(a) 1 or i (b) i or $-i$ (c) 1 or $-i$ (d) i or -1.

10. If z_1 and z_2 are two complex numbers satisfying the equation

$$\left| \frac{z_1 + z_2}{z_1 - z_2} \right| = 1,$$

then z_1/z_2 is a number which is:

(a) positive real   (b) negative real

(c) zero   (d) None of these.

11. If z_1 and z_2 are any two complex numbers, then

$$\left| z_1 + \sqrt{z_1^2 - z_2^2} \right| + \left| z_1 - \sqrt{z_1^2 - z_2^2} \right|$$

is equal to:

(a) $|z_1|$ (b) $|z_2|$

(c) $|z_1 + z_2|$ (d) $|z_1 + z_2| + |z_1 - z_2|$.

12. (z_1, z_2) and (z_3, z_4) are two pairs of conjugate complex numbers, then

$$\arg\left(\frac{z_1}{z_3} \right) + \arg\left(\frac{z_2}{z_4} \right)$$

is equal to:

(a) 0   (b) $\pi/2$ (c) π (d) $-\pi/2$.

13. If z_1 and z_2 are conjugate complex numbers and z_3 and z_4 are also conjugate, then $\arg\left(\dfrac{z_3}{z_2} \right)$ is equal to :

(a) $\arg\left(\dfrac{z_1}{z_4} \right)$ (b) $\arg\left(\dfrac{z_4}{z_1} \right)$ (c) $\arg\left(\dfrac{z_2}{z_4} \right)$ (d) $\arg\left(\dfrac{z_1}{z_3} \right)$.

14. Let z_1 and z_2 be two complex numbers such that
$$|z_1 + z_2| = |z_1| + |z_2|.$$
Then
(a) $\arg(z_1) = \arg(z_2)$ (b) $\arg(z_1) + \arg(z_2) = 0$
(c) $\arg(z_1 z_2) = 0$ (d) None of these.

15. For any two complex numbers z_1, z_2 and any two real numbers a and b,
$|az_1 - bz_2|^2 + |bz_1 + az_2|^2$ is equal to:
(a) $(a + b)(|z_1|^2 + |z_2|^2)$ (b) $(a^2 + b^2)(|z_1|^2 + |z_2|^2)$
(c) $(a^2 + b^2)(|z_1| + |z_2|)$ (d) None of these.

16. For any two complex numbers z_1 and z_2, we have $|z_1 + z_2|^2 = |z_1|^2 + |z_2|^2$.
Then

(a) $\operatorname{Re}\left(\dfrac{z_1}{z_2}\right) = 0$ (b) $\operatorname{Im}\left(\dfrac{z_1}{z_2}\right) = 0$
(c) $\operatorname{Re}(z_1 z_2) = 0$ (d) $\operatorname{Im}(z_1 z_2) = 0$.

17. If z_1, z_2 and z_3 are complex numbers such that

$$|z_1| = |z_2| = |z_3| = \left|\frac{1}{z_1} + \frac{1}{z_2} + \frac{1}{z_3}\right| = 1,$$

then $|z_1 + z_2 + z_3|$ is
(a) equal to 1   (b) less than 1
(c) greater than 3   (d) equal to 3.

18. If $\arg(z) < 0$, then $\arg(-z) - \arg(z)$ is equal to
(a) π (b) $-\pi$ (c) $-\pi/2$ (d) $\pi/2$.

19. If α is an nth root of unity other than unity itself, then the value of
$1 + \alpha + \alpha^2 + \ldots + \alpha^{n-1}$ is
(a) 0   (b) 1   (c) -1 (d) None of these.

20. The number of solutions of the equation $z^2 = \bar{z}$ is
(a) 2   (b) 3   (c) 4   (d) None of these.

21. The number of solutions of $z^2 + 2\bar{z} = 0$ is
(a) 4   (b) 3   (c) 2   (d) 5.

22. For all complex numbers z_1, z_2 satisfying $|z_1| = 12$ and $|z_2 - 3 - 4i| = 5$, the minimum value of $|z_1 - z_2|$ is
(a) 0   (b) 2   (c) 7   (d) 17.

23. The solution of the equation $|z| - z = 1 + 2i$ is

(a) $\dfrac{3}{2} - 2i$ (b) $\dfrac{3}{2} + 2i$ (c) $2 - \dfrac{3}{2}i$ (d) None of these.

24. Given that the equation $z^2 + (p + iq)z + r + is = 0$ where p, q, r and s are non-zero, has a real root. Then
(a) $pqr = r^2 + p^2 s$ (b) $prs = q^2 + r^2 p$
(c) $qrs = p^2 + s^2 q$ (d) $pqs = s^2 + q^2 r$.

25. For any complex number z, the minimum value of $|z| + |z - 1|$ is

    (a) 1   (b) 0   (c) 1/2   (d) 3/2.

26. The maximum value of $|z|$ when z satisfies the condition $\left| z - \dfrac{2}{z} \right| = 2$ is:

    (a) $\sqrt{3} - 1$ (b) $\sqrt{3}$ (c) $\sqrt{3} + 1$ (d) $\sqrt{2} + \sqrt{3}$.

27. If $\begin{vmatrix} 6i & -3i & 1 \\ 4 & 3i & -1 \\ 20 & 3 & i \end{vmatrix} = x + iy,$ then

    (a) $x = 3, y = 1$ (b) $x = 1, y = 3$ (c) $x = 0, y = 3$ (d) $x = 0 = y.$

28. If $a^2 + b^2 = 1$, then $\dfrac{1 + a + ib}{1 + a - ib}$ is equal to

    (a) $a + ib$ (b) $a - ib$ (c) $b + ia$ (d) $b - ia.$

ANSWERS

1. (c)   2. (c)   3. (b)   4. (a)   5. (b)   6. (c)   7. (d)   8. (c)   9. (c)

10. (c)   11. (d)   12. (a)   13. (a)   14. (a)   15. (b)   16. (a)   17. (a)   18. (a)

19. (a)   20. (c)   21. (a)   22. (b)   23. (a)   24. (d)   25. (a)   26. (c)   27. (d)

28. (a)

GEOMETRICAL REPRESENTATION OF COMPLEX NUMBERS

2.1. Introduction. In this chapter, it will be shown how the complex numbers and the various compositions in the set of complex numbers can be *geometrically* represented. The idea of representing complex numbers by points on a plane had occurred to several mathematicians but Gauss was the first mathematician who conceived the idea and also systematically employed the same for developing the Theory.

It will become clear to the reader in the course of the book that the possibility of the representation of complex numbers by points on a plane has proved very useful and provided a great stimulus for most of the ideas, concepts and lines of development of the Theory of Functions of a Complex Variable. This representation of complex numbers by points of a plane corresponds to that of real numbers by the points of a straight line.

We shall also in this chapter formulate, in terms of complex numbers, such elementary considerations regarding circles and straight lines in a plane as are pertinent to the technique of representation of complex numbers by points on a plane.

In addition to the representation of complex numbers by points on a plane, we shall also consider the representation of these numbers by points on a sphere. This latter idea is due to *Riemann* (1826 – 1866).

2.2. Representation of complex numbers by points on a plane. Complex co-ordinates of a point. Relatively to any two fixed perpendicular lines on a plane as co-ordinate axes, we represent a complex number, $a + ib$, by the point, P, whose rectangular cartesian co-ordinates are a, b. Also $a + ib$ is called the *Complex Co-ordinate* of the point P.

Thus any complex number, α, is represented by the point with rectangular cartesian co-ordinates:

$$[\Re(\alpha), \Im(\alpha)].$$

Also we may see that the cartesian co-ordinates of the point with complex co-ordinate, α, are

$$\left[\frac{1}{2}(\alpha + \overline{\alpha}), \frac{1}{2i}(\alpha - \overline{\alpha})\right].$$

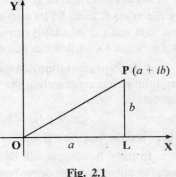

Fig. 2.1

In the following, a point representing any complex number α, will often be referred to as just the point α.

The above manner of representation sets up a one-one correspondence between the set of complex numbers and the set of points on a plane.

The X-axis which is the locus of points with real complex co-ordinates is known as the *Real axis* and the Y-axis which is the locus of points with imaginary complex co-ordinates is known as the *Imaginary axis*.

Also, we have

$$|\alpha| = OP, \arg \alpha = \angle XOP,$$

where P represents the complex number α, so that the modulus of a complex number is the distance from the origin of the corresponding point and the angle which the line joining the origin to the point makes with X-axis measured in the positive direction starting from X-axis is its argument (Fig. 2.2).

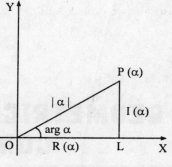

Fig. 2.2

2.3. Complex numbers represented as vectors. Sometimes it is useful to think of a complex number $\alpha = a + ib$ *as represented by the vector*

$$\overrightarrow{OP}$$

where P is the point with rectangular cartesian co-ordinates (a, b). Thus, modulus and the argument of the complex number give the magnitude and the direction of the corresponding vector and *vice-versa* (Fig. 2.3).

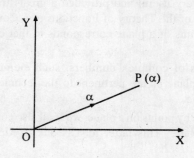

Fig. 2.3

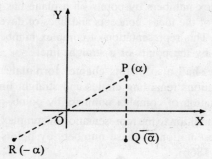

Fig. 2.4

Representation of $\overline{\alpha}$ and $-\alpha$. It is easy to see that if, a complex number α is represented by the point P, then, (*i*) its conjugate, α, is represented by the reflection Q of the point P in the real axis and (*ii*) its additive inverse $-\alpha$, is represented by the point R such that PR is bisected at the origin O, so that the point R is the reflection of the point P in the origin O (Fig. 2.4).

2.4. Representation of Algebraic Operations. We shall now give constructions which, starting from the points representing the given numbers α, β enable us to obtain points representing the numbers

$$\alpha + \beta, \ \alpha - \beta, \ \alpha\beta, \ \alpha \div \beta$$

where for the last case $\beta \neq 0$.

In the following, it will be supposed that α, β denote any complex numbers whatsoever represented by the points P and Q (Fig. 2.5).

2.4.1. Sum. The sum $\alpha + \beta$ is represented by the point R which is the fourth vertex of the parallelogram drawn with OP and OQ as adjacent sides.

This follows from the fact that the point R is such that the segments OR and PQ have the same mid-point and the

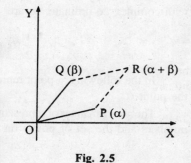

Fig. 2.5

Cartesian co-ordinates of the mid-point of the segment PQ are

$$\left[\frac{1}{2}(a+c), \frac{1}{2}(b+d) \right],$$

where $\alpha = a + ib$, $\beta = c + id$.

2.4.2. Difference. Let $-\beta$ be represented by Q' so that QQ' is bisected at the point O (Fig. 2.6). Then the point R representing

$$\alpha - \beta = \alpha + (-\beta),$$

is the fourth vertex of the parallelogram with OP and OQ' as adjacent sides.

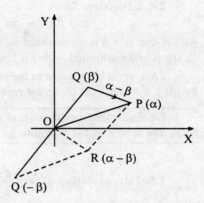

As OQ is equal and parallel to RP, we see that ORPQ is also a parallelo-gram and therefore,

$$\overline{OR} = \overline{QP}$$

so that the vector $\overrightarrow{OP}$ represents the complex number $\alpha - \beta$.

Fig. 2.6

It follows that the *complex number*

$$\alpha - \beta$$

is represented by the vector whose initial and final points represent the complex numbers β and α respectively.

Clearly, therefore

$$| \alpha - \beta | = QP$$

and arg $(\alpha - \beta)$ is equal to the angle through which the positive direction of the real axis has to rotate in the positive direction so as to be parallel to the vector $\overrightarrow{QP}$.

2.4.3. Product. We write

$$\alpha = r_1 (\cos \theta_1 + i \sin \theta_1), \quad \beta = r_2 (\cos \theta_2 + i \sin \theta_2).$$

Thus, we have

$$\alpha\beta = r_1 r_2 [\cos (\theta_1 + \theta_2) + i \sin (\theta_1 + \theta_2)]$$

$\Rightarrow$ $r_1 r_2$ is the modulus and $\theta_1 + \theta_2$, an argument of $\alpha\beta$.

This suggests the following construction for the point R representing the product $\alpha\beta$.

The line OR is obtained on rotating OP, through an angle, arg β and multiplying the same with the modulus $|\beta|$.

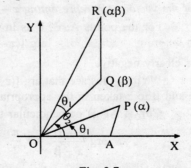

Also, if we take a point A on the real axis such that OA = 1, then the point R representing the product $\alpha\beta$ is the third vertex R of the triangle OQR directly similar to the triangle OAP (Fig. 2.7).

In fact, because of the direct similarity of the triangles OAP and OQR, we have

Fig. 2.7

$$\frac{OR}{OQ} = \frac{OP}{OA} \quad \Rightarrow \quad OR = OP \cdot OQ = r_1 r_2,$$

and $\qquad \angle XOR = \angle XOQ + \angle QOR$

$$= \angle XOQ + \angle XOP = \theta_2 + \theta_1.$$

Ex. Give the construction for multiplication with i.

2.4.4. Division. Since

$$\alpha \div \beta = \gamma \quad \Rightarrow \quad \alpha = \beta\gamma$$

we see that $\alpha \div \beta$ is represented by the point R such that if OR be rotated through an angle equal to arg β and multiplied with $|\beta|$, we get the point P representing α.

Thus, if OP be rotated in the negative direction through an angle equal to arg β and divided by $|\beta|$, we arrive at the point representing the number α/β.

Ex. Show that the nth roots of unity are the vertices of a regular polygon of n sides; the origin being the centre of the polygon.

2.5. Interpretation of $\arg \dfrac{z - \alpha}{z - \beta}$.

We shall in this section see how to describe the angle arg $[(z - \alpha)/(z - \beta)]$ in terms of the points A, B, P representing the complex numbers α, β, z respectively. A combination such as $(z - \alpha)/(z - \beta)$ will occur quite frequently in the following.

The numbers

$$z - \alpha, \ z - \beta$$

are represented by the vectors

$$\overrightarrow{AP} \text{ and } \overrightarrow{BP}$$

respectively (Fig. 2.8).

Thus, we see that *the principal value of*

$$arg \ \frac{z - \alpha}{z - \beta}$$

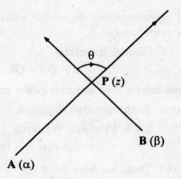

Fig. 2.8

is the angle, θ, $-\pi < \theta \le \pi$, through which the vector $\overrightarrow{BP}$ representing $z - \beta$ has to rotate to coincide with the direction of the vector $\overrightarrow{AP}$ representing $z - \alpha$.

For the points A, B, P as in the above figure

$$arg \ [(z - \alpha)/(z - \beta)]$$

is clearly negative.

We may thus see that arg $[(z - \alpha)/(z - \beta)]$ denotes the angle between the lines joining α to z and β to z taken in the appropriate sense.

Cor. If AP is perpendicular to BP, then

$$arg \ \frac{z - \alpha}{z - \beta} = \pm \frac{\pi}{2},$$

so that the number $[(z - \alpha)/(z - \beta)]$ is imaginary.

Ex. Examine the variation in arg $[(z - \alpha)/(z - \beta)]$, when the point z moves

(*i*) over a circle through the points α, β.

(*ii*) along the straight line joining the points α, β.

2.6. Straight lines in terms of complex numbers.

2.6.1. Complex equation of a straight line through two given points z_1 and z_2. If z be any point on the straight line joining z_1 and z_2, we have

$$\arg \frac{z - z_1}{z_1 - z_2} = 0 \text{ or } \pi$$

$\Rightarrow \quad (z - z_1)/(z_1 - z_2)$ is a real number

$\Rightarrow \quad \dfrac{z - z_1}{z_1 - z_2} = \overline{\left(\dfrac{z - z_1}{z_1 - z_2}\right)} = \dfrac{\bar{z} - \bar{z}_1}{\bar{z}_1 - \bar{z}_2},$

$\Rightarrow \quad z(\bar{z}_1 - \bar{z}_2) - \bar{z}(z_1 - z_2) + (z_1\bar{z}_2 - \bar{z}_1 z_2) = 0,$

as the required complex equation of the line.

Multiplying by i, we obtain

$$zi(\bar{z}_1 - \bar{z}_2) - \bar{z}i(z_1 - z_2) + i(z_1\bar{z}_2 - \bar{z}_1 z_2) = 0.$$

We denote the coefficient of $\bar{z}$ by α, so that the coefficient of z which is the conjugate of that of z will be α. Again as $\bar{z}_1 z_2$ is the conjugate of $z_1\bar{z}_2$, the number $z_1\bar{z}_2 - \bar{z}_1 z_2$ is imaginary and the number $i(z_1\bar{z}_2 - \bar{z}_1 z_2)$ is real. We write

$$i(z_1\bar{z}_2 - \bar{z}_1 z_2) = r, \text{ where } r \text{ is real.}$$

Thus, the equation of any line takes the form

$$\bar{\alpha} z + \alpha \bar{z} + r = 0,$$

where r is real and α is not zero.

2.6.2. General equation of a line. We have seen above that the equation of a straight line is of the form

$$\bar{\alpha} z + \alpha \bar{z} + r = 0, \ \alpha \neq 0, \ r \text{ is real} \qquad \qquad ...(1)$$

where α and r are constants.

Now replacing α and z by $a + ib$ and $x + iy$ respectively, we obtain
$2(ax + by) + r = 0,$

so that it follows that the equation (1) represents a straight line, if, α is a non-zero constant and r is a real constant.

Thus, the general equation of a straight line is of the form

$$\bar{\alpha} z + \alpha \bar{z} + r = 0, \ \alpha \neq 0, \ r \text{ is real.}$$

Ex. Find the equation of the right bisector of the join of the points α, β.

[**Hint.** For any point, z on the right bisector, we have

$$|z - \alpha| = |z - \beta| \ \Leftrightarrow \ \{(z - \alpha)(\bar{z} - \bar{\alpha}) = (z - \beta)(\bar{z} - \bar{\beta})\}$$

2.6.3. Reflection points for a straight line. Two given points P, Q are reflection points for a given straight line, if the given line is the right bisector of the segment PQ.

We shall prove that

two points z_1, z_2 will be reflection points for the straight line

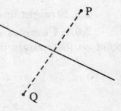

$$\bar{\alpha} z + \alpha \bar{z} + r = 0 \qquad \qquad ...(1)$$

if and only if

$$\bar{\alpha} z_1 + \alpha \bar{z}_2 + r = 0 \qquad \qquad ...(2)$$

Fig. 2.9

Firstly suppose that z_1, z_2 are the reflection points for the straight line (1) so that for any point z on the line, we have

$$|z - z_1| = |z - z_2|$$

$$\Rightarrow \qquad (z - z_1)(\bar{z} - \bar{z}_1) = (z - z_2)(\bar{z} - \bar{z}_2)$$

$$\Rightarrow \qquad z(\bar{z}_2 - \bar{z}_1) + \bar{z}(z_2 - z_1) + (z_1\bar{z}_1 - z_2\bar{z}_2) = 0 \qquad ...(3)$$

The relation (3) is true for any point z on the given line (1) and accordingly (3), thought of as the equation of the given line, must be the same as (1). Thus, there exists a number $k \neq 0$ such that

$$\bar{\alpha} = k(\bar{z}_2 - \bar{z}_1), \quad \alpha = k(z_2 - z_1), \quad r = k(z_1\bar{z}_1 - z_2\bar{z}_2).$$

These give

$$\bar{\alpha} z_1 + \alpha \bar{z}_2 = k(z_2\bar{z}_2 - z_1\bar{z}_1) = -r$$

$$\Rightarrow \qquad \bar{\alpha} z_1 + \alpha \bar{z}_2 + r = 0,$$

which is the same as (2).

Now, suppose that the condition (2) is satisfied.

Subtracting (2) from (1), we see that for any point z on the given line, we have

$$\alpha(z - z_1) + \alpha(\bar{z} - \bar{z}_2) = 0$$

$$\Rightarrow \qquad \alpha(z - z_1) = -\alpha(\bar{z} - \bar{z}_2) = -\alpha\overline{(z - z_2)}$$

$$\Rightarrow \qquad |\bar{\alpha}(z - z_1)| = |-\alpha\overline{(z - z_2)}|$$

$$\Rightarrow \qquad |\bar{\alpha}||z - z_1| = |-\alpha||\overline{z - z_2}|$$

$$\Rightarrow \qquad |z - z_1| = |z - z_2|, \text{ for } \alpha \neq 0$$

$$\Rightarrow \qquad z_1, z_2 \text{ are reflection points for the line (1).}$$

2.7. Circles in terms of complex numbers.

2.7.1. Equation of a circle with given centre and radius. *(Himachal 2005)*

If z be any point on the circle with centre z_1 and radius ρ (Fig. 2.10), we have

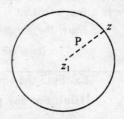

$$|z - z_1| = \rho,$$

$$\Rightarrow \qquad (z - z_1)(\bar{z} - \bar{z}_1) = \rho^2$$

$$\Rightarrow \qquad z\bar{z} - \bar{z}_1 z - z_1\bar{z} + (z_1\bar{z}_1 - \rho^2) = 0$$

which is of the form

$$z\bar{z} + \bar{\alpha} z + \alpha\bar{z} + r = 0, \; r \text{ is real.}$$

Fig. 2.10

2.7.2. General equation of a circle. We have seen above that the equation of circle is of the form

$$z\bar{z} + \bar{\alpha} z + \bar{\alpha}\bar{z} + r = 0, \; r \text{ is real} \qquad \qquad ...(1)$$

Re-writing this as

$$(z + \alpha)(\bar{z} + \bar{\alpha}) = \alpha\bar{\alpha} - r,$$

$\Rightarrow \qquad\qquad |z + \alpha|^2 = \alpha\bar{\alpha} - r,$

we see that the equation (1) represents a circle if r is real and

$$\alpha\bar{\alpha} - r \geq 0.$$

Thus, *the general equation of a circle is*

$$z\bar{z} + \bar{\alpha}z + \alpha\bar{z} + r = 0; \ r \ is \ real \ and \ \alpha\bar{\alpha} - r \geq 0.$$

2.7.3. Condition for four given points to be concyclic.

Let z_1, z_2, z_3 and z_4 be four given points. We denote the given points by A, B, C and D respectively.

The four points A, B, C and D are concyclic.

$\Rightarrow \quad \angle ACB, \angle ADB$ are either equal or differ by π.

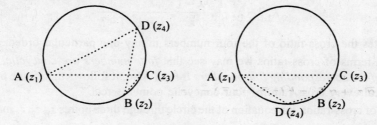

Fig. 2.11

$\Rightarrow \quad \arg \dfrac{z_3 - z_1}{z_3 - z_2}, \arg \dfrac{z_4 - z_1}{z_4 - z_2}$ are either equal or differ by π

$\Rightarrow \quad \arg \left[\left(\dfrac{z_3 - z_1}{z_3 - z_2} \right) \div \left(\dfrac{z_4 - z_1}{z_4 - z_2} \right) \right]$ is 0 or π

$\Rightarrow \quad \left(\dfrac{z_3 - z_1}{z_3 - z_2} \right) \div \left(\dfrac{z_4 - z_1}{z_4 - z_2} \right)$ is real

$\Rightarrow \quad \left(\dfrac{z_3 - z_1}{z_3 - z_2} \right) \left(\dfrac{z_4 - z_2}{z_4 - z_1} \right)$ is real.

Thus, we see that if the four points z_1, z_2, z_3 and z_4 are concyclic, the number

$$\dfrac{(z_3 - z_1)(z_4 - z_2)}{(z_3 - z_2)(z_4 - z_1)} \ \text{is real.}$$

Cor. Equation of the circle through three points z_1, z_2, z_3.

Let z be any point on the circle through the 3 given points. \qquad (*Rajsthan 2000*)

The points z_1, z_2, z_3 and z are concyclic.

$\Rightarrow \quad \dfrac{(z_2 - z_1)(z - z_3)}{(z - z_1)(z_2 - z_3)}$ is real.

$\Rightarrow \quad \dfrac{(z_2 - z_1)(z - z_3)}{(z - z_1)(z_2 - z_3)} = \dfrac{(\bar{z}_2 - \bar{z}_1)(\bar{z} - \bar{z}_3)}{(\bar{z} - \bar{z}_1)(\bar{z}_2 - \bar{z}_3)}.$

This is the required equation of the circle.

Note 1. Cross-ratio of four points on a plane. As in Projective Geometry, cross-ratio of four numbers z_1, z_2, z_3 and z_4 taken in *this order*, is defined to be equal to

$$\frac{(z_2 - z_1)(z_4 - z_3)}{(z_4 - z_1)(z_2 - z_3)}$$

and is denoted by the symbol

$$(z_1, z_2, z_3, z_4).$$

It can be shown that *any* cross-ratio of four given numbers, depending, as it does, upon the order of the numbers, is capable of taking only six different values for all the 24 possible different orders of the four numbers.

Also, these six different values are,

$$\lambda,\; 1 - \lambda,\; \frac{1}{\lambda},\; \frac{\lambda - 1}{\lambda},\; \frac{\lambda}{\lambda - 1},\; \frac{1}{1 - \lambda}$$

where λ denotes the cross-ratio of the four numbers in any one particular order.

Thus, in terms of cross-ratios we may see that *four numbers are concyclic, if and only if, a cross-ratio of the corresponding four numbers is real*. Also, it follows that if one of the six cross-ratios being real every cross-ratio of four concyclic points is real.

In terms of cross-ratios, the equation of the circle through three points z_1, z_2, z_3 may be described as

$$(z_1, z_2, z_3, z) = (\bar{z}_1, \bar{z}_2, \bar{z}_3, z).$$

Note 2. It can be seen that the cross-ratio (z_1, z_2, z_3, z_4) of four points z_1, z_2, z_3, z_4 will also be real, if the points are collinear. In fact, in case of collinearity of the four points, we have :

$$\arg \frac{z_2 - z_1}{z_3 - z_2},\; \arg \frac{z_4 - z_1}{z_4 - z_2}$$

are *separately* 0 or π so that

$$\arg \left[\left(\frac{z_3 - z_1}{z_3 - z_2} \right) \div \left(\frac{z_4 - z_1}{z_4 - z_2} \right) \right]$$

is either 0 or π and accordingly

$$\frac{(z_3 - z_1)(z_4 - z_2)}{(z_3 - z_2)(z_4 - z_1)} = (z_1, z_2, z_3, z_4)$$

is real.

Conversely, we can show that if the *cross-ratio*

$$(z_1, z_2, z_3, z_4)$$

is real, then the four points are either concyclic or collinear.

In fact, if this cross-ratio is real, then

$$\arg \left[\left(\frac{z_3 - z_1}{z_3 - z_2} \right) \div \left(\frac{z_4 - z_1}{z_4 - z_2} \right) \right]$$

is 0 or π so that

$$\arg \frac{z_3 - z_1}{z_3 - z_2},\; \arg \frac{z_4 - z_1}{z_4 - z_2}$$

are either equal or differ by π and accordingly the points will be collinear, if these arguments are *separately* 0 or π and concyclic in the alternative case.

Thus, we may say that the *necessary and sufficient condition for four points to be concyclic or collinear is that any cross-ratio of the four points is real.*

2.7.4. Inverse points with respect to a circle.

Two points P, Q are said to be inverse with respect to a circle with centre O and radius ρ, *if*

(i) *the points O, P, Q are collinear and*

(ii) $OP \cdot OQ = \rho^2$.

We shall now prove that *two points z_1, z_2 will be inverse points with respect to the circle*

$$z\bar{z} + \bar{\alpha}z + \alpha\bar{z} + r = 0 \qquad \ldots(1)$$

if and only if

$$z_1\bar{z}_2 + \bar{\alpha}z_1 + \alpha\bar{z}_2 + r = 0 \qquad \ldots(2)$$

We re-write (1) as

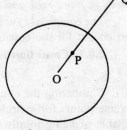

Fig. 2.11

$$(z + \alpha)(\bar{z} + \bar{\alpha}) = \bar{\alpha}\alpha - r = \rho^2 \text{ (say)}$$

$$\Leftrightarrow \qquad |z + \alpha| = \rho$$

so that, $-\alpha$ is the centre and ρ, the radius of the given circle (1).

Now z_1, z_2 will be inverse points for the circle with centre, $-\alpha$ and radius ρ, if and only if, we have

$$\arg (z_1 + \alpha) = \arg (z_2 + \alpha) \qquad \ldots(3)$$

$$|z_1 + \alpha| \, |z_2 + \alpha| = \rho^2 \qquad \ldots(4)$$

We shall now replace these *two* conditions by an equivalent *single* condition.

Since

$$\arg (z_2 + \alpha) = - \arg \overline{(z_2 + \alpha)}$$

We can re-write (3) as

$$\arg (z_1 + \alpha) = - \arg \overline{(z_2 + \alpha)}$$

$$\Leftrightarrow \qquad \arg [(z_1 + \alpha) \overline{(z_2 + \alpha)}] = 0,$$

$$\Leftrightarrow \qquad (z_1 + \alpha) \overline{(z_2 + \alpha)} \qquad \ldots(5)$$

is a positive real number.

Also (4) is equivalent to

$$|z_1 + \alpha| \, |z_2 + \alpha| = \rho^2,$$

$$\Leftrightarrow \qquad |(z_1 + \alpha) \overline{(z_2 + \alpha)}| = \rho^2 \qquad \ldots(6)$$

The conditions (5) and (6) are both equivalent to the single condition

$$(z_1 + \alpha) \overline{(z_2 + \alpha)} = \rho^2$$

$$\Leftrightarrow \qquad z_1\bar{z}_2 + \bar{\alpha}z_1 + \alpha\bar{z}_2 + r = 0, \text{ for } \alpha\bar{\alpha} - \rho^2 = r.$$

Hence the result.

Note 1. It will be seen in terms of the definition of inverse points given above, every point *other than the centre of the circle* possesses a unique inverse. It will be possible to remove this exception in § 3.3.1, by the introduction of the *infinite point*.

Note 2. Inverse points for the unit circle. The circle $|z| = 1$ is known as the *unit circle* and it may be seen either directly from the definition or from the condition obtained above that two points z_1, z_2 will be inverse for the unit circle $|z| = 1$, if and only if $\bar{z}_1, z_2 = 1$. *It follows that the inverse of any point z_1, with respect to the unit circle $|z| = 1$ is $1/\bar{z}_1$.*

2.8. Joint family of circles and straight lines. Considering the general equations of a straight line and a circle as obtained in § 2.6.2 and § 2.7.4, we see that the *general equation of the joint family of straight lines and circles can be taken to be*

$$p z\bar{z} + \bar{\alpha}z + \alpha\bar{z} + r = 0, \qquad \qquad ...(1)$$

where p, r are real and $\alpha\bar{\alpha} - pr \geq 0$.

The equation (1) will represent a straight line if $p = 0$ and a circle if $p \neq 0$. Thus, any consideration carried out for the equation (1) will relate to the joint family of straight lines and circles.

2.8.1. Condition for two points to be inverse for

$$p z\bar{z} + \bar{\alpha}z + \alpha\bar{z} + r = 0 \qquad \qquad ...(1)$$

Comparing the conditions for two points z_1, z_2 to be reflection points for a straight line and inverse points for a circle obtained in § 2.6.3 and § 2.7.4 respectively, we see that they are both capable of being jointly formulated as follows:

Two points z_1, z_2 are inverse points or reflection points, as the case may be, for (1) if and only if

$$p z_1\bar{z}_2 + \alpha\bar{z}_2 + \bar{\alpha}z_1 + r = 0.$$

Note. In view of the results obtained above, we shall often indifferently talk of a circle or straight line both as a circle and also of inverse points or reflection points both for straight lines as well as circles. Thus, we may speak of inverse points for a straight line and of reflection points for a circle. This consolidated treatment is possible only because of the results obtained above. [Refer also to Note 2 after § 2.7.3]

2.9. Two families of circles. In this section, we shall consider two families of circles. An important relation between these two families will also be found later on.

2.9.1. *The equation*

$$\left| \frac{z - z_1}{z - z_2} \right| = \lambda$$

where λ is a non-negative parameter, represents a family of circles such that z_1, z_2 are inverse points for every member of the family.

The given equation is

$$\Leftrightarrow \qquad \frac{(z - z_1)(\bar{z} - \bar{z}_1)}{(z - z_2)(\bar{z} - \bar{z}_2)} = \lambda^2$$

$$\Leftrightarrow \qquad (1 - \lambda^2)\bar{z}z + (\bar{z}_2\lambda^2 - \bar{z}_1)z + (z_2\lambda^2 - z_1)\bar{z}$$

$$+ (z_1\bar{z}_1 - \lambda^2 z_2\bar{z}_2) = 0 \qquad \qquad ...(1)$$

which is known to represent a circle for every non-negative value of λ.

We may now easily see that the condition for z_1, z_2 to be inverse points (§ 2.7.4) is satisfied for the circle (1) whatever λ may be. Hence the result.

Thus, in particular, the centre of every circle of the family must be collinear with the points z_1, z_2. Also directly we may see that the centre

$$\frac{z_1 - \lambda^2 z_2}{1 - \lambda^2}$$

of the circle (1) divides the join of z_1, z_2 externally in the ratio $\lambda^2 : 1$.

Taking $\lambda = 1$, we see that the right bisector of the join of the points z_1, z_2 is also a member of the family in question. The points z_1, z_2 are inverse for this line as well.

2.9.2. *The equation*

$$\arg\left(\frac{z - z_1}{z - z_2}\right) = \mu,$$

where μ is a real parameter, represents a family of circles every member of which passes through the two points z_1, z_2.

The locus of the point z such that

$$\arg\left(\frac{z - z_1}{z - z_2}\right) = \mu,$$

where μ is given, is an arc of a circle through the two points z_1, z_2. Also, the remaining part of the circle of which this arc is a part is given by

$$\arg\left(\frac{z - z_1}{z - z_2}\right) = \mu + \pi.$$

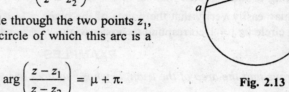

Fig. 2.13

Thus we have the result as stated.

The straight line joining the points z_1, z_2 is itself a member of the family, arising as it does for $\mu = 0$ and π.

2.10. Representation of complex numbers by points of a sphere. Riemann sphere. Stereographic projection.

It is possible to represent complex numbers by points on a sphere. Obviously, this relates to the possibility of establishing one-to-one correspondence between the set of points on a *sphere* K and that of points on a *plane* π and this correspondence is easily obtained *by associating to each point P of the sphere K, the point P′ of the plane π where the line VP meets the plane; V being a fixed point of the sphere*. Here the point V of the sphere is an exception in as much as no point of the plane corresponds to the point V of the sphere.

To consider the various properties of this correspondence, we now proceed to express the same algebraically.

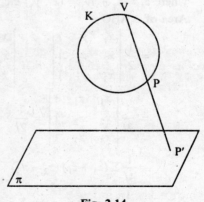

Fig. 2.14

We suppose that the radius of the sphere K is unity. Also, we suppose that the plane π passes through the centre O of the sphere K and the point V is the one where the line through O perpendicular to the plane π meets the sphere (Fig. 2.15).

We take the point O as origin, the line OV as Z-axis and any two perpendicular lines through O in the plane π as X-axis and Y-axis.

Let P (X, Y, Z) be any point on the sphere and P′ $(x, y, 0)$ the point on the π plane where VP meets the same. We have

$$X^2 + Y^2 + Z^2 = 1 \qquad \ldots(1)$$

The three points $(0, 0, 1)$, (X, Y, Z), $(x, y, 0)$ being collinear, we have

$$\frac{X}{x} = \frac{Y}{y} = \frac{Z-1}{-1}. \qquad ...(2)$$

From (1) and (2), we obtain, taking $z = x + iy$,

$$X = \frac{2x}{x^2 + y^2 + 1} = \frac{z + \bar{z}}{z\bar{z} + 1} \qquad ...(3)$$

$$Y = \frac{2y}{x^2 + y^2 + 1} = \frac{z - \bar{z}}{i(z\bar{z} + 1)} \qquad ...(4)$$

$$Z = \frac{x^2 + y^2 - 1}{x^2 + y^2 + 1} = \frac{z\bar{z} - 1}{z\bar{z} + 1} \qquad ...(5)$$

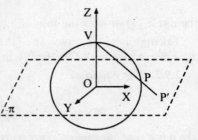

Fig. 2.15

The equations (3), (4) and (5) express co-ordinates (X, Y, Z) of the point on the sphere corresponding to the complex number z.

We may easily verify that the points of the plane π $(z = 0)$ which are inverse with respect to the unit circle $|z| = 1$ correspond to points of the sphere which are symmetric to the plane π.

EXAMPLES

1. *Prove that the area of the triangle whose vertices are the points z_1, z_2, z_3 on the Argand's diagram is*

$$\sum \left[\frac{(z_2 - z_3)|z_1|^2}{4iz_1} \right].$$

Show that the triangle is equilateral if

$$z_1^2 + z_2^2 + z_3^2 = z_1 z_2 + z_2 z_3 + z_3 z_1.$$

(Ravishankar 2001, Indore 2004, Agra 2001, 2005)

Solution. Let the points A, B, C be z_1, z_2, z_3 respectively Fig. (2.16),
where $z_1 = x_1 + iy_1 = (x_1, y_1)$ etc.
Area of $\triangle$ ABC

$$= \frac{1}{2} \begin{vmatrix} x_1 & y_1 & 1 \\ x_2 & y_2 & 1 \\ x_3 & y_3 & 1 \end{vmatrix} = \frac{1}{2i} \begin{vmatrix} x_1 & x_1 + iy_1 & 1 \\ x_2 & x_2 + iy_2 & 1 \\ x_3 & x_3 + iy_3 & 1 \end{vmatrix}$$

$$= \frac{1}{2i} \begin{vmatrix} x_1 & z_1 & 1 \\ x_2 & z_2 & 1 \\ x_3 & z_3 & 1 \end{vmatrix} = \frac{1}{2i} \sum x_1 (z_2 - z_3)$$

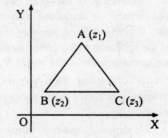

Fig. 2.16

$$= \frac{1}{4i} \sum (z_1 + \bar{z}_1)(z_2 - z_3)$$

$$= \frac{1}{4i} \left[\sum z_1 (z_2 - z_3) + \sum \bar{z}_1 (z_2 - z_3) \right]$$

$$= \frac{1}{4i} \left[0 + \sum \frac{z_1 \bar{z}_1 (z_2 - z_3)}{z_1} \right]$$

$$= \sum \left[\frac{|z_1|^2 (z_2 - z_3)}{4iz_1} \right].$$

If the triangle is equilateral, then AB = BC = CA

or
$$|z_1 - z_2| = |z_2 - z_3| = |z_3 - z_1| \qquad ...(1)$$

From the first two, we get

$$|z_1 - z_2|^2 = |z_2 - z_3|^2$$

$$\Rightarrow \qquad (z_1 - z_2)(\bar{z}_1 - \bar{z}_2) = (z_2 - z_3)(\bar{z}_2 - \bar{z}_3) \qquad ...(2)$$

$$\Rightarrow \qquad \frac{z_1 - z_2}{\bar{z}_2 - \bar{z}_3} = \frac{z_2 - z_3}{\bar{z}_1 - \bar{z}_2}$$

$$= \frac{z_1 - z_2 + z_2 - z_3}{\bar{z}_2 - \bar{z}_3 + \bar{z}_1 - \bar{z}_2} = \frac{z_1 - z_3}{\bar{z}_1 - \bar{z}_3}.$$

From the last two ratios of (1), we have

$$(z_2 - z_3)(\bar{z}_2 - \bar{z}_3) = (z_3 - z_1)(\bar{z}_3 - \bar{z}_1) \qquad ...(3)$$

Multiplying both sides of (2) and (3), we get

$$(z_1 - z_3)(z_2 - z_3) = (z_1 - z_3)^2$$

$$\Rightarrow \qquad z_1 z_2 - z_2^2 - z_1 z_3 + z_2 z_3 = z_1^2 + z_3^2 - 2z_1 z_3$$

$$\Rightarrow \qquad z_1^2 + z_2^2 + z_3^2 = z_1 z_2 + z_2 z_3 + z_3 z_1.$$

2. *The roots z_1, z_2, z_3 of the equation $x^3 + 3ax^2 + 3bx + c = 0$ in which a, b, c are complex numbers correspond to the points A, B, C on the Gaussian plane. Find the centroid of the triangle ABC and show that it will be equilateral if $a^2 = b$.*

Solution. From given equation

$$\Sigma z_1 = -3a, \ \Sigma z_1 z_2 = 3b, \ z_1 z_2 z_3 = -c; \text{ centroid is } \frac{1}{3}\Sigma z_1 = -a.$$

Condition for the triangle to be equilateral from Example 1 is

$$\Sigma z_1^2 = \Sigma z_1 z_2$$

$$\Rightarrow \qquad \Sigma z_1^2 + 2\Sigma z_1 z_2 = 3\Sigma z_1 z_2$$

$$\Rightarrow \qquad (\Sigma z_1)^2 = 3\Sigma z_1 z_2 \Rightarrow 9a^2 = 3 \cdot 3b$$

$$\Rightarrow \qquad a^2 = b.$$

3. *If z_1, z_2, z_3 are the vertices of an isosceles triangle right-angled at the vertex z_2, prove that $z_1^2 + 2z_2^2 + z_3^2 = 2z_2(z_1 + z_3)$.* (Osmania 2004)

Solution. We are given that angle between lines AB and CB is $\pi/2$.

$$\therefore \quad \text{amp}\left(\frac{z_2 - z_1}{z_2 - z_3}\right) = \frac{\pi}{2}$$

$$\Rightarrow \quad \frac{z_2 - z_1}{z_2 - z_3} \text{ is purely imaginary so that its real part is zero.}$$

But we know that $\text{Re } z = \frac{1}{2}(z + \bar{z})$.

$$\therefore \qquad \frac{1}{2}\left(\frac{z_2 - z_1}{z_2 - z_3} + \frac{\bar{z}_2 - \bar{z}_1}{\bar{z}_2 - \bar{z}_3}\right) = 0$$

$$\Rightarrow \qquad \frac{z_2 - z_1}{z_2 - z_3} = - \frac{\overline{z}_2 - \overline{z}_1}{\overline{z}_2 - \overline{z}_3} \qquad\qquad ...(1)$$

Again as the triangle is isosceles, we have AB = CB.

$$\therefore \qquad\qquad |z_2 - z_1| = |z_2 - z_3|$$
$$\Rightarrow \qquad\qquad |z_2 - z_1|^2 = |z_2 - z_3|^2$$
$$\Rightarrow \qquad (z_2 - z_1)(\overline{z}_2 - \overline{z}_1) = (z_2 - z_3)(\overline{z}_2 - \overline{z}_3)$$
$$\Rightarrow \qquad\qquad \frac{z_2 - z_1}{z_2 - z_3} = \frac{\overline{z}_2 - \overline{z}_3}{\overline{z}_2 - \overline{z}_1} \qquad\qquad ...(2)$$

Multiplying both sides of (1) and (2), we get

$$\left(\frac{z_2 - z_1}{z_2 - z_3} \right)^2 = -1$$

$$\Rightarrow \qquad z_1{}^2 + 2z_2{}^2 + z_3{}^2 = 2z_2(z_1 + z_3).$$

4. *Similar triangles BCX, CAY and ABZ are described on the sides of a triangle ABC. Show that centroids of the triangles ABC and XYZ are coincident.*

Solution. Let the vertices of the triangles ABC and XYZ be a, b, c and z_1, z_2, z_3 respectively. Since the three triangles are similar, therefore, the ratios of the corresponding sides are the same,

i.e., $$\frac{CX}{BC} = \frac{AY}{CA} = \frac{BZ}{AB}$$

$$\Rightarrow \qquad \frac{z_1 - c}{c - b} = \frac{z_2 - a}{a - c} = \frac{z_3 - b}{b - a}$$

$$= \frac{\Sigma z_1 - \Sigma a}{0}.$$

Hence, $$\Sigma z_1 = \Sigma a$$

$$\Rightarrow \qquad \frac{1}{3} \Sigma z_1 = \frac{1}{3} \Sigma a.$$

Therefore, the centroids of the two triangles XYZ and ABC are coincident.

5. *If A, B, C, D are four points in a plane, then prove that*
$$AD \cdot BC \leq BD \cdot CA + CD \cdot AB.$$

Solution. Let the points A, B, C, D be z_1, z_2, z_3, z_4 respectively.

Write AD as $-(z_1 - z_4)$ etc., then we can easily verify the identity
$$-(z_1 - z_4)(z_2 - z_3) = (z_2 - z_4)(z_3 - z_1) + (z_3 - z_4)(z_1 - z_2).$$

Taking modulus of both sides, we get
$$|-(z_1 - z_4)(z_2 - z_3)| = |(z_2 - z_4)(z_3 - z_1) + (z_3 - z_4)(z_1 - z_2)|.$$

Now apply $|z_1 z_2| = |z_1| \, |z_2|$ and $|z_1 + z_2| \leq |z_1| + |z_2|$.

6. *If A, B, C and D are the points z_1, z_2, z_3 and z_4 respectively, show that if $z_1 z_2 + z_3 z_4 = 0$ and $z_1 + z_2 = 0$, then the points A, B, C and D are concyclic.*

Solution. Condition for four points to be concyclic is

$$\frac{(z_4 - z_1)(z_3 - z_2)}{(z_4 - z_2)(z_3 - z_1)} \text{ is purely real.}$$

L.H.S. on multiplication reduces to

$$\frac{(z_4 z_3 + z_1 z_2) - (z_1 z_3 + z_4 z_2)}{(z_4 z_3 + z_1 z_2) - (z_2 z_3 + z_1 z_4)}$$

$$= \frac{0 - [z_1 z_3 + z_4 (-z_1)]}{0 - (-z_1 z_3 + z_1 z_4)} \quad \text{by given conditions}$$

$$= \frac{z_1 z_4 - z_1 z_3}{-(z_1 z_4 - z_1 z_3)} = -1, \quad i.e., \text{ purely real.}$$

Hence, the four points are concyclic.

7. *Find all circles which are orthogonal to* $|z| = 1$ *and* $|z - 1| = 4.$

Solution. Let $|z - \alpha| = k$ ...(1)

where $\alpha = a + bi$ and a, b, k are real, be the circle which cuts the circles

$$|z| = 1 \qquad\qquad ...(2)$$

and $\qquad\qquad |z - 1| = 4 \qquad\qquad ...(3)$

orthogonally.

Now, two circles will cut orthogonally if the sum of the squares of their radii is equal to the square of the distance between their centres. Thus, the circle (1) will cut the circles (2) and (3) orthogonally if

$$k^2 + 1 = |\alpha - 0|^2 = \alpha\overline{\alpha}$$

and $\qquad\qquad k^2 + 16 = |\alpha - 1|^2 = (\alpha - 1)(\overline{\alpha} - 1)$

$$= \alpha\overline{\alpha} - \alpha - \overline{\alpha} + 1$$

i.e., if $\qquad\qquad \alpha\overline{\alpha} - k^2 = 1$ and $\alpha\overline{\alpha} = k^2 - \alpha - \overline{\alpha} - 15 = 0.$

These relations give

$$1 - \alpha - \overline{\alpha} - 15 = 0 \implies \alpha + \overline{\alpha} = -14$$

$$\implies \qquad\qquad 2a = -14 \implies a = -7$$

and so, $\qquad\qquad \alpha = -7 + bi$

and $\qquad\qquad k^2 = |\alpha|^2 - 1 = (-7)^2 + b^2 - 1 = 48 + b^2.$

Hence the required family of the circles is

$$|z + 7 - bi| = \sqrt{(48 + b^2)}.$$

8. *Show that the perpendicular distance of a point d (d is a complex number) on the Argand plane from the line* $\overline{a} z + a \overline{z} + b = 0$ *(a is a complex number and b is real) is*

$$\frac{|a\overline{d} + \overline{a}d + b|}{2|a|}$$

Solution. Equation of line is

$$\overline{a}z + a\overline{z} + b = 0$$

Pur $z = x + iy$, then we have

$$(a + \overline{a})x + (\overline{a} - a)iy + b = 0$$

Let $\qquad\qquad d = d_1 + id_2$

Distance of the line from d

$$= \frac{|(a + \overline{a}) d_1 + (\overline{a} - a)id_2 + b|}{\sqrt{(a + \overline{a})^2 + [(\overline{a} - a)i]^2}}$$

$$= \frac{|a (d_1 - id_2) + \overline{a} (d_1 + id_2) + b|}{\sqrt{(a + \overline{a})^2 - (\overline{a} - a)^2}}$$

$$= \frac{|a\overline{d} + \overline{a}d + b|}{\sqrt{4\overline{a}a}}$$

$$= \frac{|a\overline{d} + \overline{a}d + b|}{\sqrt{4 |a|^2}}$$

$$= \frac{|a\overline{d} + \overline{a}d + b|}{2|a|}.$$

9. *Find the equation of the circle in complex form which touches the line* $iz + \overline{z} + 1 + i = 0$ *and the lines* $(2 - i) z = (2 + i)\overline{z}$ *and* $(2 + i) z + (i - 2)\overline{z} - 4i = 0$ *are the normal of the circle.*

Solution. The given normals of circle are

$$(2 - i) z = (2 + i)\overline{z} \qquad \qquad ...(1)$$

$$(2 + i) z + (i - 2)\overline{z} - 4i = 0 \qquad \qquad ...(2)$$

Replace $\overline{z}$ from (2) with the help of (1)

$$(2 + i) z + (i - 2)\overline{z} - 4i = 0$$

$$\Rightarrow \qquad (2 + i) z + \frac{(4i - 3)(2 - i)}{(2 + i)(2 - i)} z = 4i$$

$$\Rightarrow \qquad (2 + i) z + \frac{(11i - 2)}{5} z = 4i$$

$$\Rightarrow \qquad (16i + 18) z = 20i$$

$$\Rightarrow \qquad z = \frac{5i}{4i + 2} = \frac{10i + 20}{20} = \left(1 + \frac{i}{2}\right)$$

As the point of intersection of two normals in a circle is its centre, hence

$$\text{Centre} \equiv z = \left(1 + \frac{i}{2}\right)$$

Tangent to the circle is

$$iz + \overline{z} + (1 + i) = 0$$

$$\Rightarrow \qquad \frac{iz}{1 + i} + \frac{\overline{z}}{1 + i} + 1 = 0$$

$$\Rightarrow \qquad (1 + i) z + (1 - i)\overline{z} + 2 = 0$$

Radius of circle = perpendicular distance from centre on the tangent

$$\therefore \qquad r = \frac{\left|\dfrac{(1 + i)(2 + i)}{2} + \dfrac{(1 - i)(2 - i)}{2} + 2\right|}{|1 + i| + |1 - i|} = \frac{3}{2\sqrt{2}}.$$

∴ Equation of the circle is

$$\left| z - \left(1 + \frac{i}{2} \right) \right| = \frac{3}{2\sqrt{2}}.$$

10. *A, B, C are the points representing the complex number z_1, z_2, z_3 respectively on the complex plane and the circumcentre of the triangle ABC lies at the origin. If the altitude of the triangle through the vertex A meets the circumcircle again at P, then prove that P represents the complex number $-z_2 z_3 / z_1$.*

Solution. ∵ AD is perpendicular to BC, hence AP is ⊥ to BC

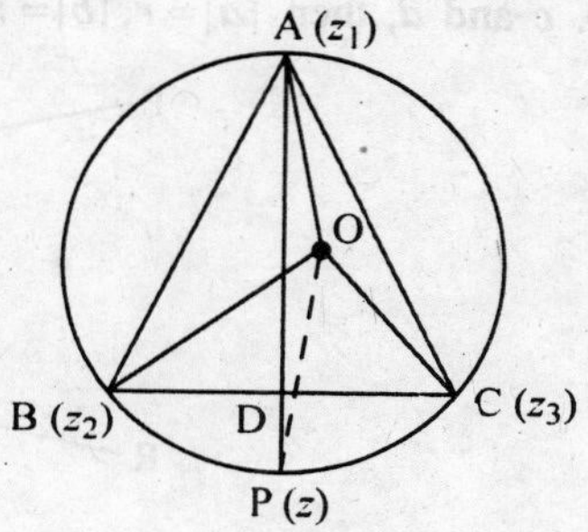

then

$$\arg \left(\frac{z_1 - z}{z_3 - z_2} \right) = \pi / 2$$

∴

$$\operatorname{Re} \left(\frac{z_1 - z}{z_3 - z_3} \right) = 0$$

⇒

$$\frac{\dfrac{z_1 - z}{z_3 - z_2} + \dfrac{\bar{z}_1 - \bar{z}}{\bar{z}_3 - \bar{z}_2}}{2} = 0 \qquad \ldots(1)$$

Fig. 2.17

But O is the circumcentre of ∆ABC, then

$$OP = OA = OB = OC$$

i.e.,

$$|z| = |z_1| = |z_2| = |z_3|$$

⇒

$$|z|^2 = |z_1|^2 = |z_2|^2 = |z_3|^2$$

⇒

$$z\bar{z} = z_1 \bar{z}_1 = z_2 \bar{z}_2 = z_3 \bar{z}_3$$

⇒

$$\frac{\bar{z}_1}{\bar{z}} = \frac{z}{z_1} \qquad \qquad \ldots(2)$$

$$\frac{\bar{z}_2}{\bar{z}} = \frac{z}{z_3} \qquad \qquad \ldots(3)$$

and

$$\frac{\bar{z}_3}{\bar{z}} = \frac{z}{z_2} \qquad \qquad \ldots(4)$$

From (1)

$$\frac{z_1 - z}{z_3 - z_2} + \frac{\dfrac{\bar{z}_1}{\bar{z}} - 1}{\dfrac{\bar{z}_3}{\bar{z}} - \dfrac{\bar{z}_1}{\bar{z}}} = 0$$

⇒

$$\frac{z_1 - z}{z_3 - z_2} + \frac{\dfrac{z}{z_1} - 1}{\dfrac{z}{z_3} - \dfrac{z}{z_2}} = 0$$

⇒

$$\left(\frac{z_1 - z}{z_3 - z_2} \right) \left(1 + \frac{z_2 z_3}{z z_1} \right) = 0$$

⇒

$$1 + \frac{z_2 z_3}{z z_1} = 0 \qquad \left(\because \frac{z_1 - z}{z_3 - z_2} \neq 0 \right)$$

$\Rightarrow$
$$z = -\frac{z_2 z_3}{z_1}.$$

11. *Two different non-parallel lines meet the circle $|z| = r$ in the points a, b and c, d respectively. Prove that these lines meet in the point z given by*

$$z = \frac{a^{-1} + b^{-1} - c^{-1} - d^{-1}}{a^{-1}b^{-1} - c^{-1}d^{-1}}.$$

Solution. Let two non-parallel straight lines PQ, RS meet the circle $|z| = r$ in the points a, b, c and d, then $|a| = r, |b| = r, |c| = r$ and $|d| = r$.

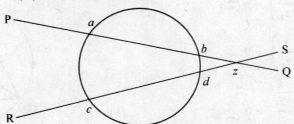

Fig. 2.18

or
$$|a|^2 = |b|^2 = |c|^2 = |d|^2 = r^2$$
$\Rightarrow$
$$a\bar{a} = b\bar{b} = c\bar{c} = d\bar{d} = r^2$$
$\Rightarrow$
$$\bar{a} = \frac{r^2}{a}, \bar{b} = \frac{r^2}{b}, \bar{c} = \frac{r^2}{c} \text{ and } \bar{d} = \frac{r^2}{d}$$

For line PQ, points a, b, z are collinear, then

$$\begin{vmatrix} z & \bar{z} & 1 \\ a & \bar{a} & 1 \\ b & \bar{b} & 1 \end{vmatrix} = 0$$

$\Rightarrow$
$$z(\bar{a} - \bar{b}) - \bar{z}(a - b) + (a\bar{b} - \bar{a}b) = 0$$

$\Rightarrow$
$$z\left(\frac{r^2}{a} - \frac{r^2}{b}\right) - \bar{z}(a - b) + \left(\frac{ar^2}{b} - \frac{br^2}{a}\right) = 0$$

$\Rightarrow$
$$\frac{r^2}{ab}z + \bar{z} - \frac{r^2}{ab}(a + b) = 0$$

$\Rightarrow$
$$\frac{z}{ab} + \frac{\bar{z}}{r^2} - \frac{(a + b)}{ab} = 0 \qquad (1)$$

Similarly, for line RS

$$\frac{z}{cd} + \frac{\bar{z}}{r^2} - \frac{(c + d)}{cd} = 0 \qquad (2)$$

$\therefore$ Subtracting (1) and (2), we have

$$z\left(\frac{1}{ab} - \frac{1}{cd}\right) - \frac{(a + b)}{ab} + \frac{(c + d)}{cd} = 0$$

$$\Rightarrow \qquad z(a^{-1}b^{-1} - c^{-1}d^{-1}) = a^{-1} + b^{-1} - c^{-1}d^{-1}$$

$$\Rightarrow \qquad z = \frac{a^{-1} + b^{-1} - c^{-1} - d^{-1}}{a^{-1}b^{-1} - c^{-1}d^{-1}}.$$

12. Let z_1, z_2, z_3 be three non-zero complex numbers and $z_1 \neq z_2$. If

$$\begin{vmatrix} |z_1| & |z_2| & |z_3| \\ |z_2| & |z_3| & |z_1| \\ |z_3| & |z_1| & |z_2| \end{vmatrix} = 0$$

then prove that

(i) z_1, z_2, z_3 lie on a circle with the centre at origin.

(ii) $arg\left(\dfrac{z_3}{z_2}\right) = arg\left(\dfrac{z_3 - z_1}{z_2 - z_1}\right)^2$

Solution. Let $z_1 = r_1(\cos\alpha + i\sin\alpha)$, $z_2 = r_2(\cos\beta + i\sin\beta)$ and $z_3 = r_3(\cos\gamma + i\sin\gamma)$

$$\therefore \qquad |z_1| = r_1, |z_2| = r_2, |z_3| = r_3$$

and $arg(z_1) = \alpha, arg(z_2) = \beta, arg(z_3) = \gamma$.

From the given condition

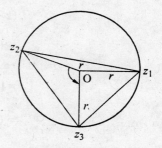

Fig. 2.19

$$\begin{vmatrix} r_1 & r_2 & r_3 \\ r_2 & r_3 & r_1 \\ r_3 & r_1 & r_2 \end{vmatrix} = 0$$

$$\Rightarrow \quad (r_1 + r_2 + r_3)(r_1^2 + r_2^2 + r_3^2 - r_1r_2 - r_2r_3 - r_3r_1) = 0$$

$$\Rightarrow \quad \frac{1}{2}(r_1 + r_2 + r_3)[(r_1 - r_2)^2 + (r_2 - r_3)^2 + (r_3 - r_1)^2] = 0$$

Since, $\qquad\qquad r_1 + r_2 + r_3 \neq 0$

$$\therefore \qquad (r_1 - r_2)^2 + (r_2 - r_3)^2 + (r_3 - r_1)^2 = 0$$

It is possible only when

$$r_1 - r_2 = r_2 - r_3 = r_3 - r_1 = 0$$

i.e., $\qquad\qquad r_1 = r_2 = r_3$

or $\qquad\qquad |z_1| = |z_3| = |z_3| = r \text{ (say)}$

Hence, z_1, z_2, z_3 lie on a circle with the centre at the origin.

Now, in $\Delta O z_2 z_3$

$$arg\left(\frac{z_3 - 0}{z_2 - 0}\right) = \angle z_2 O z_3$$

$$\Rightarrow \qquad arg\left(\frac{z_3}{z_2}\right) = \angle z_2 O z_3$$

In $\Delta z_2\, z_1\, z_3$,

$$\arg\left(\frac{z_3 - z_1}{z_2 - z_1}\right) = \angle z_2 z_1 z_3 = \frac{1}{2}\, \angle z_2 O z_3$$

$$= \frac{1}{2}\arg\left(\frac{z_3}{z_1}\right)$$

$$\therefore \qquad \arg\left(\frac{z_3}{z_1}\right) = 2\arg\left(\frac{z_3 - z_1}{z_2 - z_1}\right)$$

$$\Rightarrow \qquad \arg\left(\frac{z_3}{z_1}\right) = \arg\left(\frac{z_3 - z_1}{z_2 - z_1}\right)^2$$

13. *Find u and v, the real and imaginary parts of* $(z - 1)\,(\cos\alpha - i\sin\alpha) + (z - 1)^{-1}$ *(cos α + i sin α) where* $\alpha \in R$ *and z is a complex number. Prove that the locus of the points in the Argand's diagram representing the complex numbers z such that v = 0 is a circle of unit radius with centre* (1, 0) *or a straight line through the point* (1, 0).

Solution. Let $z = x + iy$, then

$$(z - 1)(\cos\alpha - i\sin\alpha) + (z - 1)^{-1}(\cos\alpha + i\sin\alpha)$$

$$= \{(x - 1) + iy\}(\cos\alpha - i\sin\alpha) + \frac{1}{(x - 1) + iy}\,(\cos\alpha + i\sin\alpha)$$

$$= [(x - 1) + iy](\cos\alpha - i\sin\alpha) + \frac{(x - 1) - iy}{(x - 1)^2 + y^2}\,(\cos\alpha + i\sin\alpha)$$

$$= (x - 1)\cos\alpha - i(x - 1)\sin\alpha + iy\cos\alpha + y\sin\alpha$$

$$+ \frac{(x - 1)\cos\alpha + y\sin\alpha}{(x - 1)^2 + y^2} + i\frac{(x - 1)\sin\alpha - y\cos\alpha}{(x - 1)^2 + y^2}$$

$$= \left[(x - 1)\cos\alpha + y\sin\alpha + \frac{(x - 1)\cos\alpha + y\sin\alpha}{(x - 1)^2 + y^2}\right]$$

$$+ i\left[y\cos\alpha - (x - 1)\sin\alpha + \frac{(x - 1)\sin\alpha - y\cos\alpha}{(x - 1)^2 + y^2}\right]$$

$$= u + iv$$

$$\Rightarrow \qquad u = [(x - 1)\cos\alpha + y\sin\alpha]\left[1 + \frac{1}{(x - 1)^2 + y^2}\right]$$

and

$$v = [y\cos\alpha - (x - 1)\sin\alpha]\left[1 - \frac{1}{(x - 1)^2 + y^2}\right]$$

If $v = 0$, then

$$y\cos\alpha - (x - 1)\sin\alpha = 0 \qquad\qquad \dots(1)$$

or

$$1 - \frac{1}{(x - 1)^2 + y^2} = 0$$

or $$(x - 1)^2 + y^2 = 1 \qquad (2)$$

Equation (1) is the eqn. of a straight line passing through the point (1, 0) and the eqn. (2) represents the equation of a circle whose centre is (1, 0) and radius 1.

14. *A represents the number 6i, B the number 3 and P some number z. If P moves so that PA = 2 PB, show that the locus of P is a circle whose equation is*

$$z\bar{z} = (4 + 2i)z + (4 - 2i)\bar{z}$$

Also, find the radius and the complex number corresponding to the centre of the circle.

Solution. Given $PA = 2PB$

$\Rightarrow$ $\qquad |z - 6i| = 2|z - 3|$

$\Rightarrow$ $\qquad |z - 6i|^2 = 4|z - 3|^2$

$\Rightarrow$ $\qquad (z - 6i)\overline{(z - 6i)} = 4(z - 3)\overline{(z - 3)}$

$\Rightarrow$ $\qquad (z - 6i)(\bar{z} + 6i) = 4(z - 3)(\bar{z} - 3)$

$\Rightarrow$ $\qquad z\bar{z} + 6iz - 6i\bar{z} + 36 = 4(z\bar{z} - 3z - 3\bar{z} + 9)$

$\Rightarrow$ $\qquad z\bar{z} = (4 + 2i)z + (4 - 2i)\bar{z}$ ...(1)

This is the locus of P.

The general equation of circle is

$$z\bar{z} + a\bar{z} + \bar{a}z + b = 0$$

whose centre is $-a$ and radius $= -\sqrt{a\bar{a} - b}$.

On comparing with equation (1), the locus of P is a circle where $a = -(4 - 2i)$, $b = 0$ and $\bar{a} = -(4 + 2i)$. Since $-a$ is the complex number correspoinding to the centre of the curcle, the centre of the circle is to the $4 - 2i$ and

$$\text{radius} = \sqrt{a\bar{a} - b} = \sqrt{-(4 - 2i)\{-(4 + 2i)\} - 0}$$

$$= \sqrt{20} = 2\sqrt{5}$$

EXERCISES

1. Prove geometrically that

(a) $|\alpha + \beta| \le |\alpha| + |\beta|$

(b) $|\alpha - \beta| \ge ||\alpha| - |\beta||$

(c) $|\alpha + \beta|^2 + |\alpha - \beta|^2 = 2(|\alpha|^2 + |\beta|^2)$.

2. If α, β, γ are three vertices of a parallelogram, find the vertex opposite to α.

(**Ans.** $\beta + \gamma - \alpha$)

3. Give the condition for 3 points z_1, z_2, z_3 to be collinear.

$$\left(\textbf{Ans.} \ \frac{z_3 - z_1}{z_2 - z_1} \text{ is real} \right)$$

4. Give the loci of the point z where

(a) $|z| < 1$

(b) $|z - 1| \ge 2$

(c) $|z - 2 + i| < 1$

(d) $\left| z - \dfrac{3}{4} \right| \ge \dfrac{3}{2}$

(e) $|z| \ge 2$, $\Im(z) \ge 0$ (f) $|z| \le 1$, $0 \le \arg z \le \dfrac{\pi}{3}$

(g) $0 < \Re(z) \le 2$ (h) $0 < \Re(iz) \le 2$

(i) $|z - 1| + |z + 1| = 3$ (j) $\Re(z^2) = 1$

(k) $\Im(z^2) = 2$ (l) $|\Im(z)|^2 = \Re(z^2)$

(m) $\arg \dfrac{z-1}{z+1} = \mu$ for $\mu = \pm\dfrac{\pi}{3}, \pm\dfrac{2\pi}{3}$

(n) $\left|\dfrac{z-1}{z+1}\right| = k$ for $k = 2, \dfrac{1}{2}$ (o) $\left|\dfrac{z-1}{z+1}\right| \le 2$

(p) $\left|\dfrac{z-i}{z+i}\right| \ge 2$ (q) $|z^2 - 1| = a > 0$

(r) $|z^2 - 1| < 1$ (*Kumaon 1998*)   (s) $|z^2 - 1| > 2$.

Ans.

(a) The interior of the circle with centre O, and radius 1.

(b) The exterior and frontier of the circle with centre 1 and radius 2.

(c) The interior of the circle with centre $2 - i$ and radius 1.

(d) The exterior and frontier of the circle with centre 3/4 and radius 3/2.

(e) The region common to the exterior and frontier of the circle with centre O and radius 2 and the upper semi-plane including the real axis.

(f) The interior and frontier of the region bounded by the unit circle, positive real axis and the line through the origin making an angle $\pi/3$ with the real axis.

(g) The infinite rectangular strip bounded by the imaginary axis and the line parallel to the same at a distance 2 together with points on the latter.

(h) The infinite rectangular strip bounded by the real axis and the line parallel to the same at a distance $- 2$ together with points on the latter.

(i) The ellipse with foci $1, - 1$ and major axis 3.

(j) The rectangular hyperbola $x^2 - y^2 = 1$.

(k) The rectangular hyperbola $xy = 1$.

(l) The two lines through the origin making angles $\pm \tan^{-1}(1/2)$ with the real axis.

(m) The two circles $x^2 + y^2 \pm (2/\sqrt{3})\, y - 1 = 0$.

(n) The two circles $3(x^2 + y^2) \pm 10x + 3 = 0$.

(o) The interior and frontier of the circle $3(x^2 + y^2) + 10x + 3 = 0$.

(p) The exterior and frontier of the circle $3(x^2 + y^2) + 10y + 3 = 0$.

(q) The curve $r^4 - 2r^2 \cos 2\theta + (1 - a^2) = 0$.

(r) The interior of the curve $r^2 = 2 \cos 2\theta$.

(s) The exterior of the curve $r^4 - 2r^2 \cos 2\theta = 3$.]

5. Find the locus of the point z where

(i) $z = \alpha + \beta t$ (ii) $z = \alpha t + \beta/t$

(iii) $z = \alpha \cos t + \beta \sin t$ (iv) $z = \alpha + 2\beta t + \gamma t^2$

where α, β, γ are constants, $\beta \div \alpha$ is non-real and t is a real parameter.

Ans.

(*i*) Straight line joining the points α, $\alpha + \beta$.

(*ii*) Hyperbola.

(*iii*) Ellipse.

(*iv*) A parabola or a straight line according as β/γ is not or is real.

6. Show that the locus of the point z, where $z = \dfrac{\alpha + \beta t}{\gamma + \delta t}$; t, a real parameter is a straight line or a circle according as γ/δ is real or non-real; α, β, γ, δ being constant complex numbers such that $\alpha\delta - \beta\gamma \neq 0$.

7. If z, w are two complex numbers and

$$w = \frac{2z}{1 + |z|^2},$$

find the curves in the z-plane on which

(*i*) the real part of w is constant,

(*ii*) the imaginary part of w is constant.

A point w_0 in the w-plane is such that the following two curves in the z-plane touch each other:

(*i*) $\Re(w) = u_0$,   (*ii*) $\Im(w) = v_0$.

Show that all such points (u_0, v_0) in the w-plane lie on a circle.

[**Ans.** (*i*) A family of coaxial circles.

      (*ii*) A family of coaxial circles.]

8. Find the equation of the circle described on the join of the points α, β as diameter.

[**Ans.** $2z\bar{z} - (\bar{\alpha} + \bar{\beta})z - (\alpha + \beta)\bar{z} + (\alpha\bar{\beta} + \bar{\alpha}\beta) = 0$]

9. Find the equations of the circles through the points

(*a*) $1, i, 1 + i$,   (*b*) $3 + i, 2 + 2i, 1 + i$.

Find also their centres and radii.

[**Ans.** (*a*) $2z\bar{z} + (i - 1)z - (i + 1)\bar{z} = 0$, $\dfrac{1}{2}(i + 1)$, $\dfrac{1}{\sqrt{2}}$

     (*b*) $z\bar{z} + (i - 2)z - (i + 2)\bar{z} + 4 = 0$, $2 + i$, 1]

10. Find the inverses of the point, $-i$, for each of the circles in the preceding exercise.

$\left[\text{**Ans.** } (a) \ \dfrac{2}{5} + \dfrac{1}{5}i, \ (b) \ \dfrac{7}{4} + \dfrac{3}{4}i\right]$

11. Show that the two triangles with vertices α, β, γ; α', β', γ' are directly similar if

$$\Sigma\alpha(\beta' - \gamma') = 0.$$

12. Show that the triangle with vertices α, β, γ will be equilateral if and only if

$$\alpha^2 + \beta^2 + \gamma^2 = \alpha\beta + \beta\gamma + \gamma\alpha.$$

                                                              (*Kumaon 2000*)

13. The roots α, β, γ of the equation

$$x^3 + 3px^2 + 3qx + r = 0,$$

in which p, q, r are complex numbers correspond to the points A, B, C on the plane. Find the centroid of the triangle ABC and show that it will be equilateral if and only if $p^2 = q$.

14. The vertices of a triangle are given by the numbers z_1, z_2, z_3; show that the centroid, the circumcentre and the orthocentre of the triangle are respectively given by the numbers

$$\frac{z_1 + z_2 + z_3}{3}, \frac{\Sigma z_1 \bar{z}_1 (z_2 - z_3)}{\Sigma (\bar{z}_2 z_3 - z_2 \bar{z}_3)}, \frac{\Sigma z_1^2 (\bar{z}_2 - \bar{z}_3) + \Sigma z_1 \bar{z}_1 (z_2 - z_3)}{\Sigma (z_1 \bar{z}_2 - \bar{z}_1 z_2)}.$$

[**Hint.** The circumcentre z is given by

$$|z - z_1| = |z - z_2| = |z - z_3|$$

$$\Leftrightarrow \quad (z_1)(\bar{z} - \bar{z}_1) = (z - z_2)(\bar{z} - \bar{z}_2) = (z - z_3)(\bar{z} - \bar{z}_3).$$

Also the orthocentre z is given by

$$\Re\left(\frac{z - z_1}{z_2 - z_3}\right) = 0 = \Re\left(\frac{z - z_2}{z_3 - z_1}\right)$$

$$\Leftrightarrow \qquad \frac{z - z_1}{z_2 - z_3} + \frac{\bar{z} - \bar{z}_1}{\bar{z}_2 - \bar{z}_3} = 0, \quad \frac{z - z_2}{z_3 - z_1} + \frac{\bar{z} - \bar{z}_2}{\bar{z}_3 - \bar{z}_1} = 0.]$$

15. The circumcentre of a triangle ABC is at the origin and the points A, B, C are represented by complex numbers α, β, γ respectively. Prove that the points D, E, F represented by

$$-\frac{\beta\gamma}{\alpha}, \quad -\frac{\gamma\alpha}{\beta}, \quad -\frac{\alpha\beta}{\gamma}$$

are the points in which the perpendiculars from A, B, C to the opposite sides of the triangle meet the circumcircle again.

Prove also

(i) that the orthocentre of the triangle ABC is represented by $\alpha + \beta + \gamma$;

(ii) that the incentre of the triangle ABC represents one of the values of $\sqrt{\beta\gamma} + \sqrt{\gamma\alpha} + \sqrt{\alpha\beta}$.

[You may assume without proof that the orthocentre of the triangle ABC is the incentre of the triangle DEF.]

16. Find the length of perpendicular from $z_0 = 2 + 3i$ on the straight line

$$(1 - 2i) z + (1 + 2i) \bar{z} + 3 = 0$$

$$\left[\textbf{Ans.} \frac{19}{2\sqrt{5}}\right]$$

17. If z_1, z_2, z_3 be the complex numbers represented by the vertices A, B, C respectively of a triangle ABC in anticlockwise order, show that

$$\left|\Sigma \frac{z_2 - z_3}{z_1}\right| z_1|^2 \bigg| \cos A - 2iR[(z_1 - z_2)(\bar{z}_1 - \bar{z}_3)] \sin A = 0.$$

18. Find the equations of two lines making an angle of 45° with the line $(2 - i) z + (2 + i) \bar{z} + 3 = 0$ and passing through $(- 1, 4)$.

[**Ans.** $(1 - 3i) z + (1 + 3i) \bar{z} - 22 = 0$ and $(3 + i) z + (3 - i) \bar{z} + 14 = 0$]

19. Two different non-parallel lines meet the circle $|z| = r$. One of them at points a and b and the other which is tangent to the circle at c. Show that the point of intersection of two lines is

$$\frac{2c^{-1} - a^{-1} - b^1}{c^{-2} - a^{-1} b^{-1}}$$

20. A is a point in the Argand plane. On the circle with OA as diameter, are taken two points B and C so that $\angle AOB = \angle BOC = \theta$. If O is the origin and A, B, C represent the complex z_1, z_2, z_3 respectively, show that $z_2^2 \cos 2\theta = z_1 z_3 \cos^2 \theta$.

OBJECTIVE QUESTIONS

For each of the following questions, four alternatives are given for the answer. Only one of them is correct. Choose the correct alternative.

1. The curve represented by $\left| \dfrac{z - z_1}{z - z_2} \right| = c$, where $|c| \neq 1$, is

   (*a*) straight line   (*b*) circle

   (*c*) ellipse   (*d*) None of these.

2. If z lies on the circle $|z| = 1$, then $2/z$ lies on

   (*a*) a plane   (*b*) a straight line

   (*c*) a circle   (*d*) None of these.

3. The points z_1, z_2, z_3 and z_4 in the complex plane are the vertices of a parallelogram taken in order if and only if

   (*a*) $z_1 + z_2 + z_3 + z_4 = 0$ (*b*) $z_1/z_2 = z_3/z_4$

   (*c*) $z_1 + z_3 = z_2 + z_4$ (*d*) $z_1 + z_2 = z_3 + z_4$.

4. If z_1, z_2 and z_3 are in harmonic progression, then they lie on a/an

   (*a*) circle   (*b*) straight line

   (*c*) plane   (*d*) ellipse.

5. The complex numbers z_1, z_2 and z_3 satisfying $\dfrac{z_1 - z_3}{z_2 - z_3} = \dfrac{1 - i\sqrt{3}}{2}$ are the vertices of a triangle which is

   (*a*) of area zero   (*b*) right-angled isosceles

   (*c*) equilateral   (*d*) obtuse-angled isosceles.

6. The area of the triangle formed by the complex numbers $z, iz, z + iz$ in the Argand's diagram is

   (*a*) $\dfrac{1}{2}|z|^2$ (*b*) $|z|^2$

   (*c*) $2|z|^2$ (*d*) None of these.

7. If the complex numbers z_1, z_2, z_3 are in A.P., they lie on a/an

   (*a*) ellipse   (*b*) straight line   (*c*) parabola   (*d*) circle.

8. Let α be a complex number such that $|a| < 1$ and $z_1, z_2, ...$ be vertices of a polygon such that $z_k = 1 + \alpha + \alpha^2 + ... + \alpha^{k-1}$. Then the vertices of the polygon lie within a circle

   (*a*) $\left| z - \dfrac{1}{1-a} \right| = |1 - a|$ (*b*) $|z - (1 - a)| = |1 - a|$

   (*c*) $\left| z - \dfrac{1}{1-a} \right| = \dfrac{1}{|1-a|}$ (*d*) $|z - a| = a$.

9. If $z = x + iy$ and $w = \dfrac{1 - iz}{z - i}$, then $|w| = 1$ implies that in the complex plane

(a) z lies on real axis

(b) z lies on imaginary axis

(c) z lies on a unit circle

(d) z lies inside a unit circle.

10. The points representing the complex number z for which

$$\arg\left(\frac{z - 2}{z + 2}\right) = \frac{\pi}{3}$$

lies on

(a) a parabola

(b) an ellipse

(c) a straight line

(d) a circle.

11. If $\dfrac{z + 1}{z + i}$ is a purely imaginary number, then z lies on

(a) a circle

(b) an ellipse

(c) a straight line

(d) imaginary axis.

12. If the vertices of a triangle are $-3 + i$, $8 + 5i$, $-2 - 3i$, the modulus of the complex number representing the centroid of this triangle is

(a) 2   (b) $\sqrt{2}$ (c) $2\sqrt{2}$ (d) 4.

13. If the points represented by complex numbers $z_1 = \alpha + i\beta$, $z_2 = \gamma + i\delta$ and $z_1 - z_2$ are collinear, then

(a) $\alpha\delta - \beta\gamma = 0$

(b) $\alpha\delta + \beta\gamma = 0$

(c) $\alpha\beta - \gamma\delta = 0$

(d) $\alpha\gamma - \beta\delta = 0$.

14. If z_1, z_2, z_3, z_4 represent the vertices of a rhombus taken in the anticlockwise order, then

(a) $z_1 - z_2 + z_3 - z_4 = 0$

(b) $z_1 + z_2 + z_3 + z_4 = 0$

(c) $\operatorname{amp}\left(\dfrac{z_1 - z_2}{z_3 - z_4}\right) = \dfrac{\pi}{2}$

(d) $\operatorname{amp}\left(\dfrac{z_2 - z_4}{z_1 - z_3}\right) = 0$.

15. If z_1, z_2 be two complex numbers representing the points on the circles $|z| = 1$ and $|z_2| = 2$ respectively, then

(a) max. $|2z_1 + z_2| = 4$

(b) min. $|z_1 - z_2| = 2$

(c) $\left| z_2 + \dfrac{1}{z_1} \right| \geq 3$

(d) None of these.

16. Let a and b be two fixed non-zero complex numbers and z is a variable complex number. If the lines $a\bar{z} + \bar{a}z + 1 = 0$ and $b\bar{z} + \bar{b}z - 1 = 0$ are mutually perpendicular, then

(a) $ab + \bar{a}\bar{b} = 0$

(b) $ab - \bar{a}\bar{b} = 0$

(c) $\bar{a}b - a\bar{b} = 0$

(d) $a\bar{b} + \bar{a}b = 0$

17. The points A, B and C represent the complex numbers $z_1, z_2, (1 - i)z_1 + iz_2$ respectively on the complex plane. The triangle ABC is

(a) isosceles but not right-angled

(b) right-angled but not isosceles

(c) isosceles and right - angled

(d) None of these.

18. The complex number z_1, z_2 and z_3 satisfying $\dfrac{z_1 - z_3}{z_2 - z_3} = \dfrac{1 - i\sqrt{3}}{2}$ are the vertices of a triangle which is

(a) of area zero

(b) right-angled isosceles

(c) equilateral

(d) obtuse-angled isosceles.

ANSWERS

1. (b) **2.** (c) **3.** (c) **4.** (b) **5.** (c) **6.** (a) **7.** (b) **8.** (c) **9.** (a)

10. (d) **11.** (a) **12.** (b) **13.** (a) **14.** (a) **15.** (a) **16.** (d) **17.** (c) **18.** (c)

BILINEAR TRANSFORMATIONS

3.1. Introduction. In this chapter, we shall be concerned with the geometry of the complex valued functions of a complex variable such that

$$f(z) = \frac{a + bz}{c + dz}$$

for all those values of z for which the expression $(a + bz)/(c + dz)$ is defined; a, b, c, d being given complex numbers and c, d not being both zero.

We write

$$w = \frac{a + bz}{c + dz}. \qquad \qquad ...(1)$$

The geometry arises when the numbers z and w are represented by points on the same or different planes and we regard (1) as associating to a point z of the z-plane, a point w of the w-plane. From this geometric point of view, the correspondence set up by (1) is known as *Transformation* or a *Mapping*. Moreover, (1) being equivalent to the relation

$$dwz + cw - bz - a = 0,$$

which is linear in w as well as z, the transformation determined by (1) is known as a *Bilinear Transformation*. Often the relation (1) itself is called a Bilinear Transformation. Bilinear transformations are also called Mobius Transformations since the first study of such transformations goes back to A.F. Mobius (1790 – 1868).

The point, w, will be called the bilinear image or the transform of the point z.

The study will of course include the consideration of the properties which are preserved, *i.e.*, which remain *invariant* when a bilinear transformation is carried out.

A simple basic fact about (1) may be first noticed.

If w_1, w_2 correspond respectively to z_1, z_2 in (1), we have

$$w_2 - w_1 = \frac{a + bz_2}{c + dz_2} - \frac{a + bz_1}{c + dz_1}$$

$$= \frac{(ad - bc)(z_1 - z_2)}{(c + dz_1)(c + dz_2)} \qquad \qquad ...(2)$$

so that, if $ad - bc = 0$, then $w_2 - w_1 = 0$, whatever z_1, z_2 may be distinct or same.

Thus, we see that if $ad - bc = 0$, then the relation (1) associates to *each* value of z the *same* value of w. Also if $ad - bc \neq 0$, then we deduce from (2), that the relation (1) associates different values of w to different values of z, *i.e.*,

$$z_1 \neq z_2 \iff w_1 \neq w_2.$$

56

Excluding the obviously uninteresting case which arises when $ad - bc = 0$, we shall, in the following, always assume that

$$ad - bc \neq 0.$$

The number, $ad - bc$, is called the *Jacobian* or the *Determinant* of the transformation. It may be remarked that if $ad - dc \neq 0$ then c, d cannot both be zero.

3.2. Extended Complex Plane. Infinite Point. Consider a bilinear transformation

$$w = \frac{a + bz}{c + dz}, \quad ad - bc \neq 0 \qquad \qquad ...(1)$$

Let $\qquad\qquad d \neq 0$.

To each value of $z \neq - c/d$, the transformation associates a value of w. Again, solving (1) for z in terms of w, we obtain

$$z = -\left(\frac{-a + cw}{b - dw}\right) \qquad\qquad ...(2)$$

and see that each $w \neq b/d$ is a correspondent of some z.

Thus, *if $d \neq 0$ the bilinear transformation* (1) *associates to each $z \neq - c/d$ a value of w and each $w \neq b/d$ is an associate of a value of z and the association between z and w is one-one.*

Thus, the domain of the function defined by

$$f(z) = \frac{a + bz}{c + dz}, \quad d \neq 0$$

consists of the entire set of complex numbers excluding $- c/d$ and the range also consists of the entire set of complex numbers excluding b/d.

In geometric terms, we see that if $d \neq 0$ the transformation maps one-one the entire z-plane with the exception of the point, $- c/d$, on the entire w-plane with the exception of the point b/d.

If $d = 0$ so that as assumed earlier $c \neq 0$, then to each complex number z without exception corresponds a value of w.

Now $ad - bc \neq 0$ and $d = 0 \Rightarrow c \neq 0$. In this case each w is an associate of some z.

Thus, if $d = 0$ so that $c \neq 0$, the domain as also the range is the entire set of complex numbers.

Now it is possible to make a statement wherefor the exceptions referred to above do not appear. For this purpose we adjoin a new number, called *Infinity* to the set of complex numbers and a corresponding point, called *Infinite point* or the point at infinity to the complex plane. The infinite number and the infinite point will both be denoted by the symbol ∞ and it will be supposed, as a matter of definition, that the number ∞ thus introduced has the following algebraic relationship with the other complex numbers.

$$\infty \pm a = \infty \quad \forall \quad a \neq \infty,$$

$$\infty \cdot a = \infty \quad \forall \quad a \neq 0,$$

$$\frac{a}{\infty} = 0 \text{ and } \frac{\infty}{a} = \infty \quad \forall \quad a \neq \infty,$$

$$\frac{a}{0} = \infty \quad \forall \quad a \neq 0.$$

Further ∞ itself will be, by definition, regarded as the conjugate of ∞. It will thus be seen that

$$\infty + \infty, \quad \infty - \infty, \quad \infty \cdot 0, \quad \infty/\infty, \quad 0/0$$

have not been defined so that ∞ is not capable of free algebraic manipulation.

The complex plane to which the point at infinity has been adjoined will always be referred to as the *Extended Complex Plane*.

Thus, we can now say that the bilinear transformation

$$w = \frac{a + bz}{c + dz}, \quad ad - bc \neq 0$$

maps one-one the extended z-plane into the extended w-plane such that

$$z = \infty \text{ corresponds to } w = b/d,$$

and $\qquad\qquad\qquad\qquad z = -c/d$ corresponds to $w = \infty$,

so that the exceptional points have now been taken care of.

We thus see that a bilinear transformation is one-one from the extended complex plane onto itself.

3.3. Vertex of stereographic projection corresponding to the point at infinity. It was seen in § 2.10 that the stereographic projection of a sphere onto a plane establishes one-one correspondence between the points of the plane and all the points of the sphere with the exception of the vertex of projection. The correspondence between the point (X, Y, Z) of the sphere and the point z on the plane is given by

$$X = \frac{z + \bar{z}}{z\bar{z} + 1}, \quad Y = \frac{z - \bar{z}}{i\,(z\bar{z} + 1)}, \quad Z = \frac{z\bar{z} - 1}{z\bar{z} + 1} \qquad\qquad \text{[See § 2.10]}$$

Dividing by $z\bar{z}$ and taking $z = \infty$, we see that the point on the sphere corresponding to $z = \infty$ is (0, 0, 1) which is the vertex of projection.

Thus, we see that the *stereographic projection establishes one-one correspondence between the points of the sphere and the points of the extended plane; the vertex of projection on the sphere corresponding to the point at infinity on the plane.* In other words, the stereographic projection defines a one-one function from the sphere onto the extended complex plane.

3.3.1. Centre of a circle as the inverse of the point at infinity. In terms of the definition of inverse points for a circle given in § 2.7.4, we have seen that every point other than the centre possesses a unique inverse point. We now remove this exception by saying that *centre of a circle and the point at infinity are inverse points for the circle.* The definition can be seen to be consistent with the condition (§ 2.7.4).

$$pz_1\bar{z}_2 + \alpha\bar{z}_2 + \bar{\alpha}z_1 + r = 0, \qquad\qquad\qquad\qquad ...(1)$$

for two points z_1, z_2 to be inverse for the circle

$$pz\bar{z} + \alpha\bar{z} + \bar{\alpha}z + r = 0. \qquad\qquad\qquad\qquad ...(2)$$

From (1), we have

$$\bar{z}_2 = -\frac{r + \alpha\bar{z}_1}{\alpha + pz_1} \qquad\qquad\qquad\qquad ...(3)$$

Also the centre of the circle (2) is $-\alpha/p$. Taking $z_1 = -\alpha/p$ in (3), we see that $\bar{z}_2$ and, therefore, also z_2 is equal to ∞.

3.3.2. Straight line as a circle through the point at infinity. A member

$$pz\bar{z} + \alpha\bar{z} + \bar{\alpha}z + r = 0, \qquad\qquad\qquad\qquad ...(1)$$

of the family of straight lines and circles will pass through the point at ∞ if and only if $p = 0$, as may be seen on dividing (1) by $z\bar{z}$ and putting $z = \infty$, $\bar{z} = \infty$.

Thus, a *straight line may be thought of as a circle through the point at infinity* so that the straight line through two given points z_1, z_2 can be thought of as the circle through the three points z_1, z_2 and ∞.

3.4. Resultant and Inverse.

3.4.1. Resultant of two bilinear transformations.   *(Kerala 2001)*

Consider any two bilinear transformations

$$Z = \frac{a_1 + b_1 z}{c_1 + d_1 z}, \quad a_1 d_1 - b_1 c_1 \neq 0. \qquad \qquad ...(1)$$

$$w = \frac{a_2 + b_2 Z}{c_2 + d_2 Z}, \quad a_2 d_2 - b_2 c_2 \neq 0. \qquad \qquad ...(2)$$

The equations (1) and (2) associate to each value of z a value of w. From (1) and (2), eliminating Z, we obtain the transformation

$$w = \frac{(a_2 c_1 + b_2 a_1) + (a_2 d_1 + b_1 b_2)\, z}{(c_2 c_1 + d_2 a_1) + (c_2 d_1 + d_2 b_1)\, z}, \qquad \qquad ...(3)$$

with the determinant

$$(a_2 c_1 + b_2 a_1)(c_2 d_1 + d_2 b_1) - (a_2 d_1 + b_2 b_1)(c_2 c_1 + d_2 a_1)$$

$$= -(a_1 d_1 - b_1 c_1)(a_2 d_2 - b_2 c_2) \neq 0.$$

Thus, we see that the transformation (3) associating z to w is also bilinear. This bilinear transformation is the *Resultant* or the *Composite* of the bilinear transformations (1) and (2), taken in this order.

Note. *Denoting the transformations* (1) *and* (2) *by P, Q we may write*

$$Z = P\,(z), \quad w = Q\,(Z)$$

From these we obtain

$$w = Q\,[P\,(z)],$$

so that we have

$$w = (QP)\,(z).$$

3.4.2. Inverse of a bilinear transformation. Re-writing

$$w = \frac{a + bz}{c + dz}, \quad ad - bc \neq 0 \qquad \qquad ...(1)$$

as

$$z = \frac{a - cw}{-b + dw}, \quad ad - (-b)(-c) \neq 0 \qquad \qquad ...(2)$$

we see that the correspondence of w to z as given by (2) is also bilinear. The bilinear transformation (2) is called the *Inverse* of (1).

Note. *The composite of the functions defined by* (1) *and* (2) *in this order keeps z invariant. The function I defined by I$\,(z) = z \;\forall\; z$ is called the Identity function.*

If we write (1) *as*

$$w = P\,(z)$$

then we write

$$z = P^{-1}\,(w),$$

thus, denoting the inverse of the transformation P by the symbol P^{-1}.

3.5. The Linear Group.

Theorem. *The set of all bilinear transformations form a non-abelian group under the product of transformations.*

From § 3.4.1, we have the product of two bilinear transformations is a bilinear transformation so that the **closure axiom** is satisfied.

The **associative law**

$$(T_1 T_2) T_3 = T_1 (T_2 T_3)$$

follows from the fact that this law holds for arbitrary mappings.

The **identity mapping** I defined by $w = I(z) = z$ is a bilinear transformation so that I serves as an identity element.

The **inverse** of the transformation

$$w = T(z) = \frac{az + b}{cz + d} \text{ is } z = T^{-1}(w) = \frac{dw - b}{-cw + a}.$$

For

$$T^{-1} T(z) = T^{-1} \left(\frac{az + b}{cz + d} \right) = \frac{d \left(\dfrac{az + b}{cz + d} \right) - b}{- c \left(\dfrac{az + b}{cz + d} \right) + a}$$

$$= \frac{(ad - bc) z}{(ad - bc)} = z$$

Similarly, $TT^{-1}(w) = w$

$$\therefore \qquad T^{-1} T = I = TT^{-1}$$

Thus the set of all bilinear transformations form a group under the product of transformations. Since in general $T_1 T_2(z) \neq T_2 T_1(z)$, this group is non-abelian.

EXAMPLE

Consider the transformations

$$w = T_1(z) = \frac{z + 2}{z + 3}, \quad w = T_2(z) = \frac{z}{z + 1}.$$

Find (a) $T_1^{-1}(w)$, (b) $T_1 T_2(z)$ and (c) $T_2^{-1} T_1(z)$.

Solution. *(a)* $w = \dfrac{z + 2}{z + 3} \Rightarrow wz + 3w = z + 2$

$$\Rightarrow \qquad z = \frac{2 - 3w}{w - 1}$$

$$\therefore \qquad T_1^{-1}(w) = \frac{2 - 3w}{w - 1}.$$

(b) $\qquad T_1 T_2(z) = T_1 \left(\dfrac{z}{z + 1} \right)$

$$= \frac{\dfrac{z}{z+1} + 2}{\dfrac{z}{z+1} + 3} = \frac{3z+2}{4z+3}.$$

(c) $$w = T_2 = \frac{z}{z+1} \implies T_2^{-1}(z) = -\frac{w}{w-1}$$

$$\therefore \quad T_2^{-1} T_1(z) = T_2^{-1}\left(\frac{z+2}{z+3}\right)$$

$$= -\frac{\dfrac{z+2}{z+3}}{\dfrac{z+2}{z+3} - 1} = z + 2.$$

3.6. Critical Points. By bilinear transformation

$$w = \frac{az+b}{cz+d} \qquad \qquad \dots(1)$$

we have

$$z = \frac{b-wd}{wc-a} \qquad \qquad \dots(2)$$

The transformation (1) associates a unique point of the w-plane to any point of z-plane except the point $z = -\dfrac{d}{c}$ when $c \neq 0$. The transformation (2) associates a unique point of z-plane to any point of w-plane except the point $w = \dfrac{a}{c}$, $c \neq 0$. These points $z = -\dfrac{d}{c}$ and $w = \dfrac{a}{c}$ are mapped into the points $w = \infty$ and $z = \infty$ respectively.

From (1), $$\frac{dw}{dz} = \frac{ad-bc}{(cz+d)^2},$$

This $\implies$ $$\frac{dw}{dz} = \begin{cases} \infty, & \text{if } z = -d/c \\ 0, & \text{if } z = \infty. \end{cases}$$

The points $z = -d/c$, $z = \infty$ are called **critical points**.

3.7. Expression of a given bilinear transformation as the resultant of bilinear transformations with simple geometric imports.

Consider the bilinear transformation

$$w = \frac{a+bz}{c+dz}, \quad ad-bc \neq 0$$

Firstly suppose that $d = 0$. Then $c \neq 0$ and we can re-write the given bilinear transformation as

$$w = \frac{b}{c} z + \frac{a}{c},$$

which is clearly the resultant of the bilinear transformations

$$Z = \frac{b}{c} z, \quad w = Z + \frac{a}{c}.$$

Now, suppose that d ≠ 0.

We write

$$t = c + dz \iff z = (t - c)/d,$$

Thus, we have

$$w = \frac{a + b\,(t - c)/d}{t} = \frac{ad - ac}{d} \cdot \frac{1}{t} + \frac{b}{d}$$

so that, the given bilinear transformation is the resultant of bilinear transformations :

$$u = \frac{1}{t}, \quad v = \frac{ad - bc}{d}\,u, \quad w = v + \frac{b}{d}.$$

It has thus been proved that *every bilinear transformation is the resultant of bilinear transformations of the form*

$$w = z + \alpha, \quad w = \beta z, \quad w = (1/z).$$

In the following section, it is shown that each of these three types of bilinear transformations is capable of a simple geometric interpretation.

3.8. Geometrical significance of the transformations

$$w = z + \alpha, \quad w = \beta z, \quad w = (1/z)$$

3.8.1. $w = z + \alpha$. Translation. (*Kerala 2001*)

Let the numbers z and α be denoted by the points P and A so that P is a variable and A is a fixed point.

Completing the parallelogram with OA, OP as adjacent sides, we see that P' is the point

$$z + \alpha = w.$$

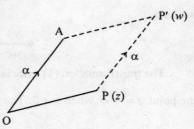

Here the vector $\overrightarrow{PP'}$ represents the number α.

Fig. 3.1

Thus, we see that *the image P' of any point P is obtained by subjecting the plane to a* **translation** *defined by the number* α.

3.8.2. $w = \beta z$. Resultant of Magnification and Rotation.

Let z and β be represented by the points P and B. Then the point P' representing w is such that

$$\angle\,POP' = \angle\,AOB = \arg \beta$$

$$OP' = OB \cdot OP$$

$$= |\,\beta\,|\,OP.$$

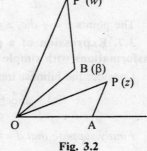

Thus, we see that the point P' is obtained from the point P on rotating the segment OP through an angle equal to arg β and magnifying the segment thus obtained in the ratio $|\,\beta\,|$. This shows that the transformation $w = \beta z$ is the resultant of a *Rotation* and a *magnification*.

Fig. 3.2

We shall have only rotation if β is unimodular, *i.e.* if $|\,\beta\,| = 1$ and only magnification if arg β is zero, *i.e.*, if β is real and positive.

3.8.3. $w = (1/z)$. Resultant of inversions in the real axis and in the unit circle. Clearly $w = (1/z)$ is the resultant of

$$Z = \bar{z}, \quad w = 1/\bar{z}$$

of which the former is reflection in the real axis and the latter is reflection in the unit circle.

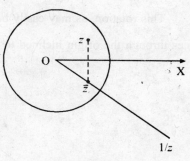

Thus, we see that the transformation $w = 1/z$ is the resultant of inversions in the real axis and in the unit circle.

Conclusion. Summing up the results obtained in the present and in the preceding section, we see that *every bilinear transformation is the resultant of a series of translations, rotations, magnifications and inversions.*

Fig. 3.3

Ex. Show that ∞ is mapped on itself by every translation, magnification and rotation but not by inversion in a circle.

3.9. A given bilinear transformation as resultant of an even number of inversions.

(Rajsthan 2002)

It will now be established that *every bilinear transformation can be expressed as the resultant of an* **even** *number of inversions.* To show this we will prove that every translation, magnification and rotation can be thus expressed.

Translation. $w = z + \alpha$.

It is easy to see that this translation is the resultant of two reflections in any two parallel lines which are perpendicular to the vector represented by α and whose distance from each other is equal to $\dfrac{1}{2} | \alpha |$.

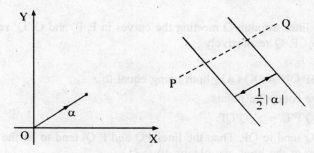

Fig. 3.4

Magnification. $w = | \beta | z$. This is equal to the resultant of two inversions in the concentric circles

$$| z | = a, \; | z | = b,$$

a, b being two real numbers such that

$$| \beta | = b^2/a^2.$$

In fact, the inverse of the point z in the circle

$$| z | = a$$

is the point $a^2 / \bar{z}$ and that of $a^2 / \bar{z}$ in the circle $| z | = b$ is the point $\qquad b^2 z/a^2 = \beta/z.$

Rotation. $w = \gamma z$, where $| \gamma | = 1.$

Let $\arg \gamma = \theta.$

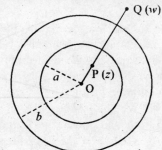

Fig. 3.5

This rotation, as may easily be seen, is equal to the resultant of two reflections in any two lines through the origin inclined to each other at an angle $\frac{1}{2}\theta$.

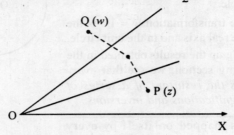

Fig. 3.6

3.10. Angle preserving property of Bilinear Transformations.

Theorem. *Every bilinear transformation is angle preserving.*

The theorem states that the angle between any two curves through a point is equal to the angle between their bilinear transforms, equality of angles being considered both in magnitude as well as in sense.

The proof of the theorem will be based on the following property of transformation by inversion:

*The angle between two curves is **equal** in magnitude but **opposite** in sense to the angle between their inverses for any circle.*

We now proceed to prove it.

Let C_1 be a given curve and let C_1' be its inverse for a circle whose centre is O, and radius is r.

Draw any two lines through O meeting the curves in P, P′ and Q, Q′ respectively. Now P′, Q′ are the inverses of P, Q respectively.

We have

$$OP \cdot OP' = OQ \cdot OQ', \text{ both being equal to } r^2.$$

$\Rightarrow$ P, P′, Q, Q′ are concyclic points.

$\Rightarrow$ $\angle Q'P'L = \angle Q'QP.$ ...(1)

Let the line OQ tend to OP. Then the lines PQ and P′Q′ tend to be the tangents to the two curves at P, P′. Thus, in the limit, we obtain, from (1)

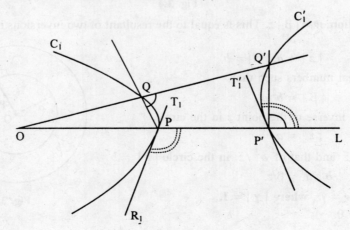

Fig. 3.7

$$\angle T_1'P'L = \angle P'PR_1$$

$\Rightarrow \qquad \angle T_1'P'L = \pi - \angle T_1PL$ ...(2)

Considering now the two curves C_1, C_2 intersecting at P and their inverses C_1', C_2' intersecting at P' and making use of the above result (2) for the two pairs of curves C_1, C_1'; C_2, C_2', we see that

$$\angle T_2'P'T_1' = \angle T_1PT_2.$$

The case of reflection in a straight line can also be easily disposed of.

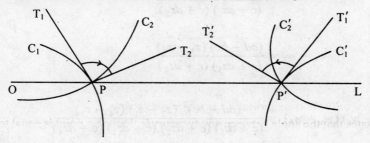

Fig. 3.8

Thus, we have proved the result stated above for inversion.

Now as each bilinear transformation is expressible as the resultant of an **even** number of inversions and for each inversion the sense of the angle changes while its magnitude is preserved, we deduce that *every bilinear transformation preserves the angle both in magnitude as well as in sense.*

Ex. Show that the circles

$$\left| \frac{z - \alpha}{z - \beta} \right| = \lambda, \quad \arg\left(\frac{z - \alpha}{z - \beta} \right) = \mu$$

cut each other orthogonally.

3.11. Cross-Ratio. *If* z_1, z_2, z_3, z_4 *are distinct points, then the ratio*

$$\frac{(z_4 - z_1)(z_2 - z_3)}{(z_2 - z_1)(z_4 - z_3)}$$ *(Kerala 2001)*

is called the cross-ratio of z_1, z_2, z_3, z_4 *and is denoted by* (z_1, z_2, z_3, z_4).

3.11.1. Theorem. *If, for a bilinear transformation,*

$$w_1, \ w_2, \ w_3, \ w_4$$

are the transforms of

$$z_1, \ z_2, \ z_3, \ z_4$$

respectively, then

$$(w_1, \ w_2, \ w_3, \ w_4) = (z_1, \ z_2, \ z_3, \ z_4).$$

OR

A bilinear transfromation preserves cross-ratio. *(M.S. Univ. 2007)*

Consider a bilinear transformation

$$w = \frac{a + bz}{c + dz} \qquad (ad - bc \neq 0)$$

$$\Rightarrow \qquad w_i = \frac{a + bz_i}{c + dz_i} \qquad (i = 1, 2, 3, 4).$$

We have

$$w_2 - w_1 = \frac{a + bz_2}{c + dz_2} - \frac{a + bz_1}{c + dz_1}$$

$$= \frac{(ad - bc)(z_1 - z_2)}{(c + dz_1)(c + dz_2)}.$$

Similarly

$$w_4 - w_3 = \frac{(ad - bc)(z_3 - z_4)}{(c + dz_3)(c + dz_4)}.$$

Thus

$$(w_2 - w_1)(w_4 - w_3) = \frac{(ad - bc)^2 (z_2 - z_1)(z_4 - z_3)}{(c + dz_1)(c + dz_2)(c + dz_3)(c + dz_4)}$$

Similarly

$$(w_4 - w_1)(w_2 - w_3) = \frac{(ad - bc)^2 (z_4 - z_1)(z_2 - z_3)}{(c + dz_1)(c + dz_2)(c + dz_3)(c + dz_4)}$$

It follows that

$$\frac{(w_2 - w_1)(w_4 - w_3)}{(w_4 - w_1)(w_2 - w_3)} = \frac{(z_2 - z_1)(z_4 - z_3)}{(z_4 - z_1)(z_2 - z_3)},$$

$$\Rightarrow \qquad (w_1, w_2, w_3, w_4) = (z_1, z_2, z_3, z_4).$$

Theorem. *The cross-ratio (z_1, z_2, z_3, z_4) is real if and only if the four points z_1, z_2, z_3, z_4 lie on a circle or on a straight line.*(Kerala 2001)

$$(z_1, z_2, z_3, z_4) = \frac{(z_1 - z_2)}{(z_2 - z_3)} \bigg/ \frac{(z_4 - z_1)}{(z_3 - z_4)}$$

$$\therefore \arg(z_1, z_2, z_3, z_4) = \arg\left(\frac{z_1 - z_2}{z_2 - z_3}\right) - \arg\left(\frac{z_4 - z_1}{z_3 - z_4}\right).$$

Hence the difference of the angles on the right hand side is 0 or $\pm \pi$ depending on the **relative** position of the points z_1, z_2, z_3, z_4 if and only if these points lie on a circle and the **cross-ratio** (z_1, z_2, z_3, z_4) is real if and only if the four points lie on a circle.

3.12. Preservation of the family of straight lines and circles.

Theorem. *Every bilinear transform of a circle or a straight line is again a circle or a straight line.*

(GNDU 2004, Rohtak 2001, Kanpur 2006)

The theorem states that the family of straight lines and circles goes over onto itself as a result of every bilinear transformation.

We shall give two proofs.

First Proof. The family of circles and straight lines is characterised by the property that the cross-ratio of any four points on any member of the family is real (Refer Cor. to § 2.7.3) and further every bilinear transformation is cross-ratio preserving.

Hence the result.

Second Proof. The equation of any member of the family of circles and straight lines is of the form

$$p z\bar{z} + \alpha\bar{z} + \bar{\alpha}z + r = 0 \qquad\qquad ...(1)$$

where p, r are real and $\alpha\bar{\alpha} \geq pr$.

The transform of (1) by any bilinear transformation

$$w = \frac{a + bz}{c + dz} \quad\Rightarrow\quad z = \frac{-a + cw}{b - dw},$$

is $\qquad p\, \dfrac{-a + cw}{b - dw} \cdot \dfrac{-\bar{a} + \bar{c}\bar{w}}{\bar{b} - \bar{d}\bar{w}} + \alpha\, \dfrac{-\bar{a} + \bar{c}\bar{w}}{\bar{b} - \bar{d}\bar{w}} + \alpha\, \dfrac{-a + cw}{b - dw} + r = 0$

$\Rightarrow \qquad p(-a + cw)(-\bar{a} + \bar{c}\bar{w}) + \alpha(-\bar{a} + \bar{c}\bar{w})(b - dw)$

$$+ \alpha(-a + cw)(\bar{b} - \bar{d}\bar{w}) + r(b - dw)(\bar{b} - \bar{d}w) = 0$$

$\Rightarrow \qquad q w\bar{w} + \beta\bar{w} + \bar{\beta}w + s = 0, \qquad\qquad ...(2)$

where

$$q = pc\bar{c} - (\alpha\bar{c}d + \bar{a}c\bar{d}) + rd\bar{d},$$

$$\beta = -pa\bar{c} + \alpha b\bar{c} + \bar{\alpha}a\bar{d} - rbd,$$

$$\bar{\beta} = -p\bar{a}c + \bar{\alpha}\bar{b}c + \alpha\bar{a}d - r\bar{b}d,$$

$$s = pa\bar{a} - (\alpha\bar{a}b + \bar{a}a\bar{b}) + rb\bar{b}.$$

Clearly q and s are real. Also,

$\beta\bar{\beta} - qs = (\alpha\bar{\alpha} - pr)(b\bar{b}c\bar{c} + a\bar{a}d\bar{d} - a\bar{b}\bar{c}d - \bar{a}bc\bar{d})$

$$= (\alpha\bar{\alpha} - pr)(\bar{b}\bar{c} - \bar{a}\bar{d})(bc - ad)$$

$$= (\alpha\bar{\alpha} - pr)\,|\,bc - ad\,|^2 \geq 0.$$

Thus, the equation (2) represents a circle or a straight line.

Hence the theorem.

3.13. Preservation of the configuration formed by a circle and a pair of inverse points for the same.

Theorem. *If A, B are inverse points for a circle Γ and A', B', Γ' are bilinear transforms of A, B, Γ, then A', B' are also inverse points for Γ'.*

Let z_1, z_2 be inverse points for

$$p z\bar{z} + \alpha\bar{z} + \bar{\alpha}z + r = 0, \qquad\qquad ...(1)$$

so that we have the condition

$$p z_1\bar{z}_2 + \alpha\bar{z}_2 + \bar{\alpha}z_1 + r = 0, \qquad\qquad ...(2)$$

which is obtained from (1) on changing $z, \bar{z}$ to $z_1, \bar{z}_2$ respectively.

Consider now the bilinear transformation

$$w = \frac{a + bz}{c + dz}, \quad ad - bc \neq 0 \qquad\qquad ...(3)$$

with the inverse transformation

$$z = \frac{-a + cw}{b - dw} \qquad\qquad ...(4)$$

The transform of (1) is

$$p\,\frac{-a + cw}{b - dw} \cdot \frac{-\overline{a} + \overline{cw}}{\overline{b} - \overline{dw}} + \alpha\,\frac{-\overline{a} + \overline{cw}}{\overline{b} - \overline{dw}} + \overline{\alpha}\,\frac{-a + cw}{b - dw} + r = 0 \qquad ...(5)$$

Also the condition (2), when re-written in terms of w_1, w_2 gives

$$p\,\frac{-a + cw_1}{b - dw_1} \cdot \frac{-\overline{a} + \overline{cw}_2}{\overline{b} - \overline{dw}_2} + \alpha\,\frac{-\overline{a} + \overline{cw}_2}{\overline{b} - \overline{dw}_2} + \overline{\alpha}\,\frac{-a + cw_1}{b - dw_1} + r = 0 \qquad ...(6)$$

Now the condition (6), obtained as it is from (5), on changing $w, \overline{w}$ to $w_1, \overline{w}_2$ respectively, shows that the points w_1, w_2 are inverse for the circle (5).

Hence the theorem.

3.14. Fixed points of a bilinear transformation. (*GNDU 2004*)

In this section, we shall be concerned with points which coincide with their transforms for a given bilinear transformation. Such points may be called *fixed points* of the transformation.

Consider a bilinear transformation

$$w = \frac{a + bz}{c + dz}, \quad ad - bc \neq 0 \qquad\qquad ...(1)$$

and suppose that w and z are represented by points on the same plane.

A point z which coincides with its transform satisfies the equation

$$z = \frac{a + bz}{c + dz},$$

$$\Leftrightarrow \quad dz^2 + (c - b)\,z - a = 0 \qquad\qquad ...(2)$$

This equation will be satisfied by more than two values of z, if and only if

$$d = 0, \; c - b = 0, \; a = 0,$$

i.e., if and only if the transformation (1) is the identity transformation

$$w = z.$$

Every point is a fixed point for the identity transformation.

We exclude this obviously uninteresting case.

Now suppose that (1) is *not* the identical transformation.

Firstly suppose that $d \neq 0$. In this case the equation (2) has the roots

$$\frac{(b - c) \pm \sqrt{(b - c)^2 + 4ad}}{2d},$$

so that we have one or two fixed points according as

$$(b - c)^2 + 4ad$$

is zero or non-zero; the fixed point or points being non-infinite.

Now suppose that $d = 0$, so that $c \neq 0$. In this case, we have

$$w = \frac{a}{c} + \frac{b}{c}\,z.$$

For this transformation, ∞ is easily seen to be one fixed point. Any other possible fixed point is given by

$$z = \frac{a}{c} + \frac{b}{c} z$$

$\Leftrightarrow$ $\qquad (c - b) z = a.$

Thus, if $(c - b) \neq 0$, the transformation has two fixed points ∞ and $a/(c - b)$ and if $(c - b) = 0$, the transformation has only one fixed point ∞.

We have, therefore, the following *four* possibilities for fixed points of a bilinear transformation

$$w = \frac{a + bz}{c + dz}, \ ad - bc \neq 0.$$

I. $d \neq 0, (b - c)^2 + 4ad \neq 0$, Two non-infinite fixed points.

II. $d \neq 0, (b - c)^2 + 4ad = 0$, One non-infinite fixed point.

III. $d = 0, b - c \neq 0$, One infinite and the other non-infinite, fixed point.

IV. $d = 0, b - c = 0, a \neq 0$, One infinite fixed point.

3.15. Normal form of a bilinear transformation. The four cases will now be considered one by one.

3.15.1. When there are two non-infinite fixed points.

Theorem. *Every bilinear transformation with two non-infinite fixed points* α, β *is of the form*

$$\frac{w - \alpha}{w - \beta} = k \frac{z - \alpha}{z - \beta}.$$

Suppose that the bilinear transformation with α, β as fixed points maps any point $z = \gamma$ onto $w = \delta$. Thus, the transforms of

$$\alpha, \beta, \gamma, z$$

are

$$\alpha, \beta, \delta, w$$

respectively. Therefore, by the preservation of cross-ratio property, we have

$$(\alpha, \gamma, \beta, z) = (\alpha, \delta, \beta, w)$$

$\Leftrightarrow$ $\qquad \dfrac{(\gamma - \alpha)(z - \beta)}{(z - \alpha)(\gamma - \beta)} = \dfrac{(\delta - \alpha)(w - \beta)}{(w - \alpha)(\delta - \beta)}$

$\Leftrightarrow$ $\qquad \dfrac{w - \alpha}{w - \beta} = k \dfrac{z - \alpha}{z - \beta}$

where we have written k for

$$(\delta - \alpha)(\gamma - \beta)/(\delta - \beta)(\gamma - \alpha).$$

Note 1. Elliptic, Hyperbolic and Loxodromic Transformations.

Consider the two conjugate systems S and T of circles such that α, β are common points for the system S and limiting points for the system T. These families are given by

$$\arg \frac{z - \alpha}{z - \beta} = \lambda, \ \frac{z - \alpha}{z - \beta} = \mu;$$

λ, μ being two real parameters.

It can be easily seen that these two systems are separately preserved, *i.e.*, each member of either system is mapped onto a member of the same system, by means of transformation

$$\frac{w - \alpha}{w - \beta} = k \frac{z - \alpha}{z - \beta}$$

In fact

$$\arg\left(\frac{z - \alpha}{z - \beta}\right) = \lambda \qquad\qquad ...(7)$$

is mapped onto

$$\arg\left(\frac{w - \alpha}{w - \beta}\right) = \arg k + \lambda$$

and

$$\left|\frac{z - \alpha}{z - \beta}\right| = \mu \qquad\qquad ...(8)$$

is mapped onto

$$\left|\frac{w - \alpha}{w - \beta}\right| = |k|\mu.$$

As a particular case, we see that if k is real so that arg k is 0 or $-\pi$, then each circle (7) of the system S is mapped onto itself and if k is unimodular, then each member (8) of the system T is mapped onto itself.

The bilinear transformation is said to be *hyperbolic* and *elliptic* respectively in these two cases. Thus, the *transformation is hyperbolic if k is real and elliptic if k is unimodular*. In any other case, it is called *Loxodromic*.

It is easy to see that a loxodromic transformation can be expressed as the resultant of an elliptic and a hyperbolic transformation.

Note 2. The transformation

$$\frac{w - \alpha}{w - \beta} = k \frac{z - \alpha}{z - \beta}$$

can be re-written as

$$(\alpha, w, \beta, z) = k.$$

If now z is any point of a circle through α, β and k is real, then w, the image of z, is also a point of the same circle. This follows from the fact that the cross-ratio (α, w, β, z) being real, the four points α, w, β, z are concyclic. This gives another proof of the fact that if k is real, then every circle through α, β is mapped onto itself.

3.15.2. When there is only one non-finite fixed point.

Theorem. *Every bilinear transformation with a single non-infinite fixed point, α, is of the form*

$$\frac{1}{w - \alpha} = \frac{1}{z - \alpha} + k.$$

Suppose that α is the only non-infinite fixed point of the transformation

$$w = \frac{a + bz}{c + dz}, \qquad\qquad ...(1)$$

so that α is the only root of the equation

$$dz^2 + (c - b)\, z - a = 0. \qquad \qquad ...(2)$$

We, therefore, have

$$dz^2 + (c - b)\, z - a = d\, (z - \alpha)^2$$

and accordingly

$$c - b = -2d\alpha \qquad \Rightarrow b = c + 2d\alpha$$
$$-a = d\alpha^2 \qquad \Rightarrow a = -d\alpha^2,$$

Thus, (1) takes the form

$$w = \frac{-d\alpha^2 + (c + 2d\alpha)\, z}{c + dz}$$

$$\Rightarrow \qquad \frac{1}{w - \alpha} = \frac{1}{z - \alpha} + \frac{d}{c + d\alpha} = \frac{1}{z - \alpha} + k, \text{ say}$$

Hence the theorem.
Here

$$k = \frac{d}{c + d\alpha} = \frac{2d}{b + c} \text{ for } \alpha = \frac{b - c}{2d}.$$

Note 3. Parabolic Transformations. A bilinear transformation with only one fixed point is called *parabolic*.

Ex. Examine the behaviour of the two families of circles S and T such that each number of S touches a given straight line at a point α and each number of T touches another straight line perpendicular to the first also at α, for parabolic transformations with fixed point α.

3.15.3. When ∞ and $\alpha \neq \infty$ are two fixed points.

If

$$w = \frac{a + bz}{c + dz},$$

be the transformation, we have $d = 0$.

$$\therefore \qquad w = \frac{a}{c} + \frac{b}{c}\, z.$$

Also

$$\alpha = \frac{a}{c} + \frac{b}{c}\, \alpha.$$

By subtracting, we obtain

$$w - \alpha = \frac{b}{c}\, (z - \alpha) = k\, (z - \alpha). \qquad \qquad ...(1)$$

Hence the result.

This transformation is the resultant of magnification and rotation about the point α.

3.15.4. When ∞ is the only fixed point so that $d = 0$ and $b = c$, then the transformation is the translation

$$w = z + \frac{a}{c}.$$

EXAMPLES

1. *What is the form of a bilinear transformation which has one fixed point α and the other fixed point ∞ ?*

Solution. Let the bilinear transformation be

$$w = \frac{az + b}{cz + d}.$$

In this case $c = 0$, $a - d \neq 0$, then

$$w = \frac{a}{d} z + \frac{b}{d}.$$

As finite fixed point is α, hence

$$\alpha = \frac{a}{d} \alpha + \frac{b}{d}$$

$$\Rightarrow \qquad w - \alpha = \frac{a}{d} (z - \alpha)$$

$$\Rightarrow \qquad w - \alpha = \lambda (z - \alpha), \text{ where } \frac{a}{d} = \lambda.$$

2. *Find the fixed points and the normal form of the following bilinear transformations*:

(*i*) $w = \dfrac{3z - 4}{z - 1}$ (*ii*) $w = \dfrac{3iz + 1}{z + i}$

(*iii*) $w = \dfrac{(2 + i) z - 2}{z + i}$ (*iv*) $w = \dfrac{z}{2 - z}.$ (*Kanpur 2004*)

Is any of these transformations hyperbolic, elliptic or parabolic ?

Solution. (*i*) In this case, the fixed points are given by

$$z = \frac{3z - 4}{z - 1} \qquad \Rightarrow z^2 - 4z + 4 = 0$$

$$\Rightarrow \qquad (z - 2)^2 = 0 \qquad \Rightarrow z = 2.$$

$z = 2$ is the only fixed point, so the transformation is parabolic.

To obtain the normal form, we have

$$wz - w = 3z - 4$$

$$\Rightarrow \qquad (w - 2) (z - 2) + 2z + 2w - w - 3z = 0$$

$$\Rightarrow \qquad (w - 2) (z - 2) - (z - 2) + (w - 2) = 0$$

$$\Rightarrow \qquad 1 - \frac{1}{w - 2} + \frac{1}{z - 2} = 0$$

$$\Rightarrow \qquad \frac{1}{w - 2} = \frac{1}{z - 2} + 1.$$

(*ii*) Fixed points are given by

$$z = \frac{3iz + 1}{z + i} \qquad \Rightarrow \qquad z^2 - 2iz - 1 = 0$$

$$\Rightarrow \qquad (z - i)^2 = 0.$$

Since $z = i$ is the only fixed point, the transformation is parabolic.

To put in the normal form, we have

$$wz + iw - 3iz - 1 = 0$$

$$\Rightarrow \qquad (w - i)(z - i) + 2iw - 2iz = 0$$

$$\Rightarrow \qquad (w - i)(z - i) + 2i(w - i) - 2i(z - i) = 0$$

$$\Rightarrow \qquad 1 + \frac{2i}{z - i} - \frac{2i}{w - i} = 0$$

$$\Rightarrow \qquad \frac{1}{w - i} = \frac{1}{z - i} - \frac{i}{2}.$$

(*iii*) Fixed points are

$$z = \frac{(2 + i)z - 2}{z + 1} \quad \Rightarrow \quad z^2 - 2z + 2 = 0$$

$$\Rightarrow \qquad z = \frac{2 \pm \sqrt{4 - 8}}{2} = 1 \pm i$$

$$\therefore \qquad 1 + i \text{ and } 1 - i \text{ are the fixed points.}$$

To put in the normal form, we have

$$w - (1 + i) = \frac{(2 + i)z - 2}{z + i} - (1 + i)$$

$$= \frac{z - (1 + i)}{z + i}$$

and

$$w - (1 - i) = \frac{(2 + i)z - 2}{z + i} - (1 - i)$$

$$= \frac{z - (1 - i) + 2iz - 2 - 2i}{z + i}$$

$$= \frac{(1 + 2i)[z - (1 - i)]}{z + i}$$

$$\therefore \qquad \frac{w - (1 + i)}{w - (1 - i)} = \frac{z - (1 + i)}{(1 + 2i)[z - (1 - i)]}$$

$$= \frac{1 - 2i}{5} \cdot \frac{z - (1 + i)}{z - (1 - i)}.$$

which is the required normal form.

Here $\lambda = \dfrac{1 + 2i}{5}$ which is neither real nor $|\lambda| = 1$.

$\therefore$ The transformation is loxodromic.

(*iv*) The fixed points are given by

$$z = \frac{z}{2 - z} \quad \Rightarrow \quad z = 0, \ z = 1.$$

Thus, 0 and 1 are the fixed points.

To obtain the normal form, we have

$$w = \frac{z}{2-z} \quad \text{and} \quad w - 1 = \frac{2z-2}{2-z}$$

$$\therefore \quad \frac{w}{w-1} = \frac{z}{2z-2} = \frac{1}{2} \cdot \frac{z}{z-1}.$$

Here $\lambda = \frac{1}{2}$ which is real.

Hence it is a hyperbolic transformation.

3.16. Determination of Bilinear Transformations under given conditions. The general bilinear transformation

$$w = \frac{a+bz}{c+dz}, \quad ad - bc \neq 0$$

contains three parameters, *viz.*, three ratios

$$a : b : c : d.$$

It may, therefore, be expected that a bilinear transformation would be determined so as to satisfy three conditions each of which is such that it gives rise to one relation between the parameters. In particular, we expect that a bilinear transformation may be determined so as to map any three distinct points z_1, z_2, z_3 on three given distinct points w_1, w_2, w_3. This would require the solution of the following three linear homogeneous equations in a, b, c, d:

$$dw_1 z_1 + cw_1 - bz_1 - a = 0,$$
$$dw_2 z_2 + cw_2 - bz_2 - a = 0,$$
$$dw_3 z_3 + cw_3 - bz_3 - a = 0.$$

Proceeding in this manner, we may not, however, be easily able to decide upon the existence and the uniqueness of the solution. On the other hand, we shall, employing the fact of the invariance of cross-ratio, be easily able to show that the required bilinear transformation is unique and also obtain the same.

Now any bilinear transformation which maps three distinct points z_1, z_2, z_3 on the three distinct points w_1, w_2, w_3 respectively must be such that

$$(z_1, z_2, z_3, z) = (w_1, w_2, w_3, w) \qquad \qquad \text{...(1)}$$

where z, w are general points.

Re-writing (1), we have

$$\frac{(z_2 - z_1)(z - z_3)}{(z - z_1)(z_2 - z_3)} = \frac{(w_2 - w_1)(w - w_3)}{(w - w_1)(w_2 - w_3)} \qquad \qquad \text{...(2)}$$

Thus, we see that if there exists a bilinear transformation mapping z_1, z_2, z_3 on w_1, w_2, w_3 respectively, it must be of the form (2). Further we may easily see that the transformation (2) is bilinear and that putting $z = z_1, z_2, z_3$ in (2), we do obtain $w = w_1, w_2, w_3$ respectively.

Thus, *the bilinear transformation mapping three given distinct points z_1, z_2, z_3 on w_1, w_2, w_3 respectively is unique and is given by* (2).

Cor. 1. *There exists a bilinear transformation which maps a given circle on another given circle.*

If we select any three distinct points on one circle and any three distinct points on the other, then the linear transformation which maps one set of three points onto the other would also map the first circle on the other because of the facts that (*i*) three points fix a circle;

(*ii*) every bilinear transformation maps a circle or a straight line on a circle or a straight line and in the present case the transform cannot be a straight line.

Clearly the bilinear transformation, in question, is *not* unique.

Cor. 2. *There exists a bilinear transformation which maps a given circle on another given straight line.*

This can be done by mapping a point of the given circle on the infinite point.

3.17. Some special bilinear transformations. In this section, we shall obtain the general bilinear transformations which map the

(*a*) real axis on itself;

(*b*) unit circle on itself;

(*c*) real axis on the unit circle.

3.17.1. Determination of the totality of Bilinear Transformations which map the real axis on the real axis.

A bilinear transformation which maps the real axis in the z-plane on the real axis in the w-plane is such that some three points x_1, x_2, x_3 on the real axis in the z-plane are mapped on $0, 1, \infty$ respectively lying on the real axis in the w-plane. Also the bilinear transformation which maps any three distinct real numbers x_1, x_2, x_3 on $0, 1, \infty$ is a bilinear transformation of the required type.

The bilinear transformation mapping x_1, x_2, x_3 on $0, 1, \infty$ respectively is given by

$$(0, 1, \infty, w) = (x_1, x_2, x_3, z)$$

$$\Rightarrow \quad \frac{(1 - 0)(w - \infty)}{(w - 0)(1 - \infty)} = \frac{(x_2 - x_1)(z - x_3)}{(z - x_1)(x_2 - x_3)}$$

$$\Rightarrow \quad w = \frac{(x_2 - x_3)(z - x_1)}{(x_2 - x_1)(z - x_3)} \qquad \qquad \text{...(1)}$$

$$= \frac{a + bz}{c + dz} \qquad \qquad \text{...(2)}$$

where

$$a = - x_1 (x_2 - x_3), \ b = (x_2 - x_3), \ c = - x_3 (x_2 - x_1), \ d = (x_2 - x_1).$$

Here

$$ad - bc = - (x_1 - x_2)(x_2 - x_3)(x_3 - x_1) \neq 0$$

for x_1, x_2, x_3 are distinct.

It will be seen that

$$x_1, x_2, x_3 \text{ are real } \Leftrightarrow \ a, b, c, d \text{ are real.}$$

Thus, we see that the totality of bilinear transformations which map the real axis onto itself is given by

$$w = \frac{a + bz}{c + dz}$$

where a, b, c, d are real numbers.

Bilinear transformations of the half-planes I $(z) > 0$, I $(z) < 0$.

From (2), we have

$$w = \frac{a + b\overline{z}}{c + d\overline{z}}$$

$\Rightarrow$ $$w - \bar{w} = \frac{(bc - ad)\,(z - \bar{z})}{(c + dz)\,(c + d\bar{z})} = \frac{(bc - ad)}{|\,c + dz\,|^2}\,(z - \bar{z})$$

$\Rightarrow$ $$I\,(w) = \frac{(bc - ad)}{|\,c + dz\,|^2}\,I\,(z).$$

Thus, we see that the transformation (2) which *maps the real axis on the real axis will map the region $I\,(z) > 0$, i.e., the upper half-plane, onto the half-plane $I\,(w) > 0$ or the half-plane $I\,(w) < 0$ according as the determinant $(ad - bc)$ of the transformation is negative or positive.*

We may similarly obtain the bilinear transformation of the half-plane $I\,(z) < 0$.

In terms of x_1, x_2, x_3, we may see that the transformation (1) will map $I\,(z) > 0$ onto $I\,(w) > 0$ or $I\,(w) < 0$ according as the orientation of the points x_1, x_2, x_3 on the real axis is the same or different from that of the points $0, 1, \infty$ on the real axis.

EXAMPLES

1. *Find the bilinear transformation which maps the points $z_1 = 2$, $z_2 = i$ and $z_3 = -2$ into the points $w_1 = 1$, $w_2 = i$ and $w_3 = -1$.*

Solution. Let the transformation be

$$w = \frac{az + b}{cz + d} \qquad \qquad ...(1)$$

Substituting the given values in (1), we get

$$1 = \frac{2a + b}{2c + d} \quad \Rightarrow \quad 2a + b - 2c - d = 0 \qquad ...(2)$$

$$i = \frac{ai + b}{ci + d} \quad \Rightarrow \quad ai + b + c - di = 0 \qquad ...(3)$$

and

$$-1 = \frac{-2a + b}{-3c + d} \quad \Rightarrow \quad 2a - b + 2c - d = 0 \qquad ...(4)$$

Adding (2) and (4), we get

$$2b - 4c = 0 \quad \Rightarrow \quad b = 2c.$$

From (3) we have

$$ai + 2i + c - 2ai = 0 \quad \Rightarrow \quad ai = 3c.$$

These relations yield

$$a = \frac{d}{2} = \frac{3c}{i} = \frac{3b}{2i} \quad \Rightarrow \quad \frac{a}{1} = \frac{d}{2} = \frac{c}{i/3} = \frac{b}{2i/3}.$$

Substituting these in (1), we get

$$w = \frac{z + 2i/3}{(i/3)\,z + 2} = \frac{3z + 2i}{iz + 6}.$$

2. *Find a bilinear transformation which transforms the unit circle $|\,z\,| = 1$ into the real axis in such a way that the point $z_1 = 1$ is mapped into $w_1 = 0$, the point $z_2 = i$ is mapped into $w_2 = 1$ and the point $z_3 = -1$ is mapped into $w_3 = \infty$. Into what regions the interior and exterior of the circle are mapped ?*

Solution. Points $z_1 = 1$, $z_2 = i$ and $z_3 = -1$ lie on the circle $|\,z\,| = 1$ and the points $w_1 = 0$, $w_2 = 1$ and $w_3 = \infty$ lie on the real axis of the w-plane. Hence the required transformation obtained by substituting these values is

$$\frac{(w - 0)\,(1 - \infty)}{(0 - 1)\,(\infty - w)} = \frac{(z - 1)\,(i + 1)}{(1 - i)\,(-1 - z)}$$

$$\Rightarrow \qquad w = -\frac{(z - 1)\,(i + 1)^2}{(z + 1)\,(1 + i)\,(1 - i)} = -\frac{(z - 1)\cdot 2i}{(z + 1)\cdot 2}$$

$$\Rightarrow \qquad w = \frac{i\,(1 - z)}{1 + z}.$$

The inverse transformation is

$$z = -\frac{w - i}{w + i} \quad \Rightarrow \quad |\,z\,| = \left|\frac{w - i}{w + i}\right|.$$

Here $|\,z\,| = 1$ is transformed into $1 = \left|\dfrac{w - i}{w + i}\right|$ or, $|\,w - i\,| = |\,w + i\,|$ which is the real axis of the w-plane. Also the centre $z = 0$ of the circle $|\,z\,| = 1$ is transformed into the point $w = i$ of the w-plane. Thus interior of the circle $|\,z\,| = 1$ is mapped into the upper half-plane.

Again, $w = -i$ corresponds to $z = \infty$, it follows that the exterior of the circle $|\,z\,| = 1$ is transformed into lower half of the w-plane.

3.18. Determination of the totality of bilinear transformations which map $|\,z\,| = 1$ onto $|\,w\,| = 1$.

(Rajsthan 2001, 2004; Avadh 2007)

As in the preceding case, the required totality can be obtained by considering all possible choices of triads z_1, z_2, z_3 on $|\,z\,| = 1$ and mapping the same on some three fixed points say, 1, i, -1 on $|\,w\,| = 1$.

We shall, however, find it more convenient to pursue another type of argument which is based on the property of the preservation by a bilinear transformation of the configuration formed by a circle and two inverse points.

Suppose that
$$w = \frac{a + bz}{c + dz} \qquad \qquad \dots(1)$$
is a transformation mapping $|\,z\,| = 1$ onto $|\,w\,| = 1$.

Now $w = 0$, $w = \infty$ are inverse points for $|\,w\,| = 1$ and they are the transforms of

$$z = -\frac{a}{b}, \; z = -\frac{c}{d}$$

respectively so that

$$-\frac{a}{b}, \; -\frac{c}{d}$$

are inverse points for $|\,z\,| = 1$.

Thus, if we write
$$\alpha = -a/b,$$
then we must have
$$-\frac{c}{d} = \frac{1}{\bar{\alpha}}.$$

Thus, we can re-write (1) as

$$w = \frac{b}{d}\cdot\frac{(a/b) + z}{(c/d) + z}$$

$$= \frac{b}{d} \cdot \frac{(-\alpha + z)}{-(1/\bar{\alpha}) + z}$$

$$\frac{b\bar{\alpha}}{d} = \frac{z - \alpha}{\bar{\alpha}z - 1} = k \frac{z - \alpha}{\bar{\alpha}z - 1}, \text{ say}$$

where we have written $k = b\bar{\alpha}/d$.

Also, we must have $|w| = 1$, when $|z| = 1 \Leftrightarrow z\bar{z} = 1$.

Now
$$|w| = |k| \left| \frac{z - \alpha}{\bar{\alpha}z - 1} \right| = \frac{|z - \alpha|}{|\bar{\alpha}z - z\bar{z}|}$$

$$= \frac{|\bar{z} - \bar{a}|}{|z||\bar{a} - \bar{z}|} = |k| \qquad \qquad \qquad ...(1)$$

Thus, we see that $|k| = 1$.

We have thus shown that *every bilinear transformation which maps* $|z| = 1$ *onto* $|w| = 1$ *must* **necessarily** *be of the form*

$$w = k \frac{z - \alpha}{\bar{\alpha}z - 1}, \qquad \qquad ...(2)$$

where, α, *may be any number and* k *is unimodular.*

We may also see that for every number α and every unimodular number k, the transformation (2) does map $|z| = 1$ onto $|w| = 1$. In fact, we have

$$|w| = |k| \cdot \left| \frac{z - \alpha}{\bar{\alpha}z - 1} \right|$$

$$= \left| \frac{\bar{z} - \bar{a}}{\bar{\alpha}z - z\bar{z}} \right| = 1, \text{ if } |z| = 1.$$

We thus see that *the totality of bilinear transformations which map* $|z| = 1$ *onto* $|w| = 1$ *is given by*

$$w = k \frac{z - \alpha}{\bar{\alpha}z - 1} \qquad \qquad ...(3)$$

where α *is a number and* k *is unimodular.*

We shall now examine the *mappings of the interior and the exterior of* $|z| = 1$ *brought about by* (3).

We have

$$\bar{w} = k \frac{\bar{z} - \alpha}{\alpha\bar{z} - 1}.$$

$\Rightarrow$
$$w\bar{w} - 1 = k\bar{k} \frac{z - \alpha}{\bar{\alpha}z - 1} \cdot \frac{\bar{z} - \bar{a}}{\alpha\bar{z} - 1} - 1$$

$$= \frac{(1 - \alpha\bar{a})(z\bar{z} - 1)}{|\alpha\bar{z} - 1|^2}, \text{ for } k = 1.$$

This shows that the bilinear transformation (3) which maps

$$|z| = 1 \text{ onto } |w| = 1$$

will map

$$|z| < 1 \text{ onto } |w| < 1 \text{ or } |w| > 1$$

according as

$$|\alpha| < 1 \text{ or } |\alpha| > 1.$$

3.19. Determination of the totality of bilinear transformations which maps the real axis I $(z) = 0$ onto the unit circle $|w| = 1$.

(*Garhwal, 2001, 2003, 2005, Rohilkhand, 2002, Meerut 2004, Ravishankar 2002*)

Suppose that

$$w = \frac{a + bz}{c + dz} \qquad \qquad ...(1)$$

is a bilinear transformation which maps I $(z) = 0$ onto $|w| = 1$.

Now the points $w = 0, \infty$ which are inverse points for $|w| = 1$ are the images of the points $z = -a/b, -c/d$ respectively. Thus $-a/b, -c/d$ must be reflection points for the real axis.

Thus, if we write

$$-a/b = \alpha, \text{ then } -c/d = \overline{\alpha}$$

We can thus re-write (1) as

$$w = \frac{b}{d} \cdot \frac{z + (a/b)}{z + (c/d)} = \frac{b}{a} \cdot \frac{z - \alpha}{z - \overline{a}} = k \frac{z - \alpha}{z - \overline{a}} \quad \text{say} \qquad ..(2)$$

We require that $|w| = 1$ when z is real.

Thus

$$\left| \frac{z - \alpha}{z - \overline{a}} \right| = 1,$$

when z is real, we see that in (1), k, must necessarily be unimodular.

Hence we see that a bilinear transformation which maps I $(z) = 0$ onto $|w| = 1$ is *necessarily* of the form

$$w = k \frac{z - \alpha}{z - \overline{a}}, \text{ where } |k| = 1.$$

Conversely also we can show that the transformation

$$w = k \frac{z - \alpha}{z - \overline{a}} \qquad \qquad ...(3)$$

where α is any number and k is unimodular does map I $(z) = 0$ onto $|w| = 1$.

Again

$$w = \frac{k(z - \alpha)}{z - \overline{a}} \text{ and } |k| = 1.$$

$$\Rightarrow \qquad w\overline{w} - 1 = \frac{(z - \overline{z})|\alpha - \overline{a}|}{|z - \overline{a}|^2} = \frac{-4I(z)I(\alpha)}{|z - \overline{a}|^2}$$

This shows that the bilinear transformation which maps

$$I(z) = 0 \text{ onto } |w| = 1$$

will map

$$I(z) > 0 \text{ onto } |w| > 1 \text{ or } |w| < 1$$

according as

$$I(\alpha) < 0 \text{ or } I(\alpha) > 0.$$

Note. The reader should carefully notice that in each of the three cases above, we are interested in the determination of *all* the bilinear transformations rather than any one bilinear transformation with an assigned property.

Theorem. *Given any two circles, there exists a bilinear transformation which maps them onto a pair of intersecting or parallel straight lines or onto a pair of concentric circles.*

There are three possibilities that the two given circles intersect in

(*a*) two points, (*b*) one point, *i.e.*, may touch, (*c*) no point.

In case (*a*), any bilinear transformation which maps one of the two points of intersection onto ∞ will map the two given circles onto two straight lines which pass through the image of the second points of intersection of the two given circles. Thus the two images are two intersecting straight lines in this case.

In case (*b*), any bilinear transformation which maps the common point of two circles onto ∞ will map the two circles onto two straight lines having no common point, *i.e.*, onto two parallel lines.

Consider case (*c*) now. First transform one of the two given circles onto a straight line.

Suppose now the images of the two given circles are a circle C with centre L and a straight line *l*.

Let M be the foot of the perpendicular from L on the line *l*. Let MP be tangent to the circle C. Draw the circle C′ with centre M and radius MP. This circle cuts C and *l* both orthogonally.

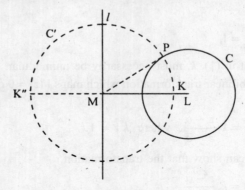

Fig. 3.9

Consider a bilinear transformation which maps the point K onto ∞. This transformation will map the circle C′ and the line LM onto a pair of orthogonal lines intersecting at the image K″ of K and cutting orthogonally the images of the circle C and the line *l*. Thus these latter are circles with common centre at K″.

3.20. Some More Bilinear Transformations. In this section we will discuss some more special bilinear transformations. For this we will make use of § 3.12 and § 3.13.

3.20.1. Determination of bilinear transformation which transforms R (z) ≥ 0 into the unit circle | *w* | ≤ 1.   (*Ravishankar 2001*)

Suppose the bilinear transformation

$$w = \frac{az + b}{cz + d} \qquad \qquad ...(1)$$

transforms the half-plane R $(z) \geq 0$ into the circle $| w | \leq 1$.

Now (1) is expressible as

$$w = \frac{a}{c} \cdot \frac{z + (b/a)}{z + (d/c)} \qquad \qquad ...(2)$$

This $\Rightarrow c \neq 0$, otherwise the points at infinity in the two planes would correspond.

The points z and $-\bar{z}$ symmetrical about the imaginary axis R $(z) = 0$ will correspond to $w = 0$ and $w = \infty$, the inverse points of the circle $| w | = 1$. Thus

$$-\frac{b}{a} = \alpha, \quad -\frac{d}{c} = -\bar{\alpha}. .$$

Then (2) takes the form

$$w = \frac{a}{c} \left(\frac{z - \alpha}{z + \bar{\alpha}} \right) \qquad \qquad ...(3)$$

The point $z = 0$ on the boundary of the half-plane R $(z) \geq 0$ must correspond to a point on the boundary of $| w | = 1$ so that

$$1 = | w | = \left| \frac{a}{c} \right| \cdot \left| \frac{0 - \alpha}{0 + \bar{\alpha}} \right| = \left| \frac{a}{c} \right|$$

so that $\frac{a}{c} = e^{i\lambda}$, where λ is real.

Hence

$$w = e^{i\lambda} \left(\frac{z - \alpha}{z + \bar{\alpha}} \right) \qquad \qquad ...(4)$$

Evidently $z = \alpha$ gives $w = 0$. But $w = 0$ is an interior point of the circle $| w | = 1$.

Hence $z = \alpha$ must be a point of the right half-plane, *i.e.*, R $(\alpha) > 0$. With this condition, (4) is the required transformation.

To verify the transformation, we have

$$w\bar{w} - 1 = \left(\frac{z - \alpha}{z + \bar{\alpha}} \right) e^{i\lambda} \cdot \left(\frac{\bar{z} - \bar{\alpha}}{z + \alpha} \right) e^{-i\lambda} - 1$$

$$= \frac{z\bar{z} + \alpha\bar{\alpha} - z\bar{\alpha} - \alpha\bar{z} - (z\bar{z} + \alpha\bar{\alpha} + z\alpha + \bar{z}\bar{\alpha})}{(z + \bar{\alpha})(z + \alpha)}$$

$$= \frac{- z(\alpha + \bar{\alpha}) - \bar{z}(\alpha + \bar{\alpha})}{| z + \bar{\alpha} |^2} = \frac{-(z + \bar{z})(\alpha + \bar{\alpha})}{| z + \bar{\alpha} |^2} = \frac{-2R(\alpha) \cdot 2R(z)}{| z + \bar{\alpha} |^2}$$

$$= \frac{4R(\alpha) \cdot R(z)}{| z + \bar{\alpha} |^2} = 1 - | w |^2 \qquad \qquad ...(5)$$

Also, we have proved that R $(\alpha) > 0$.

Now from (5), it is clear that

(*i*) R $(z) = 0$ corresponds to $1 - | w |^2 = 0$, or $| w | = 1$.

(*ii*) R $(z) > 0$ corresponds to $1 - | w |^2 > 0$, or $| w | < 1$.

Finally, R $(z) \geq 0$ corresponds to $| w | \leq 1$, by virtue of the transformation (4).

3.20.2. Determination of bilinear transformation which transforms the circle $|z| \leq \rho$ onto the circle $|w| \leq \rho'$.

(*Garhwal, 2004; Rohilkhand, 2001, Rajsthan 2000*)

Suppose the transformation

$$w = \frac{az + b}{cz + d} \qquad \qquad ...(1)$$

transforms $|z| \leq \rho$ onto the circle $|w| \leq \rho'$.

From (1) we have

$$w = \frac{a}{c} \cdot \frac{z + (b/a)}{z + (d/c)} \qquad \qquad ...(2)$$

Clearly $c \neq 0$, otherwise the point of infinity in the two planes would correspond.

Transformation (2) maps a circle of z-plane into a circle of w-plane and inverse points transform into inverse points.

If $w = 0$, then (2) $\Rightarrow$ $z = -b/a$.

If $w = \infty$, then (2) $\Rightarrow$ $z = -d/c$.

Thus, $w = 0$, $w = \infty$ the inverse points of $|w| = \rho'$ are the transforms of $z = -b/a$, $z = -d/c$ respectively. Hence we may write

$$-\frac{b}{a} = \alpha, \quad -\frac{d}{c} = \frac{\rho^2}{\bar{\alpha}}, \text{ such that } |\alpha| \leq \rho.$$

[For α and $\rho^2/\bar{\alpha}$ are the inverse points of the circle $|z| = \rho$.]

Hence by (2) we have

$$w = \frac{a}{c} \cdot \frac{z - \alpha}{z - (\rho^2/\bar{\alpha})} \quad \Rightarrow \quad w = \frac{a\alpha}{c} \left(\frac{z - \alpha}{\bar{\alpha} z - \rho^2} \right) \qquad ...(3)$$

Now (3) satisfies the conditions $|z| \leq \rho$ and $|w| \leq \rho'$.

Hence for $|z| = \rho$, we must have $|w| = \rho'$ so that (3) becomes

$$|w| = \rho' = \left| \frac{a\bar{\alpha}}{c} \right| \cdot \left| \frac{z - \alpha}{\bar{\alpha} z - z\bar{z}} \right|$$

$$= \left| \frac{a\bar{\alpha}}{c} \right| \cdot \left| \frac{1}{z} \right| \left| \frac{z - \alpha}{\overline{z - \alpha}} \right| \text{ as } z\bar{z} = \rho^2$$

But $\quad |z - \alpha| = |\overline{z - \alpha}|$

Hence $\quad \rho\rho' = \left| \frac{a\bar{\alpha}}{c} \right|$ and so $\frac{a\bar{\alpha}}{c} = \rho\rho' e^{i\lambda}$

Thus (3) becomes

$$w = \rho\rho' e^{i\lambda} \left(\frac{z - \alpha}{z\bar{\alpha} - \rho^2} \right) \text{ such that } |\alpha| < \rho,$$

where λ is real.

This is the required transformation.

Theorem. To show that the region $|z - z_0| \leq R$ is mapped conformally on $|w| \leq 1$ by the transformation

$$w = \frac{R(z - \alpha) e^{i\lambda}}{R^2 - (z - z_0)(\bar{\alpha} - \bar{z}_0)}$$

where λ is real and $z = \alpha$ is the point which is transformed into the origin.

Let

$$w = \frac{az + b}{cz + d}, \quad ad - bc \neq 0 \qquad \qquad ...(1)$$

be the required transformation. The points $w = 0$ and $w = \infty$ which are inverse points with respect to $|w| = 1$ are transformed into

$$z = -\frac{b}{a} \text{ and } z = -\frac{d}{c}$$

respectively and consequently $-b/a$, $-d/c$ must be inverse points with respect to the circle $|z - z_0| = R$. Now for the point $z = \alpha$ the inverse point with respect to the circle $|z - z_0| = R$ is

$$z_0 + \frac{R^2}{\bar{\alpha} - \bar{z}_0}.$$

Hence if we set $-\dfrac{b}{a} = \alpha$, then

$$-\frac{d}{c} = z_0 + \frac{R^2}{\bar{\alpha} - \bar{z}_0}.$$

Substituting these values in (1), we get

$$w = \frac{a}{c} \cdot \frac{z - \alpha}{z - z_0 - \dfrac{R^2}{\bar{\alpha} - \bar{z}_0}} = \frac{a(\bar{\alpha} - \bar{z}_0)}{c} \cdot \frac{z - \alpha}{(z - z_0)(\bar{\alpha} - \bar{z}_0) - R^2} \qquad ...(2)$$

Now we have $|w| = 1$ when $|z - z_0| = R$, i.e., when

$$(z - z_0)(\bar{z} - \bar{z}_0) = R^2.$$

Hence

$$1 = |w| = \left| \frac{a(\bar{\alpha} - \bar{z}_0)}{c} \right| \left| \frac{z - \alpha}{(z - z_0)(\bar{\alpha} - \bar{z}_0) - (z - z_0)(\bar{z} - \bar{z}_0)} \right|$$

$$= \left| \frac{a(\bar{\alpha} - \bar{z}_0)}{c} \right| \left| \frac{z - \alpha}{(z - z_0)(\bar{\alpha} - \bar{z})} \right|$$

$$= \left| \frac{a(\bar{\alpha} - \bar{z}_0)}{c} \right| \cdot \frac{1}{R} \qquad \left[\because |z - \alpha| = |\bar{\alpha} - \bar{z}| \text{ and } |z - a| = R \right]$$

or $\left| \dfrac{a(\bar{\alpha} - \bar{z}_0)}{c} \right| = R.$

Hence we may write $\left| \dfrac{a(\bar{\alpha} - \bar{z}_0)}{c} \right| = R^{i\mu}$, where μ is real.

Substituting in (2), we get

$$w = \frac{R(z - \alpha)}{(z - z_0)(\bar{\alpha} - \bar{z}_0) - R^2} e^{i\lambda}.$$

Putting $\mu = \lambda + \pi$, the transformation becomes

$$w = \frac{R(z - \alpha)}{(z - z_0)(\overline{\alpha} - \overline{z}_0) - R^2} e^{i\pi} \cdot e^{i\lambda}$$

$\Rightarrow \qquad\qquad w = \frac{R(z - \alpha)}{R^2 - (z - z_0)(\overline{\alpha} - \overline{z})} e^{i\lambda}$ \hfill ...(3)

where λ is real.

It is evident that $z = \alpha$ is transformed into the origin. Hence, (3) is the required transformation.

EXAMPLES

1. *Show that the transformation* $w = \dfrac{2z + 3}{z - 4}$ *transforms the circle* $x^2 + y^2 - 4x = 0$ *into the straight line* $4u + 3 = 0$ *and explain why the curve obtained is not a circle.*

(Garhwal, 2002, 2007; Kanpur 2005; Rohilkhand 2007)

Solution. $z = x + iy \Rightarrow z\overline{z} = x^2 + y^2, \; z + \overline{z} = 2x$

$w = u + iv \Rightarrow w + \overline{w} = 2u.$

From the given transformation, we have

$$z = \frac{4w + 3}{w - 2} \qquad\qquad ...(1)$$

The given circle is

$$x^2 + y^2 - 4x = 0 \Rightarrow z\overline{z} - 2(z + \overline{z}) = 0 \qquad ...(2)$$

Putting for z from (1) in (2), we get the transformed equation in w-plane as

$$\frac{4w + 3}{w - 2} \cdot \frac{4\overline{w} + 3}{\overline{w} - 2} - 2\left[\frac{4w + 3}{w - 2} + \frac{4\overline{w} + 3}{\overline{w} - 2} \right] = 0$$

$\Rightarrow \quad (16w\overline{w} + 12\overline{w} + 12w + 9) - 2[(4w\overline{w} + 3\overline{w} - 8w - 6) + (4w\overline{w} - 8\overline{w} + 3w - 6)] = 0$

$\Rightarrow \qquad\qquad\qquad\qquad\qquad 2(w + \overline{w}) + 3 = 0 \Rightarrow 2(2u) + 3 = 0$

$\Rightarrow \quad 4u + 3 = 0$, which is a straight line.

Explanation. We know that $\left| \dfrac{z - p}{z - q} \right| = \lambda$ represents a circle ($\lambda > 0$) and in case $\lambda = 1$ it is a straight line. In other words, straight line is a particular case of circle.

2. *Show that the transformation* $w = \dfrac{5 - 4z}{4z - 2}$ *transforms the circle* $|z| = 1$ *into a circle of radius unity in the w-plane and find the centre of this circle.*

Solution. From the given transformation we have

$$z = \frac{2w + 5}{4(w + 1)} \qquad\qquad ...(1)$$

$|z| = 1 \Rightarrow z\overline{z} = 1$ and hence from (1) we have

$$\frac{2w + 5}{4(w + 1)} \cdot \frac{2\overline{w} + 5}{4(\overline{w} + 1)} = 1$$

$\Rightarrow$ $\qquad\qquad 4w\overline{w} + 10\,(w + \overline{w}) + 25\ = 16\,[w\overline{w} + (w + \overline{w}) + 1]$

$\Rightarrow$ $\qquad\qquad 12w\overline{w} + 6\,(w + \overline{w}) - 9\ = 0$

$\Rightarrow$ $\qquad\qquad 12\,(u^2 + v^2) + 6\,(2u) - 9\ = 0$

$\Rightarrow$ $\qquad\qquad u^2 + v^2 + u - (3/4) = 0.$

It represents a circle in the w-plane whose centre is $(-1/2,\ 0)$ and radius $\sqrt{(1/4) + (3/4)} = 1.$

3. *Show that both the transformations* $w = \dfrac{z - i}{z + i}$ *and* $w = \dfrac{i - z}{i + z}$ *transform* $|\,w\,| \le 1$ *into upper half-plane* $I\,(z) \ge 0.$

$\qquad\qquad\qquad\qquad\qquad\qquad\qquad\qquad\qquad\qquad$ (*Rohilkhand, 2004; Kerala 2001*)

Solution. $\quad w\overline{w} - 1\ = \dfrac{z - i}{z + i} \cdot \dfrac{\overline{z} + i}{\overline{z} - i} - 1$

$\qquad\qquad\qquad\qquad = \dfrac{2i\,(z - \overline{z})}{|z + i|^2} = \dfrac{2i\,(2iy)}{|z + i|^2} = -\dfrac{4I\,(z)}{|z + i|^2}.$

The same result will be obtained if we choose the second transformation.

Now $\qquad |\,w\,|^2 - 1\ = -\dfrac{4y}{|\,z + i\,|^2}$ $\qquad\qquad\qquad\qquad\qquad\qquad$ $[\because\ I\,(z) = y]$

$|\,w\,| = 1$ corresponds to $y = 0,$ *i.e.*, real axis of z-plane.

$|\,w\,| < 1$ corresponds to $y > 0,$ *i.e.*, $I\,(z) > 0,$ *i.e.*, upper-half of z-plane.

4. *Find a bilinear transformation which maps the circle* $|\,w\,| \le 1$ *into the circle* $|\,z - 1\,| < 1$ *and maps* $w = 0,\ w = 1$ *respectively into* $z = 1/2,\ z = 0.$ *Show also that the transformation is uniquely determined.*

Solution. Let the required transformation be

$$w\ = \frac{az + b}{cz + d} = \frac{a}{c} \cdot \frac{z + (b/c)}{z + (d/c)} \qquad\qquad\qquad\qquad\qquad\qquad …(1)$$

Refer Theorem 3.13 we know that bilinear transformation (1) transforms circles and inverse points into inverse points. Here $z = -b/c$ and $z = -d/c$ are inverse points w.r.t. the circle $|\,z - 1\,| = 1.$

Now the inverse points of $|\,w\,| = 1$ are $w = 0$ and $w = \infty$ and we are given that $w = 0$ is mapped onto $z = \dfrac{1}{2}.$

$\therefore z = \dfrac{1}{2} = \alpha$ (say) is one inverse point w.r.t. the circle $|\,z - 1\,| = 1$ whose other inverse point will be

$z_0 + \dfrac{R^2}{\overline{\alpha - \overline{z_0}}},$ where $z_0 = 1$ the centre, $R = 1,\ \alpha = 1/2.$

$\therefore$ The other inverse point is

$$1 + \frac{1}{\dfrac{1}{2} - 1} = -1.$$

$\therefore z = -b/c = 1/2$ and $z = -d/c = -1$ are the inverse points so that from (1), we get

$$w\ = \frac{a}{c} \cdot \frac{z - (1/2)}{z + 1} = \frac{a}{2c} \cdot \frac{2z - 1}{z + 1} \qquad\qquad\qquad\qquad\qquad …(2)$$

Now, $w = 1$ corresponds to $z = 0$ and hence from (2), we have

$$1 = \frac{a}{2c}\left(\frac{0-1}{0+1}\right) \quad \Rightarrow \quad \frac{a}{2c} = -1.$$

Hence,

$$w = -\frac{2z-1}{z+1} = \frac{1-2z}{1+z}$$

is the required bilinear transformation.

5. *Show that if $(a - d)^2 + 4bc \neq 0$, then for the transformation* $w = \dfrac{az + b}{cz + d}$ *there are two*

unequal numbers α and β such that $\dfrac{w - \alpha}{w - \beta} = \lambda\left(\dfrac{z - \alpha}{z - \beta}\right)$, *where λ is a constant.*

(Rohilkhand 2003)

Show also that the radius of the circle in the w-plane corresponding to the circle in the

z-plane which has as diameter the line joining the points $z = \alpha$, $z = \beta$ is $\left|\dfrac{\alpha - \beta}{2\cos\theta}\right|$, *where θ is*

the argument of λ.

Solution. For the first part, see § 3.14.

We know that the equation of the circle on the join of α and β as diameter is

$$\text{amp.}\left(\frac{z-\alpha}{z-\beta}\right) = \frac{\pi}{2} \quad \Rightarrow \quad \frac{z-\alpha}{z-\beta} \text{ is purely imaginary.}$$

$\Rightarrow \qquad \text{Re}\left(\frac{z-\alpha}{z-\beta}\right) = 0 \quad \Rightarrow \quad \frac{1}{2}\left[\frac{z-\alpha}{z-\beta} + \overline{\left(\frac{z-\alpha}{z-\beta}\right)}\right] = 0$

$\Rightarrow \qquad \dfrac{z-\alpha}{z-\beta} + \overline{\left(\dfrac{z-\alpha}{z-\beta}\right)} = 0$

Now, $\qquad \dfrac{z-\alpha}{z-\beta} = \dfrac{1}{\lambda}\left(\dfrac{w-\alpha}{w-\beta}\right)$ ...(1)

$\Rightarrow \qquad \overline{\left(\dfrac{z-\alpha}{z-\beta}\right)} = \dfrac{1}{\overline{\lambda}}\cdot\left(\dfrac{\overline{w}-\overline{\alpha}}{\overline{w}-\overline{\beta}}\right)$ ...(2)

Hence from (1), by the help of (2), we get

$$\frac{1}{\lambda}\cdot\frac{w-\alpha}{w-\beta} + \frac{1}{\overline{\lambda}}\cdot\frac{\overline{w}-\overline{\alpha}}{\overline{w}-\overline{\beta}} = 0$$

or $\qquad \overline{\lambda}\,(w-\alpha)(\overline{w}-\overline{\beta}) + \lambda\,(w-\beta)(\overline{w}-\overline{\alpha}) = 0$

$\Rightarrow \quad (\lambda + \overline{\lambda})\,w\overline{w} - (\overline{\alpha}\lambda + \beta\overline{\lambda})\,w - (\alpha\overline{\lambda} + \beta\lambda)\,\overline{w} + \alpha\overline{\beta}\lambda + \beta\overline{\alpha}\lambda = 0$ ...(3)

Now if $\lambda = re^{i\theta}$, then $\overline{\lambda} = re^{-i\theta}$

$\Rightarrow \qquad \lambda + \overline{\lambda} = 2r\cos\theta.$

Then (3) reduces to

$$w\overline{w} - \frac{r\,(\overline{\alpha}e^{i\theta} - \overline{\beta}e^{-i\theta})}{2r\cos\theta}\,w - \frac{r\,(\alpha e^{-i\theta} + \beta e^{i\theta})}{2r\cos\theta}\,\overline{w}$$

$$+ \frac{r\,(\alpha\overline{\beta}e^{-i\theta} + \beta\overline{\alpha}e^{i\theta})}{2\cos\theta} = 0$$

$$\Rightarrow \quad w\overline{w} - \frac{(\overline{\alpha}e^{i\theta} - \overline{\beta}e^{-i\theta})}{2\cos\theta}\,w - \frac{(\alpha e^{-i\theta} + \beta e^{i\theta})}{2\cos\theta}\,\overline{w}$$

$$+ \frac{(\alpha\overline{\beta}e^{-i\theta} + \beta\overline{\alpha}e^{i\theta})}{2\cos\theta} = 0.$$

This is of the form $z\overline{z} + b\overline{z} + \overline{b}z + c = 0$

where $b = -\dfrac{(\alpha e^{-i\theta} + \beta e^{i\theta})}{2\cos\theta}$ so that

$$\overline{b} = -\frac{(\overline{\alpha}e^{i\theta} + \overline{\beta}e^{-i\theta})}{2\cos\theta}.$$

Its radius $= \sqrt{(bb' - c)}$.

Now

$$bb' - c = \frac{1}{(2\cos\theta)^2}\,[(\alpha e^{-i\theta} + \beta e^{i\theta})\,(\overline{\alpha}e^{i\theta} + \overline{\beta}e^{-i\theta})$$

$$- (\alpha\overline{\beta}e^{-i\theta} + \beta\overline{\alpha}e^{i\theta})\,(e^{i\theta} + e^{-i\theta})]$$

$$\therefore \qquad r^2 = \frac{1}{(2\cos\theta)^2}\,[(\alpha\overline{\alpha} + \beta\overline{\beta}) - (\alpha\overline{\beta} + \overline{\alpha}\beta)]$$

(All other terms cancel)

$$= \frac{1}{(2\cos\theta)^2}\,[\alpha\,(\overline{\alpha} - \overline{\beta}) - \beta\,(\overline{\alpha} - \overline{\beta})]$$

$$= \frac{1}{(2\cos\theta)^2}\,[(\alpha - \beta)\,(\overline{\alpha} - \overline{\beta})]$$

$$= \frac{1}{(2\cos\theta)^2}\,[|\,\alpha - \beta\,|^2]$$

$\therefore$ Radius $\quad r = \dfrac{|\,\alpha - \beta\,|}{2\cos\theta} = \left|\dfrac{\alpha - \beta}{2\cos\theta}\right|.$

6. *Prove that the transformation* $\overline{a}wz - bw - \overline{b}z + a = 0$ *maps the circle* $|\,z\,| = 1$ *on the circle* $|\,w\,| = 1$ *if* $|\,b\,| \neq |\,a\,|$.

Find the condition that the interior of the first circle may be mapped onto the interior of the second. Show also that, in this transformation the fixed points either are inverse points with respect to the unit circle or lie on that circle.

Solution. From the given relation

$$z = \frac{bw - a}{\overline{a}w - \overline{b}} \qquad\qquad ...(1)$$

$\therefore$
$$z\overline{z} - 1 = \frac{bw - a}{\overline{a}w - \overline{b}} \cdot \frac{\overline{b}\overline{w} - \overline{a}}{a\overline{w} - b} - 1$$

$$= \frac{(b\overline{b} - a\overline{a})\, w\overline{w} + (a\overline{a} - b\overline{b})}{|\overline{a}w - \overline{b}|^2}$$

or
$$|z|^2 - 1 = \frac{[|b|^2 - |a|^2][|w|^2 - 1]}{|\overline{a}w - \overline{b}|^2}, \text{ where } |b| \neq |a|$$

From above we conclude the following:

$$|\overline{z}| = 1 \text{ corresponds to } |w| = 1.$$

Also if $|b| > |a|$ *i.e.* $|b|^2 - |a|^2$ is +ve, then

$$|z|^2 - 1 < 0, \text{ if } |w|^2 - 1 < 0,$$

i.e., the interiors correspond provided $|b| > |a|$ which is the required condition.

For fixed points, $w = z$ and hence putting $w = z$ in the given relation, we get

$$\overline{a}z^2 - (b + \overline{b})z + a = 0 \qquad \qquad \qquad ...(2)$$

If the roots of (2) be z_1 and z_2, then $z_1 z_2 = a/\overline{a}$

$$|z_1 z_2| = \left|\frac{a}{\overline{a}}\right| \quad \Rightarrow \quad |z_1||z_2| = 1 \qquad \qquad ...(3)$$

If z_1 and z_2 are distinct then relation (3) shows that they are inverse points w.r.t. the circle $|z| = 1$. In case z_1 and z_2 are equal then from (3) $|z_1|^2 = 1$ which shows that $z_1 (= z_2)$ lie on the circle $|z| = 1$.

7. *Express the relation* $w = \dfrac{13iz + 75}{3z - 5i}$ *in the form where*

$$\frac{w - a}{w - b} = k\left(\frac{z - a}{z - b}\right)$$

a, b, k are constants. Show that the circle in the z-plane whose centre is at z = 0 and radius 5 is transformed into the circle in the w-plane on the line w = a and w = b as diameter and the points in the z-plane which are exterior to the former circle are transformed into the points in the w-plane within the latter circle.

Solution.
$$w = \frac{13iz + 75}{3z - 5i}$$

$\Rightarrow$
$$\frac{w - a}{w - b} = \frac{(13i - 3a)z + (75 + 5ia)}{(13i - 3b)z + (75 + 5ib)}$$

$$= \left(\frac{13i - 3a}{13i - 3b}\right)\left(\frac{z - \dfrac{75 + 5ia}{3a - 13i}}{z - \dfrac{75 + 5ib}{3b - 13i}}\right)$$

Now choose $\dfrac{75 + 5ia}{5a - 13i} = a \quad \Rightarrow \quad 3a^2 - 18ia - 75 = 0$

$\Rightarrow$
$$a^2 - 6ia - 25 = 0 \quad \Rightarrow \quad a = \frac{6i \pm \sqrt{(-36 + 100)}}{2}$$

$\Rightarrow$ $\qquad\qquad\qquad a = 3i \pm 4.$

Similarly we shall have $b = 3i \pm 4.$

The case when $a = b$ both sides are identical and hence $a \neq b$ we may choose $a = i - 4$ and $b = 3i + 4.$

Also $\qquad\qquad k = \dfrac{13i - 3a}{13i - 3b} = \dfrac{13i - (9i - 12)}{13i - (9i + 12)}$

$$= \dfrac{4i + 12}{4i - 12} = \dfrac{i + 3}{i - 3}$$

$$= \dfrac{(i + 3)^2}{i^2 - 9} = \dfrac{-1 + 9 + 6i}{-10} = \dfrac{4 + 3i}{-5}.$$

$\therefore$ Amp $k = \tan^{-1}(b/a) = \tan^{-1}(3/4).$

Hence the required form is

$$\frac{w - a}{w - b} = k\left(\frac{z - a}{z - b}\right).$$

2nd part. Now take a point on the circle $|z| = 5$ so that $z = 5e^{i\theta}$. We have to show that this circle is transformed to a circle in w-plane on line joining a and b as diameter for which we will show that

$$\text{amp.} \left(\frac{w - a}{w - b}\right) = \frac{\pi}{2}.$$

From (1), we have

$$\text{amp} \left(\frac{w - a}{w - b}\right) = \text{amp } k + \text{amp } (z - a) - \text{amp } (z - b)$$

$$= \text{amp } k + \text{amp } [5e^{i\theta} - (3i - 4)] - \text{amp } [5e^{i\theta} - (3i + 4)]$$

$$= \tan^{-1}(3/4) + \text{amp } [(5\cos\theta + 4) + i(5\sin\theta - 3)]$$

$$\qquad\qquad\qquad - \text{amp } [(5\cos\theta - 4) + i(5\sin\theta - 3)]$$

$$= \tan^{-1}(3/4) + \tan^{-1}\frac{5\sin\theta - 3}{5\cos\theta + 4} - \tan^{-1}\frac{5\sin\theta - 3}{5\cos\theta - 4}$$

$$= \tan^{-1}(3/4) + \tan^{-1}(4/3)$$

$$\qquad\qquad\qquad\qquad \left[\because \tan^{-1}a - \tan^{-1}b = \tan^{-1}\frac{a - b}{1 + ab}\right]$$

$$= \tan^{-1}\frac{(3/4) + (4/3)}{1 - (3/4)(4/3)} = \frac{\pi}{2}.$$

$\therefore \qquad$ amp $\left(\dfrac{w - a}{w - b}\right) = \dfrac{\pi}{2}.$

This equation represents a circle on the join of a and b as diameter.

Above relation shows that points on $|z| = 5$ correspond to points on the circle in w-plane on the join of points a and b as diameter.

3rd part. Any point outside the circle $|z| = 5$ can be expressed as

$$z = 5re^{i\theta}, \text{ where } r > 1.$$

$$\therefore \qquad z - a = 5r \ (\cos\theta + i\sin\theta) - (3i - 4)$$

$$= (5r\cos\theta + 4) + i\ (5r\sin\theta - 3)$$

$$z - b = (5r\cos\theta - 4) + i\ (5r\sin\theta - 3)$$

$$\therefore \text{amp}\ (z - a) - \text{amp}\ (z - b)$$

$$= \tan^{-1}\frac{5r\sin\theta - 3}{5r\cos\theta + 4} - \tan^{-1}\frac{5r\sin\theta - 3}{5r\cos\theta + 4}$$

$$= \tan^{-1}\frac{8\,(3 - 5r\sin\theta)}{25r^2 - 7 - 30r\sin\theta}, \text{ where } r > 1$$

$$< \tan^{-1}\frac{8\,(3 - 5r\sin\theta)}{25 - 7 - 30r\sin\theta}$$

$$= \tan^{-1}\frac{8\,(3 - 5r\sin\theta)}{6\,(3 - 5r\sin\theta)} = \tan^{-1}\,(4/3)$$

Now $\qquad \dfrac{w - a}{w - b} = k\,\dfrac{z - a}{z - b}$, where $\text{amp}\ k = \tan^{-1}\,(3/4)$

$$\therefore \qquad \text{amp}\left(\frac{w - a}{w - b}\right) = \text{amp}\ k + \text{amp}\ (z - a) - \text{amp}\ (z - b)$$

$$< \tan^{-1}\,(3/4) + \tan^{-1}\,(4/3)$$

$$= \tan^{-1}\frac{(3/4) + (4/3)}{1 - 1} = \frac{\pi}{2}$$

$$\therefore \quad \text{amp}\left(\frac{w - a}{w - b}\right) < \frac{\pi}{2}.$$

This gives points on the circle which are inside the circle

$$\text{amp}\left(\frac{w - a}{w - b}\right) = \frac{\pi}{2},$$

i.e., the circle on the join of a and b as diameter in w-plane.

Above relation shows that points exterior to $|z| = 5$ correspond to points inside the circle in the w-plane on the join of a and b as diameter.

8. *Show that* $\displaystyle\int\frac{ds}{y}$ *is an invariant with respect to the transformation* $w = \dfrac{az + b}{cz + d}$ *where a, b, c, d are real numbers such that ad − bc = 1 and ds* $= \sqrt{(dx^2 + dy^2)}$.

Solution. $\qquad z = x + iy \quad \Rightarrow \quad dz = dx + idy$

$$\therefore \qquad |\,dz\,| = \sqrt{(dx^2 + dy^2)} = ds,$$

$$w = \frac{az + b}{cz + d} \quad \Rightarrow \quad z = \frac{b - dw}{cw - a}$$

$$\therefore \qquad dz = \frac{(ad - bc)}{(cw - a)^2}\,dw = \frac{1}{(cw - a)^2}\,dw$$

$$\therefore \qquad |\,dz\,| = \frac{1}{|\,c - aw\,|^2}\,|\,dw\,|$$

or

$$ds = \frac{1}{|\,cw - a\,|^2}\,d\sigma \qquad \qquad ...(1)$$

where $d\sigma$ is the elementary arc in w-plane.

$$2iy = z - \overline{z} = \frac{b - dw}{cw - a} - \frac{b - d\overline{w}}{c\overline{w} - a} \quad \text{as } a, b, c, d \text{ are real.}$$

$$= \frac{(ad - bc)(w - \overline{w})}{|\,cw - a\,|^2} = \frac{w - \overline{w}}{|\,cw - a\,|^2} = \frac{2iv}{|\,cw - a\,|^2}$$

$$\therefore \qquad \frac{y}{v} = \frac{1}{|\,cw - a\,|^2} \qquad \qquad ...(2)$$

Hence from (1) by the help of (2), we get

$$ds = \frac{y}{v}\,d\sigma \quad \Rightarrow \quad \frac{ds}{y} = \frac{d\sigma}{v}$$

or

$$\int \frac{ds}{y} = \int \frac{d\sigma}{v}.$$

Above relation shows that $\displaystyle\int \frac{ds}{y}$ is invariant under given transformation.

9. *Discuss the application of the transfermation* $w = (iz + 1)/(z + i)$ *to the areas in the z-plane which are respectively inside and outside the unit circle with its centre at the origin.*

Solution. The given transformation is

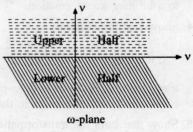

$$w = \frac{iz + 1}{z + i}$$

$$= \frac{i(x + iy) + 1}{x + iy + i}$$

$$\Rightarrow \qquad u + iv = \frac{(i - y) + ix}{x + i(1 + y)}$$

ω-plane

Fig. 3.9

$$= \frac{\{1 - y + ix\}\{x - i(1 + y)\}}{\{x + i(1 + y)\}\{x - i(1 + y)\}}$$

$$= \frac{2x + i(x^2 + y^2 - 1)}{x^2 + (1 + y)^2}$$

$$\Rightarrow \qquad u = \frac{2x}{x^2 + (1 + y)^2} \qquad ...(i)$$

$$\Rightarrow \qquad v = \frac{x^2 + y^2 - 1}{x^2 + (x + y)^2} \qquad ...(ii)$$

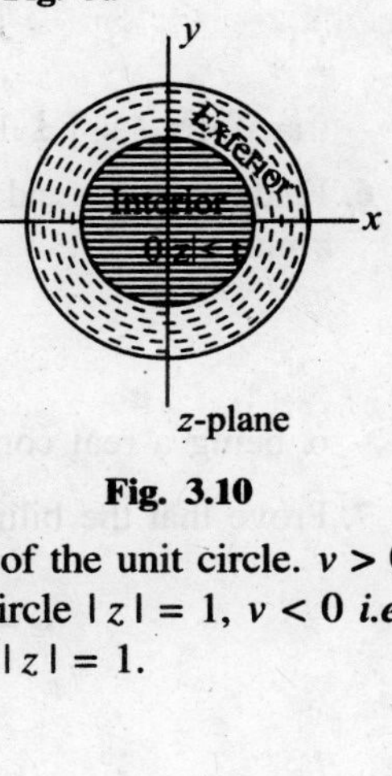

z-plane

Fig. 3.10

Clearly, $v = 0$, *i.e.*, real axis corresponds to $|z| = 1$, *i.e.*, boundary of the unit circle. $v > 0$, *i.e.*, upper half of w-plane corresponds to $|z| > 1$, *i.e.*, exterior of the circle $|z| = 1$, $v < 0$ *i.e.*, lower half of w-plane corresponds to $|z| < 1$, *i.e.*, interior of the circle $|z| = 1$.

EXERCISES

1. Express the following bilinear transformations as resultants of translations, rotations, magnifications and inversions:

(a) $\quad w = \dfrac{2 - 3z}{3 + 4z}$, (b) $\quad w = \dfrac{(1 + i) - 3z}{2 - i + iz}$, (c) $\quad w = \dfrac{2 - iz}{i + 3z}$.

[**Ans.** (a) $z_1 = z + \dfrac{3}{4}$, $z_2 = 1/z_1$, $z_3 = \dfrac{17}{16} z_2$, $w = -\dfrac{3}{4} + z_3$

(b) $z_1 = z + (2i + 1)$, $z_2 = 1/z_1$, $z_3 = (2i - 5) z_2$, $w = 3i + z_3$

(c) $z_1 = z + \dfrac{1}{3} i$, $z_2 = 1/z_1$, $z_3 = \dfrac{5}{9} z_2$, $w = -\dfrac{1}{3} i + z_3$]

2. Express the bilinear transformations

(a) $\quad w = z + (1 + i)$ (b) $\quad w = 4iz$

as resultants of inversions.

[**Ans.** (a) $z_1 = \dfrac{(1 + i) \bar{z}}{i - 1}$, $w = \dfrac{2 - (i + 1) \bar{z}_1}{1 - i}$

(b) $z_1 = \dfrac{1}{\bar{z}}$, $z_2 = \dfrac{4}{\bar{z}_1}$, $z_3 = \bar{z}_2$, $w = \dfrac{i - 1}{i + 1} \bar{z}_3$]

Of course these inversions are not unique

$$-\dfrac{7i}{8}, \dfrac{9}{8}, \dfrac{i}{4}$$

3. Show that two successive inversions with respect to an arbitrary pair of circles are equivalent to a bilinear transformation.

4. Show that the relation

$$w = \dfrac{iz + 2}{4z + i},$$

transforms the real axis in the z-plane to a circle in the w-plane. Find the centre and the radius of the circle and the point in the z-plane which is mapped on the centre of the circle.

5. Show that both the transformations

$$w = \dfrac{z + i}{z - i} \text{ and } w = \dfrac{i + z}{i - z}$$

transform $| w | \leq 1$ into the lower half-plane I $(z) \leq 0$.

6. Find the radius and centre of the circle in the w-plane which corresponds to the real axis in the z-plane where

$$w = \dfrac{ze^{i\alpha} - i}{z - ie^{i\alpha}};$$

α being a real constant. (**Ans.** radius : sinh α, centre : (cosh α, 0))

7. Prove that the bilinear transformation

$$w = \dfrac{1 + z}{1 - z}$$

maps the region $|z| \leq 1$ onto the half-plane R $(w) \geq 0$.

Find also the region in the w-plane corresponding to the region

$$|z| \leq \rho < 1.$$

$$\left[\textbf{Ans.} \quad \left| w - \frac{1+\rho^2}{1-\rho^2} \right| \leq \frac{2\rho}{1-\rho^2} \right]$$

8. The numbers a, b, c, d are real and $ad - bc > 0$. If

$$w = \frac{az + b}{cz + d},$$

and z describes the upper-half of the circle $|z| = 1$, show that w describes the upper-half of the circle described on the line joining the points

$$\frac{a+b}{c+d} \quad \text{and} \quad \frac{a-b}{c-d}$$

as diameter.

9. If a, b, c, d are real and $ad - bc \neq 0$, show that the transformation

$$w = \frac{a + bz}{c + dz}$$

transforms, in general, circles having their centres on the real axis into circles having their centres on the real axis.

10. If λ is real and a, c are complex numbers such that $|a| > |c|$, show that the bilinear transformation

$$w = (\cos \lambda + i \sin \lambda) \frac{az + \overline{c}}{cz + \overline{a}}$$

maps the inside of the circle $|z| = 1$ on the inside of the circle

$$|w| = 1.$$

If, further, the point $z = 1$ is the only invariant point, show that the transformation may be written in the form

$$\frac{1}{w-1} = \frac{1}{z-1} + \frac{1}{k},$$

where $k = 1 + (\overline{a}/c)$.

11. If λ is real and a, b are complex numbers such that $|a| > |b|$, show that the bilinear transformation

$$w = e^{i\lambda} \frac{az + b}{\overline{a} + \overline{b}z}$$

maps the inside of the circle $|z| = 1$ on the inside of the circle $|w| = 1$.(*Garwhal 2006*)

If further the point $z = 1$ is the only invariant point, show that the transformation may be put in the form

$$\frac{1}{w-1} = \frac{1}{z-1} + \frac{1}{k},$$

where $k = 1 + (\overline{a}/\overline{b})$.

12. Prove that if n is an integer, greater than unity, the transformation

$$w = \left(2 \cos \frac{\pi}{n} - z \right)^{-1}$$

is periodic with period n. Taking $n = 3$, indicate by diagrams the regions into which the interior of the circle $|z| = 1$ is carried by successive applications of the transformation.

[Use the normal form of the given transformation, $viz.$,

$$\frac{w - \alpha}{w - \alpha^{-1}} = \left(\cos \frac{2\pi}{n} + i \sin \frac{2\pi}{n} \right) \frac{z - \alpha}{z - \alpha^{-1}}$$

where $\alpha = \cos \dfrac{\pi}{n} + i \sin \dfrac{\pi}{n}$.]

13. If α, β are two fixed points of the transformation

$$w = \frac{a + bz}{c + dz} ; \ ad \neq bc,$$

show that

$$\frac{w - \alpha}{w - \beta} = \lambda \frac{z - \alpha}{z - \beta},$$

where λ is a root of the equation

$$(bc - ad) \, t^2 - (b^2 + c^2 + 2ad) \, t + (bc - ad) = 0 \text{ in } t.$$

Show further that the transformation iterated a certain number of times is the identity transformation if and only if λ is a root of unity.

14. Find all the bilinear transformations.

$$w = T \, (z),$$

such that

$$T \, [T \, \{T \, (z)\}] = z.$$

$$\left[\textbf{Ans.} \ \frac{w - \alpha}{w - \beta} = \lambda \frac{z - \alpha}{z - \beta}, \text{ where } \alpha, \ \beta \text{ are arbitrary and } \lambda \text{ is a} \atop \text{cube root of unity, other than } 1. \right].$$

15. Find the fixed points and the normal forms for the following bilinear transformations:

(a) $w = \dfrac{-2 + (2 + i) z}{i + z}$ (b) $w = \dfrac{1 + 3iz}{i + z}$

(c) $w = \dfrac{z - 1}{z + 1}$ *(Kanpur 2003, 2005)*

$$\left[\textbf{Ans.} \ (a) \ 1 \pm i, \ \frac{w - (i + 1)}{w + (i + 1)} = \frac{3 - 2iz - (1 + i)}{13z + (1 + i)}. \right.$$

$$\left. (b) \ i, \ \frac{i}{w - i} = \frac{1}{z - i} - \frac{i}{2} \ (c) \ i, -i, \ \frac{w - i}{w + i} = -i \left(\frac{z - i}{z + 1} \right) \right]$$

16. Find the bilinear transformation for which α is the only fixed point and which maps β on γ.

$$\left[\textbf{Ans.} \ \frac{1}{(\beta - \gamma)(w - \alpha)} = \frac{1}{(\beta - \gamma)(z - \alpha)} + \frac{1}{(\gamma - \alpha)(\beta - \alpha)}. \right]$$

17. Find the bilinear transformation which maps
   (a) $1, -i, 2$ on $0, 2, -i$ respectively.
   (b) $1, -1, \infty$ on $1+i, 1-i, 1$ respectively.   (*M.S. Univ. 2007*)

$$\left[\text{Ans. } (a)\ w = 2\frac{z-1}{(1+i)z-2},\ (b)\ w = \frac{z+i}{z}.\right]$$

18. Find the bilinear transformation which maps $z = 1, i, -1$ respectively onto $w = i, 0, -i$.
   For this transformation, find the images of
   (a) $|z| < 1,$ (b) $|z| \le \rho < 1.$

$$\left[\text{Ans. } w = \frac{i-z}{i+z};\ (a)\ \Re\,(w) > 0,\ (b)\ \left| w - \frac{1+\rho}{1-\rho}\right| \le \frac{2\sqrt{\rho}}{1-\rho},\right.$$

i.e., the interior and frontier of the circle with centre $\dfrac{1+\rho}{1-\rho}$ and radius $2\sqrt{\rho/(1-\rho)}.\Big]$

19. Find the bilinear transformation which maps $z = -1, 1, \infty$ respectively onto $w = -i, -1, i$.
   For this transformation, find the images of
   (a) $I(z) < 0,$ (b) $I(z) = 1, R(z) \ge \upsilon.$

$$\left[\text{Ans. } w = i\frac{z+(1+2i)}{z+(1-2i)};\right.$$

   (a) $|w| < 1$, (b) The arc of the circle $|w + i| = 2$ contained on and in the interior of the circle $|w + (2-i)| = 2.]$

20. Determine the most general bilinear transformation which transforms the circle $|z| = 1$ onto $|w| = 1$. What is the most general transformation when the further restriction is imposed that the points $z = 1, -1$ are to have images $w = 1, -1$ respectively ?

$$\left[\text{Ans. } w = k\frac{\alpha-z}{\alpha z-1},\ \text{where } |k| = 1;\ w = \frac{\alpha-z}{\alpha z-1},\ \text{where } \alpha \text{ is real.}\right]$$

21. Find the most general bilinear transformation of the region

$$|z-2| > 4 \text{ into the region } |w| < 1.$$

$$\left[\text{Ans. } w = k\frac{(4+2\alpha)-\alpha z}{(4\overline{\alpha}+2)-z},\ |k| = 1,\ |\alpha| < 1.\right]$$

22. Find the bilinear transformation which maps the circle $|z| = 1$ onto the circle $|w-1| = 1$ and maps $z = 0, z = 1$ onto $w = 1/2, w = 0$ respectively and show that the transformation is uniquely determined.

   Examine also the correspondence between the interiors and the exteriors of the circles.

$$\left[\text{Ans. } w = \frac{1-z}{2+z}.\ \text{Interior corresponding to the interior.}\right]$$

23. Given the bilinear transformation

$$w = \frac{a+bz}{c+dz},\ ad-bc \ne 0$$

and a point z_1. Further z_n, for every positive integral value of n, is defined by

$$z_{n+1} = \frac{a + bz_n}{c + dz_n}.$$

Show that if the transformation is elliptic, then all the points z_n lie on a circle and the number

of distinct points z_n is infinite if and only if $[(\arg z_1)/2\pi]$ is irrational.

24. Find the most general transformation of the type

$$w = \frac{a + bz}{c + dz},$$

which maps I $(z) > 0$ onto $|w| < 1$ and $|z| < 1$ onto I $(w) > 0$.

$$\left[\text{Ans. } w = \bar\alpha\, \frac{z - \alpha}{z - \bar\alpha}, \text{ where } |\alpha| = 1 \text{ and } I\,(\alpha) > 0. \right]$$

OBJECTIVE QUESTIONS

For each of the following questions, four alternatives are given for the answer. Only one of them is correct. Choose the correct alternative.

1. Critical points of the bilinear transformation $w = \dfrac{az + b}{cz + d}$ are

   (a) $z = -d/c,\ z = 0$ (b) $z = -d/c,\ z = \infty$

   (c) $z = 0,\ z = \infty$ (d) $z = -d/c,\ z = -b/a.$

2. The points which coincide with their transformations are called

   (a) fixed points   (b) critical points

   (c) bilinear points   (d) conformal points.

3. If z_1, z_2, z_3, z_4 are distinct points in the order in which they are written, then number of distinct cross-ratios is

   (a) 4 !   (b) 4^4 (c) 6   (d) 1.

4. Cross-ratio of z_1, z_2, z_3, z_4 is real if and only if the four points are

   (a) · coplanar   (b) concyclic

   (c) collinear   (d) None of these.

5. There is only one value of z for which $w = z$ in bilinear transformation $w = \dfrac{az + b}{cz + d}$, if

   (a) $(a - d)^2 + 4bc = 0$ (b) $(a - d)^2 + 4bc \ne 0$

   (c) $(a - d)^2 = 4bc$ (d) $(a - d)^2 \ne 4bc.$

6. A bilinear transformation $w = \dfrac{az + b}{cz + d}$ having only one fixed point is called

   (a) loxodromic   (b) elliptic   (c) parabolic   (d) hyperbolic.

7. A bilinear transformation is called loxodromic if it is

   (a) hyperbolic but not elliptic or parabolic

   (b) parabolic but not hyperbolic

   (c) elliptic but not hyperbolic

   (d) neither hyperbolic nor elliptic or parabolic.

8. Bilinear transformation which maps the half-plane I $(z) \geq 0$ onto the circular disc $|w| \leq 1$ is

(a) $w = e^{i\lambda} \left(\dfrac{z - \alpha}{z - \bar{\alpha}} \right)$

(b) $w = e^{i\lambda} \left(\dfrac{z - \alpha}{z + \bar{\alpha}} \right)$

(c) $w = e^{i\lambda} \left(\dfrac{z - \alpha}{\bar{\alpha}z - 1} \right)$

(d) None of these.

9. Bilinear transformation which transforms the unit circle $|z| \leq 1$ into the unit circle $|w| \leq 1$ is

(a) $w = e^{i\lambda} \left(\dfrac{z - \alpha}{z - \bar{\alpha}} \right)$

(b) $w = e^{i\lambda} \left(\dfrac{z - \alpha}{z + \bar{\alpha}} \right)$

(c) $w = e^{i\lambda} \left(\dfrac{z - \alpha}{\bar{\alpha}z - 1} \right)$

(d) $w = e^{i\lambda} \left(\dfrac{z - \alpha}{\bar{\alpha}z + 1} \right)$.

10. Transformation $w = \dfrac{az + b}{cz + d}$ transforms the unit circle in the w-plane into straight line in the z-plane if

(a) $b/a = d/c$

(b) $|a| = |c|$

(c) $bc + ad = 0$

(d) $bc - ad = 0$.

ANSWERS

1. (b) **2.** (a) **3.** (c) **4.** (b) **5.** (a) **6.** (c) **7.** (d) **8.** (a) **9.** (c)
10. (b)

TOPOLOGICAL CONSIDERATIONS

4.1. Introduction. In Chapter 1, we defined complex numbers and also considered Algebra of the same. In the present chapter, we shall introduce the concepts of *Limit* and *Continuity* which underlie Analysis. It will be seen that these notions of Limit and Continuity are developments of the notion of *Neighbourhood of a point.*

That aspect of the set of complex numbers which renders possible the introduction of the notion of *Neighbourhood of a point* and the allied notions of *Limit* etc., is known as *Topology* in contrast to the *Algebra* introduced in Chapter 1. It may, however, be mentioned that no attempt would be made here to introduce Topology of the set of complex numbers in a manner free from Algebra so that we would relate the basic notion of Neighbourhood to Algebra.

4.2. Neighbourhood of a Point. Firstly we shall define two special types of sets known as *Circular domain* and *Rectangular domain.*

4.2.1. Circular Domain. If α is a complex number and ρ a positive number, then the set S of points z such that

$$|z - \alpha| < \rho$$

is called a *Circular domain.*

The number α will be referred to as the centre and ρ as the radius of this circular domain.

4.2.2. Rectangular Domain. The set of complex numbers z such that:

$$a < R(z) < b, \; c < I(z) < d,$$

where a, b, c, d are real numbers is called a *Rectangular domain* and would be denoted by the symbol R $(a, b; c, d)$ or simply $(a, b; c, d)$.

The numbers $b - a$ and $d - c$ will be referred to as the lengths of the sides of this rectangular domain.

4.2.3. Neighbourhood of a point. Def. *Any circular or rectangular domain of which a given point is a member is called a neighbourhood of the point.*

4.2.4. Neighbourhood of infinity. *The set of numbers z such that $|z| > k$, where k is any positive real number, is called a neighbourhood of infinity.*

Ex. 1. S_1 is the circular domain defined by $|z| < \rho$ and S_2 is the rectangular domain defined by $-\rho < R(z) < \rho, \; -\rho < I(z) < \rho$; show that $S_1 \subset S_2$.

Ex. 2. Show that every rectangular neighbourhood of a point ξ contains a circular neighbourhood of ξ with its centre at ξ and *vice-versa.*

Ex. 3. Show that the intersection of any two neighbourhoods of a point contains a neighbourhood of the point.

Ex. 4. Show that if a neighbourhood of a point ξ contains only a finite number of members of a set S, then there exists a neighbourhood of ξ, which contains no member of S, other than possibly ξ.

4.3. Interior, Exterior and Frontier Points of a Set. Relative to a given set S, a given point, ξ may have any one of the following *three* behaviours:

I. There exists a neighbourhood of ξ consisting of members of S only.

II. There exists a neighbourhood of ξ consisting of members of the complement S^c only, *i.e.*, consisting of no member of S.

III. In *every* neighbourhood of ξ, there exist members of S as well as of S^c, *i.e.*, members belonging to S as well as not belonging to S^e.

The point ξ is said to be an *Interior point, Exterior point* and *Frontier point* according as it satisfies the conditions I, II and III above respectively.

From the above definitions, it is clear that an interior (exterior) point of a set is an exterior (interior) point of the complement of the set. Further a frontier point of a set is as well as a frontier point of the complement of the set.

4.3.1. Interior, Exterior and Frontier of a set. The sets of all interior points, exterior points and frontier points of a set S are respectively called *the Interior, the Exterior* and *the Frontier* of the set and will be denoted by

$$S_i, S_e, S_f$$

respectively.

It is clear that the interior (exterior) of a set S is the exterior (interior) of its complement S^c. Also the frontier of a set S is as well as the frontier of its complement S^c.

It may be also observed that if C denotes the entire set of complex numbers, we have

$$C = S_i \cup S_e \cup S_f,$$

and that the sets S_i, S_e, S_f are pairwise disjoint so that

$$\phi = S_i \cap S_e, \ \phi = S_e \cap S_f, \ \phi = S_f \cap S_i$$

where ϕ denotes the set containing no point known as the *null set* or the *void set*.

4.3.2. Classification of Frontier points. Limiting points. Isolated points. Firstly we introduce the important concept of *limiting point* of a set.

Def. *A point ξ is called a limiting point of a set S, if every neighbourhood of ξ contains an infinite number of members of S.*

A limiting point of a set may or may not be a member of the set.

It is easy to see that if ξ is *not* a limiting point of a set S, then there exists a neighbourhood of ξ, containing, at the most, only one member of S, *viz.*, ξ itself.

It is clear that while every interior point, of a set is also a limiting point of the set, no exterior point of a set will be a limiting point thereof.

Further any frontier point ξ of a set may have any one of the following three properties ·

I. ξ is a limiting point of S but not of S^c,

II. ξ is a limiting point of S^c but not of S,

III. ξ is a limiting point of S as well as of S^c.

The possibility that ξ is neither a limiting point of S nor of S^c cannot arise.

Firstly, we consider the case I. As ξ is a frontier point, every neighbourhood of ξ contains points of S as well as of S^c. Thus, ξ being not a limiting point of S^c, we conclude that there exists a neighbourhood of ξ such that ξ is the only point of this neighbourhood belonging to S^c. In other words, *there exists, in this case, a neighbourhood of ξ such that every member of the same, other than ξ, belongs to S.*

In this case we say that ξ is an *isolated* point of S^c. Clearly ξ is, in this case, a limiting point of S without being a member thereof.

In case II, the point ξ can be shown to be an **isolated point** of S.

Thus, a frontier point of a set S may be (*i*) an isolated point of S, or (*ii*) an isolated point of S^c or (*iii*) an isolated point of neither S nor S^c.

Also a frontier point of S, if not a member of S, must necessarily be a limiting point of S.

Ex. Show that a frontier point of a set is either a limiting point or a member of the set and may as well be both.

4.3.3. Derived sets. *The set of all the limiting points of a set S is called its derived set and denoted by* S'

Ex. Show that

(*i*) $(S_1 \cup S_2)' = S_1' \cup S_2'$

(*ii*) $(S_1 \cap S_2)' \subset S_1' \cap S_2'$.

4.3.4. Closure of a set. *The union of the interior and the frontier of a set S is called the closure of the set and is denoted by* $\overline{S}$.

Thus, by definition

$$\overline{S} = S_i \cup S_f \qquad \qquad ...(1)$$

It may be easily seen that the closure of a set is also its union and its derived set

i.e.,
$$\overline{S} = S \cup S' \qquad \qquad ...(2)$$

One difference between (1) and (2) is that in case (1) the two sets S_i, S are disjoint but in case (2) the sets S, S' may not be disjoint.

·**Note.** The reader would notice that associated with each set S, we have defined the sets denoted by

$$S^c, \ S_i, \ S_e, \ S_f, \ S', \ \overline{S}.$$

Ex. Show that a point ξ belongs to the closure of a set S if and only if every neighbourhood of ξ contains a point of S.

4.4. Open and Closed Sets.

4.4.1. Open sets. *A set which coincides with its interior is said to be open.* Thus a set S is open if

$$S = S_i.$$

Since every point of an open set is, by definition, an interior point thereof, it follows that some neighbourhood of each point of an open set consists only of the points of the set. Also no frontier point of an open set belongs to the same.

Illustrations. The following are some cases of open sets:

(*a*) $|z| < 1$ (*b*) $|z| > 1$

(*c*) $2 < |z| < 3$ (*d*) R $(z) > 0$

(*e*) $|z - 1| < 1$ and R $(z) < 0$

(*f*) $|z - 1| < 1$ or $|z - 4| < 1$.

The following sets are *not* open:

(*a*) $|z| \leq 1$,   (*b*) I $(z) \leq 0$,   (*c*) $2 \leq |z| < 3$.

Ex. 1. Show that the union of an *Arbitrary* family of open sets is an open set.

Ex. 2. Show that the intersection of a *Finite* family of open sets is an open set. Give an example to show that the result may *not* be true for an *Infinite* family of open sets.

4.4.2. Closed sets. *A set whose complement is open is called closed.* It is important to note that a closed set is characterised by saying that *a set is closed if and only if every limiting point of the set belongs to the set.*

Suppose that S is a closed set and ξ is a limiting point of the same. We may easily show that $\xi \in S$.

Now suppose that every limiting point ξ of a set S belongs to S. We shall show that the complement S^c of S is open.

Let, η, be any member of S^c. Then, η, is not a member of S and accordingly it cannot be a limiting point of S. Thus some neighbourhood of, η, contains no member of S so that this neighbourhood of, η, contain only members of S^c. Hence the result.

We may also see that a set is closed if and only if it coincides with its closure.

Illustrations. The following are some cases of closed sets:

(a) $|z| \le 1$,

(b) R $(z) \le 0$,

(c) The closure of every set is closed.

Ex. Show that

(i) $\overline{\overline{S}} = \overline{S}$.

(ii) $\overline{S_1 \cup S_2} = \overline{S_1} \cup \overline{S_2}$.

4.4.3. Bounded sets. *A set S is said to be bounded if there exists a positive number k such that*

$$|z| < k \; \forall z \in S.$$

A set which is not bounded is said to be unbounded.

Ex. Show that a set is unbounded if and only if infinity is a limiting point of the same.

4.4.4. Compact sets. *A set is called compact if it is bounded as well as closed.*

4.4.5. Closed rectangular domain and closed circular domain. The closures of rectangular and circular domains are called closed rectangular and closed circular domains respectively.

Thus, the set defined by

$$|z - \xi| \le \rho$$

is a closed circular domain and that defined by

$$a \le R \, (z) \le b, \, c \le I \, (z) \le d$$

is a closed rectangular domain.

Note. The reader may note that there exist sets which are neither open nor closed. Thus, for example, any open interval of the real axis is neither a closed nor an open set of complex numbers.

Ex. 1. Show that the frontier of every set is closed.

Ex. 2. Show that the closure of a closed set coincides with itself.

Ex. 3. Show that

(i) the intersection of an *arbitrary* family of closed sets is a closed set.

(ii) the union of a *finite* family of closed sets is a closed set. Give an example to show that the result may not be true if the family is *infinite*.

4.5. Connected Sets. Intuitively speaking, a connected set is one which can be thought of as one piece. We shall, however, give here a precise formulation of this important notion of *connected sets*. This notion is fundamental in the study of the Theory of Analytic Functions.

Def. *A set S is said to be connected if it is such that when expressed as a union of* **any** *two disjoint non-null sets* S_1, S_2, *then either* S_1 *contains a limiting point of* S_2 *or* S_2 *contains a limiting point of* S_1.

Ex. 1. Show that a line punctured at a point is *not* a connected set and that a circle punctured at a point is a connected set.

Ex. 2. What do you mean by saying that a set is not connected?

Theorem. *Every interval, open, closed or semi-open, of the real axis is a connected set.*

Let S be an interval of the real axis and let

$$S = S_1 \cup S_2$$

be *an* expression of S as a union of disjoint non-null sets S_1, S_2.

Let a, b be any points of S_1, S_2 respectively. **Take** $c = \dfrac{1}{2}(a + b)$. Then, c, belongs either to S_1 or to S_2. Of the two intervals $[a, c]$ and $[c, b]$, we select the one of which the two end points belong to the different sets S_1, S_2 respectively and call the same $[a_1, b_1]$. We now deal with $[a_1, b_1]$ as we dealt with $[a_2, b_2]$. Proceeding in this manner, we obtain a sequence of intervals $[a_n, b_n]$ such that

$$a_n \in S_1, \ b_n \in S_2$$

and

$$(b_n - a_n) = \frac{1}{2^n}(b - a).$$

It is then easily seen that we thus arrive at a point ξ such that:

$$\lim a_n = \xi = \lim b_n.$$

Clearly then ξ is a limiting point of S_1 as well as of S_2.

Also ξ is a point of S and as such either a point of S_1 or S_2. Hence, the interval S is a connected set.

Ex. Prove also the converse of the preceding theorem, *viz.*, that the only connected subsets of the real axis are intervals.

4.6. Domains and Continua. In the study of functions of complex variables, we shall usually be concerned with two special types of sets which we now define.

Def. Domain. *An open connected set is called a domain.*

Def. Continuum. *A closed connected set is called a continuum.*

Def. Closed Domain. *The closure of a domain is called a closed domain.*

Thus a closed domain arises as the union of a domain and its frontier. For the sake of a sharp contrast, a domain may sometimes be referred to as an open domain even though in relation to a domain, which is necessarily, by definition open, the word "open" is superfluous.

The circular domain and the rectangular domain as defined in § 4.2.1 and § 4.2.2 are actually domains in the sense of the definition of a domain given above.

Note. We should distinguish between what we have called the domain of a function and the domain as we now define. A domain in the present sense is a subset of the set of complex numbers which is open as well as connected.

4.6.1. Characterisation of domains.

Theorem. *An open set is connected if and only if it* **cannot** *be expressed as a union of two disjoint non-null open sets.*

Firstly suppose that S is a connected open set. Let, if possible

$$S = S_1 \cup S_2$$

where S_1, S_2 are disjoint, non-null and open. By definition of connected sets, either a limiting point of S_1 is a member of S_2 or a limiting point of S_2 is a member of S_1. Suppose that a limiting point ξ of S_1 is a member of S_2.

Since S_2 is an open set and $\xi \in S_2$, there exists a neighbourhood of ξ consisting entirely of points of S_2 and as such ξ cannot be a limiting point of S_1. We thus arrive at a contradiction. Hence we see that *an open connected set cannot be expressed as a union of disjoint, non-null and open sets.*

To prove the converse suppose that S is open but *not* connected. There must then exist two disjoint non-null sets S_1, S_2 such that

$$S = S_1 \cup S_2$$

and such that no limiting point of S_1 is a member of S_2 and no limiting point of S_2 is a member of S_1.

Let ξ be any point of S_1. Then $\xi \in S$.

As S is an open set, there exists a neighbourhood of ξ consisting entirely of members of S. Also since ξ is neither a limiting point nor a member of S_2, some neighbourhoods of ξ consist of no point of S_2. Combining these two facts we see that there exists a neighbourhood of ξ consisting of members of S_1 only. Thus S_1 is an open set. Similarly S_2 is an open set.

Thus S has been expressed as a union of disjoint, non-null, open sets so that every open set which is *not* connected can be expressed as a union of disjoint, non-null and open sets.

Hence the theorem.

4.6.2. Characterisation of continua.

Theorem. *A closed set is connected if and only if it cannot be expressed as a union of two disjoint, non-null and closed sets.*

The proof is left to the reader.

Ex. 1. Give examples of sets which are:

(a) Compact as well as connected,

(b) Compact but not connected,

(c) Connected but not compact,

(d) Neither compact nor connected.

Ex. 2. Describe the following sets as:

(a) Compact or otherwise,

(b) Connected or otherwise,

(i) $|z| < 1$,   (ii) $|z| \le 1$,

(iii) $|z| \ge 1$,   (iv) $|z| \le 1, z \ne 0$,

(v) $|z| \le 1$, $I(z) \ne 0$,   (vi) $2 \le |z| \le 3$,

(vii) $R(z) \ge 0$,   (viii) $|z| > 1$, $R(z) \ne 0$.

4.7. A Theorem on nests of closed rectangular domains.

Theorem : *If* $R_n [a_n, b_n; c_n, d_n]$

is a sequence of closed rectangular domains such that

(i) $R_{n-1} \subset R_n, \forall n$ and

(ii) *the sequences*

$$\{b_n - a_n\}, \{d_n - c_n\}$$

of the lengths of the sides of the domains both tend to zero, then **there exists one and only one** *point common to every closed rectangular domain, i.e., the intersection of all the closed rectangular domains consists of one and only one point.*

Because of (i), the sequences

$$\{a_n\} \text{ and } \{c_n\}$$

are bounded and monotonically increasing and the sequences

$$\{b_n\} \text{ and } \{d_n\}$$

are bounded and monotonically decreasing.

Thus, these four sequences are all convergent.

Again, because of (ii),

$$\lim a_n = \lim b_n = \xi, \text{ say}$$
$$\lim c_n = \lim d_n = \eta, \text{ say.}$$

Since now

$$a_n \le \xi \le b_n, c_n \le \eta \le d_n \ \forall n$$

we see that the point (ξ, η), *i.e.*, $\xi + i\eta$ belongs to every R_n.

Finally, if possible, let

$$\xi_1 + i\eta_1, \xi_2 + i\eta_2$$

be two distinct points belonging to every R_n, so that

either $\xi_1 \ne \xi_2$ or $\eta_1 \ne \eta_2$

Also $a_n \le \xi_1, \xi_2 \le b_n$,

$\Rightarrow$ $|\xi_2 - \xi_1| \le b_n - a_n$,

and $c_n \le \eta_1, \eta_2 \le d_n$

$\Rightarrow$ $|\eta_2 - \eta_1| \le d_n - c_n$,

and thus, by virtue of (ii),

$$\xi_1 = \xi_2, \eta_1 = \eta_2,$$

so that we arrive at a contradiction.

Thus, we have proved the theorem.

Ex. Prove the following *generalisation* of the above theorem :

If $\{S_n\}$ is a sequence of bounded closed sets such that

(i) $S_{n+1} \subset S_n$,

(ii) $\lim\limits_{n \to \infty} d_n = 0$;

d_n being the diameter of S_n, then there exists one and only one point $\xi + i\eta$ which belongs to every S_n.

[By the diameter d_n of a bounded set S_n is meant the upper bound of the positive real numbers $| \alpha - \beta |$ where α, β are any two members of S_n.]

4.8. Bolzano-Weierstrass Theorem. We shall now state and prove a theorem regarding the existence of limiting points of a set.

Theorem. *Every infinite bounded set has at least one limiting point.*

Let S be any infinite bounded set. The set being bounded, there exists a positive number k such that
$$| z | < k, \quad \forall \quad z \in S.$$
Also, therefore, every $z \in S$ is a point of the closed rectangular domain
$$R \, [- k, \, k; - k, \, k].$$

Now, divide R into four equal closed rectangular domains by lines parallel to the axes. The given set being infinite, at least one of these four closed rectangular domains must contain an infinite number of members of S.

Let
$$R_1 \, [a_1, \, b_1; \, c_1, \, d_1]$$
be any one of the four closed domains containing an infinite number of members of S.

Again divide R_1 into four equal parts and select any one
$$R_2 \, [a_2, \, b_2; \, c_2, \, d_2]$$
of these containing an infinite number of members of S.

Continuing in this manner, we obtain a sequence of closed rectangular domains
$$R_n \, [a_n, \, b_n; \, c_n, \, d_n]$$
such that

(*i*) each R_n contains an infinite number of members of S;

(*ii*) $R_{n+1} \subset R_n$, $\quad \forall \quad n$;

(*iii*) $b_n - a_n = \dfrac{k}{2^{n-1}}, \, d_n - c_n = \dfrac{k}{2^{n-1}}.$

Now the condition (*iii*) implies
$$\lim (b_n - a_n) = 0 = \lim (d_n - c_n).$$

Thus, the conditions of the preceding theorem on rectangles are satisfied and there exists, therefore, a point $\xi + i\eta \in R_n$, for every n.

Consider now *any* rectangular neighbourhood of $\xi + i\eta$. There will then exist a positive integer n such that R_n is contained in this neighbourhood. Hence the rectangular neighbourhood, in question, of $\xi + i\eta$ contains an infinite number of members of S. Thus $\xi + i\eta$ is a limiting point of S.

Hence the theorem.

Note. Extended Plane. For the extended plane, we can omit the word 'Bounded' and simply say that *every infinite set has a limiting point.*

If the set is bounded, then the preceding theorem holds and if it is unbounded, then $z = \infty$ is a limiting point of the set. In fact if the set is not bounded, then every neighbourhood $| z | > k$ of ∞ contains an infinite number of members of the set; k being any arbitrary positive number.

4.9. Heine-Borel Theorem. We shall now prove an important theorem which belongs to a class of what are known as *Covering Theorems*. In this connection, we state that a set Σ of sets is said to be a *cover* of a set S if every point of the set S is a member of some member of Σ.

Theorem. *If S is any compact set and Σ is any set of open rectangular domains such that every point of S belongs to some member of Σ, then there exists a **finite** subset σ of Σ such that every point of S is also a point of some member of σ.*

The theorem states that if any set Σ of open rectangular domains covers a compact set S, then there exists a finite sub-set σ of Σ also covering S.

Proof. Suppose that the theorem is *not* true. Since S being compact is bounded, there exists a positive number k, such that every member of S is a member of the closed rectangular domain

$$R\ [-k,\ k;\ -k,\ k].$$

Divide R into four equal closed rectangular domains by lines parallel to the axes. The theorem being assumed *not* true, the part of S contained in at least one of these four closed domains must be such that it cannot be covered by any finite subset of Σ. Let any one such closed domain be

$$R_1\ [a_1,\ b_1;\ c_1,\ d_1].$$

We now deal with R_1 as we did with R. Continuing in this manner, we obtain a sequence of closed rectangular domains

$$R_n\ [a_n,\ b_n;\ c_n,\ d_n]$$

such that

(*i*) the part of S contained in no R_n can be covered by finite sub-set of Σ;

(*ii*) $R_{n+1} \subset R_n$;

(*iii*) $b_n - a_n = \dfrac{k}{2^{n-1}},\ d_n - c_n = \dfrac{k}{2^{n-1}}.$

The condition (*iii*) implies that

$$\lim (b_n - a_n) = 0 = \lim (d_n - c_n).$$

There exists, therefore, by § 4.8 a point $\xi + i\eta$ belonging to every R_n.

The result may be briefly stated as follows:

Every cover of a compact set consisting of open rectangular domains admits of a finite sub-cover.

As each R_n necessarily contains an infinite number of members of S, we see that $\xi + i\eta$ is a limiting point of S. The set S being closed, it follows that

$$\xi + i\eta \in S.$$

The point $\xi + i\eta$ being a member of S, there exists a member; say R', of Σ such that

$$\xi + i\eta \in R'.$$

Also there exists an integer m such that

$$R_m \subset R'.$$

Thus we deduce that the part of S contained in R_m is covered by a *single* member of Σ so that we arrive at a contradiction of (*i*) above.

Hence the assumption of the theorem being not true is wrong and accordingly the theorem is proved.

Cor. We shall now state and prove the theorem in the form in which we employ circular instead of rectangular domains to cover a given compact set.

If S is a compact set and Σ is any set of open circular domains such that each point of S is the centre of some member of Σ so that Σ covers S, then there exists a finite sub-set of Σ which already covers S.

If now any point ξ, of S is the centre of a member A of Σ, then it is also necessarily a point of the *open rectangular domain R whose sides are parallel to the axes and which is inscribed in A.

---

* The reader may easily formulate in abstract terms the content of this statement.

Thus, associated to the covering of S formed of the set Σ of circular domains, we have also a covering of S formed of the set Σ_1, of rectangular domains. Then, by the above theorem, there exists a finite sub-set σ_1, of Σ_1, covering S. The finite sub-set σ of Σ consisting of circular domains described about the rectangles of σ_1, is then the covering whose existence was intended to be established.

EXAMPLE

Given the point set $S = \{i, i/2, i/3, i/4, \ldots\}$ or briefly $\{i/n\}$.

(a) Is S bounded?

(b) What are its limit points, if any?

(c) Is S closed?

(d) What are its interior or boundary points?

(e) Is S open?

(f) Is S connected?

(g) Is S an open region or domain?

(h) What is the closure of S?

(i) What is the complement of S?

(j) Is S countable?

(k) Is S compact?

(l) Is the closure of S compact?

Solution. (a) The set S is bounded for every point $z \in S, |z| < 2$ (for example), i.e., all points of S lie inside the circle of radius 2 with centre at the origin.

(b) Every deleted neighbourhood of $z = 0$ contains points of S, a limit point is $z = 0$. It is the only limit point. Note that as S is bounded and infinite, Bolzano-Weierstrass Theorem predicts at least one limit point.

(c) S is not closed, since the limit point $z = 0 \neq$ S.

(d) Every delta neighbourhood of any point i/n (i.e., every circle of radius δ with centre at i/n) contains points which belong to S and points which do not belong to S implying that every point of S, as well as the point $z = 0$, is a boundary point. S has no interior points.

(e) S does not contain any interior points. Hence it cannot be open. Thus, S is neither open nor closed.

(f) If any two points of S are joined by a polygonal path, then there are points on this path which do not belong to S and hence S is not connected.

(g) As S is not an open connected set, it is not an open region or domain.

(h) The closure of S contains the points of the set S together with the limit point zero, i.e., $\{0, i, i/2, i/3, \ldots\}$.

(i) Complement of S = set of all points which do not belong to S i.e. all points $z \neq i, i/2, i/3, \ldots$.

(j) There is one-one correspondence between the elements of S the natural numbers 1, 2, 3, ... as indicated below:

$$
\begin{array}{ccccccc}
i & i/2 & i/3 & i/4 & \ldots & \ldots & i/n \\
\updownarrow & \updownarrow & \updownarrow & \updownarrow & \ldots & \ldots & \updownarrow \\
1 & 2 & 3 & 4 & \ldots & \ldots & n
\end{array}
$$

Hence the set S is countable.

(k) The set S is bounded but not closed, hence it is not compact.

(l) The closure of S is bounded as well as closed, hence it is compact.

4.10. Limits. Let $w = f(z)$ be a complex valued function of a complex variable defined in S and let σ be a given complex number. We then say that $f(z)$ tends to the limit l as z tends to a and write in symbols

$$\lim_{z \to a} f(z) = l \qquad \qquad ...(1)$$

if, to each positive number ε, arbitrarily assigned, there corresponds a positive number δ such that

$$|f(z) - l| < \varepsilon$$

when

$$0 < |z - a| < \delta \; and \; z \in S.$$

Expressed in terms of the concept of 'Neighbourhood', the above definition means that to each neighbourhood N of the point l, there corresponds a *deleted neighbourhood N_1 of a such that for every point z of the intersection of N_1 and S, $f(z)$ belongs to N,

i.e., $$z \in N_1 \cap S \; \Rightarrow \; f(z) \in N.$$

Again, adopting a rather crude way of expression, we say that the equality (1) is equivalent to the statement that w is near l when z is near a.

Of course in any given case,

$$\lim_{z \to a} f(z)$$

may not exist.

Note. In the above we have not said anything as to the number a being or not being a member of the S. It will, however, be seen that the definition as given turns out to be almost devoid of any content if a is *not* a limiting point of S, for in this case there will be a neighbourhood of a in which the only member of S is at the most a. It will thus be appropriate if we assume a to be a limiting point of S and then talk of

$$\lim_{z \to a} f(z).$$

Ex. From the definition deduce that if $\lim f(z) = l$, then $\lim |f(z)| = |l|$. Also show that the converse is not true.

Note. We may also give meanings to the statements

$$\lim_{z \to a} f(z) = \infty, \quad \lim_{z \to \infty} f(z) = l, \quad \lim_{z \to \infty} f(z) = \infty.$$

Thus, we say that

$$\lim_{z \to a} f(z) = \infty$$

if to every positive number k, however large, there corresponds a positive number δ such that

$$|f(z)| > k$$

for

$$0 < |z - a| < \delta, z \in S.$$

In other words, it means that to every neighbourhood N of ∞, there corresponds a deleted neighbourhood N_1, of a such that

$$z \in N_1 \cap S \; \Rightarrow \; f(z) \in N.$$

We may now easily give similar meanings to the other two statements.

---

* Deleted neighbourhood of a point means a neighbourhood of the point excluding the point itself. Thus $0 < |z - a| < \delta$ is a deleted neighbour-hood of the point a.

4.11. Limit in terms of real and imaginary parts.

Let
$$w = f(z)$$
determine the two real functions
$$u = u(x, y), \, v = v(x, y),$$
which are respectively the real and imaginary parts of $f(z)$.

We have of course
$$z = x + iy, f(z) = u(x, y) + iv(x, y).$$

It can be proved that if $a = a_1 + ia_2$, $l = l_1 + il_2$, then
$$\lim_{z \to a} f(z) = l$$
$$\Leftrightarrow \lim_{(x, y) \to (a_1, a_2)} u(x, y) = l_1, \quad \lim_{(x, y) \to (a_1, a_2)} v(x, y) = l_2.$$

We have
$$f(z) - l = [u(x, y) + iv(x, y)] - (l_1 + il_2)$$
$$= (u - l_1) + i(v - l_2).$$

Also
$$|u - l_1| \le |f(z) - l|, \, |v - l_2| \le |f(z) - l| \qquad \text{...(1)}$$

and
$$|f(z) - l| \le |u - l_1| + |v - l_2| \qquad \text{...(2)}$$

The two results can now be proved with the help of the inequalities (1) and (2).

The above results may also be stated as follows:
$$\lim_{z \to a} f(z) = l,$$
$$\Leftrightarrow \lim R[f(z)] = R(l) \text{ and } \lim I[f(z)] = I(l).$$

From this we may deduce that
$$\lim f(z) = l \quad \Rightarrow \quad \lim \overline{f(z)} = \overline{l}.$$

4.12. Algebraic operations with limits.
As in the case of Real Variables, it can be proved that *if $f(z)$ and $F(z)$ are two functions such that*
$$\lim_{z \to a} f(z) = l, \quad \lim_{z \to a} F(z) = m$$
then
$$lim \, [f(z) \pm F(z)] = l \pm m, \qquad \text{...(I)}$$
$$lim \, [f(z) \cdot F(z)] = lm, \qquad \text{...(II)}$$
$$lim \, [f(z) / F(z)] = l/m, \text{ when } m \ne 0 \qquad \text{...(III)}$$

Here it is of course understood that the two functions $f(z)$ and $F(z)$ are defined for the same set.

The proofs are similar to those in the case of Real Variables, depending as they do, upon the relations
$$|\alpha\beta| = |\alpha||\beta|, \, |\alpha + \beta| \le |\alpha| + |\beta|$$
between the absolute values.

The results will now be proved one by one.

I. Let $\varepsilon > 0$ be a given number.

We have

$$| [f(z) + F(z)] - (l + m) | = | [f(z) - l] + [F(z) - m] |$$
$$\leq | f(z) - l | + | F(z) - m |. \qquad \ldots(1)$$

As

$$\lim_{z \to a} f(z) = l, \quad \lim_{z \to a} f(z) = m$$

there exist positive numbers δ_1, δ_2 such that

$$| f(z) - l | < \frac{1}{2} \varepsilon \text{ for } 0 < | z - a | \leq \delta_1, \qquad \ldots(2)$$

$$F(z) - m | < \frac{1}{2} \varepsilon \text{ for } 0 < | z - a | \leq \delta_2 \qquad \ldots(3)$$

Let $\delta = \min (\delta_1, \delta_2)$.

Then from (1), (2) and (3), we deduce that

$$| [f(z) + F(z)] - (l + m) | < \varepsilon \text{ for } 0 < | z - a | \leq \delta.$$

so that

$$\lim [f(z) + F(z)] = l + m = \lim f(z) + \lim F(z).$$

The case of difference may be similarly discussed.

II. We have

$$f(z) F(z) - lm = F(z) [f(z) - l] + l [F(z) - m]$$

$$\Rightarrow \quad | f(z) F(z) - lm | \leq | F(z) | | f(z) - l | + | l | | F(z) - m |, \qquad \ldots(1)$$

Since $\lim_{z \to a} F(z) = m$, there exists a positive number δ_1 such that

$$| F(z) - m | < 1 \text{ for } 0 < | z - a | \leq \delta_1.$$

From this we deduce that

$$| F(z) | < | m | + 1 \text{ for } 0 < | z - a | \leq \delta_1. \qquad \ldots(2)$$

Now, let $\varepsilon > 0$ be a given positive number.

Since $\lim_{z \to a} f(z) = l$ and $\lim_{z \to a} F(z) = m$ there exist positive numbers δ_2, δ_3 such that

$$| f(z) - l | < \frac{\varepsilon}{2 (| m | + 1)} \text{ for } 0 < | z - a | \leq \delta_2 \qquad \ldots(3)$$

$$F(z) - m | < \frac{\varepsilon}{2 (| l | + 1)} \text{ for } 0 < | z - a | \leq \delta_3 \qquad \ldots(4)$$

Let $\delta = \min (\delta_1, \delta_2, \delta_3)$.

Then from (1), (2), (3) and (4), we deduce that

$$| f(z) F(z) - lm | < \varepsilon \text{ for } 0 < | z - a | \leq \delta$$

so that

$$\lim_{z \to a} [f(z) F(z)] = lm.$$

III. We have

$$\frac{f(z)}{F(z)} - \frac{l}{m} = \frac{m [f(z) - l] - l [F(z) - m]}{m F(z)}$$

$\Rightarrow$
$$\left| \frac{f(z)}{F(z)} - \frac{l}{m} \right| \leq \frac{1}{|F(z)|} \left[|f(z) - l| + \frac{|l|}{|m|} |F(z) - m| \right] \qquad \ldots(1)$$

Since $\lim\limits_{z \to a} F(z) = m \neq 0$, there exists a positive number δ_1 such that

$$|F(z) - m| < \frac{1}{2}|m| \text{ for } 0 < |z - a| \leq \delta_1$$

From this we deduce that

$$\frac{1}{2}|m| < |F(z)| \text{ for } 0 < |z - a| \leq \delta_1 \qquad \ldots(2)$$

Now, let $\varepsilon > 0$ be a given positive number.

Since $\lim\limits_{z \to a} f(z) = l$, $\lim\limits_{z \to a} F(z) = m$, there exist positive numbers δ_2 and δ_3 such that

$$|f(z) - l| < \frac{\varepsilon}{4}|m| \text{ for } 0 < |z - a| \leq \delta_2 \qquad \ldots(3)$$

$$|F(z) - m| < \frac{|m|^2}{|l| + 1} \cdot \frac{\varepsilon}{4} \text{ for } 0 < |z - a| \leq \delta_3 \qquad \ldots(4)$$

Then from (1), (2), (3) and (4), we deduce that

$$\left| \frac{f(z)}{F(z)} - \frac{l}{m} \right| \leq \frac{\varepsilon}{2} + \frac{\varepsilon}{2} = \varepsilon \text{ for } 0 < |z - a| \leq \delta,$$

where $\delta = \min(\delta_1, \delta_2, \delta_3)$.

Hence

$$\lim \frac{f(z)}{F(z)} = \frac{l}{m}.$$

Ex. From IJ deduce that if $\lim f(z) = l$, then $\lim |f(z)| = |l|$.

In fact we have

$$|f(z)|^2 = f(z)\,\overline{f(z)}.$$

Note. Some of the above statements can easily be extended to include cases of infinite limits, *i.e.*, when l or m, or both are infinite and also when a is infinite.

In fact each of the above results remain true when a is ∞. Also we can have l, m or both infinite only if the corresponding algebraic combination is meaningful.

Thus, the reader may prove the following results:

(i) $\lim f(z) = l \neq \infty$, $\lim F(z) = \infty \Rightarrow \lim [f(z) + F(z)] = \infty$.

(ii) $\lim f(z) = l \neq 0$, $\lim F(z) = \infty \Rightarrow \lim [f(z) F(z)] = \infty$.

In this case l may be infinite.

(iii) $\lim f(z) = l \neq 0$, $\lim F(z) = 0 \Rightarrow \lim [f(z) \div F(z)] = \infty$.

4.13. Continuity. *A function* $w = f(z)$ *defined in a set S is said to be continuous at a point* $a \in S$, *if*

$$\lim_{z \to a} f(z) = f(a)$$

i.e., if $\lim\limits_{z \to a} f(z)$ exists and equals the value $f(a)$ of $f(z)$ for $z = a$.

Further $f(z)$ is said to be continuous in S, if it is continuous at every point of S.

It may also be easily shown that *if a function $f(z)$ is continuous, then the real and imaginary parts thereof are also continuous and conversely.*

4.13.1. Continuity of the algebraic combinations of continuous functions. With the help of the results of § 4.12 and the definition of continuity, it at once follows that if $f(z)$, F (z) are continuous at $z = a$, then $f(z) +$ F $(z), f(z)\cdot$F (z) and $f(z) /$ F (z) are also continuous at $z = a$ provided that for the last case of division F $(a) \neq 0$.

4.14. Uniform Continuity. Suppose that $w = f(z)$ is continuous in S and a is a point of S. Then because of the continuity there corresponds, to each $\varepsilon > 0$, a $\delta > 0$ such that

$$| f(z) - f(a) | < \varepsilon \text{ when } | z - a | \leq \delta \qquad \text{...(1)}$$

It is clear that (1) will also be true for any smaller positive value of δ.

In (1), δ depends not only upon ε but also upon a. The question now arises, "Is it possible to choose a $\delta > 0$ which may hold *uniformly* for every point a whatsoever, belonging to S after $\varepsilon > 0$ has been assigned and fixed ?" One may be inclined to reply in the affirmative and to say that the smallest of all the values of δ for different points of S would be the number sought for. This approach, however, overlooks the important question of the *existence* of the *smallest* value. Of course, the lower bound of the set of the values of δ which are all positive would certainly exist, but, it may not, a prior, be assumed to be non-zero.

It would now be shown that the answer to the question posed above is certainly in the affirmative when the domain S of definition and continuity of $f(z)$ is compact, *i.e.*, bounded and closed. Thus we prove the following theorem.

Theorem. *If $f(z)$ is continuous in a compact set S, then to every given $\varepsilon > 0$, there corresponds a number $\delta > 0$, such that*

$$| f(z_1) - f(z_2) | < \varepsilon$$

when z_1, z_2 are any two members of S satisfying the inequality

$$| z_1 - z_2 | < \delta.$$

Let $\varepsilon > 0$ be a given number. Then to each $a \in$ S, there corresponds a circular domain

$$| z - a | < \rho_a,$$

with centre a and radius ρ_a such that for every point z which belongs to this domain and to S, we have

$$| f(z) - f(a) | < \frac{1}{2} \varepsilon.$$

For any two points z_1, z_2 of this domain, we have

$$| f(z_1) - f(z_2) | = | f(z_1) - f(a) + f(a) - f(z_2) |$$
$$\leq | f(z_1) - f(a) | + | f(z_2) - f(a) | < \varepsilon.$$

We now suppose that associated to each point $a \in$ S is a circular domain C_a with centre a and radius $\frac{1}{2} \rho_a$. The set Σ of these circular domains covers the compact set S and is such that each point $a \in$ S is the centre of some circular domain of this system. Hence by the corollary to the Heine-Borel Theorem, there exists a finite sub-set σ of Σ which also covers S. Let δ be the smallest of the *finite* set of the radii of the circular domains of the sub-set σ. We shall show that this number δ has the requisite property.

Consider now any two points z_1, z_2 of S such that
$$|z_2 - z_1| < \delta.$$
Let a_m be the centre of the circular domain of the set σ to which z_1 belongs so that
$$|z_1 - a_m| < \frac{1}{2}\rho_{am}.$$
We then have
$$|z_2 - a_m| = |z_2 - z_1 + z_1 - a_m|$$
$$\leq |z_2 - z_1| + |z_1 - a_m|$$
$$< \delta + \frac{1}{2}\rho_{am} \leq \frac{1}{2}\rho_{am} + \frac{1}{2}\rho_{am} = \rho_{am}.$$

Thus, we see that z_1, z_2 belong to the circular domain with centre a_m and radius ρ_{am} and accordingly we have
$$|f(z_2) - f(z_1)| < \varepsilon.$$
Hence the theorem.

Note. The theorem proved above is often stated as follows:

A function defined and continuous in a compact set is uniformly continuous.

4.15. Compactness preserving character of continuous mappings.

Theorem. *The range of a function continuous in a compact set is itself compact.*

This theorem may also be briefly stated as follows:

Every continuous image of a compact set is compact.

As seen in the proof of the preceding theorem, there exists a finite set of circular domains
$$C_1, C_2, \ldots\ldots\ldots, C_i, \ldots\ldots\ldots, C_k$$
with centres
$$a_1, a_2, \ldots\ldots\ldots, a_i, \ldots\ldots\ldots, a_k$$
and radii
$$\rho_1, \rho_2, \ldots\ldots\ldots, \rho_i, \ldots\ldots\ldots, \rho_k$$
such that
$$|f(z) - f(a_i)| < \varepsilon, \text{ for } |z - a_i| < \rho_i \text{ and } z \in S$$
and the finite set of circular domains covers S.

Now for any z in C_i, we have
$$|f(z) - f(a_i)| < \varepsilon$$
from which we deduce that
$$|f(z)| < |f(a_i)| + \varepsilon.$$
If now, λ be the greatest of the finite set of numbers
$$|f(a_i)| + \varepsilon, \ i = 1, 2, \ldots\ldots\ldots, k$$
we deduce that
$$|f(z)| < \lambda, \quad \forall \ z \in S.$$
Thus, the range is bounded.

Now to prove that the range is closed also.

Let ξ be a limiting point of the range T and let, if possible, ξ not belong to T. Then

$$f(z) - \xi = 0, \quad \forall \quad z \in S.$$

It follows that the function $1 / [f(z) - \xi]$ is continuous and hence also bounded.

Let now K be any positive number, however large. As ξ is a limiting point of the range T, there exist points $z \in S$ such that we have

$$|f(z) - \xi| < 1/K; \quad f(z) \in T$$

$$\Rightarrow \quad \left| \frac{1}{f(z) - \xi} \right| > K$$

so that we arrive at a contradiction of the fact that the function

$$1 / [f(z) - \xi]$$

is bounded.

Hence the range is closed also.

Thus we have proved the theorem.

4.16. Connectedness preserving character of continuous mappings. Theorem. *Every continuous image of a connected set is connected.*

Let S be the domain and T the range of a continuous function

$$w = f(z).$$

Let, further, S be a connected set. We shall then prove that T is also a connected set. Let

$$T = T_1 \cup T_2, \qquad \qquad ...(1)$$

be *an* expression of T as union of disjoint, non-null sets T_1 and T_2.

Then because of (1), we have

$$S = S_1 \cup S_2$$

where the images of S_1, S_2 are T_1, T_2 respectively. Surely, S_1, S_2 are disjoint and non-null. As S is connected, some limiting point, of S_1 belong to S_2 or that of S_2 belongs to S_1. Let a limiting point ξ of S_1 belong to S_2. Then

$$f(\xi) \in T_2.$$

Consider any neighbourhood

$$|w - f(\xi)| < \varepsilon \qquad \qquad ...(2)$$

of

$$f(\xi).$$

Because of continuity there exists a positive number δ such that (2) holds for

$$|z - \xi| < \delta \qquad \qquad ...(3)$$

As ξ is a limiting point of S_1, the neighbourhood (3) of ξ contains an infinite number of members z of S_1. Thus an infinite number of members of T_1 belong to the neighbourhood (1) of $f(\xi)$ and accordingly $f(\xi)$ is a limiting point of T_1 and belongs to T_2. Thus T is a connected set.

Hence the theorem.

Note. It is interesting to notice that the *continuous image of a domain may not be a domain*. As for example, $w = |z|$ maps every domain on a sub-set of the real axis which is clearly not open. In fact a continuous image of an open set may *not* be open. Continuous image of a bounded continuum is, however, a bounded continuum. In the following chapter we shall consider the types of mappings which preserve the character of a set being a domain.

4.17. Curves. Consider a complex function

$$z = z \, (t), \, a \le t \le b$$

defined in an interval $[a, b]$ of the real axis so that to each number, t, such that $a \le t \le b$, there corresponds a complex number z. Here we have a complex valued function of a real variable. Then the range of this function $z \, (t)$ defined in an interval of a real axis is called a *curve*. This curve is said to be continuous, if the function $z \, (t)$ is continuous. In what follows, we shall always be considering continuous curves and a '*curve*' *will be always regarded as continuous*.

Thus, *a curve is a continuous image of a closed interval of the real axis*.

Being the continuous image of a bounded closed set, a curve is necessarily bounded and closed.

A curve may be thought of as having two *orientations* according as t varies from a to b or b to a.

4.17.1. Simple curves. *A curve* $z = z \, (t)$ *is said to be simple if the function* $z \, (t)$ *is one-one*, *i.e.*, no two different values of t correspond to the same value of z. Thus, *a simple curve is a continuous* **one-one** *image of an interval of the real axis*.

4.17.2. Simple closed curves. A curve given by $z = z \, (t)$, $a \le t \le b$, is said to be simple closed, if no two different values of t other than, a and b, correspond to same value of z and

$$z \, (a) = z \, (b).$$

A simple closed curve can be thought of as a continuous one-one image of the unit circle $|z| = 1$.

4.17.3. *Jordan Curve. A simple closed curve is called a Jordan curve.*

Theorem. *A curve is a connected set.*

This follows from the facts that

  (*i*) a continuous image of a connected set is connected,

  (*ii*) a curve is a continuous image of an interval of the real axis, and

 (*iii*) an interval of the real axis is a connected set.

Cor. *A curve*

$$z = z \, (t)$$

where $z \, (t)$ *is defined in a closed interval* $[a, b]$ *is a continuum.*

4.18. Jordan Curve

Theorem. Relative to the circle $|z| = 1$, which is a Jordan curve, we obtain two disjoint domains given by

$$|z| < 1, |z| > 1$$

such that $|z| = 1$ is the common frontier of both these domains and the union of these two domains and the curve is the entire set of complex numbers.

Of these two domains, the one defined by $|z| < 1$ which is bounded is called the *interior* and the other one is called the *exterior* of the curve $|z| = 1$.

This result is capable of generalisation to any Jordan curve whatsoever. We now state this generalisation.

Relative to any Jordan curve C, *there exist two disjoint domains* S_1, S_2 *such that* C *is the common frontier of both* S_1, S_2 *and the union of* S_1, S_2, *where* C *is the entire set of complex numbers*.

Of the two domains S_1, S_2, the one which is bounded is called the interior and the other one not bounded is called the exterior of the Jordan curve.

Adopting a rather inexact, but intuitive way, we may state this result as follows:

Every Jordan curve determines an interior and an exterior domain.

The rigorous proof of the theorem which involves very intricate and profound arguments is beyond the scope of this book. We shall, therefore, only assume the truth of the theorem expecting the reader to appreciate only the intuitive content of the same.

It should, however, be carefully understood that, as a result of Jordan Theorem, we are justified in talking of the interior and the exterior of a Jordan curve.

4.18.1. Orientation of a Jordan Curve. An oriented Jordan curve is said to be positively or negatively oriented according as

$$\arg (z - \xi)$$

changes by $+ 2\pi$ or $- 2\pi$ while z completely describes the oriented curve and ξ is any point in the interior of the curve.

If ξ belongs to the exterior of the curve then $\arg (z - \xi)$ undergoes no change while z describes the oriented curve completely.

4.19. Connectivity of a domain. Simply connected and multiply connected domains. *A domain is called simply connected if the frontier thereof consists of a single continuum.*

In general *a domain is called m-ply connected if the frontier of the same consists of m distinct continua.*

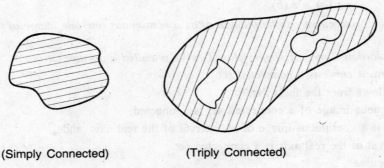

(Simply Connected)   (Triply Connected)

Fig. 4.1

A useful characterisation of simply connected domains is as follows:

A domain is simply connected if the interior of every Jordan curve in the domain belongs to the domain.

The proof will not be given here.

The domain $| z | < 1$ is simply connected but the domains given by

$$0 < | z | < 1, | 1 | < | z | < 2$$

are both doubly connected.

4.20. Connectedness of line segments and polygonal lines. If a, b be any two points, then the set of points

$$a + t (b - a), 0 \le t \le 1$$

is the *line segment* joining the points, a, b. This line, being a continuous image of the interval $[0, 1]$ of the real axis is a connected set.

A *polygonal line* is a continuous curve consisting of a system of line segments. Thus, if the polygonal line consists of the line segments joining the pairs of points

$$a_1, a_2; a_2, a_3; \ldots\ldots\ldots; a_{k-1}, a_k,$$

then the polygonal line is the curve given by

$$z = \begin{cases} a_1 + t\,(a_2 - a_1),\ 0 \leq t \leq 1, \\ a_2 + (t-1)\,(a_3 - a_2),\ 1 \leq t \leq 2, \\ \dots\ \dots\ \dots\ \dots \\ \dots\ \dots\ \dots\ \dots \\ a_{k-1} + (t-k-1)\,(a_k - a_{k-1}),\ k-1 \leq t \leq k. \end{cases}$$

Being a continuous image of the interval $[0, k]$ of the real axis, we see that the polygonal line is a connected set.

4.21. Another useful characterisation of open connected sets by polygonal lines. Theorem.
An open set is connected if and only if any two points of the same can be joined by a polygonal line in the set.

Firstly suppose that S is an open connected set.

Let, if possible, a, b be two points of S which *cannot* be joined by a polygonal line in S.

Let S_1 denotes the set of all those points of S which can be joined to a, by a polygonal line in S and S_2 the set of all those points of S which cannot be thus joined to a. Then $a \in S_1$ and $b \in S_2$. Thus, S_1, S_2 are disjoint and non-null and

$$S = S_1 \cup S_2.$$

We shall show that S_1, S_2 are open sets.

Let ξ be any point of S_1. There exists a neighbourhood of ξ consisting entirely of points of the open set S. Since every point of this neighbourhood can be joined to ξ, by a line segment in S, we see that every such point can as well be joined to a, by a polygonal line in S.

Thus, there exists a neighbourhood of ξ consisting entirely of points of S_1. Thus, S_1 is an open set.

Suppose now that η is any point of S_2. There exists a neighbourhood of η, consisting entirely of points of the open set S. No point of this neighbourhood can be joined to a, by a polygonal line in S, for, otherwise the point η could as well be so joined to a, *viz.*, the point in question. Thus, we see that S_2 is an open set.

Hence we have

$$S = S_1 \cup S_2,$$

where S_1, S_2 are disjoint, non-null, open sets. This is a contradiction of the fact that S is connected. Hence the result.

We now consider the converse.

Suppose that an open set S is such that any two points of the same can be joined by a polygonal line in S.

Let, if possible, S *be not connected.* Then there exists two disjoint, non-null sets S_1, S_2 such that

$$S = S_1 \cup S_2$$

and no limiting point of S_1 belongs to S_2 and no limiting point of S_2 belongs to S_1.

Let, a, b be two points of S_1, S_2 respectively and Σ be the polygonal line in S joining a, b.

Also let Σ_1, Σ_2 be the parts of the polygonal line contained in S_1, S_2 respectively. We then have

$$\Sigma = \Sigma_1 \cup \Sigma_2.$$

As Σ is connected, either a limiting point of Σ_1 belongs to Σ_2 or that of Σ_2 belongs to Σ_1.

Suppose that a limiting point of Σ_1 is a member of Σ_2. Since a limiting point of Σ_1 is also a limiting point of S_1, we deduce that a limiting point of S_1 belongs to S_2. Thus, we have a contradiction and accordingly S is a connected set.

Note. The above characterisation holds good for open sets only and not for closed sets. For example, $|z| = 1$ is a closed and connected set but no two points of the same can be joined by a polygonal line in the set.

4.22. Branch Line and Branch Point. *A point is called a branch point of a function $f(z)$ if some of the branches interchange as the independent variable z describes a closed path about it.*

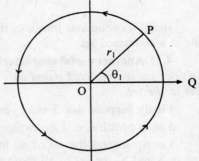

Let $w = f(z) = z^{1/2}$ be a multivalued complex function.

$$f(z) = r^{1/2} e^{i\theta/2} \qquad [\because \ z = re^{i\theta}]$$

Now make a complete circuit in anticlockwise direction around the origin O starting from any point $P(z_1)$ whose amplitude is θ_1 (say).

$$\therefore \qquad\qquad w = r_1^{1/2} e^{i\theta_1/2} \text{ at P.}$$

Fig. 4.2

After a complete circuit we again arrive at P so that
$\theta = \theta_1 + 2\pi$

$$\Rightarrow \qquad w = r_1^{1/2} e^{i(\theta_1 + 2\pi)/2} = r_1^{1/2} e^{i\left(\frac{1}{2}\theta_1 + \pi\right)}$$

$$= -r_1^{1/2} e^{-i\frac{1}{2}\theta_1}.$$

This shows that we have not obtained the same value of w with which we started.

Hence we are on one branch of the function $w = z^{1/2}$ when $0 \le \theta \le 2\pi$ and on the second branch when $2\pi \le \theta \le 4\pi$.

Evidently each branch of the function is single valued. For keeping the function single valued an *artificial barrier* OQ, where Q is supposed at infinity is made. The artificial barrier is called *branch line* or *branch cut* or *cross cut* and the point O is called the *branch point*. We may however have any other line from O as an artificial barrier in place of OQ.

In a similar manner we can show that $f(z) = \log z$ has a branch point at $z = 0$.

4.23. Period. A function $f(z)$ is said to be of period w if
$$f(z + w) = f(z).$$

The function e^z is of period $2\pi i$.

For $e^{(z + 2\pi i)} = e^z$.

EXERCISES

1. Show that a limiting point of any subset of a set is also a limiting point of the set.

2. Find the limiting points of the sets given below; n ranging over all positive integral values:

   (a) $n^{1/n} + i^n$

   (b) $2^{1/n} + 2w^n$, where $w = \frac{1}{2}(-1 + \sqrt{3}\ i)$

   (c) $n^{1/n} + 3w^n$, where $w = \frac{1}{2}(-1 - \sqrt{3}\ i)$

(d) $\dfrac{n-1}{n+1} \cos \dfrac{n\pi}{3}$

(e) $\dfrac{n+1}{n} \sin \dfrac{n\pi}{6}$

(f) $\dfrac{n-1}{n+1} \cos \dfrac{n\pi}{3} + i\left(\dfrac{n+1}{n}\right) \sin \dfrac{n\pi}{6}$

(g) $\dfrac{n-1}{n+1} \sin^2 \dfrac{n\pi}{10}$.

[**Ans.** (a) $1 \pm i, 0, 2$

(b) $\pm\sqrt{3}\, i, 3$

(c) $\dfrac{-1 \pm 3\sqrt{3}\, i}{2}, 4$

(d) $\pm 1, \pm \dfrac{1}{2}$

(e) $\pm 1, \pm \dfrac{\sqrt{3}}{2}, \pm \dfrac{1}{2}, 0$

(f) $1, -1 \pm i, \dfrac{1}{2} + \dfrac{1}{2}i, -\dfrac{1}{2} \pm \dfrac{\sqrt{3}}{2}i$

(g) $0, \dfrac{3 \pm \sqrt{5}}{8}, \dfrac{5 \pm \sqrt{5}}{8}, 1]$

3. Show that the following functions are continuous for every value of z:

(a) R (z)
(b) I (z)
(c) $|z|$
(d) $\bar{z}$
(e) z^2
(f) c, a constant.

4. Show that a polynomial
$$f(z) = a_0 z^n + a_1 z^{n-1} + \ldots\ldots\ldots + a_n$$
is continuous in every domain.

5. Show that a rational function
$$f(z) = \dfrac{a_0 z^n + a_1 z^{n-1} + \ldots\ldots + a_n}{b_0 z^m + b_1 z^{m-1} + \ldots\ldots + b_m}$$

wherefor the numerator and denominator have no common factor are continuous in every domain to which does not belong a zero of the denominator.

6. The functions
$$\dfrac{I(z)}{z}, \dfrac{R(z)}{z}, \dfrac{z}{|z|}, \dfrac{R(z^2)}{|z|^2}, \dfrac{z\,R(z)}{|z|}$$

are defined for $z \neq 0$. Which of them may be suitably defined at $z = 0$ so as to become continuous at this point ?

$$\left[\textbf{Ans. Only } \dfrac{z\,R(z)}{|z|}\right]$$

OBJECTIVE QUESTIONS

For each of the following questions, four alternatives are given for the answer. Only one of them is correct. Choose the correct alternative.

1. Any circular domain of which a given point is a member is called
   (a) neighbourhood
   (b) interior
   (c) exterior
   (d) frontier.

2. If every neighbourhood of a point ξ contains an infinite number of members of a set S, then ξ is
   (a) interior point
   (b) limiting point
   (c) infinite point
   (d) singular point.

3. The set of all the limiting points of a set is called
   - (a) limit set
   - (b) derived set
   - (c) closed set
   - (d) open set.

4. The union of the interior and the frontier of set is called
   - (a) exterior of set
   - (b) compactness of set
   - (c) closure of set
   - (d) characteristic of set.

5. A closed connected set is called
   - (a) continuum
   - (b) domain
   - (c) closure
   - (d) compact set.

6. Every infinite bounded set has
   - (a) no limiting point
   - (b) infinite limiting points
   - (c) only one limiting point
   - (d) at least one limiting point.

7. A curve is a
   - (a) derived set
   - (b) compact set
   - (c) connected set
   - (d) None of these.

ANSWERS

1. (a)   **2.** (b)   **3.** (b)   **4.** (c)   **5.** (a)   **6.** (d)   **7.** (c)

ANALYTIC FUNCTIONS

5.1. Introduction. In this chapter, we shall consider the notion of differentiability applicable to the complex valued functions of a complex variable. It will be seen that this notion constitutes a departure from that of continuity inasmuch as the differentiability of a function of a complex variable is **not** just equivalent to the differentiability of the real and imaginary parts thereof as is the case with continuity. This fact leads to *Cauchy-Riemann Partial Differential Equations* and their important geometric consequence.

Following Cauchy (1789 – 1857), the notion of *Analytic Functions* will be given in terms of differentiability. It may be remarked that Weierstrass adopted the method of power series for the purpose. It will, however, be seen in Chapter 9 that these two approaches of Cauchy and Weierstrass are essentially equivalent. The geometric aspect of Analytic Functions which had been emphasised by Riemann (1826 – 1866) is examined later on in this chapter.

Far reaching properties of Analytic Functions can only be arrived at with the help of the Cauchy's fundamental theorem involving the notion of integration. This will be taken up in Chapters 8 and 9.

5.2. Differentiable Functions of a Complex Variable. Let $w = f(z)$ be defined in any domain D closed or otherwise. Let $z \in$ D.

Then, as in real variables, $f(z)$ is said to be differentiable or derivable at any point $z \in$ D, if

$$\lim_{h \to 0} \frac{f(z+h) - f(z)}{h} \qquad \qquad ...(1)$$

exists and also, in the event of differentiability, *i.e.*, of the existence of the limit (1), the limit is called the **Derivative** or the **Differential Coefficient** at z and denoted by $f'(z)$ or $df(z)/dz$.

If $f(z)$ be differentiable at z, then writing

$$\frac{f(z+h) - f(z)}{h} - f'(z) = \varepsilon,$$

we obtain the relation

$$f(z+h) - f(z) = hf'(z) + h\varepsilon,$$

where ε is a function of h tending to zero with h.

5.2.1. Differentiability and Continuity. As in real variables, we may show that *differentiability implies continuity but not conversely.* (*Meerut 2002; Kerala 1998*)

We write

$$f(z+h) - f(z) = \frac{f(z+h) - f(z)}{h} \cdot h$$

Again $f(z)$ is differentiable at z.

$\Rightarrow$
$$\lim \, [f\,(z+h)-f\,(z)] \; = \; \lim \, \frac{f\,(z+h)-f\,(z)}{h}\cdot \lim \, h$$
$$= \; f'\,(z)\cdot 0 \; = \; 0$$

$\Rightarrow$
$$\lim_{h\to 0} \, f\,(z+h) \; = \; f\,(z)$$

$\Rightarrow$ $f\,(z)$ is continuous at z.

To see that the converse is *not true*, we consider
$$f\,(z) \; = \; \overline{z} \; = \; x - iy$$

and show that $f\,(z)$ is continuous but not differentiable for $z = 0$.

We have
$$|\,f\,(z) - f\,(0)\,| \; = \; |\,\overline{z} - 0\,| = |\,z\,| < \varepsilon \;\; \text{when} \;\; |\,z - 0\,| < \varepsilon$$

so that $f\,(z)$ is continuous for $z = 0$.

Also
$$\frac{f\,(0+h)-f\,(0)}{h} \; = \; \frac{p-iq}{p+iq},$$

where $h = p + iq$.

Now,
$$\lim \, \frac{p-iq}{p+iq}$$

depending as it does on $\lim \, (p/q)$ does not exist when $(p, q) \to (0, 0)$, *i.e.*, when $p \to 0$ and $q \to 0$.

Note. The reader may even show that $f\,(z) = \overline{z}$ is continuous for every z and differentiable for no z.

EXAMPLES

1. *Prove that the function $f\,(z) = |\,z\,|^2$ is continuous everywhere but no where differentiable except at the origin.*

(*Banglore 2003, Mumbai 2001, 2004; Meerut 2001, 2003; Kanpur 2004; GNDU 2003*)

Solution. We have $|\,z\,| = \sqrt{(x^2 + y^2)}$ $\therefore$ $|\,z\,|^2 = x^2 + y^2$ ...(1)

But $x^2 + y^2$ is continuous everywhere, hence it follows that $|\,z\,|^2$ is everywhere continuous.

Now
$$f'\,(z) \; = \; \lim_{\Delta z \to 0} \, \frac{|\,z + \Delta z\,|^2 - |\,z\,|^2}{\Delta z}$$
$$= \; \lim_{\Delta z \to 0} \, \frac{(z + \Delta z)\,(\overline{z} + \Delta \overline{z}) - z\overline{z}}{\Delta z}$$
$$= \; \lim_{\Delta z \to 0} \, \left[\overline{z} + \Delta \overline{z} + z\cdot \frac{\Delta \overline{z}}{\Delta z} \right]$$
$$= \; \lim_{\Delta z \to 0} \, \left[\overline{z} + z\,\frac{\Delta \overline{z}}{\Delta z} \right] \quad (\because \; \Delta \overline{z} \to 0 \text{ as } \Delta z \to 0) \qquad \text{...(1)}$$

Let $\Delta z = \rho\,(\cos \theta + i \sin \theta) \Rightarrow \Delta \overline{z} = \rho\,(\cos \theta - i \sin \theta)$

$\Rightarrow \qquad \dfrac{\Delta \bar{z}}{\Delta z} = \dfrac{\cos \theta - i \sin \theta}{\cos \theta + i \sin \theta} = (\cos \theta - i \sin \theta)(\cos \theta + i \sin \theta)^{-1}$

$$= (\cos \theta - i \sin \theta)^2 = \cos 2\theta - i \sin 2\theta$$

Now $\displaystyle \lim_{\Delta z \to 0} \dfrac{\Delta \bar{z}}{\Delta z}$ does not tend to unique limit as it depends upon arg Δz, where z is a non-zero point. Hence from (1), it follows that $f'(z)$ is not unique, *i.e.*, $f(z)$ is non-differentiable for any non-zero value of z. When $z = 0$, the value of $f'(z)$, *i.e.*, $f'(0)$ is zero and is unique implying thereby that the function is differentiable at $z = 0$.

2. *If* $f(z) = \dfrac{x^3 y\,(y - ix)}{x^6 + y^2}$ $(z \neq 0)$, $f(0) = 0$, *prove that :* $\dfrac{f(z) - f(0)}{z} \to 0$ *as* $z \to 0$

along any radius vector but not as $z \to 0$ *in any manner.*

(*Kumaon, 1991, 93; Gorakhpur, 1992, 94, 95, 97*)

Solution. Let $z \to 0$ along $y = mx$. Then, we have

$$\lim_{z \to 0} \dfrac{f(z) - f(0)}{z} = \lim_{z \to 0} \dfrac{x^3 y\,(y - ix)}{(x^6 + y^2)(x + iy)}$$

$$= \lim_{x \to 0} \dfrac{x^3\, mx\,(mx - ix)}{(x^6 + m^2 x^2)(x + imx)} = \lim_{x \to 0} \dfrac{m\,(m - i)\cdot x^2}{(m^2 + x^4)(1 + im)} = 0.$$

Further, let $z = 0$ along $y = x^3$. So that, we have

$$\lim_{z \to 0} \dfrac{f(z) - f(0)}{z} = \lim_{x \to 0} \dfrac{x^6\,(x^3 - ix)}{(x^6 + x^6)(x + ix^3)}$$

$$= \lim_{x \to 0} \dfrac{(x^2 - i)}{2\,(1 + ix^2)} = -\dfrac{1}{2}\, i.$$

5.3. Geometrical Interpretation of the Derivative. Let z_0 be a point P in the z-plane and let w_0 be its image P' in the w-plane under the transformation $w = f(z)$. Let $f(z)$ be a single valued function so that the point z_0 maps only to one point w_0. Now give z_0 an increment Δz so as to obtain the point Q. The point Q has the image Q' in the w-plane. Evidently P'Q' represents the complex number $\Delta w = f(z_0 + \Delta z) - f(z_0)$. Hence the derivative of $f(z)$ at $z = z_0$, if it exists, is given by

$$= \lim_{\Delta z \to 0} \dfrac{f(z_0 + \Delta z) - f(z_0)}{\Delta z} = \lim_{P \to Q} \dfrac{Q'P'}{QP}$$

$$= \text{Limit of the ratio Q'P' to QP as Q approaches point P.}$$

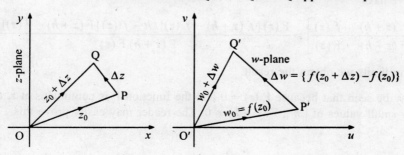

Fig. 5.1

5.4. Analytic Function

(Kumaon 2001; Osmania 2004; Rohilkhand, 2002, 2003, 2004; UPPCS 2002, 2004; Gorakhpur, 2000, 2001, 2003, 2004; Garhwal, 2001, 2005, 2006; Kanpur 2005; Rohtak, 2001)

A one valued function $f(z)$ which is defined and differentiable at each point of a domain D is said to be *analytic* in that domain. A function is said to be analytic at a point if its derivative exists not only at that point but in δ-neighbourhood ($|z - z_0| < \delta$) of that point.

The terms *regular* and *holomorphic* are sometimes used as synonymous for analytic. A function $f(z)$ may be differentiable in a domain except possible for a finite number of points. These points are called *singular points* or *singularities* of $f(z)$ in that domain.

5.4.1. Elementary rules of differentiation. The elementary rules for the differentiation of functions of a complex variable are the same as those of real variables. Thus we shall show that if two functions $f(z)$ and F (z) are differentiable at a point z, then so are also their sum, difference, product and quotient provided that in the last case denominator F $(z) \neq 0$.

Also,

$$[f(z) \pm F(z)]' = f'(z) \pm F'(z) \tag{I}$$

$$[f(z) F(z)]' = f(z) F'(z) + f'(z) F(z) \tag{II}$$

$$\left[\frac{f(z)}{F(z)}\right]' = \frac{F(z) f'(z) - f(z) F'(z)}{[F(z)]^2} \tag{III}$$

We now prove these results.

I. We have

$$\frac{[f(z+h) \pm F(z+h)] - [f(z) \pm F(z)]}{h} = \frac{f(z+h) - f(z)}{h} \pm \frac{F(z+h) - F(z)}{h}$$

so that the result now follows on taking limits as $h \to 0$.

II. We have

$$\frac{f(z+h) F(z+h) - f(z) F(z)}{h} = F(z+h) \cdot \frac{f(z+h) - f(z)}{h} + f(z) \cdot \frac{F(z+h) - F(z)}{h}.$$

Also because of the differentiability and the consequential continuity of F (z), we have

$$\lim_{h \to 0} F(z + h) = F(z).$$

We obtain the result on taking the limits.

III. We have

$$\frac{1}{h}\left[\frac{f(z+h)}{F(z+h)} - \frac{f(z)}{F(z)}\right] = \frac{F(z)[f(z+h) - f(z)]/h - f(z)[F(z+h) - F(z)]/h}{F(z+h) F(z)}.$$

Taking limits we obtain the result.

It may be seen that because F $(z) \neq 0$ and the function F is continuous at z, therefore, for sufficiently small values of $|h|$, F $(z + h) \neq 0$. The reader may easily prove this.

5.4.2. *Chain Rule.* Suppose that $Z = f(z)$ is defined in a domain D_1 and $w = \phi(Z)$ is defined in a domain D_2 and that the range of $Z = f(z)$ is contained in the domain of D_2 of $w = \phi(z)$. Then $w = \phi[f(z)]$ is a function of z defined in D_1.

We shall now prove that *if* $Z = f(z)$ *is differentiable at* z *and* $w = \phi(Z)$ *is differentiable at the corresponding* Z, *then* w *is a differentiable function of* z *and*

$$\frac{dw}{dz} = \frac{dw}{dZ} \cdot \frac{dZ}{dz} = \phi'(Z) f'(z).$$

Because of the differentiability of $f(z)$, we have a relation of the form

$$k = f(z + h) - f(z) = hf'(z) + h\varepsilon_1, \text{ where } \varepsilon_1 \to 0 \text{ as } h \to 0 \qquad \qquad ...(1)$$

Also because of the differentiability of $\phi(Z)$, we have

$$\phi(Z + h) - \phi(Z) = k\phi'(Z) + \varepsilon_2 k, \text{ where } \varepsilon_2 \to 0 \text{ as } k \to 0 \qquad \qquad ...(2)$$

From (1) and (2), we have

$$\phi[f(z + h)] - \phi[f(z)] = \phi(Z + k) - \phi(Z)$$

$$= [hf'(z) + \varepsilon_1 h]\, \phi'(Z) + \varepsilon_2 [hf'(z) + \varepsilon_1 h]$$

$$= hf'(z)\, \phi'(Z) + h[\varepsilon_1 \phi'(z) + \varepsilon_2 f'(z) + \varepsilon_2 \varepsilon_1]$$

$$= hf'(z)\, \phi'(Z) + h\varepsilon_3, \text{ (say)}$$

where

$$\varepsilon_3 = \varepsilon_1 \phi'(z) + \varepsilon_2 f'(z) = \varepsilon_2 \varepsilon_1 \to 0.$$

Thus, we see that $w = \phi[f(z)]$ is differentiable at z and

$$\frac{dw}{dz} = \phi'(Z) f'(z).$$

This is known as *Chain Rule.*

5.5. Derivatives of Polynomials and Rational Functions. Directly from definition, it can be shown that the derivative of z is 1 and that of a constant c is 0,

i.e.,
$$\frac{dz}{dz} = 1, \quad \frac{dc}{dz} = 0.$$

If n is a positive integer, we have

$$\frac{dz^n}{dz} = \lim_{h \to 0} \frac{(z + h)^n - z^n}{h}$$

$$= \lim_{h \to 0} \left[nz^{n-1} + \frac{n(n-1)}{2!} hz^{n-2} + ... + h^{n-1} \right]$$

$$= nz^{n-1} \qquad \qquad \text{[Refer § 4.11]}$$

If $n = -m$ is any negative integer so that m is a positive integer, we have, for $z \neq 0$

$$\frac{dz^n}{dz} = \frac{d}{dz}\left(\frac{1}{z^m}\right) = \frac{z^m \cdot 0 - 1 \cdot mz^{m-1}}{z^m} \qquad \qquad \text{[Refer § 5.4.1]}$$

$$= (-m)\, z^{-m-1} = nz^{n-1}.$$

Again, if

$$f(z) = a_0 z^n + a_1 z^{n-1} + ... + a_{n-1} z + a_n,$$

is a polynomial, we have, employing the results obtained above and the result of § 5.4.1 (*iii*)

$$f'(z) = na_0 z^{n-1} + (n-1) a_1 z^{n-2} + \dots + a_{n-1}.$$

Finally if

$$f(z) = \frac{P(z)}{Q(z)},$$

is a rational function; P (z), Q (z) being polynomials, we have, using in § 5.4.1

$$f'(z) = \frac{P'(z) Q(z) - P(z) Q'(z)}{[Q(z)]^2}$$

the result holding for every z for which Q (z) ≠ 0.

Note. The derivative of z^n when n is any rational number will be obtained later on in this chapter. The case when n is a complex number whatsoever will be considered in the following chapter.

5.6. Necessary and Sufficient Conditions for f(z) to be Analytic (Cauchy-Riemann Partial Differential Equations)

5.6.1. The necessary conditions for f (z) to be analytic.

Theorem *If f (z) = u (x, y) + iv (x, y) is differentiable at any point z = x + iy, then the real and imaginary parts u (x, y), v (x, y) of f (z) are also differentiable at (x, y) and*

$$u_x = v_y, u_y = -v_x.$$

(Avadh 2004, Osmania 2004, Gorakhpur 2005, Rohilkhand 2002, 2004, Gauhati 2001, Kanpur 2003, 2005, 2006, 2007 Calicut 2004, Utkal 2003, Kerala 2001, UPPCS 2004, Meerut 2006, Ravishankar 2003, Indore 2005)

Since f (z) is differentiable at z, we have a relation of the form

$$f(z + h) - f(z) = hf'(z) + h\varepsilon \qquad \qquad \dots(1)$$

where ε depends upon h and ε → 0 as h → 0.

We write

$$h = p + iq, f'(z) = \alpha + i\beta, \varepsilon = \varepsilon_1 + i\varepsilon_2.$$

Then, we can rewrite (1) as

$$[u(x + p, y + q) - u(x, y)] + i[v(x + p, y + q) - v(x, y)]$$
$$= (p + iq)(\alpha + i\beta) + (\varepsilon_1 + i\varepsilon_2)(p + iq) \qquad \dots(2)$$

Equating real and imaginary parts in (2), we obtain

$$u(x + p, y + q) - u(x, y) = p\alpha - q\beta + p\varepsilon_1 - q\varepsilon_2, \qquad \dots(3)$$

$$v(x + p, y + q) - v(x, y) = p\beta + q\alpha + q\varepsilon_2 + q\varepsilon_1 \qquad \dots(4)$$

The relations (3) and (4) show that the functions u (x, y) and v (x, y) are differentiable at (x, y) and

$$u_x = \alpha, u_y = -\beta; v_x = \beta, v_y = \alpha \qquad \dots(5)$$

From (5) we obtain the relation

$$u_x = v_y, u_y = -v_x \qquad \dots(6)$$

Connecting the partial derivatives of the functions u and v.

The two partial differential equations (6) are known as *Cauchy-Riemann Partial Differential Equations.*

We may also see that

$$f'(z) = \alpha + i\beta$$

$$= u_x + iv_x = -i(u_y + iv_y).$$

Ex. 1. Verify the Cauchy-Riemann equations for the function z^n, where n is any positive integer. Also verify the same for $1/z$ at any point $z \neq 0$.

Ex. 2. Show that the Cauchy-Riemann equations are *not* satisfied for any of the functions

$$w = R(z), \; w = I(z), \; w = \bar{z}, \; w = |z|, \; w = \bar{z}/z,$$

at any point z. Also show directly that these functions are *not* differentiable for any point z.

Theorem 2. Sufficient conditions for $f(z)$ to be analytic.

(Converse of the preceding Theorem 1). *If the real and imaginary parts u and v of $f(z)$ are both differentiable at (x, y) and satisfy the Cauchy-Riemann partial differential equations*

$$u_x = v_y, \; u_y = -v_x \qquad \qquad ...(1)$$

then $f(z)$ is differentiable at $z = x + iy$.

(*Banglore 2003, Indore 2005, Meerut 2000, 2003 Gauhati 2004, Kanpur 2004, 2006, Ravishankar 2002*)

We have

$$\frac{f(z+h) - f(z)}{h}$$

$$= \frac{[u(x+p, y+q) - u(x, y)] + i[v(x+p, y+q) - v(x, y)]}{p + iq} \qquad ...(2)$$

Since, the functions u and v are differentiable at (x, y), we have relations of the form

$$u(x+p, y+q) - u(x, y) = pu_x + qu_y + \varepsilon_1 p - \varepsilon_2 q \qquad ...(3)$$

$$v(x+p, y+q) - v(x, y) = pv_x + qv_y + \varepsilon_3 p + \varepsilon_4 q \qquad ...(4)$$

where $\varepsilon_1, \varepsilon_2, \varepsilon_3, \varepsilon_4$ are functions of p, q tending to zero as $p \to 0$ and $q \to 0$.

From (2), (3) and (4), making use of (1), we obtain

$$\frac{f(z+h) - f(z)}{h}$$

$$= \frac{(pu_x - qv_x + \varepsilon_1 p - \varepsilon_2 q) + i(pv_x + qu_x + \varepsilon_3 p + \varepsilon_4 q)}{p + iq}$$

$$= \frac{(p+iq)(u_x + iv_x)}{p+iq} + \frac{p}{p+iq}\varepsilon_1 + \frac{q}{p+iq}\varepsilon_2 + \frac{ip}{p+iq}\varepsilon_3 + \frac{iq}{p+iq}\varepsilon_4$$

$$\Rightarrow \left| \frac{f(z+h) - f(z)}{h} - (u_x + iv_x) \right| \leq |\varepsilon_1| + |\varepsilon_2| + |\varepsilon_3| + |\varepsilon_4| \qquad ...(5)$$

for

$$\left| \frac{p}{p+iq} \right| \leq 1, \; \left| \frac{q}{p+iq} \right| \leq 1, \; \left| \frac{ip}{p+iq} \right| \leq 1, \; \left| \frac{iq}{p+iq} \right| \leq 1.$$

From the relation (5), we see that

$$\frac{f(z+h)-f(z)}{h} \to u_x + iv_x \text{ as } h \to 0.$$

Hence the theorem.

5.7. Analytic Functions in a Domain. If a function is differentiable at each point of a domain, then we say that the function is *Analytic* or *Regular Analytic* in the domain.

Further, a function is said to be *Analytic at a point*, if it is analytic in some domain enclosing the point, *i.e.*, in some neighbourhood of the point.

If $f(z)$ is analytic in a domain D, then it will be proved in Chapter 9 that the derivative $f'(z)$ which is also a function defined in D is itself analytic in D. In particular, therefore, $f'(z)$ is continuous in D. It will also thus follow that a *function which is differentiable once in any domain is also infinitely differentiable in the domain.*

Note. In this note, we consider the latitude which one may have in fixing the real and imaginary parts of an analytic function. Once we specify the real part $u(x, y)$ of an analytic function $f(z)$, then we see, as a result of the Cauchy-Riemann equations, that the partial derivatives v_x and v_y of the imaginary part v of the function $f(z)$ are automatically fixed inasmuch as

$$v_x = -u_y, \ v_y = u_x.$$

This shows that the specification of the real part $u(x, y)$ of an analytic function leads to the specification of its imaginary part to within an arbitrary additive constant.

We are not completely free even in the choice of $u(x, y)$ as we shall now see. As stated above, the derivative $f'(z)$ of an analytic function $f(z)$ is itself analytic so that the functions $u(x, y)$ and $v(x, y)$ also possess continuous second order partial derivatives at every point of the domain.

Now

$$u_x = v_y, \ u_y = -v_x$$
$$\Rightarrow \qquad u_{xx} = v_{xy}, \ u_{yy} = -v_{yx}$$

Also because of continuity,

$$v_{xy} = v_{yx}.$$

Thus we have

$$u_{xx} + u_{yy} = 0,$$

i.e.,
$$\frac{\partial^2 u}{\partial x^2} + \frac{\partial^2 u}{\partial y^2} = 0 \qquad \qquad ...(1)$$

This shows that the real part, u, of an analytic function must satisfy the second order partial differential equation (1).

This equation is known as the *Laplace's* or the *Potential* equation and every solution thereof is known as a *Harmonic* function or a *Potential* function.

It may be shown that the imaginary part, v, also satisfies the same Laplace's equation. Thus, we see that the *real and imaginary parts of an analytic function are both harmonic functions.*

Given any harmonic function u, we may determine a *conjugate harmonic* function v to within an arbitrary constant with the help of the Cauchy-Riemann equations and thereby define an analytic function $u + iv$.

5.7.1. Determination of the conjugate function. *If $f(z) = u + iv$ is an analytic function where both $u(x, y)$ and $v(x, y)$ are conjugate functions. Being given one of these say $u(x, y)$ to determine the other $v(x, y)$.*

Since v is a function of (x, y), therefore, we have

$$dv = \frac{\partial v}{\partial x}\, dx + \frac{\partial v}{\partial y}\, dy$$

$$= -\frac{\partial u}{\partial y}\, dx + \frac{\partial u}{\partial x}\, dy \qquad \qquad \dots(1)$$

by Cauchy-Riemann equations.

But the right hand side of (1) is of the form

$$M dx + N dy,$$

where $M = -(\partial u / \partial y)$ and $N = (\partial u / \partial x)$.

So that $\qquad \dfrac{\partial M}{\partial y} = \dfrac{\partial}{\partial y}\left(-\dfrac{\partial u}{\partial y}\right) = -\dfrac{\partial^2 u}{\partial y^2}.$

and $\qquad \dfrac{\partial N}{\partial x} = \dfrac{\partial}{\partial x}\left(\dfrac{\partial u}{\partial x}\right) = \dfrac{\partial^2 u}{\partial x^2}.$

Again u is a harmonic function, therefore it satisfies Laplace's equation,

i.e., $\qquad \dfrac{\partial^2 u}{\partial x^2} + \dfrac{\partial^2 u}{\partial y^2} = 0 \quad \text{or} \quad \dfrac{\partial^2 u}{\partial y^2} = -\dfrac{\partial^2 u}{\partial x^2} \quad \Rightarrow \quad \dfrac{\partial M}{\partial y} = \dfrac{\partial N}{\partial x}.$

This implies that equation (1) satisfies the condition of exact differential equation and hence it can be integrated so as to obtain v.

5.7.2. Polar form of Cauchy-Riemann conditions.

(Avadh 2003, Agra 2003, Banglore 2001, Kerala 2001, Kumaon 2001, 2004, Manipur 2004, Mumbai 2000, Garhwal, 2000, 2005, 2006, Gorakhpur 2001, 2004, Kanpur 2004, Rohilkhand, 2001, 2003, 2004)

We have

$$x = r \cos\theta,\ y = r \sin\theta,$$

so that $\qquad r^2 = x^2 + y^2 \text{ and } \theta = \tan^{-1}(y/x).$

$\Rightarrow \qquad \dfrac{\partial r}{\partial x} \equiv \dfrac{x}{r} = \cos\theta,\ \dfrac{\partial r}{\partial y} = \sin\theta,$

$$\frac{\partial \theta}{\partial x} = \frac{1}{1 + (y^2/x^2)}\left(-\frac{y}{x^2}\right) = -\frac{\sin\theta}{r} \text{ and } \frac{\partial \theta}{\partial y} = \frac{\cos\theta}{r}.$$

Now, $\qquad \dfrac{\partial u}{\partial x} = \dfrac{\partial u}{\partial r}\cdot\dfrac{\partial r}{\partial x} + \dfrac{\partial u}{\partial \theta}\cdot\dfrac{\partial \theta}{\partial x} = \dfrac{\partial u}{\partial r}\cdot\cos\theta - \dfrac{\partial u}{\partial \theta}\cdot\dfrac{\sin\theta}{r}$

$$\frac{\partial u}{\partial y} = \frac{\partial u}{\partial r}\cdot\frac{\partial r}{\partial y} + \frac{\partial u}{\partial \theta}\cdot\frac{\partial \theta}{\partial y} = \frac{\partial u}{\partial r}\cdot\sin\theta + \frac{\partial u}{\partial \theta}\cdot\frac{\cos\theta}{r}$$

And similarly, $\qquad \dfrac{\partial v}{\partial y} = \dfrac{\partial v}{\partial r}\cdot\cos\theta - \dfrac{\partial v}{\partial \theta}\cdot\dfrac{\sin\theta}{r}$

and $\qquad \dfrac{\partial v}{\partial y} = \dfrac{\partial v}{\partial r}\cdot\sin\theta + \dfrac{\partial v}{\partial \theta}\cdot\dfrac{\cos\theta}{r}$

Cauchy-Riemann equations in cartesian form are

$$\frac{\partial u}{\partial y} = \frac{\partial v}{\partial y},\ \frac{\partial u}{\partial y} = -\frac{\partial v}{\partial x}.$$

Substituting in these equations from above, we have

$$\frac{\partial u}{\partial r} \cdot \cos \theta + \frac{\partial u}{\partial \theta} \cdot \frac{\sin \theta}{r} = \frac{\partial v}{\partial r} \cdot \sin \theta + \frac{\partial v}{\partial \theta} \cdot \frac{\cos \theta}{r} \qquad \ldots(1)$$

and

$$\frac{\partial u}{\partial r} \cdot \sin \theta + \frac{\partial u}{\partial \theta} \cdot \frac{\cos \theta}{r} = -\frac{\partial v}{\partial r} \cdot \cos \theta + \frac{\partial v}{\partial \theta} \cdot \frac{\sin \theta}{r} \qquad \ldots(2)$$

Multiplying (1) by cos θ and (2) by sin θ, and adding, we get

$$\frac{\partial u}{\partial r} = \frac{1}{r} \frac{\partial v}{\partial \theta}$$

Again, multiplying (1) by sin θ and (2) by cos θ, and subtracting, we have

$$\frac{\partial u}{\partial \theta} = -r \frac{\partial v}{\partial r}.$$

$$\Rightarrow \qquad \frac{\partial u}{\partial r} = \frac{1}{r} \frac{\partial v}{\partial \theta} \qquad \ldots(3)$$

and

$$\frac{\partial u}{\partial \theta} = -r \frac{\partial v}{\partial r} \qquad \ldots(4)$$

Relations (3) and (4) are Cauchy-Riemann equations in polar form.

5.8. Derivative of *w* in polar form.

We have

$$w = u + iv$$

$$\therefore \qquad \frac{\partial w}{\partial x} = \frac{\partial u}{\partial x} + i \frac{\partial v}{\partial x}.$$

But

$$\frac{dw}{dz} = \frac{\partial w}{\partial x}$$

$$= \frac{\partial w}{\partial r} \cdot \frac{\partial r}{\partial x} + \frac{\partial w}{\partial \theta} \cdot \frac{\partial \theta}{\partial x}$$

$$= \frac{\partial w}{\partial r} \cdot \cos \theta - \left(\frac{\partial u}{\partial \theta} + i \frac{\partial v}{\partial \theta} \right) \cdot \frac{\sin \theta}{r} \qquad (\because \ w = u + iv)$$

$$= \frac{\partial w}{\partial r} \cdot \cos \theta - \left(-r \frac{\partial v}{\partial r} - i \cdot r \cdot \frac{\partial u}{\partial r} \right) \cdot \frac{\sin \theta}{r}$$

[From eqns. (3) and (4) of § 5.7.2]

$$= \frac{\partial w}{\partial r} \cdot \cos \theta - i \left(\frac{\partial u}{\partial r} + i \frac{\partial v}{\partial r} \right) \cdot \sin \theta$$

$$= \frac{\partial w}{\partial r} \cdot \cos \theta - i \frac{\partial w}{\partial r} \cdot \sin \theta$$

$$= (\cos \theta - i \sin \theta) \frac{\partial w}{\partial r}.$$

This is the derivative of *w*.

Again,

$$\frac{\partial w}{\partial z} = \frac{\partial w}{\partial r} \cdot \frac{\partial r}{\partial x} + \frac{\partial w}{\partial \theta} \cdot \frac{\partial \theta}{\partial x}$$

$$= \left(\frac{\partial u}{\partial r} + i \frac{\partial v}{\partial r} \right) \cdot \cos \theta - \frac{\partial w}{\partial \theta} \cdot \frac{\sin \theta}{r} \qquad (\because \; w = u + iv)$$

$$= \left(\frac{1}{r} \cdot \frac{\partial v}{\partial \theta} - i \cdot \frac{1}{r} \cdot \frac{\partial u}{\partial \theta} \right) \cdot \cos \theta - \frac{\partial w}{\partial \theta} \cdot \frac{\sin \theta}{r}$$

[From eqns. (3) and (4) of § 5.7.2]

$$= -\frac{i}{r} \left(\frac{\partial u}{\partial \theta} + i \frac{\partial v}{\partial \theta} \right) \cdot \cos \theta - \frac{\partial w}{\partial \theta} \cdot \frac{\sin \theta}{r} \quad (\text{since} \;\; w = u + iv)$$

$$= -\frac{i}{r} (\cos \theta - i \sin \theta) \frac{\partial w}{\partial \theta},$$

This also is a derivative of w.

$$\Rightarrow \qquad \frac{dw}{dz} = (\cos \theta - i \sin \theta) \frac{\partial w}{\partial r} = -\frac{i}{r} (\cos \theta - i \sin \theta) \frac{\partial w}{\partial \theta}.$$

5.8.1. Orthogonal System. *Two curves are said to be orthogonal to each other, when they intersect at right angle at each of their points of intersection.*

To show that, if $w = f(z) = u + iv$ be an analytic function of $z = x + iy$, then the family of curves $u(x, y) = c_1$ and $v(x, y) = c_2$ form an orthogonal system.

(Kanpur 2003, Kerala 97, 99, 2001)

For the curve $u(x, y) = c_1$, we have on differentiating

$$\frac{\partial u}{\partial x} dx + \frac{\partial u}{\partial y} dy = 0, \quad i.e., \quad \frac{dy}{dx} = -\frac{\partial u / \partial x}{\partial u / \partial y}$$

And for the curve $v(x, y) = c_2$, we have on differentiating

$$\frac{\partial v}{\partial x} dx + \frac{\partial v}{\partial y} dy = 0, \quad i.e., \quad \frac{dy}{dx} = -\frac{\partial v / \partial x}{\partial v / \partial y}.$$

The product of the above two values of (dy/dx) is

$$= \left(-\frac{\partial u / \partial x}{\partial u / \partial y} \right) \times \left(-\frac{\partial v / \partial x}{\partial v / \partial y} \right)$$

$$= \left(\frac{\partial v / \partial y}{\partial v / \partial x} \right) \times \left(-\frac{\partial v / \partial x}{\partial v / \partial y} \right) = -1 \qquad (\text{Since } u_x = v_y, \; u_y = -v_x)$$

Hence the two curves $u = c_1$ and $v = c_2$ are orthogonal, and since c_1 and c_2 are parameters, therefore, we say that the two family of curves $u = c_1$ and $u = c_2$ form an orthogonal system.

5.8.2. Harmonic Functions. *Any function of x, y which possesses continuous partial derivatives of the first and second orders and satisfies Laplace's equation is called a harmonic function.*

(Kanpur 2000)

Theorem: *If $f(z) = u + iv$ is an analytic function, then u and v are both harmonic functions.*

(Garhwal 2003, Meerut 2001)

Let $f(z) = u + iv$, be an analytic function, then we have

$$\frac{\partial u}{\partial x} = \frac{\partial v}{\partial y} \quad \text{and} \quad \frac{\partial u}{\partial y} = \frac{-\partial v}{\partial x} \qquad \qquad ...(1)$$

Also, because u and v are the real and imaginary parts of an analytic function, therefore derivatives of u and v, of all orders, exist and are continuous functions of x and y so that we have

$$\frac{\partial^2 v}{\partial x\, \partial y} = \frac{\partial^2 v}{\partial y\, \partial x} \qquad \qquad ...(2)$$

Differentiating equations (1), we have

$$\frac{\partial^2 u}{\partial x^2} = \frac{\partial^2 v}{\partial x\, \partial y} \quad \text{and} \quad \frac{\partial^2 u}{\partial y^2} = -\frac{\partial^2 v}{\partial y\, \partial x}$$

Adding these we have

$$\frac{\partial^2 u}{\partial x^2} + \frac{\partial^2 u}{\partial y^2} = 0 \text{ by virtue of (2)} \qquad \qquad ...(3)$$

Similarly,

$$\frac{\partial^2 v}{\partial x^2} + \frac{\partial^2 v}{\partial y^2} = 0.$$

Hence both u and v satisfy Laplace's equation.

$$\frac{\partial^2 v}{\partial x^2} + \frac{\partial^2 v}{\partial y^2} = 0$$

Therefore both u and v are harmonic functions.

Such functions u and v are called **conjugate harmonic functions** or simple **conjugate functions.**

EXAMPLES

1. *Show that an analytic function in a domain with its derivative zero for every point of the domain is constant.*

Solution. We have to show that if $f'(z)$ is zero for every point of a domain D, then $f(z)$ is constant in D. We have for such a function

$$f(z) = u + iv$$
$$\Rightarrow \qquad f'(z) = u_x + iv_x$$

so that $f'(z) = 0$

$$\Rightarrow \qquad u_x = 0,\ v_x = 0.$$

Also therefore

$$v_y = 0,\ u_y = 0$$

Surely,

$$u_x = 0,\ u_y = 0$$

$\Rightarrow \quad u$ is a constant.

Again

$$v_x = 0,\ v_y = 0$$

$\Rightarrow \quad v$ is a constant.

It follows that $f(z) = u + iv$ is a constant.

In the following we also give another proof.

Since any two points of D can be connected by a polygonal line in D, (§ 4.20) it is sufficient to prove that $f(z)$ has the same value at the two end points a, b of a line segment.

Consider now a line segment π of length l and end points a, b.

Let $\varepsilon > 0$ be a given number.

Because of the derivative being zero, each point z' of the line segment π possesses a neighbourhood such that for each point z'' of the same

$$\left| \frac{f(z') - f(z'')}{z' - z''} \right| < \frac{\varepsilon}{2l},$$

$\Rightarrow \qquad\qquad |f(z') - f(z'')| < \frac{\varepsilon}{2l} |z' - z''|.$

By the Heine-Borel Theorem, there exists a finite number of these neighbourhoods covering the line segment π, so that we have a finite sequence of points

$$a = z_1, \ldots, z_{k-1}, z_k, \ldots, z_{n-1}, z_n = b$$

such that any two consecutive points of the same lie in one such neighbourhood.

Thus, we have

$$|f(z_k) - f(z_{k-1})| < \frac{\varepsilon}{l} |z_k - z_{k-1}|,$$

for $k = 2, 3, \ldots, n$.

We have

$$|f(b) - f(a)| = \left| \sum_{k=2}^{n} [f(z_k) - f(z_{k-1})] \right|$$

$$\leq \sum_{k=2}^{n} |f(z_k) - f(z_{k-1})|$$

$$\leq \frac{\varepsilon}{l} \Sigma |z_k - z_{k-1}| < \varepsilon.$$

As ε is an arbitrary positive number, we obtain

$$f(b) = f(a).$$

Hence the result.

2. *Show that an analytic function with constant modulus in a domain is constant.*

Solution. Let $\quad f(z) = u + iv$

so that

$$|u + iv| = |f(z)| = c,$$

$\Rightarrow \qquad\qquad u^2 + v^2 = c^2.$

$\Rightarrow \qquad\qquad uu_x + vv_x = 0,$

and $\qquad\qquad uu_y + vv_y = 0.$

By Cauchy-Riemann equations, these become

$$uu_x - vu_y = 0,$$

$$uu_y + vu_x = 0.$$

From these, on eliminating u_y, we obtain

$$(u^2 + v^2)\, u_x = 0.$$

Thus at every point z wherefor

$$w = u + iv \neq 0$$

we have $u_x = 0,$

and similarly also $u_y = 0,\ v_x = 0,\ v_y = 0.$

From considerations of continuity, we see that at every point of the domain the four partial derivatives of u, v are all zero and hence u, v and accordingly $f(z) = u + iv$ is constant.

3. *For what values of z do the function w defined by the following equations ceases to be analytic ?*

$$z = \sin u \cosh v + i \cos u \sinh v \qquad\qquad w = u + iv.$$

Solution. $z = \sin u \cosh v + i \cos u \sinh v$ ...(1)

$\Rightarrow$ $\dfrac{\partial z}{\partial u} = \cos u \cosh v - i \sin u \sinh v.$

Again, $\dfrac{dz}{dw} = \dfrac{\partial z}{\partial u} = \cos u \cosh v - i \sin u \sinh v$ ...(2)

Squaring and adding (1) and (2), we have

$$z^2 + \left(\frac{dz}{dw}\right)^2 = (\sin^2 u + \cos^2 u)(\cosh^2 v - \sinh^2 v) = 1$$

i.e., $\dfrac{dz}{dw} = \sqrt{(1 - z^2)}.$

Hence w ceases to be analytic when:

$$\frac{dz}{dw} = 0,$$

i.e, when $z = \pm 1$.

4. *For what values of z the function defined by the following equations ceases to be analytic?*

$$z = \log \rho + i\phi,$$

where $w = \rho (\cos \phi + i \sin \phi)$.

Solution. Let $w = f(r, \theta)$ and $z = r(\cos \theta + i \sin \theta)$, then we have

$$\frac{dw}{dz} = (\cos \theta - i \sin \theta)\frac{\partial w}{\partial r}.$$

Here $z = \log \rho + i\phi$ and $w = \rho(\cos \phi + i \sin \phi)$

$\Rightarrow$ $\dfrac{dz}{dw} = (\cos \phi - i \sin \phi)\dfrac{\partial z}{\partial \rho}$ [Using the above result]

$$= (\cos \phi - i \sin \phi)\frac{1}{\rho}$$

$$= \frac{(\cos \phi - i \sin \phi)(\cos \phi + i \sin \phi)}{w} = \frac{1}{w}.$$

Hence w is analytic so long as $(1/w) \neq 0$, *i.e.,* so long as w is finite.

5. *Show that the functions $f(z) = e^{-z^{-4}}$ $(z \neq 0)$ and $f(0) = 0$ is not analytic at $z = 0$, although Cauchy-Riemann equations are satisfied at the point. How would you explain this?*

(*Rohilkhand, 2003, Indore 2004, Ravishankar 2000, Garhwal, 2004, Meerut 2002, 2003, Kanpur 2001, Rohtak 2001, 2005*)

Solution. Here

$$u + iv = e^{-(x + iy)^{-4}}$$

or

$$u + iv = e^{-\dfrac{(x - iy)^4}{(x^2 + y^2)^4}}$$

$$= e^{-\dfrac{1}{(x^2 + y^2)^4}[(x^4 + y^4 - 6x^2y^2) - i4xy(x^2 - y^2)]}$$

$$u = e^{-\dfrac{x^4 + y^4 - 6x^2y^2}{(x^2 + y^2)^4}} \cdot \cos\left[\dfrac{4xy(x^2 - y^2)}{(x^2 + y^2)^4}\right]$$

$$v = -e^{-\dfrac{x^4 + y^4 - 6x^2y^2}{(x^2 + y^2)^4}} \cdot \sin\left[\dfrac{4xy(x^2 - y^2)^2}{(x^2 + y^2)^4}\right]$$

At $z = 0$,

$$\frac{\partial u}{\partial x} = \lim_{x \to 0} \frac{u(x, 0) - u(0, 0)}{x} = \lim_{x \to 0} \frac{e^{-x^{-4}}}{x}$$

$$= \lim_{x \to 0} \left[\frac{1}{x \cdot e^{(1/x^4)}}\right] = 0.$$

$$\frac{\partial u}{\partial y} = \lim_{y \to 0} \frac{u(0, y) - u(0, 0)}{y} = \lim_{y \to 0} \frac{e^{-y^{-4}}}{y}$$

$$= \lim_{y \to 0} \left[\frac{1}{y \cdot e^{(1/y^4)}}\right] = 0$$

$$\frac{\partial v}{\partial x} = \lim_{x \to 0} \frac{v(x, 0) - v(0, 0)}{x} = \lim_{x \to 0} \frac{0}{x} = 0$$

$$\frac{\partial v}{\partial y} = \lim_{y \to 0} \frac{v(0, y) - v(0, 0)}{y} = \lim_{y \to 0} \frac{0}{y} = 0.$$

Hence Cauchy-Riemann equations are satisfied at $z = 0$.

But

$$f'(0) = \lim_{z \to 0} \frac{f(z) - f(0)}{z} = \lim_{z \to 0} \frac{1}{ze^{(1/z^4)}}$$

$$= \lim_{z \to 0} \frac{1}{re^{i(\pi/4)}} \cdot \frac{1}{\exp(-r^{-4})}, \text{ taking } z = re^{i(\pi/4)}$$

$$= \lim_{r \to 0} \frac{1}{re^{i(\pi/4)}} \cdot \frac{1}{\exp(-1/r^4)} = \infty.$$

Showing that $f'(z)$ does not exist at $z = 0$ and hence $f(z)$ is not analytic at $z = 0$.

Note. $f(z)$ may not be analytic at $z = z_0$ if merely the Cauchy-Riemann conditions are satisfied there. In addition to this $f'(z)$ must exist and should be unique at z_0 and at every point in the neighbourhood of z_0.

6. *Prove that the function* $f(z) = u + iv$, *where*

$$f(z) = \frac{x^3(1 + i) - y^3(1 - i)}{x^2 + y^2} \quad (z \neq 0), \ f(0) = 0$$

is continuous and that Cauchy-Riemann equations are satisfied at the origin, yet f' (z) does not exist there. (*Agra 2004, Meerut 2001, Gorakhpur 2003, Garhwal 2003*)

OR

Give an example of a function whose real and imaginary parts have continuous partial derivative of all order at a point and yet function is not differentiable.

(*Banglore 2001, 2004; Kurukshetra 2003*)

Solution. Here $u = \dfrac{x^3 - y^3}{x^2 + y^2}$, $v = \dfrac{x^3 + y^3}{x^2 + y^2}$ (where $z \neq 0$).

Here we see that both u and v are finite for all values of $z \neq 0$, so u and v are rational and finite for all values of $z \neq 0$. Hence $f(z)$ is continuous where $z \neq 0$.

At the origin, $u = 0$, $v = 0$.   [Since $f(0) = 0$]

Hence u and v are both continuous at the origin; consequently $f(z)$ is continuous at the origin.

Now, at the origin

$$\frac{\partial u}{\partial x} = \lim_{x \to 0} \frac{u(x, 0) - u(0, 0)}{x} = \lim_{x \to 0} \left(\frac{x}{x}\right) = 1$$

$$\frac{\partial u}{\partial y} = \lim_{y \to 0} \frac{u(0, y) - u(0, 0)}{y} = \lim_{y \to 0} \left(\frac{-y}{+y}\right) = -1$$

$$\frac{\partial v}{\partial x} = \lim_{x \to 0} \frac{v(x, 0) - v(0, 0)}{x} = \lim_{x \to 0} \left(\frac{x}{x}\right) = 1$$

$$\frac{\partial v}{\partial y} = \lim_{y \to 0} \frac{v(0, y) - v(0, 0)}{y} = \lim_{y \to 0} \left(\frac{y}{y}\right) = 1$$

$\Rightarrow \qquad \dfrac{\partial u}{\partial x} = \dfrac{\partial v}{\partial y}$ and $\dfrac{\partial u}{\partial y} = -\dfrac{\partial v}{\partial x}$.

$\therefore$ Cauchy-Riemann equations are satisfied at $z = 0$.

Again, $f'(0) = \lim_{z \to 0} \dfrac{f(z) - f(0)}{z}$

$$= \lim_{x \to 0} \left[\frac{(x^3 - y^3) + i(x^3 + y^3)}{x^2 + y^2} \cdot \frac{1}{x + iy} \right]$$

Let $z \to 0$ along $y = x$, then we have

$$f'(0) = \lim_{x \to 0} \frac{x^3 - x^3 + i(x^3 + x^3)}{x^2 + x^2} \cdot \frac{1}{x + ix}$$

$$= \lim_{x \to 0} \frac{2i}{2(1 + i)} = \frac{1}{2}(1 - i).$$

Further, let $z \to 0$ along $y = 0$, then we have

$$f'(0) = \lim_{x \to 0} \frac{x^3(1 + i)}{x^3} = 1 + i.$$

Hence $f'(0)$ is not unique. Thus $f'(z)$ does not exist at the origin.

7. *Examine the nature of the function*

$$f(z) = \frac{x^2 y^5 (x + iy)}{x^4 + y^{10}}, z \neq 0$$

$$f(0) = 0$$

in the region including the origin.   (*Meerut 2002, Amrawati 2001, 2005; Purvanchal 2004*)

Solution. Here,

$$u + iv = \frac{x^2 y^5 (x + iy)}{x^4 + y^{10}}$$

Then

$$u = \frac{x^3 y^5}{x^4 + y^{10}}, \quad u = \frac{x^2 y^6}{x^4 + y^{10}}$$

At the origin,

$$u_x = \lim_{x \to 0} \frac{u(x,0) - u(0,0)}{x}$$

$$= \lim_{x \to 0} \frac{0 - 0}{x} = 0$$

$$u_y = \lim_{y \to 0} \frac{u(0,y) - u(0,0)}{y}$$

$$= \lim_{y \to 0} \frac{(0 - 0)}{y} = 0$$

Similarly, $u_x = 0$, $u_y = 0$

Hence Cauchy-Riemann equations are satisfied at the origin.

But

$$\lim_{z \to 0} \frac{f(z) - f(0)}{z}$$

$$= \lim_{z \to 0} \left[\frac{x^2 y^5 (x + iy)}{x^4 + y^{10}} - 0 \right] \frac{1}{x + iy} \qquad \text{since } f(0) = 0 \text{ and } z = x + iy$$

$$= \lim_{\substack{x \to 0 \\ y \to 0}} \frac{x^2 y^5}{x^4 + y^{10}}$$

$$= \lim_{x \to 0} \frac{x^2 m^5 x^5}{x^4 + m^{10} x^{10}}$$

if $z \to 0$ along the radius vector $y = mx$

$$= \lim_{x \to 0} \frac{m^5 x^3}{1 + m^{10} x^6} = 0$$

and

$$= \lim_{x \to 0} \frac{x^2 x^2}{x^4 + x^4} = 0 \quad (\text{if } z \to 0 \text{ along the curve } y^5 = x^2)$$

$$= \frac{1}{2}$$

showing that $f'(0)$ does not exist.

Hence, $f(z)$ is not analytic at origin although Cauchy-Riemann equations are satisfied there.

8. *Show that the function*

$$f(z) = \sqrt{(|xy|)}$$

is not regular at the origin, although Cauchy-Riemann equations are satisfied at that point.

　　　(Meerut 2000; Agra 2000, 2004, 2005; Kanpur 2003, 2005, 2006, Banglore 2004)

　　　Solution. Let the function be

$$f(z) = u(x, y) + iv(x, y)$$

and　　　　　　$$f(z) = \sqrt{(|xy|)},$$

equating real and imaginary parts, we get

$$u(x, y) = \sqrt{(|xy|)}, \ v(x, y) = 0$$

At the origin,

$$\frac{\partial u}{\partial x} = \underset{x \to 0}{Lt} \frac{u(x, 0) - u(0, 0)}{x}$$

$$= \underset{x \to 0}{Lt} \frac{0 - 0}{x} = 0$$

$$\frac{\partial u}{\partial y} = \underset{y \to 0}{Lt} \frac{u(0, y) - u(0, 0)}{y}$$

$$= \underset{y \to 0}{Lt} \frac{0 - 0}{y} = 0$$

$$\frac{\partial v}{\partial x} = \underset{x \to 0}{Lt} \frac{v(0, y) - v(0, 0)}{x}$$

$$= \underset{x \to 0}{Lt} \frac{0 - 0}{x} = 0$$

$$\frac{\partial v}{\partial y} = \underset{y \to 0}{Lt} \frac{v(0, y) - v(0, x)}{y}$$

$$= \underset{y \to 0}{Lt} \frac{0 - 0}{y} = 0$$

Hence Cauchy-Riemann equations are satisfied at the origin.

Again,　　　　　$$f'(0) = \underset{z \to 0}{Lt} \frac{f(z) - f(0)}{z}$$

$$= \underset{\substack{x \to 0 \\ y \to 0}}{Lt} \frac{\sqrt{|mx^2|}}{x + imx}$$　　　　　Let $z \to 0$ along $y = mx$

$$= \frac{\sqrt{|m|}}{1 + im}$$

this depends on m, *i.e.*, $f'(0)$ is not unique.

　　　Hence $f(z)$ is not analytic at the origin although Cauchy-Riemann equations are satisfied there.

　　　9. *If n is real, show that $r^n (\cos n\theta + i \sin n\theta)$ is analytic except possibly when r = 0, and that its derivative is $nr^{n-1} [\cos (n-1) \theta + i \sin (n-1) \theta]$.*

Solution. Let $w = r^n (\cos n\theta + i \sin n\theta) \equiv f(z) \equiv u + iv$.

So, here $u = r^n \cos n\theta$, $v = r^n \sin n\theta$

then
$$\frac{\partial u}{\partial r} = nr^{n-1} \cos n\theta, \quad \frac{\partial v}{\partial r} = nr^{n-1} \sin n\theta$$

$$\frac{\partial u}{\partial \theta} = -nr^n \sin n\theta, \quad \frac{\partial v}{\partial \theta} = nr^n \cos n\theta.$$

Thus, we see that
$$\frac{\partial u}{\partial r} = \frac{1}{r}\frac{\partial v}{\partial \theta}, \text{ and } \frac{1}{r}\frac{\partial u}{\partial \theta} = -\frac{\partial v}{\partial r}.$$

That is, Cauchy-Riemann conditions are satisfied.

Hence the function $w = r^n (\cos n\theta + i \sin n\theta)$ is analytic, if (dw/dz) exists for all finite values of z.

We have
$$\frac{dw}{dz} = (\cos \theta - i \sin \theta)\frac{\partial w}{\partial r}$$

$$= (\cos \theta - i \sin \theta)\cdot nr^{n-1} (\cos n\theta + i \sin n\theta)$$

$$= nr^{n-1} [\cos (n-1)\theta + i \sin (n-1)\theta].$$

Thus, dw/dz exists for all finite values of r including zero, except when $r = 0$ and $n \leq 1$.

10. *If $w = f(z) = u + iv$ be an analytic function of $z = x + iy$, show that the curves $u = constant$, $v = constant$ represented on the z-plane intersect at right angles.*

Solution. $f(z) = u + iv$ is a regular function of z, the functions u and v will satisfy Cauchy-Riemann equations

$$\frac{\partial u}{\partial x} = \frac{\partial v}{\partial y} \text{ and } \frac{\partial v}{\partial x} = -\frac{\partial u}{\partial y} \qquad ...(1)$$

whence, multiplying these, we get

$$\frac{\partial u}{\partial x}\cdot\frac{\partial v}{\partial x} + \frac{\partial u}{\partial y}\cdot\frac{\partial v}{\partial y} = 0.$$

This is the condition that the curves $u = $ constant and $v = $ constant, intersect at right angles.

Thus, if $f(z)$ is a regular function of z, then the curves

$u = R[f(z)] = $ *constant and $v = I[f(z)] = $ constant form an orthogonal system, i.e., they intersect at right angles.*

11. *Prove that $u = y^3 - 3x^2y$ is a harmonic function. Determine its harmonic conjugate and then find the corresponding analytic function $f(z)$ in terms of z.*

(Garhwal 2006; Rohilkhand 2004)

Solution. $u = y^3 - 3x^2y$ ...(1)

$\Rightarrow$
$$\frac{\partial u}{\partial x} = -6xy; \quad \frac{\partial u}{\partial y} = 3y^2 - 3x^2; \quad \frac{\partial^2 u}{\partial x^2} = -6y, \quad \frac{\partial^2 u}{\partial y^2} = 6y$$

$\therefore$
$$\frac{\partial^2 u}{\partial x^2} + \frac{\partial^2 u}{\partial y^2} = -6y + 6y = 0$$

$\Rightarrow$ u satisfies Laplace's equation; hence u is a harmonic function. Further, let v be the harmonic conjugate to u, then we have

$$dv = \frac{\partial v}{\partial x}\, dx + \frac{\partial v}{\partial y}\, dy = -\frac{\partial u}{\partial y}\, dx + \frac{\partial u}{\partial x}\, dy$$

[Since $u_x = v_y$ and $u_x = -v_y$]

$$= -(3y^2 - 3x^2)\, dx - 6xy\, dy$$
$$= -(3y^2\, dx + 6xy\, dy) + 3x^2\, dx.$$

Integrating,

$$v = -3xy^2 + x^3 + c.$$

This is the harmonic conjugate to u.

Now, $f(z) = u + iv = y^3 - 3x^2y + i\,(-3xy^2 + x^3 + c)$

$$= i\,(x + iy)^3 + ic = iz^3 + ic.$$

12. *If $u = x^3 - 3xy^2$, show that there exists a function $v\,(x, y)$ such that $w = u + iv$ is analytic in a finite region.*

Solution. $u = x^3 - 3xy^2$

$\Rightarrow$ $\frac{\partial u}{\partial x} = 3x^2 - 3y^2,\ \frac{\partial u}{\partial y} = -6xy,\ \frac{\partial^2 u}{\partial x^2} = 6x,\ \frac{\partial^2 u}{\partial y^2} = -6x.$

$\therefore$ $\frac{\partial^2 u}{\partial x^2} + \frac{\partial^2 u}{\partial y^2} = 6x - 6x = 0.$

Thus, the given function u satisfies Laplace's equation and is therefore a harmonic function. Further v is a function of (x, y).

$\therefore$ $dv = \frac{\partial v}{\partial x}\, dx + \frac{\partial v}{\partial y}\, dy$

$$= -\frac{\partial u}{\partial y}\, dx + \frac{\partial u}{\partial x}\, dy \qquad \text{(by Cauchy-Riemann equations)}$$

$$= 6xy\, dx + (3x^2 - 3y^2)\, dy$$

$$= (6xy\, dx + 3x^2\, dy) - 3y^2\, dy.$$

Integrating this equation, we get

$$v = 3x^2y - y^3 + c,$$

where c is a constant.

$\therefore$ $f(z) = u + iv$

$$= x^3 - 3xy^2 + i\,(3x^2y - y^3 + c)$$

$$= (x + iy)^3 + ic = z^3 + ic,$$

$\Rightarrow$ $f(z) = z^3 + ic.$

$\Rightarrow$ $f'(z) = 3z^2,$

which exists for all finite values of z.

Hence $f(z)$ is analytic in any finite region.

13. *If ϕ and ψ are functions of x and y satisfying Laplace's equation, show that $(s + it)$ is analytic, where:*

$$s = \frac{\partial \phi}{\partial y} - \frac{\partial \psi}{\partial x} \quad \text{and} \quad t = \frac{\partial \phi}{\partial x} + \frac{\partial \psi}{\partial y}. \qquad \textit{(Kanpur 2000)}$$

Solution. Since ϕ and ψ both satisfy Laplace's equation

$$\therefore \qquad \frac{\partial^2 \phi}{\partial x^2} + \frac{\partial^2 \phi}{\partial y^2} = 0, \text{ and } \frac{\partial^2 \psi}{\partial x^2} + \frac{\partial^2 \psi}{\partial y^2} = 0.$$

Take

$$s = \frac{\partial \phi}{\partial y} - \frac{\partial \psi}{\partial x}, \text{ and } t = \frac{\partial \phi}{\partial x} + \frac{\partial \psi}{\partial y},$$

$$\Rightarrow \qquad \frac{\partial s}{\partial x} = \frac{\partial^2 \phi}{\partial x \partial y} - \frac{\partial^2 \psi}{\partial x^2} \text{ and } \frac{\partial t}{\partial y} = \frac{\partial^2 \phi}{\partial y \partial x} + \frac{\partial^2 \phi}{\partial y^2}$$

$$\Rightarrow \qquad \frac{\partial s}{\partial x} - \frac{\partial t}{\partial y} = -\left(\frac{\partial^2 \psi}{\partial x^2} + \frac{\partial^2 \psi}{\partial y^2} \right) = 0 \qquad\qquad (\because \ \psi \text{ is harmonic})$$

$$\therefore \qquad \frac{\partial s}{\partial x} = \frac{\partial t}{\partial y}.$$

Also

$$\frac{\partial s}{\partial y} = \frac{\partial^2 \phi}{\partial y^2} - \frac{\partial^2 \psi}{\partial y \partial x} \text{ and } \frac{\partial t}{\partial x} = \frac{\partial^2 \phi}{\partial x^2} + \frac{\partial^2 \psi}{\partial x \partial y}$$

$$\Rightarrow \qquad \frac{\partial s}{\partial y} + \frac{\partial t}{\partial x} = \frac{\partial^2 \phi}{\partial x^2} + \frac{\partial^2 \phi}{\partial y^2} = 0 \qquad\qquad (\text{Since } \phi \text{ is harmonic})$$

$$\therefore \qquad \frac{\partial s}{\partial y} = -\frac{\partial t}{\partial x}.$$

Hence we have proved

$$\frac{\partial s}{\partial x} = \frac{\partial t}{\partial y} \text{ and } \frac{\partial s}{\partial y} = -\frac{\partial t}{\partial x},$$

i.e., Cauchy-Riemann equations are satisfied.

Hence $(s + it)$ is an analytic function.

5.9. To construct a function $f(z)$ when one conjugate function is given.

Let $f(z) = u + iv$ be analytic function, when u and v are the conjugate functions (i.e., both u and v satisfy Laplace's equation). If either of them, say u is given, then to form $f(z)$.

As u is already given, the function $f(z)$ can be constructed if either only v is found out, or function $f(z)$ as a whole is directly found out.

First method to construct $f(z)$ when one of the conjugate functions, say $u(x, y)$ is given, is to determine only v as has been done in the last article and then the function $f(z)$ so constructed is $u + iv$.

The other method to construct $f(z)$ directly without finding v is due to Milne-Thomson and is an elegant method given below:

$$x = \frac{1}{2}(z + \bar{z}) \text{ and } y = \frac{1}{2i}(z - \bar{z})$$

$$\therefore \qquad f(z) \equiv u\left[\frac{z + \bar{z}}{2}, \frac{z - \bar{z}}{2i} \right] + iv\left[\frac{z + \bar{z}}{2}, \frac{z - \bar{z}}{2i} \right] \qquad\qquad ...(1)$$

This relation can be regarded as a formal identity in two independent variables z and $\bar{z}$. Putting $\bar{z} = z$, we get

$$f(z) = u(z, 0) + iv(z, 0).$$

Again $w = f(z) = u + iv$

$\Rightarrow$ $f'(z) = \dfrac{dw}{dz} = \dfrac{\partial w}{\partial x} = \dfrac{\partial u}{\partial x} + i\,\dfrac{\partial v}{\partial x}$

$\qquad\qquad\qquad = \dfrac{\partial u}{\partial x} - i\,\dfrac{\partial u}{\partial y}$

by Cauchy-Riemann equations.

Hence if we write

$$\frac{\partial u}{\partial x} \equiv \phi_1(x, y) \text{ and } \frac{\partial u}{\partial y} \equiv \phi_2(x, y)$$

we have

$$\frac{dw}{dz} \text{ or } f'(z) = \phi_1(x, y) - i\phi_2(x, y)$$

$$\qquad\qquad = \phi_1(z, 0) - i\phi_2(z, 0)$$

$$[\because \ \bar{z} = z \ \Rightarrow \ x = z, y = 0]$$

Integrating it,

$$f(z) = \int [\phi_1(z, 0) - i\phi_2(z, 0)]\, dz + c$$

where c is an arbitrary constant.

Thus function $f(z)$ is constructed when $u(x, y)$ is given.

Similarly if $v(x, y)$ is given, it can be shown that

$$f(z) = \int [\psi_1(z, 0) + i\psi_2(z, 0)]\, dz + c$$

where $\psi_1(x, y) = \dfrac{\partial v}{\partial y}$ and $\psi_2(x, y) = \dfrac{\partial v}{\partial x}$.

EXAMPLES

1. *Prove that the function* $u = e^x(x\cos y - y\sin y)$ *satisfies Laplace's equation and find the corresponding analytic function* $f(z) = u + iv$.

(*Kanpur 2003, 2006; Rohilkhand, 2001, 2004; Rohtak 2000;*
Meerut 2004, Gorakhpur 2005 Garhwal, 2007)

Solution. $u = e^x(x\cos y - y\sin y)$ ...(*i*)

$\Rightarrow$ $\dfrac{\partial u}{\partial x} = e^x(x\cos y - y\sin y + \cos y) = \phi_1(x, y),$

and $\dfrac{\partial u}{\partial y} = e^x(-x\sin y - y\cos y - \sin y) = \phi_2(x, y).$

By Milne's method, we have

$$f'(z) = \phi_1(z, 0) - i\phi_2(z, 0) = e^z(z + 1).$$

Integrating, we get

$$f(z) = \int e^z(z + 1)\, dz = ze^z + c.$$

Thus $f(z) = ze^z + c.$

2. *Prove that the function*

$$u = x^3 - 3xy^2 + 3x^2 - 3y^2 + 1$$

satisfies Laplace's equation and determine the corresponding analytic function u + iv.

(*Meerut 2001*)

Solution. Here $u = x^3 - 3xy^2 + 3x^2 - 3y^2 + 1$.

$\Rightarrow$

$$\frac{\partial u}{\partial x} = 3x^2 - 3y^2 + 6x = \phi_1(x, y) \text{ (say)}$$

$$\frac{\partial u}{\partial y} = -6xy - 6y = \phi_2(x, y) \text{ (say)}.$$

$$\frac{\partial^2 u}{\partial x^2} = 6x^2 + 6, \ \frac{\partial^2 u}{\partial y^2} = -6x - 6$$

$\therefore$

$$\frac{\partial^2 u}{\partial x^2} + \frac{\partial^2 u}{\partial y^2} = 6x + 6 - 6x - 6 = 0.$$

$\Rightarrow$ u satisfies Laplace's equation.

Hence u is a harmonic function. By Milne's method, we then have

$$f'(z) = \phi_1(z, 0) - i\phi_2(z, 0) = (3z^2 + 6z).$$

Now integrating it, we get

$$f(z) = \int (3z^2 + 6z) \, dz = z^3 + 3z^2 + c.$$

Thus $\qquad f(z) = z^3 + 3z^2 + c.$

3. *If $f(z) = u + iv$ is an analytic function of $z = x + iy$ and $u - v = e^x(\cos y - \sin y)$, find $f(z)$ in terms of z.*

(*Agra 2001, 2005; Garhwal 2004, Kanpur 2004*)

Solution. We have $u + iv = f(z)$ $\quad \therefore \quad iu - v = if(z)$

Adding, we get $(u - v) + i(u + v) = (1 + i)f(z) = F(z)$ (say).

Let us put $u - v = U$ and $u + v = V$, then $F(z) = U + iV$ is an analytic function.

Now, $\qquad U = u - v = e^x(\cos y - \sin y)$

$\Rightarrow$

$$\frac{\partial U}{\partial x} = e^x(\cos y - \sin y) = \phi_1(x, y) \text{ (say)}$$

and

$$\frac{\partial U}{\partial y} = e^x(-\sin y - \cos y) = \phi_2(x, y) \text{ (say)}.$$

By Milne's method, we have

$$F'(z) = \phi_1(z, 0) - i\phi_2(z, 0) = (e^z + ie^z) = (1 + i)e^z.$$

Integrating it, we get

$$F(z) = \int (1 + i)e^z \, dz + c = (1 + i)e^z + c$$

i.e., $\qquad (1 + i)f(z) = (1 + i)e^z + c$

or $\qquad f(z) = e^z + c_1.$

4. *If $u - v = (x - y)(x^2 + 4xy + y^2)$ and $f(z) = u + iv$ is an analytic function of $z = x + iy$, find $f(z)$ in terms of z.*

Solution. We have $u + iv = f(z)$ $\quad \therefore \quad iu - v = if(z)$.

Adding these,

$$(u - v) + i (u + v) = (1 + i) f(z) = F(z), \text{ say}$$

where $F(z)$ is analytic because $f(z)$ is so.

Now, let $U = u - v$ and $V = u + v$, then $F(z) = U + iV$ is also an analytic function.

Now, $\qquad\qquad U = u - v \equiv (x - y)(x^2 + 4xy + y^2),$

$$\therefore \qquad\qquad \frac{\partial U}{\partial x} = 3x^2 + 6xy - 3y^2 = \phi_1(x, y)$$

and $\qquad\qquad \frac{\partial U}{\partial y} = 3x^2 - 6xy - 3y^2 = \phi_2(x, y).$

Then by Milne's method, we have

$$F(z) = \int [\phi_1(z, 0) - i\phi_2(z, 0)]\, dz + c$$

$$= \int (3z^2 - i\, 3z^2)\, dz + c = (1 - i) z^3 + c.$$

$\Rightarrow \qquad (1 + i) f(z) = (1 - i) z^3 + c \qquad\qquad [\because\ F(z) = (1 + i) f(z)]$

$\Rightarrow \qquad\qquad f(z) = \dfrac{1 - i}{1 + i} z^3 + \dfrac{c}{1 + i} = -iz^3 + c_1.$

$\Rightarrow \qquad\qquad f(z) = -iz^3 + c_1.$

5. *If $f(z) = u + iv$ is an analytic function of*

$$z = x + iy \text{ and } u - v = \frac{e^y - \cos x + \sin x}{\cosh y - \cos x},$$

find $f(z)$ subject to the condition $f(\pi / 2) = \dfrac{3 - i}{3}.$

(Garhwal, 2001)

Solution. We have $u + iv = f(z)$ $\therefore$ $iu - v = if(z).$

On adding, we have

$$u - v + i(u + v) = (1 + i) f(z) = F(z) \text{ (say)}$$

i.e., $\qquad\qquad (u - v) + i(u + v) = F(z).$

Now, let $U = u - v$ and $V = u + v$, then $U + iV = F(z)$ is an analytic function.

Further, $\qquad U = \dfrac{e^y - \cos x + \sin x}{\cosh y - \cos x} = \dfrac{\cosh y + \sinh y - \cos x + \sin x}{\cosh y - \cos x}$

$$= 1 + \frac{\sinh y + \sin x}{\cosh y - \cos x} = \left(1 - \frac{\sin x + \sinh y}{\cos x - \cosh y}\right).$$

$\Rightarrow \qquad\qquad \dfrac{\partial U}{\partial x} = \dfrac{-1 - \sin x \sinh y + \cos x \cosh y}{(\cos x - \cosh y)^2} = \phi_1(x, y)$

and $\qquad\qquad \dfrac{\partial U}{\partial y} = \dfrac{1 - \sin x \sinh y - \cos x \cosh y}{(\cos x - \cosh y)^2} = \phi_2(x, y).$

Then by Milne's method, we have

$$F'(z) = [\phi_1(z, 0) - i\phi_2(z, 0)]$$

$$= -\frac{1}{1 - \cos z} - i\,\frac{1}{1 - \cos z}$$

$$= -(1 + i)\,\frac{1}{1 - \cos z} = -\frac{1}{2}(1 + i)\,\text{cosec}^2\,\frac{z}{2}.$$

Integrating it, we get

$$F(z) = -\frac{i}{2}(1 + i)\int \text{cosec}^2\,\frac{z}{2}\,dz + c = (1 + i)\cot\frac{z}{2} + c$$

i.e., $\qquad (1 + i)\,f(z) = (1 + i)\cot(z/2) + c \qquad\qquad [\because\ (1 + i)\,f(z) = F(z)]$

or $\qquad\qquad f(z) = \cot(z/2) + c_1.$

Again, when $\qquad z = \dfrac{\pi}{2},\ f\left(\dfrac{\pi}{2}\right) = \dfrac{3 - i}{2}\ \therefore\ c_1 = \dfrac{3 - i}{2} - 1 = \dfrac{1 - i}{2}.$

$\Rightarrow \qquad\qquad f(z) = \cot\dfrac{z}{2} + \dfrac{1}{2}(1 - i).$

6. *Show that* $\left(\dfrac{\partial^2}{\partial x^2} + \dfrac{\partial^2}{\partial y^2}\right) \equiv 4\,\dfrac{\partial^2}{\partial z\partial\bar{z}}.$

Solution. We have $x + iy = z,\ x - iy = \bar{z}.$

$\therefore \qquad\qquad x = \dfrac{1}{2}(z + \bar{z}),\ y = -\dfrac{i}{2}(z - \bar{z})$ $\qquad\qquad\qquad$ ...(1)

Now, $\qquad\qquad \dfrac{\partial x}{\partial z} = \dfrac{1}{2},\ \dfrac{\partial x}{\partial\bar{z}} = \dfrac{1}{2};\ \dfrac{\partial y}{\partial z} = -\dfrac{i}{2},\ \dfrac{\partial y}{\partial\bar{z}} = \dfrac{i}{2}$

Again, $\qquad\qquad \dfrac{\partial}{\partial z} \equiv \dfrac{\partial}{\partial x}\cdot\dfrac{\partial x}{\partial z} + \dfrac{\partial}{\partial y}\cdot\dfrac{\partial y}{\partial z} = \dfrac{1}{2}\left(\dfrac{\partial}{\partial x} - i\dfrac{\partial}{\partial y}\right)$

and $\qquad\qquad \dfrac{\partial}{\partial\bar{z}} = \dfrac{\partial}{\partial x}\cdot\dfrac{\partial x}{\partial\bar{z}} + \dfrac{\partial}{\partial y}\cdot\dfrac{\partial y}{\partial\bar{z}} = \dfrac{1}{2}\left(\dfrac{\partial}{\partial x} + i\dfrac{\partial}{\partial y}\right).$

Hence $\qquad\qquad \dfrac{\partial^2}{\partial z\partial\bar{z}} \equiv \dfrac{1}{2}\left(\dfrac{\partial}{\partial x} - i\dfrac{\partial}{\partial y}\right)\cdot\dfrac{1}{2}\left(\dfrac{\partial}{\partial x} + i\dfrac{\partial}{\partial y}\right)$

$\Rightarrow \qquad\qquad 4\,\dfrac{\partial^2}{\partial z\partial\bar{z}} \equiv \left(\dfrac{\partial^2}{\partial x^2} + \dfrac{\partial^2}{\partial y^2}\right).$

7. *If* $f(z) = u + iv$ *is an analytic function of* $z = x + iy$, *and* ψ *is any function of* x *and* y *with differential coefficients of the first two orders, then*

$$\left(\dfrac{\partial\psi}{\partial x}\right)^2 + \left(\dfrac{\partial\psi}{\partial y}\right)^2 = \left[\left(\dfrac{\partial\psi}{\partial u}\right)^2 + \left(\dfrac{\partial\psi}{\partial v}\right)^2\right]|f'|z|^2$$

(Kumaon, 2002; Garhwal, 1999)

and $\qquad\qquad \dfrac{\partial^2\psi}{\partial x^2} + \dfrac{\partial^2\psi}{\partial y^2} = \left(\dfrac{\partial^2\psi}{\partial u^2} + \dfrac{\partial\psi}{\partial v^2}\right)^2 |f'(z)|^2.$

Solution. We have

$$\frac{\partial \psi}{\partial x} = \frac{\partial \psi}{\partial u} \cdot \frac{\partial u}{\partial x} + \frac{\partial \psi}{\partial v} \cdot \frac{\partial v}{\partial x} \qquad \qquad ...(1)$$

and

$$\frac{\partial \psi}{\partial y} = \frac{\partial \psi}{\partial u} \cdot \frac{\partial u}{\partial y} + \frac{\partial \psi}{\partial v} \cdot \frac{\partial v}{\partial y}$$

$$= -\frac{\partial \psi}{\partial u} \cdot \frac{\partial v}{\partial x} + \frac{\partial \psi}{\partial v} \cdot \frac{\partial u}{\partial x} \qquad \qquad ...(2)$$

$$[\text{as } u_x = v_y, \ u_y = -v_x]$$

Squaring and adding (1) and (2), we have

$$\left(\frac{\partial \psi}{\partial x}\right)^2 + \left(\frac{\partial \psi}{\partial y}\right)^2 = \left[\left(\frac{\partial \psi}{\partial u}\right)^2 + \left(\frac{\partial \psi}{\partial v}\right)^2\right]\left[\left(\frac{\partial u}{\partial x}\right)^2 + \left(\frac{\partial v}{\partial x}\right)^2\right]$$

$$= \left[\left(\frac{\partial \psi}{\partial u}\right)^2 + \left(\frac{\partial \psi}{\partial v}\right)^2\right] |f'(z)|^2 \qquad \left[\because f'(z) = \frac{\partial u}{\partial x} + i\frac{\partial v}{\partial x}\right]$$

2nd Part. Result (1) can be re-written as

$$\frac{\partial}{\partial x} \equiv \frac{\partial u}{\partial x} \cdot \frac{\partial}{\partial u} + \frac{\partial v}{\partial x} \cdot \frac{\partial}{\partial v} \text{ and also } \frac{\partial}{\partial y} \equiv -\frac{\partial v}{\partial x} \cdot \frac{\partial}{\partial u} + \frac{\partial u}{\partial x} \cdot \frac{\partial}{\partial v}$$

$$\Rightarrow \qquad \frac{\partial}{\partial x} + i\frac{\partial}{\partial y} \equiv \left(\frac{\partial u}{\partial x} \cdot \frac{\partial}{\partial u} + \frac{\partial v}{\partial x} \cdot \frac{\partial}{\partial v}\right) + i\left(-\frac{\partial v}{\partial x} \cdot \frac{\partial}{\partial u} + \frac{\partial u}{\partial x} \cdot \frac{\partial}{\partial v}\right)$$

$$\equiv \left(\frac{\partial u}{\partial x} - i\frac{\partial v}{\partial x}\right)\frac{\partial}{\partial u} + i\left(\frac{\partial u}{\partial x} - i\frac{\partial v}{\partial x}\right)\frac{\partial}{\partial v}$$

i.e.

$$\frac{\partial}{\partial x} + i\frac{\partial}{\partial y} \equiv \left(\frac{\partial u}{\partial x} - i\frac{\partial v}{\partial x}\right)\left(\frac{\partial}{\partial u} + i\frac{\partial}{\partial v}\right) \qquad ...(3)$$

Similarly, $\quad \dfrac{\partial}{\partial x} - i\dfrac{\partial}{\partial y} \equiv \left(\dfrac{\partial u}{\partial x} + i\dfrac{\partial v}{\partial x}\right)\left(\dfrac{\partial}{\partial u} - i\dfrac{\partial}{\partial v}\right) \qquad ...(4)$

Multiplying (3) and (4) columnwise, we have

$$\left(\frac{\partial}{\partial x} + i\frac{\partial}{\partial y}\right)\left(\frac{\partial}{\partial x} - i\frac{\partial}{\partial y}\right) \equiv \left[\left(\frac{\partial u}{\partial x}\right)^2 + \left(\frac{\partial v}{\partial x}\right)^2\right]\left(\frac{\partial^2}{\partial u^2} + \frac{\partial^2}{\partial v^2}\right)$$

i.e.,

$$\left(\frac{\partial^2}{\partial x^2} + \frac{\partial^2}{\partial y^2}\right) \equiv |f'(z)|^2\left(\frac{\partial^2}{\partial u^2} + \frac{\partial^2}{\partial v^2}\right)$$

or

$$\left(\frac{\partial^2}{\partial x^2} + \frac{\partial^2}{\partial y^2}\right)\psi = |f'(z)|^2\left(\frac{\partial^2}{\partial u^2} + \frac{\partial^2}{\partial v^2}\right)\psi$$

or

$$\frac{\partial^2 \psi}{\partial x^2} + \frac{\partial^2 \psi}{\partial y^2} = \left(\frac{\partial^2 \psi}{\partial u^2} + \frac{\partial^2 \psi}{\partial v^2}\right)|f'(z)|^2 .$$

8. *If f (z) is an analytic function of z, prove that*

$$\left(\frac{\partial^2}{\partial x^2} + \frac{\partial^2}{\partial y^2}\right) |\, Re\, f\, (z)\,|^2 \; = \; 2\,|\, f'\, (z)\,|^2 \;.$$ *(Garhwal, 2003)*

Solution. Let $f(z) = u + iv$, so $Re\, f(z) = u$.

We have

$$\frac{\partial}{\partial x}(u^2) = 2u\frac{\partial u}{\partial x} \quad \text{and} \quad \frac{\partial^2}{\partial x^2}(u^2) = 2\left(\frac{\partial u}{\partial x}\right)^2 + 2u\frac{\partial^2 u}{\partial x^2} \qquad \text{...(1)}$$

Similarly $\quad \dfrac{\partial^2}{\partial y^2}(u^2) = 2\left(\dfrac{\partial u}{\partial y}\right)^2 + 2u\dfrac{\partial^2 u}{\partial y^2}$ \qquad \qquad \text{...(2)}

$$\Rightarrow \quad \left(\frac{\partial^2}{\partial x^2} + \frac{\partial^2}{\partial y^2}\right)u^2 = 2\left[\left(\frac{\partial u}{\partial x}\right)^2 + \left(\frac{\partial u}{\partial y}\right)^2\right] + u\left(\frac{\partial^2 u}{\partial x^2} + \frac{\partial^2 u}{\partial y^2}\right)$$

$$= 2\left[\left(\frac{\partial u}{\partial x}\right)^2 + \left(\frac{\partial u}{\partial y}\right)^2\right] \qquad\qquad [\because\ u \text{ is a harmonic function}]$$

$$= 2\left[\left(\frac{\partial u}{\partial x}\right)^2 + \left(\frac{\partial v}{\partial x}\right)^2\right] \qquad\qquad\qquad [\because\ u_y = -v_x]$$

$$= 2\,|\, f'\, (z)\,|^2 \qquad\qquad \left[\begin{array}{l} \because\ f'\, (z) = \dfrac{\partial w}{\partial x} = \dfrac{\partial u}{\partial x} + i\dfrac{\partial v}{\partial x}, \\ \text{where}\ u = f\,(z) = u + iv. \end{array}\right]$$

$$\Rightarrow \qquad\qquad \left(\frac{\partial^2}{\partial x^2} + \frac{\partial^2}{\partial y^2}\right)u^2 = 2\,|\, f'\,(z)\,|^2$$

$$\Rightarrow \qquad\qquad \left(\frac{\partial^2}{\partial x^2} + \frac{\partial^2}{\partial y^2}\right)|\, Re\, f\,(z)\,|^2 = 2\,|\, f'\,(z)\,|^2 \qquad [\text{Since } Re\, f(z) = u]$$

Aliter. Let $f(z) = u + iv$, so that $\overline{f(z)} = u - iv$

$$\Rightarrow \qquad u = \frac{1}{2}[f\,(z) + \overline{f\,(z)}].$$

Now, $\left(\dfrac{\partial^2}{\partial x^2} + \dfrac{\partial^2}{\partial y^2}\right)|\, Re\, f\,(z)\,|^2$

$$= \left(\frac{\partial^2}{\partial x^2} + \frac{\partial^2}{\partial y^2}\right)|u|^2 = 4\frac{\partial^2}{\partial z\partial\bar{z}}|u|^2$$

$$= 4\frac{\partial^2}{\partial z\partial\bar{z}}\left|\frac{1}{2}[f\,(z) + \overline{f\,(z)}]\right|^2$$

$$= \frac{\partial^2}{\partial z\partial\bar{z}}\{f\,(z) + \overline{f\,(z)}\}\,[\overline{f\,(z)} + f\,(z)] \qquad [\because\ |\overline{f\,(z)} + f\,(z)|^2 = f\,(z)\,\overline{f\,(z)}]$$

$$= \frac{\partial^2}{\partial z \partial \bar{z}} [f(z) + \overline{f(z)}]^2 = \frac{\partial}{\partial z} \cdot \frac{\partial}{\partial \bar{z}} [f(z) + \overline{f(z)}]^2$$

$$= \frac{\partial}{\partial z} \cdot 2 \{f(z) + \overline{f(z)}\} \overline{f'(z)} = \{f'(z) \overline{f'(z)}\}$$

$$= 2 |f'(z)|^2 \qquad\qquad\qquad [\because |z|^2 = z\bar{z}]$$

9. *If* $f(z) = u + iv$ *is a regular function of z in any domain prove that*

(i) $\left(\dfrac{\partial^2}{\partial x^2} + \dfrac{\partial^2}{\partial y^2} \right) |f(z)|^{p-2} = p^2 |f(z)|^{p-2} |f'(z)|^2 .$

(ii) $\left(\dfrac{\partial^2}{\partial x^2} + \dfrac{\partial^2}{\partial y^2} \right) |u|^p = p(p-1) |u|^{p-2} |f'(z)|^2 .$ *(Mumbai 2000, Andhra 2000)*

Solution. We know that $\left(\dfrac{\partial^2}{\partial x^2} + \dfrac{\partial^2}{\partial y^2} \right) \equiv 4 \dfrac{\partial^2}{\partial z \partial \bar{z}}.$

(i) $\left(\dfrac{\partial^2}{\partial x^2} + \dfrac{\partial^2}{\partial y^2} \right) |f(z)|^p = 4 \dfrac{\partial^2}{\partial z \partial \bar{z}} |f(z)|^p$

$$= 4 \frac{\partial^2}{\partial z \partial \bar{z}} [f(z) \overline{f(z)}]^{p/2} = 4 \frac{\partial^2}{\partial z \partial \bar{z}} [f(z)]^{p/2} \cdot [\overline{f(z)}]^{p/2}$$

$$= 4 \frac{\partial}{\partial z} [\{f(z)\}^{p/2} \cdot (p/2) \{\overline{f(z)}\}^{(p/2)-1} \cdot \overline{f'(z)}]$$

$$= 4 [(p/2)(z)^{(p/2)-1} \cdot f'(z) \cdot (p/2) \{\overline{f(z)}\}^{(p/2)-1} \cdot \overline{f'(z)}]$$

$$= p^2 [f(z) \overline{f(z)}]^{(p/2)-1} \{f'(z) \overline{f'(z)}\}$$

$$= p^2 |f(z)^2|^{(p/2)-1} |f'(z)|^2$$

$$= p^2 |f(z)|^{p-2} |f'(z)|^2 .$$

(ii) We have $u + iv = f(z)$ and $u - iv = \overline{f(z)}$;

$$\therefore \qquad u = \frac{1}{2} [f(z) + \overline{f(z)}].$$

Now $\left(\dfrac{\partial^2}{\partial x^2} + \dfrac{\partial^2}{\partial y^2} \right) |u|^p = 4 \dfrac{\partial^2}{\partial z \partial \bar{z}} |u|^p$

$$= 4 \frac{\partial^2}{\partial z \partial \bar{z}} \left| \frac{1}{2} \{f(z) + \overline{f(z)}\} \right|^p$$

$$= \frac{4}{2^p} \frac{\partial^2}{\partial z \partial \bar{z}} |\{f(z) + \overline{f(z)}\}^2|^{p/2}$$

$$= \frac{4}{2^p} \frac{\partial^2}{\partial z \partial \bar{z}} [\{f(z) + \overline{f(z)}\} \{\overline{f(z)} + f(z)\}]^{p/2}$$

$$= \frac{4}{2^p} \frac{\partial^2}{\partial z \partial \bar{z}} \{f(z) + \overline{f(z)}\}^p$$

$$= \frac{4}{2^p} \frac{\partial}{\partial \bar{z}} p \, \{f(z) + \overline{f(z)}\}^{p-1} f'(z)$$

$$= (4/2^p) \cdot p\,(p-1)\, \{f(z) + \overline{f(z)}\}^{p-2} f'(z) \, \overline{f'(z)}$$

$$= (4/2^p) \cdot p\,(p-1)\, [\{f(z) + \overline{f(z)}\}^2]^{(1/2)\,(p-2)} \, |f'(z)|^2$$

$$= (4/2^p)\, p\,(p-1)\, [\{f(z) + \overline{f(z)}\}\,\{\overline{f(z)} + f(z)\}]^{(1/2)\,(p-2)} \, |f'(z)|^2$$

$$= (4/2^p)\, p\,(p-1)\, [|\,f(z) + \overline{f(z)}\,|^2]^{(1/2)\,(p-2)} \, |f'(z)|^2$$

$$= p\,(p-1) \left[\left|\frac{1}{2}\,\{f(z) + \overline{f(z)}\}\right|^2\right]^{(1/2)\,(p-2)} |f'(z)|^2$$

$$= p\,(p-1)\, [\,|\,u\,|^{(2)\,(1/2)\,(p-2)}]\, |f'(z)|^2$$

$$= p\,(p-1)\, |\,u\,|^{p-2}\, |f'(z)|^2.$$

10. *If $w = f(z)$ is a regular function of z; prove that*

$$\left(\frac{\partial^2}{\partial x^2} + \frac{\partial^2}{\partial y^2}\right) \log |f'(z)| = 0.$$

If $|f'(z)|$ is the product of a function of x and a function of y, show that
$$f'(z) = \exp(\alpha z^2 + \beta z^2 + \gamma),$$
where α is a real and β and γ are complex constants.   (*Kanpur 2002*)

Solution. We know that $\left(\dfrac{\partial^2}{\partial x^2} + \dfrac{\partial^2}{\partial y^2}\right) \equiv 4\,\dfrac{\partial^2}{\partial z \partial \bar{z}}.$

$$\Rightarrow \quad \left(\frac{\partial^2}{\partial x^2} + \frac{\partial^2}{\partial y^2}\right) \{\log |f'(z)|\}$$

$$= 4 \frac{\partial^2}{\partial z \partial \bar{z}} \{\log |f'(z)|\}$$

$$= 4 \frac{\partial^2}{\partial z \partial \bar{z}} \left\{\frac{1}{2} \log |f'(z)|^2\right\}$$

$$= 2 \frac{\partial^2}{\partial z \partial \bar{z}} [\log \{f'(z)\, \overline{f'(z)}\}]$$

$$= 2 \frac{\partial^2}{\partial z \partial \bar{z}} [\log f'(z) + \log \overline{f'(z)}]$$

$$= 2 \frac{\partial}{\partial \bar{z}} \left\{\frac{f''(z)}{f'(z)}\right\} = 0.$$

2nd Part. Let $|f'(z)| = \phi(x)\,\psi(y)$, where $\phi(x)$ is a function of x alone and $\psi(y)$ is a function of y alone. Here $\phi(x)$ and $\psi(y)$ are either both positive or negative.

Now, $$\left(\frac{\partial^2}{\partial x^2} + \frac{\partial^2}{\partial y^2}\right) \log |f'(z)| = 0$$

$$\Rightarrow \qquad \left(\frac{\partial^2}{\partial x^2} + \frac{\partial^2}{\partial y^2}\right)[\log \phi (x) + \log \psi (y)] = 0$$

$$\Rightarrow \qquad \frac{d^2}{dx^2} \log \phi (x) + \frac{d^2}{dy^2} \log \psi (y) = 0$$

$$\Rightarrow \qquad \frac{d^2}{dx^2} \log \phi (x) = - \frac{d^2}{dy^2} \log \psi (y) = \text{constant } c, \text{ say.}$$

Now $\dfrac{d^2}{dx^2} \log \phi (x) = c$ (a real constant)

and $\qquad \dfrac{d^2}{dy^2} \log \psi (y) = - c.$

$$\Rightarrow \qquad \log \phi (x) = \frac{1}{2} cx^2 + dx + e$$

$$\Rightarrow \qquad \phi (x) = \exp \left(\frac{1}{2} cx^2 + dx + e\right)$$

Similarly $\qquad \psi (y) = \exp \left(-\frac{1}{2} cy^2 + d'y + e'\right),$

where d, e, d', e' are real constants.

$$\Rightarrow \qquad |f'(z)| = \phi (x) \psi (y)$$

$$= \exp \left[\frac{c}{2} (x^2 - y^2) + dx + d'y + e + e'\right] \qquad ...(1)$$

Now $|\exp (\alpha z^2 + \beta z + \gamma)|$
$$= |\exp \{\alpha (x + iy)^2 + (a + ib)(x + iy) + (c + id)\}|,$$

where $\beta = a + ib$ and $\gamma = c + id$
$$= \exp \{\alpha (x^2 - y^2) + ax - by + c\}, \qquad [\because |e^{A + B}| = e^A]$$

which is of the same form as (1).

So, we can write $f'(z) = \exp (\alpha z^2 + \beta z + \gamma).$

11. *Show that an analytic function with constant modulus is constant.*
Solution. Let an analytic function be $f(z) = u + iv.$

(Calicut 2004, M.S. Univ. 2007, Amritsar 2000, Kanpur 2003)

Then $\qquad |f(z)|^2 = u^2 + v^2.$

But $\qquad |f(z)| = \text{constant} = c \text{ (say)}, (c \neq 0)$

$\therefore \qquad |f(z)|^2 = u^2 + v^2 = c^2 \qquad ...(1)$

Now differentiating (1) partially w.r.t. x and y respectively, we have

$$2u \frac{\partial u}{\partial x} + 2v \frac{\partial v}{\partial x} = 0 \text{ or } u \frac{\partial u}{\partial x} + v \frac{\partial v}{\partial x} = 0 \qquad ...(2)$$

and $\qquad 2u \dfrac{\partial u}{\partial y} + 2v \dfrac{\partial v}{\partial y} = 0 \text{ or } - u \dfrac{\partial v}{\partial x} + v \dfrac{\partial u}{\partial x} = 0 \qquad ...(3)$

Squaring and adding (2) and (3), we have

$$(u^2 + v^2)\left[\left(\frac{\partial u}{\partial x}\right)^2 + \left(\frac{\partial v}{\partial x}\right)^2\right] = 0$$

i.e.

$$\left(\frac{\partial u}{\partial x}\right)^2 + \left(\frac{\partial v}{\partial x}\right)^2 = 0 \qquad\qquad [\because \ u^2 + v^2 \neq 0]$$

or

$$|f'(z)|^2 = 0 \qquad\qquad [\text{Since } f'(z) = u_x + iv_x]$$

i.e.

$$f'(z) = 0 \ \Rightarrow \ f(z) = \text{constant.}$$

5.10. The inverse of an analytic function. Neigbhourhood preserving mappings. Suppose that $w = f(z)$ is analytic at a point z_0 and $f'(z_0) \neq 0$. Then, by definition, there exists a neighbourhood of z_0 at every point of which $f(z)$ is differentiable so that $f'(z)$ exists and is continuous.

We write

$$w = u + iv, \qquad z = x + iy;$$
$$w_0 = u_0 + iv_0, \qquad z_0 = x_0 + iy_0.$$

Then $w = f(z)$ determines two real functions

$$\left.\begin{array}{l} u = u(x, y) \\ v = v(x, y) \end{array}\right\} \qquad\qquad\qquad ...(1)$$

which are defined in a certain neighbourhood of (x_0, y_0) and which possess continuous first order partial derivatives in the same neighbourhood. Further the Jacobian of the transformation (1),

$$= \begin{vmatrix} u_x & u_y \\ v_x & v_y \end{vmatrix} = \begin{vmatrix} u_x & u_y \\ -u_y & u_x \end{vmatrix}$$

$$= (u_x)^2 + (u_y)^2 = |f'(z)|^2 \neq 0$$

at the point (x_0, y_0).

Therefore, as proved in Real Variables, the pair of functions in (1) determine the inverses

$$x = x(u, v) \text{ and } y = y(u, v)$$

such that

(*i*) $x_0 = x(u_0, v_0)$ and $y_0 = y(u_0, v_0)$

(*ii*) the functions $x(u, v)$ and $y(u, v)$ are defined in a *certain neighbourhood N' of (u_0, v_0) and map the same on a neighbourhood N of (x_0, y_0)*;

(*iii*) the functions possess continuous first order partial derivatives in the neighbourhood N' of (u_0, v_0).

We now state the following theorem :

Theorem. *Let $w = f(z)$ be analytic at a point z_0 and let $f'(z_0) \neq 0$. Then $w = f(z)$ maps one-one a certain neighbourhood N of z_0 onto a neighbourhood N' of $w_0 = f(z_0)$ so that each point $w \in N'$ is the image of one and only one point $z \in N$. Further this inverse function $z = F(w)$ of $w = f(z)$ is also analytic at w_0 and $F(w) = 1/f'(z)$.*

The first part has already been proved above and only the second remains to be proved.

Let $w_0 + k$ be any point in the neighbourhood N' of w_0. Then there exists one and only one point $z_0 + h \in N$ such that

$$w_0 + k = f(z_0 + h) \ \Leftrightarrow \ z_0 + h = F(w_0 + k).$$

Also $h \neq 0$ if $k \neq 0$.

We have

$$\frac{F(w_0 + k) - F(w_0)}{k} = \frac{z_0 + h - z_0}{k}$$

$$= \left(\frac{k}{h}\right)^{-1} = \left[\frac{f(z_0 + h) - f(z_0)}{h}\right]^{-1}.$$

Let $k \to 0$. Then, $F(w)$ being continuous, we have $h \to 0$. Thus

$$F'(w_0) = [f'(z_0)]^{-1} = 1/f'(z_0) \qquad \qquad ...(1)$$

Further $f'(z)$ being continuous and non-zero at z_0, there exists a neighbourhood of z_0 at no point of which $f'(z)$ is 0. Thus, restricting our attention to a suitable neighbourhood of w_0, we see that the conclusion (1) applies to each point w in a certain neighbourhood of w_0.

It follows that $F(w)$ is analytic at w_0 and

$$F(w) = 1/f'(z),$$

for corresponding points in certain neighbourhoods of w_0 and z_0 respectively.

Note. It is important to notice that under the given conditions, the transformation $w = f(z)$ *maps a neighbourhood N of z onto a neighbourhood N' of w* so that as z sweeps N, then w sweeps N' In this connection, the following two points should be specially noted.

1. There is no point in N' which is not the image of a point in N.

2. No point in N' is the image of two different points in N.

Both these facts are expressed by the statement *that $w = f(z)$ maps one-one a neighbourhood N of z_0 onto a neighbourhood N' of w_0.*

5.11. Domain preserving character of analytic mappings. *Let $w = f(z)$ be analytic in a domain D_1 and $f'(z) \neq 0$ for all z in D_1. Then, if D_1 is mapped on D_2, then D_2 is itself a domain.*

In other words, *an analytic function with nowhere zero derivative maps a domain onto a domain.*

The range D_2 is open, for, as proved in the preceding theorem, a neighbourhood of each point w of D_2 is the image of a neighbourhood of its pre-image z in D_1 and accordingly each point of D_2 is an interior point thereof. Also, D_2 is connected, for it is a continuous image of a connected set D_1 (Refer § 4.15). Thus, D_2 is a domain.

Thus, we may say that *an analytic function with non-zero derivative preserves domains.*

It should, however, be remembered that correspondence between the domains D_1 and D_2 may not be one-one.

For example, consider $w = z^2$

and the domain D_1 defined by $1 < |z| < 3$.

The range D_2 is defined by $1 < |w| < 9$.

The derivative, $2z$, is not zero for any point of D_1. The mapping of D_1 onto D_2 is not, however, one-one. In particular, we may see that $z = 2$ and $z = -2$ are both mapped on $w = 4$ so that a neighbourhood of $w = 4$ is the image of a neighbourhood of 2 as also of a neighbourhood of, -2, both lying in D_1.

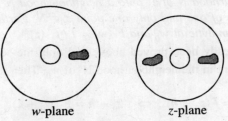

w-plane z-plane

Fig. 5.2

Note. It may be noticed that the domain preserving property of an analytic function with a non-vanishing derivative does not take account of the full implication of the fact of differentiability of the function and of the equivalent fact of its real and imaginary parts satisfying the Cauchy-Riemann partial differential equations. In this connection, it will be seen that the vital point in the argument pursued in § 5.7, relates to the non-vanishing of the Jacobian

$$\begin{vmatrix} u_x & u_y \\ v_x & v_y \end{vmatrix}$$

which fact was related to the non-vanishing of the derivative $f'(z)$ through the employment of Cauchy-Riemann equations. The non-vanishing of the Jacobian may, however, arise without u, v satisfying the Cauchy-Riemann equations as, for example, is the case for

$$w = \bar{z} = x - iy,$$

wherefor the Jacobian

$$= \begin{vmatrix} 1 & 0 \\ 0 & -1 \end{vmatrix} = -1 \neq 0.$$

The function $w = \bar{z}$ is domain preserving without being analytic.

The full implication of Cauchy-Riemann equations is brought out in terms of another property, viz., that of *Angle preserving* as is considered in the following section.

5.12. Angle preserving property of analytic mappings. Let $w = f(z)$ be analytic at a point z_0 and let $f'(z_0) \neq 0$. We have then seen that the given function maps one-one a certain neighbourhood of z_0 onto a neighbourhood of w_0. We shall now prove an important geometric characteristic of this mapping, viz., that angle between any two curves through z_0 is equal in magnitude as well as in sense to the angle between their images through w_0.

Let $z_0 + h$ be any point on a curve C through z_0 and $w_0 + k$ the corresponding point on the image curve Γ through w_0.

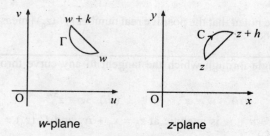

w-plane   z-plane

Fig. 5.3

We then have

$$f'(z_0) = \lim_{h \to 0} \frac{(w_0 + k) - w_0}{(z_0 + h) - z_0} = \lim_{h \to 0} \frac{k}{h} \qquad \text{...(1)}$$

We write

$$h = r(\cos\theta + i\sin\theta), \quad k = \rho(\cos\varphi + i\sin\varphi)$$

$$\therefore \quad \frac{k}{h} = \frac{\rho}{r}[\cos(\varphi - \theta) + i\sin(\varphi - \theta)] \qquad \text{...(2)}$$

From (1) and (2), we obtain

$$\lim \frac{\rho}{r} = |f'(z_0)|, \qquad \text{...(3)}$$

$$\lim(\varphi - \theta) = \arg[f'(z_0)] \qquad \text{...(4)}$$

If the tangents to the two curves C and Γ through z_0 and w_0 respectively make angles ψ and ψ' with the real axis, we have

$$\lim \theta = \psi, \lim \varphi = \psi' \qquad \qquad ...(5)$$

Thus, we obtain from (4) and (5),

$$\psi' - \psi = \lim (\varphi - \theta) = \arg [f'(z_0)],$$

$$\Rightarrow \qquad \psi' = \psi + \arg [f'(z_0)].$$

This, shows that the tangent to the image curve Γ is obtained on rotating the tangent to the curve C through an angle equal to arg $[f'(z_0)]$ and this angle is the same irrespective of the curve C.

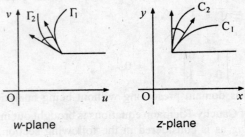

w-plane   *z*-plane

Fig. 5.4

Thus, if ψ_1, ψ_2 be the angles which the tangents to two curves C_1, C_2 and ψ_1', ψ_2' be the angles which the tangents to the image curves Γ_1, Γ_2 make with the real axis, we have

$$\psi_1' = \psi_1 + \arg f'(z_0),$$

$$\psi_2' = \psi_2 + \arg f'(z_0),$$

$$\Rightarrow \qquad \psi_2' - \psi_1' = \psi_2 - \psi_1.$$

Hence the theorem.

Note. It may also be noted that the positive real number $|f'(z_0)|$ measures what may be called the *Magnification* at z_0.

Ex. 1. Find the angle through which the tangent to any curve through $1 + i$ is rotated by the transformations:

(i) $w = z^3$,   (ii) $w = z^4$,   (iii) $w = z^5$.

Ex. 2. If $w = f(z) = u + iv$ is analytic at $z_0 = x_0 + iy_0$ and $f'(z_0) \neq 0$, show that the curves

$$u(x, y) = u(x_0, y_0), v(x, y) = v(x_0, y_0)$$

intersect each other orthogonally at (x_0, y_0).

5.12.1. Converse of the preceding result.

Let $w = f(z) = u + iv,$

where we suppose that both the functions u, v are differentiable at and near a point (x, y).

Let, further, C_1, C_2 be *any* two curves through the point (x, y) possessing tangents there at and let Γ_1, Γ_2 be their images.

We will now show that if the angle between the curves Γ_1 and Γ_2 is the same, in both magnitude and sense, as that between the curves C_1 and C_2, then Cauchy-Riemann equations are satisfied, *i.e.*, $f(z)$ is analytic.

Firstly we consider any curve C through the point (x, y) and its image curve Γ through the point (u, v). Let the curve C be given by

$$z = z(t)$$

or equivalently by

$$x = x(t),\ y = y(t).$$

Then the curve Γ is given by

$$u = u[x(t), y(t)] = u(t),\ (\text{say})$$

and

$$v = v[x(t), y(t)] = v(t),\ (\text{say}).$$

We suppose that (dx/dt) and (dy/dt) are not both zero at (x, y), for, otherwise the curve C would not have a tangent at (x, y).

Then we have

$$\left.\begin{array}{l} \dfrac{du}{dt} = u_x \dfrac{dx}{dt} + u_y \dfrac{dy}{dt}, \\[2mm] \dfrac{dv}{dt} = v_x \dfrac{dx}{dt} + v_y \dfrac{dy}{dt}, \end{array}\right\} \qquad \ldots(1)$$

We now suppose that

$$\begin{vmatrix} u_x & u_y \\ v_x & v_y \end{vmatrix} \neq 0 \qquad \ldots(2)$$

This guarantees that a neighbourhood of (x, y) is mapped one-one onto a neighbourhood of (u, v).

As a consequence of (2), we see that (du/dt) and (dv/dt) in (1) are not both zero so that the curve Γ has a tangent at (u, v).

Suppose now that $du/dt \neq 0$ and $dv/dt \neq 0$.

We then obtain from (1),

$$\frac{dv}{du} = \frac{v_x + v_y (dy/dx)}{u_x + u_y (dy/dx)}.$$

If then ψ, ψ' are the angles which the tangents to the curve C and Γ make with the real axis, we have

$$\tan \psi' = \frac{v_x + v_y \tan \psi}{u_x + u_y \tan \psi}.$$

$$\therefore \quad \tan(\psi' - \psi) = \frac{\tan \psi' - \tan \psi}{1 + \tan \psi' \tan \psi}$$

$$= \frac{\dfrac{v_x + v_y \tan \psi}{u_x + u_y \tan \psi} - \tan \psi}{1 + \left(\dfrac{v_x + v_y \tan \psi}{u_x + u_y \tan \psi}\right) \tan \psi}$$

$$= \frac{(v_x + p v_y) - p(u_x + p u_y)}{(u_x + p u_y) + p(v_x + p v_y)}. \qquad \ldots(2)$$

where we have written p for $\tan \psi$.

We now suppose that $\psi' - \psi$ is constant for all corresponding pairs of curves C and Γ and write $\tan(\psi' - \psi) = k$.

Thus we have

$$k = \frac{(v_x + pv_y) - p(u_x + pu_y)}{(u_x + pu_y) + p(v_x + pv_y)} \quad \forall \quad p \qquad \qquad ...(3)$$

$$\Rightarrow \quad (kv_y + u_y) p^2 + [k(u_y + v_x) + (u_x - v_y)] p + (ku_x - v_x) = 0 \qquad ...(4)$$

is an identity in p.

This implies that

$$kv_y + u_y = 0, \qquad \qquad ...(5)$$

$$k(u_y + v_x) + (u_x - v_y) = 0, \qquad \qquad ...(6)$$

$$\underline{k}v_x - v_x = 0. \qquad \qquad ...(7)$$

Subtracting (5) from (7), we obtain

$$k(u_x - v_y) - (v_x + u_y) = 0 \qquad \qquad ...(8)$$

From (6) and (8), we obtain

$$k[(u_y + v_x)^2 + (u_x - v_y)^2] = 0.$$

If $k \neq 0$, then we have

$$u_y + v_x = 0$$

$$u_x - v_y = 0$$

$$\Rightarrow \qquad \qquad u_x = v_y, u_y = -v_x$$

so that the Cauchy-Riemann equations are satisfied.

In case $k = 0$, then, we see from (4) that

$$p^2 u_y + (u_x - v_y) p - v_x = 0$$

is an identity.

$$\Rightarrow \qquad \qquad u_y = 0, u_x = v_y, v_x = 0$$

so that again the Cauchy-Riemann equations are satisfied.

Ex. Verify from (2) that $\tan(\psi' - \psi)$ is constant if Cauchy-Riemann equations are satisfied.

EXERCISES

1. Find the domains in which the following functions are analytic. Find also the derivatives of the functions.

(a) $\dfrac{z^2 - 1}{z^2 + 1}$, (b) $\dfrac{1}{z^3 + 1}$, (c) $\dfrac{1}{(z^4 + 1)^2}$.

[**Ans.** (a) Every domain of which $\neq i$ are not the members, $4z/(z^2 + 1)^2$.

(b) Every domain of which the three cube roots of -1 are not the members, $-3z^2/(z^3 + 1)^2$.

(c) Every domain of which the four fourth roots of -1, are not the members, $-8z^3/(z^4 + 1)^4$.]

2. If $f(z)$ is a regular function of z in any domain, prove that

(i) $\nabla^2 |f(z)|^2 = 4|f'(z)|^2$,

(ii) $\nabla^2 |f(z)|^p = p^2 |f(z)|^{p-2} |f'(z)|^2$,

where ∇^2 is the operator

$$\frac{\partial^2}{\partial x^2} + \frac{\partial^2}{\partial y^2}.$$

3. If $u(x, y)$ is the real part of an analytic function $f(z)$, show that every nth order partial derivative of $u(x, y)$ is the real part of the nth derivative of $f(z)$ multiplied with a suitable power of i.

4. If u, v are the real and imaginary parts of an analytic function, show that

$$\frac{\partial u}{\partial s} = \frac{\partial v}{\partial n},$$

where $\partial u/\partial s$ and $\partial v/\partial n$ denote the directional derivatives of u along two directions s, n such that the direction s coincides with the direction n on rotation through $+\frac{1}{2}\pi$.

[**Note.** This result may be thought of as a generalisation of Cauchy-Riemann equations.]

5. Find the analytic functions of which the following functions are real parts:
   (a) $e^{-x}\{(x^2 - y^2)\cos y + 2xy \sin y\}$. (*Avadh 2004*)
   (b) $\sin 2x/(\cosh 2y + \cos 2x)$.
   [**Ans.** (a) $e^{-x}(x + iy)^2 (\cos y - i \sin y) + ci$
   (b) $\tan(x - iy)$.]

6. Show that the function
$$f(z) = \sin x \cosh y + i \cos x \sinh y$$
is continuous as well as analytic everywhere.

7. Show that the function $f(z) = xy + iy$ is every where continuous but is not analytic.

(*Kanpur 2003*)

8. If $w = f(z) = \dfrac{1 + z}{1 - z}$, find (i) $\dfrac{dw}{dz}$ and (ii) determine where $f(z)$ is non-analytic.

$$\left[\textbf{Ans.} \ (i) \ \frac{2}{1 - z^2}, \quad (ii) \ z = 1.\right]$$

9. Show that the function $u = \cos x \cosh y$ is harmonic and find its harmonic conjugate.
   [**Ans.** $-\sin x \sinh y + c$] (*Avadh 2007*)

10. Show that the function $u(x, y) = e^x \cos y$ is harmonic. Determine its harmonic conjugate $v(x, y)$ and the analytic function.
    [**Ans.** $e^x \sin y + c$ and $e^z + d$]

11. Prove that if $w = f(z) = u + iv$ is analytic in a region R, then:

$$\frac{dw}{dz} = \frac{\partial w}{\partial x} = -i\frac{\partial w}{\partial y}.$$

12. Show that the function
$$u = \sin x \cos y + 2 \cos x \sinh y + x^2 - y^2 + 4xy$$
satisfies Laplace's equation and determine the corresponding analytic function $f(z) = u + iv$.
    [**Ans.** $(1 - 2i)(\sin z + z^2) + c$]

13. If $u + v = \dfrac{2 \sin 2x}{e^{2y} - e^{-2y} - 2 \cos 2x}$ and $f(z) = u + iv$ is an analytic function of $z = x + iy$,

find $f(z)$ in terms of z.

(Kerala 2001; Kumaon 2000; Rohilkhand, 1992; Garhwal, 1995)

$$\left[\textbf{Ans. } \frac{1}{2}(1+i) \cot z + c \right]$$

14. If $f(z) = u + iv$ is an analytic function of z and $u - v = \dfrac{\cos x + \sin x - e^{-y}}{2 \cos x - e^y - e^{-y}}$, find $f(z)$ subject

to the condition $f(\pi/2) = 0$.   (Garhwal, 2002; Rohilkhand, 2005; Kumaon, 1997)

$$\left[\textbf{Ans. } \frac{1}{2}\left(1 - \cot \frac{z}{2}\right) \right]$$

15. If $u = \dfrac{\sin 2x}{\cosh 2y + \cos 2x}$, find the corresponding analytic function $f(z) = u + iv$.

[**Ans.** $\tan z + c$]   [Kumaon 2003]

16. If $u = (x - 1)^3 - xy^2 + 3y^2$, determine v so that $u + iv$ is a regular function of $u + iv$.

[**Ans.** $3x^2 y - 6xy - y^3 + c$]   (Kanpur 2005)

17. If $f(z)$ is a regular function of z, prove that $\left(\dfrac{\partial^2}{\partial x^2} + \dfrac{\partial^2}{\partial y^2}\right) |f(z)|^2 = 4|f'(z)|^2$.

(Kerala 2001)

OBJECTIVE QUESTIONS

For each of the following questions, four alternatives are given for the answer. Only one of them is correct. Choose the correct alternative.

1. If at $z = a$, $\lim\limits_{\Delta z \to 0} \dfrac{\Delta w}{\Delta z}$ depends on amp (Δz); then $f(z)$ is

   (a) differentiable at $z = a$ (b) not differentiable at $z = a$

   (c) differentiable except at $z = a$ (d) None of these.

2. $f(z) = \bar{z}$ is

   (a) continuous for every z, not differentiable for any z

   (b) continuous for some values of z, differentiable for every z

   (c) discontinuous for every z, differentiable for every z

   (d) neither continuous nor differentiable.

3. Functions satisfying Laplace's equation are known as

   (a) regular   (b) homomorphic

   (c) harmonic   (d) conjugate.

4. An analytic function with constant modulus   (Kanpur 2003)

   (a) is variable   (b) is constant

   (c) is zero   (d) does not exist.

5. Function $f(z) = xy + iy$ is
   (a) everywhere continuous and analytic
   (b) everywhere continuous but not analytic
   (c) discontinuous but analytic everywhere
   (d) neither continuous nor analytic.

6. For a function $f(z) = u + iv$ to be analytic, Cauchy-Riemann equation
   (a) $u_x = v_y, u_y = -v_x$ (b) $u_x = -v_y, u_y = v_x$
   (c) $u_x = v_y, u_y = v_x$ (d) $u_x = -v_y, u_y = -v_x.$

   (Kanpur 2003, Garhwal 2004, Rahilkhand 2003)

7. Polar force of Caurhy-Riemann condition is:
   (a) $\dfrac{\partial u}{\partial r} = -\dfrac{1}{r}\dfrac{\partial v}{\partial \theta}, \dfrac{\partial u}{\partial \theta} = -r\dfrac{\partial v}{\partial r}$ (b) $\dfrac{\partial u}{\partial r} = -\dfrac{1}{r}\dfrac{\partial v}{\partial \theta}, \dfrac{\partial u}{\partial \theta} = r\dfrac{\partial v}{\partial r}$

   (c) $\dfrac{\partial u}{\partial r} = -\dfrac{1}{r}\dfrac{\partial \theta}{\partial v}, \dfrac{\partial u}{\partial \theta} = -r\dfrac{\partial v}{\partial r}$ (d) $\dfrac{\partial u}{\partial r} = \dfrac{1}{r}\dfrac{\partial v}{\partial \theta}, \dfrac{\partial u}{\partial \theta} = -r\dfrac{\partial v}{\partial r}.$

8. Value of $\dfrac{dw}{dz}$ in polar form is:
   (a) $-\dfrac{i}{r}(\cos\theta - i\sin\theta)\dfrac{\partial w}{\partial r}$ (b) $\dfrac{i}{r}(\cos\theta - i\sin\theta)\dfrac{\partial w}{\partial r}$

   (c) $\dfrac{i}{r}(\cos\theta - i\sin\theta)\dfrac{\partial w}{\partial r}$ (d) $(\cos\theta - i\sin\theta)\dfrac{\partial w}{\partial r}.$

9. Function $z = \sin u \cos v + i \cos u \sinh v$ will cease to be analytic at
   (a) $z = 0$ (b) $z = \pm 1$
   (c) $z = \pm i$ (d) None of these.

10. If $w = u + iv$ be anlytic function of $z = x + iy$, then the families of curves $u(x, y) = c_1$ and
   $v(x, y) = c_2$ form:
   (a) Orthogonal system   (b) Conjugate system
   (c) Harmonic systam   (d) Analytic system.

11. If $u = \dfrac{1}{2}\log(x^2 + y^2)$ is harmonic then its harmonic conjugate is:
   (a) $\log(y/x) + c$ (b) $\log(x/y) + c$
   (c) $\tan^{-1}(y/x) + c$ (d) $\tan^{-1}(x/y) + c.$

12. Harmonic conjugate of the function $e^x \cos y$ is
   (a) $e^{-x}\cos y + c$ (b) $e^x \sin y + c$
   (c) $e^{-x}\sin y + c$ (d) None of these.   *(Rohilkhand 2003)*

13. Function $u = e^x(x\cos y - y\sin y)$ satisfies Laplace's equation, then corresponding analytic
   function $f(z)$ is:
   (a) $e^z + c$ (b) $e^{-z} + c$
   (c) $ze^z + c$ (d) $\dfrac{1}{z}e^z + c.$

14. Value of $\left(\dfrac{\partial^2}{\partial x^2} + \dfrac{\partial^2}{\partial y^2} \right)$ is:

(a) $4 \dfrac{\partial^2}{\partial z \, \partial \overline{z}}$

(b) $2 \dfrac{\partial^2}{\partial z \, \partial \overline{z}}$

(c) $-4 \dfrac{\partial^2}{\partial z \, \partial \overline{z}}$

(d) $-2 \dfrac{\partial^2}{\partial z \, \partial \overline{z}}$.

ANSWERS

1. (b) **2.** (a) **3.** (c) **4.** (b) **5.** (b) **6.** (a) **7.** (c) **8.** (d) **9.** (b)

10. (a) **11.** (c) **12.** (b) **13.** (c) **14.** (a).

INFINITE SERIES–POWER SERIES
(Elementary Transcendental Functions)

6.1. Introduction. This chapter is devoted to the consideration of *Power Series* and of the *Elementary Transcendental Functions*. It will be seen that the *Exponential Function* which will be defined by means of a power series will form the basis for defining other functions : *Logarithmic, Generalised Power, Trigonometric* and *Hyperbolic*.

This chapter will also deal with those of the parts of the subject of the *Convergence of Sequences* and *Infinite Series* which are necessary for the purpose of this chapter. Chapter 12 will deal with *Infinite Products* and *Uniform Convergence* of infinite series and products.

6.2. Convergent Sequences. *A sequence is a function defined on the set of positive integers.* For any arbitrary sequence, the value associated to the positive integer n is usually denoted by the symbol z_n and the sequence itself by the symbol $\{z_n\}$.

We shall now define a convergent sequence.

Def. *A sequence $\{z_n\}$ is said to be convergent, if there exists a number l and to every number $\varepsilon > 0$, there corresponds a corresponding positive integer m such that*

$$| z_n - l | < \varepsilon, \ \forall \ n \geq m.$$

Also then l is said to be the *limit* of the sequence, and we write $\lim z_n = l$. We may also say that the sequence $\{z_n\}$ tends to l or converges to l.

A sequence which is not convergent will be referred to as *Divergent*.

It may be easily shown that a convergent sequence cannot tend to two different limits.

Ex. Prove the following results:

1. The limit of a convergent sequence is also a limiting point of the sequence and the unique limiting point for the matter of that.
2. A sequence with more than one limiting point cannot be convergent.
3. A convergent sequence is necessarily bounded.
4. Every re-arrangement of a convergent sequence is convergent. [A sequence $\{Z_n\}$ is said to be a re-arrangement of a sequence $\{z_n\}$ if the ranges of the two sequences are the same.]
5. Every sub-sequence of a convergent sequence is convergent, and that a non-convergent sequence can have a convergent sub-sequence.
6. A bounded sequence is convergent if and only if it has a unique finite limiting point.

6.2.1. *Convergence in terms of real sequences.*

Theorem. *A sequence $\{z_n\}$ is convergent if and only if the two real sequences $\{R(z_n)\}$ and $\{I(z_n)\}$ are **both** convergent and also, in the event of convergence,*

$$lim \; z_n = lim \; [R \; (z_n)] + i \, . \, lim \; [I \; (z_n)].$$

We write

$$z_n = x_n + iy_n.$$

Let $\{z_n\}$ be convergent with limit $l = l_1 + il_2$.

We have

$$z_n - l = (x_n - l_1) + i \; (y_n - l_2)$$

$\Rightarrow$ $\qquad\qquad | z_n - l | \leq | x_n - l_1 | + | y_n - l_2 |$ ...(1)

Also we have

$$| x_n - l_1 | \leq | z_n - l |, \; | y_n - l_2 | \leq | z_n - l |$$ ...(2)

Thus, from (2) we deduce that

$$lim \; z_n = l_1 + il_2 \quad \Rightarrow \quad \begin{cases} lim \; x_n = l_1 \\ lim \; y_n = l_2 \end{cases}$$

Again let

$$lim \, x_n = l_1, \; lim \, y_n = l_2.$$

We write $\quad l_1 + il_2 = l.$

We deduce from (1) that $lim \; z_n = l.$

6.3. Necessary and sufficient condition for a sequence to be convergent. We shall obtain a form of necessary and sufficient condition for the convergence of sequences.

6.3.1. Cauchy's General Principle of Convergence

Theorem. *A necessary and sufficient condition for a sequence $\{z_n\}$ to be convergent is that to a given positive number ε, there corresponds a positive integer m such that*

$$| z_{n+p} - z_n | < \varepsilon \; \forall \; n \geq m \; and \; \forall \; p \geq 0.$$

The condition is necessary. Let the sequence be convergent. Then there exists a number l such that to a given positive number ε there corresponds a positive number m, such that

$$| z_n - l | < \frac{1}{2} \varepsilon, \; \forall \; n \geq m.$$

Also therefore

$$| z_{n+p} - l | < \frac{1}{2} \varepsilon, \quad \forall \quad n \geq m \; and \; p \geq 0.$$

It follows that

$$| z_{n+p} - z_n | = | z_{n+p} - l + l - z_n |$$
$$\leq | z_{n+p} - l | + | l - z_n |$$
$$< \frac{1}{2} \varepsilon + \frac{1}{2} \varepsilon, \; when \; n \geq m, p \geq 0.$$

Thus, to every given positive ε, there corresponds an integer m such that

$$| z_{n+p} - z_n | < \varepsilon \; \forall \; n \geq m, p \geq 0.$$

Hence the condition is necessary.

The condition is sufficient. Firstly we shall prove that under the given condition the sequence is bounded.

Taking $\varepsilon = 1$, we see that there exists a positive integer m such that

$$| z_{m+p} - z_m | < 1 \; \forall \; p \geq 0$$ ...(1)

Also
$$|z_{m+p}| - |z_m| \leq |z_{m+p} - z_m| \qquad \qquad ...(2)$$
From (1) and (2), we see that
$$|z_{m+p}| \leq |z_m| + 1 \quad \forall \quad p \geq 0.$$
Then if k be the greatest of the non-negative numbers
$$|z_1|, |z_2|, ..., |z_{m-1}|, |z_{m+1}|$$
which are finite in number, we see that
$$|z_n| < k,$$
for all n implying that the sequence is bounded.

Now two cases are possible. Either the sequence has only a finite or an infinite number of distinct values. In case it has only a finite number of distinct values, then under the given condition there must exist a positive integer m such that for $n \geq m$, z_n remains constant. In this case the sequence converges to the constant value in question.

Now suppose that the sequence has an *infinite* number of distinct values. Being infinite and bounded, the sequence must have at least one limiting point. It will now be shown, that as a consequence of the given condition, the sequence cannot have two distinct limiting points.

Suppose that l_1 and l_2 are two limiting points. Let ε be *an* arbitrary positive number.

The given condition being assumed true, there exists a positive integer m_0 such that
$$|z_{n+p} - z_n| < \frac{1}{3}\varepsilon, \quad \forall \quad n \geq m_0 \text{ and } p \geq 0.$$

Also l_1 and l_2 being limiting points, there exist integers m_1 and m_2, both $\geq m_0$ such that
$$|z_{m_1} - l_1| < \frac{1}{3}\varepsilon, \ |z_{m_2} - l_2| < \frac{1}{3}\varepsilon.$$

As m_1, m_2 are both $\geq m_0$, we have also
$$|z_{m_2} - z_{m_1}| < \frac{1}{3}\varepsilon.$$

Thus
$$|l_1 - l_2| = |l_1 - z_{m_1} + z_{m_1} - z_{m_2} + z_{m_2} - l_2|$$
$$\leq |l_1 - z_{m_1}| + |z_{m_1} - z_{m_2}| + |z_{m_2} - l_2|$$
$$< \frac{1}{3}\varepsilon + \frac{1}{3}\varepsilon + \frac{1}{3}\varepsilon = \varepsilon.$$

As $|l_1 - l_2|$ is non-negative and ε is an arbitrary positive number, we see that we must have
$$|l_1 - l_2| = 0 \quad \Rightarrow \quad l_1 = l_2.$$

Thus, the sequence has one and only one limiting point.

Let l be the *unique* limiting point of the sequence.

Again, let ε be any positive number. As l is the unique limiting point of the sequence, there can exist, at the most, only a finite number of members of the bounded sequence not lying in the neighbourhood
$$|z - l| < \varepsilon$$
of l.

If now, m, be the greatest of the suffixes of z_n which lie outside $|z - l| < \varepsilon$, we see that
$$|z_n - l| < \varepsilon, \quad \forall \quad n \geq m.$$
Thus, the sequence converges to the limit l. Hence the condition is also sufficient.

6.4. Cauchy Sequence. *A sequence* $< z_n >$ *is said to be a Cauchy (or fundamental) sequence if to each* $\varepsilon > 0$, *there exists a positive integer* n_0 *such that*

$$|z_m - z_n| < \varepsilon, \quad \forall \quad m, n \geq n_0.$$

Theorem. *Every convergent sequence is a Cauchy sequence.*

Let $< z_n >$ converges, to z_0. Then to each $\varepsilon > 0$, there exists n_0 such that

$$|z_n - z_0| < \varepsilon/2, \quad \forall \quad n \geq n_0.$$

Hence if $m \geq n_0$, $n \geq n_0$,

then $\qquad |z_m - z_0| < \varepsilon/2$ and $|z_n - z_0| < \varepsilon/2$ $\qquad\qquad$ ...(1)

$\therefore \qquad |z_m - z_n| = |z_m - z_0 + z_0 - z_n|$

$$\leq |z_m - z_0| + |z_0 - z_n|$$

$$< \varepsilon/2 + \varepsilon/2 = \varepsilon.$$

Hence $< z_n >$ is a Cauchy sequence.

Remark. It can be proved easily by the reader that C is **complete.** By this we mean that every Cauchy sequence in C is convergent. Hence we may conclude:

A sequence in C is convergent if and only if it is a Cauchy sequence.

This is known as **Cauchy's criterion for convergence of sequence.**

6.5. Algebraic operations with limits of sequences. As in § 4.12, it can be shown that if

$$\{z_n\}, \ \{w_n\}$$

are two convergent sequences with limits l, m respectively, then the sequences

$$\{z_n \pm w_n\}, \ \{z_n w_n\}, \ \{z_n \div w_n\}$$

are also convergent with limits

$$l \pm m, \ lm, \ l \div m$$

respectively, provided that for the last case $m \neq 0$.

6.6. Convergence of Infinite Series. Let

$$u_1 + u_2 + \ldots + u_n + \ldots,$$

denoted by Σu_n, be a series whose members are complex numbers.

In terms of the notion of '*Sum*' as defined in Chapter 1, the sum of an infinite series is *not* meaningful inasmuch as there is no last term and the process of successive summation will not terminate. The notion of 'Limit' is inevitable for dealing with infinite series and for this purpose the concept of convergent sequences is basic.

We now set up a sequence $\{s_n\}$ of *partial sums* where

$$s_n = u_1 + u_2 + \ldots + u_n.$$

Then the series is said to be convergent if the sequence $\{s_n\}$ *is convergent, and, in the event of convergence,* $\lim s_n$ *is called the sum of the infinite series* Σu_n.

6.6.1. Convergence in terms of real series. As in § 4.11, we can show that a series Σu_n is convergent if and only if the two real term series

$$\Sigma R \ (u_n) \ \text{and} \ \Sigma I \ (u_n)$$

are both convergent. This can be easily proved by considering the three sequences of partial sums of the three series

$$\Sigma u_n, \Sigma R \ (u_n) \ \text{and} \ \Sigma I \ (u_n).$$

Notation. In the following, the sum of a convergent series Σu_n will often be denoted by the symbol (Σu_n).

6.6.2. The following important points about infinite series are all capable of simple proofs.

(a) If Σu_n and Σv_n are two convergent series, then the series $\Sigma (u_n \pm v_n)$ are also convergent and
$$[\Sigma (u_n \pm v_n)] = (\Sigma u_n) \pm (\Sigma v_n).$$
This means that the sum of the series $\Sigma (u_n + v_n)$ is equal to the sums of those of (Σu_n) and (Σv_n) and so also for the case of difference.

(b) The fact or otherwise of the convergence of a series is not affected by omitting or introducing a *finite* number of terms.

(c) If a series Σu_n is convergent, then so is also convergent any other series obtained by bracketing at will any finite systems of successive terms of the series.

If Σv_n is the series obtained from Σu_n by means of the process referred to here, then the sequence $\{s_n\}$ of partial sums of Σv_n is clearly a sub-sequence of the sequence $\{S_n\}$ of partial sums of Σu_n so that if $\{S_n\}$ has a unique limiting point, then that must be the unique limiting point of $\{s_n\}$ as well.

The student should, however, remember that while we can introduce brackets we cannot always remove the same.

The proofs of the above results are left to the reader.

(d) The general term u_n of a convergent series Σu_n *necessarily* tends to zero. In fact we have $u_n = s_n - s_{n-1}$ so that $\lim u_n = s - s = 0$. This condition, however, is not sufficient.

6.7. Cauchy's General Principle of Convergence for a Series. Analogous to the principle of convergence for a sequence, we have the following for a series.

The necessary and sufficient condition for Σu_n to be convergent is that to a given positive number ε, there corresponds a positive integer m such that
$$| u_{n+1} + u_{n+2} + \ldots + u_{n+p} | < \varepsilon, \quad \forall \ n \geq m, p \geq 0.$$
The proof follows immediately from the corresponding theorem for sequences (§ 6.6).

The necessary and sufficient condition for the convergence of the sequence $\{s_n\}$, *i.e.*, for the series Σu_n is that to a given $\varepsilon > 0$, there corresponds a positive integer m such that
$$| s_{n+p} - s_n | < \varepsilon \quad \forall \ n \geq m, p \geq 0,$$
$\Rightarrow$
$$| u_{n+1} + u_{n+2} + \ldots + u_{n+p} | < \varepsilon \quad \forall \ n \geq m, p \geq 0.$$
Hence the proof.

6.8. Absolute convergence of a series. *A series Σu_n is said to be absolutely convergent if the real positive term series $\Sigma | u_n |$ is convergent.*

We shall now prove that an *absolutely convergent series is also convergent.*

Let Σu_n be an absolutely convergent series and let ε be a given positive number. Now, $\Sigma | u_n |$ being a convergent series, there exists a positive integer m such that
$$| u_{n+1} | + \ldots + | u_{n+p} | < \varepsilon, \quad \forall \ n \geq m, p \geq 0 \qquad \qquad ..(1)$$
Also $\forall \ n$ and $\forall \ p$,
$$| u_{n+1} + \ldots + u_{n+p} | \leq | u_{n+1} | + \ldots + | u_{n+p} | \qquad \qquad ...(2)$$
From (1) and (2), we see that there exists a positive integer m such that
$$| u_{n+1} + \ldots + u_{n+p} | < \varepsilon \quad \forall \ n \geq m, p \geq 0.$$
Hence Σu_n is convergent.

Note 1. We can also state the above result in another useful form as follows :

A sufficient condition for the convergence of the series Σu_n is that the series $\Sigma | u_n |$ converges.

Note 2. $\Sigma | u_n |$ being a real positive term series, its convergence can be examined by means of the usual comparison tests for positive term series developed in real variables.

Note 3. *A series which is convergent without being absolutely convergent is called a conditionally convergent series.*

Note 4. The fundamental distinction between conditionally and absolutely convergent series is brought out by the considerations concerning **Re-arrangements** of a series in § 6.6.

Note 5. We can easily show that if a series Σu_n is absolutely convergent, then the two corresponding real term series

$$\Sigma R\,(u_n) \text{ and } \Sigma I\,(u_n)$$

are also absolutely convergent and conversely.

These results are again easy consequences of the inequalities

$$|\,u_n\,| \leq |\,R\,(u_n)\,| + |\,I\,(u_n)\,|,$$
$$|\,R\,(u_n)\,| \leq |\,u_n\,| \text{ and } |\,I\,(u_n)\,| \leq |\,u_n\,|.$$

6.8.1. Tests for the absolute convergence of complex term series. It is obvious that a test for the convergence of a positive term series can be restated as one for the absolute convergence of a complex term series. Here we state the following tests which are adaptations of those of D' Alembert's and Raabe's Tests for positive term series.

I. *A series Σu_n will be absolutely convergent, if*

$$\lim_{n \to \infty} \left|\frac{u_{n+1}}{u_n}\right| = l < 1.$$

II. *A series Σu_n will be absolutely convergent, if*

$$\lim_{n \to \infty} \left[n \left\{ \left|\frac{u_n}{u_{n+1}}\right| - 1 \right\} \right] = l > 1.$$

The following result can also be easily established:

If Σu_n and Σv_n are two series such that Σu_n is absolutely convergent and

$$\lim \frac{|\,v_n\,|}{|\,u_n\,|} = l, \; (l \neq \infty)$$

then Σv_n is also absolutely convergent.

6.9. Abel's* and Dirichilet's* tests for complex term series. We shall now obtain two tests which are useful for the investigation of convergence which is not necessarily absolute.

Theorem *If Σa_n converges and $\Sigma\,|\,v_n - v_{n+1}\,|$ converges, then $\Sigma a_n v_n$ also converges.*
We write

$$s_n = a_1 + a_2 + \dots + a_n,$$

so that the series Σa_n being convergent, $\lim s_n$ exists.
Let

$$\lim s_n = s.$$

We write

$$S_n = a_1 v_1 + a_2 v_2 + \dots + a_n v_n.$$

The series $\Sigma\,|\,v_n - v_{n+1}\,|$ being convergent, the series $\Sigma\,(v_n - v_{n+1})$ is also convergent. Denoting by σ_n the sum of n terms of this latter series, we have

$$\sigma_n = (v_1 - v_2) + (v_2 - v_3) + \dots + (v_n - v_{n+1})$$
$$= v_1 - v_{n+1}$$

---

* Abel (1802-29) and Dirichilet (1805-59).

$\Rightarrow$ $v_{n+1} = v_1 - \sigma_n.$

This shows that

$$\lim v_{n+1}$$

exists. Let this be denoted by v.

The sequence $\{s_n\}$, being convergent, is bounded, so that there exists a number k such that $|s_n| < k \ \forall \ n$.

Now

$$
\begin{aligned}
S_{n+p} - S_n &= a_{n+1}v_{n+1} + a_{n+2}v_{n+2} + \ ..... + a_{n+p}v_{n+p} \\
&= (s_{n+1} - s_n)\, v_{n+1} + (s_{n+2} - s_{n+1})\, v_{n+2} \\
&\qquad\qquad\qquad + \ ..... + (s_{n+p} - s_{n+p-1})\, v_{n+p} \\
&= - s_n v_{n+1} + (v_{n+1} - v_{n+2})\, s_{n+1} + (v_{n+2} - v_{n+3})\, s_{n+2} \\
&\qquad + \ ..... + (v_{n+p-1} - v_{n+p})\, s_{n+p-1} + v_{n+p}s_{n+p} \qquad ...(1)
\end{aligned}
$$

From (1), we have

$$
\begin{aligned}
|\, S_{n+p} - S_n\,| &\le |\, v_{n+p}s_{n+p} - s_n v_{n+1}\,| \\
&\quad + k\, \{|\, v_{n+1} - v_{n+2}\,| + \ ..... + |\, v_{n+p-1} - v_{n+p}\,|\} \qquad ...(2)
\end{aligned}
$$

Let, ε be any given positive number.

Now since

$$\lim_{n \to \infty} (v_{n+p}s_{n+p} - s_n v_{n+1}) = vs - sv = 0,$$

there exists a positive integer m_1 such that

$$|\, v_{n+p}s_{n+p} - s_n v_{n+1}\,| < \varepsilon/2 \ \forall \ n \ge m_1,\, p \ge 0 \qquad\qquad ...(3)$$

Also because $\Sigma\, |\, v_n - v_{n+1}\,|$ is convergent there exists by Cauchy's general principle of convergence a positive integer m_2, such that

$$|\, v_{n+1} - v_{n+2}\,| + ... + |\, v_{n+p-1} - v_{n+p}\,| < \varepsilon/2k \ \forall \ n \ge m_2,\, p \ge 0. \qquad ...(4)$$

From (2), (3) and (4), we deduce that

$$|\, S_{n+p} - S_n\,| < \varepsilon \ \forall \ n \ge \max\,(m_1,\, m_2),\, p \ge 0.$$

Hence the series $\Sigma a_n v_n$ is convergent.

Cor. As a special case, we may deduce from above *that if $\{v_n\}$ is a positive monotonically decreasing sequence and the series Σa_n is convergent, then $\Sigma a_n v_n$ is convergent.*

The convergence of $\Sigma\, |\, v_n - v_{n+1}\,|$ is an easy consequence of the assumed character of the sequence $\{v_n\}$.

Theorem *If the sequence of partial sums of a series Σa_n is bounded and if $\Sigma\, |\, v_n - v_{n+1}\,|$ converges and $\lim v_n = 0$, then the series $\Sigma a_n v_n$ is convergent.*

We adopt the notation of the preceding theorem. The sequence $\{s_n\}$ being bounded, there exists a positive number k such that

$$|s_n| < k, \ \forall \ n.$$

From (1) of the preceding theorem, we have, for all n:

$$
\begin{aligned}
|\, S_{n+p} - S_n\,| &\le k\, |\, v_{n+1}\,| + k\, |\, v_{n+p}\,| \\
&\quad + k\, \{|\, v_{n+1} - v_{n+2}\,| + \ ..... + |\, v_{n+p-1} - v_{n+p}\,|\} \qquad ...(5)
\end{aligned}
$$

As $\Sigma\, |\, v_{n+1} - v_{n+2}\,|$ is convergent, there exists a positive integer m_1, such that

$$|\, v_{n+1} - v_{n+2}\,| + ... + |\, v_{n+p-1} - v_{n+p}\,| < \varepsilon/3k \ \forall \ n \ge m_1,\, p \ge 0 \qquad ...(6)$$

Also because $\lim v_n = 0$, there exists a positive integer m_2 such that

$$|\, v_{n+1}\,| < \varepsilon/3k \ \forall \ n \ge m_2 \qquad\qquad\qquad ...(7)$$

$\Leftrightarrow$ $\qquad\qquad |v_{n+p}| < \varepsilon/3k \;\forall\; n \geq m_2, p \geq 0$ $\qquad\qquad\qquad$ ...(8)

From (5), (6), (7) and (8), we deduce that

$\qquad |S_{n+p} - S_n| < \varepsilon \;\forall\; n \geq \max{(m_1, m_2)}$ and $p \geq 0$.

Hence $\Sigma a_n v_n$ is convergent.

Cor. As a special case of the above, we may deduce that if $\{v_n\}$ is a positive monotonically decreasing sequence tending to zero, and the sequence of partial sums of Σa_n is bounded, then the series $\Sigma a_n v_n$ is convergent.

EXAMPLES

1. *The geometric series*

$$1 + z + z^2 + \dots + z^n + \dots$$

converges if and only if $|z| < 1$. *Also the convergence is absolute.*

Solution. The series

$$1 + |z| + |z|^2 + \dots + |z|^n + \dots$$

being a real term geometric series with common ratio $|z|$ is convergent if and only if $|z| < 1$.

Thus, the given series is absolutely convergent when $|z| < 1$.

Also the series is divergent for $|z| \geq 1$, for the general term z^n does not tend to 0 as $n \to \infty$ in this case.

2. *The series*

$$\sum_{n=1}^{\infty} \frac{nz^{n-1}}{z^n - (1 + n^{-1})^n}$$

converges absolutely if $|z| < 1$.

Solution. We have, if $|z| < 1$,

$$|z^n - (1 + n^{-1})^n| \geq (1 + n^{-1})^n - |z^n| \geq (1 + n^{-1})^n - 1.$$

Since when $n \to \infty$, $(1 + n^{-1})^n \to e$ and $2 < e < 3$, we see that for sufficiently large values of n, $(1 + n^{-1})^n - 1 > 1$ and accordingly for such values of n,

$$|z^n - (1 + n^{-1})^n| > 1 \;\Leftrightarrow\; \frac{1}{|z^n - (1 + n^{-1})^n|} < 1.$$

Also $\Sigma n z^{n-1}$ can be easily seen to be absolutely convergent when $|z| < 1$. Hence the result.

3. *Consider for convergence the series*

$$\sum \frac{(-1)^n}{z+n}.$$

Solution. Here we apply Theorem II, § 6.9. We take

$$a_n = (-1)^n, \; v_n = 1/(z+n).$$

Clearly the sequence of partial sums of the series Σa_n is bounded.

Also

$$v_n - v_{n+1} = \frac{1}{z+n} - \frac{1}{z+n+1} = \frac{1}{(z+n)(z+n+1)}.$$

Writing

$$u_n = \frac{1}{n^2},$$

we see that

$$\frac{|v_n - v_{n+1}|}{|u_n|} \to 1 \text{ as } n \to \infty.$$

Since $\Sigma |u_n|$ is convergent, we see that the series $\Sigma |v_n - v_{n+1}|$ is also convergent. Finally we see that

$$v_n = \frac{1}{z+n} \to 0 \text{ as } n \to \infty.$$

Thus, we see that the series

$$\sum \frac{(-1)^n}{z+n}$$

is convergent for every value of z other than a negative integer.

6.10. Rearrangements of a Series. A series Σv_n is said to be a rearrangement of Σu_n if every v_n is some u_n and every u_n is some v_n. We shall now prove two theorems in connection with rearrangements of series.

Theorem *If Σu_n is an absolutely convergent series and Σv_n is **any** rearrangement of the same, then the series Σv_n is also convergent and has the same sum as Σu_n.*

This theorem will be proved in three steps.

First Step. *When Σu_n is a **positive** term series.*

We write
$$S_n = u_1 + u_2 + \ldots.. + u_n,$$
$$\sigma_n = v_1 + v_2 + \ldots.. + v_n.$$

Now, Σu_n being a convergent positive term series, the sequence $\{S_n\}$ is bounded and monotonically increasing. Let $\lim S_n = S$.

Now, as Σv_n is a rearrangement of Σu_n, to each positive integer n there corresponds a positive integer m such that

$$\sigma_n \leq S_m \leq S \qquad \ldots(1)$$

so that σ_n is also bounded above. Thus Σv_n is also a convergent series and its sum S' is, by (1), such that

$$S' \leq S \qquad \ldots(2)$$

Further Σu_n being also a rearrangement of the positive term series Σv_n, we may similarly see that

$$S \leq S' \qquad \ldots(3)$$

From (2) and (3) we deduce that
$$S = S'.$$

Second Step. *When Σu_n is an absolutely convergent **real** term series.*

We define the two sequences $\{a_n\}$, $\{b_n\}$ as follows:

$$a_n = \begin{cases} u_n, & \text{when } u_n \geq 0, \\ 0, & \text{when } u_n < 0; \end{cases} \quad b_n = \begin{cases} -u_n, & \text{when } u_n \leq 0, \\ 0, & \text{when } u_n > 0. \end{cases}$$

By virtue of the definitions of $\{a_n\}$ and $\{b_n\}$, we may see that

$$u_n = a_n - b_n, \qquad \ldots(1)$$
$$|u_n| = a_n + b_n. \qquad \ldots(2)$$

Corresponding to the sequence $\{v_n\}$, we may similarly define two sequences $\{c_n\}$ and $\{d_n\}$ such that

$$v_n = c_n - d_n, \quad\quad\quad ...(3)$$

$$|v_n| = c_n + d_n. \quad\quad\quad ...(4)$$

From (1) and (2), we have

$$a_n = \frac{1}{2}[u_n + |u_n|], \quad b_n = \frac{1}{2}[|u_n| - u_n].$$

As Σu_n and $\Sigma |u_n|$ are both convergent, we deduce that Σa_n and Σb_n are also convergent, and

$$(\Sigma a_n) = \frac{1}{2}[(\Sigma u_n) + (\Sigma |u_n|)], \quad\quad\quad ...(5)$$

$$(\Sigma b_n) = \frac{1}{2}[(\Sigma |u_n|) - (\Sigma u_n)], \quad\quad\quad ...(6)$$

where (Σa_n) denotes the sum of Σa_n and so on.

Now Σa_n and Σb_n are convergent positive term series and Σc_n, Σd_n are rearrangements respectively of the same. Hence by Step I, these latter series are also convergent and

$$(\Sigma c_n) = (\Sigma a_n), \quad (\Sigma d_n) = (\Sigma b_n) \quad\quad\quad ...(7)$$

Now from (3) and (4), we see that Σv_n and $\Sigma |v_n|$ are convergent and

$$\begin{aligned}
(\Sigma v_n) &= (\Sigma c_n) - (\Sigma d_n) \\
&= (\Sigma a_n) - (\Sigma b_n) & \text{[From (7)]} \\
&= (\Sigma u_n) & \text{[From (5) and (6)]}
\end{aligned}$$

Thus, Σv_n is convergent, and in fact absolutely convergent, with sum equal to that of Σu_n.

Third Step. *When Σu_n is an absolutely convergent* **complex** *term series.*

We have

$$u_n = R(u_n) + i[I(u_n)], \quad v_n = R(v_n) + i[I(v_n)].$$

As Σu_n is absolutely convergent, therefore (Refer Note 5 of § 6.3) the corresponding real term series $\Sigma R(u_n)$ and $\Sigma I(u_n)$ are also absolutely convergent.

Further, Σv_n being a rearrangement of Σu_n, we see that

$$\Sigma R(v_n) \text{ and } \Sigma I(v_n)$$

are also respectively rearrangements of the real absolutely convergent series

$$\Sigma R(u_n) \text{ and } \Sigma I(u_n)$$

and as such they are absolutely convergent and

$$[\Sigma R(v_n)] = [\Sigma I(u_n)], \quad [\Sigma R(v_n)] = [\Sigma I(u_n)].$$

Again, therefore, Σv_n is absolutely convergent and

$$\begin{aligned}
(\Sigma v_n) &= [\Sigma R(v_n)] + i[\Sigma I(v_n)] \\
&= [\Sigma R(u_n)] + i[\Sigma I(u_n)] \\
&= (\Sigma u_n).
\end{aligned}$$

Thus, we have completed the proof of the theorem.

Theorem II. *If Σu_n is any conditionally convergent* **real** *term series and σ is* **any** *given real number, then there exists a rearrangement Σv_n of Σu_n such that Σv_n converges to σ.*

The series Σu_n being conditionally convergent, the series $\Sigma |u_n|$ must be divergent to infinity.

As in the second step of the preceding theorem, we define a_n and b_n, so that we have

$$u_n = a_n - b_n,$$

$$| u_n | = a_n + b_n,$$

and accordingly

$$a_n = \frac{1}{2} (u_n + | u_n |), \quad b_n = \frac{1}{2} (| u_n | - u_n).$$

As Σu_n is convergent and $\Sigma \mid u_n \mid$ is divergent to infinity, we see that the series Σa_n and Σb_n are also both divergent to infinity.

Clearly Σa_n and Σb_n can be thought of as consisting respectively of the positive terms and of the absolute values of the negative terms of the series.

We now give the process of construction of Σv_n. Firstly suppose that σ is positive.

We start writing the positive terms of the given series in the order in which they appear and stop when the sum attained *just* exceeds σ. This means that if we have written m_1 terms, then the sum of m_1 terms is greater than σ and that of $(m_1 - 1)$ terms less than σ.

Again we start writing negative terms and stop when the sum of all the positive and negative terms written is just less than σ. In this manner, we alternatively write positive and negative sets of terms.

It may now be seen that the sum of any number of terms of the new series differs from σ by the absolute value of the last positive or negative term used.

Now, Σu_n being convergent,

$$\lim_{n \to \infty} u_n = 0.$$

Thus, if ε be any given positive number, there exists a positive integer m such that

$$| u_n | < \varepsilon, \ \forall \ n \geq m.$$

We now suppose that the process of rearrangement has been carried far enough that the first m terms

$$u_1, \ u_2, \ ....., \ u_m$$

of the given series have been accommodated in the rearrangement Σv_n.

Thus, there exists a positive integer N such that

$$| S_n - \sigma | < \varepsilon \ \forall \ n \geq N,$$

where S_n denotes the sum of the first n terms of the series

$$v_1 + v_2 + ... \ .$$

The proof when σ is negative can be easily modified.

Note. By a suitable modification of the above proof, it may be shown that for any given conditionally convergent series, a rearrangement can be found such that the same diverges to $+ \infty$ or $- \infty$ or oscillates finitely or infinitely.

6.10.1. Rearrangements of Complex Term Series. If Σu_n is not absolutely convergent, then at least one of the two real term series

$$\Sigma R \ (u_n), \ \Sigma I \ (u_n)$$

will not be absolutely convergent, *i.e.*, will be conditionally convergent. By a suitable rearrangement we can, therefore, effect in one of the two series any prescribed change of behaviour relative to convergence. But a rearrangement of one of the two series will automatically *fix* the rearrangement and, therefore, the behaviour of the other. However, this way of arguing cannot lead us further inasmuch as there is no immediate way of knowing the possibly altered behaviour of the second as a result of change in the first. All that we can say is that *rearrangement of a conditionally convergent complex term series may alter the behaviour thereof.*

We also *state without proof* the following more precise result in this connection.

If Σu_n is conditionally convergent, it may be transformed by an appropriate arrangement into another series which is convergent and whose sum may be prescribed to have either any arbitrary value in the whole complex plane or any value on a particular straight line in the plane according to the circumstances of the case.

6.11. Multiplication of Series. Definition of Product Series. If Σu_n and Σv_n be two given series, then the series Σw_n, where

$$w_n = (u_1 v_n + u_2 v_{n-1} + \ldots + u_n v_1)$$

is called the *Product Series* of the given series.

For suggestion behind this definition, reference may be made to the following section on power series.

We shall now prove the following theorem:

The product series Σw_n of any two absolutely convergent series Σu_n and Σv_n is also absolutely convergent and

$$(\Sigma w_n) = (\Sigma u_n)(\Sigma v_n),$$

so that the sum of the product series is equal to the product of the sums of the two series.

The proof will be given in four steps.

First Step. We start considering the doubly infinite array

$$
\begin{array}{llllll}
u_1 v_1 & u_1 v_2 & u_1 v_3 & u_1 v_4 & \cdots & \cdots & \cdots \\
u_2 v_1 & u_2 v_2 & u_2 v_3 & u_2 v_4 & \cdots & \cdots & \cdots \\
u_3 v_1 & u_3 v_2 & u_3 v_3 & u_3 v_4 & \cdots & \cdots & \cdots \\
u_4 v_1 & u_4 v_2 & u_4 v_3 & u_4 v_4 & \cdots & \cdots & \cdots \\
\cdots & \cdots & \cdots & \cdots & \cdots & \cdots
\end{array}
$$

and define a new series Σa_n, where a_n consists of the sum of the members of the nth square and are not contained in the $(n-1)$th square.

Thus

$$a_n = u_1 v_n + u_2 v_n + \ldots + u_n v_n + u_n v_{n-1} + u_n v_{n-2} + \ldots + u_n v_1.$$

If S'_n, S''_n, σ_n denote the sums of first n terms of the series

$$\Sigma u_n, \Sigma v_n, \Sigma a_n$$

we have, as may be easily seen,

$$\sigma_n = S'_n S''_n.$$

$\therefore$ σ_n is convergent and

$$\lim \sigma_n = (\lim S'_n)(\lim S''_n)$$
$$= S'S'',$$

where S', S'' are the sums of the given series Σu_n, Σv_n. Thus Σa_n is convergent with sum $S'S''$.

Second Step. Consider now the array

$$
\begin{array}{llll}
u_1 v_1 & u_1 v_2 & u_1 v_3 & \cdots & \cdots & \cdots \\
u_2 v_1 & u_2 v_2 & u_2 v_3 & \cdots & \cdots & \cdots \\
u_3 v_1 & u_3 v_2 & u_3 v_3 & \cdots & \cdots & \cdots \\
\cdots & \cdots & \cdots & \cdots & \cdots
\end{array}
$$

and the series Σb_n, where b_n consists of the sum of the members in the nth square and are not contained in the $(n-1)$th.

Thus

$$b_n = |u_1 v_n| + |u_2 v_n| + \ldots + |u_n v_n| + |u_n v_{n-1}| + \ldots + |u_n v_1|.$$

As in Case I, we can, by considering the convergence of $\Sigma |u_n|$ and $\Sigma |v_n|$, show that Σb_n is convergent.

Third Step. By the theorem on removal of brackets, for positive term series, we see that the series

$$|u_1 v_1| + |u_1 v_2| + |u_2 v_2| + |u_2 v_1| + |u_1 v_3| + \ldots \qquad \ldots(1)$$

is convergent and therefore the series

$$u_1 v_1 + u_1 v_2 + u_2 v_2 + u_2 v_1 + u_1 v_3 + \ldots \qquad \ldots(2)$$

is absolutely convergent.

By (c) of § 6.2.2, on insertion of brackets and the theorem on rearrangement, we see that the two series Σw_n and Σa_n obtained on appropriately rearranging and inserting brackets are convergent have the *same* sum as the series (2). But the sum of Σa_n as shown in the first step, is $S'S''$. Therefore, the series Σw_n is convergent with sum $S'S''$.

Fourth Step. Since

$$|w_1| + \ldots + |w_n| \leq \{|u_1| + \ldots + |u_n|\} \, \{|v_1| + \ldots + |v_n|\},$$

it follows that the series $\Sigma |w_n|$ is convergent, *i.e.*, Σw_n is absolutely convergent.

6.12. Power Series. *(Kanpur 1998)*

So far we have been concerned with series with constant terms only. We shall now consider a special type of series — known as *Power Series*, with variable terms.

A series of the type

$$a_0 + a_1 (z - a) + a_2 (z - a)^2 + \ldots + a_n (z - a)^n + \ldots$$

also written as

$$\sum_{n=0}^{\infty} a_n (z - a)^n, \qquad \ldots(1)$$

is called a *power series*, involving as it does different integral powers of $(z - a)$. In the following, we shall consider the power series

$$\sum_{n=0}^{\infty} a_n z^n \qquad \ldots(2)$$

for, as may be at once seen, the consideration of a series of type (1) can be always reduced to that of a series of type (2).

6.12.1. Certain theorems on power series.

Theorem *The power series $\Sigma a_n z^n$ is*

(i) *either convergent for all values of z,*

(ii) *or converges for z = 0 only,*

(iii) *or converges for z in some region of the complex plane.*

We shall establish the above by the help of suitable examples.

(i) Consider the power series $\Sigma u_n = \sum \dfrac{z^n}{n!}$.

$$u_n = \frac{z^n}{n!}, \quad u_{n+1} = \frac{z^{n+1}}{(n+1)!}$$

$$\lim_{n \to \infty} \left| \frac{u_{n+1}}{u_n} \right| = \lim_{n \to \infty} \left| \frac{z}{n+1} \right| = \lim_{n \to \infty} \frac{|z|}{n+1} = 0 < 1.$$

Hence by ratio test power series converges absolutely for all values of z.

(*ii*) Consider the series $\Sigma\ (n\ !)\ z^n$.

Now, if $z \neq 0$ then $\lim\limits_{n \to \infty} (n\ !)\ z^n = \infty$.

Hence the series is not convergent for values of $z \neq 0$.

If however $z = 0$ then the above limit is zero and hence the series converges.

(*iii*) Consider the geometric series $\sum\limits_{n=0}^{\infty} z^n$.

We know that it converges for $|\ z\ | < 1$ and diverges for $|\ z\ | \geq 1$.

Hence the power series converges for z in some region of the complex plane.

Theorem (Abel's Theorem). *If a power series $\Sigma a_n z^n$ converges for a particular value z_0 of z, then it converges for all values of z for which $|\ z\ | < |\ z_0\ |$.*

(*Rohilkhand, 2000, Kanpur 2007*)

Let us suppose that $\Sigma a_n z_0^n$ converges, then by definition

$$\lim\limits_{n \to \infty}\ a_n z_0^n = 0.$$

Hence we can find a number $N > 0$ such that

$$|\ a_n z_0^n\ | \leq N \text{ for all values of } n.$$

Now $$|\ a_n z^n\ | \leq N \left|\ \frac{z}{z_0}\ \right|^n$$

But as $|\ z\ | < |\ z_0\ |$ the geometric series

$$\sum \left|\ \frac{z}{z_0}\ \right|^n$$

is convergent.

Therefore by comparison test, the series $\Sigma a_n z^n$ is absolutely convergent for all values of z for which $|\ z\ | < |\ z_0\ |$.

Theorem (Cauchy-Hadamard Theorem). *For any power series $\Sigma a_n z^n$, there are three possible behaviours:*

(*i*) *The series diverges for every value of z other than 0.*

(*ii*) *The series converges for every value of z.*

(*iii*) *There exists a positive number r such that the series converges for every z such that $|\ z\ | < r$, and diverges for every z such that $|\ z\ | > r$.*

Also

$$r = 1 \div \overline{lim}\ |\ a_n\ |^{1/n}$$

where $\overline{lim}\ |a_n|^{1/n}$ denotes the upper limit of the real sequence, $|a_n|^{1/n}$.   (*Rohilkhand, 1995*)

Consider the sequence

$$b_n = \{|\ a_n\ |^{1/n}\},$$

of positive real numbers, formed in terms of the sequence $\{a_n\}$ of the coefficients of the given power series. Three cases arise:

I. The sequence $\{b_n\}$ is not bounded.

II. The sequence $\{b_n\}$ is bounded with upper limit zero.

III. The sequence $\{b_n\}$ is bounded with upper limit different from zero.

We shall consider these three cases one by one.

I. *The sequence $\{b_n\}$ is not bounded*. It will be shown that in this case the series does not converge for any non-zero value of z.

Let $z \neq 0$ be any given number. Let k be a positive real number.

Since $\{|a_n|^{1/n}\}$ is not bounded there exist values for which

$$|a_n|^{1/n} > \frac{k}{|z|} \quad \Rightarrow \quad |a_n z^n| > k^n > k, \ (k > 1)$$

This shows that the sequence $\{|a_n z^n|\}$ is **not** bounded and accordingly the series $\Sigma a_n z^n$ does not converge.

II. *The sequence $\{b_n\}$ has upper limit, equal to 0*. It will be shown that in this case the series converges for every value of z.

We have

$$0 \leq \underline{\lim} |a_n|^{1/n} \leq \overline{\lim} |a_n|^{1/n} = 0,$$

$$\underline{\lim} |a_n|^{1/n} = \overline{\lim} |a_n|^{1/n} = 0.$$

Thus, the sequence $\{|a_n|^{1/n}\}$ is convergent with limit 0.

If, now, z be any given non-zero number, there exists a positive integer m such that

$$|a_n|^{1/n} < \frac{1}{2|z|} \quad \forall \quad n \geq m,$$

$$\Rightarrow \qquad |a_n z^n| < \left(\frac{1}{2}\right)^n \quad \forall \quad n \geq m.$$

Comparing now the two positive term series

$$|a_m z^m| + |a_{m+1} z^{m+1}| + \ldots\ldots, \tag{1}$$

$$(1/2)^m + (1/2)^{m+1} + \ldots\ldots, \tag{2}$$

we see that the series (1) is convergent and accordingly the series $\Sigma a_n z^n$ is absolutely convergent.

III. *The sequence $\{|a_n|^{1/n}\}$ is bounded with non-zero upper limit μ.*

It will be shown that the series converges absolutely for every z such that $|z| < r$ and does not converge for any z such that $|z| > r$, where $r = 1/\mu$.

Let, now, z be a given number such that

$$|z| < r.$$

Let again z_0 be a number such that

$$|z| < |z_0| < r,$$

$$\Rightarrow \qquad \frac{1}{|z|} > \frac{1}{|z_0|} > \frac{1}{r} = \mu.$$

As $1/|z_0|$ is greater than the upper limit, it follows that there exists a positive integer m such that

$$|a_n|^{1/n} < \frac{1}{|z_0|}, \quad \forall \quad n \geq m$$

$\Rightarrow$ $\qquad\qquad |a_n z_0{}^n| < 1, \quad \forall \ \ n \geq m.$

Now

$$|a_n z^n| = |a_n z_0{}^n| - \left|\frac{z}{z_0}\right|^n < \left|\frac{z}{z_0}\right|^n, \quad \forall \ n \geq m$$

Comparing the two positive term series

$$|a_m z^m| + |a_{m+1} z^{m+1}| + \ldots \qquad\qquad \ldots(3)$$

$$\left|\frac{z}{z_0}\right|^m + \left|\frac{z}{z_0}\right|^{m+1} + \ldots,$$

where $\left|\dfrac{z}{z_0}\right| < 1$, we see that the series (3) is convergent. It then follows that the series

$$\Sigma a_n z^n,$$

is absolutely convergent.

Let, now, z be any number such that $|z| > r$ so that

$$\frac{1}{|z|} < \frac{1}{r} = \mu.$$

As $1/|z|$ is less than the upper limit μ, it follows that for an infinite number of values of n,

$$|a_n|^{1/n} > \frac{1}{|z|} \quad \Rightarrow \quad |a_n z^n| > 1.$$

Thus, $\lim (a_n z^n)$ cannot be zero and therefore the series cannot be convergent.

1. The theorem can also be stated in the following briefer form, for we may take $r = 0$ and $r = \infty$ in the cases I and II respectively.

For every power series $\Sigma a_n z^n$, there exists a non-negative real number r such that for every $|z| < r$, the series is absolutely convergent and for every $|z| > r$, the series is not convergent.

The number r is called the **Radius of Convergence** of the power series.

2. The above theorem does not make any statement concerning points z such that $|z| = r$. In fact, no general statement is possible and all conceivable types of behaviours are possible for point z such that $|z| = r$.

3. The series

$$\Sigma a_n (z - a)^n$$

converges for every z such that $|z - a| < r$ and does not converge for any z such that $|z - a| > r$, where

$$r = \frac{1}{\lim |a_n|^{1/n}}.$$

4. *If*

$$\lim \frac{a_{n+1}}{a_n}$$

exists and is equal to μ, then the radius of convergence of the power series $\Sigma a_n z^n$ is $1/\mu$.

This is a consequence of the fact that if $\lim |a_{n+1}/a_n|$ exists, then

$$\lim |a_n|^{1/n}$$

also exists and the two limits are equal.

Circle and Radius of Convergence of a Power Series. *The circle* $|z| = r$ *which includes in its interior* $|z| < r$ *all the values of z for which the power series* $\Sigma a_n z^n$ *converges, is called the circle of convergence of the series. The radius R of this circle is called the radius of convergence.*

(Avadh 2004; Kanpur 1998)

By Theorem III, we see that the radius of convergence r of a power series is given by

$$\frac{1}{r} = \overline{\lim} \, |a_n|^{1/n} \qquad \qquad ...(1)$$

This is known as **Hadamard's Formula** for the radius of convergence.

In practice, there is a simpler formula for finding r. It is given by

$$\frac{1}{r} = \lim_{n \to \infty} \left| \frac{a_{n+1}}{a_n} \right| \qquad \qquad ...(2)$$

provided the limit exists; whether finite or infinite.

The formula (2) follows from (1) and the Cauchy's second theorem on limits which states:

If $< u_n >$ *is a sequence of positive constants, then*

$$\lim_{n \to \infty} (u_n)^{1/n} = \lim_{n \to \infty} \left(\frac{u_{n+1}}{u_n} \right)$$

provided the limit on the right hand side exists; whether finite or infinite.

Note that nothing is said about convergence on the boundary of the circle $|z| = R$. It may converge or diverge on the boundary.

In view of the above definition, theorem III may be stated as:

A power series converges absolutely and uniformly within its circle of convergence and diverges outside it.

Theorem *The power series* $\sum_{n=0}^{\infty} a_n z^{n-1}$ *obtained by differentiating the power series* $\Sigma a_n z^n$ *has the same radius of convergence as the original series* $\Sigma a_n z^n$. *(Rohilkhand, 1999)*

From the definition of radius of convergence

$$\frac{1}{r} = \lim_{n \to \infty} |a_n|^{1/n} \quad \text{for } \Sigma a_n z^n$$

and

$$\frac{1}{r'} = \lim_{n \to \infty} |n a_n|^{1/n} \quad \text{for } \Sigma n a_n z^{n-1}.$$

In order to prove $r = r'$, we have to establish that

$$\lim_{n \to \infty} n^{1/n} = 1.$$

Now by Cauchy's theorem on limits, we have

$$\lim_{n \to \infty} a_n^{1/n} = \lim_{n \to \infty} \frac{a_{n+1}}{a_n}$$

$$\therefore \quad \lim_{n \to \infty} n^{1/n} = \lim_{n \to \infty} \frac{n+1}{n} = \lim_{n \to \infty} \left(1 + \frac{1}{n} \right)$$

$$= 1.$$

Hence $r = r'$.

Theorem *The sum function $f(z)$ of the power series $\sum\limits_{n=0}^{\infty} a_n z^n$ represents an analytic function at every point inside the circle of convergence of the power series.*

Further, every power series possesses derivatives of all orders within its circle of convergence and these derivatives are obtained through term by term differentiation of the series.

Or

Every power series represents an analytic function inside its circle of convergence.

(Banglore 2001, 2003, Mumbai 2001, Rohtak 2000, Rohilkhand, 2002 U.P.P.C.S. 2002)

Sum function. *If $f(z) = \sum\limits_{0}^{\infty} a_n z^n$, then $f(z)$ is called the sum function of the series.*

Let r be the radius of convergence of a given power series

$$\sum_{n=0}^{\infty} a_n z^n$$

and let $f(z)$ be its sum function.

It will be shown that $f(z)$ is analytic in the domain

$$|z| < r.$$

The radius of convergence of the power series

$$\sum_{n=0}^{\infty} n a_n z^{n-1};$$

the first term being zero, is also r.

In fact, if we write $b_n = n a_n$, we have

$$|b_n|^{1/n} = n^{1/n} |a_n|^{1/n} \text{ so that } \overline{\lim} |b_n|^{1/n} = \overline{\lim} |a_n|^{1/n}$$

for $\lim n^{1/n} = 1$.

Let z be any point of the domain $|z| < r$.

Then there exists a positive number ρ such that

$$|z| < \rho < r.$$

Take $z + h$ any point such that

$$|z + h| \le \rho < r,$$

so that $z + h$ is also a point of the domain

$$|z| < r.$$

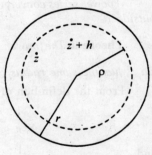

Fig. 6.1

We now have

$$\frac{f(z+h) - f(z)}{h} - \sum_{n=0}^{\infty} n a_n z^{n-1}$$

$$= \frac{\sum\limits_{n=0}^{\infty} a_n (z+h)^n - \sum\limits_{n=0}^{\infty} a_n z^n}{h} - \sum_{n=0}^{\infty} n a_n z^{n-1}$$

$$= \sum_{n=0}^{v} \left[a_n \frac{(z+h)^n - z^n}{h} - n a_n z^{n-1} \right]$$

$$+ \sum_{n=v+1}^{\infty} a_n \frac{(z+h)^n - z^n}{h} - \sum_{n=v+1}^{\infty} na_n z^{n-1} \qquad \qquad ...(1)$$

where v is any positive integer whatsoever.

Since $\sum_{n=0}^{\infty} na_n z^{n-1}$ is convergent, there exists, by definition, a positive integer m_1 such that $\forall \; v > m_1$

$$\left| \sum_{n=v+1}^{\infty} na_n z^{n-1} \right| < \varepsilon / 3; \qquad \qquad ...(2)$$

ε being a given positive number.

Now, we have

$$\frac{(z+h)^n - z^n}{(z+h) - z} = (z+h)^{n-1} + (z+h)^{n-2} z + ... + z^{n-1}$$

$$\therefore \left| \frac{(z+h)^n - z^n}{h} \right| < [| z+h |^{n-1} + | z+h |^{n-2} | z | + ... + | z |^{n-1}]$$

$$\leq (\rho^{n-1} + \rho^{n-2} \rho + ... + \rho^{n-1})$$
$$= n\rho^{n-1}.$$

Also, therefore,

$$\left| a_n \frac{(z+h)^n - z^n}{h} \right| \leq n | a_n | \rho^{n-1}.$$

As the series $\sum_{n=0}^{\infty} n | a_n | \rho^{n-1}$ is convergent, there exists a positive integer m_2 such that $\forall \; v > m_2$

$$\left| \sum_{n=v+1}^{\infty} n | a_n | \rho^{n-1} \right| < \varepsilon / 3$$

and hence also

$$\left| \sum_{n=v+1}^{\infty} a_n \frac{(z+h)^n - z^n}{h} \right| < \varepsilon / 3 \qquad \qquad ...(3)$$

Now, $m = \max (m_1, m_2).$

We have, from (1) taking m for v, and making use of (2) and (3)

$$\left| \frac{f(z+h) - f(z)}{h} - \sum_{n=0}^{\infty} na_n z^{n-1} \right|$$

$$\leq \left| \sum_{n=0}^{m} a_n \left[\frac{(z+h)^n - z^n}{h} - na_n z^{n-1} \right] \right|$$

$$+ \left| \sum_{n=m+1}^{\infty} a_n \frac{(z+h)^n - z^n}{h} \right| + \left| \sum_{n=m+1}^{\infty} na_n z^{n-1} \right|$$

$$< \left| \sum_{n=0}^{m} a_n \left[\frac{(z+h)^n - z^n}{h} - nz^{n-1} \right] \right| + \frac{\varepsilon}{3} + \frac{\varepsilon}{3}.$$

Also, because $a_n \dfrac{(z+h)^n - z^n}{h} \to na_n z^{n-1}$ as $h \to 0$,

and

$$\left| \sum_{n=0}^{m} a_n \left[\frac{(z+h)^n - z^n}{h} - nz^{n-1} \right] \right| \qquad \qquad ...(4)$$

is the sum of a *finite* number of terms only, we see that there exists a positive number δ such that for $|h| < \delta$, this sum is $< \varepsilon/3$.

Thus for $|h| < \delta$, we have

$$\left| \frac{f(z+h) - f(z)}{h} - \sum_{n=0}^{\infty} na_n z^{n-1} \right| < \varepsilon,$$

$\Rightarrow$

$$\lim_{h \to 0} \frac{f(z+h) - f(z)}{h} = \sum_{n=0}^{\infty} na_n z^{n-1}.$$

Hence $f(z)$ is derivable in the domain $|z| < r$ and

$$f'(z) = \sum_{n=0}^{\infty} na_n z^{n-1}$$

so that $f'(z)$ is given on term by term differentiation of the series for $f(z)$.

Thus $f(z)$ is analytic in $|z| < r$.

Cor. 1. *As the radius of convergence of the derived series $\Sigma na_n z^{n-1}$ is also r, we see that $f'(z)$ is also analytic in $|z| < r$. Successively differentiating and applying the theorem, we see that the sum function $f(z)$ of a power series with radius of convergence r possesses derivatives of every order in the domain $|z| < r$ and that the various derivatives are obtained through term by term differentiation of the series.*

Also further

$$a_n = \frac{f_n(0)}{n!}.$$

This follows on differentiating n times and putting $z = 0$.

Cor. 2. If instead of the series $\sum_{n=0}^{\infty} a_n z^n$, we consider the series

$$\sum_{n=0}^{\infty} a_n (z-a)^n,$$

with radius of convergence r, then the sum function $f(z)$ of this series is convergent in the domain $|z - a| < r$.

Moreover, as in Cor. 1,

$$a_n = \frac{f_n(a)}{n!}.$$

Note. The converse of the theorem above will be proved in Chapter 9. There it will be shown that if $f(z)$ is analytic in a certain circle with its centre at a, then $f(z)$ can be expressed as the sum of power series in terms of the powers of $(z - a)$.

Theorem VI. (Abel's Limit Theorem). *If $\sum\limits_0^\infty a_n$ converges, then $f(z) = \sum\limits_0^\infty a_n z^n$ tends to $f(1)$ as $z \to 1$ in such a manner that $|1 - z| / (1 - |z|)$ remains bounded.(Sagar 1999, 2003)*

There is no loss of generality if we suppose that $\sum\limits_0^\infty a_n = 0$, since this can be obtained by adding a constant to a_0. We have $f(1) = 0$. Now set

$$s_n = a_0 + a_1 + a_2 + \dots + a_n$$

and consider the identity

$$
\begin{aligned}
s_n(z) &= a_0 + a_1 z + a_2 z^2 + \dots + a_n z^n \\
&= s_0 + (s_1 - s_0) z + (s_2 - s_1) z^2 + \dots + (s_n - s_{n-1}) z^n \\
&= s_0 (1 - z) + s_1 (z - z^2) + \dots + s_{n-1} (z^{n-1} - z^n) + s_n z^n \\
&= (1 - z)(s_0 + s_1 z + \dots + s_{n-1} z^{n-1}) + s_n z^n.
\end{aligned}
$$

But $s_n z^n \to 0$, we can write

$$f(z) = (1 - z) \sum\limits_0^\infty s_n z^n.$$

Since $|1 - z| / (1 - |z|)$ remains bounded, there exists a positive constant k such that

$$|1 - z| / (1 - |z|) \le k \qquad \dots (1)$$

Again, since $s_n \to 0$ as $n \to \infty$, for given $\varepsilon > 0$ there exists a positive integer m such that $n \ge m$ implies $|s_n| < \varepsilon$. $\qquad \dots (2)$

Now

$$
\begin{aligned}
|f(z)| &= \left| (1 - z) \sum\limits_0^\infty s_n z^n \right| \\
&\le \left| (1 - z) \sum\limits_0^{m-1} s_n z^n \right| + \left| (1 - z) \sum\limits_m^\infty s_n z^n \right| \\
&\le |1 - z| \left| \sum\limits_0^{m-1} s_n z^n \right| + |1 - z| \sum\limits_m^\infty |s_n| |z|^n \\
&< |1 - z| \left| \sum\limits_0^{m-1} s_n z^n \right| + |1 - z| \sum\limits_m^\infty \varepsilon |z|^n \times 6 \text{ by (2)} \\
&= |1 - z| \left| \sum\limits_0^{m-1} s_n z^n \right| + |1 - z| \frac{\varepsilon |z|^m}{(1 - |z|)} \text{ (Summing the G.P.)} \\
&\le |1 - z| \left| \sum\limits_0^{m-1} s_n z^n \right| + \frac{\varepsilon |1 - z|}{(1 - |z|)} \\
&\le |1 - z| \left| \sum\limits_0^{m-1} s_n z^n \right| + k\varepsilon \text{ by (1).}
\end{aligned}
$$

The first term of right hand side can be made as small as we please by taking z sufficiently close to 1. It follows that $f(z) \to 0 = f(1)$ as $z \to 1$ subject to the stated conditions.

EXAMPLES

1. *Find the radii of convergence of the following power series*:

(a) $\sum \dfrac{1}{n^n} z^n$ (*Kerala 1999, 2003, Kanpur 2003*)

(b) $\sum \dfrac{z^n}{n!}$

(c) $\sum \dfrac{n!}{n^n} z^n$ (*Kanpur 2004*)   (d) $\sum 2^{\sqrt{n}} z^n$

(e) $\sum \left(1 + \dfrac{1}{n}\right)^{n^2} z^n$ (f) $\sum \dfrac{1}{n^p} z^n$.

Solution. (a) We have

$$a_n = \frac{1}{n^n}$$

$\Rightarrow$
$$|a_n|^{1/n} = \frac{1}{n} \to 0, \text{ as } n \to \infty.$$

Thus ∞, is the radius of convergence so that the series converges for every value of z.

(b) We have

$$a_n = \frac{1}{n!}, \quad a_{n+1} = \frac{1}{(n+1)!}$$

Thus

$$\left|\frac{a_{n+1}}{a_n}\right| = \frac{1}{n+1} \to 0.$$

Hence ∞, is the radius of convergence.

(c) We have

$$a_n = \frac{n!}{n^n} \text{ so that } a_{n+1} = \frac{(n+1)!}{(n+1)^{n+1}}.$$

Thus

$$\frac{a_{n+1}}{a_n} = \frac{1}{\left(1 + \dfrac{1}{n}\right)^n} \to \frac{1}{e} \text{ as } n \to \infty.$$

Hence e is the radius of convergence.

(d) We have

$$a_n = 2^{\sqrt{n}}$$

$\Rightarrow$
$$a_n^{1/n} = 2^{\sqrt{1/n}} \to 1 \text{ as } n \to \infty.$$

Hence 1 is the radius of convergence.

(e) We have

$$a_n = \left(1 + \frac{1}{n}\right)^{n^2}$$

so that

$$| a_n |^{1/n} = \left(1 + \frac{1}{n}\right)^n \to e.$$

Hence e^{-1}, is the radius of convergence.

(f) We have

$$a_n = \frac{1}{n^p}, \quad a_{n+1} = \frac{1}{(n+1)^p}.$$

Thus

$$\frac{a_{n+1}}{a_n} = \frac{1}{\left(1 + \frac{1}{n}\right)^p} \to 1.$$

Hence 1 is the radius of convergence.

2. *Show that* :

(i) Σz^n *does not converge at any point of the circle of convergence.*

(ii) $\Sigma z^n/n^2$ *converges at every point on the circle of convergence.*

(iii) $\Sigma z^n/n$ *converges at every point of the circle of convergence other than 1.*

(iv) $\Sigma z^{np}/n$ *converges at every point of the circle of convergence with the exception of p, points.*

Solution. (i) The radius of convergence is 1. For every point z on the circle of convergence, we have

$$| z^n | = | z |^n = 1$$

so that, the general term does *not* tend to zero.

Hence the series does not converge for any point on the circle of convergence.

(ii) The radius of convergence is 1. Also for any point z on the circle of convergence,

$$\left| \frac{z^n}{n^2} \right| = \frac{| z |^n}{n^2} = \frac{1}{n^2}.$$

Also the series $\Sigma \, (1/n^2)$ is known to converge so that $\Sigma \, (z^n/n^2)$ converges absolutely for every point on the circle of convergence.

(iii) The radius of convergence is 1. Also for $z = 1$,

$$\frac{z^n}{n} = \frac{1}{n}$$

and the series $\Sigma \, (1/n)$ is not convergent.

To prove that the series is convergent for every other point on the circle of convergence, we shall use theorem II.

Take

$$a_n = z^n, \quad v_n = \frac{1}{n}.$$

Then

$$| 1 + z + \ldots + z^n | = \left| \frac{1 - z^n}{1 - z} \right|, \quad z \neq 1$$

$$\leq \frac{1+|z|^n}{|1-z|} = \frac{2}{|1-z|}$$

so that the sequence of partial sums of the series Σa_n is bounded.

Also $\qquad v_n - v_{n+1} = \frac{1}{n} - \frac{1}{n+1} = \frac{1}{n(n+1)}$

so that $\Sigma |v_n - v_{n+1}|$ is a convergent series.

Further $\qquad \lim v_n = \lim \frac{1}{n} = 0.$

Thus the series $\Sigma a_n v_n$, i.e., the series

$$\Sigma z^n/n$$

converges for every z other than 1 on the circle of convergence.

    (iv) We write $z^p = Z$. Then, by (iii) above, we see that the series $\Sigma z^{np}/n$ converges for every point z on the circle of convergence other than the points z for which $z^p = 1$. These latter are the p points.

    3. *Find the radius of convergence of the series*

$$\frac{z}{2} + \frac{1\cdot3}{2\cdot5}z^2 + \frac{1\cdot3\cdot5}{2\cdot5\cdot8}z^3 + \dots\dots \qquad\qquad (G.N.D.U.\ 2000)$$

Solution. $\qquad a_n = \dfrac{1\cdot3\cdot5\ \dots\ (2n-1)}{2\cdot5\cdot8\ \dots\ (3n-1)}$

$$a_{n+1} = \frac{1\cdot3\cdot5\ \dots\ (2n-1)\,(2n+1)}{2\cdot5\cdot8\ \dots\ (3n-1)\,(3n+2)}$$

$$\therefore\qquad \frac{a_{n+1}}{a_n} = \frac{3n+2}{2n+1} = \frac{3+\dfrac{2}{n}}{2+\dfrac{1}{n}}$$

$$\therefore\qquad \frac{1}{r} = \lim_{n\to\infty}\left|\frac{a_{n+1}}{a_n}\right| = \frac{3}{2} \implies r = \frac{2}{3}.$$

    4. *Find the radius of convergence of the power series*

$$f(z) = \sum_0^\infty \frac{z^n}{2^n+1} \qquad\qquad (Avadh\ 2005,\ Meerut\ 2004)$$

and prove that $(2-z)f(z) - 2 \to 0$ *as* $z \to 2.$

Solution. $\qquad a_n = \dfrac{1}{2^n+1}, \quad a_{n+1} = \dfrac{1}{2^{n+1}+1}$

$$\frac{1}{r} = \lim_{n\to\infty}\left|\frac{a_{n+1}}{a_n}\right| = \lim_{n\to\infty}\frac{1}{2\cdot2^n+1}\cdot(2^n+1)$$

$$= \lim_{n\to\infty}\frac{1+\dfrac{1}{2^n}}{2+\dfrac{1}{2^n}} = \frac{1}{2} \implies r = 2.$$

$$f(z) = \sum_{0}^{\infty} \frac{z^n}{2^n + 1} < \sum_{0}^{\infty} \frac{z^n}{2^n}$$

$$= 1 + \frac{z}{2} + \frac{z^2}{2^2} + \ldots = \frac{1}{1 - z/2} = \frac{2}{2 - z}$$

because $|z| < 2$ for all z within the circle of convergence.

$$\therefore \lim_{z \to 2} (2 - z) f(z) = \lim_{z \to 2} (2 - z) \cdot \frac{2}{2 - z} = 2$$

$$\Rightarrow \quad (2 - z) f(z) - 2 \to 0 \text{ as } z \to 2.$$

5. *If r_1 and r_2 are the radii of convergence of the power series $\Sigma a_n z^n$ and $\Sigma b_n z^n$ respectively, then show that the radius of convergence of the power series $\Sigma a_n b_n z^n$ is $r_1 r_2$.* (Kerala 2001)

Solution. $\quad \dfrac{1}{r_1} = \lim_{n \to \infty} |a_n|^{1/n}, \quad \dfrac{1}{r_2} = \lim_{n \to \infty} |b_n|^{1/n}$ (By hypothesis)

If r be the radius of convergence of $\Sigma a_n b_n z^n$, then

$$\frac{1}{r} = \lim_{n \to \infty} |a_n b_n|^{1/n} = \lim_{n \to \infty} |a_n|^{1/n} \lim_{n \to \infty} |b_n|^{1/n},$$

$$= \frac{1}{r_1} \cdot \frac{1}{r_2} \quad \Rightarrow \quad r = r_1 r_2.$$

6. *Find the domain of convergence of the following power series*

(a) $\displaystyle\sum \left(\frac{iz - 1}{2 + i} \right)^n$ \qquad (b) $\displaystyle\sum \left(\frac{2i}{z + 1 + i} \right)^n$

(c) $\displaystyle\sum \frac{1 \cdot 3 \cdot 5 \ldots (2n - 1)}{n!} \left(\frac{1 - z}{z} \right)^n.$ \qquad (Rohilkhand, 2001)

Solution. (a) $\quad u_n = \left(\dfrac{iz - 1}{2 + i} \right)^n, \quad u_{n+1} = \left(\dfrac{iz - 1}{2 + i} \right)^{n+1}$

$$\lim_{n \to \infty} \left| \frac{u_{n+1}}{u_n} \right| = \lim_{n \to \infty} \left| \frac{iz - 1}{2 + i} \right| = \frac{|iz - 1|}{\sqrt{5}}.$$

The series is convergent if $\dfrac{|iz - 1|}{\sqrt{5}} < 1$

$$\Rightarrow \qquad |iz + i^2| < \sqrt{5} \quad \Rightarrow \quad |i(z + i)| \le 5$$

$$\Rightarrow \qquad |z + i| < 5, \text{ as } |i| = 1.$$

This relation implies that the given series is convergent for those points z which lie inside the circle whose radius is $\sqrt{5}$ and is centred at the point $z = -i$.

(b) $\qquad u_n = \left(\dfrac{2i}{z + 1 + i} \right)^n, \quad u_{n+1} = \left(\dfrac{2i}{z + 1 + i} \right)^{n+1}$

$$\lim_{n \to \infty} \left| \frac{u_{n+1}}{u_n} \right| = \lim_{n \to \infty} \left| \frac{2i}{z + 1 + i} \right|$$

$$= \frac{2}{|z+1+i|}, \text{ as } |i| = 1$$

∴ The series is convergent if

$$\frac{2}{|z+1+i|} < 1$$

⇒ if $|z+1+i| > 2$.

This implies that the given series is convergent for all those points z which lie outside the circle centred at $z = -(1+i)$ and of radius 2.

(c) $$u_n = \frac{1 \cdot 3 \cdot 5 \ldots (2n-1)}{n!} \left(\frac{1-z}{z}\right)^n$$

$$u_{n+1} = \frac{1 \cdot 3 \cdot 5 \ldots (2n-1)(2n+1)}{(n+1)!} \left(\frac{1-z}{z}\right)^{n+1}$$

$$\lim_{n \to \infty} \left| \frac{u_{n+1}}{u_n} \right| = \lim_{n \to \infty} \left| \frac{n!}{(n+1)!} \cdot (2n+1) \left(\frac{1-z}{z}\right) \right|$$

$$= \lim_{n \to \infty} \left| \frac{2n+1}{n+1} \cdot \frac{1-z}{z} \right| = 2 \cdot \frac{|1-z|}{|z|}.$$

The series is convergent if

$$2 \frac{|1-z|}{|z|} < 1 \quad \Rightarrow \quad 4|1-z|^2 < |z|^2$$

⇒ $$4(1-z)(1-\bar{z}) < z\bar{z}$$

⇒ $$4 - 4(z+\bar{z}) + 3z\bar{z} < 0$$

⇒ $$z\bar{z} - \frac{4}{3} \cdot (z+\bar{z}) + \frac{4}{3} < 0$$

⇒ $$z\bar{z} - \frac{4}{3}(z+\bar{z}) + \frac{16}{9} < \frac{16}{9} - \frac{4}{3}$$

⇒ $$\left(z - \frac{4}{3}\right)\left(\bar{z} - \frac{4}{3}\right) < \frac{4}{9}$$

⇒ $$\left| z - \frac{4}{3} \right|^2 < \frac{4}{9} \quad \Rightarrow \quad \left| z - \frac{4}{3} \right| < \frac{2}{3}.$$

This relation implies that the given series is convergent for those points z which lie inside the circle centred at $z = 4/3$ and radius = 2/3.

7. *Find the region of convergence of the following power series:*

(a) $$\sum_{n=1}^{\infty} \frac{(z+2)^{n-1}}{(n+1)^3 \, 4^n},$$

(b) $$\sum_{n=1}^{\infty} n! z^n,$$ *(Gujarat 2004)*

(c) $$\sum_{n=1}^{\infty} \frac{(-1)^{n-1} z^{2n-1}}{(2n-1)!}.$$

Solution. (a) Clearly for $z = -2$ the given series is convergent. Excluding $z = -2$, we have

$$\lim_{n \to \infty} \left| \frac{u_{n+1}}{u_n} \right| = \lim_{n \to \infty} \left| \left(\frac{n+1}{n+2} \right)^3 \cdot \frac{1}{4} (z + 2) \right|$$

$$= \frac{1}{4} |z + 2|.$$

Therefore, the given series is convergent if the above limit is less than 1,

i.e., $\dfrac{|z + 2|}{4} < 1 \Rightarrow |z + 2| < 4.$

The point $z = -2$ is included in $|z + 2| < 4$.

However, if $\dfrac{|z + 2|}{4} = 1$, i.e., $|z + 2| = 4$, then the test fails.

In this case

$$|u_n| = \left| \frac{(z + 2)^{n-1}}{(n+1)^3 \cdot 4^n} \right| = \frac{1}{4 (n+1)^3} < \frac{1}{n^3}, \text{ as } |z + 2| = 4.$$

But $\Sigma (1/n^3)$ is convergent as $p = 3$, i.e. > 1 and $|u_n| \le |v_n|$ and $\Sigma |v_n|$ is convergent therefore the given series is also convergent absolutely.

Combining the two results, we conclude that the given series converges within and on the circle whose centre is at $z = -2$ and radius $= 4$.

(b) Clearly for $z = 0$ the series is convergent. Hence excluding $z = 0$, we have

$$\lim_{n \to \infty} \left| \frac{u_{n+1}}{u_n} \right| = \lim_{n \to \infty} |(n + 1) z| = \infty > 1 \text{ if } |z| \ne 0.$$

Therefore, the given series does not converge for any z except for $z = 0$.

(c) Clearly for $z = 0$ the series is convergent. Hence excluding $z = 0$, we have

$$\lim_{n \to \infty} \left| \frac{u_{n+1}}{u_n} \right| = \lim_{n \to \infty} \left| - \frac{(2n-1)!}{(2n+1)!} z^2 \right|$$

$$= \lim_{n \to \infty} \frac{|z|^2}{(2n+1)(2n)} = 0 < 1.$$

Hence the given series converges for all values of z.

8. *For what values of z does the series*

$$\sum_{n=0}^{\infty} (-1)^n (z^n + z^{n+1})$$

converge and find its sum?

Solution. Clearly the series converges for $z = 0$.

$$u_n = (-1)^n (z^n + z^{n+1})$$

$$u_{n+1} = (-1)^{n+1} (z^{n+1} + z^{n+2}) = - (-1)^n z (z^n + z^{n+1})$$

$$\therefore \quad \lim_{n \to \infty} \left| \frac{u_{n+1}}{u_n} \right| = \lim_{n \to \infty} |z| = |z|.$$

Hence the given series is convergent if $|z| < 1$ and the point $z = 0$ is included in $|z| < 1$.

Let S_n be the sum of first n terms of the series.

$$\therefore \quad S_n = (1 - z + z^2 - \ldots \text{ to } n \text{ terms}) + (z - z^2 + z^3 - \ldots \text{ to } n \text{ terms})$$

$$= \frac{1 - (-z)^n}{1 + z} + z \cdot \frac{1 - (-z)^n}{1 + z}$$

$$= (1 + z) \cdot \frac{1 - (-z)^n}{1 + z} = 1 - (-z)^n$$

$$\therefore \quad S = \lim_{n \to \infty} S_n = 1 \text{ as } |z| < 1.$$

9. *For what values of z does the series*

$$\sum_{n=1}^{\infty} \frac{1}{(z^2 + 1)^n}$$ (C.S.I.R. (Net) 2005)

converges and find its sum ?

Solution. Clearly

$$\lim_{n \to \infty} \left| \frac{u_{n+1}}{u_n} \right| = \lim_{n \to \infty} \left| \frac{1}{z^2 + 1} \right| = \frac{1}{|z^2 + 1|}.$$

Hence the series converges if $\dfrac{1}{|z^2 + 1|} < 1$ or $|z^2 + 1| > 1.$

Let $S_n (z)$ be the sum of first n terms of the given series, then

$$S_n = \frac{1}{(z^2 + 1)} + \frac{1}{(z^2 + 1)^2} + \ldots + n \text{ terms}$$

$$= \frac{1}{(z^2 + 1)} \cdot \frac{1 - \dfrac{1}{(z^2 + 1)^n}}{1 - \dfrac{1}{z^2 + 1}}$$

$$= \frac{1}{z^2} \left[1 - \frac{1}{(z^2 + 1)^n} \right].$$

Then

$$S(z) = \lim_{n \to \infty} S_n (z) = \lim_{n \to \infty} \frac{1}{z^2} \left[1 - \frac{1}{(z^2 + 1)^n} \right]$$

$$= \frac{1}{z^2}, \text{ as } |z^2 + 1| > 1.$$

10. *Examine the behaviour of the power series*

$$\sum \frac{z^{4n}}{4n + 1}$$

on the circle of convergence.

Solution. Here

$$a_n = \frac{1}{4n + 1}, \quad a_{n+1} = \frac{1}{4n + 5}$$

$$\frac{1}{r} = \lim_{n \to \infty} \left| \frac{a_{n+1}}{a_n} \right| = \lim_{n \to \infty} \left| \frac{4n+1}{4n+5} \right| = 1$$

$\therefore \qquad\qquad r = 1.$

Hence the circle of convergence is of radius 1 and centred at $z = 0$.

Now at the points $z = \pm 1, \pm i$ ($|z| = 1$) on the circle of convergence the given series takes the form $\Sigma [1/(4n+1)]$ which we know is divergent on comparison with a divergent series $\Sigma (1/n)$. Thus the given series is not convergent for points $z = \pm 1, \pm i$ on the circle of convergence.

Now, we shall examine the behaviour of the series for every value of z on the circle of convergence except $z = \pm 1, \pm i$. For this we shall make use of Dritchilet's test.

Let $\displaystyle\sum \frac{z^{4n}}{4n+1} = \Sigma a_n u_n$ where $a_n = z^n$, $u_n = \dfrac{1}{4n+1}$.

The following conditions are satisfied.

(i)
$$|S_n| = |\Sigma a_n| = |1 + z^4 + z^8 + \dots + z^{(4n-1)}|$$

$$= \left| \frac{1 - (z^4)^n}{1 - z^4} \right| \le \frac{1 + |z|^{4n}}{|1 - z^4|}, \; z \ne \pm 1, \pm i$$

$$= \frac{2}{|1 - z^4|} \text{ on } |z| = 1.$$

This proves that the sequence $< S_n >$ of partial sums is bounded.

(ii)
$$\lim_{n \to \infty} u_n = \lim_{n \to \infty} \frac{1}{4n+1} = 0.$$

(iii) $\displaystyle \Sigma (u_n - u_{n+1}) = \sum \left(\frac{1}{4n+1} - \frac{1}{4n+5} \right)$

$$= \sum \frac{4}{(4n+1)(4n+5)}.$$

This is convergent as is clear on comparison with $\Sigma 1/n^p$.

Therefore the series

$$\Sigma a_n u_n = \sum \frac{z^{4n}}{4n+1}$$

is convergent for every value of z other than $z = \pm 1$, $z = \pm i$ on the circle of convergence.

11. *Examine the behaviour of the series*

$$\sum_{n=2}^{\infty} \frac{z^n}{n (\log n)^2}$$

on the circle of convergence.   (*Rohilkhand, 2000*)

Solution. Here

$$a_n = \frac{1}{n (\log n)^2}, \quad a_{n+1} = \frac{1}{(n+1) [\log (n+1)]^2}$$

$\therefore \qquad\qquad \dfrac{a_n}{a_{n+1}} = \dfrac{n+1}{n} \cdot \left[\dfrac{\log (n+1)}{\log n} \right]^2$

$$= \frac{n+1}{n} \cdot \left[\frac{\log n \, (1+1/n)}{\log n} \right]^2$$

$$= \left(1 + \frac{1}{n} \right) \left[\frac{\log n + \log \, (1+1/n)}{\log n} \right]^2$$

$$= \left(1 + \frac{1}{n} \right) \left(\frac{\log n + \frac{1}{n} - \frac{1}{2n^2} + \dots}{\log n} \right)^2$$

$$= \left(1 + \frac{1}{n} \right) \left(1 + \frac{1}{n \log n} - \frac{1}{2n^2 \log n} + \dots \right)^2$$

$$\therefore \quad \frac{1}{r} = \lim_{n \to \infty} \left| \frac{a_{n+1}}{a_n} \right| = 1 \implies r = 1.$$

Hence the radius of the circle of convergence is 1 and its centre is at $z = 0$.

Now for every point on the circle of convergence

$$\left| \frac{z^n}{n \, (\log n)^2} \right| = \frac{|z|^n}{|n \, (\log n)^2|} = \frac{1}{n \, (\log n)^2}$$

as $|z| = 1$ on the circle.

But by Cauchy's condensation test we know that

$$\sum_{n=2}^{\infty} \frac{1}{n \, (\log n)^2}$$

is convergent for every point z on the circle of convergence.

6.13. Exponential, Trigonometric and Hyperbolic Functions of a Complex Variable. We shall now define Exponential, Trigonometric and Hyperbolic functions of a complex variable and obtain some of their basic properties. We start with a theorem.

Theorem. *The power series*

$$\sum_{n=0}^{\infty} \frac{z^n}{n!} = 1 + z + \frac{z^2}{2!} + \dots + \frac{z^n}{n!} + \dots$$

is absolutely convergent for every value of z.

Here we have

$$a_n = \frac{1}{n!}.$$

$$\implies \quad \frac{a_{n+1}}{a_n} = \frac{1}{n+1} \to 0 \text{ as } n \to \infty.$$

Thus for the power series, in question, the radius of convergence is infinity and accordingly the series converges for every value of z.

Exponential Function. Def. *The sum function of the everywhere convergent series*

$$\sum \frac{z^n}{n!}$$

is called the Exponential Function z and is denoted by E (z).

The function E (z) is defined for every value of z and is also, by the preceding § 6.10, analytic in every domain and

$$d[\text{E}\,(z)]/dz = \text{E}\,(z)$$

with the initial value E $(0) = 1$.

Again by definition, $\dfrac{d}{dz}[\text{E}(z)] = \text{E}(z)$ for all z and so E (z) is an analytic function of z in the whole complex plane.

Also it is evident from the power series that E (z) *never vanishes.*

Note. The definition of E (z) shows that when z is real and equal to x, then E (z) is same as e^x, as defined in real variables. We have here avoided writing the indicial form e^z and have instead written E (z). It is because we have not so far defined the generalised power a^b where a, b are complex numbers and, moreover, it will be seen that this is in general infinite valued. Thus the symbol e^z, interpreted as 'e raised to the power z' is in general infinite valued. It will however be seen that E (z) denotes one of the values of e^n.

6.13.1. The addition theorem for the Exponential Function.

Theorem. $\qquad$ $E\,(z_1 + z_2) = E\,(z_1)\,E\,(z_2)$,

for any pair of numbers z_1, z_2.

We have

$$\text{E}\,(z_1) = 1 + z_1 + \frac{z_1^2}{2!} + \ldots + \frac{z_1^n}{n!} + \ldots$$

$$\text{E}\,(z_2) = 1 + z_2 + \frac{z_2^2}{2!} + \ldots + \frac{z_2^n}{n!} + \ldots$$

As these two series are absolutely convergent, we can use the multiplication theorem of § 6.8.

The $(n + 1)$th term of the product

$$= \frac{z_2^n}{n!} + \frac{z_2^{n-1}}{(n-1)!}\cdot\frac{z_1}{1!} + \frac{z_2^{n-2}}{(n-2)!}\cdot\frac{z_1^2}{2!} + \ldots + \frac{z_1^n}{n!}$$

$$= \frac{1}{n!}\left[z_2^n + n z_2^{n-1} z_1 + \frac{n\,(n-1)}{2!}\, z_2^{n-2} z_1^2 + \ldots + z_1^n \right]$$

$$= \frac{1}{n!}(z_2 + z_1)^n.$$

The product series therefore

$$= 1 + (z_1 + z_2) + \frac{(z_1 + z_2)^2}{2!} + \ldots + \frac{(z_1 + z_2)^n}{n!} + \ldots$$

$$= \text{E}\,(z_1 + z_2).$$

Thus we have proved that

$$\text{E}\,(z_1 + z_2) = \text{E}\,(z_1)\,\text{E}\,(z_2),\ \forall\ z_1\ \text{and}\ z_2.$$

Cor. *Non-vanishing of E (z)*. From the addition formula, we deduce that

$$E (z) E (- z) = E (0) = 1.$$

This shows that E $(z) \neq 0$, for any value of z.

6.13.2. Trigonometrical functions sin z, cos z.

We *define* sin z and cos z in terms of the exponential function E (z) as follows for all z:

$$\sin z = \frac{E (iz) - E (- iz)}{2i}, \quad \cos z = \frac{E (iz) + E (- iz)}{2i}.$$

Clearly sin z and cos z are defined for every value of z.

Employing the power series for E (z), we may see that we have the following power series for sin z and cos z:

$$\sin z = z - \frac{z^3}{3!} + \frac{z^5}{5!} - ..... + \frac{(-1)^n z^{2n+1}}{(2n+1)!} + ...$$

$$\cos z = 1 - \frac{z^2}{2!} + \frac{z^4}{4!} - ..... + \frac{(-1)^n z^{2n}}{(2n)!} + ...$$

Clearly sin z and cos z are real when z is real.

We may also, by Cauchy-Hadamard Theorem of § 6.12.1 directly verify that these power series are convergent for every value of z. Also they are analytic in every domain and

$$\frac{d}{dz} (\sin z) = \cos z, \quad \frac{d}{dz} (\cos z) = - \sin z.$$

We may easily verify that

$$\sin (- z) = - \sin z \text{ and } \cos (- z) = \cos z$$

$$\sin 0 = 0 \text{ and } \cos 0 = 1.$$

Note. Clearly the definitions of sin z and cos z agree with those of sin x and cos x when z is the real number x.

Euler's Equation. From above we obtain the Euler's relation

$$E (iz) = \cos z + i \sin z.$$

Thus we have if $z = \alpha + i\beta$,

$$E (\alpha + i\beta) = E (\alpha) E (i\beta) = E (\alpha) (\cos \beta + i \sin \beta),$$

so that E (α) is the modulus and β the argument of E $(\alpha + i\beta)$.

6.13.3. *Addition formulae for sin z and cos z.* We have

$$E [i (z_1 + z_2)] = E (iz_1) E (iz_2).$$

$\Rightarrow$ $$\cos (z_1 + z_2) + i \sin (z_1 + z_2) = (\cos z_1 + i \sin z_1) (\cos z_2 + i \sin z_2).$$

Changing z_1, z_2 to $- z_1$ and $- z_2$ respectively, we obtain,

$$\cos (z_1 + z_2) - i \sin (z_1 + z_2) = (\cos z_1 - i \sin z_1) (\cos z_2 - i \sin z_2).$$

Multiplying out the right hand sides and separately adding and subtracting, we obtain

$$\cos (z_1 + z_2) = \cos z_1 \cos z_2 - \sin z_1 \sin z_2, \quad \text{...(1)}$$

$$\sin (z_1 + z_2) = \sin z_1 \cos z_2 + \cos z_1 \sin z_2 \quad \text{...(2)}$$

Changing z_2 to $- z_2$, we can obtain the corresponding results for

$$\cos (z_1 - z_2) \text{ and } \sin (z_1 - z_2).$$

In (1), if we replace z_1 by z and z_2 by $- z$, we obtain

$$\cos^2 z + \sin^2 z = 1.$$

Ex. Prove that

(i) $\sin z_1 + \sin z_2 = 2 \sin \frac{1}{2} (z_1 + z_2) \cos \frac{1}{2} (z_1 - z_2)$

(ii) $\cos z_1 + \cos z_2 = 2 \cos \frac{1}{2} (z_1 + z_2) \cos \frac{1}{2} (z_1 - z_2)$

(iii) $\sin \left(z + \frac{1}{2} \pi \right) = \cos z, \ \cos \left(z + \frac{1}{2} \pi \right) = - \sin z$

(iv) $\sin (z + \pi) = - \sin z, \ \cos (z + \pi) = - \cos z$

6.13.4. Hyperbolic functions $\sinh z$, $\cosh z$. They are defined as follows for all z:

$$\cosh z = \frac{E(z) + E(-z)}{2}, \ \sinh z = \frac{E(z) - E(-z)}{2}.$$

From these, we obtain the following power series expressions for $\sinh z$ and $\cosh z$.

$$\sinh z = z + \frac{z^3}{3!} + \frac{z^5}{5!} + \ldots + \frac{z^{2n+1}}{(2n+1)!} + \ldots \quad \ldots(1)$$

$$\cosh z = 1 + \frac{z^2}{2!} + \frac{z^4}{4!} + \ldots + \frac{z^{2n}}{(2n)!} + \ldots \quad \ldots(2)$$

Clearly $\sinh z$ and $\cosh z$ are real when z is real.

From definitions, it is clear that $\sinh z$ and $\cosh z$ are defined for every value of z, and are analytic in every domain. This fact may also be directly verified by showing that the power series (3) and (4) are convergent for every value of z.

6.13.5. Relations between Trigonometric and Hyperbolic functions. The following relations may be verified directly from the definitions:

$$\sin (iz) = i \sinh z, \ \sinh (iz) = i \sin z,$$

$$\cos (iz) = \cosh z, \ \cosh (iz) = \cos z.$$

Ex. Prove the addition formulae for $\sinh z$ and $\cosh z$.

6.14. Zeros of $\sin z$, $\cos z$.

We have

$$\sin z = \sin (x + iy)$$

$$= \sin x \cosh y + i \cos x \sinh y \quad \ldots(1)$$

$\Leftrightarrow$

$$|\sin z|^2 = \sin^2 x \cosh^2 y + \cos^2 x \sinh^2 y$$

$$= \sin^2 x (1 + \sinh^2 y) + (1 - \sin^2 x) \sinh^2 y$$

$$= \sin^2 x + \sinh^2 y.$$

Thus $\sin z = 0$ if and only if

$$\sin x = 0, \ \sinh y = 0, \ x \text{ and } y \text{ being real}$$

$\Leftrightarrow$

$$x = n\pi, \ y = 0,$$

n being any integer.

Hence *the zeros of $\sin z$ are given by $z = n\pi$; n being any integer.*

Again, we have

$$\cos z = \cos (x + iy)$$

$$= \cos x \cosh y - i \sin x \sinh y \quad \ldots(2)$$

$\Leftrightarrow$
$$| \cos z |^2 = \cos^2 x \cosh^2 y + \sin^2 x \sinh^2 y$$
$$= \cos^2 x \, (1 + \sinh^2 y) + (1 - \cos^2 x) \sinh^2 y$$
$$= \cos^2 x + \sinh^2 y.$$

Thus $\cos z = 0$ if and only if
$$\cos x = 0, \sinh y = 0$$

$\Leftrightarrow$
$$x = (2n + 1) \frac{\pi}{2}, \quad y = 0,$$

n being any integer.

Hence *the zeros of $\cos z$ are given by*
$$z = (2n + 1) \frac{\pi}{2};$$

n being any integer.

Note 1. From above we see that the zeros of $\sin z$, $\cos z$ are all real and are the same as those of $\sin x$, where x is real.

Note 2. From (1) and (2), we may easily deduce that $\sin z$ is real when z is real or when $R(z) = (2n + 1) \, \pi/2$, and $\cos z$ is real when z is real or when $R(z) = n\pi$; n being any integer.

6.15. Periods of $\sin z$, $\cos z$, E (z). *A number $k \neq 0$ is said to be a period of $f(z)$, if*
$$f(z + k) = f(z),$$

for every z.

Let k be a period of $\sin z$ so that
$$\sin (z + k) = \sin z,$$

for every z.

Putting $z = 0$, we see that k must satisfy
$$\sin k = 0 \implies k = n\pi. \qquad\qquad ....(1)$$

Further
$$\sin (z + n\pi) = (-1)^n \sin z = \sin z,$$

if and only if n is even.

Thus we see that the *periods of $\sin z$ are given by*
$$2n\pi,$$

where n is any integer.

The number 2π such that every period is an integral multiple of the same is called a *Primitive* period or often simply the period.

Further since
$$\cos z = \sin \left(\frac{1}{2}\pi + z \right),$$

we see *that 2π is also a primitive period of $\cos z$.*

Period of E (z). If k be a period of E (z), we have
$$E(z + k) = E(z), \ \forall \ z.$$

Putting $z = 0$, we see that k satisfies E $(k) = 1$.

If
$$k = \alpha + i\beta,$$

we have

$$E(\alpha + i\beta) = 1$$

$$\Leftrightarrow \quad E(\alpha)(\cos\beta + i\sin\beta) = 1$$

$$\Leftrightarrow \quad E(\alpha) = 1, \beta = 2n\pi.$$

Thus we have

$$\alpha = 0, \beta = 2n\pi.$$

Also we may verify that $\alpha + i\beta = 2in\pi$ is a period of $E(z)$.

Thus the periods of $E(z)$ are given by

$$2in\pi,$$

n being any integer and are thus all purely imaginary.

The *number $2i\pi$ is the primitive period of $E(z)$.*

6.16. Inverse of E (z). Logarithmic Function. Consider $w = E(z)$.

Now to each value of z corresponds a value of w. We shall now consider the inverse problem and examine the existence of z such that $E(z)$ has a given value w. From the foregoing, it is already clear that no value of z will correspond to $w = 0$ in view of the periodic character of $E(z)$, we see that if one value of z corresponds to a given w, then an infinite number of such values of z correspond to the same w.

Suppose now that w is given so that we have to examine the existence of $z = x + iy$ such that

$$E(x + iy) = w \quad \Leftrightarrow \quad E(x)(\cos y + i\sin y) = w.$$

This gives

$$E(x) = |w| \qquad \qquad \qquad ...(1)$$

$$y = \arg w \qquad \qquad \qquad ...(2)$$

Thus if $|w| \neq 0$, *i.e.*, $w \neq 0$, (1) gives a single value of x, *viz.*,

$$x = \log|w|.$$

Here $\log|w|$ stands for the real logarithm of the positive real number $|w|$.

Also then, from (2), y is infinite valued.

Thus we have

$$z = x + iy = \log|w| + i \arg w,$$

where arg w is infinite valued.

Def. Log _w_. By definition, we write

$$z = Log\, w,$$

if $\qquad \qquad w = E(z).$

From above we see that Log w is defined for every value of w other than 0 and that it is infinite valued; different values of the same differing from each other by integral multiples of $2i\pi$.

6.16.1. Principal value of Log _w_. We have seen that

$$Log\, w = \log|w| + i \arg w,$$

so that the different values of Log w arise for different values of arg w. The value of Log w which arises for the principal value of arg w, *i.e.*,

$$-\pi < \arg w \leq \pi$$

is called the *principal value of* Log w and is written as log w. Thus we may write

$$Log\, w = \log w + 2in\pi,$$

where n is any integer; log w denoting the principal value of Log w.

6.16.2. Logarithm of a positive real number. If w be a positive real number so that $| w | = w$ and the principal value of arg w is zero, we have

$$\text{Log } w = \log w + 2in\pi.$$

Thus log w which is the real logarithm of the positive real number w is the principal value of Log w and the other values arise on adding different integral multiples of $2i\pi$ to the real logarithm.

6.16.3. Branches of log w. The infinitely many valued function log w can be easily decomposed into *branches* all of which are single valued. All we have to do is to restrict the value of ϕ in an interval of length 2π. For example, if $0 \le \phi < 2\pi$, we obtain a branch which is known as the **principal value** of log w. Geometrically, the condition $0 \le \phi < 2\pi$ is equivalent to saying that we cannot cross the positive real axis. Another way of describing this situation is by saying that we are *cutting* the complex plane along the positive real axis. The other branches of log w may then be defined by the conditions

$$n \cdot 2\pi \le \phi < (n + 1) \cdot 2\pi.$$

All of these branches are single-valued in the complex plane cut *along the positive real axis*. If we cross the cut, we shall pass from one branch of log w to an adjacent one. The origin is called the **branch point of log w.**

Note. Note that there is nothing special about choosing the positive real axis as the site of cut. Any other continuous non-self-intersecting curve which starts at the origin and extends to infinity would be used equally well for defining a branch of log w provided one of the 'edges' of the cut is thought of as belonging to the cut plane and the other as not belonging to it. It will depend upon reasons of convenient formulations. Thus we could start by defining the principal branch by the condition $- \pi < \phi \le \pi$ and describing the other branches by the conditions

$$(2n - 1) \pi < \phi < (2n + 1) \pi.$$

In this case the cut extends from 0 to $- \infty$, *i.e.*, lies along the negative real axis.

6.17. A Law of Logarithms. *Corresponding to the addition theorem*

$$E (z_1 + z_2) = E (z_2) E (z_1) \hspace{3cm} ...(1)$$

we have the result

$$\text{Log } (w_1 w_2) = \text{Log } w_1 + \text{Log } w_2,$$

for logarithms.

Suppose that

$$w_1 = E (z_1), w_2 = E (z_2)$$

$\Rightarrow \hspace{2cm} z_1 = \text{Log } w_1, z_2 = \text{Log } w_2.$

From (1), we have

$$z_1 + z_2 = \text{Log } [E (z_1) E (z_2)]$$

$\Rightarrow \hspace{1cm} \text{Log } w_1 + \text{Log } w_2 = \text{Log } (w_1 w_2) \hspace{3cm} ...(2)$

In view of the multiple-valued character of the function Log w and of the consequent infinite possible values of either side of (2), we should see that this equality (2) means that *each value of either side is a value of the other.*

Also the reader should see that (2) may *not* hold good when each logarithm is interpreted as principal, *i.e.*, the equality

$$\log (w_1 w_2) = \log w_1 + \log w_2,$$

between principal values may *not* be true.

6.18. Analytic character of Log z. We have seen that

$$\text{Log } z = \log |z| + i \text{ arg } z.$$

Thus we see that if D be any domain not containing $z = 0$ as a point thereof and if Log z be assigned any particular value at a point $z \in$ D, then the value of Log z at every point of D is uniquely determined on the assumption of the continuous variation only. As a result, we see that in any such domain D, we can consider Log z as a single valued function of z and the different branches of Log z are separated from each other. Any one branch of Log z is of course fixed as soon as a value of Log z for any particular value of z is assigned. This, however, is not possible for domains containing $z = 0$ as a point.

Let now D be a domain *not* containing $z = 0$. Also let Log z denote any single valued branch defined in D. We write

$$w = \text{Log } z \implies z = \text{E } (w).$$

Now

$$\frac{dz}{dw} = \text{E } (w) \neq 0.$$

Therefore, by (dw/dz) exists and

$$\frac{dw}{dz} = \frac{1}{(dz/dw)} = \frac{1}{\text{E } (w)} = \frac{1}{z}.$$

Thus *Log z is analytic in D with derivative $1/z$,*

i.e., $$\frac{d}{dz} (\text{Log } z) = \frac{1}{z}.$$

This applies to every branch of Log z.

6.19. Generalised power a^b. *By definition*

$$a^b = \text{E } (b \text{ Log } a);$$

a, b being any complex number whatsoever.

Now

$$\text{Log } a = \log |a| + i (\phi + 2n\pi),$$

where, ϕ, denotes the principal value of arg a.

$\therefore$ $$a^b = \text{E } (b \log |a| + bi\phi + bi2n\pi)$$

$$= \text{E } (b \log |a|) \cdot \text{E } (ib\phi) \cdot \text{E } (2ibn\pi) \qquad \qquad ...(1)$$

Thus in general, a^b is infinite valued and different values of, a^b are obtained by giving different integral values to n in (1).

We shall now see that this definition agrees with those given before when b is a rational number.

Suppose first *that b is a positive integer m.* In this case, we have

$$\text{E } (2ibn\pi) = 1.$$

$\therefore$ $$a^b = \text{E } \{b (\log |a| + |ib\phi|)\}$$

$$= \{\text{E } (\log |a| + i\phi)\} \ \{\text{E } (\log |a| + i\phi)\} \ ..... \ b \text{ times}$$

$$= a \cdot a \ ..... \ a, \text{ taken } b \text{ times.}$$

Let now b be a negative integer. We have

$$\text{E } (2ibn\pi) = 1$$

and $$a^b = \text{E } \{b (\log |a| + i\phi)\}$$

$$= \frac{1}{E\{-b[\log|a|+i\phi)]\}}$$

$$= \frac{1}{a \cdot a \, \dots \, a, \text{ taken } (-b) \text{ times}}.$$

Finally let b be a rational number $1/q$; q being a positive integer. In this case $E\left(2i\dfrac{1}{q} \cdot n\pi\right)$ possesses q distinct values obtained by giving n the values

$$0, 1, 2, \dots, q-1$$

and the qth power of each of these values is 1.

Also

$$E\left\{\frac{1}{b}[(b\log|a|+bi\phi)]\right\} = a,$$

i.e., the qth power of $E[b\log|a|+bi\phi] = a$.

The case when $b = p/q$ is now deducible from above.

We agree to write e^z for $E(z)$ so that, as may easily be seen, e^z necessarily stands for the principal value.

6.20. Analytic character of z^n; n being any constant number. We have, by definition

$$w = z^n = E(n \operatorname{Log} z),$$

so that it is clear that a single valued function z^n can be defined in every domain which does not include $z = 0$ as a point thereof.

Thus in any domain D *not* including $z = 0$, we have

$$\frac{dw}{dz} = E(n\operatorname{Log}z)\cdot\frac{n}{2} = \frac{nz^n}{z} = nz^{n-1}, \qquad \dots(1)$$

so that w is analytic in such domains.

Note. The reader may notice that it is more conducive to clarity to write the relation (1) in the form

$$\frac{d}{dz}(z^n) = \frac{nz^{n-1}}{z},$$

which implies that the same branch of z^n is to be considered on either side.

6.21. Inverse of cos z. Consider the equation

$$w = \cos z \qquad \dots(1)$$

in z where w is given. In view of the periodic character of cos z, it is clear that if one value of z corresponds to a given w, then an infinite number of such values correspond to the same w.

We have

$$w = \frac{E(iz) + E(-iz)}{2}.$$

$$\therefore \quad E(iz)^2 - 2w\,E(iz) + 1 = 0, \text{ for } E(-iz) = 1/E(iz).$$

As the constant term of this quadratic equation is $1 \neq 0$, we see that no root of this equation is zero.

$$\therefore \quad E(iz) = w \pm \sqrt{w^2 - 1} \qquad \dots(2)$$

The two values of E (*iz*) are reciprocals of each other. If we write

$$\alpha = w + \sqrt{w^2 - 1}, \text{ then } \frac{1}{\alpha} = w - \sqrt{w^2 - 1}.$$

Thus the values of *z* satisfying the equations

$$E(iz) = \alpha, \qquad\qquad\qquad ...(3)$$
$$E(iz) = 1/\alpha, \qquad\qquad\qquad ...(4)$$

are the values of *z* satisfying (1).

Now (3) and (4) give

$$iz = \log |\alpha| + i \arg \alpha,$$

$$iz = \log \left| \frac{1}{\alpha} \right| + i \arg \left(\frac{1}{\alpha} \right).$$

Also

$$\log \frac{1}{|\alpha|} = - \log |\alpha|.$$

Further if θ denotes the principal value of arg α, then $- \theta$ denotes the principal value of arg $(1/\alpha)$.

Thus the different values of *z* are all given by

$$z = - i \log |\alpha| + \arg \alpha + 2n\pi;$$
$$z = i \log |\alpha| - \arg \alpha + 2n\pi,$$

where *n* is any integer whatsoever.

Thus we may write

$$z = 2n\pi \pm (\arg \alpha - i \log |\alpha|),$$

n being any integer. This gives the general value of *z*.

Of course we write $z = \cos^{-1} w$, if $w = \cos z$.

6.22. Derivative of $\cos^{-1} z$.

$$w = \cos^{-1} z$$

$$= \frac{1}{i} \log [z + \sqrt{z^2 - 1}]$$

$$= \frac{1}{i} \log [z + i \sqrt{1 - z^2}].$$

[Refer to (2) of the preceding section]

This shows that the multiple valued character of *w* arises on two accounts which consists in *w* involving two multiple valued functions, *viz.*, $\sqrt{1 - z^2}$ and the logarithm.

Now ± 1 are the two branch points of $\sqrt{1 - z^2}$. Also we may easily see that $z + i \sqrt{1 - z^2}$ cannot be zero for any value of *z*. Thus we deduce that we look upon *w* as a single valued function of *z* in any domain D which does not include the two points ± 1 in its interior; the function being fixed by assigning the value of $\sqrt{1 - z^2}$ and of $\log [z + i \sqrt{1 - z^2}]$ for any given $z \in D$. Hence by the chain rule on page 128, we have

$$\frac{dw}{dz} = \frac{1}{i} \frac{1 - \dfrac{iz}{\sqrt{1 - z^2}}}{z + i\sqrt{1 - z^2}} = -\frac{1}{\sqrt{1 - z^2}}$$

so that the derivative is expressed in terms of the particular value assigned to $\sqrt{1 - z^2}$.

6.23. Inverse of sin z. Consider the equation

$$w = \sin z,$$

where w is known and z unknown.

We have

$$w = \frac{E\,(iz) - E\,(-iz)}{2i},$$

$$\Leftrightarrow \qquad [E\,(iz)]^2 - 2iw\,E\,(iz) - 1 = 0,$$

$$\Leftrightarrow \qquad E\,(iz) \in \{iw + \sqrt{1 - w^2},\ iw - \sqrt{1 - w^2}\}$$

If we write

$$iw + \sqrt{1 - w^2} = \alpha$$

so that

$$iw - \sqrt{1 - w^2} = -1/\alpha$$

we have

$$E\,(iz) \in \{\alpha,\ -1/\alpha\}.$$

Now

$$E\,(iz) = \alpha$$

$$\Rightarrow \qquad iz = \log |\alpha| + i \arg \alpha$$

$$\Rightarrow \qquad z = -i \log |\alpha| + \arg \alpha \qquad\qquad\qquad ...(1)$$

and

$$E\,(iz) = -1/\alpha$$

$$\Rightarrow \qquad iz = \log |-1/\alpha| + i \arg (-1/\alpha)$$

$$\qquad\qquad = -\log |\alpha| + i \arg (-1/\alpha)$$

$$\Rightarrow \qquad z = i \log |\alpha| + \arg (-1/\alpha) \qquad\qquad\qquad ...(2)$$

6.24. Derivative of $\sin^{-1} z$. We write

$$w = \sin^{-1} z$$

$$= -i \log [iz + \sqrt{1 - z^2}\,].$$

Thus as in the preceding section, we can show that $w = \sin^{-1} z$ is analytic in every domain to which do not belong the points ± 1 and

$$\frac{dw}{dz} = \frac{1}{\sqrt{1 - z^2}}.$$

EXERCISES

1. Give an example of a sequence $\{z_n\}$ of real numbers for which

$$\lim_{n \to \infty} z_n = \infty,$$

in the sense of the theory of complex numbers whereas the limit does not exist in the sense of the theory of real numbers. Explain this fact making use of the geometrical representation of the extended plane.

2. Examine the convergence of the sequences

(a) z^n, (b) $z^n/(n!)$,

for different values of z.

[**Ans.** (a) Convergent for $|z| < 1$ and $z = 1$.

(b) Convergent to zero for every z.]

3. The sequence of complex numbers z_n satisfies the recurrence relation

$$z_n = \frac{1}{2}\left(z_{n-1} + \frac{a^2}{z_{n-1}}\right),$$

where a is any non-zero complex number.
Prove that:

$$\left(\frac{z_n - a}{z_n + a}\right) = \left(\frac{z_{n-1} - a}{z_{n-1} + a}\right)^2.$$

The first number of the sequence is z_0. Prove that

(i) $-\dfrac{\pi}{2} < \arg\dfrac{z_0}{a} < \dfrac{\pi}{2} \Rightarrow z_n \to a$

(ii) $\dfrac{\pi}{2} < \arg\dfrac{z_0}{a} < \dfrac{3\pi}{2} \Rightarrow z_n \to a$.

4. Investigate the behaviour of the sequence $\{z_n\}$ defined by

$$z_{n+1} = \frac{a + bz_n}{c + dz_n}, \quad (ad - bc) \neq 0;$$

a, b, c, d being given numbers and z_1 is arbitrary.

What are the necessary and sufficient conditions for the sequence $\{z_n\}$ and $\{1/z_n\}$ to converge?

5. Let $\{z_n\}$ be any sequence of complex numbers and

$$\lim_{n \to \infty} z_n = \zeta.$$

Prove that

$$\lim_{n \to \infty} \frac{z_1 + z_2 + \ldots + z_n}{n} = \zeta$$

so long as ζ is finite. By choosing a suitable sequence $\{z_n\}$, show that the statement is not generally true if $\zeta = \infty$.

6. Show that

$$\sum \frac{1}{n^z} \text{ converges absolutely when } R(z) > 1.$$

[**Hint.** We have $|n^z| = |n^{x+iy}| = |n^x||n^{iy}| = |n^x||e^{iy \log n}| = n^x$.]

7. Show that

$$\sum \frac{e^{inz}}{n^s}$$

is absolutely convergent if I $(z) \geq 0$ and R $(s) > 1$.

[**Hint.** $| e^{inz} | = | e^{in\,(x\,+\,iy)} | = | e^{-ny} | \leq 1$ if $y \geq 0$.]

8. Examine the following series for convergence:

   (a) $\sum e^{nz}$,   (b) $\sum z^n e^{nz}$,   (c) $\sum \dfrac{1}{n^i}$,   (d) $\sum \dfrac{1}{n^{2-3i}}$,

   (e) $\sum \dfrac{1}{(n+i)^i}$,   (f) $\sum \dfrac{1}{1+z^n}$,   (g) $\sum \dfrac{z^n}{1+z^n}$,   (h) $\sum \sin nz$,

   (i) $\sum \dfrac{e^{inz}}{n^2}$,   (j) $\sum \dfrac{n+1}{n^z}$,   (k) $\sum \dfrac{1}{1-z^n}$,   (l) $\sum \dfrac{z^{2n}}{1-z^{2n+1}}$,

   (m) $\sum \dfrac{(-1)^n}{z+na}$,   (n) $\sum \dfrac{(-1)^n}{z^2+n^2}$,   (o) $\sum \dfrac{1}{z+n(-1)^n}$,

   (p) $\sum \left(\dfrac{1}{n+b} - \dfrac{1}{n} \right) z^n$,   (q) $\sum \left(\dfrac{a+n}{b+n} \right) z^n$.

[**Ans.** (a) C, for R $(z) < 0$.

  (b) C, for points $z = x + iy$ such that $\sqrt{x^2 + y^2} \; e^x < 1$.

  (c) D   (d) C

  (e) D

  (f) C for $| z | > 1$ and D for $| z | \leq 1$

  (g) C for $| z | < 1$ and D for $| z | \geq 1$

  (h) C for $z = k\pi$; k being any integer.

  (i) C for I $(z) \geq 0$ (j) C for R $(z) > 2$

  (k) C for $| z |$ and D for $| z | \leq 1$

  (l) C for $| z | < 1$ with sum $z/(1 - z)$ and C for $| z | > 1$ with sum
     $1/(1 - z)$ and D for $| z | = 1$

  (m) C   (n) C

  (o) C

  (p) C for $| z | \leq 1$, D for $| z | > 1$

  (q) C for $| z | < 1$, D for $| z | \geq 1$.]

[Here C, stands for convergence and D, stands for divergence.]

9. Show that

$$\sum 3^n \sin \frac{z}{4^n}$$

converges absolutely for every value of z.

$$\left[\textbf{Hint. } 3^n \sin \frac{z}{4^n} = \left(\frac{3}{4} \right)^n \left(4^n \sin \frac{z}{4^n} \right). \right.$$

Also because

$$\lim_{n \to \infty} \left(4^n \sin \frac{z}{4^n} \right) = z,$$

there exists a number k, independent of n, but of course depending on z, such that

$$\left[\left| 4^n \sin \frac{z}{4^n} \right| < k, \ \forall \ n. \right]$$

10. Find for which values of z the series

$$\frac{\sin^2 z}{2} - \frac{\sin^4 z}{4} + \frac{\sin^6 z}{8} - \ldots\ldots + (-1)^{n+1} \frac{\sin^{2n} z}{2^n} + \ldots\ldots$$

is convergent.

[**Hint.** The series is a G.P. with common ratio $- (\sin^2 z)/2$.]

11. Show that

$$\sum_{n=1}^{\infty} c^{n^2} c^{nz}$$

is absolutely convergent for every value of z if $| c | < 1$.

12. Prove that if Σa_n is convergent and the real part of z is positive, then the series

$$\sum_{1}^{\infty} \frac{n! \, a_n}{(z+1)(z+2)\ldots\ldots(z+n)},$$

is convergent.

13. Give examples of series Σa_n, Σb_n, Σc_n with the following properties:

(i) Σa_n is convergent and Σa_n^2 is divergent.

(ii) Σb_n is convergent and Σb_n^3 is divergent.

(iii) Σc_n is convergent and both Σc_n^2 and Σc_n^3 are divergent.

14. The series Σz_n where $z_n = x_n + iy_n$ is convergent for $x_n \geq 0$ for all n and Σz_n^2 is convergent. Prove that Σz_n^2 is absolutely convergent.

15. Show that the series

$$\sum_{n=0}^{\infty} \frac{e^{2\pi niz}}{(a+n)^s}, \ (a, \text{ real})$$

is convergent for all values of s, if $I(z) > 0$ and is convergent for values of s whose real part is positive when z is real and not an integer.

16. Show that the series

$$\sum_{n=1}^{\infty} \frac{nz^{n-1} \{(1+n^{-1})^n - 1\}}{(z^n - 1) \{z^n - (1 + n^{-1})^n\}}$$

is absolutely convergent for every value of z except the values

$$1 + \left(\frac{a}{m}\right) e^{2ki\pi/m}$$

$(a = 0, 1; k = 0, 1, \ldots, m - 1; m = 1, 2, 3, \ldots).$

17. Find the radii of convergence of the following power series:

(i) $\sum z^n$ (ii) $\sum \dfrac{z^n}{n}$ (iii) $\sum \dfrac{z^n}{n^2}$ (iv) $\sum (3 + 4i)^n z^n$

(Kanpur 2005, Osmania 2004)

(v) $\sum n z^n$ (vi) $\sum \dfrac{n^n}{n!} z^n$ *(Rohilkhand, 2002)*

(vii) $\sum \left(1 - \dfrac{1}{n}\right)^{n^2} z^n$ (viii) $\sum_{2}^{\infty} \dfrac{z^n}{\log n}$ (ix) $\sum \dfrac{z^{2n}}{n}$ (x) $\sum n^{(\log n)^2} z^n$

(xi) $\sum n^{\log n} z^p$ (xii) $\sum (\log n)^n z^n$ (xiii) $\sum \dfrac{z^n}{1 + in^2}$ (xiv) $\sum \dfrac{(n!)^2}{(2n)!} z^n$

(Avadh 2004)

(xv) $\sum \dfrac{n\sqrt{2+i}}{1 + 2in} z^n$

(xvi) $\sum \dfrac{2^{-n}}{1 + in^2} z^n$ (xvii) $\sum \dfrac{in + 2}{2^n} z^n$

(xviii) $\sum \dfrac{(-1)^n}{n} (z - 2i)^n$

(xix) $\sum \left(\dfrac{n+p}{n}\right)^{n^2} z^n$, $(p$ is a real constant).

[**Ans.** (i) 1   (ii) 1   (iii) 1   (iv) 1/5   (v) 1   (vi) e^{-1} (vii) e

(viii) 1   (ix) 1   (x) e^{-p} (xi) 1   (xii) 0   (xiii) 1   (xiv) 4   (xv) 1   (xvi) 2

(xvii) 2   (xviii) 1   (xix) 1.]

18. Find the domains of convergence of the series

$$\sum n^2 \left(\frac{z^2 + 1}{1 + i}\right)^n.$$

[**Ans.** $|z^2 + 1| < \sqrt{2}$.]

19. Investigate the behaviours of the following power series on the circle of convergence:

(i) $\sum_{n=2}^{\infty} \dfrac{z^n}{n \log n}$ (ii) $\sum_{n=0}^{\infty} (-1)^n \dfrac{z^p}{n \log n}$

(iii) $\sum_{n=1}^{\infty} (-1)^n \dfrac{z^n}{n}$ *(Calicut 2004)*   (iv) $\sum_{n=2}^{\infty} \dfrac{z^{2n}}{n - \sqrt{n}}$

(v) $\sum_{n=2}^{\infty} (-1)^{n-1} \dfrac{z^{2n}}{n - \sqrt{n}}$.

[**Ans.** The series converge at all points on the circle of convergence except at

(*i*) 1   (*ii*) – 1   (*iii*) – 1   (*iv*) ± 1

(*v*) ± *i*.]

20. Show that

$$\sum \frac{(n!)^2}{(2n)!} z^n$$

does not converge at any point on the circle of convergence.

21. Discuss completely the convergence of

$$\sum_{n=1}^{\infty} \frac{z^{2n}}{n}.$$

22. If $\Sigma a_n z^n$ has radius 3 and *k* is a positive integer, obtain the radii of convergence of the series

(*a*) $\Sigma a_n^k z^n$,   (*b*) $\Sigma a_n z^{nk}$.

[**Ans.** (*a*) 3*k*, (*b*) 3^{k-1}.]

23. Find the regions of convergence of the series:

(*i*) $z + \frac{1}{2} z^2 + \frac{1}{3} z^3 + \dots$

(*ii*) $i\pi + (z-2) + \frac{1}{2}(z-2)^2 - \frac{1}{3}(z-2)^3 + \dots$

[**Ans.** (*i*) $|z| \le 1$ except at $z = 1$,   (*ii*) $|z-2| \le 1$ except at $z = 1$.]

24. Plot the points:

Log 1, Log (– 1), Log *i*, Log (– *i*), Log $(-1 - \sqrt{3}i)$

in the Argand diagram.

25. Find the loci of points for which E (*z*), sin *z*, cos *z*, sinh *z*, cosh *z* are

(*i*) purely real,   (*ii*) purely imaginary.

26. Show that the values of *i* are all real and they can be arranged in the form of an infinite G.P.

27. Show that Log *z* can have a real value if and only if *z* is positive.

28. Prove that the function $\tan^{-1} z$ is multi-valued and show that each branch is single valued in the *z*-plane 'cut' along the imaginary axis except for the segment from *i* to – *i*. Prove also that each branch is regular in the 'cut' plane.

29. Show that the principal values of z^i remain bounded for all values of *z*.

30. Explain the following paradox $- \pi i = \log(-1) = \frac{1}{2} \log(-1)^2 = \frac{1}{2} \log 1 = 0.$

31. Examine the validity of the equation $\log z^4 = 4 \log z$.

32. If $u + iv = \cosh(x + iy)$, show that

$$v = -\frac{\sin 2y}{\cosh 2x - \cos 2y}.$$

Hence show that

$$iv = \frac{1}{1 - e^{2(x-iy)}} - \frac{1}{1 - e^{2(x+iy)}}$$

and deduce that if $x < 0$, v can be expressed as the infinite series

$$-2 \sum_{r=1}^{\infty} e^{2rx} \sin 2ry.$$

OBJECTIVE QUESTIONS

For each of the following questions, four alternatives are given for the answer. Only one of them is correct. Choose the correct alternative.

1. A sequence with more than one limiting point is
   - (a) convergent always
   - (b) may be convergent
   - (c) cannot be convergent
   - (d) None of these.

2. In a convergent series, Σu_n
   - (a) necessarily tends to zero
   - (b) tends to a finite limit
   - (c) tends to an infinite limit
   - (d) necessarily tends to infinity.

3. If Σa_n converges and $\Sigma \mid v_n - v_{n+1} \mid$ converges, then
   - (a) $\Sigma (a_n + v_n)$ also converges
   - (b) $\Sigma (a_n v_n)$ also converges
   - (c) $\Sigma (a_n/v_n)$ also converges
   - (d) $\Sigma (v_n/a_n)$ also converges.

4. The product series of any two absolutely convergent series is
   - (a) convergent
   - (b) conditionally convergent
   - (c) absolutely convergent
   - (d) uniformly convergent.

5. A power series within its circle of convergence
   - (a) converges absolutely
   - (b) converges uniformly
   - (c) converges absolutely and uniformly
   - (d) diverges.

6. The primitive period for $\sin z$ is
   - (a) π
   - (b) $\pi / 2$
   - (c) 2π
   - (d) $3\pi / 2$.

7. Primitive period of $\exp (z)$ is
   - (a) 2π
   - (b) $2\pi i$
   - (c) $2n\pi$
   - (d) $2n\pi i$.

8. The sum function of the series $\sum \dfrac{z^n}{n!}$ is
   - (a) exponential function
   - (b) logarithmic function
   - (c) cosine function
   - (d) sine function.

9. Zeros of $\cos z$ are given by
   - (a) $z = n\pi$
   - (b) $z = (2n + 1) \pi$
   - (c) $z = n\pi/2$
   - (d) $z = (2n+1)\dfrac{\pi}{2}$.

ANSWERS

1. (c)   2. (a)   3. (b)   4. (c)   5. (c)   6. (c)   7. (b)   8. (a)   9. (d)

CONFORMAL MAPPINGS

7.1. Introduction. In this chapter, we shall take up only some elementary aspects of the subject of conformal mapping for, more than this is not included in the scope of this book.

In his dissertation, Riemann* stated a theorem that every simply connected domain D with at least two boundary points can be mapped one-one and conformally on the interior of the unit circle. In fact it was also shown that the mapping is uniquely determined such that the same transforms any point $a \in D$ into the origin and a given direction at a into the positive direction of the real axis.

Of course from this we at once deduce that any simply connected domain D with at least two boundary points can be conformally mapped in a unique manner on any other simply connected domain D_1 with at least two boundary points such that any given point of D corresponds to a given point of D_1 and a given direction in D corresponds to a given direction in D_1. The proof of this Riemann's theorem being not within the scope of this book, we shall only attend to a part of the constructive aspect of the subject of conformal mappings and seek to obtain transformations which map some special types of given domains onto the interior of the unit circle. We shall be in a position to consider only such domains for which the corresponding mappings are given by algebraic combinations of the elementary functions which we have so far introduced. Thus, we have necessarily first to start with the consideration of mappings given by elementary functions. Then for any given domain, we shall have to seek some suitable combination of the elementary functions. The chapter will, therefore, be divided into two parts. The first part will deal with the consideration of the mappings brought about by given elementary functions and the second part with the determination of the functions which bring about given mappings.

Here it may be stated that we have already considered in Chapter 3 the nature of the mappings brought about by functions

$$w = \frac{a + bz}{c + dz}; \quad ad - bc \neq 0.$$

For any given function, a good idea of the nature of mappings, would be always had by considering the images of the curves

$$R(z) = \text{constant}, \quad I(z) = \text{constant};$$

$$|z| = \text{constant}, \quad \arg z = \text{constant}.$$

As $R(z) = $ constant and $I(z) = $ constant are two families of mutually orthogonal curves, their images will also be, in general, two families of mutually orthogonal curves. Similarly also for the two families $|z| = $ constant, $\arg z = $ constant.

---

* Riemann : (1826-66).

7.2. Conformal Transformations.

(Sagar 1996, Kerala 1999, 2001, Calicut 2004)

If one domain D_1 is mapped onto another domain D_2 such that the mapping is one-one and continuously differentiable and is also such that any two curves in D_1 intersecting at any angle α are mapped on two curves also intersecting at the same angle α, then the mapping is called *Isogonal*. An isogonal mapping is further called *Conformal* if not only the magnitude but also the *sense* of the angle is preserved. A conformal mapping may also be called conformal transformation or representation.

Thus, by definition, if

$$w = f(z)$$

is a conformal mapping of a domain D_1 onto a domain D_2, then we necessarily have the following:

   (a) To each $z \in D_1$ corresponds one and only one $w \in D_2$ and each $w \in D_2$ thus arises from one and only one $z \in D_1$. This means that the function $f(z)$ is simple.

   (b) $f(z)$ possesses a continuous derivative in the domain D_1.

The problem of conformal mapping consists in examining the question of existence and of the determination (in the case of existence) of the function $f(z)$ which map conformally any *given* domain D_1 onto a *given* domain D_2. The examination of the question of existence is, however, beyond the scope of this book. Since the part of the subject dealing with the question of existence gives no clue as to the problem of the determination of the actual mapping in any given case, it is necessary, in any case, to examine as large a number as possible of particular functions and determine the domain which arise as the conformal maps of given domains in a given case.

The case of bilinear transformations

$$w = \frac{az + b}{cz + d}; \quad ad - bc \neq 0$$

which are special cases of conformal transformations has been already considered in details in Chapter 3 where we established their conformal character in a purely geometrical manner without reference to the notion of analyticity of a function.

7.2.1. Sufficient condition for $w = f(z)$ to represent a conformal mapping.

Let $f(z)$ be an analytic function of z in a region D of the z-plane and let $f'(z) \neq 0$ inside D. Then the mapping $w = f(z)$ is conformal at the points of D.

(Garhwal, 2007; Rohilkhand, 2000, 2006)

Let z_0 be an interior point of the region D. Further suppose that C_1 and C_2 be two continuous curves intersecting at z_0, the tangents at which the two curves make angles α_1 and α_2 respectively with the real axis. Let z_1 and z_2 be the points on the curves C_1 and C_2 respectively at the same distance r from z_0 where r is small. Hence, we can write:

$$z_1 - z_0 = re^{i\theta_1}, \quad z_2 - z_0 = re^{i\theta_2} \qquad \qquad ...(1)$$

Clearly as $r \to 0$ the line $z_1 z_0$ and $z_2 z_0$ will tend to be tangents to the curves C_1 and C_2 at z_0 and consequently we can say that

$$\theta_1 \to \alpha_1, \theta_2 \to \alpha_2 \text{ when } r \to 0.$$

Let w_0, w_1 and w_2 be the images in the w-plane of the points z_0, z_1 and z_2 respectively in the z-plane. As the point z_0 moves to z_1 along C_1 the image point moves along the curve Γ_1 from w_0 to w_1 and similarly as z_0 moves to z_2 along C_2 the image point moves, along the curve Γ_2 from w_0 to w_2.

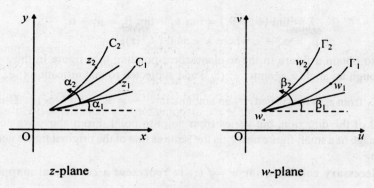

Fig. 7.1

As above suppose that tangents at w_0 to the curves Γ_1 and Γ_2 make angles β_1 and β_2 with the real axis and let

$$w_1 - w_0 = \rho_1 e^{i\phi_1} \text{ and } w_2 - w_0 = \rho_2 e^{i\phi_2}$$

$\therefore \qquad \phi_1 \to \beta_1 \text{ as } \rho_1 \to 0 \text{ and } \phi_2 \to \beta_2 \text{ as } \rho_2 \to 0.$

Now, $\qquad f'(z_0) = \lim_{z_1 \to z_0} \dfrac{f(z_1) - f(z_0)}{z_1 - z_0}$

$$= \lim_{z_1 \to z_0} \frac{w_1 - w_0}{z_1 - z_0} = \lim_{z_1 \to z_0} \frac{\rho_1 e^{i\phi_1}}{r e^{i\theta_1}}$$

$$= \lim_{z_1 \to z_0} \frac{\rho_1}{r} e^{i(\phi_1 - \theta_1)}.$$

Now, $f(z)$ being analytic it follows that $f'(z_0) \neq 0$ and as such we write $f'(z_0) = Re^{i\lambda}$ so that $R = |f'(z_0)|$ and $\lambda = amp\ [f'(z_0)]$.

$$\therefore \qquad Re^{i\lambda} = \lim_{z_1 \to z_0} \frac{\rho_1}{r} e^{i(\phi_1 - \theta_1)}.$$

Equating modulus and amplitude on both sides, we get:

$$R = \lim_{z_1 \to z_0} \frac{\rho_1}{r} \text{ and } \lim (\phi_1 - \theta_1) = \lambda$$

or $\qquad \beta_1 - \alpha_1 = \lambda \quad \Rightarrow \quad \beta_1 = \alpha_1 + \lambda.$

Proceeding exactly as above we can show that $\beta_2 = \lambda + \alpha_2$.

Clearly $\qquad \beta_1 - \beta_2 = (\lambda + \alpha_1) - (\lambda + \alpha_2) = \alpha_1 - \alpha_2.$

Above relation shows that angle between the curves Γ_1 and Γ_2 at w_0 is the same as the angle between the curves C_1 and C_2 at z_0. Also from the figure it is clear that these angles have the same sense of description. Hence, the mapping $w = f(z)$ preserves both the magnitude and sense of the angle between the tangents to the curves and as such it is a conformal mapping.

Note. We have seen above that

$$Re^{i\lambda} = \lim \frac{\rho_1}{r} e^{i(\phi_1 - \theta_1)}$$

$$\Rightarrow \qquad \lim \frac{\rho_1}{r} = R = |f'(z_0)|$$

and $$\lambda = \lim (\phi_1 - \theta_1) = \lim \phi_1 - \lim \theta_1 = \beta_1 - \alpha_1$$

or $$\beta_1 = \alpha_1 + \lambda \text{ where } \lambda = \text{amp } [f'(z)].$$

Hence, to obtain a figure in the w-plane corresponding to a figure in the z-plane it should be rotated through an angle $\lambda = \text{amp } [f'(z_0)]$ and subjected to magnification (*i.e.*, the distance of a point z_1 on C_1 from z_0 is magnified) by an amount $\lim \dfrac{\rho_1}{r} = R = |f'(z_0)|$. This magnification is independent of the direction, but varies from point to point. From above we conclude that the shape of the image of a small figure near z_0 is the same as that of the original figure under a conformal transformation.

7.2.2. Necessary condition for $w = f(z)$ to represent a conformal mapping.

If the mapping $w = f(z)$ is conformal then the function $f(z)$ is an analytic function of z.

(*Garhwal, 2002; Meerut 2000, 2004; Agra 2000*)

We have:
$$u + iv = u(x, y) + iv(x, y)$$

so that $$u = u(x, y) \text{ and } v = v(x, y).$$

Let ds and $d\sigma$ denote elementary arc lengths in the z-plane and w-plane respectively. Then
$$ds^2 = dx^2 + dy^2 \text{ and } d\sigma^2 = du^2 + dv^2.$$

Now, $$du = \frac{\partial u}{\partial x} dx + \frac{\partial u}{\partial y} dy$$

and $$dv = \frac{\partial v}{\partial x} dx + \frac{\partial v}{\partial y} dy.$$

Hence,
$$d\sigma^2 = \left(\frac{\partial u}{\partial x} dx + \frac{\partial u}{\partial y} dy \right)^2 + \left(\frac{\partial v}{\partial x} dx + \frac{\partial v}{\partial y} dy \right)^2$$

$\Rightarrow$ $$d\sigma^2 = E dx^2 + 2F dx dy + G dy^2$$

where $$E = \left(\frac{\partial u}{\partial x} \right)^2 + \left(\frac{\partial v}{\partial x} \right)^2, \quad F = \left(\frac{\partial u}{\partial x} \frac{\partial u}{\partial y} + \frac{\partial v}{\partial x} \frac{\partial v}{\partial y} \right)$$

and $$G = \left(\frac{\partial u}{\partial y} \right)^2 + \left(\frac{\partial v}{\partial y} \right)^2.$$

Now, $d\sigma : ds$ is independent of direction if
$$\frac{E}{1} = \frac{F}{0} = \frac{G}{1} = h^2 \text{ (say)}$$

where h depends on x and y only and is not zero. Thus, the conditions for an isogonal transformation are

$$\left(\frac{\partial u}{\partial x} \right)^2 + \left(\frac{\partial v}{\partial x} \right)^2 = h^2 = \left(\frac{\partial u}{\partial y} \right)^2 + \left(\frac{\partial v}{\partial y} \right)^2 \qquad ...(1)$$

and $$\left(\frac{\partial u}{\partial x} \frac{\partial u}{\partial y} + \frac{\partial v}{\partial x} \frac{\partial v}{\partial y} \right) = 0 \qquad ...(2)$$

The equations (1) are satisfied if we take

$$\frac{\partial u}{\partial x} = h \cos \alpha, \quad \frac{\partial v}{\partial x} = h \sin \alpha, \quad \frac{\partial u}{\partial y} = h \cos \beta \text{ and } \frac{\partial v}{\partial y} = h \sin \beta.$$

Substituting these values in (2), we get:

$$h^2 (\cos \alpha \cos \beta + \sin \alpha \sin \beta) = 0$$

$$\Rightarrow \qquad\qquad\qquad \cos (\alpha - \beta) = 0 \qquad\qquad\qquad\qquad [\because \ h \neq 0]$$

$$\Rightarrow \qquad\qquad\qquad \alpha - \beta = \pm \pi/2.$$

Taking $\alpha - \beta = \dfrac{\pi}{2}$, *i.e.*, $\alpha = \beta + \dfrac{\pi}{2}$, we have:

$$\frac{\partial u}{\partial x} = h \cos \left(\frac{\pi}{2} + \beta \right) = - h \sin \beta,$$

$$\frac{\partial v}{\partial x} = h \sin \left(\frac{\pi}{2} + \beta \right) = h \cos \beta.$$

Also,

$$\frac{\partial u}{\partial y} = h \cos \beta \text{ and } \frac{\partial v}{\partial y} = h \sin \beta$$

$$\Rightarrow \qquad\qquad \frac{\partial u}{\partial x} = - \frac{\partial v}{\partial y}, \ \frac{\partial v}{\partial x} = \frac{\partial u}{\partial y} \qquad\qquad\qquad\qquad ...(3)$$

Similarly taking $\alpha - \beta = - \dfrac{\pi}{2}$, *i.e.*, $\alpha = \beta - \dfrac{\pi}{2}$, we shall have:

$$\frac{\partial u}{\partial x} = \frac{\partial v}{\partial y}, \ \frac{\partial v}{\partial x} = - \frac{\partial u}{\partial y} \qquad\qquad\qquad\qquad ...(4)$$

The equations (4) are the well-known Cauchy-Riemann equations, showing that $f(z)$ is an analytic function of z. The equations (3) reduce to (4), if we write $- v$ for v, *i.e.*, if we take the image figure obtained by the reflection in the real axis of the w-plane. Thus, equations (3) correspond to isogonal but not a conformal transformation. Hence, it is shown that if the transformation $w = f(z)$ is conformal, then $f(z)$ must be an analytic function of z.

Note. We know that if ξ is an analytic function of w and w is an analytic function of z, then ξ is an analytic function of z. Hence, if a region D of the z-plane is represented conformally on a region D′ of the w-plane and the region D′ in its turn on a region D″ of the ξ-plane the transformation from the z-plane to the ξ-plane will be conformal.

Cor. 1. There are some transformations which preserve magnitudes of the angle only but not their signs. For example, the transformation $w = \bar{z} = x - iy$ maps every point into its reflection in the real axis and consequently the angles are preserved but their signs are changed. In general, this is true for every transformation of the form

$$w = f(\bar{z}) \qquad\qquad\qquad\qquad ...(1)$$

where $f(z)$ is analytic.

As a matter of fact, the transformation (1) is the combination of the two transformations

(a) $\xi = \bar{z}$ \qquad\qquad\qquad\qquad\qquad\qquad (b) $w = f(\xi)$.

As shown above, in (a) the angles are preserved but their signs are changed and in (b) both the angles and signs are preserved since $f(\xi)$ is an analytic function of $\xi = \bar{z}$. Hence, (1) *represents a transformation which is isogonal but not conformal.*

Cor. 2. *A small arc in the z-plane through the point* z_0 *is magnified in the ratio* $|f'(z_0)|: 1$ *in the w-plane under the transformation* $w = f(z)$ *where* $f(z)$ *is regular and* $f'(z) \neq 0$.

Since $f(z)$ is analytic, therefore, Cauchy-Riemann equations give

$$u_x = v_y \text{ and } u_y = -v_x \qquad \qquad ...(1)$$

$$du = \frac{\partial u}{\partial x} dx + \frac{\partial u}{\partial y} dy = \frac{\partial u}{\partial x} dx - \frac{\partial v}{\partial x} dy$$

$$dv = \frac{\partial v}{\partial x} dx + \frac{\partial v}{\partial y} dy = \frac{\partial v}{\partial x} dx + \frac{\partial u}{\partial x} dy$$

$$\therefore \qquad d\sigma^2 = du^2 + dv^2 = \left[\left(\frac{\partial u}{\partial x} \right)^2 + \left(\frac{\partial v}{\partial x} \right)^2 \right] (dx^2 + dy^2)$$

or $\qquad d\sigma^2 = ds^2 \left| \frac{\partial u}{\partial x} + i \frac{\partial v}{\partial x} \right|^2$

$$= ds^2 \left| \frac{\partial w}{\partial x} \right|^2 \qquad \qquad [\because \quad w = u + iv]$$

or $\qquad d\sigma^2 = ds^2 \left| \frac{\partial w}{\partial z} \right|^2 = ds^2 |f'(z)|^2 .$

$\Rightarrow \qquad d\sigma = |f'(z)| \, ds.$

Hence, a small arc through a point z_0 in the z-plane is magnified in the ratio $|f'(z)| : 1$ in the w-plane under conformal transformation $w = f(z)$.

Cor. 3. The case when $f'(z_0) = 0$. We have seen in Theorem 7.2.1 that the transformation $w = f(z)$ is conformal at $z = z_0$ if $f(z)$ is analytic at z_0, i.e., $f'(z_0) \neq 0$. Let us now suppose that $f'(z_0) = 0$ and that $f'(z_0)$ has a zero of $(n-1)^{th}$ order at the point z_0. Hence, first $(n-1)$ derivatives of $f(z)$ vanish at z_0 but $f^n(z_0) \neq 0$.

Expanding $f(z)$ by Taylor's theorem, we get:

$$f(z) = f(z_0) + (z - z_0) f'(z_0) + \frac{(z - z_0)^2}{2!} f''(z_0)$$
$$+ ..... + \frac{(z - z_0)^n}{n!} f^n(z_0).$$

Hence $f(z_1) - f(z_0) = 0 + 0 + 0 + ... + a_n (z_1 - z_0)^n$

where $\qquad a_n = \dfrac{f^n(z_0)}{n!}$

$\Rightarrow \qquad w_1 - w_0 = a_n (z_1 - z_0)^n$

$\Rightarrow \qquad \rho_1 e^{i\phi_1} = \text{Re}^{i\lambda} [r e^{i\theta_1}]^n = Rr^n e^{i(n\theta_1 + \lambda)}.$

Equating modulus and amplitude on both sides, we get:

$$\lim \phi_1 = \lim (n\theta_1 + \lambda) = n\alpha_1 + \lambda.$$

Similarly, $\qquad \lim \phi_2 = n\alpha_2 + \lambda$

$\Rightarrow \qquad \lim (\phi_1 - \phi_2) = n (\alpha_1 - \alpha_2).$

This shows that angle between the curves at w_0 in the w-plane is not the same as the angle between the curves at z_0 in the z-plane. Hence, the conformal property of maintaining the magnitude of the angle is not holding good in this case.

7.2.3. *Superficial Magnification.* It has already been shown that in a conformal transformation $w = f(z)$, the linear magnification at any point z is $|f'(z)|$ provided $f'(z) \neq 0$. It will now be proved that the superficial magnification is $|f'(z)|^2$.

Let D denotes a closed domain in the z-plane and D′ be the corresponding closed domain in the w-plane. If A denotes the area of D′, then

$$A = \iint_{D'} du\,dv = \iint_{D} \left| \frac{\partial(u, v)}{\partial(x, y)} \right| dx\,dy \qquad \qquad ...(1)$$

by a well-known theorem for change of variables in a double integral.

Now,
$$\frac{\partial(u, v)}{\partial(x, y)} = \frac{\partial u}{\partial x} \cdot \frac{\partial v}{\partial y} - \frac{\partial v}{\partial x} \cdot \frac{\partial u}{\partial y}$$

$$= \frac{\partial u}{\partial x} \cdot \frac{\partial u}{\partial x} - \frac{\partial u}{\partial x}\left(-\frac{\partial v}{\partial x}\right) \qquad \text{[Using Cauchy-Riemann equations]}$$

$$= \left(\frac{\partial u}{\partial x}\right)^2 + \left(\frac{\partial v}{\partial x}\right)^2 = \left| \frac{\partial u}{\partial x} + i\frac{\partial v}{\partial x} \right|^2$$

$$= |f'(z)|^2.$$

Substituting in (1), we get:

$$A = \iint_{D} |f'(z)|^2 \, dx\,dy.$$

7.3. Some Special Transformations. The fundamental problem in the theory of conformal representation is the possibility of representing conformally a given region D of the z-plane into any given region D′ of the w-plane. Riemann stated in the Fundamental Existence Theorem that *any region with a suitable boundary can be conformally represented on a circle by a biuniform transformation.* We are more concerned with the applications of conformal representation to practical problems, *i.e.*, with the following:

Given two regions D and D′ with specified boundaries, we have to find the function $w = f$ (z) which will transform D into D′ so that the boundaries correspond.

We have found bilinear transformations for some simple cases of this type (Chapter 3). However, since for any arbitrary boundary curves there is no general method of determining the suitable regular function $f(z)$ it is of importance to be acquainted with the types of regions which correspond with each other when $f(z)$ is one of the elementary functions or a combination of such functions.

Now we propose to give some of the most useful transformations which can be effected by elementary functions.

7.3.1. *Powers. The mappings* $w = z^n$. We shall now consider the analytic function $w = z^n$ where n is a positive integer. Firstly we notice that the mapping is conformal at all points except at $z = 0$ where $dw/dz = nz^{n-1} = 0$. Also we notice that the correspondence between z and w is n to 1.

We consider the polar forms
$$z = r(\cos\theta + i\sin\theta), \quad w = \rho(\cos\varphi + i\sin\varphi)$$

for z and w and obtain

$$\rho(\cos\varphi + i\sin\varphi) = r^n(\cos n\theta + i\sin n\theta)$$

$$\Rightarrow \qquad \rho = r^n, \quad \varphi = n\theta.$$

The following facts about this mapping may easily be seen to be true.

(a) The circles r = constant about the origin go over into circles ρ = constant about the origin.

(b) Rays emanating from the origin go over into rays emanating from the origin. Also the angle between two rays emanating from the origin is not preserved but multiplied with n. This means that the mapping at the origin instead of being conformal has the property of multiplying angles by n.

(c) A circular sector (wedge) with its vertex at the origin is mapped into a circular sector (wedge) with vertex at the origin and with n times the central angle.

(d) The interior of a wedge with vertex angle π/n, i.e., the domain defined by

$$0 < \arg z < \pi/n$$

is conformally mapped onto the entire upper half-plane

$$I(w) > 0.$$

(e) The interior of a wedge with vertex angle $2\pi/n$, i.e., the domain defined by

$$0 < \arg z < 2\pi/n$$

is conformally mapped onto the entire w-plane *cut* along the entire positive real axis, i.e., on the complementary domain of the positive real axis. The cut introduced is often called a *Slit* and the plane is referred to as slit along the positive real axis.

Ex. Examine the correspondence of the frontiers of the pairs of domains referred to above in (c), (d) and (e).

7.3.2. Special Power. *The mapping $w = z^2$.*

(*Gauhati 2007, Kanpur 2003; Rohilkhand, 1999*)

To examine this mapping which is conformal at all points z except at $z = 0$, we consider the cartesian forms

$$z = x + iy, \quad w = u + iv$$

for z and w and obtain

$$u + iv = (x + iy)^2 = x^2 - y^2 + 2ixy$$
$$\Rightarrow \qquad u = x^2 - y^2, \quad v = 2xy.$$

We shall consider the images in the w-plane of the lines $x = a$, $x = b$ parallel to the imaginary axis in the z-plane.

We now have the following facts:

(a) The line $x = a > 0$ corresponds to the curve

$$u = a^2 - y^2, \quad v = 2ay$$

where y is to be thought of as a parameter varying from $-\infty$ to $+\infty$.

Eliminating y, we obtain

$$v^2 = 4a^2 (a^2 - u)$$

which is a parabola with its vertex at $(a^2, 0)$, focus at the origin and which opens towards the negative side of the u-axis.

Also the two parts of the line $x = a$ lying below and above the real axis separately correspond to the two parts of the parabola lying below and above the real axis in the w-plane.

The same parabola in the w-plane is also the image of the line $x = -a$ in the z-plane; the upper (lower) part of the parabola corresponding to the lower (upper) part of the line.

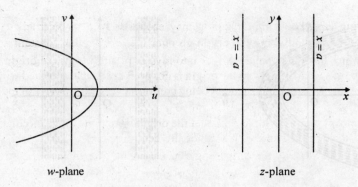

Fig. 7.2

(*b*) This infinite strip of the *z*-plane included between the lines
$$x = a, \ x = b, \ (a > 0, \ b > 0)$$
as well as the infinite strip between the lines
$$x = -a, \ x = -b$$
is conformally mapped on the domain included between the parabolas
$$v^2 = 4a^2 (a^2 - u), \ v^2 = 4b^2 (b^2 - u).$$

This follows from the fact that the first strip in the *z*-plane is swept out by the line $x = p$ and the domain in the *w*-plane by the parabola $v^2 = 4p^2 (p^2 - u)$ as p moves from a to b.

Similarly about the second strip in the *z*-plane.

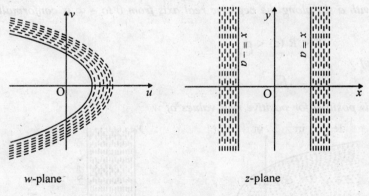

Fig. 7.3

(*c*) By making, *b*, tend to infinity, we may see that the semi-plane to the right of $x = a$, i.e., the domain given by R (*z*) > *a* is conformally mapped on the exterior, not containing the origin, of the parabola $v^2 = 4a^2 (a^2 - u)$. The domain given by R (*z*) < − *a* is also mapped on the same exterior.

Thus, $w = z^2$ maps conformally the semi-plane R (*z*) > *a* onto the **exterior** of the parabola $v^2 = 4a^2 (a^2 - u)$; *a* being positive.

We shall now consider the **interior** of the parabola.

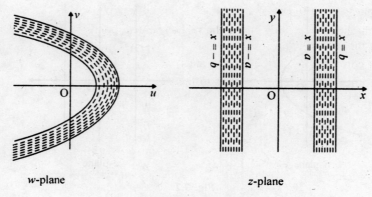

w-plane   z-plane

Fig. 7.4

(d) By considering $x = p$ and making p tend to zero, we *may see that the domain*

$$0 < \mathrm{R}\,(z) < a$$

is conformally mapped on the entire **interior** *of the parabola*

$$v^2 = 4a^2\,(a^2 - u)$$

with a **slit** *along the negative real axis from 0 to* $- \infty$.

This result can also be stated as follows:

The interior of the parabola

$$v^2 = 4a^2\,(a^2 - u)$$

in the w-plane with a slit along the negative real axis from 0 to $- \infty$ *is conformally mapped on the domain*

$$0 < \mathrm{R}\,(z) < a$$

by that branch of

$$z = \sqrt{w}$$

for which $\sqrt{w}$ *is positive for positive real values of w.*

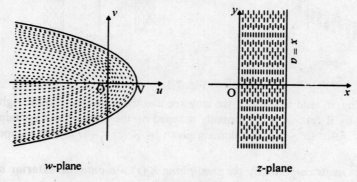

w-plane   z-plane

Fig. 7.5

For conformal mapping of the *entire* interior of the parabola, *i.e.*, without any slit whatsoever.

(e) Consider now the image of the part of the line $x = a$ lying above the real axis only. We may see that

$$0 \le \mathrm{R}\,(z) < a,\; \mathrm{I}\,(z) \ge 0$$

corresponds to the interior of the part of the parabola lying above the real axis.

In fact it may be seen that:

(*i*) the part of the line $x = a$ lying above the real axis corresponds to the part of the parabola lying above the real axis;

(*ii*) the line OA corresponds to the line OV; and

(*iii*) the positive imaginary axis corresponds to the negative real axis.

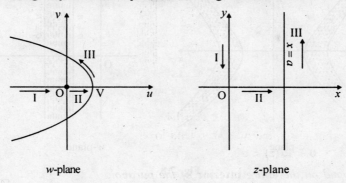

w-plane   z-plane

Fig. 7.6

It may be directly noticed that the mapping has ceased to be conformal at $z = 0$ in asmuch as two perpendicular directions through $z = 0$ go over to the same direction at $w = 0$.

7.3.3. *The inverse mapping* $z = \sqrt{w}$. We now consider the images in the z-plane of the lines $u = a$, $v = b$ in the w-plane. We have:

$$u = x^2 - y^2, \quad v = 2xy.$$

We notice the following points:

(*a*) The line $u = a > 0$ corresponds to the rectangular hyperbola

$$x^2 - y^2 = a$$

whose transverse axis lies along the real axis and conjugate axis along the imaginary axis.

It may however be seen that either branch of the hyperbola is the complete image of the line, depending as to which branch of $\sqrt{w}$ we employ for the purpose.

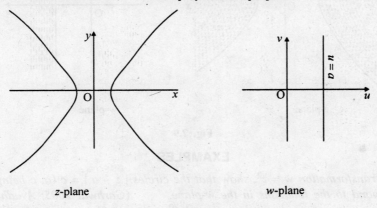

z-plane   w-plane

Fig. 7.7

(*b*) The infinite strip bounded by $u = a$, $u = b$, *i.e.*, the domain given by

$$a < R(w) < b$$

s conformally mapped on either domain in the z-plane bounded by the branches of the rectangular

hyperbolas
$$x^2 - y^2 = a, \ x^2 - y^2 = b$$
separately lying to the right and to the left of the imaginary axis in the z-plane.

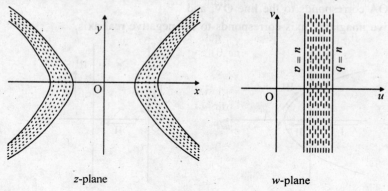

Fig. 7.8

Here the domain on the right is obtained for the branch for which z is $\sqrt{a}$ for $w = a > 0$ and the domain on the left is obtained for the branch for which z is $-\sqrt{a}$ for $w = a > 0$.

(c) Letting b tend to ∞, we see that the domain
$$R\,(w) > a$$
is conformally mapped separately on the interiors of the two branches of the hyperbola $x^2 - y^2 = a$; the two mappings corresponding to the two branches of $\sqrt{w}$. It will be noticed that the domains in question do not contain the critical points $w = 0$, $z = 0$ respectively.

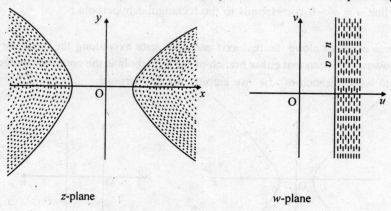

Fig. 7.9

EXAMPLES

1. *By the transformation $w = z^2$, show that the circles $|z - a| = c$ (a, c being real) in the z-plane correspond to the limacons in the w-plane.*   (*Garhwal 2005; Avadh 2003, 2005*)

Solution. $|z - a| = c \ \Rightarrow \ z - a = ce^{i\theta}$
$$\Rightarrow \qquad z = a + ce^{i\theta}.$$
$$w = z^2 \ \Rightarrow \ w = (a + ce^{i\theta})^2 = a^2 + 2ace^{i\theta} + c^2 e^{2i\theta}$$
$$\Rightarrow \qquad w - a^2 + c^2 = c^2 + 2ace^{i\theta} + c^2 e^{2i\theta}$$

$$= ce^{i\theta} (ce^{i\theta} + ce^{-i\theta} + 2a) = ce^{i\theta} (2c \cos \theta + 2a)$$
$$= 2ce^{i\theta} (a + c \cos \theta).$$

Now transforming the pole in the w-plane to the point $a^2 - c^2$ the above equation becomes
$$w = Re^{i\phi} = 2ce^{i\theta} (a + c \cos \theta).$$

Equating modulus and amplitude, we get:
$$R = 2c (a + c \cos \theta) \text{ and } \phi = \theta$$

or $$R = 2c (a + c \cos \phi).$$

This represents a limacon in the w-plane. In particular when $c = a$ then circle becomes $| z - a | = a$ and limacon becomes the cardioid
$$R = 2a^2 (1 + \cos \phi)$$

and the pole remains at the original position.

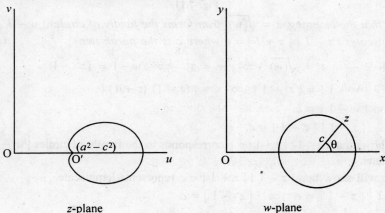

z-plane   w-plane

Fig. 7.10

2. *Discuss the application of the transformation $w = z^2$ to the area in the first quadrant of the z-plane bounded by the axis and the circles $| z | = a, | z | = b \ (a > b > 0)$. Is the transformation conformal?*
                                                                            (*Meerut 2000*)

Solution. Let $\quad w = Re^{i\phi}$ and $z = re^{i\theta}$

$\therefore \quad\quad\quad\quad | w | = R$ and $| z | = r.$

Also, $\quad\quad\quad w = z^2 \implies Re^{i\phi} = r^2 e^{2i\theta}.$

Equating modulus and amplitude, we have:
$$R = r^2 \text{ and } \phi = 2\theta \text{ or } | w | = | z |^2 \text{ and } \phi = 2\theta.$$

Hence, the given quadrant $| z | = a, 0 \leq \theta \leq \pi/2$ in the z-plane is transformed into semi-circle $| w | = | z |^2 = a^2$, i.e., $| w | = a^2$ where $0 \leq \phi \leq \pi$ as $\phi = 2\theta.$

In a similar manner the quadrant $| z | = b, 0 \leq \theta \leq \pi/2$ is transformed into the semi-circle $| w | = b^2, 0 \leq \phi \leq \pi.$

Hence, the area in the first quadrant of the z-plane bounded by the axes and the circles $| z | = a$ and $| z | = b \ (a > b > 0)$ is transformed into the angular regions between the two semi-circles $| w | = a^2$ and $| w | = b^2$ in the upper half of the w-plane. Also for the given region the transformation is obviously conformal because $\dfrac{dw}{dz} = 2z$ which is not zero at any point of the region. The same is shown in the figure.

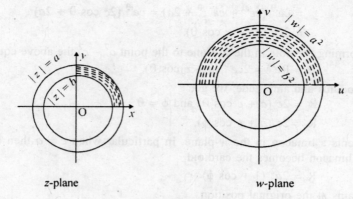

z-plane   w-plane

Fig. 7.11

3. Show that the mapping $z = \sqrt{(w)}$ transforms the family of circles $|w - 1| = c$ into the family of lemniscates $|z - 1||z + 1| = c$ where c is the parameter.   (Avadh 2004)

Solution. $z = \sqrt{(w)} \Rightarrow w = z^2 \Rightarrow w - 1 = (z^2 - 1)$

$\Rightarrow$ $|w - 1| = |z^2 - 1| \Rightarrow c = |(z - 1)(z + 1)|$

when $|w - 1| = c.$

$\Rightarrow$ $|z - 1||z + 1| = c.$

Above shows that $|z - 1||z + 1| = c$ corresponds to the family of circles $|w - 1| = c$ where c is the parameter.

Now we will show that $|z - 1||z + 1| = c$ represents lemniscate.

$|z - 1||z + 1| = c \Rightarrow |z^2 - 1| = c$

$\Rightarrow$ $z^2 - 1 = ce^{i\lambda} \Rightarrow z^2 = 1 + ce^{i\lambda}.$

$\Rightarrow$ $(re^{i\theta})^2 = a^2 e^{2i\alpha}$ (say)

$\Rightarrow$ $r^2 e^{2i\theta} = a^2 e^{2i\alpha} \Rightarrow r^2 = a^2 e^{-2i(\theta - \alpha)}$

$\Rightarrow$ $r^2 = a^2 [\cos 2(\theta - \alpha) - i \sin 2(\theta - \alpha)].$

Equating real part, we get:

$$r^2 = a^2 \cos 2(\theta - \alpha).$$

This equation represents lemniscate of Bernoulli whose axis is inclined at an angle α to the real axis.

4. Show that the transformation $w(z + i)^2 = 1$ maps the interior of the circle $|z| = 1$ in the z-plane on the exterior of the parabola

$$1/R = 2(1 - \cos \phi)$$

where $Re^{i\phi} = w.$

Solution. $w(z + i)^2 = 1 \Rightarrow z + i = \dfrac{1}{\sqrt{w}}$

$\Rightarrow$ $z = \dfrac{1}{\sqrt{w}} - i$

or $z = \dfrac{1}{\sqrt{R}} e^{-i\phi/2} - i$ where $w = Re^{i\phi}$

or
$$z = \frac{1}{\sqrt{R}}\left(\cos\frac{\phi}{2} - i\sin\frac{\phi}{2}\right) - i$$

$$= \frac{1}{\sqrt{R}}\cos\frac{\phi}{2} - i\left(\frac{1}{\sqrt{R}}\sin\frac{\phi}{2} + 1\right)$$

$$\therefore \quad |z| = \left[\frac{1}{R}\cos^2\frac{\phi}{2} + \left(\frac{1}{\sqrt{R}}\sin\frac{\phi}{2} + 1\right)^2\right]^{1/2}$$

$$\Rightarrow \quad |z| = \left(\frac{1}{R} + \frac{2}{\sqrt{R}}\sin\frac{\phi}{2} + 1\right)^{1/2}$$

$$|z| \le 1 \quad \Rightarrow \quad \frac{1}{R} + \frac{2}{\sqrt{R}}\sin\frac{\phi}{2} + 1 \le 1$$

$$\Rightarrow \qquad 1 + 2\sqrt{R}\sin\frac{\phi}{2} \le 0$$

$$\Rightarrow \qquad 1 \le -2\sqrt{R}\sin(\phi/2)$$

$$\Rightarrow \qquad 1 \le 4R\sin^2(\phi/2)$$

or $\qquad 4R\sin^2(\phi/2) \ge 1$

or $\qquad 2R(1 - \cos\phi) \ge 1.$

Hence, the unit circle $|z| = 1$ in the z-plane corresponds to the parabola $2R(1 - \cos\phi) = 1$ in the w-plane and $|z| < 1$, i.e., the interior of the circle corresponds to $2R(1 - \cos\phi) > 1$, i.e., the exterior of the parabola.

5. *In the transformation $(w + 1)^2 = 4/z$, a unit circle in the w-plane corresponds to a parabola in the z-plane and inside of the circle to the outside of the parabola.*

Or

Show that the transformation $w = 2/\sqrt{z} - 1$ transforms the region outside the parabola $y^2 = 4(1 - x)$ into the interior of the unit circle in the w-plane.

(Agra 2000, Ravishankar 2001)

Solution. Since we are considering the unit circle in the w-plane, i.e., $|w| = 1$, we take
$$w = e^{i\phi} = \cos\phi + i\sin\phi$$

Therefore, $(1 + e^{i\phi})^2 = \dfrac{4}{z} = \dfrac{4}{r}e^{-\theta i}$

i.e., $\qquad (1 + e^{i\phi}) = \dfrac{2}{\sqrt{r}}e^{-\frac{1}{2}\theta i}$

$$\Rightarrow \quad 1 + \cos\phi + i\sin\phi = \frac{2}{\sqrt{r}}\left(\cos\frac{\theta}{2} - i\sin\frac{\theta}{2}\right)$$

which gives
$$1 + \cos\phi = \frac{2}{\sqrt{r}}\cos\frac{\theta}{2}$$

and $\qquad \sin\phi = -\dfrac{2}{\sqrt{r}}\sin\dfrac{\theta}{2}.$

Therefore, $\left(\dfrac{2}{\sqrt{r}} \cos \dfrac{\theta}{2} - 1 \right)^2 + \dfrac{4}{r} \sin^2 \dfrac{\theta}{2} = 1$

$\Rightarrow$ $-\dfrac{4}{\sqrt{r}} \cos \dfrac{\theta}{2} + \dfrac{4}{r} = 0$

$\Rightarrow$ $r \cos^2 (\theta/2) = 1$

$\Rightarrow$ $\dfrac{2}{r} = 1 + \cos \theta$ or $r = \dfrac{2}{1 + \cos \theta}$ ...(1)

showing that z then describes a parabola having its focus at the origin and its latus rectum equal to 4.

Next let us take any point interior to the unit circle, say, R $(\cos \phi + i \sin \phi)$ where R < 1. Transforming as above, we obtain

$$\dfrac{2}{\sqrt{r}} \cos \dfrac{\theta}{2} - 1 = R \cos \phi, \quad \dfrac{2}{\sqrt{r}} \sin \dfrac{\theta}{2} = R \sin \phi$$

which gives $-\dfrac{4}{\sqrt{r}} \cos \dfrac{\theta}{2} + \dfrac{4}{r} = R^2 - 1 < 0$

$\therefore$ $r \cos^2 \dfrac{\theta}{2} > 1$ or $r > \dfrac{2}{1 + \cos \theta}$ ...(2)

Hence, the point corresponding to the point (R, ϕ) inside the unit circle in the w-plane lies outside the parabola in the z-plane.

6. If $w = \left(\dfrac{z - c}{z + c} \right)^2$ where c is real and +ve, find the areas of the z-plane of which the upper half of the w-plane is the conformal representation.

(*Rajasthan 2004, Mumbai 2003; Garhwal, 2003*)

Solution. $w = \left(\dfrac{z - c}{z + c} \right)^2 \Rightarrow u + iv = \left(\dfrac{x + iy - c}{x + iy + c} \right)^2$

$\Rightarrow$ $w = \left[\dfrac{(x - c) + iy}{(x + c) + iy} \cdot \dfrac{(x + c) - iy}{(x + c) - iy} \right]^2$

$= \left[\dfrac{x^2 - c^2 + y^2 + 2icy}{(x + c)^2 + y^2} \right]^2$

$\Rightarrow$ $u + iv = \dfrac{(x^2 + y^2 - c^2)^2 - 4c^2 y^2 + 4icy (x^2 + y^2 - c^2)}{[(x + c)^2 + y^2]^2}$

Equating real and imaginary parts, we get:

$u = \dfrac{(x^2 + y^2 - c^2)^2 - 4c^2 y^2}{[(x + c)^2 + y^2]^2}$ ...(1)

$v = \dfrac{4cy (x^2 + y^2 - c^2)}{[(x + c)^2 + y^2]^2}$ ...(2)

Now for upper half of the w-plane, $v \geq 0$.

Case I. *v is +ve.*

If v is +ve then from (2) both y and $x^2 + y^2 - c^2$ are either −ve or both +ve.

(*i*) $y > 0$ and $x^2 + y^2 - c^2 > 0$, *i.e.*, both +ve give z-plane exterior of the circle $x^2 + y^2 - c^2 = 0$ and in the upper half of the z-plane ($y > 0$).

(*ii*) $y < 0$ and $x^2 + y^2 - c^2 < 0$, *i.e.*, both −ve give interior of the circle $x^2 + y^2 - c^2 = 0$ and in the lower half of the z-plane ($y < 0$).

Case II. $v = 0$.

If $v = 0$ then from (2) we have either $y = 0$ or $x^2 + y^2 - c^2 = 0$.

(*i*) If $y = 0$ then from (1), we get:

$$u = \frac{(x^2 - c^2)^2}{(x + c)^4} = \left(\frac{x - c}{x + c}\right)^2.$$

If $x = c$ then $u = 0$ and if $x = -c$ then $u = \infty$.

Thus, corresponding to $v = 0$, *i.e.*, the real axis from $u = \infty$ to $u = 0$ we have the real axis in the z-plane ($y = 0$) from $x = -c$ to $x = c$.

(*ii*) If $x^2 + y^2 - c^2 = 0$ then from (1), we get:

$$u = \frac{-4c^2 y^2}{[(x + c)^2 + y^2]^2} = \frac{4c^2 (x^2 - c^2)}{[(x + c)^2 + c^2 - x^2]^2}$$

$$\Rightarrow \qquad u = \frac{4c^2 (x^2 - c^2)}{4c^2 (x + c)^2} = \frac{x - c}{x + c}.$$

If $x = c$ then $u = 0$ and if $x = -c$ then $u = -\infty$.

Thus, corresponding to $v = 0$, *i.e.*, the real axis from $u = 0$ to $u = -\infty$ we have the semi-circumference of the circle ($x^2 + y^2 - c^2 = 0$) from $x = c$ to $x = -c$. The same is shown in the figure below.

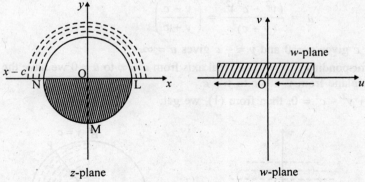

Fig. 7.12

7. *Show by means of the transformation* $w = \left(\dfrac{z - ic}{z + ic}\right)^2$ *the upper half of the w-plane may be made to correspond to the interior of a certain semi-circle in the z-plane.*

(*Ravishankar 2000, Meerut 2000, Rohilkhand 2003*)

Solution. $w = \left(\dfrac{z - ic}{z + ic}\right)^2 = \left[\dfrac{x + i(y - c)}{x + i(y + c)}\right]^2$

$$= \left[\frac{x + i(y - c)}{x + i(y + c)} \cdot \frac{x - i(y + c)}{x - i(y + c)} \right]^2$$

$$= \frac{(x^2 + y^2 - c^2 - 2icx)^2}{[x^2 + (y + c)^2]^2}$$

$\Rightarrow \qquad u + iv = \dfrac{(x^2 + y^2 - c^2)^2 - 4c^2x^2 - 4icx\,(x^2 + y^2 - c^2)}{[x^2 + (y + c)^2]^2}$

Equating real and imaginary parts, we get:

$$u = \frac{(x^2 + y^2 - c^2)^2 - 4c^2x^2}{[x^2 + (y + c)^2]^2} \qquad \qquad ...(1)$$

$$v = \frac{-4cx\,(x^2 + y^2 - c^2)}{[x^2 + (y + c)^2]^2} = \frac{4cx\,(c^2 - x^2 - y^2)}{[x^2 + (y + c)^2]^2} \qquad ...(2)$$

Now for upper half of the w-plane, $v \geq 0$.

Case I. *v is +ve, i.e., $v > 0$.*

If v is +ve then from (2) both x and $c^2 - x^2 - y^2$ are either +ve or both –ve.

(i) If $x > 0$ and $c^2 - x^2 - y^2 > 0$, i.e., $x^2 + y^2 < c^2$, i.e., both +ve then we have the interior of the circle $x^2 + y^2 - c^2 = 0$ in the right half of the z-plane ($x > 0$), i.e., interior of the semi-circle as shown in the figure.

(ii) If $x < 0$ and $c^2 - x^2 - y^2 < 0$, i.e., $x^2 + y^2 > c^2$, i.e., both –ve then we have the exterior of the circle in the left half of the z-plane ($x < 0$).

Case II. *$v = 0$.*

If $v = 0$, then from (1) we have either $x = 0$ or $x^2 + y^2 = c^2$.

(i) If $x = 0$, then from (1), we get:

$$u = \frac{(y^2 - c^2)^2}{(y + c)^4} = \left(\frac{y - c}{y + c} \right)^2.$$

Now, $y = c$ gives $u = 0$ and $y = -c$ gives $u = \infty$.

Thus, corresponding to $v = 0$, i.e., real axis from $u = \infty$ to $u = 0$ we have the imaginary axis ($x = 0$) in the z-plane from $y = -c$ to $y = c$.

(ii) If $x^2 + y^2 - c^2 = 0$, then from (1), we get:

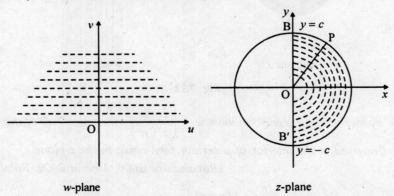

w-plane   z-plane

Fig. 7.13

$$u = \frac{-4c^2x^2}{(2c^2 + 2cy)^2} = \frac{4c^2(y^2 - c^2)}{4c^2(y + c)^2} = \frac{y - c}{y + c}.$$

If $y = c$, then $u = 0$ and if $y = -c$, then $u = -\infty$.

Thus, corresponding to $v = 0$, *i.e.*, real axis from $u = 0$ to $u = -\infty$ we have the semi-circumference of the circle $x^2 + y^2 = c^2$ from $y = c$ to $y = -c$.

Note. In the same way we can discuss the transformation $w = \left(\dfrac{z + ic}{z - ic}\right)^2$ and show that the upper half of the w-plane corresponds to the interior of the left half of the semi-circle $x^2 + y^2 - c^2 = 0$.

7.4. The mapping

$$w = \frac{1}{2}\left(z + \frac{1}{z}\right).$$

We notice that the mapping is two-to-one and that it is conformal for every z except ± 1, in that $\dfrac{dw}{dz} = \dfrac{1}{2}(1 - z^{-2})$ is non-zero for every value of z except ± 1. The inverse of

$$w = \frac{1}{2}\left(z + \frac{1}{z}\right)$$

is

$$z = w \pm \sqrt{w^2 - 1}$$

so that as expected, z is a double valued function of w. As $w = \pm 1$ are two branch points, we see that we can look upon either branch as a single valued function of w in any domain which does not include the points $w = 1$, $w = -1$ and the branch is uniquely and completely determined by fixing the value of z for a given value of w on the sole requirement of continuity.

We write polar expression for z and cartesian for w so that we write

$$z = r(\cos\theta + i\sin\theta), w = u + iv.$$

Then we have:

$$u + iv = \frac{1}{2}\left[r(\cos\theta + i\sin\theta) + \frac{1}{r}(\cos\theta - i\sin\theta)\right]$$

so that

$$u = \frac{1}{2}\left(r + \frac{1}{r}\right)\cos\theta, \quad v = \frac{1}{2}\left(r - \frac{1}{r}\right)\sin\theta.$$

We now have the following facts for this mapping.

(*a*) For $r = 1$, we have:

$$u = \cos\theta, v = 0$$

so that as z describes the unit circle once by θ varying from 0 to 2π, then the point w describes the segment of the real axis between the points 1 and -1 twice.

The reader may observe that here we clearly and directly see the non-conformal character of the mapping for the points $z = 1$ and $z = -1$.

In fact as z moves along the unit circle and passes through $z = 1$ so that its direction does not change, the image point w passes through 1 and changes its direction by π. So also for $z = -1$.

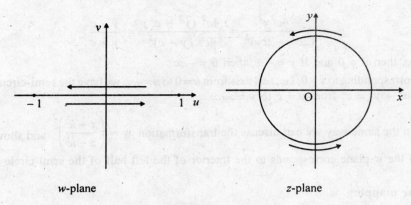

w-plane   z-plane

Fig. 7.14

(*b*) To $|z| = r > 1$ corresponds the ellipse

$$u = \frac{1}{2}\left(r + \frac{1}{r}\right)\cos\theta, \quad v = \frac{1}{2}\left(r - \frac{1}{r}\right)\sin\theta, \quad 0 \leq \theta \leq 2\pi \qquad ...(1)$$

$$\Rightarrow \qquad \frac{u^2}{\frac{1}{4}\left(r + \frac{1}{r}\right)^2} + \frac{v^2}{\frac{1}{4}\left(r - \frac{1}{r}\right)^2} = 1,$$

with foci $w = \pm 1$.

From the parametric equations (1) of the ellipse, we see that as z describes the circle $|z| = r$ once, *i.e.*, as θ varies from 0 to 2π, the point w describes the ellipse also once.

Since on changing r to $1/r$ the equation of the ellipse does not change, we see that the circle $|z| = 1/r$ also corresponds to the same ellipse (1).

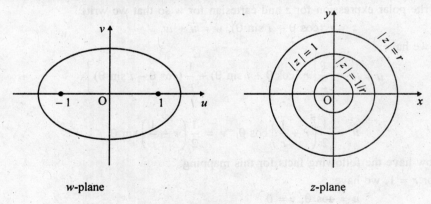

w-plane   z-plane

Fig. 7.15

(*c*) As r, starting from 1 increases, then both

$$r + \frac{1}{r} \text{ and } r - \frac{1}{r}$$

also constantly increase. This shows that each of the two shaded domains

$$r < |z| < R, \quad \frac{1}{R} < |z| < \frac{1}{r}$$

in the z-plane is conformally mapped on the domain bounded by the two confocal ellipses

$$\frac{u^2}{\frac{1}{4}\left(r+\frac{1}{r}\right)^2} + \frac{v^2}{\frac{1}{4}\left(r-\frac{1}{r}\right)^2} = 1,$$

$$\frac{u^2}{\frac{1}{4}\left(R+\frac{1}{R}\right)^2} + \frac{v^2}{\frac{1}{4}\left(R-\frac{1}{R}\right)^2} = 1.$$

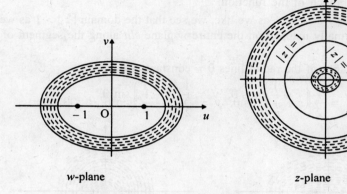

w-plane   z-plane

Fig. 7.16

(d) Letting $R \to \infty$, we see that each of the domains

$$|z| > r \quad \text{and} \quad |z| < \frac{1}{r}$$

is conformally mapped on the domain exterior to the ellipse

$$\frac{u^2}{\frac{1}{4}\left(r+\frac{1}{r}\right)^2} + \frac{v^2}{\frac{1}{4}\left(r-\frac{1}{r}\right)^2} = 1.$$

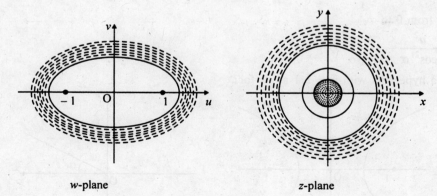

w-plane   z-plane

Fig. 7.17

Note. We may note that the exterior of the ellipse

$$\frac{u^2}{\frac{1}{4}\left(r+\frac{1}{r}\right)^2} + \frac{v^2}{\frac{1}{4}\left(r-\frac{1}{r}\right)^2} = 1$$

in the w-plane is mapped on the domain $|z| > r$ in the z-plane by that branch of

$$z = w + \sqrt{w^2 - 1}$$

for which $\sqrt{w^2 - 1}$ is positive for real values of $w > 1$.

The other domain

$$|z| < \frac{1}{r}$$

is obtained by the other branch of the function.

(e) Since we can take r as near 1 as we like, we see that the domain $|z| > 1$ as well as the domain $|z| < 1$ is conformally mapped on the entire w-plane *slit* along the segment of the real axis joining -1 to $+1$.

We consider the images of the radial lines $\theta = $ constant. We have:

$$u = \frac{1}{2}\left(r + \frac{1}{r}\right)\cos\theta, \quad v = \frac{1}{2}\left(r - \frac{1}{r}\right)\sin\theta.$$

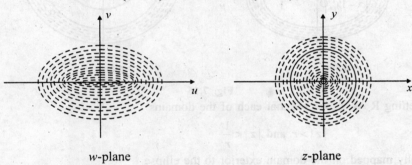

w-plane z-plane

Fig. 7.18

(a) The image of the ray $\theta = \alpha$ where $0 < \alpha < \pi/2$ such that $\cos\alpha \ne 0$, $\sin\alpha \ne 0$ is

$$u = \frac{1}{2}\left(r + \frac{1}{r}\right)\cos\alpha, \quad v = \frac{1}{2}\left(r - \frac{1}{r}\right)\sin\alpha \qquad \ldots(1)$$

r varying from 0 to ∞,

$$\Rightarrow \qquad \frac{u^2}{\cos^2\alpha} - \frac{v^2}{\sin^2\alpha} = 1 \qquad\qquad\qquad \ldots(2)$$

which is a hyperbola with $w = \pm 1$ as its foci.

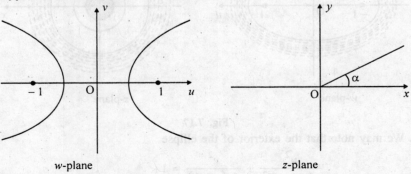

w-plane z-plane

Fig. 7.19

As r varies from 0 to ∞, the point (u, v) describes the branch of the hyperbola (2) lying to the right of the imaginary axis. The lower part of this branch is described as r varies from 0 to 1 and the upper part as r varies from 1 to ∞.

The second branch of the hyperbola is the complete image of either of the two rays $\theta = \pi - \alpha$ and $\theta = \pi + \alpha$.

(*b*) The wedge defined by the lines $\theta = \alpha$, $\theta = \beta$, *i.e.*, the domain

$$\alpha < \arg z < \beta$$

is mapped conformally on the domain bounded by the two branches lying to the right of the imaginary axis of the hyperbolas

$$\frac{u^2}{\cos^2 \alpha} - \frac{v^2}{\sin^2 \alpha} = 1, \quad \frac{u^2}{\cos^2 \beta} - \frac{v^2}{\sin^2 \beta} = 1.$$

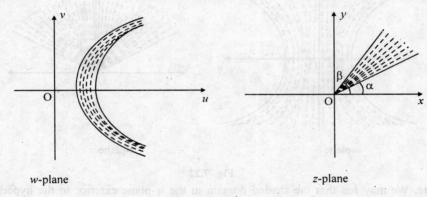

w-plane   z-plane

Fig. 7.20

(*c*) Suppose that $\beta = \pi/2$. Then the image of the positive imaginary axis is

$$u = 0, \quad v = \frac{1}{2}\left(r - \frac{1}{r}\right)$$

r varying from 0 to ∞. This image is the entire imaginary axis in the w-plane.

Thus, the wedge shaped domain

$$\alpha < \arg z < \pi/2$$

is conformally mapped on the domain bounded by the imaginary axis and the branch of the hyperbola on the right.

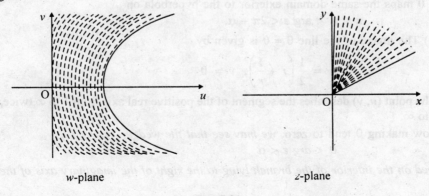

w-plane   z-plane

Fig. 7.21

(*d*) With the help of (*a*) and (*c*), we see that the domain defined by

$$\alpha < \arg z < \pi - \alpha$$

is conformally mapped on the domain bounded by the two branches of the hyperbola

$$\frac{u^2}{\cos^2 \alpha} - \frac{v^2}{\sin^2 \alpha} = 1 \qquad\qquad\qquad ...(1)$$

We may see that the domain defined by

$$\pi + \alpha < \arg z < 2\pi - \alpha$$

is also conformally mapped on the same domain exterior to the hyperbola (1).

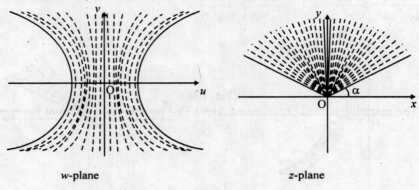

w-plane   z-plane

Fig. 7.22

Note. We may see that the shaded domain in the *w*-plane exterior to the hyperbola (1) is conformally mapped on the domain in the *z*-plane defined by

$$\alpha < \arg z < \pi - \alpha$$

by that branch of

$$z = w + \sqrt{w^2 - 1}$$

for which $\sqrt{w^2 - 1} = i$ for $w = 0$.

The other branch for which

$$\sqrt{w^2 - 1} = -i$$

for $w = 0$ maps the same domain exterior to the hyperbola on

$$\pi + \alpha < \arg z < 2\pi - \alpha.$$

(*e*) The image of the line $\theta = 0$ is given by

$$u = \frac{1}{2}\left(r + \frac{1}{r}\right), \quad v = 0$$

so that the point (u, v) describes the segment of the positive real axis from 1 to ∞ twice, as *r* varies from 0 to ∞.

Now making θ tend to zero, *we may see that the wedge*

$$0 < \arg z < \alpha$$

is mapped on the interior of the branch lying to the right of the imaginary axis of the hyperbola

$$\frac{u^2}{\cos^2 \alpha} - \frac{v^2}{\sin^2 \alpha} = 1,$$

with a slit along the positive real axis from 1 to ∞.

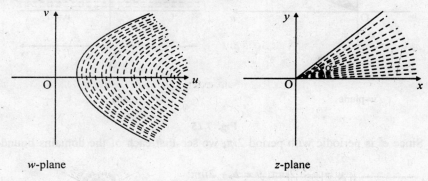

w-plane   z-plane

Fig. 7.23

7.5. The mapping $w = e^z$. (*Rohilkhand 2006*) This mapping is conformal for every value of z. Also the correspondence between z and w is infinity-to-one; the function being periodic with period $2i\pi$.

Also for the inverse function

$$z = \log w,$$

$w = 0$, is the branch point so that each branch of z defines a single valued function of w in any domain not including $w = 0$ and the branch is uniquely and completely determined by fixing the value of log w for a given value of w on the assumption of continuity alone.

Using the Cartesian and polar forms

$$z = x + iy, \; w = \rho \, (\cos \phi + i \sin \phi)$$

for z and w respectively, we have:

$$\rho \, (\cos \phi + i \sin \phi) = e^x \, (\cos y + i \sin y)$$

$\Rightarrow$ $\qquad\qquad\qquad \rho = e^x, \; \phi = y.$

We now have the following facts for this mapping :

(*i*) Consider any line $y = a$ where $0 < a < 2\pi$ in the z-plane. Since e^x varies from 0 to ∞ monotonically as x varies from $-\infty$ to $+\infty$, we see that the image of the line $y = a$ is the ray, $\phi = a$, excluding the origin.

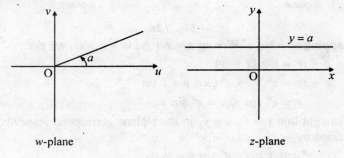

w-plane   z-plane

Fig. 7.24

(*ii*) To the domain in the z-plane bounded by the lines $y = a$, $y = b$ where $(b - a) < 2\pi$, corresponds the wedge in the w-plane bounded by the radial lines $\phi = a$, $\phi = b$.

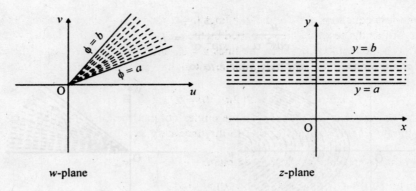

Fig. 7.25

(*iii*) Since e^z is periodic with period $2i\pi$, we see that each of the domains bounded by the lines

$$y = a + 2in\pi, \; y = b + 2in\pi;$$

n being any integer; corresponds to the same wedge in the w-plane.

Note. We may specially note that the infinite rectangular strip bounded by $y = 0$, $y = \pi$ in the z-plane corresponds to the domain

$$I\,(w) > 0$$

in the w-plane.

Further we see that we can also look upon $z = \log w$ as a conformal mapping of $I\,(w) > 0$ on the infinite rectangular strip $0 < I\,(z) < \pi$ brought about by that branch of $\log w$ which is defined by assigning the value $i\pi/2$ to $\log i$.

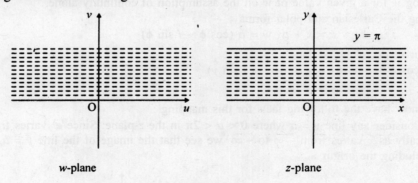

Fig. 7.26

7.6. The mapping $w = \log z$. Writing $z = x + iy$, $w = u + iv$, we get:

$$u + iv = \log (x + iy)$$

$\Rightarrow$ $$x + iy = e^{u + iv} = e^u \cdot (\cos v + i \sin v)$$

$\Rightarrow$ $$x = e^u \cos v, \; y = e^u \sin v.$$

Hence, the straight line $x = x_1$, $y = y_1$ in the z-plane correspond respectively to the curves in the w-plane defined by

$$e^u \cos v = x_1, \; e^u \sin v = y_1.$$

Again, writing $w = u + iv$ and $z = re^{i\theta}$, we get :

$$u + iv = \log r + i\theta \quad \therefore \quad u = \log r, \; v = \theta.$$

From these equations, we see that the lines $\theta = \alpha$ for varying α are mapped onto the straight lines $v = \alpha$. In fact the sectorial area bounded by the rays $\theta = \alpha_1$, $\theta = \alpha_2$ is mapped onto the infinite strip parallel to the real axis between the lines $v = \alpha_1$ and $v = \alpha_2$. In particular, the infinite strips $0 \le v \le 2\pi$ is the image of the whole z-plane cut along the positive real axis from 0 to ∞. Also every parallel strip

$$n \cdot 2\pi \le v \le (n + 1) \cdot 2\pi \quad (n = 0, \pm 1, \pm 2, \ldots)$$

is the image of the same cut-plane. Also the circles defined by $r = r_1$ in the z-plane are mapped onto the straight line $u = \log r_1$ parallel to the imaginary axis.

From the given transformation, we obtain $\dfrac{dw}{dz} = \dfrac{1}{z}$. The derivative is, therefore, infinite at the origin and so the mapping is not conformal there.

7.7. The mapping $w = z^{1/\alpha}$. The above transformation maps wedges or sectors into half-plane. Let $z = re^{i\theta}$ and $w = \rho e^{i\phi}$.

$\therefore \qquad \rho e^{i\theta} = r^{1/\alpha} e^{i\theta/\alpha}$.

Equating modulus and amplitude on both sides, we get:

$$\rho = r^{1/\alpha} \qquad \qquad \ldots(1)$$

$$\phi = \theta/\alpha \text{ or } \theta = \alpha\phi \qquad \qquad \ldots(2)$$

From (2) we observe that $0 < \theta < \pi\alpha$

$\Rightarrow \qquad \qquad 0 < \phi < \pi$.

From above it is quite clear that an infinite wedge of central angle $\pi\alpha$ in the z-plane with one vertex at the origin and one arm along the real axis corresponds to the upper half of the w-plane.

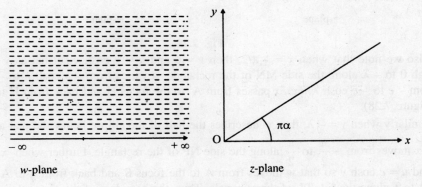

w-plane z-plane

Fig. 7.27

Again from (1) we conclude that $r = $ constant $\Rightarrow \rho$ is constant showing thereby that circles in the z-plane correspond to circles in the w-plane and in particular unit circle $|z| = 1$ and $|w| = 1$ correspond because when $r = 1$, $\rho = 1$.

Hence, the sector cut-off from the wedge $0 < \arg z < \pi\alpha$ by an arc of a unit circle $|z| = 1$ is transformed into the unit semi-circle $|w| = 1$ in the upper half of the w-plane.

7.8. The Trigonometric Transformations

7.8.1. The mapping $w = c \sin z$. The transformation can be written as

$$u + iv = c \sin (x + iy) = c \sin x \cosh y + ic \cos x \sinh y$$

Hence, equating real and imaginary parts, we get:

$$u = c \sin x \cosh y, \; v = c \cos x \sinh y \qquad \qquad \ldots(1)$$

Eliminating x, we get:

$$\frac{u^2}{c^2 \cosh^2 y} + \frac{v^2}{c^2 \sinh^2 y} = 1 \qquad ...(2)$$

For varying values of y, the equation (2) represents a family of confocal ellipses having the foci at $(\pm c, 0)$. To examine this transformation more closely, we consider a rectangle in the z-plane bounded by the lines

$$x = \pm \frac{1}{2}\pi, \quad y = \pm \lambda \quad (\lambda = 0).$$

For all values of x between $-\dfrac{\pi}{2}$ and $\dfrac{\pi}{2}$, $\cos x$ is positive. Hence, when $y = \lambda$, v is positive and u varies from $c \cosh \lambda$ to $- c \cosh \lambda$.

It follows that the half of the ellipse from A to A′ above the real axis is covered as x moves along the side of the rectangle from L to M.

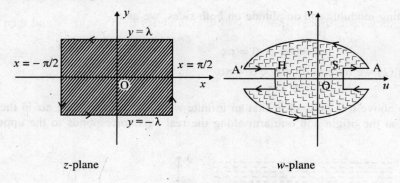

z-plane   w-plane

Fig. 7.28

Also we note that when $x = - \pi/2$, then $v = 0$ and $u = - \cosh y$ so that as y varies from λ through 0 to $- \lambda$ along the side MN of the rectangle, u varies from $- c \cosh \lambda$ to $- c$ and then back from $- c$ to $- c \cosh \lambda$, i.e., x passes from A′ to the focus H and back from H to A′. (Refer to the figure 7.28).

Similarly when $y = - \lambda$, then w describes the half of the ellipse below the real axis from A′ to A as x moves from $-\dfrac{\pi}{2}$ to $\dfrac{\pi}{2}$ along the side NP of the rectangle. Further when $x = \dfrac{\pi}{2}$, then $v = 0$ and $u = c \cosh y$ so that w moves from A to the focus S and back from S to A as y moves from $- \lambda$ to λ along the side PL of the rectangle. Thus, the boundary of the rectangle in the z-plane bounded by the lines $x = \pm \dfrac{1}{2}\pi, v = \pm \dfrac{1}{2}\lambda$ corresponds to the boundary of the ellipse

$$\frac{u^2}{c^2 \cosh^2 \lambda} + \frac{v^2}{c^2 \sinh^2 \lambda} = 1 \qquad ...(3)$$

with two slits from extremities of the major axis each to the nearer focus. The reader can easily see that the interiors also correspond. When $\lambda = 0$, the ellipse reduces to the segment of the real axis from $u = - c$ to $u = c$. Also note that the same region of the w-plane corresponds to the rectangular regions defined by the lines

$$x = (2n \pm 1)\frac{\pi}{2}, \quad y = \pm \lambda,$$

where $n = ... - 3, - 2, - 1, 0, 1, 2, 3, ... $.

Of course $n = 0$ corresponds to the region already considered. It follows that the regions bounded by the ellipse (3) with two cuts from the extremities of the major axis each to the nearer focus is described an infinite number of times as z moves on the infinite strip between the lines $y = -\lambda$ and $y = \lambda$. This is because of the fact that the mapping $w = \sin z$ is many-one.

Again, eliminating y from (1), we get:

$$\frac{u^2}{c^2 \sin^2 x} - \frac{v^2}{c^2 \cos^2 x} = 1 \qquad \qquad \text{...(4)}$$

The equation (4) represents a family of confocal hyperbolas with the foci at $(\pm c, 0)$ for varying values of x. It should not be thought that the curve (1) for fixed values of x consists of both the branches of the hyperbola (4). To show this, we consider the images of the lines $x = -\dfrac{\pi}{2}$, $x = -a$, $x = a$ and $x = \dfrac{\pi}{2}$ where $0 < a < \dfrac{\pi}{2}$. We observe that when $x = -\dfrac{\pi}{2}$, $v = 0$ and $u = -c$ cosh y.

Hence, as v varies from $-\infty$ through 0 to ∞, u varies from $-\infty$ to $-c$ and then back to $-\infty$.

When $x = -a$, then $u = -c \sin a \cosh y$, $v = c \cos a \sinh y$.

Hence, when y varies from $-\infty$ to ∞, u is a negative and v varies from $-\infty$ to ∞ so that the line $x = -a$ corresponds to the left hand branch of the hyperbola

$$\frac{u^2}{c^2 \sin^2 a} - \frac{v^2}{c^2 \cos^2 a} = 1 \qquad \qquad \text{...(5)}$$

Similarly, we can show that the line $x = a$ corresponds to the right hand branch of the hyperbola (5) and the line $x = \dfrac{\pi}{2}$ corresponds to the slit from c to ∞ traversed twice. Also evidently the imaginary axis $x = 0$ in the z-plane corresponds to the imaginary axis $u = 0$ of the w-plane. The reader can easily verify that the infinite strip between $x = -a$ and $x = a$ corresponds to the region of the w-plane which lies between the two branches of the hyperbola (5) as shown in the figure 7.29.

It is easy to see that the infinite strip in the z-plane between the lines

$$x = -\frac{\pi}{2} \quad \text{and} \quad x = \frac{\pi}{2}$$

corresponds to the whole of the w-plane with slits extending respectively from $-c$ to $-\infty$ and from c to ∞.

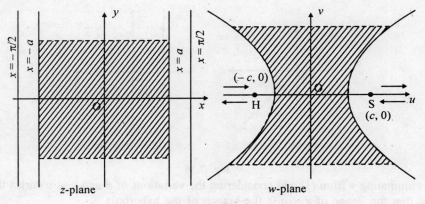

Fig. 7.29

To sum up, the mapping $w = \sin z$ transforms the one-parameter families of straight lines parallel to the x-axis and y-axis but distance from the lines

$$x = \frac{m\pi}{2} \quad (m = 0, \pm 1, \pm 3, \pm 5, \ldots)$$

or $\qquad\qquad\qquad y = 0,$

into a one parametric family of confocal ellipses and a one parametric family of confocal hyperbolas respectively with common foci at the points, $w = \pm c$.

The conformal property holds at every point of the z-plane except at the points

$$z = \frac{m\pi}{2} \quad (m = 0, \pm 1, \pm 3, \pm 5, \ldots)$$

whose images are precisely the foci $w = \pm c$. The families of ellipses and hyperbolas must form an orthogonal system in the w-plane since they are the images of two orthogonal families of straight lines in the z-plane.

7.8.2. The mapping $w = \cos z$. The mapping is conformal for every value of z except those for which the derivative, $-\sin z$, is zero, $i.e.$, for $z = n\pi$. Also the correspondence between z and w is infinity to one; $\cos z$ being periodic with the period 2π.

For the inverse function

$$z = \cos^{-1} w,$$

we have two branch points ± 1 so that each branch defines z as a single valued function of w in any domain not containing the points ± 1.

Consider now the Cartesian forms for z and w

$$z = x + iy, \ w = u + iv.$$

We have then

$$u + iv = \cos (x + iy)$$
$$= \cos x \cosh y - i \sin x \sinh y.$$
$$\Rightarrow \qquad u = \cos x \cosh y, \ v = - \sin x \sinh y.$$

We now have the following facts:

(a) The image of $x = a$ is the curve

$$u = \cos a \cosh y, \ v = - \sin a \sinh y \qquad\qquad \ldots(1)$$

y being the parameter varying from $-\infty$ to $+\infty$.

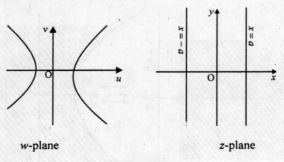

w-plane   z-plane

Fig. 7.30

On eliminating y from (1) and considering the variations of u and v as y varies from $-\infty$ to ∞, we see that the image of $x = a$ is the branch of the hyperbola

$$\frac{u^2}{\cos^2 a} - \frac{v^2}{\sin^2 a} = 1 \qquad \qquad ...(2)$$

lying to the right of the imaginary axis. Here we have considered, a, as any number such that $0 < a < \pi/2$.

The second branch of the hyperbola is the image of the line $x = \pi - a$.

The foci of the hyperbola (2) are ± 1.

(b) The domain contained between the two branches lying on the right of the imaginary axis of the hyperbolas

$$\frac{u^2}{\cos^2 a} - \frac{v^2}{\sin^2 a} = 1, \quad \frac{u^2}{\cos^2 b} - \frac{v^2}{\sin^2 b} = 1$$

is the conformal image of the domain bounded by $x = a$, $x = b$ where $0 < a, b < \pi/2$.

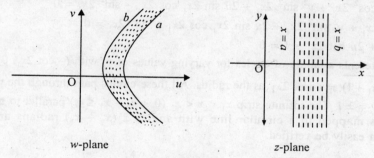

w-plane   z-plane

Fig. 7.31

(c) The image of the line $x = \pi/2$ is given by

$$u = 0, \quad v = - \sinh y$$

which is the complete imaginary axis in the w-plane.

Also the image of the line $x = 0$ given by

$$u = \cosh y, \quad v = 0;$$

y varying from $-\infty$ to $+\infty$, is the segment of the positive real axis from 1 to $+\infty$ taken twice.

(d) From above, making b tend to $\pi/2$ and a to 0, we see *that the domain*

$$0 < R(z) < \pi/2$$

is conformally mapped on the semi-plane to the right of the imaginary axis slit along the positive real axis from 1 to $+\infty$ by the transformation

$$w = \cos z.$$

7.8.3. The mapping $w = \tan z$. We have: *(Meerut 2003)*

$$u + iv = \tan(x + iy) = \frac{\sin(x + iy)}{\cos(x + iy)}$$

$$= \frac{2 \sin(x + iy) \cos(x - iy)}{2 \cos(x + iy) \cos(x - iy)}$$

$$= \frac{\sin 2x + i \sinh 2y}{\cos 2x + \cosh 2y}$$

$\Rightarrow$ $$u = \frac{\sin 2x}{\cos 2x + \cosh 2y}, \quad v = \frac{\sinh 2y}{\cos 2x + \cosh 2y}$$

The straight line $\dot{x} = x_1$ is mapped into the curve

$$u = \frac{\sin 2x_1}{\cos 2x_1 + \cosh 2y}, \quad v = \frac{\sinh 2y}{\cos 2x_1 + \cosh 2y}$$

with y as a parameter. These may be written as:

$$u \cosh 2y = \sin 2x_1 - u \cos 2x_1 \qquad \qquad ...(1)$$

and
$$\sinh 2y = v \cos 2x_1 + v \cosh 2y$$

$$= v \cos 2x_1 + v \left(\frac{\sin 2x_1}{u} - \cos 2x_1 \right) \quad \text{[From (1)]}$$

or
$$u \sinh 2y = v \sin 2x_1 \qquad \qquad ...(2)$$

To eliminate y from (1) and (2), square and subtract the equations (1) and (2),

$$u^2 (\cosh^2 2y - \sinh^2 2y) = \sin^2 2x_1 + u^2 \cos^2 2x_1 - 2u \sin 2x_1 \cos 2x_1 - v^2 \sin^2 2x_1$$

$$\Rightarrow \quad u^2 - u^2 \cos^2 2x_1 + v^2 \sin^2 2x_1 + 2u \sin 2x_1 \cos 2x_1 - \sin^2 2x_1 = 0$$

$$\Rightarrow \quad u^2 \sin^2 2x_1 + v^2 \sin^2 2x_1 + 2u \sin 2x_1 \cos 2x_1 - \sin^2 2x_1 = 0$$

$$\Rightarrow \quad u^2 + v^2 + 2u \cot 2x_1 - 1 = 0.$$

This represents a family of circles for varying values of x_1 with $(- \cot 2x_1, 0)$ as the centre and $\sqrt{(\cot^2 2x_1 + 1)} = \text{cosec } 2x_1$ as the radius. All these circles pass through the points $(0, \pm 1)$, i.e., through $w = \pm i$. The infinite strip $x_1 < x < x_2$ ($0 < x_2 - x_1 \le \pi$) parallel to the real axis in the z-plane is mapped to a circular line with angles $2(x_2 - x_1)$ radians and vertices at $w = \pm i$ as can easily be verified.

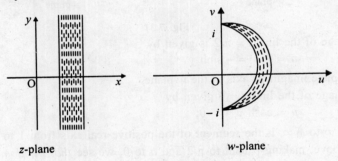

z-plane   w-plane

Fig. 7.32

Similarly the family of straight lines $y = y_1$ for varying values of y_1 is mapped into the family of circles

$$u^2 + v^2 - 2v \coth 2y_1 + 1 = 0.$$

Note. The transformation $w = \tan z$ can also be considered as the result of two transformations. For we have:

$$w = \frac{1}{i} \cdot \frac{e^{iz} - e^{-iz}}{e^{iz} + e^{-iz}} = \frac{1}{i} \cdot \frac{e^{2iz} - 1}{e^{2iz} + 1}.$$

We write
$$\xi = e^{2iz} \qquad \qquad ...(1)$$

and
$$w = \frac{1}{i} \frac{\xi - 1}{\xi + 1} \qquad \qquad ...(2)$$

In (1), straight lines parallel to the x-axis and y-axis in the z-plane transform respectively into straight lines through the origin and circle with centre at the origin in the ξ-plane.

In (2), which is bilinear, straight line through the origin and circles and to the family of orthogonal circles in the w-plane.

7.8.4. The mapping $w = tan^2 \left(\dfrac{\pi \sqrt{z}}{4a} \right)$.
(*Kerala 2003, Rohilkhand 1997*)

By means of this transformation, one shall be able to map the circular region $|w| \le 1$ into the inside and the boundary of the parabola

$$y^2 = 4a^2 (a - x).$$

The given transformation can be written as:

$$= \tan^2 \left(\frac{\pi \sqrt{z}}{4a} \right) = \frac{1 - \cos \left(\dfrac{\pi \sqrt{z}}{2a} \right)}{1 + \cos \left(\dfrac{\pi \sqrt{z}}{2a} \right)}.$$

This transformation can be considered as a combination of the following three transformations:

$$w = \tan^2 \frac{\xi}{2} = \frac{1 - \cos \xi}{1 + \cos \xi}, \quad \xi = \frac{1}{2} \pi t \text{ and } t = \sqrt{z}$$

where $w = u + iv$, $\zeta = \xi + i\eta$, $t = \sigma + i\tau$ and $z = x + iy$.

We first consider the infinite strip in the ζ-plane between the line $\xi = 0$, $\xi = \pi/2$. Writing $\zeta = \dfrac{1}{2} \pi + i\eta$, we see from the first of the above transformations that

$$|w| = \left| \frac{1 - \cos \left(\dfrac{1}{2} \pi + i\eta \right)}{1 + \cos \left(\dfrac{1}{2} \pi + i\eta \right)} \right| = \left| \frac{1 + i \sinh \eta}{1 - i \sinh \eta} \right|$$

$$= \frac{\sqrt{(1 + \sinh^2 \eta)}}{\sqrt{(1 + \sinh^2 \eta)}} = 1.$$

Hence, as η moves from $-\infty$ to ∞ along the line $\xi = \dfrac{1}{2} \pi$, w describes the unit circle $|w| = 1$ once. Again on $\xi = 0$, we have $\xi = ih$ so that $\cos x = \cos i\eta = \cosh h$ and

$$w = \frac{1 - \cosh \eta}{1 + \cosh \eta}$$

which is real. Thus, as η moves from $+\infty$ to 0, w goes from -1 to 0 and as η moves from 0 to $-\infty$, w goes back from 0 to -1. Hence, the infinite strip

$$0 \le \xi \le \frac{1}{2} \pi$$

corresponds to the circular region $|w| \le 1$ with a slit extending from 0 to -1 as shown below.

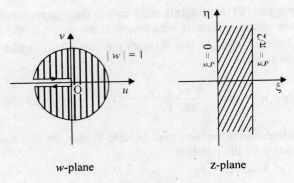

w-plane   z-plane

Fig. 7.33

It is easy to see that the interiors correspond. The infinite strip in the t-plane corresponding to the strip

$$0 \leq \xi \leq \pi/2$$

is evidently given by $0 \leq \sigma \leq a$. Finally we examine the region in the z-plane corresponding to the strip $0 \leq \sigma \leq a$ in the t-plane under the transformation $t = \sqrt{z}$.

We have:

$$(\sigma + i\tau)^2 = x + iy$$

so that

$$\sigma^2 - \tau^2 = x, \quad 2\sigma\tau = y.$$

Eliminating σ, we get:

$$\sigma^2 - \frac{y^2}{4\sigma^2} = x \implies y^2 = 4\sigma^2 (\sigma^2 - x)$$

which represents a family of parabolas for varying values of σ. In particular $\sigma = a$ corresponds to the parabola

$$y^2 = 4a^2 (a^2 - x).$$

Also as $\sigma \to 0$, the parabola gets narrower and ultimately becomes a slit extending from the origin (which is the focus here) to $-\infty$. Thus, the infinite strip $0 \leq \sigma \leq a$ corresponds to the region inside and on the boundary of the parabola

$$y = 4a^2 (a^2 - x).$$

It is evident that the interiors correspond. The regions are shown below:

Note that the transformation

$$w = \tan^2 \left(\frac{\pi \sqrt{z}}{4a} \right)$$

maps the region inside the parabola

$$y^2 = 4a^2 (a^2 - x)$$

in a one-to-one correspondence onto the inside of the circle

$$|w| = 1$$

since the real axis of the z-plane from $-\infty$ to 0 corresponds to the real axis of the w-plane from -1 to 0. In fact, the slits in the z-plane and w-plane are not required for the direct transformation from the w-plane to the z-plane. They are needed only for the subsidiary transformations in order to show the correspondence between boundaries of the various regions.

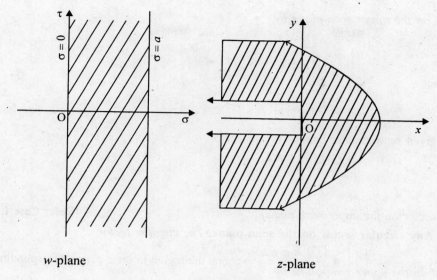

w-plane   z-plane

Fig. 7.34

We further observe that

$$\frac{dw}{dz} = 2 \tan\left(\frac{\pi \sqrt{z}}{4a}\right) \cdot \sec^2\left(\frac{\pi \sqrt{z}}{4a}\right) \cdot \frac{\pi}{4a} \cdot \frac{1}{2\sqrt{z}}$$

$$= \frac{\pi}{4a \sqrt{z}} \tan\left(\frac{\pi \sqrt{z}}{4a}\right) \sec^2\left(\frac{\pi \sqrt{z}}{4a}\right).$$

We see that (dw/dz) tends to a finite non-zero limit as $z \to 0$. It follows that the points $z = 0$ and $w = 0$ are not critical points of the transformation. Accordingly the representation is one-to-one and conformal.

7.9. Mapping of given domains onto the interior of the unit circle or the upper half-plane. We shall now catalogue some domains, which, by means of the elementary transformations or their algebraic combinations, can be mapped onto the interior of the unit circle. In some cases we may consider the mapping onto the upper semi-plane, for, as we have seen, the upper semi-plane can be conformally mapped onto the interior of the unit circle by means of a bilinear transformation.

We may also remark that the interior of any circle is conformally equivalent to the interior or the exterior of any other circle, for, by a suitable bilinear transformation, we can always conformally map two such domains.

Further any two semi-planes are conformally equivalent.

I. Wedge on the semi-plane. The wedge

$$0 < \arg z < \pi/n$$

is mapped on the upper semi-plane

$$I(w) > 0$$

by the transformation

$$w = z^n.$$ [Refer § 7.3.1 (d), page 213]

II. Semi-circular domain on the semi-plane. *The semi-circular domain*

$$|z| < 1, I(z) > 0$$

is mapped on the upper semi-plane by

$$w = \left(\frac{1 + z}{1 - z}\right)^2.$$

In fact

$$Z = \frac{1 + z}{1 - z}$$

maps the given semi-circular domain on the sector

$$0 < \arg Z < \pi/2$$

and

$$w = z^2$$

maps the sector on the upper semi-plane.   [Refer Case I, above]

III. Any circular sector on the semi-plane. *The circular sector*

$$|z| < 1, \; 0 < \arg z < \pi/n$$

is mapped on the upper semi-plane by

$$w = \left(\frac{1 + z^n}{1 - z^n}\right)^2.$$

The transformation

$$Z = z^n$$

maps the given circular sector onto the semi-circle

$$|Z| < 1, \; 0 < \arg Z < \pi.$$

Now refer to the Case II above.

IV. Infinite rectangular strip on the semi-plane. *The infinite rectangular strip*

$$0 < I(z) < \pi$$

is mapped on the upper semi-plane by the transformation

$$w = e^z.$$ [Refer § 7.5, page 231]

V. Semi-infinite rectangular strip on the semi-plane. *The semi-infinite rectangular strip*

$$-\infty < R(z) < 0, \; 0 < I(z) < \pi$$

is mapped on the upper semi-plane by the transformation

$$w = \left(\frac{1 + e^z}{1 - e^z}\right)^2.$$

The transformation

$$Z = e^z$$

maps the given semi-infinite rectangular strip on the semi-circular domain

$$|Z| < 1, \; 0 < \arg Z < \pi$$

which is then mapped on the upper semi-plane by

$$w = \left(\frac{1 + Z}{1 - Z}\right)^2.$$ [Refer Case II, above]

VI. The exterior of the ellipse on the interior of the unit circle. The exterior of the ellipse

$$\frac{x^2}{a^2} + \frac{y^2}{b^2} = 1,$$

$$a = \frac{1}{2}\left(r + \frac{1}{r}\right), \quad b = \frac{1}{2}\left(r - \frac{1}{r}\right)$$

is mapped on the interior of the unit circle $|w| = 1$ by

$$w = r(z + \sqrt{z^2 - 1}).$$

Here $\sqrt{z^2 - 1}$ denotes that branch of the function for which $\sqrt{z^2 - 1}$ takes negative values for those real values of z which are greater than one.

The function

$$Z = z + \sqrt{z^2 - 1}$$

maps the exterior of the ellipse on the interior of the circle $|Z| = 1/r$. [Refer § 7.4 (d)] and $w = rZ$ maps this interior on the interior of the unit circle $|w| = 1$.

VII. Exterior of a parabola onto the semi-plane. *The exterior of the parabola*

$$y^2 = 4a^2(a^2 - x) \qquad (a > 0)$$

is mapped on the upper semi-plane by

$$w = i(\sqrt{z - a}).$$

Here $\sqrt{z}$ denotes that branch for which $\sqrt{z}$ is positive for positive values of z.

The function

$$Z = \sqrt{z}$$

maps conformally the exterior of the given parabola onto the domain $R(Z) > a$ [§ 7.3.3 (c), page 214] and $w = i(Z - a)$ maps this latter domain on the upper semi-plane.

VIII. Interior of a parabola onto the interior of the unit circle. *The interior of the parabola*

$$y^2 = 4a^2(a^2 - x) \qquad (a > 0)$$

is mapped on the domain $|w| < 1$ by the transformation

$$w = \tan^2\left(\frac{\pi\sqrt{z}}{4a}\right).$$

The transformation

$$w = \tan^2\left(\frac{\pi\sqrt{z}}{4a}\right),$$

is the resultant of the following.

$$Z = \sqrt{z}, \quad T = \frac{\pi}{2a}Z, \quad P = \cos T, \quad w = \frac{1 - P}{1 + P}.$$

Now $Z = \sqrt{z}$ maps the given interior with the slit along the negative real axis from $z = 0$ to $z = -\infty$ onto $0 < R(Z) < a$.

Again $T = \pi Z/2a$ maps the domain $0 < R(z) < a$ onto the domain $0 < RT < \pi/2$.

Also the transformation

$$P = \cos T$$

maps the rectangular strip $0 < R(T) < \pi/2$ onto the semi-plane to the right of the imaginary axis with the slit along the positive real axis from $P = 1$ to ∞.[Refer § 7.8.2 (d)]

The transformation

$$w = \frac{1 - P}{1 + P}$$

maps the semi-plane to the right of the imaginary axis with slit along the positive real axis from $P = 1$ to ∞ on the interior of the unit circle with slit along the negative real axis from $w = 0$ to -1.

Combining all these transformations, we see that

$$w = \tan^2\left(\frac{\pi\sqrt{z}}{4a}\right)$$

maps the interior of the given parabola with slit along the negative real axis from $z = 0$ to $z = -\infty$ onto the interior of the unit circle $|w| = 1$ with slit along the negative real axis from $w = 0$ to $w = -1$.

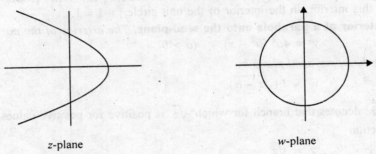

z-plane   w-plane

Fig. 7.35

We notice that for the function (1) (dw/dz) is not zero for $z = 0$.

In fact

$$\frac{dw}{dz} = \frac{\tan\left(\dfrac{\pi\sqrt{z}}{2a}\right)}{\left(\dfrac{\pi\sqrt{z}}{2a}\right)} \cdot \sec^2\left(\frac{\pi\sqrt{z}}{4a}\right) \cdot \frac{2a}{\pi}$$

$$= \frac{2a}{\pi} \text{ for } z = 0.$$

Thus, the mapping is conformal even for $z = 0$.

Also we may see that as z moves along the negative real axis from $z = 0$ to $z = -\infty$, w moves along the negative real axis from $w = 0$ to $w = -1$.

In fact for $z = -t = i^2 t$ for $t > 0$, we have:

$$w = \tan^2\left(\frac{\pi\sqrt{z}}{4a}\right) = \tan^2\left(\frac{i\pi\sqrt{t}}{4a}\right)$$

$$= \left[i\tanh\left(\frac{\pi\sqrt{t}}{4a}\right)\right]^2 = -\tanh^2\left(\frac{\pi\sqrt{t}}{4a}\right),$$

so that w varies from 0 to -1 as t varies from 0 to $+\infty$.

Hence, the result.

IX. Interior of a branch of a hyperbola onto semi-plane. *The interior of either branch of the hyperbola*

$$x^2 - y^2 = a$$

is mapped on the upper semi-plane by

$$w = i\,(z^2 - a).$$ [Refer § 7.3.3]

X. Exterior of the two branches of a hyperbola, *i.e.*, **the simply connected domain bounded by the two branches on semi-plane.** *The simply connected domain bounded by the two branches of the hyperbola*

$$\frac{x^2}{\cos^2 \alpha} - \frac{y^2}{\sin^2 \alpha} = 1$$

is mapped on the upper semi-plane by

$$w = e^{-i\alpha}(z + \sqrt{z^2 - 1})^{\frac{\pi}{\pi - 2\alpha}}$$ ...(1)

The result can be easily obtained by considering (1) as the resultant of

$$Z = z + \sqrt{z^2 - 1},\ \ T = Z^{\frac{\pi}{\pi - 2\alpha}},\ \ w = e^{-i\alpha}\,T.$$ [Refer § 7.4 (d)]

Here $\sqrt{z^2 - 1}$ denotes that branch of this function which takes the value i for $z = 0$.

XI. Convex lens onto a semi-plane. A convex lens formed by two circular arcs which intersect at an angle π/n at the points $z = a$ and $z = b$ is mapped into the upper semi-plane by

$$w = \left(e^{-i\alpha}\,\frac{z - a}{z - b}\right)^n.$$

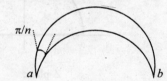

The transformation

$$Z = (z - a)/(z - b)$$

maps the two arcs on two rays through $Z = 0$ and, because of conformality, these rays will be inclined to each other at an angle π/n.

Fig. 7.36

Then, for a suitable value of α,

$$T = e^{-i\alpha}\,Z,$$

maps the interior of the wedge formed by these rays onto

$$0 < \arg T < \pi/n.$$

XII. Closed Crescent *formed by two circles touching each other; one of the circles being contained in the other.*

If $z = 0$ be the point of contact, then $Z = 1/z$ maps the crescent onto an infinite strip bounded by two parallel lines. Then by a suitable magnification and rotation represented by a bilinear transformation,

$$T = f(z)$$

this strip can be mapped onto $0 < I\,(T) < \pi$.

Finally $w = e^T$

maps this latter strip into the upper semi-plane.

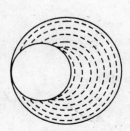

Fig. 7.37

EXAMPLES

1. *Show that the transformation*

$$w = \frac{1 + z^2}{1 - z^2},$$

maps the interior of the positive quadrant of the unit circle in the z-plane conformally on the interior of the positive quadrant of the w-plane. Discuss also the correspondence between the boundaries of the two domains.

Solution. We have:

$$\frac{dw}{dz} = \frac{4z}{(1 - z^2)^2} = 0 \text{ for } z = 0.$$

We write:

$$Z = z^2 \qquad \qquad ...(1)$$

$$\Rightarrow \qquad w = \frac{1 + Z}{1 - Z} \qquad \qquad ...(2)$$

The interior of the positive quadrant of the unit circle in the z-plane is mapped conformally on the interior of the part of the unit circle lying above the real axis in the Z-plane.

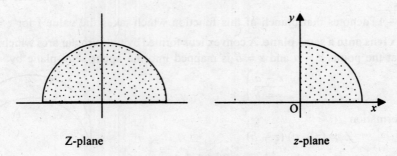

Z-plane   z-plane

Fig. 7.38

We now rewrite (2) as

$$Z = \frac{w - 1}{w + 1}$$

$$\Rightarrow \qquad 1 - Z\bar{Z} = 1 - \frac{w - 1}{w + 1} \cdot \frac{\bar{w} - 1}{\bar{w} - 1}$$

$$= \frac{(w + 1)(\bar{w} + 1)(w - 1)(\bar{w} - 1)}{|w + 1|^2}$$

$$= \frac{2(w + \bar{w})}{|w + 1|^2} = \frac{4R(w)}{|w + 1|^2} \qquad \qquad ...(3)$$

so that

$$|Z| < 1 \quad \Rightarrow \quad R(w) > 0.$$

Also,

$$I(Z) = \frac{Z - \bar{Z}}{2i} = \left(\frac{w - 1}{w + 1} + \frac{\bar{w} - 1}{\bar{w} + 1} \right) \frac{1}{2i}$$

$$= \frac{2(w - \overline{w})}{|w + 1|^2 \, 2i} \qquad \qquad ...(4)$$

$$= \frac{2I(w)}{|w + 1|^2}$$

so that $\qquad I(Z) > 0 \quad \Rightarrow \quad I(w) > 0.$

Thus, to each point Z in the interior of the semi-circle wherefor $|Z| < 1$ and $I(Z) > 0$, there corresponds a point w such that $R(w) > 0$ and $I(w) > 0$, i.e., a point in the interior of the first quadrant.

Also we see from above that each point w in the interior of the first quadrant wherefor $R(w) > 0$ and $I(w) > 0$ is the image of a point Z in the interior of the semi-circle wherefor $|Z| < 1$ and $I(Z) > 0$.

The correspondence is clearly conformal in the given domain of the z-plane.

The following correspondence between the boundaries may be easily established:

(i) As z varies from 0 to 1, w varies from 1 to ∞ along the real axis in the w-plane.

(ii) As z varies from 1 to i along the arc of the unit circle in the first quadrant, w moves from ∞ to 0 along the imaginary axis in the w-plane.

(iii) As z varies from i to 0 along the imaginary axis in the z-plane, w varies from 0 to 1 along the real axis in the w-plane.

Clearly the mapping is not conformal for $z = 0$.

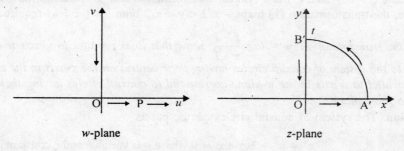

w-plane   z-plane

Fig. 7.39

In fact we see that the directions of the real and the imaginary axes inclined to each other at an angle of $\pi/2$ at $z = 0$ correspond both to the direction of the real axis at $w = 1$ which corresponds to $z = 0$.

2. *Show that the transformation*

$$w = \tanh^{-1} z,$$

maps the upper half of the z-plane conformally on the strip $0 < v < \frac{1}{2}\pi.$

Solution. We have:

$$w = \frac{1}{2} \log \frac{1 + z}{1 - z}$$

We write:

$$Z = \frac{1 + z}{1 - z} \qquad \qquad ...(1)$$

$$S = \log Z \qquad \qquad ...(2)$$

$$w = \frac{1}{2} S \qquad \qquad ...(3)$$

The transformation (1) maps
$$I(z) > 0 \text{ onto } I(Z) > 0.$$

The transformation (2) maps
$$I(Z) > 0 \text{ onto } 0 < I(S) < \pi.$$

The transformation (3) maps
$$0 < I(S) < \pi \text{ onto } 0 < I(w) < \frac{1}{2}\pi.$$

Hence, the result.

3. *Show that the transformation* $w = \tanh(z/2)$ *maps the strip* $-\pi/2 < y < \pi/2$ *onto* $|w| < 1$.

Solution. We have:

$$w = \tanh(z/2) = \frac{e^{z/2} - e^{-z/2}}{e^{z/2} + e^{-z/2}} = \frac{e^z - 1}{e^z + 1} \qquad \text{...(1)}$$

Let
$$\zeta = \xi + i\eta = e^z \qquad \text{...(2)}$$

Then
$$w = \frac{\zeta - 1}{\zeta + 1} \qquad \text{...(3)}$$

Thus, (1) is the resultant of (2) and (3).

Proceeding as in § 7.5, we will see that the strip $-\pi/2 < y < \pi/2$ is transformed onto the right half-plane $\xi > 0$. Again (3) is a bilinear transformation and so it transforms $\xi > 0$ onto $|w| < 1$. Hence, the transformation (1) maps $-\pi/2 < y < \pi/2$ onto $|w| < 1$ as required.

4. *In the transformation* $w = \log \dfrac{z-1}{z+1}$ *show that lines parallel to v-axis in the w-plane correspond to the system of coaxial circles having their centres on the x-axis in the z-plane. Also that lines parallel to u-axis in the w-plane correspond to coaxial circles having their centres on the y-axis in the z-plane.*

Solution. The system of coaxial circles can be put as

or

$$\left.\begin{array}{l} x^2 + y^2 + 2gx + c = 0 \text{ where } g \text{ is variable and } c \text{ constant} \\ x^2 + y^2 + 2fy + c = 0 \text{ where } f \text{ is variable and } c \text{ constant} \end{array}\right\} \qquad \text{...(1)}$$

Also, $\log(x + iy) = \log\sqrt{x^2 + y^2} + i\tan^{-1}(y/x)$.

$$w = \log\left(\frac{z-1}{z+1}\right) = \log(x - 1 + iy) - \log(x + 1 + iy)$$

$\Rightarrow$
$$w = \left[\frac{1}{2}\log\{(x-1)^2 + y^2\} + i\tan^{-1}\frac{y}{x-1}\right]$$

$$-\left[\frac{1}{2}\log\{(x+1)^2 + y^2\} + i\tan^{-1}\frac{y}{x+1}\right]$$

$\Rightarrow$
$$u + iv = \frac{1}{2}\log\frac{(x-1)^2 + y^2}{(x+1)^2 + y^2} + i\left(\tan^{-1}\frac{y}{x-1} - \tan^{-1}\frac{y}{x+1}\right)$$

$$\therefore \qquad u = \frac{1}{2} \log \frac{(x-1)^2 + y^2}{(x+1)^2 + y^2} \qquad \qquad ...(2)$$

$$v = \tan^{-1} \frac{y}{x-1} - \tan^{-1} \frac{y}{x+1} = \tan^{-1} \left(\frac{2y}{x^2 + y^2 - 1} \right) \qquad ...(3)$$

Case I. Lines parallel to v-axis, *i.e.*, $u = 0$ are $u = c$ where c is a parameter.

Hence, from (2) on putting $u = c$, we get:

$$e^{2c} = \frac{(x-1)^2 + y^2}{(x+1)^2 + y^2}$$

$$\Rightarrow \qquad \frac{e^{2c}}{1} = \frac{x^2 + y^2 + 1 - 2x}{x^2 + y^2 + 1 + 2x} \qquad \text{[Applying componendo and dividendo]}$$

$$\frac{e^{2c} + 1}{e^{2c} - 1} = \frac{x^2 + y^2 + 1}{-2x}$$

$$\Rightarrow \qquad x^2 + y^2 + 2gx + 1 = 0$$

where $\qquad g = \dfrac{e^{2c} + 1}{e^{2c} - 1}$ is a parameter.

By (1), the above equation represents a family of coaxial circles having their centres on x-axis in the z-plane.

Case II. Lines parallel to u-axis, *i.e.*, $v = 0$ are $v = d$ where d is a parameter.

Hence, from (3), we have:

$$\tan d = \frac{2y}{x^2 + y^2 - 1}$$

$$\Rightarrow \qquad x^2 + y^2 - 2y \cot d - 1 = 0.$$

By (1), the above equation represents a family of coaxial circles having their centres on y-axis in the z-plane.

5. *If $w = \tan^2 z/2$, show that the strip in the z-plane between $x = 0$ and $x = \pi/2$ is represented on the interior of the unit circle in the w-plane, cut along the real axis from $w = -1$ to $w = 0$.*

Solution. $\qquad w = \tan^2 (z/2) = \dfrac{1 - \cos z}{1 + \cos z} = \dfrac{1 - \cos (x + iy)}{1 + \cos (x + iy)}$

$$\Rightarrow \qquad w = \frac{(1 - \cos x \cosh y) + i \sin x \sinh y}{(1 + \cos x \cosh y) - i \sin x \sinh y} \qquad ...(1)$$

(*i*) If $x = \pi/2$, then from (1), we have:

$$w = \frac{1 + i \sinh y}{1 - i \sinh y}$$

$$\therefore \qquad |w| = \left[\frac{1 + \sinh^2 y}{1 + \sinh^2 y} \right]^{1/2} = 1.$$

This shows that the line $x = \pi/2$ in the z-plane corresponds to the unit circle $|w| = 1$ in the w-plane.

(*ii*) If $x = 0$, then from (1), we have:

$$w = \frac{1 - \cosh y}{1 + \cosh y} = \frac{2 - e^y - e^{-y}}{2 + e^y + e^{-y}} = \text{a real quantity.}$$

This shows that the line $x = 0$ in the z-plane corresponds to some real portion of the w-plane.

Now, $\lim\limits_{y \to \infty} e^{-y} = 0$ and $\lim\limits_{y \to -\infty} e^y = 0.$

When $y = -\infty, \ w = \lim\limits_{y \to -\infty} \dfrac{2 - e^y - e^{-y}}{2 + e^y + e^{-y}}$

$$= \lim\limits_{y \to \infty} \frac{2e^y - e^{2y} - 1}{2e^y + e^{2y} + 1} = -1.$$

When $y = 0, \ x = \dfrac{1 - \cosh y}{1 + \cosh y} = \dfrac{1 - 1}{2} = 0.$

When $y = \infty, \ w = \lim\limits_{y \to \infty} \dfrac{2 - e^y - e^{-y}}{2 + e^y + e^{-y}}$

$$= \lim\limits_{y \to \infty} \frac{2e^{-y} - 1 - e^{2y}}{2e^{-y} + 1 + e^{-2y}} = -1.$$

Above shows that as z travels along $x = 0$ from $y = -\infty$ to $y = \infty$ in the z-plane, w travels along the real portion of the w-plane, *i.e.*, real axis from -1 to 0 and back again from 0 to -1. This shows that the line $x = 0$ in the z-plane corresponds to a cut from $u = -1$ to $u = 0$.

(*iii*) Lastly we have to prove that the interiors correspond.

From (1), we have:

$$|w| = \frac{\sqrt{(1 - \cos x \cosh y)^2 + \sin^2 x \sinh^2 y}}{\sqrt{(1 + \cos x \cosh y)^2 + \sin^2 x \sinh^2 y}}.$$

When $0 < x < \pi/2$ then $1 - \cos x \cosh y < 1 + \cos x \cosh y$. Hence, when $0 < x < \pi/2$ we have $|w| < 1$ which represents the interior of the unit circle in the w-plane. This relation shows that the interior of the strip between $x = 0$ and $x = \pi/2$ in the z-plane corresponds to the interior of the unit circle $|w| = 1$ in the w-plane. This is exhibited in the figure below.

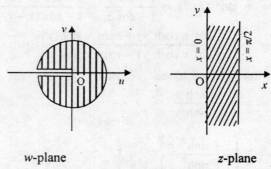

w-plane   z-plane

Fig. 7.40

6. *Show that the transformation*

$$w = \frac{i\,(z + ic)^2 - (z - ic)^2}{i\,(z + ic)^2 + (z - ic)^2}$$

conformally maps the interior of the semi-circle $|\,z\,| = 1$, $R\,(z) > 0$ *onto the interior of the unit circle* $|\,w\,| = 1$.

Solution. The transformation can be written as

$$w = \frac{i - \left(\dfrac{z - ic}{z + ic}\right)^2}{i + \left(\dfrac{z - ic}{z + ic}\right)^2}$$

which is the combination of the transformations

$$\zeta = \left(\frac{z - ic}{z + ic}\right)^2, \quad w = \frac{i - \zeta}{i + \zeta}.$$

First of these transformations maps the interior of the semi-circle $|\,z\,| = 1$, $R\,(z) > 0$ conformally onto the upper half of the ζ-plane. Second transformation may be written as

$$\zeta = \frac{i\,(1 - w)}{1 + w}.$$

Writing $w = u + iv$, $\zeta = \xi + i\eta$, we get:

$$\xi + i\eta = \frac{i\,(1 - u - iv)}{1 + u + iv}$$

$\Rightarrow$
$$\eta = \frac{1 - u^2 - v^2}{(1 + u)^2 + v^2}.$$

Hence, the real axis $\eta = 0$ of the ζ-plane corresponds to the circle $u^2 + v^2 = 1$, *i.e.*, $|\,w\,| = 1$. Also the upper half of the ζ-plane defined by $\eta > 0$ corresponds to the region

$$1 - u^2 - v^2 > 0 \quad \Rightarrow \quad u^2 + v^2 < 1 \quad \Rightarrow \quad |\,w\,| < 1.$$

Thus, the upper half of the ζ-plane corresponds to the interior of the unit circle $|\,w\,| = 1$.

7. *Show that the transformation*

$$w = \left(\frac{z + i}{z - i} + 1\right)^2$$

maps the real axis in the z-plane onto a cardioid in the w-plane. Indicate the region of the z-plane which corresponds to the interior of the cardioid.

Solution. Given transformation is the combination of the following transformations

(*i*)
$$\zeta = \frac{z + i}{z - i}, \quad t = \zeta + 1, \quad w = t^2.$$

Now consider $\zeta = \dfrac{z + i}{z - i}$. For real axis in the z-plane $y = 0$ $\therefore$ $z = x$.

$\therefore$
$$\zeta = \frac{y + i}{y - i} \quad \Rightarrow \quad |\,\zeta\,| = \frac{\sqrt{y^2 + 1}}{\sqrt{y^2 + 1}} = 1.$$

Hence, the real axis in the z-plane is transformed into the unit circle in the ζ-plane.

Again,
$$1 - \zeta\bar{\zeta} = 1 - \frac{z+i}{z-i} \cdot \frac{\bar{z}-i}{\bar{z}+i}$$

$$= \frac{(z-i)(\bar{z}+i) - (z+i)(\bar{z}-i)}{|z-i|^2}$$

$\Rightarrow$
$$1 - |\zeta|^2 = \frac{2i(z-\bar{z})}{|z-i|^2} = \frac{-4y}{|z-i|^2}.$$

For the interior of the circle $|\zeta| < 1$, y must be negative showing thereby that the interior of the unit circle corresponds to the lower half of the z-plane. This is shown in the figure below.

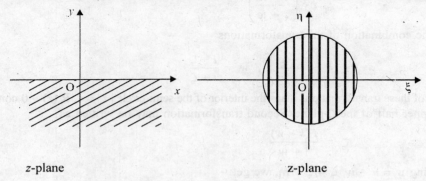

z-plane   z-plane

Fig. 7.41

(ii) $t = \zeta + 1$ or $\zeta = t - 1$ $\therefore$ $|\zeta| = 1$

$\Rightarrow$ $|t-1| = 1$ which is a circle in the t-plane with centre at $t = 1$. Above transformation is that of translation.

(iii) $w = t^2$.

Since $|t-1| = 1$ $\therefore$ $(t-1) = e^{i\theta}$

$\Rightarrow$ $t = 1 + e^{i\theta}$ and let $w = \rho e^{i\phi}$

$\therefore$ $\rho e^{i\phi} = (1 + e^{i\theta})^2 = 1 + 2e^{i\theta} + e^{2i\theta} = e^{i\theta}(e^{i\theta} + e^{-i\theta} + 2)$

$\therefore$ $\rho e^{i\phi} = e^{i\theta}(2 + 2\cos\theta).$

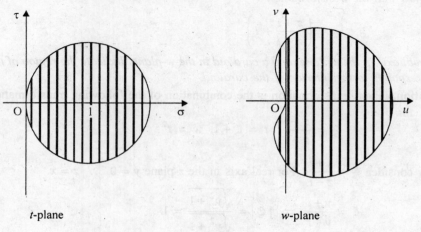

t-plane   w-plane

Fig. 7.42

Equating modulus and amplitude, we have:
$$\rho = 2 (1 + \cos \theta) \text{ and } \phi = \theta$$
$$\therefore \qquad \rho = 2 (1 + \cos \phi).$$

This represents the cardioid in the w-plane.

We can verify that the interior of the circle $| z - 1 | = 1$ corresponds to the interior of the above cardioid in the w-plane. This transformation is shown below.

8. *If $w = 2z + z^2$ prove that the circle $| z | = 1$ corresponds to a cardioid in the w-plane. Further show that the vertices of an equilateral triangle inscribed in the circle correspond to the points of contact of parallel tangents of the cardioid.*

(*Rohilkhand, 2001; Meerut 2003, Kanpur 2002, 2005*)

Solution. $\qquad w = 2z + z^2 \implies w + 1 = (z + 1)^2.$

Shift the pole to the point $(- 1, 0)$ in the w-plane, *i.e.,* write $W = w + 1$, we have:

$W = (z + 1)^2$ and any point on the unit circle $| z | = 1$ is $z = e^{i\theta}$.

$$\therefore \qquad W = (e^{i\theta} + 1)^2 = e^{i\theta} (e^{i\theta/2} + e^{- i\theta/2})^2$$
$$= e^{i\theta} \cdot (2 \cos \theta/2)^2$$

or
$$Re^{i\phi} = e^{i\theta} \cdot \left(4 \cos^2 \frac{\theta}{2} \right).$$

Equating modulus and amplitude, we get:

$$R = 4\cos^2 \frac{\theta}{2} \text{ and } \phi = \theta$$

or
$$R = 2 (1 + \cos \phi).$$

This equation represents a cardioid in the w-plane.

Therefore the circle $| z | = 1$ corresponds to a cardioid in the w-plane.

Let $\triangle$ ABC be the equilateral triangle inscribed in the unit circle $| z | = 1$.

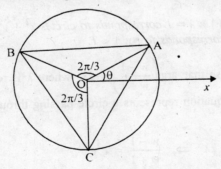

Fig. 7.43

If vectorial angle of vertex A be θ then those of B and C will be $\theta + 2\pi/3$ and $\theta + 4\pi/3$ respectively. If A′, B′, C′ be the corresponding points in the w-plane then these vectorial angles are

$$\phi, \ \phi + 2\pi/3, \ \phi + 4\pi/3 \qquad\qquad [\because \ \theta = \phi]$$

We have to establish that at these points A′, B′, C′ of the cardioid tangents are parallel to $w + 1 = W = U + iV$ (say) $= Re^{i\phi}$ where $R = 2 (1 + \cos \phi).$

$$\therefore \qquad U = R \cos \phi = 2 (1 + \cos \phi) \cos \phi$$
$$= 2 \cos \phi + 1 + \cos 2\phi$$

$$V = R \sin \phi = 2 (1 + \cos \phi) \sin \phi$$
$$= 2 \sin \phi + \sin 2\phi.$$

$\therefore \quad \dfrac{dU}{d\phi} = -2 \sin \phi - 2 \sin 2\phi = -4 \sin \dfrac{3\phi}{2} \cos \dfrac{\phi}{2}$

$\quad \dfrac{dV}{d\phi} = 2 \cos \phi + 2 \cos 2\phi = 4 \cos \dfrac{3\phi}{2} \cos \dfrac{\phi}{2}$

$\therefore \quad \tan \phi = \dfrac{dV}{dU} = \dfrac{dV}{d\phi} \Big/ \dfrac{dU}{d\phi}$

or

$$\tan \phi = \frac{4 \cos \dfrac{3\phi}{2} \cos \dfrac{\phi}{2}}{-4 \sin \dfrac{3\phi}{2} \cos \dfrac{\phi}{2}} = -\cot \frac{3\phi}{2}.$$

Putting $\qquad \phi = \phi, \phi + \dfrac{3\pi}{2}, \phi + \dfrac{4\pi}{3}$ for A', B', C' we get:

$$\tan \phi = -\cot \frac{3\phi}{2}, -\cot \frac{3}{2}\left(\phi + \frac{2\pi}{3}\right), -\cot \frac{3}{2}\left(\phi + \frac{4\pi}{3}\right)$$

$$= -\cot \frac{3\phi}{2}, -\cot \left(\frac{3}{2}\phi + \pi\right), -\cot \left(\frac{3}{2}\phi + 2\pi\right)$$

$$= -\cot (3\phi/2), -\cot (3\phi/2), -\cot (3\phi/2).$$

Since $\tan \phi$ is same for all the three points, it therefore follows that tangents at A', B', C' to the cardioid are parallel.

9. *Consider the transformation $w = \dfrac{1}{2}\left(z + \dfrac{1}{z}\right)$. By considering amp $\left(\dfrac{w-1}{w+1}\right)$ or otherwise prove that in general any circle through two points $w = \pm 1$ corresponds to two circles in the z-plane.*

In particular show that $|w| = 1$ corresponds to circles $x^2 + y^2 \pm 2y - 1 = 0$. Also find the region in the z-plane which corresponds to $|w| < 1$.

Solution. Let us suppose that $\arg\left(\dfrac{w-1}{w+1}\right) = 2\lambda$ where λ is real.

We know that above equation represents a circle passing through two fixed points $w = 1$, $w = -1$.

Now, $\quad \arg\left(\dfrac{w-1}{w+1}\right) = 2\lambda \quad \Rightarrow \quad \dfrac{w-1}{w+1} = c^2 e^{2i\lambda}$

where both c and λ are real.

But $\qquad w = \dfrac{1}{2}\left(z + \dfrac{1}{z}\right) = \dfrac{z^2 + 1}{2z}.$

Hence, putting for w, we get:

$$\left(\frac{z-1}{z+1}\right)^2 = c^2 e^{2i\lambda} \quad \Rightarrow \quad \frac{z-1}{z+1} = \pm ce^{i\lambda}$$

or $\qquad \dfrac{z-1}{z+1} = ce^{i\lambda}, \quad \dfrac{z-1}{z+1} = -ce^{i\lambda} = ce^{i(\pi + \alpha)}$

$$\therefore \qquad \arg\left(\frac{z-1}{z+1}\right) = \lambda, \quad \arg\left(\frac{z-1}{z+1}\right) = \pi + \alpha.$$

Both the above equations represent circle in the z-plane.

Second Part. By the given transformation the circle $|w| \le 1$ transforms to $\frac{1}{2}\left(z+\frac{1}{z}\right) \le 1$

$$\therefore \qquad \left(\frac{1}{2}\right)^2 \left(z+\frac{1}{z}\right)^2 \le 1 \text{ or } \left(z+\frac{1}{z}\right)\left(\bar{z}+\frac{1}{\bar{z}}\right) \le 4$$

or
$$z\bar{z} + \frac{1}{z\bar{z}} + \frac{z}{\bar{z}} + \frac{\bar{z}}{z} \le 4$$

or
$$(z\bar{z})^2 + 1 + z^2 + \bar{z}^2 \le 4z\bar{z}$$

or
$$[(z\bar{z})^2 - 2z\bar{z} + 1] + (z^2 + \bar{z}^2 - 2z\bar{z}) \le 0$$

or
$$(z\bar{z} - 1)^2 + (z - \bar{z})^2 \le 0$$

or
$$(|z|^2 - 1)^2 + (2iy)^2 \le 0$$
or
$$(x^2 + y^2 - 1)^2 - 4y^2 \le 0$$
or
$$(x^2 + y^2 + 2y - 1)(x^2 + y^2 - 2y - 1) \le 0$$
or
$$x^2 + y^2 \pm 2y - 1 \le 0.$$

Above relation shows that the circle $|w| = 1$ corresponds to both the circles $x^2 + y^2 \pm 2y - 1 = 0$ and the interior given by $|w| < 1$ corresponds to the interior given by $x^2 + y^2 \pm 2y - 1 < 0$.

10. *Prove that*

$$|z + \sqrt{(z^2 - c^2)}| + |z - \sqrt{(z^2 - c^2)}| = |z + c| + |z - c|.$$

Hence, show that if the relation between the z-plane and the w-plane be given by
$$z^2 + 2wz \cos \lambda + w^2 = 1$$
and if z describes an ellipse whose foci are the branch points in the z-plane, then w describes an ellipse whose foci are the branch points in the w-plane.

Solution. First Part. Let $z + \sqrt{(z^2 - c^2)} = x$, $z - \sqrt{(z^2 - c^2)} = y$

$$\therefore \qquad xy = z^2 - (z^2 - c^2) = c^2$$

$$x + y = 2z, \quad x - y = 2\sqrt{z^2 - c^2}$$

$$\therefore \qquad [|x| + |y|]^2 = |x|^2 + |y|^2 + 2|x||y|$$

$$= \frac{1}{2}[|x + y|^2 + |x - y|^2] + 2|xy|$$

$$= \frac{1}{2}[4|z|^2 + 4|z^2 - c^2|] + 2|c^2|$$

$$= 2|z|^2 + 2|c|^2 + 2|z + c||z - c|$$

$$= [|z + c| + |z - c|]^2$$

$$\Rightarrow \qquad |x| + |y| = |z + c| + |z - c|$$

$$\Rightarrow \qquad |z + \sqrt{(z^2 - c^2)}| + |z - \sqrt{(z^2 - c^2)}| = |z + c| + |z - c|.$$

Second Part. It should be remembered that in the case of an ellipse sum of the focal distances of any point on it is equal to the length of its major axis.

$$z^2 + z(2w \cos \lambda) + (w^2 - 1) = 0$$

or

$$w^2 + w(2z \cos \lambda) + (z^2 - 1) = 0 \qquad \qquad ...(1)$$

Solving for z and w, we have:

$$z = \frac{-2w \cos \lambda \pm \sqrt{(4w^2 \cos^2 \lambda - 4w^2 + 4)}}{2}$$

$$= -w \cos \lambda \pm i \sin \lambda \sqrt{(w^2 - \text{cosec}^2 \lambda)} \qquad \qquad ...(2)$$

$$w = \frac{-2z \cos \lambda \pm \sqrt{(4z^2 \cos^2 \lambda - 4z^2 + 4)}}{2}$$

$$= -z \cos \lambda \pm i \sin \lambda \sqrt{(z^2 - \text{cosec}^2 \lambda)} \qquad \qquad ...(3)$$

From above we conclude that the two values of z and w are equal if

$$w^2 = \text{cosec}^2 \lambda \text{ or } z^2 = \text{cosec}^2 \lambda$$

or

$$w = \pm \text{cosec } \lambda \text{ or } z = \pm \text{cosec } \lambda.$$

This gives the branch points in the w-plane and z-plane respectively.

Now if z describes an ellipse in the z-plane with foci at branch points, *i.e.*, at $z = -\text{cosec } \lambda$ and $z = \text{cosec } \lambda$ then by property (1) of ellipse, we have:

$$|z + \text{cosec } \lambda| + |z - \text{cosec } \lambda| = 2a$$

or

$$|z + \sqrt{(z^2 - \text{cosec}^2 \lambda)}| + |z - \sqrt{(z^2 - \text{cosec}^2 \lambda)}| = 2a \qquad \qquad ...(4)$$

Now from (3), we have:

$$\frac{w + z \cos \lambda}{i \sin \lambda} = \pm \sqrt{(z^2 - \text{cosec}^2 \lambda)}$$

$$\therefore z \pm \sqrt{(z^2 - \text{cosec}^2 \lambda)} = z + \frac{w + z \cos \lambda}{i \sin \lambda}$$

$$= \frac{w + z(\cos \lambda + i \sin \lambda)}{i \sin \lambda} = \frac{w + z e^{i\lambda}}{i \sin \lambda}.$$

Now put for z,

$$z \pm \sqrt{(z^2 - \text{cosec}^2 \lambda)}$$

$$= \frac{w + e^{i\lambda} [-w \cos \lambda \pm i \sin \lambda \sqrt{(w^2 - \text{cosec}^2 \lambda)}]}{i \sin \lambda}$$

$$= e^{i\lambda} \frac{[w e^{-i\lambda} - w \cos \lambda \pm i \sin \lambda \sqrt{(w^2 - \text{cosec}^2 \lambda)}]}{i \sin \lambda}$$

$$= e^{i\lambda} \frac{[(w \cos \lambda - iw \sin \lambda) - w \cos \lambda \pm i \sin \lambda \sqrt{(w^2 - \mathrm{cosec}^2 \lambda)}]}{i \sin \lambda}$$

$$= e^{i\lambda} [- w \pm \sqrt{(w^2 - \mathrm{cosec}^2 \lambda)}]$$

$$= - e^{i\lambda} [w \mp \sqrt{(w^2 - \mathrm{cosec}^2 \lambda)}]$$

$$\therefore \qquad z + \sqrt{(z^2 - \mathrm{cosec}^2 \lambda)} = - e^{i\lambda} [w - \sqrt{(w^2 - \mathrm{cosec}^2 \lambda)}]$$

$$z - \sqrt{(z^2 - \mathrm{cosec}^2 \lambda)} = - e^{i\lambda} [w + \sqrt{(w^2 - \mathrm{cosec}^2 \lambda)}].$$

Now $|- e^{i\lambda}| = 1$ and hence taking modulus of both sides of above equation and then adding, we have:

$$|z + \sqrt{(z^2 - \mathrm{cosec}^2 \lambda)}| + |z - \sqrt{(z^2 - \mathrm{cosec}^2 \lambda)}| = 2a$$

$$= [| w - \sqrt{(w^2 - \mathrm{cosec}^2 \lambda)}| + | w + \sqrt{(w^2 - \mathrm{cosec}^2 \lambda)}|] \qquad \text{[By (4)]}$$

$$\therefore \qquad | w + \sqrt{(w^2 - \mathrm{cosec}^2 \lambda)}| + | w - \sqrt{(w^2 - \mathrm{cosec}^2 \lambda)}| = 2a$$

or $\qquad | w + \mathrm{cosec}\, \lambda | + | w - \mathrm{cosec}\, \lambda | = 2a.$

This relation shows that sum of the distance of a point w in the w-plane from the branch point $w = \mathrm{cosec}\, \lambda$ and $w = - \mathrm{cosec}\, \lambda$ is equal to $2a$. Therefore w describes an ellipse in the w-plane whose foci are at the branch points.

11. *Consider the correspondence of two planes represented by* $(a - b) w^2 - 2zw + a + b = 0$ *and show that z-curves corresponding to circles in the w-plane are confocal ellipses and corresponding to straight line passing through the origin are confocal hyperbolas.*

Show also that the interior of $| w | = 1$ *corresponds to the exterior of the ellipse* $\dfrac{x^2}{a^2} + \dfrac{y^2}{b^2} = 1$

in the z-plane, (a, b are real and positive).

Solution. We have:
$$2z - (a - b) w + (a + b)/w = 2x + 2iy.$$

Let (ρ, ϕ) be the polar coordinates of any point in the w-plane so that $w = \rho e^{i\phi}$, then
$$2x = [(a - b) \rho + (a + b)/\rho] \cos \phi \qquad \text{...(1)}$$

and $\qquad 2y = [(a - b) \rho - (a + b)/\rho] \sin \phi \qquad \text{...(2)}$

Eliminating ϕ, we get:

$$\frac{x^2}{\alpha^2} + \frac{y^2}{\beta^2} = 1 \qquad \text{...(3)}$$

where $\qquad 4\alpha^2 = [(a - b) \rho + (a + b)/\rho]^2$

and $\qquad 4\beta^2 = [(a - b) \rho - (a + b)/\rho]^2.$

For $\rho = $ constant or $| w | = $ constant, *i.e.*, circles in the w-plane represent ellipse for which
$$\alpha^2 - \beta^2 = (a^2 - b^2) = \text{constant}$$

showing that they are confocal.

Next eliminating ρ from (1) and (2), we get:

$$\frac{x^2}{\cos^2 \phi} - \frac{y^2}{\sin^2 \phi} = a^2 - b^2 \qquad \text{...(4)}$$

For ϕ = constant, *i.e.*, straight lines passing through the origin in the w-plane, these represent hyperbolas which are confocal, since

$$(a^2 - b^2) \cos^2 \phi - [-(a^2 - b^2) \sin^2 \phi] = a^2 - b^2 = \text{constant}.$$

The corresponding ellipses (3) will be exterior to $\dfrac{x^2}{a^2} + \dfrac{y^2}{b^2} = 1$, if $\alpha^2 > a^2$ and $\beta^2 > b^2$. We have to show that this is so, when $\rho < 1$.

Now $\alpha^2 > a^2$, if

$$(a - b)^2 \rho^2 + (a + b)^2/\rho^2 + 2 (a^2 - b^2) > 4a^2$$

i.e., if $(a - b)^2 \rho^2 + (a + b)^2/\rho^2 - (a + b)^2 - (a - b)^2 > 0$

i.e., if $(a + b)^2 (1 - \rho^2) - (a - b)^2 \rho^2 (1 - \rho^2) > 0$

i.e., if $(1 - \rho^2) [(a + b)^2 - (a - b)^2 \rho^2] > 0$

i.e., if. $1 - \rho^2 > 0$ and $(a + b)^2 > (a - b)^2 \rho^2$

which are satisfied when $\rho < 1$.

Similarly, we can show that $\beta^2 > b^2$ when $\rho > 1$.

Hence, the interior of $| w | = 1$ corresponds to the exterior of the ellipse $\dfrac{x^2}{a^2} + \dfrac{y^2}{b^2} = 1$ in the z-plane.

12. *If* $z = \dfrac{4aw \cot \alpha}{1 + 2\theta \cot \alpha - w^2}$, $0 < \alpha < \pi/4$ *show that when w describes a unit circle, z describes twice over an arc of a certain circle subtending an angle $4a$ at the centre.*

(*Rohilkhand, 1996*)

Solution. From the given relation, we have:

$$\frac{1 + 2w \cot \alpha - w^2}{w} = \frac{4a \cot \alpha}{z}$$

or

$$\frac{1}{w} - w + 2 \cot \alpha = \frac{4a \cot \alpha}{z}.$$

For the unit circle $| w | = 1$ in the w-plane $w = e^{i\phi}$ and let $z = re^{i\theta}$.

$\therefore$

$$e^{-i\phi} - e^{i\phi} + 2 \cot \alpha = \frac{4a \cot \alpha}{re^{i\theta}}$$

or

$$2 \cot \alpha - (e^{i\phi} - e^{-i\phi}) = \frac{4a \cot \alpha}{r} (\cos \theta - i \sin \theta)$$

Equating real and imaginary parts, we get:

$$2 \cot \alpha = \frac{4a \cot \alpha}{r} \cos \theta \qquad \qquad \ldots(1)$$

$$2 \sin \phi = \frac{4a \cot \alpha}{r} \sin \theta \qquad \qquad \ldots(2)$$

From (1) we obtain $r = 2a \cos \theta$ showing that the point z describes a circle whose diameter is of length $2a$ and which passes through the origin as shown in the figure below.

Again dividing (2) by (1), we get:

$$\frac{\sin \phi}{\cot \alpha} = \tan \theta \quad \text{or} \quad \tan \theta = \sin \phi \tan \alpha \qquad \qquad \ldots(3)$$

'Hence, the unit circle in the w-plane corresponds to the circle $r = 2a \cos \theta$ in the z-plane.

Second Part. For completely describing the circle $|w| = 1$ in the w-plane ϕ will vary from 0 to $\pi/2$, $\pi/2$ to π, π to $3\pi/2$, $3\pi/2$ to 2π and let us now find the corresponding path traced by z in the z-plane.

From (3), $\tan \theta = \sin \phi \tan \alpha$.

When	$\phi = 0$	$\pi/2$	π	$3\pi/2$	2π
	$\theta = 0$	α	0	$-\alpha$	0

Above shows during the complete circuit of unit circle in the w-plane the point z moves from the position $\theta = 0$ to $\theta = \alpha$, $\theta = \alpha$ to $\theta = 0$, $\theta = 0$ to $\theta = -\alpha$, $\theta = -\alpha$ to $\theta = 0$. In other words it describes twice the portion of the circle in the z-plane from $-\alpha$ to α. This portion subtends an angle 2α at the pole and hence it subtends an angle 4α at the centre.

This is clear from the figure.

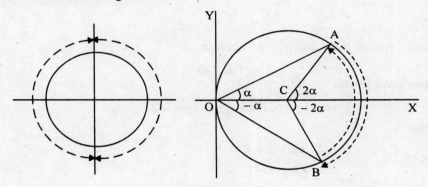

Fig. 7.44

13. *Prove that the transformation*

$$w = \frac{2z}{1 - z^2},$$

maps conformally on the circle $|w| < 1$, the domain containing the origin which is bounded by two minor arcs of the circles

$$|z - 1| = \sqrt{2} \ \text{and} \ |z + 1| = \sqrt{2}.$$

Also indicate in a diagram of the w-plane, the domains corresponding to each of the three domains into which the z-plane is divided by these two circles.

Solution. The two circles

$$|z - 1| = \sqrt{2}, \ |z + 1| = \sqrt{2}$$

both pass through the points $\pm i$ and are orthogonal.

It is now suggested that the given transformation

$$w = \frac{2z}{1 - z^2}$$

should be expressible as a resultant of transformations one of which would map the given intersecting circles onto a pair of intersecting lines. Thus, we consider a bilinear transformation which would map $-i$ and i onto 0 and ∞ respectively. One such transformation is

$$Z = \frac{z + i}{z - i}.$$

It may now be shown that the given transformation is the resultant of the transformations

$$w = i\frac{T-1}{T+1}, \quad T = Z^2 \text{ and } Z = \frac{z+i}{z-i}.$$

The mapping $Z = (z + i)/(z - i)$ would transform the given circles onto a pair of straight lines through the origin.

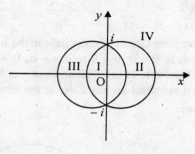

z-plane

Fig. 7.45

The two given circles

$$|z - 1| = \sqrt{2} \text{ and } |z + 1| = \sqrt{2}$$

are equivalent to

$$z\bar{z} - z - \bar{z} = 1, \quad z\bar{z} + z + \bar{z} = 1.$$

Now

$$\frac{Z - \bar{Z}}{Z + \bar{Z}} = \frac{\dfrac{z+i}{z-i} - \dfrac{\bar{z}-i}{\bar{z}+i}}{\dfrac{z+i}{z-i} + \dfrac{\bar{z}-i}{\bar{z}+i}} = \frac{i(z + \bar{z})}{(z\bar{z} - 1)}$$

$$\Rightarrow \qquad \frac{I(Z)}{R(Z)} = \frac{z + \bar{z}}{z\bar{z} - 1}.$$

The images of the two given circles therefore are

$$\frac{I(Z)}{R(Z)} = 1 \text{ and } \frac{I(Z)}{R(Z)} = -1$$

respectively.

Writing $Z = X + iY$, we see that these lines are
$$Y = X, \quad Y = -X$$
respectively.

The interiors of the two given circles are transformed to these semi-planes determined by the lines which contain the transforms

$$\frac{1+i}{1-i} = i, \quad \frac{-1+i}{-1-i} = -i$$

of the centres respectively.

Thus, the domain interior to both the circles is transformed to the portion of the Z-plane common to the two semi-planes above and is the domain marked 1.

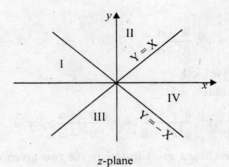

z-plane

Fig. 7.46

The transformation

$$T = Z^2,$$

transforms this domain I onto the semi-plane to the right of the imaginary axis in the T-plane.

Then, $$R = \frac{T - 1}{T + 1}$$

transforms the domain on the right of the imaginary axis on the T-plane onto the domain $|R| < 1$ on the w-plane.

Finally

$$w = iR$$

which represents rotation through a right angle, gives the interior $|w| < 1$.

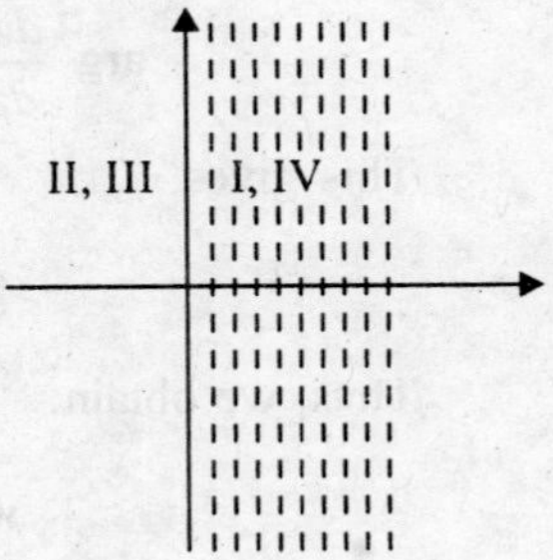

Proceeding as above, we can show that the regions marked I and IV in the figure above are mapped on $|w| < 1$ and those marked II and III on $w| > 1$.

II, III | I, IV

T-plane

Fig. 7.47

14. *Obtain a conformal mapping on the domain*

$$\frac{1}{4}\pi < arg\ z < \frac{3}{4}\pi$$

on the interior of the unit circle in which the point z = 2i is transformed into the centre of the unit circle and a direction through z = 2i is rotated through an angle π.

Determine also the image of the half-line, $arg\ z = \frac{1}{2}\pi$.

Solution. The rotation

$$T = a \qquad \qquad \qquad ...(1)$$

where $$a = e^{\frac{-i\pi}{4}}$$

maps the given domain onto

$$0 < arg\ T < \frac{1}{2}\pi \qquad \qquad ...(2)$$

The transformation

$$R = T^2 \qquad \qquad \qquad ...(3)$$

maps the domain (2) onto the upper semi-plane

$$0 < arg\ R < \pi \qquad \qquad ...(4)$$

The transformation

$$w = e^{i\beta}\,\frac{R - \alpha}{R - \alpha} \qquad\qquad ...(5)$$

maps the domain (4) onto $|w| < 1$.

Combining these we obtain

$$w = e^{i\beta}\,\frac{a^2 z^2 - \alpha}{a^2 z^2 + \overline{a}} = e^{i\beta}\,\frac{iz^2 + \alpha}{iz^2 - \overline{a}}, \quad \text{for } a^2 = -i$$

Now α, β have to be chosen so as to satisfy the two given conditions.

Putting $z = 2i$ and $w = 0$, we obtain:

$$\alpha = 4i.$$

Again, we require that

$$\arg \frac{dw}{dz} = \pi \text{ for } z = 2i.$$

This gives

$$\beta = \frac{3\pi}{2}.$$

Thus, we obtain:

$$w = -i\,\frac{z^2 + 4}{z^2 - 4},$$

as the required transformation.

Putting $z = iy$, we see that the image of the given half-line $\arg z = \frac{i}{2}\pi$ is given by

$$w = i\,\frac{4 - y^2}{4 + y^2},$$

where y varies from 0 to ∞. It may be easily seen that

$$(4 - y^2)/(4 + y^2)$$

monotonically decreases from 1 to -1 as y increases from 0 to ∞. Thus, we see that the required image is the segment of the imaginary axis from i to $-i$.

EXERCISES

1. Prove that the relation

$$w = \sin \frac{\pi z}{2a}, \quad (z = x + iy)$$

gives one-to-one correspondence between the upper semi-plane of w and the region

$$y \geq 0, \, -a \leq x \leq a.$$

Show further that the domain

$$y > 0, \, |x| < a$$

is conformally mapped on $I(w) > 0$. Examine how the mapping ceases to be conformal for

$$z = \pm a.$$

2. Prove that the transformation

$$w = \sin z$$

transforms the set S of those points z for which

$$0 < R(z) < \frac{1}{2}\pi$$

and

$$I(z) > 0$$

into the set T of those points w for which

$$R(w) > 0$$

and

$$I(w) > 0$$

in the sense that

(i)   for every point z of S, $w = \sin z$ is a point of T, and

(ii) corresponding to every point w of T, there is one and only one point z of S such that $w = \sin z$.

Into which set of points does this transformation transform the strip

$$0 < n(z) < \frac{1}{2}\pi?$$

3. Show that the relation

$$w = \cosh z$$

transforms lines parallel to the axes in the z-plane in general into confocal ellipses and hyperbolas in the w-plane and determine the exceptional cases.   (*Rohilkhand, 2002, 2004*)

Prove also that there is a one-to-one correspondence between the semi-infinite strip defined by

$$x > 0, \; 0 < y < \pi$$

and the upper half of the w-plane.

4. Show that the function $w = \sinh \pi z$ takes every value w such that $R(w) > 0$ exactly once in the domain

$$R(z) > 0, \; -\frac{1}{2} < I(z) < \frac{1}{2}.$$

5. Prove that the relation

$$z = \left(\frac{w+1}{w-1}\right)^2$$

transforms the y-axis in the z-plane onto the two circles

$$|w + i| = \sqrt{2} \text{ and } |w - i| = \sqrt{2}$$

in the w-plane.

6. Consider the transformation

$$\frac{w - 2a}{w + 2a} = \left(\frac{z - a}{z + a}\right)^2 \quad (a > 0)$$

and show that the circle

$$|7z - ia| = 5\sqrt{2}\, a$$

in the z-plane corresponds in the w-plane to the shorter of the two arcs between
$$w = 2a \quad \text{and} \quad w = -2a$$
taken twice, of the circle
$$|7w + 48ia| = 50a$$
and that the circle
$$|20z - (1 + 3i)\, a| = 15\sqrt{2}\, a$$
corresponds to a unit circle.

7. Prove that if $w = \dfrac{1}{2}(z + z^{-1})$, then, in general, circles $|z| = $ constant and lines $\arg z = $ constant correspond to conics with foci at $w = \pm 1$ in the w-plane. What exceptions are there ?

By considering the argument of $(w - 1)/(w + 1)$, or otherwise, prove that (in general) any circle through the two points $w = \pm 1$ corresponds to two circles in the z-plane. In particular, show that $|w| = 1$ corresponds to
$$x^2 + y^2 \pm 2y - 1 = 0,$$
and indicate in a diagram the regions in the z-plane which correspond to
$$|w| < 1.$$

8. What region or regions in the z-plane correspond to the interior of the circle $|w| = 1$ under the transformation
$$w = \frac{z^3 - \alpha}{z^3 - \bar{\alpha}};$$
$\alpha,\ \bar{\alpha}$ being conjugate complex constants.

9. Find the domain in the w-plane into which the positive quadrant of the circle $|z| < 1$ is mapped by the function
$$w = \left(\frac{3z - 1}{z - 3}\right)^2.$$

10. If $w = z + e^z$, determine how w moves in the w-plane as
   (*i*) z describes the imaginary axis;
   (*ii*) z describes the line $y = \pi/2$.

11. Show that, if a and c are positive, the relation
$$\frac{w - a}{w + a} = ie^{ciz},$$
maps the interior of the circle $|w| = a$,
on an infinite strip in the z-plane.

Find the curves in the w-plane which correspond to lines parallel to the real and imaginary axes in the z-plane.

12. If
$$w = u + iv = e^{\pi^2/a},$$

where $z = x + iy$ and a is positive, find the loci in the w-plane corresponding to the lines $y = 0$ and $y = a$ in the z-plane.

13. A domain D in the form of a quadrant of a circle in the z-plane is defined by

$$x > 0, \, y > 0, \, |z| < 1 \quad (z = x + iy)$$

By transforming D successively into a semi-circular domain, a quarter-plane, half-plane and a circular domain, or otherwise, find a function

$$w = f(z)$$

which represents D conformally on the domain D_1 defined by

$$|w| < 1.$$

Find what curve in D_1 corresponds to the ray

$$\arg z = \frac{1}{4}\pi$$

in D and what point in D corresponds to the point $w = 0$ in D_1?

14. If

$$\frac{w - 2}{w + 2} = a\xi^2$$

where

$$\xi = \frac{z + 1}{z - 1} \quad \text{and} \quad a > 0,$$

show that the coaxial system of circles in the z-plane having

$$z = \pm 1$$

as limiting points is transformed into the coaxial system in the w-plane with limiting points at

$$w = \pm 2.$$

Show also that the above transformation represents the half-plane $I(z) > 0$ on the whole w-plane provided that cuts are made along the whole real axis except on the segment from $w = -2$ to $w = +2$.

15. In the mapping $w = \sqrt{z}$, show that the family of circles

$$|z - 1| = \text{constant is transformed to a family of lemniscates}$$

$$|w - 1||w + 1| = \text{constant}.$$

16. Show that the relation $Z = z^2$ transforms the curve

$$x^4 + y^4 = a^2$$

of the z-plane into a certain ellipse (mapped twice) in the Z-plane and hence show that the curve can be transformed into a portion of a straight line.

17. If $w = \tanh^{-1} z$, prove that two families of coaxial circles in the z-plane having common points or limiting points at $z = \pm 1$ correspond respectively to lines parallel to the real or imaginary axes in the w-plane.

18. Describe the image curves of the circles

$$|z| = r, \, (r < 1)$$

by the transformation

$$w = z/(1 - z)^2.$$

19. Map the domain defined by

$$|z| < 1, \quad \left| z - \frac{1}{2} \right| > \frac{1}{2}$$

conformally onto the unit circle so that $z = -\dfrac{1}{2}$ maps onto $w = 0$ and $dw/dz > 0$ at that point.

[This latter condition geometrically implies that at the point $z = -\dfrac{1}{2}$, each direction remains invariant.]

20. Map the common part of the two domains

$$|z| < 1, \; |z - 1| < 1$$

on the inside of the unit circle.

21. Find the transformation which maps conformally the domain given by

$$|2z - i| > 1, \; |z| < 1$$

onto the upper semi-plane so that $z = 0$ is mapped on $w = 1$.

[The two circles $|2z - i| = 1$, $|z| = 1$ touch each other at $z = i$. Let $Z = f(z)$ so that $z = i, 0, -i$ are mapped on $Z = \infty, 0, \pi i$ respectively.

Then

$$Z = 2\pi i z/(z - i).$$

The transforms in the w-plane are two parallel straight lines with distance π from each other. Then

$$w = e^Z = e^{2\pi i z/(z - i)},$$

is the transformation sought.]

22. Find the transformation which maps conformally the semi-circle

$$|z| < 1, \; I(z) > 0$$

onto the unit circle $|w| < 1$ so that $z = i/2$ maps onto $w = 0$ and dw/dz for $z = i/2$ is positive.

23. Map the outside of the parabola $y^2 = 4ax$ onto $|w| < 1$ so that $z = 0$ and $z = -a$ correspond to $w = 1$ and $w = 0$ respectively.

24. Find the transformation which maps conformally the interior of the right hand branch of the hyperbola

$$x^2 - y^2 = a^2$$

onto $|w| < 1$ so that the focus corresponds to $w = 0$ and the vertex to $w = -1$.

25. Map the outside of the ellipse

$$x^2/a^2 + y^2/b^2 = 1$$

onto $|w| < 1$.

26. Map the domain $x^2 - y^2 \geq 1$, $x > 0$ conformally onto $I(w) > 0$ so that $z = 1$ is mapped on $w = 0$.

27. Map the domain $x^2 + 4y \geq 0$ conformally onto $I(w) > 0$ so that $z = 0$ is mapped on $w = -1$.

28. Map the domain $|z| < 1$ by

$$w = \frac{z}{(1 + z)^2}.$$

$$\left[w = \frac{1}{Z+2}, \; Z = z + \frac{1}{z} \right]$$

29. Show that the function

$$w = \frac{iz^2 + z + i}{-iz^2 + z - i},$$

maps $|z| < 1$ conformally onto a domain obtained from the w-plane   by omitting the points of a slit going from $(-3 + 4i)/5$ via 1 to $(-3 - 4i)/5$ along the circle
$$|w| = 1.$$

$$\left[w = \frac{(1 + iz)}{(1 - iz)}, \; Z = z + \frac{1}{z} \right]$$

30. Show that

$$w = i \cosh \left(\frac{\pi \sqrt{z}}{2a} \right)$$

maps conformally the interior of the parabola

$$y^2 = 4a^2 (x + a^2)$$

onto the upper semi-plane of the w-plane.

31. Considering successively the transformations

$$z = R^2, \; R = \frac{T - 1}{T + 1}, \; T = S^{\frac{\alpha}{2\pi}}$$

$$S = \frac{w + \sqrt{w^2 - 4}}{2}$$

where $\sqrt{w^2 - 4}$ denotes the branch such that $\sqrt{w^2 - 4} < 0$ if $w > 2$, show that the interior of a branch of the hyperbola

$$\frac{u^2}{(2 \cos \alpha)^2} - \frac{v^2}{(2 \sin \alpha)^2} = 1, \quad (w = u + iv, \; 0 < \alpha < \pi/2)$$

in the w-plane is mapped onto $|z| < 1$.

32. Show that the transformation

$$w = \frac{(1 + z^3)^2 - i (1 + z^3)^2}{(1 - z^3)^2 + i (1 - z^3)^2},$$

maps the domain

$$|z| < 1, \; 0 < \arg z < \pi/3$$

conformally on

$$|w| < 1.$$

Discuss also the correspondence between the boundaries of the two domains.

33. Show that the transformation

$$w = \frac{-2ai}{\pi} \log z \quad (a > 0)$$

maps the semi-plane $R(z) > 0$ conformally on the strip
$$|R(w)| > a.$$

Further deduce that

$$w = \frac{-2hi}{\pi} \log \frac{1+z}{1-z}$$

maps $|z| < 1$ conformally on
$$|R(w)| < a.$$

34. Map conformally the interior of the unit circle $|z| = 1$ slit along the real axis from $z = 1$ to $z = -a$, $(1 > a > 0)$, onto a circle about the origin of the w-plane so that $z = 0$ is mapped onto $w = 0$ and $dw/dz = 1$ for $z = 0$.

35. Find the transformation which maps the exterior of the symmetric lens of the following figure in a one-to-one conformal manner onto the entire w-plane slit from $u = -1$ to $u = +1$ so that $z = \infty$ corresponds to $w = \infty$ and $z = 1$ corresponds to $w = 1$.

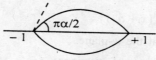

Fig. 7.48

36. Find a function $w = f(z)$ giving a conformal representation of the set of all points
$$z = re^{i\theta} \quad (0 < r < \infty, \ 0 < \theta < \alpha)$$

onto a crescent-shaped domain between the two circles forming with another the angle 2α in the w-plane.

37. In the w-plane, find the exact image of the circle $|z - 1| < 1$ by the mapping defined by
$$w = \log(z - 1).$$

38. Obtain a conformal transformation of the domain $|z| < 1$ into the whole w-plane cut along the negative real axis.

39. Obtain the most general conformal mapping of the interior of the unit circle on the exterior of the ellipse

$$\left(\frac{u}{\cosh \alpha}\right)^2 + \left(\frac{v}{\sinh \alpha}\right)^2 = 1, \ (\alpha > 0)$$

$$w = u + iv.$$

40. Map the inside of the crescent bounded by the circles
$$x^2 + y^2 = 1, \ x^2 + y^2 + 2y - 1 = 0$$

onto the half of the circle $|w| = 1$ lying to the right of the imaginary axes.

41. Show that the transformation

$$w = \frac{1 + z^2}{1 - z^2}$$

maps the interior of the positive quadrant of the unit circle in the z-plane conformally on the interior of the positive quadrant of the w-plane. Discuss also the correspondence between the boundaries of the two domains.

42. Show that the transformation

$$w (z + i)^2 = 1$$

maps the interior of the circle $|z| = 1$ in the z-plane on the exterior of the parabola

$$\frac{1}{\rho} = 2 (1 - \cos \phi)$$

where $w = \rho e^{i\phi}$ in the w-plane.

43. If

$$(z + 1)^2 = 4 / Z,$$

show that the unit circle in the z-plane corresponds to the parabola

$$R \cos^2 (\theta / 2) = 1$$

in the z-plane and the inside of the circle to the outside of the parabola. (*Rohilkhand 2005*)

44. If

$$w = \left(\frac{z + c}{z - c} \right)^2$$

where c is real and positive, find the area of the z-plane of which the upper half of the w-plane is the conformal representation.

45. If

$$w = \frac{1}{2} \left(z + \frac{1}{z} \right).$$

then prove that in general circles $|z| = $ constant and lines $\arg z = $ constant correspond to conics with foci at $w = \pm 1$ in the w-plane.

OBJECTIVE QUESTIONS

For each of the following questions, four alternatives are given for the answer. Only one of them is correct. Choose the correct alternative.

1. In a conformal transformation
 (*a*) Magnitude of the angle is preserved
 (*b*) Sense of rotation is preserved
 (*c*) Sense of rotation as well as the magnitude of the angle is preserved
 (*d*) Only magnitude is preserved.

2. Under conformal transformation $w = f(z)$ a small arc through a point z_0 in the z-plane is magnified in the w-plane in the ratio
 (*a*) $|f'(z)| : 1$ (*b*) $|f'(z)|^2 : 1$
 (*c*) $|f(z)| : 1$ (*d*) $|f(z)|^2 : 1.$

3. The transformation $w = z^n$, n being a +ve integer is
 (*a*) Conformal at every point except at $z = 0$
 (*b*) Conformal at every point including $z = 0$

    (*c*) Isogonal transformation only

    (*d*) Neither isogonal nor conformal.

4. Transformation $w = z^{1/\alpha}$ maps

    (*a*) Half-planes into circles   (*b*) Wedges or sectors into half-planes

    (*c*) Half-planes into confocal hyperbolas   (*d*) None of these.

5. Critical points of the transformation $w = \dfrac{1}{2}\left(z + \dfrac{1}{z}\right)$ are

    (*a*) $-\infty, 0$ (*b*) $0, \infty$

    (*c*) ± 1 (*d*) $\pm \infty$.

6. The transformation $w = f(\bar{z})$ is

    (*a*) Both isogonal and conformal   (*b*) Isogonal but not conformal

    (*c*) Conformal but not isogonal   (*d*) Neither isogonal nor conformal.

7. The exterior of the ellipse on the interior of the unit circle is mapped by the transformation

    (*a*) $w = r\left(z + \sqrt{z^2 - 1}\right)$ (*b*) $w = re^z$

    (*c*) $w = \left(\dfrac{1 + z^n}{1 - z^n}\right)^2$ (*d*) $w = i\left(\sqrt{z} - a\right)$.

8. The transformation $w = \left(\dfrac{1 + z^n}{1 - z^n}\right)^2$ maps

    (*a*) Semi-circular domain on the semi-plane

    (*b*) Wedge on a semi-plane

    (*c*) Any circular sector on the semi-plane

    (*d*) Semi-infinite rectangular strip on the semi-plane.

9. To map a convex lens onto a semi-plane we use the transformation

    (*a*) $w = \left(e^{-i\alpha} \dfrac{z - a}{z - b}\right)^n$ (*b*) $w = e^{-i\alpha}\left(z + \sqrt{z^2 - 1}\right)^{\frac{\pi}{\pi - 2\alpha}}$

    (*c*) $w = i(z^2 - a)$ (*d*) None of these.

ANSWERS

1. (*c*)   **2.** (*a*)   **3.** (*a*)   **4.** (*b*)   **5.** (*c*)   **6.** (*b*)   **7.** (*a*)   **8.** (*c*)   **9.** (*a*)

COMPLEX INTEGRATION

8.1. Introduction. This chapter will deal with the notion of *Integrability* and *Integral* of a complex function along an *oriented* curve in the complex plane. In view of the fact, that this subject is to be related to *Analytic Functions* whose study is the main purpose of this book, we shall not obtain necessary and sufficient conditions for integrability and instead only consider an important sufficient condition for the same. Thus, we shall prove that a function is integrable along a curve if the curve is *rectifiable* and the function is continuous along the same. Some elementary properties of integration will also be obtained.

The following section of the chapter deals with the notion of *Oriented* and *Rectifiable Curves*.

8.2. Some Important Definitions

1. **Partition :** Let $[a, b]$ be a closed interval where a, b are real numbers. Then the set of points

$$P = \{t_0, t_1, t_2, \ldots, t_n\},$$

where $a = t_0 < t_1 < t_2 < t_3 < \ldots < t_n = b$ is called a *partition* of the interval $[a, b]$.

The greatest of the numbers $t_1 - t_2$, $t_0 - t_1$, $\ldots, t_n - t_{n-1}$ is called the *norm* of the partition P and is denoted by $|$ P $|$.

2. **Continuous arc :** If a point z on an arc is such that

$$z = \phi(t) + i\psi(t) \qquad\qquad \ldots(A)$$

then we may write

$$x = \phi(t) \qquad\qquad \ldots(1)$$
$$y = \psi(t) \qquad\qquad \ldots(2)$$

If $\phi(t)$ and $\psi(t)$ are real continuous functions of the real variable t defined in the range $\alpha \le t \le \beta$, then the arc is called a *continuous arc*.

3. **Multiple point :** If the equation (A) or say the equations (1) and (2) are satisfied by more than one values of t in the given range, then the point z, or say the point (x, y) is called a *multiple point* of the arc.

4. **Jordan arc :** A continuous arc without multiple points is called a *Jordan arc*.

Thus, for a point z on a Jordan curve, z as expressed in equation (A) is single-valued and $\phi(t)$, $\psi(t)$ are continuous. In addition if $\phi'(t)$ and $\psi'(t)$ are also continuous in the range $\alpha \le t \le \beta$, then the arc is called a *regular arc* of a Jordan curve.

A **continuous Jordan curve** consists of a chain of finite number of continuous arcs.

5. **Contour :** By contour we mean a *Jordan curve consisting of continuous chain of a finite number of regular arcs.*

(*Meerut* 2002, 2003)

If A be the starting point of the first arc and B the end point of the last arc, then integral

along such a curve is written as $\int\limits_{A}^{B} f(z)\, dz$.

If the starting point A of the arc coincides with the end point B of the last arc then the contour AB is said to be closed.

The integral along such closed contour is written as $\int_{C} f(z)\, dz$, and is read as *integral f (z)*

taken over the closed contour C. Although $\int_{C} f(z)\, dz$ does not indicate the direction along the curve, but it is conventional to take the direction positive which is anticlockwise, unless indicated otherwise.

8.2.1. Orientation of a curve. Let $z = z (t)$ be a given curve, the real parameter t taking up values between the given real numbers a and b. Then we can regard, t, as varying from a to b or from b to a. This gives rise to the concept of an *oriented curve*; the orientation depending upon the manner of description of the curve corresponding to t varying from a to b or from b to a. If the curve, while t varies from a to b, is denoted by C, then we agree to denote the curve corresponding to t varying from b to a by $-$ C.

Thus, an oriented curve is an ordered set of points; the order being induced by the manner in which t varies.

8.3. Rectifiable Curve : Let
$$z = z (t) = x (t) + iy (t),$$
be a given curve and let t take up values between a and b.

We suppose that $a < b$.

Let the interval $[a, b]$ be divided into any finite arbitrary number of sub-intervals
$$[t_0, t_1], \ldots, [t_{r-1}, t_r], \ldots, [t_{n-1}, t_n],$$
where $a = t_0 < t_1 < \ldots < t_{r-1} < t_r < \ldots < t_{n-1} < t_n = b$.

We may denote this division of the interval $[a, b]$ by the symbol
$$D (t_0, \ldots, t_{r-1}, t_r, \ldots, t_n) \text{ or Simply by D.}$$

We write
$$z_r = z (t_r),$$

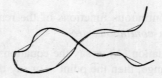

Fig. 8.1

and consider the sum
$$S (D) = \Sigma \mid z_r - z_{r-1} \mid,$$
so that a sum S (D) corresponds to every division of the interval $[a, b]$. Clearly, S (D) denotes the length of the polygonal line with vertices
$$z_0, z_1, \ldots, z_{r-1}, z_r, \ldots, z_{n-1}, z_n$$
which are points on the given curve.

Def. *The curve is said to be rectifiable if the set of the sums S (D) obtained for different divisions D of $[a, b]$ is bounded.*

Further, if the curve is rectifiable, the upper bound of the set of the sums is called the Length of the curve.

If $a > b$, then we carry out the process referred to above for the interval $[b, a]$ instead of that for $[a, b]$.

We may note that the notions of rectifiability and length of a curve are independent of its orientation, *i.e.*, they are the same for C and $- $ C.

Note. Here we have not obtained any form of conditions for the rectifiability of a curve.

An important form of the necessary and sufficient conditions for the rectifiability of a curve $z = z(t) = x(t) + iy(t)$ is that the functions $x(t)$, $y(t)$ are both of *bounded variation* in $[a, b]$.

In § 8.3, however, it will be seen that a curve $z = z(t)$ is rectifiable if $x(t)$ and $y(t)$ possess continuous derivatives in the interval $[a, b]$ so that this gives the sufficient condition for rectifiability.

8.3.1. *A property of rectifiable curves.* Let C be any curve

$$z = z(t),$$

where $a \leq t \leq b$.

Let, now, c be any number between a and b and let the two curves $z = z(t)$ corresponding to t, varying in the intervals $[a, c]$ and $[c, b]$ be denoted by C_1 and C_2 respectively. It will now be shown that *if C is rectifiable, then C_1 and C_2 are also rectifiable and conversely.*

Further, in the case of rectifiability

$$l = l_1 + l_2 \qquad \qquad ...(1)$$

where l_1, l_2 and l denote the lengths of C_1, C_2 and C respectively.

Firstly suppose that C is rectifiable.

Let D_1, D_2 be *any two* divisions of the intervals $[a, c]$, $[c, b]$ respectively. These two divisions give rise to a division of $[a, b]$ which we may denote by D.

Clearly, then we have:

$$S(D) = S(D_1) + S(D_2).$$

Since C is rectifiable, therefore

$$S(D) \leq l.$$

Hence C_1, C_2 are also rectifiable.

Now suppose that C_1, C_2 are rectifiable.

Let D be any division of $[a, b]$ and let D' be the division of $[a, b]$ obtained on adjoining to the division points of D an extra division point C if it be not already there. Then clearly

$$S(D) \leq S(D').$$

Also, let D_1, D_2 be the divisions of $[a, c]$ and $[c, b]$ induced by the division D' of $[a, b]$ so that

$$S(D') = S(D_1) + S(D_2).$$

Thus,

$$S(D) \leq S(D_1) + S(D_2).$$

As C_1, C_2 are rectifiable, we have:

$$S(D_1) \leq l_1, \ S(D_2) \leq l_2$$

$$\therefore \qquad \qquad S(D) \leq l_1 + l_2 \qquad \qquad ...(2)$$

and accordingly C is rectifiable.

Now to prove the relation (1).

Let $\varepsilon > 0$ be any arbitrary number.

By definition of upper bound, there exist divisions D_1, D_2 of $[a, c]$, $[c, b]$ such that

$$S(D_1) \geq l_1 - \frac{1}{2}\varepsilon, \quad S(D_2) \geq l_2 - \frac{1}{2}\varepsilon.$$

If D be the division of $[a, b]$ induced by D_1, D_2, we have:
$$S(D) = S(D_1) + S(D_2) \geq l_1 + l_2 - \varepsilon.$$

Also,
$$S(D) \leq l.$$

Thus,
$$l_1 + l_2 - \varepsilon \leq l.$$

As ε is arbitrary, we deduce
$$l_1 + l_2 \leq l.$$

Also, as in (2), we have, for *any* division D of $[a, b]$,
$$S(D) \leq l_1 + l_2$$

so that
$$l \leq l_1 + l_2.$$

Thus,
$$l = l_1 + l_2.$$

8.4. Integral along an oriented curve. Let an oriented curve C be given by
$$z = z(t),$$

t varying from a to b or b to a as the case may be. We suppose that t varies from a to b.

Also, let $f(z)$ be any function defined on D.

Let
$$a = t_0, t_1, \ldots, t_{r-1}, t_r, \ldots, t_{n-1}, t_n = b$$

be any set of division points. We denote this division by D.

Let further, α_r, be any value of t lying between t_{r-1} and t_r. We write:
$$z(t_r) = z_r, z(\alpha_r) = \xi_r.$$

We now set up the sum

$$S = (z_1 - z_0) f(\xi_1) + \ldots + (z_r - z_{r-1}) f(\xi_r) + \ldots + (z_n - z_{n-1}) f(\xi_n)$$

$$= \sum_{r=1}^{n} (z_r - z_{r-1}) f(\xi_r).$$

To each division D and each choice of α_r, there corresponds a sum S.

Def. *The function $f(z)$ is said to be integrable over C, if there exists a number I such that to each $\varepsilon > 0$, there corresponds a $\delta > 0$ so that*
$$|S - I| < \varepsilon,$$

for every division whose norm $\leq \delta$ and for every choice of α_r.

Also, then I is said to be the line integral or simply the integral of $f(z)$ over C and we write
$$\int_C f(z) \, dz = I.$$

Also, we write

$$S(D) = \sum_{r=1}^{n} (z_r - z_{r-1}) f(z_r).$$

The norm of a division D given by

$$a = t_0, t_1, \ldots, t_{r-1}, t_r, \ldots, t_{n-1}, t_n = b$$

means the greatest of the lengths

$$|t_1 - t_0|, |t_2 - t_1|, \ldots, |t_r - t_{r-1}|, \ldots, |t_n - t_{n-1}|$$

of the sub-intervals in which $[a, b]$ has been divided.

A division D' is said to be *consecutive* to or finer than a division D, if it has as its division points those of the division D and possibly some more.

Also, any sum S is called an **Approximating Sum** for the integral.

8.5. Sufficient Condition for Integrability. Theorem. *A continuous function $f(z)$ over a continuous rectifiable curve C is integrable.*

Thus, we shall show that

$$\int_C f(z)\, dz$$

exists if C is a continuous rectifiable curve and $f(z)$ is continuous over C.

The theorem will be proved in two steps preceded by a lemma.

Lemma. Now $f(z)$ is a continuous function of z over C and $z = z(t)$ is a continuous function of t. Hence, $f[z(t)]$ is a continuous function of t, and accordingly also uniformly continuous. Thus, if $\varepsilon > 0$ be any number, then there exists $\delta > 0$ such that

$$|f(z_r) - f(z_{r-1})| < \varepsilon \text{ when } |t_r - t_{r-1}| \le \delta,$$

where $z_r = z(t_r)$, $z_{r-1} = z(t_{r-1})$.

We shall now prove that *if D_1 be any division of norm $\le \delta$ and D_2 be any division consecutive to D_1, then*

$$|S(D_2) - S(D_1)| < \varepsilon l.$$

Suppose that D_1 is given by the points

$$a = t_0, t_1, \ldots, t_{r-1}, t_r, \ldots, t_{n-1}, t_n = b.$$

Suppose further that in the case of the division D_2 the sub-interval $[t_{r-1}, t_r]$ is sub-divided by the points

$$\beta_1, \beta_2, \ldots, \beta_k.$$

We write:

$$\eta_1 = z(\beta_1), \eta_2 = z(\beta_2), \ldots, \eta_k = z(\beta_k).$$

Then

$$S(D_2) - S(D_1)$$

$$= \sum_{r=1}^{n} [(\eta_1 - z_{r-1}) f(\eta_1) + (\eta_2 - \eta_1) f(\eta_2)$$

$$+ \ldots + (z_r - \eta_k) f(z_r) - (z_r - z_{r-1}) f(z_r)]$$

$$= \sum_{r=1}^{n} [(\eta_1 - z_{r-1}) \{f(\eta_1) - f(z_r)\} + (\eta_2 - \eta_1) \{f(\eta_2) - f(z_r)\}$$

$$+ \ldots + (z_r - \eta_k) \{f(z_r) - f(z_{r-1})\}]$$

$$\therefore S(D_2) - S(D_1) < \sum_{r=1}^{n} [|\eta_1 - z_{r-1}|\varepsilon + |\eta_2 - \eta_1|\varepsilon + \dots + |z_1 - \eta_k|\varepsilon]$$

$$\le \varepsilon l.$$

Note. The reader may note that in terms of our definition,

$$S(D)$$

is uniquely defined as soon as any division D is given. This, however, is not the case for the sum S, which depends also upon the choice of points between the points of division of D.

First Step. *Let*

$$D_1, D_2, \dots, D_n, \dots,$$

be any sequence of divisions such that each is consecutive to its predecessor and such that the sequence

$$\rho_1, \rho_2, \dots, \rho_n, \dots,$$

of norms of the divisions tends to zero. Then the sequence

$$S(D_1), S(D_2), \dots, S(D_n), \dots,$$

of sums is convergent.

As $f(z)$ is a continuous function of z and $z = z(t)$ is a continuous function of t, therefore, $f[z(t)]$ is a continuous function of t.

Now, let ε, be any given positive number.

Then by virtue of the uniform continuity of $f(z)$ as a function of t, we see that there exists a positive number δ such that

$$|f(z_r) - f(z_{r-1})| < \frac{\varepsilon}{l} \text{ when } |t_r - t_{r-1}| \le \delta.$$

Here $z_r = z(t_r)$ and $z_{r-1} = z(t_{r-1})$.

As $\rho_n \to 0$, there exists a positive integer m such that

$$|\rho_n| < \delta \quad \forall \quad n \ge m.$$

Thus, $\forall \ n \ge m$ and any $p \ge 0$, we have

$$|S(D_n) - S(D_{n+p})| < \frac{\varepsilon}{l} l = \varepsilon. \quad \text{(Lemma)}$$

Hence, by Cauchy's general principle of convergence for a sequence, the sequence
$$S(D_n)$$
is convergent.

Let its limit be denoted by I.

Second Step. Let, ε, be any given positive number.

Again, by virtue of uniform continuity, there exists a positive number δ such that

$$|f(z_r) - f(z_{r-1})| < \frac{\varepsilon}{4l} \text{ when } |t_r - t_{r-1}| \le \delta.$$

Let D be any division

$$a = t_0, t_1, \dots, t_{r-1}, t_r, \dots, t_{n-1}, t_n = b$$

with norm $\le \delta$ and let α_r be any value of t lying between t_{r-1} and t_r.

Also, we write

$$z_r = z(t_r) \text{ and } \xi_r = z(\alpha_r).$$

Consider, now .

$$S = \sum_{r=1}^{n} (z_r - z_{r-1}) \, f\,(\xi_r), \quad S\,(D) = \sum_{r=1}^{n} (z_r - z_{r-1}) \, f\,(z_r).$$

$$\therefore \qquad |S - S\,(D)| \leq \sum_{r=1}^{n} |z_r - z_{r-1}| \, |f\,(\xi_r) - f\,(z_r)|.$$

Since $|\alpha_r - t_r| \leq |t_r - t_{r-1}| \leq \delta$, we have
$$|f\,(\xi_r) - f\,(z_r)| < \varepsilon/4l.$$

$$\therefore \qquad |S - S\,(D)| \leq \sum_{r=1}^{n} |z_r - z_{r-1}| \frac{\varepsilon}{4l} = \frac{\varepsilon}{4} \qquad\qquad \dots(1)$$

Consider now any sequence of divisions $\{D_n\}$ such that D_{n+1} is consecutive to D_n for every n and such that $\rho_n \to 0$ where ρ_n is the norm of D_n. Let
$$\lim S\,(D_n) = I.$$

Since $\rho_n \to 0$, there exists a positive integer m_1 such that
$$|\rho_n| < \delta \quad \forall \quad n \geq m_1.$$

Also, there exists a positive integer m_2 such that
$$|S\,(D_n) - I| < \varepsilon/4 \quad \forall \quad n \geq m_2 \qquad\qquad \dots(2)$$

Let $m = \max.\,(m_1, m_2)$.

Let D' be a division having as its division points those of D as well as of D_m. The norm of each of D and D_m being $\leq \delta$ and D' being consecutive to both D and D_m, we have, by the lemma,

$$|S\,(D') - S\,(D)| < \varepsilon/4 \qquad\qquad \dots(3)$$
$$|S\,(D') - S\,(D_m)| < \varepsilon/4 \qquad\qquad \dots(4)$$

From (1), (2), (3) and (4), we deduce that
$$|S - I| = |S - S\,(D) + S\,(D) - S\,(D') + S\,(D') - S\,(D_m) + S\,(D_m) - I|$$
$$\leq |S - S\,(D)| + |S\,(D) - S\,(D')|$$
$$+ |S\,(D') - S\,(D_m)| + |S\,(D_m) - I|$$
$$< \varepsilon/4 + \varepsilon/4 + \varepsilon/4 + \varepsilon/4 = \varepsilon.$$

Thus, we see that $f\,(z)$ is integrable over C and I is the integral.

Cor. From above it follows that if $f\,(z)$ be continuous over a continuous rectifiable curve C and if $\{D_n\}$ be any sequence of divisions such that each member of the same is consecutive to the preceding and if the sequence of norms $\{\rho_n\}$ of the divisions tends to zero, then the integral

$$\int_C f\,(z)\,dz$$

is equal to the limit of the convergent sequence
$$\{S\,(D_n)\}.$$

Note. The result arrived at in the course of the above investigation will be found useful in the following:

If an approximating sum S corresponds to a division of norm $\leq \delta$ such that for
$$|t_r - t_{r-1}| \leq \delta,$$
we have $\qquad\qquad\qquad |f\,(z_r) - f\,(z_{r-1})| < \varepsilon/4l,$
then, for such a sum
$$|S - I| < \varepsilon.$$

Here $z_r = z(t_r), z_{r-1} = z(t_{r-1}).$

A sequence of divisions $\{D_n\}$ with the properties referred to here will be called a *distinguished sequence* of divisions.

8.6. Some properties of Integrals. In the following, it will be understood that the functions $f(z)$, $F(z)$ etc., are continuous over given continuous rectifiable curves.

8.6.1. *Additive properties of Integrals.*

Theorem *If $f(z)$ and $F(z)$ are continuous over a continuous rectifiable curve C, so that $f(z)$, $F(z)$ and $f(z) + F(z)$ are all integrals over C, then*

$$\int_C [f(z) + F(z)]\, dz = \int_C f(z)\, dz + \int_C F(z)\, dz.$$

Let $\{D_n\}$ be any distinguished sequence of divisions.

If $S(D_n)$, $S'(D_n)$, $S''(D_n)$ be approximating sums for the functions
$$f(z) + F(z), f(z), F(z)$$ corresponding to the division D_n, we have
$$S(D_n) = S'(D_n) + S''(D_n).$$

Proceeding to the limit when n tends to infinity, we obtain

$$\int_C [f(z) + F(z)]\, dz = \int_C f(z)\, dz + \int_C F(z)\, dz.$$

Theorem II. *If $f(z)$ is continuous over a continuous rectifiable curve C and C_1, C_2 are two parts of C, then*

$$\int_C f(z)\, dz = \int_{C_1} f(z)\, dz + \int_{C_2} f(z)\, dz.$$

Here we may suppose that the curve C corresponds to the interval $[a, b]$ and C_1, C_2 to $[a, c]$, $[c, b]$ respectively where c is any number between a and b.

Let $\{D_n'\}$, $\{D_n''\}$ be two distinguished sequences of divisions of $[a, c]$ and $[c, b]$ respectively. Let $\{D_n\}$ be the distinguished sequence of divisions for $[a, b]$ such that the points of division of D_n are those of D_n' as well as of D_n''.

We then have

$$S(D_n) = S(D_n') + S(D_n'')$$

where the three sums refer to the divisions D_n, D_n', D_n'' of the intervals $[a, b]$, $[a, c]$, $[c, b]$ respectively.

Letting n tend to infinity, we obtain

$$\int_C f(z)\, dz = \int_{C_1} f(z)\, dz + \int_{C_2} f(z)\, dz.$$

8.6.2. $\int_C k\, f(z)\, dz = k \int_C f(z)\, dz,$

where k is any constant.

The proof follows at once on considering a distinguished sequence of divisions.

8.6.3. $\int_C f(z)\, dz = - \int_{-C} f(z)\, dz.$

This result is an easy consequence of the definition.

8.6.4. Integral estimation.

$$\left| \int_C f(z) \, dz \right| \leq Ml,$$

where, l, is the length of the curve C and M is a number such that

$$|f(z)| \leq M \ \forall \ z \in C. \qquad\qquad (Poorvanchal, 1995; GNDU 2000)$$

We have:

$$S(D) = \Sigma(z_r - z_{r-1}) f(z_r)$$

$$\Rightarrow \qquad\qquad |S(D)| \leq \Sigma|z_r - z_{r-1}||f(z_r)|$$

$$\leq M \Sigma|z_r - z_{r-1}| \leq Ml.$$

Thus, if D_n be any distinguished sequence of divisions, we have

$$|S(D_n)| \leq Ml$$

for all n and hence in the limit

$$\left| \int_C f(z) \, dz \right| \leq Ml.$$

8.7. Evaluation of $\int_C f(z) \, dz$. Reduction of Real Integrals. We now suppose that the curve C is continuously differentiable. This means that the function

$$z = z(t)$$

defining the curve C possesses a continuous derivative $z'(t)$ for every value of t in $[a, b]$. Of course

$$z'(t) = \lim_{h \to 0} \frac{z(t+h) - z(t)}{h}.$$

If further we write

$$z(t) = x(t) + iy(t),$$

then the continuously differentiable character of $z(t)$ implies that $x(t)$ and $y(t)$ are also continuously differentiable and

$$z'(t) = x'(t) + iy'(t).$$

Also, let

$$f[z(t)] z'(t) = u(t) + iv(t).$$

We shall now prove the following:

If C defined by

$$z = z(t)$$

is continuously differentiable and $f(z)$ is continuous over C, then the curve C is rectifiable and

$$\int_C f(z) \, dz = \int_a^b [u(t) + iv(t)] \, dt$$

$$= \int_a^b u(t) \, dt + i \int_a^b v(t) \, dt.$$

Thus, here

$$\int_C f(z) \, dz$$

is expressed in terms of the real integrals

$$\int_a^b u(t)\,dt, \quad \int_a^b v(t)\,dt.$$

First we prove the rectifiability of C.

Let D defined by the points

$$a = t_0, t_1, ..., t_{r-1}, t_r, ..., t_{n-1}, t_n = b$$

be any division of $[a, b]$.

We write:

$$z_r = z(t_r) = x(t_r) + iy(t_r).$$

We have:

$$\Sigma \,|\, z_r - z_{r-1}\,| \;=\; \Sigma \,|\, z(t_r) - z(t_{r-1})\,|$$

$$= \Sigma \,[\,x(t_r) - x(t_{r-1})\,] + i\,[\,y(t_r) - y(t_{r-1})\,]$$

$$\leq \Sigma \,|\, x(t_r) - x(t_{r-1})\,| + \Sigma \,|\, y(t_r) - y(t_{r-1})\,| \qquad \text{...(1)}$$

By Lagrange's mean value theorem in Real Analysis, we see that there exist numbers α_r, β_r belonging to the interval

$$[t_{r-1}, t_r]$$

such that

$$x(t_r) - x(t_{r-1}) = (t_r - t_{r-1})\, x'(\alpha_r) \qquad \text{...(2)}$$

$$y(t_r) - y(t_{r-1}) = (t_r - t_{r-1})\, y'(\beta_r) \qquad \text{...(3)}$$

Further $x'(t)$ and $y'(t)$ being continuous, they are bounded. There exists, therefore, a number k such that

$$|\,x'(t)\,| \leq k, \;\; |\,y'(t)\,| \leq k \qquad \text{...(4)}$$

for all t in $[a, b]$.

From (1), (2), (3) and (4), we deduce that

$$\Sigma \,|\, z_r - z_{r-1}\,| \leq 2k\,\Sigma\,|\,t_r - t_{r-1}\,| = 2k\,(b-a).$$

Thus, the curve C is rectifiable.

To prove the second part, we have

$$\Sigma\,(z_r - z_{r-1})\,f(z_r)$$

$$= \Sigma\,[(t_r - t_{r-1})\,x'(\alpha_r) + i\,(t_r - t_{r-1})\,y'(\beta_r)]\,[\varphi(t_r) + i\,\psi(t_r)],$$

where we have written

$$f(z) = \varphi(t) + i\,\psi(t).$$

Thus, we write

$$\Sigma\,(z_r - z_{r-1})\,f(z_r) = (S_1 + S_2) + i\,(S_3 + S_4) \qquad \text{...(5)}$$

where

$$S_1 = \Sigma\,(t_r - t_{r-1})\,x'(\alpha_r)\,\varphi(t_r) \qquad \text{...(6)}$$

$$S_2 = -\,\Sigma\,(t_r - t_{r-1})\,y'(\beta_r)\,\psi(t_r) \qquad \text{...(7)}$$

$$S_3 = \Sigma\,(t_r - t_{r-1})\,x'(\alpha_r)\,\psi(t_r) \qquad \text{...(8)}$$

$$S_4 = \Sigma\,(t_r - t_{r-1})\,y'(\beta_r)\,\varphi(t_r) \qquad \text{...(9)}$$

These sums have now to be considered one by one. We have

$$S_1 = \Sigma (t_r - t_{r-1}) \, x'(t_r) \, \varphi(t_r)$$
$$+ \Sigma (t_r - t_{r-1}) [x'(\alpha_r) - x'(t_r)] \, \varphi(t_r) \qquad \qquad ...(10)$$

Now $x'(t)$, being continuous, is uniformly continuous. Thus, to every $\varepsilon > 0$, there corresponds a $\delta > 0$ such that

$$| x'(\xi) - x'(\eta) | < \varepsilon,$$

when

$$| \xi - \eta | \le \delta.$$

Now taking D to be any division with norm $\le \delta$, we see that

$$| \Sigma (t_r - t_{r-1}) [x'(\alpha_r) - x'(t_r)] \, \varphi(t_r) |$$
$$\le \Sigma (t_r - t_{r-1}) \, k_1 \varepsilon = k_1 \varepsilon \, \Sigma (t_r - t_{r-1}) = k_1 \varepsilon \, (b - a) \qquad ...(11)$$

where k_1 is a number such that

$$| \varphi(t) | < k_1 \text{ for } t \text{ in } [a, b].$$

Letting the norm tend to zero, we now see from (10) and (11) that

$$\lim S_1 = \int_a^b \varphi(t) \, x'(t) \, dt \qquad \qquad ...(12)$$

Similarly

$$\lim S_2 = - \int_a^b \psi(t) \, y'(t) \, dt \qquad \qquad ...(13)$$

$$\lim S_3 = \int_a^b \psi(t) \, x'(t) \, dt \qquad \qquad ...(14)$$

$$\lim S_4 = \int_a^b \varphi(t) \, y'(t) \, dt \qquad \qquad ...(15)$$

Thus, we see that

$$\int_C f(z) \, dz = \left[\int_a^b \varphi(t) \, x'(t) \, dt - \int_a^b \psi(t) \, y'(t) \, dt \right]$$
$$+ i \left[\int_a^b \psi(t) \, x'(t) \, dt + \int_a^b \varphi(t) \, y'(t) \, dt \right]$$
$$= \int_a^b (\varphi x' - \psi y') \, dt + i \int_a^b (\varphi y' + \psi x') \, dt.$$

Also

$$f[z(t)] \, z'(t) = [\varphi(t) + i\psi(t)] \, [x'(t) + iy'(t)]$$
$$= (\varphi x' - \psi y') + i \, (\varphi y' + \psi x').$$

Hence, the theorem.

Note. The reader must have learnt in Real Variables that the length of the curve
$$z = z(t) = x(t) + iy(t),$$
where $x(t)$ and $y(t)$ are continuously differentiable, is equal to the definite integral
$$\int_a^b \sqrt{\left(\frac{dx}{dt}\right)^2 + \left(\frac{dy}{dt}\right)^2}\, dt = \int_a^b |z'(t)|\, dt.$$

8.8. Approximation. It will now be seen that any line integral can be approximated to by means of an integral along a polygon to any given degree of approximation. Obviously, for this purpose, we would take the polygon whose vertices lie on the given curve and which vertices are employed for any approximating sum. Thus, we shall prove the following:

If $f(z)$ is continuous in a domain G and C is any continuous rectifiable curve in G, then to every $\varepsilon > 0$, there corresponds a polygon Γ in G and with vertices on C such that

$$\left| \int_C f(z)\, dz - \int_\Gamma f(z)\, dz \right| < \varepsilon.$$

Let $f(z)$ be continuous in a bounded domain G and let C be a continuous rectifiable curve in G.

The frontier G_f of G is a bounded closed set.

Also C is a bounded closed set.

Consider now the set S of distances

$$|\xi - \eta|$$

where ξ is a point of G_f and η of C. Let d denote the lower bound of this set, S of distances. Surely no member of S is zero, for the sets S and G_f have no member in common. Further we shall show that the lower bound d of S cannot be zero.

Let, if possible, $d = 0$. Then there exists a sequence of distances

$$|\xi_1 - \eta_1|, \ldots, |\xi_n - \eta_n|, \ldots, \quad \xi_n \in G_f, \; \eta_n \in C \qquad \ldots(1)$$

which converges to 0.

Let, ξ, be any limiting point of the infinite bounded sequence $\{\xi_n\}$. As G_f is closed, we have $\xi \in G_f$. There exists, therefore, a sub-sequence

$$\xi^{(1)}, \xi^{(2)}, \ldots, \xi^{(n)}, \ldots,$$

of the sequence $\{\xi_n\}$ which converges to ξ. Now the sub-sequence

$$|\xi^{(1)} - \eta^{(1)}|, |\xi^{(2)} - \eta^{(2)}|, \ldots, |\xi^{(n)} - \eta^{(n)}|, \ldots,$$

of the sequence $\{|\xi_n - \eta_n|\}$.

(1) also converges to zero and since

$$\eta^{(n)} = \xi^{(n)} - [\xi^{(n)} - \eta^{(n)}]$$

we see that

$$\lim \eta^{(n)} = \xi.$$

As C is a closed set,

$$\lim \eta^{(n)} = \xi \in C.$$

Thus, C and G_f have a point ξ in common and we arrive at a contradiction.

Hence, $d \neq 0$.

Let, now, G_1, denote the set of all those points which are at a distance $\leq \frac{1}{2}d$ from C. Then G_1 is bounded, closed and is contained in G.   (Prove it)

Hence, $f(z)$ is uniformly continuous in G_1.

Let, l, be the length of C and $\varepsilon > 0$ be any given number.

Then there exists a $\delta_0 > 0$, such that

$$|f(z') - f(z'')| < \varepsilon/8l$$

when z' and z'' are any two points of G_1 such that

$$|z' - z''| \leq \delta_0.$$

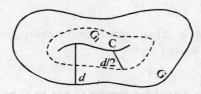

Fig. 8.2

Also since $z(t)$ is uniformly continuous in $a \leq t \leq b$, there exists a positive number δ such that

$$|z(t') - z(t'')| \leq \delta_0 \text{ when } |t' - t''| \leq \delta.$$

From above it follows that corresponding to any pair of points t', t'' for which $|t' - t''| \leq \delta$, we have

$$|f[z(t')] - f[z(t'')]| < \varepsilon/8l.$$

Consider now any division D of $[a, b]$ with norm $< \delta$, determined by the points

$$a = t_0, t_1, \ldots, t_{r-1}, t_r, \ldots, t_{n-1}, t_n = b$$

and the sum

$$S = \Sigma(z_r - z_{r-1}) f(z_r), \text{ where } z_r = z(t_r).$$

Also, let Γ denote the polygon inscribed in C with vertices

$$z_0, z_1, \ldots, z_{r-1}, z_r, \ldots, z_n.$$

Supposing $\delta_0 \leq d/2$, we see that $|z_r - z_{r-1}| \leq d/2$. Because of this, it can now be easily seen that the polygon Γ belongs to G_1.

Consider now, the two integrals

$$I_\Gamma = \int_\Gamma f(z)\, dz, \quad I_C = \int_C f(z)\, dz,$$

along the polygon Γ and the given curve C respectively. The sum S can be regarded as approximating both for Γ as well as for C.

Since the divisions of C and Γ are such that for any pair of points α, β of the same segment thereof, we have

$$|f(\alpha) - f(\beta)| < \varepsilon/8l.$$

$\therefore$ $$|S - I_\Gamma| < \frac{\varepsilon}{8l} 4l = \frac{\varepsilon}{2},$$

$$|S - I_C| < \frac{\varepsilon}{8l} 4l = \frac{\varepsilon}{2}.$$ (Refer note after § 8.5)

From these we conclude that

$$|I_C - I_\Gamma| < \varepsilon.$$

Hence, the theorem.

8.9. Differentiation Under Integral Sign. Functions defined by Integrals. Let $f(z)$ be a function which is continuous on any continuous rectifiable curve C and let ξ be any point of the complex plane *not* lying on C.

As $(z - \xi) \neq 0$ for any point $z \in C$, we see that $f(z)/(z - \xi)$ is continuous on C.

We write

$$\varphi(\xi) = \int_C \frac{f(z)}{(z - \xi)}\, dz.$$

It will now be shown that $\varphi(\xi)$ is analytic in the entire complex plane except on C, i.e., in the complement domain of C and that

$$\varphi'(\xi) = \int_C \frac{f(z)}{(z - \xi)^2}\, dz,$$

so that $\varphi'(\xi)$ is obtained on differentiating the integrand under integral sign with respect to ξ.

Let d be the distance of ξ from the curve C so that d is the lower bound of

$$|z - \xi|$$

for every point z on C. Also, therefore,

$$|z - \xi| \geq d \ \forall \ z \in C.$$

The circular domain

$$|z - \xi| < \frac{1}{2} d$$

will not contain any point of C.

We take $\xi + h$ any point in the interior of this domain so that $\xi + h$ does not lie on C.

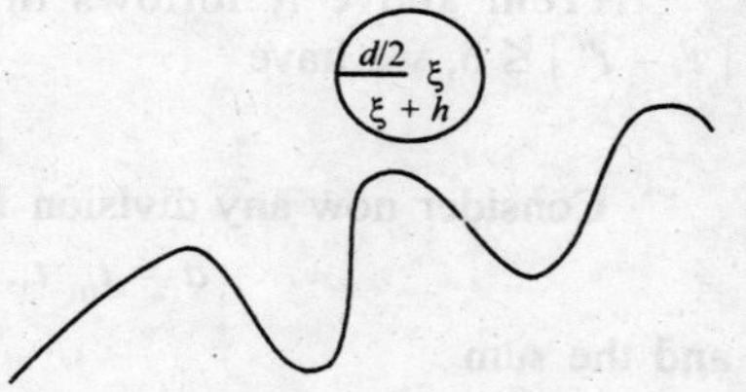

We now have

Fig. 8.3

$$\varphi(\xi) = \int_C \frac{f(z)}{(z - \xi)}\, dz$$

$$\varphi(\xi + h) = \int_C \frac{f(z)}{[z - (\xi + h)]}\, dz$$

$$\therefore \ \varphi(\xi + h) - \varphi(\xi) = \int_C f(z)\left[\frac{1}{[z - (\xi + h)]} - \frac{1}{(z - \xi)}\right] dz$$

$$= \int_C \frac{h\, f(z)}{(z - \xi)\,[z - (\xi + h)]}\, dz$$

$$\Rightarrow \quad \frac{\varphi(\xi + h) - \varphi(\xi)}{h} = \int_C \frac{f(z)}{(z - \xi)\,[z - (\xi + h)]}\, dz.$$

Now, we have

$$\frac{\varphi(\xi + h) - \varphi(\xi)}{h} - \int_C \frac{f(z)}{(z - \xi)^2}\, dz$$

$$= \int_C f(z) \left[\frac{1}{(z - \xi)\{z - (\xi + h)\}} - \frac{1}{(z - \xi)^2} \right] dz$$

$$= \int_C \frac{h f(z)}{(z - \xi)^2 [z - (\xi + h)]} dz \qquad \ldots(1)$$

Also, for every point z on C, we have

$$|z - \xi| \geq d \qquad \ldots(2)$$

$$|z - (\xi + h)| \geq |z - \xi| - |h| \geq |d| - |h| \qquad \ldots(3)$$

Further $f(z)$ being continuous on the continuous curve C, there exists a positive constant M such that

$$|f(z)| \leq M \quad \forall \ z \in C \qquad \ldots(4)$$

From (1), (2), (3) and (4), we deduce that

$$\left| \frac{\varphi(\xi + h) - \varphi(\xi)}{h} - \int_C \frac{f(z)}{(z - \xi)^2} dz \right| < |h| \frac{Ml}{d^2 (d - |h|)}$$

where l is the length of C.

$$\Rightarrow \qquad \lim_{h \to 0} \frac{\varphi(\xi + h) - \varphi(\xi)}{h} = \int_C \frac{f(z)}{(z - \xi)^2} dz$$

so that $\varphi(\xi)$ is differentiable and

$$\varphi'(\xi) = \int_C \frac{f(z)}{(z - \xi)^2} dz.$$

8.10. Generalisation. *It will now be shown by the method of induction that* $\varphi(\xi)$ *is differentiable any number, n, of times and that*

$$\varphi^n(\xi) = (n!) \int_C \frac{f(z)}{(z - \xi)^{n+1}} dz.$$

The result has been seen to be true for $n = 1$.

Suppose now that it is true for $n - 1$, so that we assume that

$$\varphi^{n-1}(\xi) = (n - 1)! \int_C \frac{f(z)}{(z - \xi)^n} dz.$$

Taking, $\xi + h$, as above, we have

$$\varphi^{n-1}(\xi + h) = (n - 1)! \int_C \frac{f(z)}{[z - (\xi + h)]^n} dz$$

$$\therefore \qquad \varphi^{n-1}(\xi + h) - \varphi^{n-1}(\xi)$$

$$= (n - 1)! \int_C f(z) \left[\frac{1}{\{z - (\xi + h)\}^n} - \frac{1}{(z - \xi)^n} \right] dz$$

$$\Rightarrow \qquad \frac{\varphi^{n-1}(\xi + h) - \varphi^{n-1}(\xi)}{h}$$

$$= (n-1)! \int_C f(z) \frac{\sum\limits_{r=1}^{n} (z-\xi)^{n-r} [z-(\xi+h)]^{r-1}}{[z-(\xi+h)]^n (z-\xi)^n} \, dz.$$

Thus,

$$\frac{\varphi^{n-1}(\xi+h) - \varphi^{n-1}(\xi)}{h} - n! \int_C \frac{f(z)}{(z-\xi)^{n+1}} \, dz$$

$$= (n-1)! \int_C f(z) \frac{\sum\limits_{r=1}^{n} (z-\xi)^{n-r+1} [z-(\xi+h)]^{r-1} - n [z-(\xi+h)]^n}{[z-(\xi+h)]^n (z-\xi)^{n+1}} \, dz$$

$$= (n-1)! \int_C f(z) \frac{\sum\limits_{r=1}^{n} (z-\xi)^{n-r+1} (z-\xi-h)^{r-1} - (z-\xi-h)^n}{(z-\xi)^{n+1} (z-\xi-h)^n} \, dz$$

$$= (n-1)! \int_C f(z) \sum_{r=1}^{n} \left[\frac{(z-\xi)^{n-r+1} - (z-\xi-h)^{n-r+1}}{(z-\xi)^{n+1} (z-\xi-h)^{n-r+1}} \right] dz$$

$$\doteq (n-1)! \sum_{r=1}^{n} \int_C f(z) \frac{(z-\xi)^{n-r+1} - (z-\xi-h)^{n-r+1}}{(z-\xi)^{n+1} (z-\xi-h)^{n-r+1}} \, dz$$

$$= h (n-1)! \sum_{r=1}^{n} \int_C f(z) \frac{\sum\limits_{p=0}^{n-r} (z-\xi)^{n-r-p} (z-\xi-h)^{p}}{(z-\xi)^{n+1} (z-\xi-h)^{n-r+1}} \, dz$$

$$= h (n-1)! \sum_{r=1}^{n} \sum_{p=0}^{n-r} \int_C \frac{f(z)}{(z-\xi)^{r+p+1} (z-\xi-h)^{n-r-p+1}} \, dz.$$

As in the first case, it can now be shown that the integral tends to 0 as $h \to 0$ for every value of r and p.

Hence, we see that $\varphi^{n-1}(\xi)$ is differentiable and

$$\varphi^{n}(\xi) = (n!) \int_C \frac{f(z)}{(z-\xi)^{n+1}} \, dz$$

so that the theorem is true for every n.

EXAMPLES

1. *Compute*

$$\int_C \frac{dz}{z}$$

where C denotes

   (i) *the square described in the positive sense with sides parallel to the axes and of lengths 2a and having its centre at the origin;*

   (ii) *the circle* $|z| = r$ *described in the positive sense.*

Solution. (*i*) We have:

$z = -ai + t$ along AB;   ...(1)

$z = a + it$ along BC;   ...(2)

$z = t + ia$ along CD;   ...(3)

$z = -a + it$ along DA;   ...(4)

In the cases (1) and (2), t varies from $-a$ to a and in the cases (3) and (4), t varies from a to $-a$.

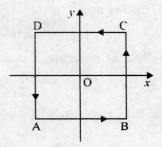

Fig. 8.4

$$\therefore \quad \int_C \frac{dz}{z}$$

$$= \int_{-a}^{a} \frac{dt}{t - ia} + \int_{-a}^{a} \frac{dt}{a + it} + \int_{a}^{-a} \frac{dt}{t + ia} + \int_{a}^{-a} \frac{dt}{-a + it}$$

$$= \int_{-a}^{a} \left(\frac{1}{t - ia} - \frac{1}{t + ia} \right) dt + \int_{-a}^{a} \left(\frac{1}{a + it} - \frac{1}{-a + it} \right) dt,$$

where we have combined first with the third and second with the fourth.

Thus,

$$\int_C \frac{dz}{z} = \int_{-a}^{a} \frac{2ia}{t^2 + a^2} \, dt + \int_{-a}^{a} \frac{2ai}{t^2 + a^2} \, dt.$$

Putting $t = au$, we get

$$\int \frac{dz}{z} = \int_{-1}^{1} \frac{2i \, du}{u^2 + 1} + \int_{-1}^{1} \frac{2i \, du}{u^2 + 1} = 4i \int_{-1}^{1} \frac{du}{u^2 + 1} = 2\pi i.$$

(*ii*) We have, for points on C,

$$z = r (\cos t + i \sin t)$$

where t varies from 0 to 2π.

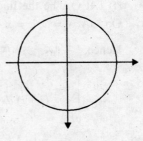

$$\therefore \quad \int_C \frac{dz}{z} = \int_{0}^{2\pi} \frac{r (-\sin t + i \cos t)}{z (\cos t + i \sin t)} \, dt$$

$$= \int_{0}^{2\pi} i \, dt = 2\pi i.$$

Fig. 8.5

2. *Show that*

(i) $\int_C k \, dz = k (b - a),$ (ii) $\int_C z \, dz = \frac{1}{2} (b^2 - a^2)$

where, k, is a constant and, C, denotes any rectifiable curve joining a to b.

(*Garhwal 2001; Poorvanchal 1992, 94*)

Solution. (*i*) In terms of the usual notation, we have for any division,

$$S = \sum_{r=1}^{n} (z_r - z_{r-1}) k = k (z_n - z_0) = k (b - a) \quad (z_0 = a, z_n = b)$$

so that, S, for every division, is the same.

It follows that

$$\int_C k \, dz = k \, (b - a).$$

(*ii*) As the integrand, z, is continuous, the integral exists. We have, for any division,

$$S = \sum_{r=1}^{n} (z_r - z_{r-1}) f(\xi_r) = \sum_{r=1}^{n} (z_r - z_{r-1}) \xi_r.$$

We take respectively $\xi_r = z_r$ and $\xi_r = z_{r-1}$ and obtain

$$S = \sum_{r=1}^{n} (z_r - z_{r-1}) z_r, \quad S' = \sum_{r=1}^{n} (z_r - z_{r-1}) z_{r-1}.$$

$$\therefore \quad S + S' = \sum_{r=1}^{n} (z_r^2 - z_{r-1}^2) = b^2 - a^2.$$

Since, S and S' both tend to the same limit

$$\int_C z \, dz,$$

we obtain

$$\int_C z \, dz = (b^2 - a^2) \Rightarrow \int_C z \, dz = \frac{1}{2} (b^2 - a^2).$$

3. *Find the value of the integral*

$$\int_0^{1+i} (x - y + ix^2) \, dz$$

(*i*) *Along the straight line from $z = 0$ to $z = 1 + i$;*

(*ii*) *Along the real axis from $z = 0$ to $z = 1$ and then along a line parallel to the imaginary axis from $z = 1$ to $z = 1 + i$.* (*Meerut, 2002; Garhwal 2000*)

Solution. Let A be the point of affix $1 + i$ and N be the point of affix 1.

(*i*) Let OA be the line from $z = 0$ to $z = 1 + i$.

On OA, $y = x$, $z = x + iy$, $dz = (1 + i) \, dx$.

Hence, $\displaystyle\int_{OA} (x - y + ix^2) \, dz$

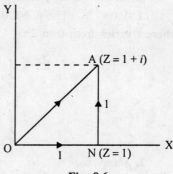

Fig. 8.6

$$= \int_0^1 ix^2 (1 + i) \, dx$$

$$= (-1 + i) \left[\frac{x^3}{3} \right]_0^2 = \frac{8}{3} (-1 + i).$$

(*ii*) The real axis from $z = 0$ to $z = 1$ is the line ON along the real axis and the line from $z = 1$ to $z = 1 + i$ a line NA parallel to the imaginary axis.

So, here the contour of integration C consists of the lines ON and NA, *i.e.*, say $C = C_1 + C_2$.

On C_1 (ON), $y = 0$, $z = x + iy = x$, $dz = dx$ and x varies from 0 to 1 and on C_2 (NA), $x = 1$, so on it $z = 1 + iy$, $dz = idy$ and y varies from 0 to 1.

Hence,

$$\int\limits_{0}^{1+i} (x - y + ix^2)\, dz = \int_{C_1 + C_2} (x - y + ix^2)\, dz$$

$$= \int_{C_1} (x - y + ix^2)\, dz + \int_{C_2} (x - y + ix^2)\, dz$$

$$= \int\limits_{0}^{1} (x + ix^2)\, dx + \int\limits_{0}^{1} (1 - y + i) \cdot i\, dy$$

$$= \left[\frac{x^2}{2} + i\, \frac{x^3}{3} \right]_0^1 + i \left[(1 + i)\, y - \frac{y^2}{2} \right]_0^1$$

$$= \left(\frac{1}{2} + \frac{i}{3} \right) + \left(\frac{1}{2} + i \right) = \frac{1}{2} + \frac{5}{6}\, i.$$

4. *Evaluate the integral*

$$\int\limits_{0}^{1+i} z^2\, dz.$$

Solution. $f(z) = z^2$ is analytic for all finite values of z, therefore its integral along a curve joining two fixed points will be the same whatever be the path.

Here we have to integrate z^2 between two fixed points $(0, 0)$ and $(1, 1)$. Choose the path of integration joining these points as a curve made up of:

(1) part of the real axis from the point $(0, 0)$ to the point $(1, 0)$. On this line $z = x$, $dz = dx$ and x varies from 0 to 1.

(2) followed by a line parallel to the imaginary axis from the point $(1, 0)$ to the point $(1, 1)$. On this line $z = 1 + iy$, $dz = idy$ and y varies from 0 to 1.

Thus,

$$\int\limits_{0}^{1+i} z^2\, dz = \int\limits_{0}^{1} x^2\, dx + \int\limits_{0}^{1} (1 + iy)^2\, i\, dy \quad \text{along the chosen path}$$

$$= \left[\frac{x^3}{3} \right]_0^1 + \left[\frac{1}{3} (1 + iy)^3 \right]_0^1$$

$$= \frac{1}{3} + \frac{1}{3} [(1 + i)^3 - 1] = \frac{1}{3} (1 + i)^3.$$

5. *Prove that*

$$\int_C \frac{1}{z - a}\, dz = 2\pi i$$

where C is given by the equation $|z - a| = R$.

Solution. On the circle C, $|z - a| = R$.

$\therefore z - a = Re^{i\theta}$, where θ varies from 0 to 2π.

So that, $dz = Re^{i\theta} \cdot id\theta$.

Hence, $\int_C \dfrac{1}{z - a} \, dz = \int_0^{2\pi} \dfrac{1}{Re^{i\theta}} \, Re^{i\theta} \cdot id\theta = i \int_0^{2\pi} d\theta = 2\pi i.$

EXERCISES

1. Evaluate

$$\int_C |z| \, dz,$$

where C is the circle

$$|z - 1| = 1$$

described in the positive sense.

$$\left[\textbf{Ans.} \ \frac{8i}{3}\right]$$

2. Find

$$\int_C I(z) \, dz,$$

where C denotes

(a) the unit circle described once in the positive direction from
$$+ 1 \text{ to } + 1.$$

(b) the straight segment from
$$z = a \text{ to } z = b.$$

(c) the circle $|z - a| = r$ traversed once in the positive direction.

$$\left[\textbf{Ans.} \ (a) - \pi, \ (b) \ \frac{1}{2}(b - a) \, I(b + a), \ (c) - \pi r^2\right]$$

3. Evaluate

$$\int_C \frac{dz}{z^m},$$

where m is any integer, positive, negative or zero and C denotes the circle $|z| = r$ traversed in the positive sense.

[**Ans.** 0, if $m \neq 1$; $2\pi i$, if $m = 1$]

4. Evaluate

$$\int_C R(z) \, dz,$$

where C denotes the

(a) straight line joining 0 to $1 + i$.

(b) straight line from 0 to i and
the straight line from 1 to $1 + i$.

(c) straight line from 0 to 1 and
the straight line from 1 to $1 + i$.

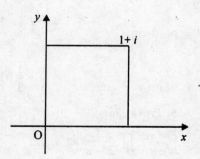

Fig. 8.7

$$\left[\textbf{Ans. } (a) \ \frac{1+i}{2}, \ (b) \ \frac{1}{2}, \ (c) \ \frac{1+2i}{2} \right]$$

5. Compute

$$\int_C \frac{dz}{\sqrt{z}},$$

where C denotes the positively oriented unit circle beginning from e^{ai} and $\sqrt{z}$ is equal to -1 for $z = 1$.

$$\left[\textbf{Ans. } -4e^{\frac{1}{2}ai} \right]$$

6. Let AB be an arc of the circle $|z| = R$ for which

$$\theta_1 \le \theta \le \theta_2;$$

and let $z f(z)$, as $R \to \infty$ tend uniformly to the limit k, which is a constant.

Prove that

$$\lim_{R \to \infty} \int_{AB} f(z) \, dz = i (\theta_2 - \theta_1) \, k.$$

[Hint. For every $\varepsilon > 0$, there exists an R_0 free from θ, such that for $|z| \ge R_0 \, |z f(z) - k| < \varepsilon$. We write $z f(z) = k + \varphi(z)$. Then

$$\int_{AB} f(z) \, dz = \int_{AB} \frac{k}{z} \, dz + \int_{AB} \frac{\varphi(z)}{z} \, dz$$

$$= ki (\theta_2 - \theta_1) + \int_{AB} \frac{\varphi(z)}{z} \, dz$$

$$\Rightarrow \qquad \left| \int_{AB} f(z) \, dz - ki (\theta_2 - \theta_1) \right|$$

$$< \frac{\varepsilon}{R} \cdot R (\theta_2 - \theta_1), \text{ when } R \ge R_0$$

$$\to 0 \text{ as } R \to \infty.]$$

7. C is the semi-circle defined by $|z| = R$, $I(z) \ge 0$. If max. $|z f(z)| \to 0$ as $R \to \infty$, prove that

$$\int f(z) \, dz \to 0 \text{ as } R \to \infty.$$

8. Prove that

$$\int_{|z| = r} z^n \, dz = 0$$

where n is any integer positive or negative other than -1.

OBJECTIVE QUESTIONS

For each of the following questions, four alternatives are given for the answer. Only one of them is correct. Choose the correct alternative.

1. A continuous arc without multiple points is called a

(a) Jordan curve   (b) Continuous arc
(c) Contour   (d) Rectifiable arc.

2. A continuous function $f(z)$ over a continuous rectifiable curve C is
(a) differentiable   (b) integrable
(c) meromorphic   (d) None of these.

3. The value of $\int_C z \, dz$ is
(a) $b - a$ (b) $b^2 - a^2$
(c) $\dfrac{1}{2}(b^2 - a^2)$ (d) None of these.

4. If C is given by the equation $|z - a| = R$, then the value of $\int_C \dfrac{dz}{z - a}$ is
(a) $2\pi i$ (b) πi
(c) $\pi i/2$ (d) None of these.

5. The value of $\int_C \dfrac{dz}{z}$, where C is the circle with centre at the origin and radius r is
(a) $\log r$ (b) πi
(c) $2\pi i$ (d) $\pi i/2$.

ANSWERS

1. (c)   2. (a)   3. (a)   4. (b)   5. (c)

Chapter 9

CAUCHY THEORY

9.1. Introduction. This chapter will be concerned with the Fundamental theorem of Function Theory which was first discovered by Cauchy (1789 – 1857) in the year 1814 and its basic consequences. Cauchy proved the theorem only under the assumption of the continuity of the derivative $f'(z)$. It was, however, in 1900 that Goursat made the discovery that the theorem remains true even if the existence only and not the continuity of $f(z)$ is assumed. In the words of Caratheodory, this discovery of Goursat had made quite a stir. On account of this discovery of Goursat, this theorem is now often justifiably known as Cauchy-Goursat theorem also.

As a consequence of the theorem, it will be shown that *a function of a complex variable which is differentiable once in any domain is ipso facto infinitely differentiable in the same.* As another consequence, we shall see that there is a strong interrelation between the values of an analytic function at different points inasmuch as the values of the same in the interior of any rectifiable Jordan curve C will be known as soon as the values on C are known.

Before proceeding to state and prove the Cauchy's theorem, we shall consider a few preliminary points about polygons in the following section.

9.2. A few preliminary points about polygons. A closed oriented polygon Γ whose sides may cross each other can be regarded as composed of a finite number of *simple* closed oriented polygons such that each side of each of the simple polygons is either a side or a part of the side of the original polygon.

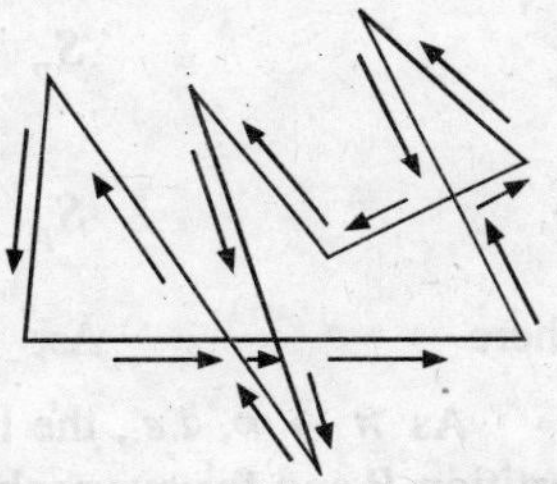

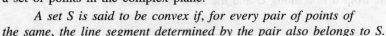

We shall now show that the *interior of any simple closed polygon can be decomposed into a finite number of triangular domains.*

To prove this, we first introduce the notion of *convexity* of a set of points in the complex plane.

Fig. 9.1

A set S is said to be convex if, for every pair of points of the same, the line segment determined by the pair also belongs to S.

The following two properties of convex sets may be easily established:

(*i*) *A semi-plane is a convex set.*

(*ii*) *The intersection of any number of convex sets is convex.*

To prove the theorem stated above, we first suppose that the interior of a simple closed polygon is convex. In this case, if P be any point in the interior of the polygon and $A_1, A_2, ..., A_n$ be the vertices of the polygon, then the line segments $PA_1, PA_2, ..., PA_n$ belong to the interior of the polygon. Thus the interior of the polygon is decomposed as a union of a finite number of triangular domains given by

$$PA_1A_2, \ PA_2A_3, \ ....., \ PA_nA_1.$$

In case the interior of the polygon is not convex, we extend each side of the polygon indefinitely in both the directions. The interior of the polygon will then be split up into a finite number of polygonal domains. Each of these latter domains, being the intersection of semi-planes is convex and the decomposition into triangles may then be carried out in the case of each of these convex sub-domains.

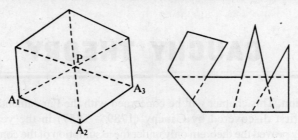

Fig. 9.2

9.3. Complex Line Integrals (Riemann's definition of integration.)

Let $z = z(t) = x(t) + iy(t)$, $a \le t \le b$ be a given curve C joining a and b and let $f(z)$ be a function of a complex variable z defined and continuous on C.

Consider the partition $P = \{a = t_0, t_1, t_2, ..., t_n = b\}$ of the interval $[a, b]$. Let $z_0, z_1, z_2, ..., z_n$ be the points on the curve corresponding to the values $t_0, t_1, t_2, ..., t_n$, i.e., $z(t_r) = z_r$. On each arc joining z_{r-1} to z_r choose a point e_r where $r = 1, 2, ..., n$ i.e., $z_{r-1} \le e_r \le z_r$; form the following sum S_p, for the partition P,

$$S_p = f(e_1)(z_1 - z_0) + f(e_2)(z_2 - z_1)$$
$$+ ... + f(e_r)(z_r - z_{r-1}) + ... + f(e_n)(z_n - z_{n-1}),$$

or
$$S_p = \sum_{r=1}^{n} f(e_r)(z_r - z_{r-1})$$

or
$$S_p = \sum_{r=1}^{n} f(e_r).\Delta z_r \qquad ...(i)$$

where
$$\Delta z_r = z_r - z_{r-1}.$$

As $n \to \infty$, i.e., the largest of the chord length $|\Delta z_r|$ approaches to zero and if for every partition P and for every choice of points e_r, the sum S_p tends to a unique limit, then the function $f(z)$ is said to be integrable from a to b along C and the limit is denoted by

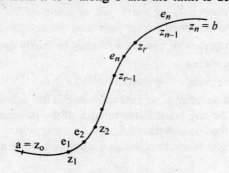

Fig. 9.3

$$\int\limits_{a}^{b} f(z)\,dz \quad \text{or} \quad \int\limits_{c} f(z)\,dz \qquad \qquad ...(ii)$$

and is called the complex line integral or briefly the line integral of $f(z)$ along the curve c or the definite integral of $f(z)$ from a to b along the curve C.

Thus $\qquad \int\limits_{C} f(z)\,dz = \lim_{n\to\infty} \sum_{r=1}^{n} f(e_r)(z_r - z_{r-1}) \qquad \qquad ...(iii)$

where $\qquad \qquad z_{r-1} \le e_r \le z_r$

If $f(z) = u(x, y) + iv(x, y) = u + iv$, where $z = x + iy$, then the complex line integral $\int\limits_{C} f(z)\,dz$ can be expressed in terms of real line integrals as

$$\int\limits_{C} (u + iv)(dx + idy)$$

$$= \int\limits_{C} (udx - vdy) + i \int\limits_{C} (vdx + udy)$$

General line integrals of the form $\int\limits_{C} pdx + qdy$ are often studied as function (or functionals) of the are C under the assumption that p, q are defined and continuous in a domain D such that C is free to vary in D. There is an important class of integrals characterised by the property that the integral over on its end points. this means that if the two arcs C_1 and C_2 have the same initial point and the same final point then

$$\int\limits_{C_1} pdx + qdy = \int\limits_{C_2} pdx + qdy$$

Theorem 1. *The following statements are equivalent:*

(i) A line integral of $f(z)$ over an arc C depends only on the end points of C.

(ii) The integral of $f(z)$ over any closed curve is zero.

Let the integral of $f(z)$ over any closed curve be zero and let C_1 and C_2 be any two arcs with the same end points. Then $C_1 - C_2$ is a closed curve so that

$$\int\limits_{C_1-C_2} f(z)dz = 0$$

$\Rightarrow \qquad \qquad \int\limits_{C_1} f(z)dz - \int\limits_{C_2} f(z)dz = 0$

Hence $\qquad \qquad \int\limits_{C_1} f(z)\,dz = \int\limits_{C_2} f(z)\,dz$

Again let the integral over any two arcs with the same end points be the same and let C be any closed curve. Then C and $- C$ have the same end points so that

$$\int\limits_{C} f(z)\,dz = \int\limits_{-C} f(z)\,dz = \int\limits_{C} f(z)\,dz$$

$\therefore \qquad \qquad 2\int\limits_{C} f(z)dz = 0, \quad i.e., \quad \int\limits_{C} f(z)\,dz = 0$

Theorem 2. *The line integral $\int_{C} pdx + qdy$, defined in a domain D, depends only on the end points of C, if and only if there exists a function $u(x, y)$ in D such that*

$$\frac{\partial u}{\partial x} = p \quad \text{and} \quad \frac{\partial u}{\partial y} = q.$$

To prove the sufficiency, suppose there exists a function $u(x, y)$ in D such that

$$\frac{\partial u}{\partial x} = p, \frac{\partial u}{\partial y} = q.$$

Then if α, β are the end points of C, we have

$$\int_C p\, dx + q\, dy = \int_C \frac{\partial u}{\partial x} dx + \frac{\partial u}{\partial y} dy$$

$$= \int_\alpha^\beta \left[\frac{\partial u}{\partial x} x'(t) + \frac{\partial u}{\partial y} y'(t) \right] dt$$

$$= \int_\alpha^\beta \frac{d}{dt} u(x(t), y(t))\, dt$$

$$= u\{x(\beta), y(\beta)\} - u\{x(\alpha), y(\alpha)\} \qquad \ldots(i)$$

Since the right hand side of (i) depends only on the end points α and β.

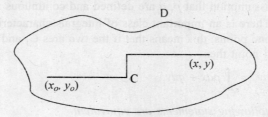

Fig. 9.4

To prove the necessity, let the line integral $\int_C p\, dx + q\, dy$ depends only on the end points of C. We consider a fixed point (x_0, y_0) in D and let (x, y) be an arbitrary point there. We join (x_0, y_0) to (x, y) by a polygonal arc C, contained in D, whose sides are parallel to the coordinate axes (Fig. 9.4). We now define a function u by

$$u(x, y) = \int_C p\, dx + q\, dy.$$

By given condition, the integral depends only on the points and so it is well defined. Further, if we select the last segment of C horizontal, then we can take y constant ($\Rightarrow dy = 0$) and suppose that x varies without changing the other segments. Choosing x as a parameter on the last segment, we get

$$u(x, y) = \int^x p(x, y)\, dx + \text{constant} \qquad \ldots(ii)$$

Since $dy = 0$ implies that $\int q\, dy$ is constant.

We do not specify the lower limit since it is immaterial for our purpose. From (ii)

$$\frac{\partial u}{\partial x} = p$$

Similarly, if we choose the last segment vertical, then it can be shown that

$$\frac{\partial u}{\partial y} = q.$$

This establishes the necessary condition.

Remarks:

(*i*) We know by definition of partial differentiation

$$du = \left(\frac{\partial u}{\partial x}\right) dx + \left(\frac{\partial u}{\partial y}\right) dy \qquad\qquad ...(i)$$

We know that $p\,dx + q\,dy$ is an exact differential if it can be written in the form (*i*). On the basis of this terminology we can say:

An integral depends only on the end point if and only if the integral is an exact differential.

(*ii*) We now determine the condition under which

$$f(z)\,dz = f(z)\,dx + i f(z)\,dy$$

is an exact differential. By definition of an exact differential, there must exist a function $F(z)$ in D such that

$$\frac{\partial F(z)}{\partial x} = f(z) \quad \text{and} \quad \frac{\partial F(z)}{\partial y} = i f(z)$$

If follows that

$$\frac{\partial F}{\partial x} = -\frac{\partial F}{\partial y} \quad \text{which is a Cauchy-Riemann equation.}$$

(*iii*) From (*i*) and (*ii*), we conclude:

The integral $\int_C f(z)\,dz$, with continuous f, depends only on the end points of C if and only if f is the derivative of an anlytic function in D.

For example, for $n \geq 0$, the function $(z-a)^n$ is the derivative of $\dfrac{(z-a)^{n+1}}{(n+1)}$ which is an analytic function in the whole complex plane. If C is any closed curve, then it follows from theorem 1 and remark (*iii*), above that

$$\int_C (z-a)^n dz = 0. \qquad\qquad ...(i)$$

If n is negative, but $\neq -1$, then also $\int_C (z-a)^n dz = 0$ for all closed curves C which do not pass though a, since in the complementary region of the point a the infinite integral is still analytic and single – valued. If $n = -1$, then (*i*) does not always hold.

9.4. Cauchy's Theorem. (*Original*)

If $f(z)$ is an analytic function of z and if $f'(z)$ is continuous at each point within and on a closed contour C, then

$$\int_C f(z)\,dz = 0.$$

(*Meerut 2003; Kanpur 1998, 2003, 2004; Garhwal 2001; Gorakhpur 1992; Poorvanchal 1993*)

Let D be the region which consists of all points within and on the contour C. If

$$P(x, y),\ Q(x, y),\ \frac{\partial Q}{\partial x},\ \frac{\partial P}{\partial y}$$

are all continuous functions of x and y in the region D, then Green's theorem states that

$$\int_C (P\, dx + Q\, dy) = \int_D \int \left(\frac{\partial Q}{\partial x} - \frac{\partial P}{\partial y} \right) dxdy.$$

Since $f(z) = u + iv$ is continuous on the simple curve C and $f'(z)$ exists and is continuous in D, therefore u, v, u_x, u_y, v_x, v_y are all continuous in D. The conditions of Green's theorem are thus satisfied. Hence

$$\int_C f(z)\, dz = \int_C (u + iv)\,(dx + idy)$$

$$= \int_C (u\, dx - v\, dy) + i \int (v\, dx + u\, dy)$$

$$= -\iint_D \left(\frac{\partial v}{\partial x} + \frac{\partial u}{\partial y} \right) dxdy + i \iint_D \left(\frac{\partial u}{\partial x} - \frac{\partial v}{\partial y} \right) dxdy = 0$$

[By Green's theorem]

$$= -\iint_D \left(\frac{\partial v}{\partial x} - \frac{\partial u}{\partial y} \right) dxdy + i \iint_D \left(\frac{\partial u}{\partial x} - \frac{\partial v}{\partial y} \right) dxdy$$

[By Cauchy-Riemann equations]

Hence $\displaystyle\int_C f(z)\, dz = 0.$

Note. *Goursat showed that for the truth of the theorem the assumption of the continuity of $f'(z)$ is unnecessary, and that Cauchy's Theorem holds if and only if $f(z)$ is analytic within and on C.*

9.5. Fundamental Cauchy Theorem. *If $f(z)$ be analytic in a simply-connected domain D and if C be any closed continuous rectifiable curve in D, then*

$$\int_C f(z)\, dz = 0.$$

(Kanpur 2002; Kumaon 2002; Garhwal 2003, 2005; Gorakhpur 2001, 2005; Lucknow 1992, 94, 96; Meerut 2001)

The theorem will be proved in *three* steps.

First Step. *When the curve C is a triangle.*

Let Δ be any triangle in the simply-connected domain D. As D is simply-connected, the interior of Δ also belongs to D.

We connect the middle points of the sides of the triangle and thus obtain four new triangles which we denote by

$$\Delta_{11}, \Delta_{12}, \Delta_{13}, \Delta_{14}.$$

Also we have

$$\int_\Delta f(z)\, dz = \int_{\Delta_{11}} f(z)\, dz + \int_{\Delta_{12}} f(z)\, dz$$

$$+ \int_{\Delta_{13}} f(z)\, dz + \int_{\Delta_{14}} f(z)\, dz \qquad ...(1)$$

where each of the four triangles is traversed in the sense in

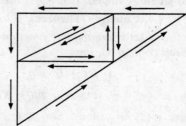

Fig. 9.5

which Δ is traversed. This follows from the fact that each side of any of these four triangles, not forming a part of the side of Δ, will be traversed twice in opposite directions and as such, on summation, the integrals along the same will vanish.

Now, from (1), we have

$$\left| \int_{\Delta} f(z)\,dz \right| \leq \left| \int_{\Delta_{11}} f(z)\,dz \right| + \left| \int_{\Delta_{12}} f(z)\,dz \right|$$

$$+ \left| \int_{\Delta_{13}} f(z)\,dz \right| + \left| \int_{\Delta_{14}} f(z)\,dz \right|.$$

Thus one at least of the four numbers on the right must be such that it is not less than $\frac{1}{4}$ th of the number on the left. We denote by Δ_1 the first one of the four triangles

$$\Delta_{11},\ \Delta_{12},\ \Delta_{13},\ \Delta_{14}$$

such that

$$\frac{1}{4}\left| \int_{\Delta} f(z)\,dz \right| \leq \left| \int_{\Delta_1} f(z)\,dz \right| \ \Rightarrow\ \left| \int_{\Delta} f(z)\,dz \right| \leq 4 \left| \int_{\Delta_1} f(z)\,dz \right| \qquad \text{...(1)}$$

Similarly, connecting the mid-points of the sides of the triangle Δ_1, we obtain a triangle Δ_2 such that

$$\left| \int_{\Delta_1} f(z)\,dz \right| \leq 4 \left| \int_{\Delta_2} f(z)\,dz \right| \qquad \text{...(2)}$$

From (1) and (2), we obtain

$$\left| \int_{\Delta} f(z)\,dz \right| \leq 4^2 \left| \int_{\Delta_2} f(z)\,dz \right|.$$

Proceeding in this manner, we obtain a sequence of triangles

$$\Delta_1,\ \Delta_2,\ .....,\ \Delta_n$$

such that

$$(i)\ \left| \int_{\Delta} f(z)\,dz \right| \leq 4^n \left| \int_{\Delta_n} f(z)\,dz \right|, \qquad \text{...(3)}$$

(ii) the length of $\Delta_n = \dfrac{l}{2^n}$, where l is the length of the triangle Δ.

(iii) $\Delta' \supset \Delta_1' \supset \Delta_2' \supset ..... \supset \Delta_n'$, where Δ_n' denotes the bounded closed triangular domain with Δ_n as frontier.

From (ii) and (iii), it follows, [Refer Ex. after § 4.7] that there exists a point z_0 which belongs to every bounded closed triangular domain Δ_n'.

Also $z_0 \in D$ so that $f(z)$ is differentiable at z_0. Thus we have

$$\lim_{z \to z_0} \frac{f(z) - f(z_0)}{z - z_0} = f'(z_0).$$

We write

$$\frac{f(z) - f(z_0)}{z - z_0} - f'(z_0) = \eta(z),$$

where $\eta(z)$ is a function of z tending to 0 as $z \to z_0$. Thus to a given $\varepsilon > 0$, there exists a $\delta > 0$ such that

$$|\eta(z)| < \varepsilon \text{ when } |z - z_0| < \delta.$$

Hence for $|z - z_0| < \delta$, we have

$$f(z) = f(z_0) + (z - z_0) f'(z_0) + (z - z_0) \eta(z) \qquad \ldots(4)$$

where $$|\eta(z)| < \varepsilon \qquad \ldots(5)$$

Also there exists a positive integer m such that $\forall\ n > m$, Δ_n' is contained in the domain $|z - z_0| < \delta$. For any point z on the triangle Δ_n whose perimeter is

$$l_n = \frac{l}{2^n},$$

we have

$$|z - z_0| \le l_n.$$

From (4) and (5), we have

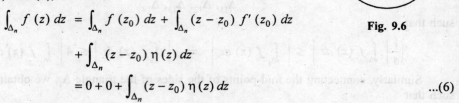

Fig. 9.6

$$\int_{\Delta_n} f(z)\, dz = \int_{\Delta_n} f(z_0)\, dz + \int_{\Delta_n} (z - z_0) f'(z_0)\, dz$$

$$+ \int_{\Delta_n} (z - z_0)\, \eta(z)\, dz$$

$$= 0 + 0 + \int_{\Delta_n} (z - z_0)\, \eta(z)\, dz \qquad \ldots(6)$$

Further, we have

$$\left| \int_{\Delta_n} (z - z_0)\, \eta(z)\, dz \right| \le l_n \cdot \varepsilon \cdot l_n = \varepsilon l_n^2 = \varepsilon \left(\frac{l}{2^n} \right)^2 \qquad \ldots(7)$$

From (3), (6) and (7), we obtain

$$\left| \int_{\Delta} f(z)\, dz \right| \le 4^n \cdot \varepsilon \cdot \left(\frac{l}{2^n} \right)^2 = \varepsilon l^2.$$

Here ε is an arbitrary positive number, howsoever small. Thus we prove that

$$\int_{\Delta} f(z)\, dz = 0.$$

Second Step. *When the curve C is any closed polygon in a simply-connected domain D.*

As the integral along any closed polygon can be expressed as a sum of integrals along triangles and as, by the first step, each of the latter integrals is zero, we see that the theorem is true for any closed polygon.

Third Step. *When C is any arbitrary continuous rectifiable closed curve in a simply-connected domain D.*

We have seen in § 8.8 that the integral

$$\int_{C} f(z)\, dz$$

can be approximated to any degree of approximation by means of an integral along a polygon in D with its vertices on C.

Suppose now that $\varepsilon > 0$ is any given number. Thus there exists a closed polygon π in D such that

$$\left| \int_{C} f(z)\, dz - \int_{\pi} f(z)\, dz \right| < \varepsilon.$$

Also by the second step, the integral

$$\int_\pi f(z)\, dz$$

along the polygon is zero. Thus we have

$$\left| \int_C f(z)\, dz \right| < \varepsilon.$$

As ε is arbitrary, we have

$$\left| \int_C f(z)\, dz \right| = 0 \;\Rightarrow\; \int_C f(z)\, dz = 0.$$

Note. The student may note that we have not required the curve C to be simple so that the integral along the *closed* curve C vanishes whether the curve is or is not simple. It is necessary however that the domain D is simply-connected.

Cor. *If $f(z)$ is analytic in a simply-connected domain D, then the integral along every rectifiable curve in D joining any two given points of D is the same i.e., is independent of the curve joining the given points.*

Let C_1 and C_2 be any two curves in D joining two given points a and b of the same.

Then if C denotes the closed curve consisting of C_1 and $- C_2$, we have, by Cauchy's theorem,

$$\int_C f(z)\, dz = 0,$$

$$\Rightarrow \qquad \int_{C_1} f(z)\, dz + \int_{-C_2} f(z)\, dz = 0,$$

$$\Rightarrow \qquad \int_{C_1} f(z)\, dz = \int_{-C_2} f(z)\, dz.$$

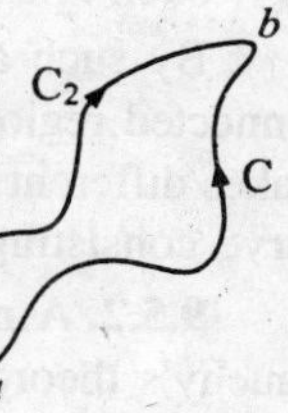

Hence the result.

Thus we find that the symbol

$$\int_a^b f(z)\, dz$$

Fig. 9.7

is meaningful inasmuch as it denotes the integral along any curve in D joining a to b.

9.5.1. Connected Region   (*Meerut 2002, 2003*)

Connected Region. A region is said to be a *connected region* if any two points of the region D can be connected by a curve which lies entirely within the region.

Simply-Connected Region. A connected region is said to be a *simply-connected region* if all the interior points of a closed curve C drawn in the region D are the points of the region D. In other words, if all the points of the area bounded by any single closed curve C drawn in the region D are the points of the region D, then the region D is said to be simply-connected.

Multi-Connected Region. If all the points of the area bounded by two or more closed curves drawn in the region D, are the points of the region D, then the region D is said to be a *multi-connected region*.

For example, let there be a number of closed curves C, C_1, C_2, C_3, ... all drawn in a certain region D.

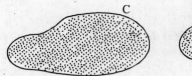 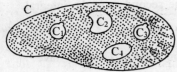

Fig. 9.8

If all the points of the area lying between the closed curves C, C_1, C_2, ... the area which is interior to C and exterior to the other curves C_1, C_2, C_3, C_4 are the points of the region D, then the region D is said to be a multi-connected region.

Cross-cut (or Cut) (*Kurukshetra 2005*). The lines drawn in a multiply-connected region without intersecting any one of the curves, which make a multi-connected region a simply-connected one are called *cuts* or *cross-cuts*.

Thus let there be a multi-connected region lying between the curves C, C_1, C_2, C_3, C_4, where C_1, C_2, C_3, C_4 lie inside C. In this region draw lines joining C to all the curves C_1, C_2, C_3, C_4, then the same region which lies between several curves C, C_1, C_2, C_3, C_4 can also be said to lie between a simple curve whose boundary consists of the boundaries of C, C_1, C_2, C_3, C_4 and the lines AB, PQ, RS, etc.

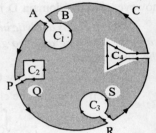

Fig. 9.9

Such lines AB, PQ, RS, ... etc. are called cuts or cross-cuts.

By such a manipulation the same region which is a multi-connected region is made a simply-connected region. This device makes different curves C, C_1, C_2, C_3, C_4 as parts of the continuous curve consisting of these curves and the cross-cuts.

9.5.2. A more general form of Cauchy's theorem. A number of statements and proofs of Cauchy's theorem under less restrictive conditions have been given. We shall here state only one such form.

If f (z) is continuous and analytic within a rectifiable Jordan curve C, then

$$\int_C f\,(z)\,dz\ = 0.$$

This form of the statement emphasises that it is not necessary for $f(z)$ to be analytic on C and that it need only be continuous on the same.

We shall, however, not prove this theorem here and only state that the proof depends upon the fact that it is possible to take a rectifiable closed curve C' in the domain interior to C such that the integral of $f(z)$ along C' is arbitrarily near to that along C.

The interior of the Jordan curve C is necessarily a simply-connected domain.

9.5.3. Extension to multiply-connected domains. *If a domain D is bounded by a system of rectifiable Jordan curves C_1, C_2, ..., C_k and if f (z) is analytic in D and continuous on C_1, C_2, ..., C_k then*

$$\int_{C_1} f\,(z)\,dz + \int_{C_2} f\,(z)\,dz + ... + \int_{C_k} f\,(z)\,dz = 0,$$

where each of the boundary curves is so described that the domain constantly lies on the left.

The same thing may be expressed by saying that

$$\int_C f\,(z)\,dz\ = 0,$$

where C denotes the entire boundary of the domain described in an appropriate manner.

Consider firstly the case of a *doubly-connected domain* D bounded by two non-intersecting rectifiable Jordan curves C_1, C_2. One of these will be in the interior of the other.

Take any two points a, b on C_1 and any two points c, d on C_2.

Join a to c and b to d by two arcs Γ_1 and Γ_2 which lie in D and do not cross each other and C_1, C_2.

It is then clear that we obtain two simply-connected domains enclosed by Jordan curves, denoted by π_1 and π_2 such that $f(z)$ is analytic in the

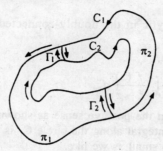

Fig. 9.10

domains and continuous on the boundary curves π_1, π_2. Thus

$$\int_{\pi_1} f(z)\, dz = 0, \quad \int_{\pi_2} f(z)\, dz = 0.$$

$\Rightarrow$
$$\int_{\pi_1} f(z)\, dz + \int_{\pi_2} f(z)\, dz = 0 \qquad \qquad ...(1)$$

Since, in the sum on the left of (1), we have to consider pairs of integrals along Γ_1, Γ_2 described in the opposite senses, we see that (1) is equivalent to

$$\int_{C_1} f(z)\, dz + \int_{C_2} f(z)\, dz = 0.$$

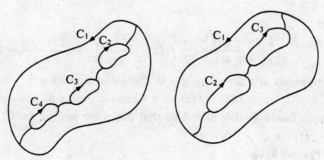

Fig. 9.11

The case of triply and other multiply-connected domains can be similarly considered by introducing connecting arcs and the consequently obtained simply-connected domains.

9.6. Cauchy's Integral Formula. *If $f(z)$ is analytic in a simply-connected domain D bounded by a rectifiable Jordan curve C and is continuous on C, then*

$$f(z) = \frac{1}{2\pi i} \int_C \frac{f(\xi)}{\xi - z}\, d\xi,$$

where z is any point of D.

(*Garhwal 2004, 2006; UPPCS 2002; Guwahati 2002; Kerala 1999, 2001;*
Avadh 2005; Meerut 2001, 03; Kumaon, 2003)

Let d be the distance of z from the curve C. Also let C_1 be any circle with its centre at z and radius ρ where $\rho < d$.

As a function of ξ,

$$\frac{f(\xi)}{\xi - z}$$

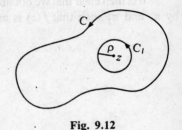

Fig. 9.12

is continuous on C, C_1 and analytic in the doubly-connected domain bounded by the same.

Hence by Cauchy's theorem,

$$\frac{1}{2\pi i} \int_C \frac{f(\xi)}{\xi - z}\, d\xi = \frac{1}{2\pi i} \int_{C_1} \frac{f(z)}{\xi - z}\, d\xi,$$

where C, C_1 are both described in the positive sense as shown in the figure. It is clear that the integral along the circle C_1 is independent of its radius and we may accordingly take the same as small as we like.

Now, we have

$$\frac{1}{2\pi i} \int_{C_1} \frac{f(\xi)}{\xi - z}\, d\xi = \frac{1}{2\pi i} \int_{C_1} \frac{f(\xi) - f(z)}{\xi - z}\, d\xi + \frac{1}{2\pi i} \int_{C_1} \frac{f(z)}{\xi - z}\, d\xi$$

$$= \frac{1}{2\pi i} \int_{C_1} \frac{f(\xi) - f(z)}{\xi - z}\, d\xi + f(z),$$

for

$$\int_{C_1} \frac{d\xi}{\xi - z} = 2\pi i.$$

Thus we have

$$\frac{1}{2\pi i} \int_C \frac{f(\xi)}{\xi - z}\, d\xi - f(z) = \frac{1}{2\pi i} \int_{C_1} \frac{f(\xi) - f(z)}{\xi - z}\, d\xi. \qquad \ldots(1)$$

As $f(\xi)$ is continuous at z for every $\varepsilon > 0$, there corresponds a $\delta > 0$ such that

$$|f(\xi) - f(z)| < \varepsilon \text{ when } |\xi - z| < \delta.$$

We now suppose that ρ is chosen $< \delta$ so that for every point ξ on C_1, we have

$$|f(\xi) - f(z)| > \varepsilon \qquad \ldots(2)$$

From (1) and (2), we have

$$\left| \frac{1}{2\pi i} \int_C \frac{f(\xi)}{\xi - z}\, d\xi - f(z) \right| < \frac{1}{2\pi} \cdot \frac{\varepsilon}{\rho} \cdot 2\pi\rho = \varepsilon.$$

As ε is arbitrary and the left-hand side does not depend upon ρ, we deduce that

$$\frac{1}{2\pi i} \int_C \frac{f(\xi)}{\xi - z}\, d\xi = f(z).$$

Cor. Gauss Mean Value Theorem. *If $f(z)$ is an analytic function on a domain D and if the circular region $|z - a| \le \rho$ is contained in D, then*

$$f(a) = \frac{1}{2\pi} \int_0^{2\pi} f(a + \rho e^{i\theta}) \, d\theta.$$

Or

The value of f(z) at the point a equals the average of its value on the boundary of the circle $|z - a| = \rho$.

Let γ denotes the circle $|z - a| \leq \rho$, contained in D.

∴ For any point on γ, $z - a = \rho e^{i\theta}$ $(0 \leq \theta \leq 2\pi)$

or $z = a + \rho e^{i\theta}$ so that $dz = \rho i e^{i\theta} \, d\theta$.

∴ By Cauchy's integral formula, we have

$$f(a) = \frac{1}{2\pi i} \oint_\gamma \frac{f(z)}{z - a} \, dz$$

$$= \frac{1}{2\pi i} \int_0^{2\pi} \frac{f(a + \rho e^{i\theta})}{\rho e^{i\theta}} \cdot i\rho e^{i\theta} \, d\theta = \frac{1}{2\pi} \int_0^{2\pi} f(a + \rho e^{i\theta}) \, d\theta.$$

9.6.1. Extension to multiply-connected domains. *If a domain D is bounded by a system of rectifiable Jordan curves* $C_1, C_2, \ldots, C_k$ *and if f(z) is analytic in D and continuous on* $C_1, C_2, \ldots, C_k,$ *then*

$$f(z) = \frac{1}{2\pi i} \int_{C_1} \frac{f(\xi)}{\xi - z} \, d\xi + \ldots + \frac{1}{2\pi i} \int_{C_k} \frac{f(\xi)}{\xi - z} \, d\xi,$$

where z is any point of D and each of the boundary curves is so described that the domain constantly lies on the left.

The same thing can be expressed by saying that

$$f(z) = \frac{1}{2\pi i} \int_C \frac{f(\xi)}{\xi - z} \, d\xi,$$

where C denotes the *entire* boundary of the domain described in an appropriate manner.

We enclose z by a Jordan curve π described positively which along with its interior belongs to the domain D.

We denote by D_1 the domain obtained on removing from D the points on π and in the interior of π. Then the boundary of D_1 is given by the Jordan curves

$$-\pi, C_1, C_2, \ldots, C_k.$$

Also, as a function of ξ, $f(\xi)/(\xi - z)$ is analytic in D_1 and continuous on the boundary of the same. We have, by § 9.6.1,

$$\frac{1}{2\pi i} \int_{-\pi} \frac{f(\xi)}{\xi - z} \, d\xi + \frac{1}{2\pi i} \int_{C_1} \frac{f(\xi)}{\xi - z} \, d\xi + \ldots + \frac{1}{2\pi i} \int_{C_k} \frac{f(\xi)}{\xi - z} \, d\xi = 0.$$

Also by the theorem given above, we have

$$f(z) = \frac{1}{2\pi i} \int_\pi \frac{f(\xi)}{\xi - z} \, d\xi.$$

Thus we have proved that

$$f(z) = \frac{1}{2\pi i} \int_{C_1} \frac{f(\xi)}{\xi - z} \, d\xi + \ldots + \frac{1}{2\pi i} \int_{C_k} \frac{f(\xi)}{\xi - z} \, d\xi.$$

Note. The Cauchy's integral formula proved above shows that the value of an analytic function at any point of the domain is known in terms of the values of the function at the boundary only.

Thus we may state that if $f(z)$ and $g(z)$ are analytic in a domain D and continuous on the boundary curve C then

$$f(z) = g(z), \ \forall \ z \in C \ \Rightarrow \ f(z) = g(z), \ \forall \ z \in D.$$

9.6.2. Poisson's Integral Formula. *If $f(z)$ is analytic in $|z| < \rho$, then*

$$f(re^{i\theta}) = \frac{1}{2\pi} \int_0^{2\pi} \frac{R^2 - r^2}{R^2 - 2Rr \cos(\theta - \varphi) + r^2} f(Re^{i\varphi}) \, d\varphi, \qquad (Meerut\ 2002)$$

where $re^{i\theta}$ is any point of the domain

$$|z| < \rho,$$

and R is any number such that

$$r < R < \rho.$$

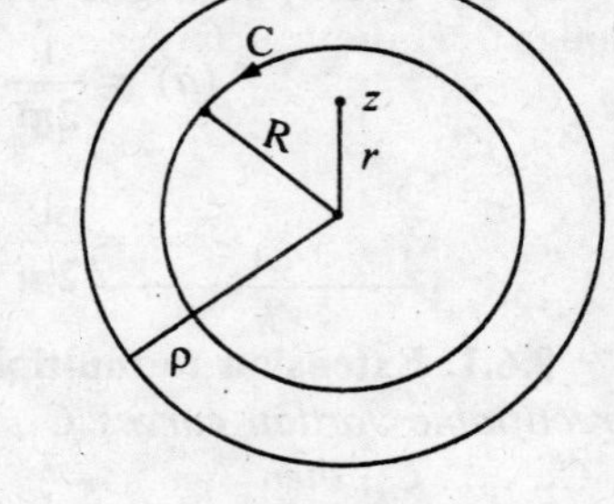

Let $z = re^{i\theta}$ be any point of the domain

$$|z| < \rho$$

and let C denote the circle

$$|z| = R$$

when $r < R < \rho$.

Fig. 9.13

By Cauchy's integral formula, we have

$$f(z) = \frac{1}{2\pi i} \int_C \frac{f(\xi)}{\xi - z} \, d\xi. \qquad \qquad \dots(1)$$

The inverse of z with respect to the circle $|z| = R$ is $R^2/\bar{z}$ and lies outside the circle so that we have

$$0 = \frac{1}{2\pi i} \int_C \frac{f(\xi)}{\xi - (R^2/\bar{z})} \, d\xi. \qquad \qquad \dots(2)$$

Subtracting (2) from (1), we obtain

$$f(z) = \frac{1}{2\pi i} \int \frac{(R^2 - z\bar{z}) f(\xi)}{(\xi - z)(R^2 - \xi\bar{z})} \, d\xi.$$

We put $\xi = Re^{i\varphi}$ and obtain

$$f(re^{i\theta}) = \frac{1}{2\pi i} \int_0^{2\pi} \frac{(R^2 - r^2) f(Re^{i\varphi}) R i e^{i\varphi}}{(Re^{i\varphi} - re^{i\theta})(R^2 - rRe^{i\varphi - i\theta})} \, d\varphi$$

$$= \frac{1}{2\pi} \int_0^{2\pi} \frac{(R^2 - r^2) f(Re^{i\varphi})}{R^2 - 2Rr \cdot \cos(\theta - \varphi) + r^2} \, d\varphi.$$

If we write

$$f(re^{i\theta}) = u(r, \theta) + iv(r, \theta),$$

then equating real and imaginary parts, we obtain

$$u(r, \theta) = \frac{1}{2\pi} \int_0^{2\pi} \frac{(R^2 - r^2) u(R, \varphi)}{R^2 - 2Rr \cos(\theta - \varphi) + r^2} \, d\varphi \qquad \qquad \dots(3)$$

and

$$v(r, \theta) = \frac{1}{2\pi} \int_0^{2\pi} \frac{(R^2 - r^2) v(R, \varphi)}{R^2 - 2Rr \cos(\theta - \varphi) + r^2} \, d\varphi \qquad \qquad \dots(4)$$

The formulae (3) and (4) express the real and imaginary parts of the value of the function at any interior point in terms of the real and imaginary parts of the values of the functions at points on the bounding circle.

9.7. Analytical character of the derivative. We shall now prove a very important property of analytic functions stated as follows:

Theorem. *The derivative of a function analytic in a domain is itself an analytic function.*

(Kanpur 2003, 2005)

We shall prove that if $f(z)$ is analytic in a domain D, then so is also $f'(z)$ in D.

Let z be any point of D.

We consider a circle C with its centre at z and radius ρ such that C along with its interior belongs to D. Let $z + h$ be any point in the interior of C. By Cauchy's integral formula, we have

$$f(z) = \frac{1}{2\pi i} \int_C \frac{f(\xi)}{\xi - z} \, d\xi, \quad f(z + h) = \frac{1}{2\pi i} \int_C \frac{f(\xi)}{\xi - (z + h)} \, d\xi,$$

$$\therefore \quad \frac{f(z + h) - f(z)}{h} = \frac{1}{2\pi i} \int \frac{f(\xi)}{(\xi - z)[\xi - (z + h)]} \, d\xi.$$

$$\therefore \quad \frac{f(z + h) - f(z)}{h} - \frac{1}{2\pi i} \int_C \frac{f(\xi)}{(\xi - z)^2} \, d\xi$$

$$= \frac{h}{2\pi i} \int \frac{f(\xi)}{(\xi - z)^2 (\xi - z - h)} \, d\xi.$$

Let M be the upper bound of $f(\xi)$ in the closed domain with the circle C as its boundary. Also for $\xi \in C$,

$$|\xi - z| = \rho, \; |\xi - z - h| \geq |\xi - z| - |h| = \rho - |h|.$$

Thus we have

$$\left| \frac{f(z + h) - f(z)}{h} - \frac{1}{2\pi i} \int_C \frac{f(\xi)}{(\xi - z)^2} \, d\xi \right| \leq \frac{|h|}{2\pi} \cdot \frac{M}{\rho^2 (\rho - |h|)} \cdot 2\pi\rho$$

$$\Rightarrow \quad \lim_{h \to 0} \frac{f(z) f(z + h) - f(z)}{h} = \frac{1}{2\pi i} \int_C \frac{f(\xi)}{(\xi - z)^2} \, d\xi$$

$$\Rightarrow \quad f'(z) = \frac{1}{2\pi i} \int_C \frac{f(\xi)}{(\xi - z)^2} \, d\xi.$$

(Kumaon 2000, UPPCS 1999, 2000, Meerut 2005, Kanpur 2003; Gorakhpur 2000)

Proceeding as above and as in § 8.9, we may show that

$$f''(z) = \frac{2}{2\pi i} \int_C \frac{f(\xi)}{(\xi - z)^3} \, d\xi.$$

As z is any point of D, we see that $f'(z)$ is analytic in D.

9.7.1. Higher Order Derivatives of an Analytic Function.

Theorem. *If a function $f(z)$ is analytic in a domain D, then $f(z)$ has, at any point $z = a$ of D, derivatives of all orders, all of which are again analytic functions in D, there values are given by*

$$f^n(a) = \frac{n!}{2\pi i} \int_C \frac{f(z)}{(z-a)^{n+1}} \, dz$$

where C is any closed contour in D surrounding the point z = a.

Let $f(z)$ be an analytic function in a domain D and C a closed contour in D surrounding the point $z = a$ of D. Then, we have

$$f'(a) = \frac{1}{2\pi i} \int_C \frac{f(z)}{(z-a)^2} \, dz \qquad \text{...(1)}$$

and

$$f''(a) = \frac{2!}{2\pi i} \int_C \frac{f(z)}{(z-a)^3} \, dz \qquad \text{...(2)}$$

Proceeding similarly, it can be shown that

$$f'''(a) = \frac{3!}{2\pi i} \int_C \frac{f(z)}{(z-a)^4} \, dz \text{ etc.}$$

Hence we can assume that for $n = m$,

$$f^m(a) = \frac{m!}{2\pi i} \int_C \frac{f(z)}{(z-a-h)^{m+1}} \, dz.$$

∴ If $(a + h)$ is a point in the small neighbourhood of the point a, then

$$f^m(a+h) = \frac{m!}{2\pi i} \int_C \frac{f(z)}{(z-a)^{m+1}} \, dz.$$

∴

$$f^m(a+h) - f^m(a)$$

$$= \frac{m!}{2\pi i} \int_C \left[\frac{1}{(z-a-h)^{m+1}} - \frac{1}{(z-a)^{m+1}} \right] f(z) \, dz$$

$$= \frac{m!}{2\pi i} \int_C \frac{\{(z-a)^{m+1} - (z-a-h)^{m+1}\}}{(z-a-h)^{m+1}(z-a)^{m+1}} \cdot f(z) \, dz$$

$$= \frac{m!}{2\pi i} \int_C \frac{\{(z-a-h)+h\}^{m+1} - (z-a-h)^{m+1}}{(z-a-h)^{m+1}(z-a)^{m+1}} \cdot f(z) \, dz$$

$$= \frac{m!}{2\pi i} \int_C \frac{1}{(z-a-h)^{m+1}(z-a)^{m+1}} \left[(z-a-h)^{m+1} + (m+1)(z-a-h)^m \right.$$

$$\left. + \frac{(m+1)m}{2!}(z-a-h)^{m-1} h^2 + \dots + h^{m+1} - (z-a-h)^{m+1} \right] f(z) \, dz$$

$$= \frac{m!}{2\pi i} \int_C \frac{(m+1)h}{(z-a-h)^{m+1}(z-a)^{m+1}} \left[(z-a-h)^m \right.$$

$$\left. + \frac{m}{2!}(z-a-h)^{m-1} h + \dots + \frac{h^m}{(m+1)} \right] f(z) \, dz$$

or $\quad \dfrac{f^m (a + h) - f^m (a)}{h} = \dfrac{(m + 1)!}{2\pi i} \left[\displaystyle\int_C \dfrac{f(z)}{(z - a - h)(z - a)^{m+1}} dz \right.$

$$+ \int_C \dfrac{h f(z)}{(z - a - h)^{m+1} (z - a)^{m+1}} \cdot \left\{ \dfrac{m}{2!} (z - a - h)^{m-1} \right.$$

$$\left. + \dfrac{m(m-1)}{3!} (z - a - h)^{m-2} h + \ldots + \dfrac{h^{m-1}}{m+1} \right\} dz \Bigg]$$

$$= \dfrac{(m + 1)!}{2\pi i} \left[\int_C \dfrac{(z - a - h) + h f(z)}{(z - a - h)(z - a)^{m+1}} dz + h \int_C \dfrac{f(z) \phi(z)}{(z - a - h)^{m+1} (z - a)^{m+1}} \right]$$

where $\quad \phi(z) = \dfrac{m}{2!} (z - a - h)^{m-1} + \dfrac{m(m-1)}{3!} (z - a - h)^{m-2} h + \ldots + \dfrac{h^{m-1}}{m+1}$ \qquad ...(3)

$$= \dfrac{(m + 1)!}{2\pi i} \int_C \dfrac{f(z)}{(z - a)^{m+1}} dz + \dfrac{(m + 1)! \, h}{2\pi i} \int_C \left[\dfrac{1}{(z - a - h)} \right.$$

$$\left. + \dfrac{\phi(z)}{(z - a - h)^{m+1}} \right] \dfrac{f(z)}{(z - a)^{m+1}} dz$$

or $\quad \dfrac{f^m (a + h) - f^m (a)}{h} - \dfrac{(m + 1)!}{2\pi i} \int_C \dfrac{f(z)}{(z - a)^{m+1}} dz = I$ \qquad ...(4)

where

$$I = \dfrac{(m + 1)! \, h}{2\pi i} \int_C \left[\dfrac{1}{(z - a - h)} + \dfrac{\phi(z)}{(z - a - h)^{m+1}} \right] \cdot \dfrac{f(z)}{(z - a)^{m+1}} dz - dz$$

or $\quad \left| \dfrac{f^m (a + h) - f^m (a)}{h} - \dfrac{(m + 1)!}{2\pi i} \int_C \dfrac{f(z)}{(z - a)^{m+1}} dz \right| = |\, I\,|$ \qquad ...(5)

Now

$$|\, I\,| = \left| \dfrac{(m + 1)! \, h}{2\pi i} \int_C \left[\dfrac{1}{(z - a - h)} + \dfrac{\phi(z)}{(z - a - h)^{m+1}} \right] \cdot \dfrac{f(z)}{(z - a)^{m+1}} dz \right|$$ \qquad ...(6)

Now we shall show that $I \to 0$ as $h \to 0$. For this we describe a circle γ with centre at $z = a$ and radius ρ such that γ lies entirely within C.

Therefore from (6), we have

$$|\, I\,| = \left| \dfrac{(m + 1)! \, h}{2\pi i} \int_\gamma \left[\dfrac{1}{(z - a - h)} + \dfrac{\phi(z)}{(z - a - h)^{m+1}} \right] \dfrac{f(z)}{(z - a)^{m+1}} dz \right|$$

$$\leq \dfrac{(m + 1)! \, |h|}{2\pi} \int_\gamma \left[\dfrac{1}{|z - a - h|} + \dfrac{|\phi(z)|}{|z - a - h|^{m+1}} \right] \dfrac{|f(z)|}{|z - a|^{m+1}} |dz|$$ \qquad ...(7)

Choosing h such that $a + h$ lies within γ and if $|\, h\,| > \rho/2$, the $|\, z - a\,| = \rho$ and $|\, z - a - h\,| \geq |\, z - a\,| \, |\, h\,| > \rho - \rho/2 = \rho/2$.

Also $f(z)$ is analytic and $\phi(z)$ given by (3) being a polynomial is also analytic and hence both functions $f(z)$ and $\phi(z)$ are bounded. If M and M' are the upper bounds of $f(z)$ and $\phi(z)$ respectively in D $i.e.$, $|\, f(z)\,| \leq M$ and $|\, \phi(z)\,| \leq M'$, then from (7), we have

$$| I | < \frac{(m+1)!\,|\,h\,|}{2\pi}\left[\frac{1}{(\rho/2)} + \frac{M'}{(\rho/2)^{m+1}}\right]\cdot\frac{M}{\rho^{m+1}}\cdot\int_{\gamma}|\,dz\,|$$

$$= \frac{(m+1)!\,|\,h\,|}{2\pi}\left[\frac{1}{(\rho/2)} + \frac{M'}{(\rho/2)^{m+1}}\right]\cdot\frac{M}{\rho^{m+1}}\cdot 2\pi\rho$$

$$= \frac{(m+1)!\,|\,h\,|}{\rho^{m}}\left[\frac{1}{(\rho/2)} + \frac{M'}{(\rho/2)^{m+1}}\right]M.$$

Clearly R.H.S. $\to 0$ as $h \to 0$. Thus $I \to 0$ as $h \to 0$.

Hence from (5), we have

$$\lim_{h \to 0} \frac{f^{m}(a+h) - f^{m}(a)}{h} = \frac{(m+1)!}{2\pi i}\int_{C}\frac{f(z)}{(z-a)^{m+1}}\,dz$$

or

$$f^{m+1}(a) = \frac{(m+1)!}{2\pi i}\int_{C}\frac{f(z)}{(z-a)^{m+1}}\,dz$$

which shows that the theorem holds for $n = m + 1$ also, if it holds for $n = m$. Also it holds for $n = 1$ and $n = 2$.

Hence it holds for every positive integral value of n *i.e.*, the nth derivative of $f(z)$, at $z = a$ is given by

$$f^{n}(a) = \frac{n!}{2\pi i}\int_{C}\frac{f(z)}{(z-a)^{n+1}}\,dz.$$

Since the derivatives of an analytic function $f(z)$ of every order exist, hence these derivatives are themselves all analytic functions.

Cor. 2. *If $f(z)$ is analytic in a domain D bounded by a finite system of rectifiable Jordan curves C_1, C_2, ..., C_k and is continuous on these boundary curves, then $\forall\; z \in D$,*

$$f^{n}(z) = \frac{n!}{2\pi i}\int_{C_1}\frac{f(\xi)}{(\xi-z)^{n+1}}\,d\xi + ... + \frac{n!}{2\pi i}\int_{C_k}\frac{f(\xi)}{(\xi-z)^{n+1}}\,\xi$$

where each boundary curve is so described that the domain lies on the left.

By Cauchy's integral formula for multiply-connected domains, we have

$$f(z) = \frac{1}{2\pi i}\int_{C}\frac{f(\xi)}{\xi-z}\,d\xi,$$

where C denotes the entire boundary of D.

We enclose z by a Jordan curve C' such that C' and its interior belong to D. Then by Cauchy's integral formula, we have

$$f(z) = \frac{1}{2\pi i}\int_{C'}\frac{f(\xi)}{\xi-z}\,d\xi.$$

Then, by § 8.9, we have

$$f^{n}(z) = \frac{n!}{2\pi i}\int_{C'}\frac{f(\xi)}{(\xi-z)^{n+1}}\,d\xi \qquad ...(1)$$

As $f(\xi)/(\xi - z)^{n+1}$ is analytic in the domain D, obtained on removing from D the points on C' and in the interior of C' and is continuous on the boundary curves $C_1, C_2, \ldots, C_k, -C'$, of the same, we have, by Cauchy's theorem

$$\int_{-C'} \frac{f(\xi)}{(\xi - z)^{n+1}}\, d\xi + \int_{C_1} \frac{f(\xi)}{(\xi - z)^{n+1}}\, d\xi + \ldots + \int_{C_k} \frac{f(\xi)}{(\xi - z)^{n+1}}\, d\xi = 0 \qquad \ldots(2)$$

From (1) and (2), we obtain the required result.

Note. The reader would note that the main point in the above proof is the result arrived at in § 8.9. In fact the demonstration given for the main theorem of this section is itself only a repetition of that of § 8.9 and as such we could omit the demonstration here and only make an appeal to § 8.9.

Cor. 3. Let $f(z)$ be analytic in a domain D and continuous on the boundary of D.

Let ξ be any point of D and let d be the distance of ξ from the boundary. Finally, let M be the upper bound of $|f(z)|$ on the boundary of D. It will then be proved that

$$|f^n(\xi)| \le \frac{n!\, Ml}{2\pi d^{n+1}},$$

where l is the length of the entire boundary.

In terms of the notation of Cor. 2 above, we have

$$|f^n(\xi)| \le \frac{n!}{2\pi} \left[\frac{M}{d^{n+1}}\, l_1 + \ldots + \frac{M}{d^{n+1}}\, l_k \right],$$

where $l_1, \ldots, l_k$ are the lengths of the curves $C_1, \ldots, C_k$ respectively.

Thus we have

$$|f^n(\xi)| \le \frac{n!\, Ml}{2\pi d^{n+1}}. \qquad (Kumaon,\ 1992;\ Rohilkhand,\ 1993;\ Lucknow,\ 1993)$$

9.8. Morera's Theorem. (Converse of Cauchy's Theorem). *If $f(z)$ be continuous in a simply-connected domain D and if*

$$\int_C f(z)\, dz = 0,$$

where C is any rectifiable Jordan curve in D, then $f(z)$ is analytic in D.

(Banglore 2003, Delhi 2000, 2004, 2005; Garhwal 2002; Kanpur 2003, 2004, 2005; Meerut 2000, 2001, 2004; Kerala 2001; Gorakhpur, 2005; Nagpur 2001)

Let a be any fixed and z any variable point of D and let C_1, C_2 be any two continuous rectifiable curves in D joining a to z. Then the curve C_1 followed by $-C_2$, is a closed rectifiable continuous curve in D so that, as given,

$$\int_{C_1} f(z)\, dz + \int_{C_2} f(z)\, dz = 0$$

$$\Rightarrow \qquad \int_{C_1} f(z)\, dz = \int_{C_2} f(z)\, dz.$$

Thus the integral along every curve in D joining a to z is the same.

Taking ξ as the variable of integration, we write

$$\varphi(z) = \int_a^z f(\xi)\, d\xi. \qquad \ldots(1)$$

The notation (1) is justified because of the fact that the integral (1) depends only upon the points a, z and not on the particular curve in D which joins a to z.

As z is a point of the domain D, there exists a circle with its centre at z such that the same along with its interior belongs to D.

Further, let $z + h$ be any point of this interior.

We have

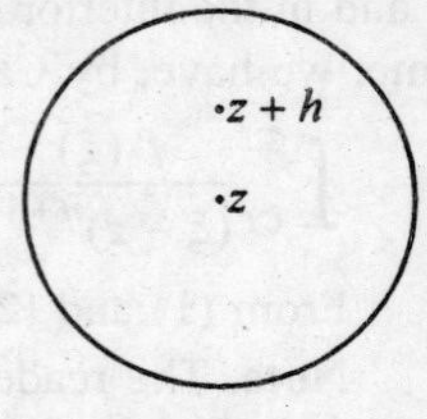

$$\varphi(z + h) - \varphi(z) = \int_a^{z+h} f(\xi)\, d\xi - \int_a^z f(\xi)\, d\xi$$

$$= \int_z^{z+h} f(\xi)\, d\xi. \qquad \qquad ...(2)$$

Fig. 9.14

The integral (2) being independent of the curve joining z to $z + h$, take the same along the straight segment from z to $z + h$.

$$\frac{\varphi(z + h) - \varphi(z)}{h} - f(z) = \frac{1}{h}\left[\int_z^{z+h} f(\xi)\, d\xi - \int_z^{z+h} f(z)\, d\xi \right]$$

$$\therefore \qquad = \frac{1}{h} \int_z^{z+h} [f(\xi) - f(z)]\, d\xi. \qquad ...(3)$$

Let $\varepsilon > 0$ be any given number. As $f(\xi)$ is continuous at z, there exists $\delta > 0$ such that
$$|f(\xi) - f(z)| < \varepsilon \text{ for } |\xi - z| > \delta.$$

Now supposing that $|h| < \delta$, we see that for every point, on the line segment joining z to $z + h$, we have

$$|f(\xi) - f(z)| < \varepsilon \qquad\qquad ...(4)$$

From (3) and (4), we obtain

$$\left| \frac{\varphi(z + h) - \varphi(z)}{h} - f(z) \right| < \frac{1}{|h|} \cdot |h| \cdot \varepsilon = \varepsilon, \text{ for } |h| < \delta.$$

$$\Rightarrow \qquad\qquad \lim_{h \to 0} \frac{\varphi(z + h) - \varphi(z)}{h} = f(z),$$

$\Rightarrow \qquad \varphi'(z)$ exists and $\varphi'(z) = f(z)$. $\qquad\qquad ...(5)$

The equality (5) holds for every $z \in$ D.

Thus we see that $f(z)$ appears as the derivative of a function and as such, by § 9.7, $f(z)$ is analytic in D.

9.9. Indefinite Integral. Def. *A function $\varphi(z)$ is said to be an indefinite integral of a function $f(z)$ in a domain D if for every $z \in$ D,*

$$\varphi'(z) = f(z).$$

We now proceed to state and prove a theorem concerning the existence of indefinite integrals.

Theorem. *The necessary and sufficient condition for a function to possess an indefinite integral in any simply-connected domain D is that the function is analytic in that domain. Also any two indefinite integrals (of the same function) differ by a constant.*

Firstly we suppose that $f(z)$ is analytic in a simply-connected domain D.

Let a be any fixed point and z any variable point in D.

As a consequence of the Cauchy's theorem, we may easily prove that the integral of $f(z)$ along every curve in D, joining a to z is the same.

Thus we write

$$\varphi(z) = \int_a^z f(\xi)\, d\xi.$$

As in the preceding theorem, we may now show that

$$\varphi'(z) = f(z).$$

Thus we see that $f(z)$ possesses an indefinite integral, *viz.*, $\varphi(z)$.

Hence every *analytic function in a simply-connected domain possesses an indefinite integral*.

Suppose now that $f(z)$ possesses an indefinite integral $\varphi(z)$ so that

$$\varphi'(z) = f(z).$$

Then $f(z)$, being the derivative of a function $\varphi(z)$, is necessarily an analytic function.

We come now to the question of uniqueness.

Let, if possible, $\varphi(z)$ and $\psi(z)$ be two indefinite integrals of an analytic function $f(z)$ in a simply-connected domain D. Then we have

$$\varphi'(z) = \psi'(z),$$

both being equal to $f(z)$.

$$\therefore \quad [\psi(z) - \varphi(z)]' = \psi'(z) - \varphi'(z) = 0.$$

*Thus

$$\psi(z) - \varphi(z)$$

is constant and accordingly we have a relation of the form

$$\psi(z) = \varphi(z) + c,$$

where c is a constant.

Hence we see that the *general indefinite integral of an analytic function in a simply-connected domain D is given by*

$$\varphi(z) + c,$$

where

$$\varphi(z) = \int_a^z f(\xi)\, d\xi,$$

and c is any arbitrary constant.

Cor. *If $f(z)$ is analytic in a simply-connected domain D and $\psi(z)$ is any indefinite integral of $f(z)$ so that $\psi'(z) = f(z)$, then*

$$\int_a^b f(z)\, dz = \psi(b) - \psi(a).$$

We write

$$\varphi(z) = \int_a^z f(\xi)\, d\xi \qquad \qquad ...(1)$$

so that, as shown above,

$$\psi(z) = \varphi(z) + c,$$

---

* The fact that an analytic function whose derivative in any domain is zero is a constant is a simple consequence of Cauchy-Riemann equations.

where c is some constant.

$$\therefore \quad \psi(a) = \varphi(a) + c = c, \text{ for } \varphi(a) = 0$$

and

$$\psi(b) = \varphi(b) + c.$$

Thus

$$\psi(b) - \psi(a) = \varphi(b) = \int_a^b f(z) \, dz. \qquad \text{[From (1)]}$$

9.10. Development of Analytic Functions as Power Series. Taylor's Theorem for Complex Functions.

(Agra 2003; Kumaon 2000, 2004 Gorakhpur 2002; Mithila 2000, 2004; Rajasthan 2003, 2005; Ravishankar 2000, 2002; Garhwal 2000)

Theorem. *If $f(z)$ is analytic in a circular domain D with centre a, then for every $z \in D$,*

$$f(z) = f(a) + (z - a) f'(a) + \ldots + \frac{(z - a)^n}{n!} f^n(a) + \ldots$$

$$= \sum_{n=0}^{\infty} \frac{(z - a)^n}{n!} f^n(a),$$

so that $f(z)$ can be expressed as a power series about a.

Let C denote the boundary of the circular domain D. Let z be any point of D.

Again, let C_1 denote any circle whose centre is a and whose radius is smaller than that of C and which contains z in its interior.

We suppose that C_1 is positively oriented. By Cauchy's integral formula, we have

$$f(z) = \frac{1}{2\pi i} \int_{C_1} \frac{f(\xi)}{\xi - z} \, d\xi.$$

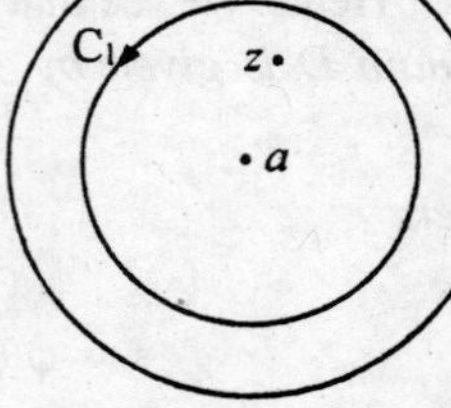

Now

$$\frac{1}{\xi - z} = \frac{1}{(\xi - a) - (z - a)}$$

$$= \frac{1}{\xi - a} \left[\frac{1}{1 - \dfrac{z - a}{\xi - a}} \right]$$

Fig. 9.15

$$= \frac{1}{\xi - a} \left[1 + \frac{z - a}{\xi - a} + \frac{(z - a)^2}{(\xi - a)^2} + \ldots + \frac{(z - a)^{n-1}}{(\xi - a)^{n-1}} \right.$$

$$\left. + \frac{(z - a)^n}{(\xi - a)^n} \frac{1}{1 - \dfrac{z - a}{\xi - a}} \right]$$

$$= \frac{1}{\xi - a} + (z - a) \frac{1}{(\xi - a)^2} + (z - a)^2 \frac{1}{(\xi - a)^3}$$

$$+ \ldots + (z - a)^{n-1} \frac{1}{(\xi - a)^n} + \frac{(z - a)^n}{(\xi - a)^n} \frac{1}{\xi - z}.$$

$$\therefore \frac{1}{2\pi i} \int_{C_1} \frac{f(\xi)}{\xi - z} d\xi = \frac{1}{2\pi i} \int_{C_1} \frac{f(\xi)}{\xi - a} d\xi + \frac{(z-a)}{2\pi i} \int_{C_1} \frac{f(\xi)}{(\xi - a)^2} d\xi$$

$$+ ..... + \frac{(z-a)^{n-1}}{2\pi i} \int_{C_1} \frac{f(\xi)}{(\xi - a)^n} d\xi + \frac{1}{2\pi i} \int_{C_1} \left(\frac{z-a}{\xi - a}\right)^n \frac{f(\xi)}{\xi - z} d\xi$$

$$= f(a) + (z-a) f'(a) + ... + \frac{(z-a)^{n-1}}{(n-1)!} f^{n-1}(a) + R_n, \text{ say, } (1)$$

where

$$R_n = \frac{1}{2\pi i} \int_{C_1} \left(\frac{z-a}{\xi - a}\right)^n \frac{f(\xi)}{\xi - z} d\xi.$$

For every point ξ on C_1,

$$\left| \frac{z-a}{\xi - a} \right|$$

is constant and less than one. We denote it by p.

Also if ρ_1 denote the radius of C_1, we have

$$|\xi - z| = |(\xi - a) - (z - a)| \geq |\xi - a| - |z - a| = \rho_1 - |z - a|.$$

Thus we have

$$|R_n| \leq \frac{1}{2\pi} \cdot 2\pi\rho_1 (p)^n \frac{M}{\rho_1 - |z - a|} = \frac{M\rho_1}{\rho_1 - |z - a|} p^n,$$

where $|f(\xi)| \leq M \ \forall \ z \in C_1$.

As $0 < p < 1$, we see that $R_n \to 0$ as $n \to \infty$.

Thus we obtain from (1),

$$f(z) = f(a) + (z - a) f'(a) + ... + \frac{(z-a)^{n-1}}{(n-1)!} f^{n-1}(a) + ...$$

$$= \sum_{n=0}^{\infty} \frac{(z-a)^n}{n!} f^n(a).$$

Cor. 1. *If $f(z)$ is analytic in any domain D and a is any point of* D, *then*

$$f(z) = \sum_{n=0}^{\infty} \frac{(z-a)^n}{n!} f^n(a),$$

where the equality holds for every point z in the largest circular domain whose centre is 'a' and which is contained in the domain D.

Fig. 9.16

This is an immediate consequence of the above theorem.

Cor. 2. *If the centre of the circle C is chosen at the origin then writing a = 0, we get*

$$f(z) = \frac{f^n(0)}{n!} z^n.$$

*Above is known as **Maclaurin's series**.*

Note. Uniqueness of Power Series Expansion. Comparing the result obtained here with that in Cor. 2, Theorem V of § 6.12.1, we see that the power series expansion of an analytic function about a point is unique.

9.10.1. An important consequence of Taylor's Theorem.

Theorem. *If $f(z)$ is analytic in any domain D, then the value $f(\xi)$ of the function at any point $\xi \in D$ can be determined in terms of the values of the function and of its different derivatives at any given point $a \in D$.*

Let the points a, ξ be joined by a continuous rectifiable curve C in D. Let the length of C be l.

Let d be the distance of C from the boundary of D. Then the interior of every circle whose centre lies on C and whose radius is d belongs to the domain D.

Let C_1 denote the circle with its centre at a and radius $3d/4$.

Then the radius of convergence of the power series

$$f(z) = f(a) + (z - a) f'(a) + ... + \frac{(z - a)^n}{n!} f^n(a) + .. \qquad ...(1)$$

is $\geq 3d/4$, for $f(z)$ is regular at every point within and on C_1.

The point z_1 on C whose distance measured along C, from a is $d/2$ is in the interior of C_1, for its straight distance from a is

$$\leq d/2 \leq 3d/4.$$

Then the values

$$f(z_1), f'(z_1), ..., f^n(z_1), ...$$

of $f(z)$ and of its different derivatives at z_1, are obtained from the series (1) and those obtained on differentiating the same successively.

Consider now the series

$$f(z) = f(z_1) + (z - z_1) f'(z_1) + ... + \frac{(z - z_1)^n}{n!} f^n(z_1) + ... \qquad ...(2)$$

whose radius of convergence is $\geq 3d/4$. Then the point z_2 on C with distance $d/2$ from z_1 measured along C, lies in the interior of the circle of convergence of (2) and as such we can find the values of the function and of its different derivatives at z_2 from (2) and its different derived series.

Proceeding in this manner, we shall, after a finite number of steps, arrive at a power series such that ξ is an interior point of the circle of convergence of the same.

If l is the length of C and, p is a positive integer such that

$$\frac{pd}{2} > l \text{ and } \frac{(p - 1)d}{2} < l,$$

then ξ lies in the interior of the circle with z_{p-1} as its centre so that we shall require $(p-1)$ points

$$z_1, z_2, ..., z_{p-1}$$

to reach ξ.

Hence the result.

Note. It is clear that the values

$$f(a), f'(a), ..., f^n(a), ...$$

depend only on the values of $f(z)$ in a neighbourhood of a.

Cor. As a particular case of the above, we deduce that if $f(z)$ is analytic in a domain D and is identically zero in a certain neighbourhood of some point of D, then $f(z)$ is zero for every point z of D.

9.10.2. Isolated character of the zeros of an analytic function. We shall now prove that *an analytic function which is not identically zero can have only isolated zeros.*

This means that if $f(z)$ is analytic in a domain and is not identically zero, and if a is a zero of $f(z)$, *i.e.,* $f(a) = 0$, then there exists a deleted neighbourhood of a for no point z of which $f(z)$ is zero.

By Taylor's Theorem, we have for a certain neighbourhood of a,

$$f(z) = f(a) + (z-a) f'(a) + ... + \frac{(z-a)^n}{n!} f^n(a) \qquad ...(1)$$

We have $f(a) = 0$.

In case

$$f(a), f'(a), ..., f^n(a), ...$$

are all zero, then we have

$$f(z) = 0,$$

in a certain neighbourhood of a and as such, by the preceding corollary, $f(z)$ is identically zero in D.

Now suppose that the coefficients are not all zero and the first non-zero coefficient is $f^m(a)$. We then obtain, from (1),

$$f(z) = (z-a)^m \left[\frac{f^m(a)}{m!} + (z-a) \frac{f^{m+1}(a)}{(m+1)!} + ... \right]$$

$$= (z-a)^m \, \varphi(z) \qquad ...(2)$$

Here $\varphi(a) \neq 0$. Also, $\varphi(z)$ is continuous at a. Then there exists a neighbourhood of a for no point z of which $\varphi(z)$ is zero. From (2) we now deduce that for every point $z \neq a$, of this neighbourhood, we have $f(z) \neq 0$.

Hence the result.

Cor. *If $f(z)$ and $g(z)$ are analytic in a domain D and are equal at a certain set of points which has a limiting point in D, then*

$$f(z) = g(z)$$

for every point z of D.

This follows on applying the result of the preceding sub-section to the function

$$f(z) - g(z).$$

9.11 Cauchy's Inequality: *If $f(z)$ is analytic within a circle C, given by $|z-a| = R$ and if $|f(a)| \leq M$ on C, then*

$$|f^n(a)| \leq \frac{Mn}{R^n}$$

We know that

$$f^n(a) = \frac{n!}{2\pi i} \int_C \frac{f(z)\, dz}{(z-a)^{n+1}}$$

Taking mod on both sides

$$|f^n(a)| = \left| \frac{n!}{2\pi i} \int_C \frac{f(z)\,dz}{(z-a)^{n+1}} \right|$$

$$\leq \frac{n!}{|2\pi i|} \int_C \frac{|f(z)|\,|dz|}{|z-a|^{n+1}}$$

$$\leq \frac{n!}{2\pi} \cdot \frac{M}{R^{n+1}} \int_0^{2\pi} R\,d\theta$$

Since $z = \mathrm{Re}^{i\theta}$, $|dz| = |i\,\mathrm{Re}^{i\theta}\,d\theta|$

$$= R\,d\theta \text{ as } |e^{i\theta}| = 1$$

$$\leq \frac{n!}{2\pi} \cdot \frac{M}{R^{n+1}} \cdot 2\pi R$$

$$\leq \frac{M.n!}{R^n}$$

9.12. Laurent Series. We shall now obtain a theorem associated with the name of *Laurent* (1841 – 1908). A series of the form

$$\sum_{n=-\infty}^{\infty} a_n\,(z-a)^n \qquad\qquad\qquad ...(1)$$

is called a *Laurent Series*. It is a sum of two series of the type

$$a_0 + a_1\,(z-a) + a_2\,(z-a)^2 + \,..... \qquad\qquad ...(2)$$

$$a_{-1}\,(z-a)^{-1} + a_{-2}\,(z-a)^{-2} + \,..... \qquad\qquad ...(3)$$

which respectively consist of the sums of the positive and negative powers of $(z-a)$.

As proved in § 6.11, the domains of convergence of these two series are of the form

$$|z-a| < R$$

$$|(z-a)^{-1}| < \rho^{-1} \;\Rightarrow\; |z-a| > \rho$$

where R and ρ are two suitably determined non-negative numbers.

Thus if $\rho < R$, we see that the domain of convergence of the Laurent series (1) is the doubly-connected domain

$$\rho < |z-a| < R$$

which may be called a *circular ring*.

If now $f(z)$ and $F(z)$ be the sums of the two series (2) and (3), then, as proved in § 6.10, these functions are respectively analytic in the domains

$$|z-a| < R \text{ and } |z-a| > \rho.$$

Thus we see *that the sum of the Laurent series* (1) *is* $f(z) + F(z)$ *which is an analytic function in the domain*

$$\rho < |z-a| < R.$$

In the following, we shall prove the converse of the result stated above.

Theorem. *Every function* $f(z)$ *analytic in the doubly-connected domain D defined by*

$$\rho < |z-a| < R$$

which is a circular ring with centre 'a' is expressible as a Laurent's series so that there exists a relation of the form

$$f(z) = \sum_{n=-\infty}^{\infty} a_n (z-a)^n.$$

(Kumaon 2003; Garhwal 2005; Merut 2000; Mumbay 2001; Ravishankar 2001)

Let z be any point of D. We draw any two positively oriented circles C_1, C_2 with radii ρ_1, ρ_2 such that

$$\rho < \rho_1 < |z-a| < \rho_2 < R.$$

Then the domain bounded by the circles C_1, C_2 lies in D and encloses the point z.

By Cauchy's integral formula for doubly-connected domains, we have

$$f(z) = \frac{1}{2\pi i} \int_{C_2} \frac{f(\xi)}{\xi-z} d\xi + \frac{1}{2\pi i} \int_{-C_1} \frac{f(\xi)}{\xi-z} d\xi$$

$$= \frac{1}{2\pi i} \int_{C_2} \frac{f(\xi)}{\xi-z} - \frac{1}{2\pi i} \int_{C_1} \frac{f(\xi)}{\xi-z} d\xi \quad ...(1)$$

For $\xi \in C_2$, we write

$$\frac{1}{\xi-z} = \frac{1}{(\xi-a)-(z-a)}$$

$$= \frac{1}{(\xi-a)\left[1-\dfrac{z-a}{\xi-a}\right]}$$

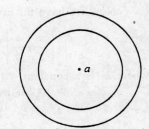

Fig. 9.17

$$= \frac{1}{(\xi-a)}\left[1+\frac{z-a}{\xi-a}+\left(\frac{z-a}{\xi-a}\right)^2\right.$$

$$+ ..... +\left(\frac{z-a}{\xi-a}\right)^{n-1} + \left.\left(\frac{z-a}{\xi-a}\right)^n \cdot \frac{1}{1-\dfrac{z-a}{\xi-a}}\right]$$

$$= \frac{1}{\xi-a} + \frac{z-a}{(\xi-a)^2} + ... + \frac{(z-a)^{n-1}}{(\xi-a)^n} + \left(\frac{z-a}{\xi-a}\right)^n \cdot \frac{1}{\xi-z}$$

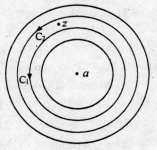

Fig. 9.18   ...(2)

Also for $\xi \in C_1$, we write

$$\frac{1}{\xi-z} = \frac{1}{(\xi-a)-(z-a)} = -\frac{1}{(z-a)}\frac{1}{1-\dfrac{\xi-a}{z-a}}$$

$$= -\frac{1}{(z-a)}\left[1+\frac{\xi-a}{z-a}+\left(\frac{\xi-a}{z-a}\right)^2 + ... + \left(\frac{\xi-a}{z-a}\right)^{n-1}\right.$$

$$\left. + \left(\frac{\xi-a}{z-a}\right)^n \frac{1}{1-\dfrac{\xi-a}{z-a}}\right]$$

$$= -\left[\frac{1}{z-a} + \frac{\xi-a}{(z-a)^2} + \ldots + \frac{(\xi-a)^{n-1}}{(z-a)^n} + \left(\frac{\xi-a}{z-a}\right)^n \cdot \frac{1}{z-\xi}\right] \qquad \ldots(3)$$

We write

$$\frac{1}{2\pi i}\int_{C_2} \frac{f(\xi)}{(\xi-a)^n}\,d\xi = a_{n-1}, \text{ where } n = 1, 2, \ldots$$

and obtain from (2),

$$\frac{1}{2\pi i}\int_{C_2} \frac{f(\xi)}{\xi-z}\,d\xi = a_0 + a_1(z-a) + a_2(z-a)^2 + \ldots + a_{n-1}(z-a)^{n-1}$$

$$+ \frac{1}{2\pi i}\int_{C_2}\left(\frac{z-a}{\xi-z}\right)^n \frac{f(\xi)}{\xi-z}\,d\xi.$$

Now we have for every point $\xi \in C_2$,

$$\left|\frac{z-a}{\xi-a}\right| = k_2, \text{ say}$$

where k_2 is a constant < 1 and

$$|\xi - z| = |(\xi-a) - (z-a)|$$

$$\geq |\xi-a| - |z-a| = \rho_2 - |z-a|.$$

Also let M_2 be a number such that

$$|f(\xi)| \leq M_2 \ \forall \ \xi \in C_3.$$

Thus we have

$$\left|\frac{1}{2\pi i}\int_{C_2}\left(\frac{z-a}{\xi-a}\right)^n \frac{f(\xi)}{\xi-z}\,d\xi\right| \leq \frac{1}{2\pi}k_2^n \frac{M_2}{\rho_2 - |z-a|}2\pi\rho_2.$$

Also since $k_2^n \to 0$ as $n \to \infty$, we see that

$$\frac{1}{2\pi i}\int_{C_2} \frac{f(\xi)}{\xi-z}\,d\xi = a_0 + a_1(z-a) + \ldots + a_n(z-a)^n + \ldots \qquad \ldots(4)$$

Again, writing

$$\frac{1}{2\pi i}\int_{C_1}(\xi-a)^n f(\xi)\,d\xi = a_{-(n+1)}, \text{ where } n = 0, 1, 2, \ldots$$

We obtain from (3)

$$\frac{1}{2\pi i}\int_{C_1} \frac{f(\xi)}{\xi-z}\,d\xi = -\left[a_{-1}(z-a)^{-1} + a_{-2}(z-a)^{-2} + \ldots + a_{-n}(z-a)^{-n}\right.$$

$$\left. + \frac{1}{2\pi i}\int_{C_1}\left(\frac{\xi-a}{z-a}\right)^n \cdot \frac{f(\xi)}{z-\xi}\,d\xi\right]$$

For every point $\xi \in C_1$, we write

$$\left|\frac{\xi-a}{z-a}\right| = k_1$$

where k_1 is a constant < 1, and
$$|z - \xi| = |(z - a) - (\xi - a)|$$
$$\geq |z - a| - |\xi - a| = |z - a| - \rho_1.$$

Also let M_1 be a number such that
$$|f(\xi)| \leq M_1 \ \forall \ \xi \in C_1.$$

Thus we have
$$\left| \frac{1}{2\pi i} \int_{C_1} \left(\frac{\xi - a}{z - a} \right)^n \frac{f(\xi)}{z - a} d\xi \right| \leq \frac{1}{2\pi} k_1^n \frac{M_1}{|z - a| - \rho_1} \cdot 2\pi \rho_1.$$

Also since $k_1^n \to 0$ as $n \to \infty$, we see that
$$\frac{1}{2\pi i} \int_{C_1} \frac{f(\xi)}{\xi - z} d\xi = -[a_{-1}(z - a)^{-1} + a_{-2}(z - a)^{-2}$$
$$+ ... + ... + a_{-n}(z - a)^{-n} + ...] \qquad ...(5)$$

From (1), (4) and (5), we obtain
$$f(z) = a_0 + a_1(z - a) + ... + a_n(z - a)^n$$
$$+ ... + a_{-1}(z - a)^{-1} + a_{-2}(z - a)^{-2} + ...$$

where
$$a_{n-1} = \frac{1}{2\pi i} \int_{C_2} \frac{f(\xi)}{(\xi - a)} d\xi, \qquad n = 1, 2, ...$$

$$a_{-(n+1)} = \frac{1}{2\pi i} \int_{C_1} (\xi - a)^n f(\xi) d\xi . \qquad n = 0, 1, 2, ...$$

As $f(\xi)/(\xi - a)^n$ and $(\xi - a)^n f(\xi)$ are both analytic in the doubly-connected domain D, we see that every circle C in this domain, with its centre at a, we have
$$a_{n-1} = \frac{1}{2\pi i} \int_C \frac{f(\xi)}{(\xi - a)^n} d\xi, \qquad n = 1, 2, ...$$

$$a_{-(n+1)} = \frac{1}{2\pi i} \int_C (\xi - a)^n f(\xi) d\xi \qquad n = 0, 1, 2, ...$$

These two separate results can be put in a uniform form as follows:
$$a_n = \frac{1}{2\pi i} \int_C \frac{f(\xi)}{(\xi - a)^{n+1}} d\xi,$$

when n is any integer; positive, negative or zero.

Thus we have proved that every function $f(z)$ analytic in a doubly-connected domain
$$\rho < |z - a| < R$$

is expressible as
$$f(z) = \sum_{n = -\infty}^{\infty} a_n (z - a)^n,$$

where
$$a_n = \frac{1}{2\pi i} \int \frac{f(\xi)}{(\xi - a)^{n+1}} d\xi,$$

and C is any circle in D with its centre at a.

9.12.1. Uniqueness of Laurent's expansion. *Suppose that we have obtained in any manner or as the definition of $f(z)$ the formula,*

$$f(z) = \sum_{m=-\infty}^{\infty} A_m (z-a)^m, \text{ integration } R_2 < |z-a| \nless R_1$$

Then the series is necessarily identical with the Laurent's series for $f(z)$ in the region.

(Agra, 2000, 2004)

Proof. If z is a point in the annulus between two concentric circles of radii R_1, R_2 ($R_2 < R_1$) with centre at $z = a$, then Laurent's series is

$$f(z) = \sum_{m=-\infty}^{\infty} a_n (z-a)^n,$$

where

$$a_n = \frac{1}{2\pi i} \int_C \frac{f(z)}{(z-a)^{n+1}} dz, \text{ where } |z-a| = r, (R_2 < r < R_1)$$

$$= \frac{1}{2\pi i} \int_C \sum_{m=-\infty}^{\infty} \frac{A_m (z-a)^m}{(z-a)^{n+1}} dz$$

$$= \frac{1}{2\pi i} \int_C \sum_{m=-\infty}^{\infty} A_m (z-a)^{m-n-1} dz$$

$$= \frac{1}{2\pi} \sum_{m=-\infty}^{\infty} A_m \int_C (z-a)^{m-n-1} dz$$

(sigma and integral are interchanged because term by term integration is possible since the series is uniformly convergent.)

$$= \frac{1}{2\pi i} \sum_{m=-\infty}^{\infty} A_m \int_0^{2\pi} [r^{m-n-1} \cdot e^{i(m-n-1)\theta}] \cdot rie^{i\theta} d\theta$$

$$[\because \quad z - a = re^{i\theta}]$$

$$= \frac{1}{2\pi} \sum_{m=-\infty}^{\infty} A_m r^{m-n} \int_0^{2\pi} e^{i(m-n)\theta} d\theta$$

$$= \frac{1}{2\pi} \sum_{m=-\infty}^{\infty} A_m r^{m-n} \cdot 0 \text{ when } m \neq n$$

$$= 0 \qquad\qquad \text{[Because then all integrals vanish.]}$$

and

$$= \frac{1}{2\pi} A_n \int_0^{2\pi} d\theta \quad \text{when } m = n$$

$$= \frac{1}{2\pi} A_n \cdot 2\pi = A_n.$$

Hence the given series is identical with the Laurent's series.

9.13. Logarithmic and Binomial Series. As an application of Taylor's Theorem, we shall find power series expansions of

$$\log (1 + z), (1 + z)^n$$

around the origin.

9.13.1. log $(1 + z)$. Now $z = -1$ where for $1 + z = 0$ is the branch point of $\log (1 + z)$. Also for every $z \neq -1$, $\log (1 + z)$ is analytic. Thus we can expand each branch of $\log (1 + z)$ about $z = 0$ and the expansion would be valid for $|z| < 1$.

For $z = 0$, we have

$$\log (1 + z) = \log 1 = 2mi\pi;$$

m being zero or any integer.

We select the principal branch for expansion defined by

$\log 1 = 0$.

We write

$$f(z) = \log (1 + z).$$

Then

$$f^n (z) = \frac{(-1)^{n-1} (n-1)!}{(1+z)^n}$$

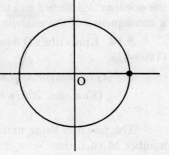

Fig. 9.19

so that $f(0) = 0$ and $f^n (0) = (-1)^{n-1} (n-1)!$

Substituting in

$$f(z) = f(0) + z \, f'(0) + \ldots + z^n \, \frac{f^n (0)}{n!} + \ldots$$

we obtain

$$\log (1 + z) = z - \frac{z^2}{2} + \frac{z^3}{3} + \ldots + (-1)^{n-1} \frac{z^n}{n} + \ldots$$

By Cor. 1, § 9.8 or directly, we may see that the radius of convergence of this series is 1.

9.13.2. $(1 + z)^\alpha$. Here also $z = -1$ is the branch point of the function and each branch of the function is analytic for every $z \neq -1$.

We can thus have a power series expansion for each branch of the function about $z = 0$ valid for $|z| < 1$.

Writing $f(z) = (1 + z)^\alpha$

we have

$$f(0) = 1^\alpha = E(\alpha \log 1) = E(2\alpha im\pi);$$

m being any integer or 0.

We select the principal branch for expansion. This is specified by defining

$$f(0) = 1^\alpha = 1.$$

Now

$$f^n (z) = \alpha (\alpha - 1) \ldots (\alpha - n + 1) \cdot \frac{(1+z)^\alpha}{(1+z)^n}.$$

Thus for the principal branch,

$$f^n (0) = \alpha (\alpha - 1) \ldots (\alpha - n + 1).$$

Making substitutions in the Taylor's formula, we obtain the power series expansion

$$(1 + z)^\alpha = 1 + \alpha z + \frac{\alpha (\alpha - 1)}{2!} z^2 + \ldots + \frac{\alpha (\alpha - 1) \ldots (\alpha - n + 1)}{n!} z^n + \ldots$$

valid for $|z| < 1$.

Note. The reader would recall that for the derivation of the Logarithmic and Binomial Series in Real Variables from Taylor's formula, it was a necessary part of the process to show that the remainder after n terms would tend to zero with n tending to infinity. In the present case, however, the position is different and simpler inasmuch as the fact of the remainder tending to zero is just a consequence of the analytic character of the functions.

9.14. Liouville's Theorem. We shall now consider a result established by *Liouville* (1809-82).

If $f(z)$ is analytic and **uniformly** *bounded in every domain, then $f(z)$ is constant.*

(Kumaon, 2001; Kanpur 1999, 2003; Poorvanchal, 1995, 97, Kerala 1999; 2001; Garhwal 2001, 2006)

The function being uniformly bounded in every domain means that there exists a positive number M such that

$$|f(z)| \le M \ \forall \ z.$$

Let D be any domain defined by

$$|z| \le R;$$

R being any positive number, however, large.

Then by Cor. 3, § 9.5.1, we have

$$|f^n(0)| \le \frac{n! M}{2\pi R^{n+1}} \cdot 2\pi R = \frac{n! M}{R^n}.$$

This inequality holds for every R, however large it may be. Letting R tend to infinity, we obtain

$$f^n(0) = 0,$$

for every n.

Again, by Taylor's theorem, we have for every z,

$$f(z) = f(z) + z \, f'(0) + \ldots\ldots + \frac{z^n}{n!} f^n(0) + \ldots\ldots.$$

$$= f(0).$$

Thus $f(z)$ is constant.

9.15. Fundamental Theorem of Algebra.

Theorem. *Every polynomial of degree ≥ 1 has at least one zero.*

(Rajsthan 2001, Kanpur 2004)

By a zero of a function is meant a number where for the value of the function is zero.

Let

$$f(z) = a_n z^n + a_{n-1} z^{n-1} + \ldots\ldots + a_2 z^2 + a_1 z + a_0, \ a_n \ne 0$$

be any polynomial.

Let, if possible, $f(z)$ have no zero *i.e.*, let

$$f(z) \ne 0 \ \forall \ z \in C.$$

Then

$$1/f(z)$$

is analytic in every domain.

Now, we have

$$\frac{1}{f(z)} = \frac{1}{z^n} \frac{1}{a_n + \dfrac{a_{n-1}}{z} + \ldots + \dfrac{a_0}{z^n}} \to 0 \text{ as } z \to \infty$$

Thus to every $\varepsilon > 0$, there corresponds an $R > 0$ such that

$$| 1 / f(z) | < \varepsilon, \text{ for } | z | > R.$$

Also $1 / f(z)$ is continuous in the bounded closed domain $| z | \leq R$ and as such it is bounded therein and accordingly there exists a number M such that

$$| 1 / f(z) | < M \text{ for } | z | \leq R.$$

Thus we see that

$$| 1 / f(z) | < \max. (M, \varepsilon) \text{ for every } z.$$

Hence by Liouville's Theorem $1 / f(z)$ is constant so that we arrive at an absurd conclusion. Thus our assumption is wrong and the polynomial $f(z)$ must have a zero.

Cor. *Every polynomial $f(z)$ of degree ≥ 1 assumes every value at least once.* This result is equivalent to the statement that the polynomial

$$f(z) - c$$

must have at least one zero; c being any number whatsoever.

9.16. Theorem of the Arithmetic Mean. An immediate and interesting consequence of the Cauchy's Integral formula is the following theorem known as the *Theorem of the Arithmetic Mean*.

Theorem. *If $f(z)$ is analytic in a circular domain with centre z and is continuous on the boundary, then the value of the function at the centre z is equal to the mean of the values of the function on the circumference.*

The theorem states that if s denotes the arc length of the circle, then, we have

$$f(z) = \frac{\int_C f(\xi)\, ds}{l}$$

where l is the length of the circle and $P(\xi)$ is any point on the circle. Let ρ be the radius of this circle.

By Cauchy's integral formula,

$$f(z) = \frac{1}{2\pi i} \int_C \frac{f(\xi)}{\xi - z}\, d\xi.$$

We have, for any point ξ on the circle,

$$\xi - z = \rho e^{i\theta}$$

$$\therefore \qquad d\xi = \rho i e^{i\theta}\, d\theta$$

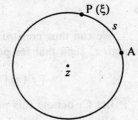

Fig. 9.20

$$\therefore \qquad f(z) = \frac{1}{2\pi i} \int_0^{2\pi} \frac{f(z + \rho e^{i\theta})}{\rho e^{i\theta}} \rho i e^{i\theta}\, d\theta$$

$$= \frac{1}{2\pi} \int_0^{2\pi} f(z + \rho e^{i\theta})\, d\theta.$$

Also we have

$$s = \rho \theta$$

where s varies from 0 to l.

Thus

$$f(z) = \frac{1}{2\pi} \int_0^1 f(z + \rho e^{i\theta}) \frac{ds}{\rho}$$

$$= \frac{\int_0^1 f(\xi) \, ds}{2\pi\rho} = \frac{\int_0^1 f(\xi) \, ds}{l}.$$

9.17. Principle of Maximum Modulus. Let $f(z)$ be analytic in a domain D and continuous on the boundary of D. As $|f(z)|$ is continuous in the closed domain formed of D and its boundary the same must be bounded above and attain its upper bound at some point of the domain. We shall now show that *the maximum value M of $|f(z)|$ is attained at a point of the boundary.* It will further be shown *that if for some point z of the interior,*

$$|f(z)| = M$$

then the function is necessarily a constant in the entire domain.

(*Kanpur 1999, 2001, 2002; Garhwal 2006, 2007; Meerut 2005*)

Let, if possible, $|f(z)|$ attain the upper bound M at a point a of the interior so that we have $|f(a)| = M.$

Let D' be a circular domain with centre a such that D' along with its boundary circle is contained in D. Then D' is a neighbourhood of a.

Then either, $|f(z)| = M$ at every point z of D' or there exists some point z_0 of D' such that $|f(z_0)| \neq M$ so that

$$|f(z_0)| = M - \varepsilon,$$

where ε is some positive number.

By virtue of the continuity of $|f(z)|$ at z_0, there exists a neighbourhood of z_0 for every point z of which

$$||f(z)| - |f(z_0)|| < \frac{1}{2} \varepsilon.$$

$$\Rightarrow \qquad |f(z)| < |f(z_0)| + \frac{1}{2} \varepsilon = M - \frac{1}{2} \varepsilon.$$

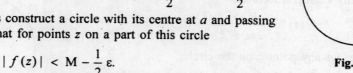

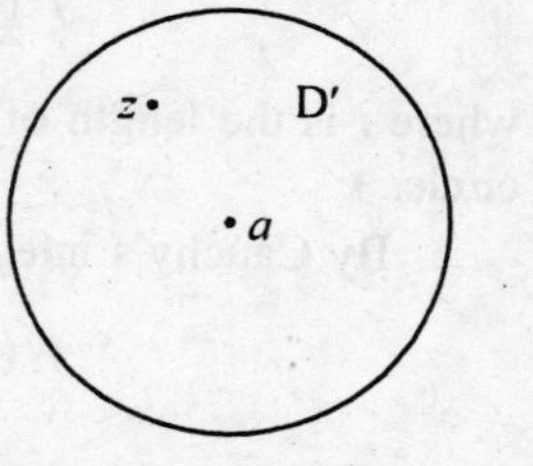

We can thus construct a circle with its centre at a and passing through z_0 such that for points z on a part of this circle

$$|f(z)| < M - \frac{1}{2} \varepsilon.$$

Fig. 9.21

Let C_1 denote this point and C_2 the remainder of this circle.

Now, by the theorem of the Arithmetic Mean, proved in the preceding section, we have

$$f(a) = \int_C \frac{f(z) \, ds}{l} = \frac{\int_{C_1} f(z) \, ds + \int_{C_2} f(z) \, ds}{l}$$

$$\Rightarrow \qquad |f(a)| \leq \frac{1}{l} \left\{ \left(M - \frac{1}{2}\varepsilon\right) l_1 + M l_2 \right\} = M - \frac{1}{2} \varepsilon \frac{l_1}{l},$$

where l_1 and l_2 are the lengths of the parts C_1 and C_2.

$$\Rightarrow \qquad M \leq M - \frac{1}{2} \varepsilon \frac{l_1}{l},$$

so that we arrive at a contradiction.

Thus $| f(z) | = M$ at every point z of the circular domain D' which is a neighbourhood of the point a.

It has thus been shown that if, a, is a point of D such that $| f(a) | = M$, then there exists a neighbourhood of a such that for every point z of the same, we have $| f(z) | = M$.

Thus the set D_1 of points z of D for which $| f(z) | = M$ is an open set.

Also we may easily see that the set D_2 of points z of D for which $f(z) | \neq M$ is an open set.

Then if D_2 is null, we see that $| f(z) | = M$ for every point of D and hence $f(z)$ is constant in D. If, however, D_2 is non-null, we have

$$D = D_1 \cup D_2, \qquad \qquad ...(1)$$

where D_1, D_2 are non-null, disjoint, open sets. As, however, D is a-connected set, such a decomposition as (1) is not possible and we arrive at a contradiction.

We have thus proved the theorem.

9.18. Minimum Modulus Principle. *If $f(z)$ is analytic within and on a closed contour C and $f(z) \neq 0$ inside C. Suppose further that $f(z)$ is not constant, then $| f(z) |$ attains its minimum value at a point on the boundary of C. In other words, if m is the minimum of $| f(z) |$ inside and on C then $| f(z) | > m \ \forall \ z$ inside C.*

$f(z)$ is analytic within and on C and $f(z) \neq 0$ inside C. Therefore $1 / f(z)$ is analytic within C. Hence by maximum modulus principle $1 / | f(z) |$ attains its maximum value on the boundary of C, so that $| f(z) |$ attains its minimum value on the boundary of C.

9.19. Schwarz's Lemma. *Let*

(i) $f(z)$ be analytic in a domain defined by $| z | < R$,

(ii) $| f(z) | \leq M \ \forall \ \varepsilon \in D$,

(iii) $f(0) = 0$.

Then $\forall \ z \in D$,

$$| f(z) | \leq M | z | / R.$$

Also if the equality occurs for any one z, then $f(z) = Mze^{i\alpha}/R$, where α is a real constant.

(Meerut 2003, 2004)

By Taylor's Theorem, we have

$$f(z) = a_0 + a_1 z + a_2 z^2 + a_3 z^3 + \ldots ,$$

where, by (i), the equality holds at least for $| z | < R$.

By (iii), $a_0 = f(0) = 0$.

Defining $f(z) / z$ to be equal to a_1 for $z = 0$, we see that

$$f(z) / z = a_1 + a_2 z + a_3 z^2 + \ldots$$

is analytic in the circular domain $| z | < R$.

Let, now, ξ be any point of this domain and let r be any positive number such that

$$| \xi | < r < R.$$

Consider now the closed circular domain

$$| z | \leq r$$

and apply the Maximum Modulus Principle to the same for the function $\phi (z) = f(z) / z$.

Thus we have

$$| \phi(\xi) | = \left| \frac{f(\xi)}{\xi} \right| \leq \frac{\max.}{| z | = r} \left| \frac{f(z)}{z} \right| \leq \frac{M}{r}.$$

Thus for every ξ such that $|\xi| \leq r$, we have

$$|f(\xi)| \leq \frac{M}{r}|\xi|.$$

As this inequality holds for every $r < R$ and the left-hand side is independent of r, we have on making $r \to R$.

$$|f(z)| \leq \frac{M|\xi|}{R}$$

$$\Rightarrow \qquad |f(z)| \leq \frac{M|z|}{R} \quad \forall \ z \in |z| < R.$$

Suppose now that we have equality for one z. Then we have equality for every z i.e., we have

$$\left|\frac{f(z)}{z}\right| = \frac{M}{R}$$

$$\Rightarrow \qquad \frac{f(z)}{z} = \frac{M}{R}e^{i\alpha} \quad \Rightarrow \quad f(z) = \frac{M}{R}e^{i\alpha}z.$$

EXAMPLES

1. *If C is a closed contour around the origin, prove that*

$$\left(\frac{a^n}{n!}\right) = \frac{1}{2\pi i}\int_C \frac{a^n e^{az}\,dz}{n!\,z^{n+1}}.$$

Hence deduce that

$$\sum_{n=0}^{\infty}\left(\frac{a^n}{n!}\right)^2 \equiv \frac{1}{2\pi}\int_0^{2\pi} e^{2a\cos\theta}\,d\theta.$$

(Garhwal 2001, I.A.S. 1998; Kumaon 2001)

Solution. Let $f(z) = e^{az} \Rightarrow f^n(z) = a^n e^{az}$.

Putting $z = 0$ in the above, we get

$$a^n = f^n(0) = \frac{1}{2\pi i}\cdot n!\int\frac{f(z)\,dz}{z^{n+1}} \qquad\qquad [\S\ 9.5.1 \text{ for } a = 0]$$

Multiplying both sides by $\dfrac{a^n}{(n!)^2}$, we get

$$\left(\frac{a^n}{n!}\right)^2 = \frac{1}{2\pi i}\int_C \frac{a^n e^{az}\,dz}{n!\,z^{n+1}}. \qquad\qquad [\because\ f(z) = e^{az}]$$

This proves the first part of the question.

$$\therefore \qquad \sum_{n=0}^{\infty}\left(\frac{a^n}{n!}\right)^2 = \sum_{n=0}^{\infty}\frac{1}{2\pi i}\cdot\frac{1}{n!}\int_C \frac{a^n e^{az}}{z^{n+1}}\,dz$$

$$= \frac{1}{2\pi i}\int_C \sum_{n=0}^{\infty}\frac{a^n e^{az}}{n!\,z^{n+1}}\,dz$$

$$= \frac{1}{2\pi i}\int_C e^{az}\left[\sum_{n=0}^{\infty}\left(\frac{a}{z}\right)^2\cdot\frac{1}{n!}\right]\frac{dz}{z}$$

$$= \frac{1}{2\pi i} \int_C e^{az} \cdot e^{a/z} \cdot \frac{dz}{z}$$

$$= \frac{1}{2\pi i} \int_C e^{a\,(z + 1/z)}\, \frac{dz}{z}.$$

Now choose C to be a circle of unit radius centred at origin *i.e.*, $|z| = 1$, so that $z = e^{i\theta}$ and $dz = ie^{i\theta}\, d\theta$.

Also

$$z + 1/z = e^{i\theta} + e^{-i\theta} = 2\cos\theta.$$

$$\therefore \quad \sum_{n=0}^{\infty} \left(\frac{a_n}{n!} \right)^2 = \frac{1}{2\pi} \int_0^{2\pi} e^{2a\cos\theta} \cdot \frac{ie^{i\theta}\, d\theta}{e^{i\theta}}$$

$$= \frac{1}{2\pi} \int_0^{2\pi} e^{2a\cos\theta}\, d\theta.$$

2. *Determine a function which shall be regular within the circle $|z| = 1$ and shall have on the circumference of this circle the value*

$$\frac{(a^2 - 1)\cos\theta + i\,(a^2 + 1)\sin\theta}{a^4 - 2a^2 \cos 2\theta + 1}$$

where $a^2 > 1$ and θ is the vectorial angle at points on the circumference.

Solution. Since $f(z)$ is analytic inside the circle $|z| = 1$, therefore it can be expanded at any point z inside it by Maclaurin's series.

$$\therefore \qquad f(z) = \sum_{n=0}^{\infty} a_n z^n$$

where

$$a_n = \frac{f^n(0)}{n!} = \frac{1}{n!} \cdot \frac{n!}{2\pi i} \int_C \frac{f(z)\, dz}{(z - 0)^{n+1}}$$

$$\Rightarrow \qquad a_n = \frac{1}{2\pi i} \int_C \frac{f(z)\, dz}{z^{n+1}} \qquad\qquad \dots(1)$$

We are given that

$$f(z) = \frac{(a^2 - 1)\cos\theta + i\,(a^2 + 1)\sin\theta}{a^4 - 2a^2 \cos 2\theta + 1} \quad \text{on } |z| = 1$$

$$= \frac{a^2(\cos\theta + i\sin\theta) - (\cos\theta - i\sin\theta)}{a^4 - a^2\,(e^{2i\theta} + e^{-2i\theta}) + 1}$$

$$= \frac{a^2 e^{i\theta} - e^{-i\theta}}{a^4 - a^2 \left(z^2 + \dfrac{1}{z^2} \right) + 1}$$

$$= \frac{a^2 z - \dfrac{1}{z}}{(a^2 - z^2)\left(a^2 - \dfrac{1}{z^2} \right)} = \frac{z\left(a^2 - \dfrac{1}{z^2} \right)}{(a^2 - z^2)\left(a^2 - \dfrac{1}{z^2} \right)}$$

$$= \frac{a}{a^2 - z^2} \text{ on the circle C} \qquad\qquad ...(2)$$

$$\therefore \quad a_n = \frac{1}{2\pi i} \oint_C \frac{z}{a^2 - z^2} \cdot \frac{dz}{z^{n+1}} \qquad\qquad \text{[by (1) and (2)]}$$

$$= \frac{1}{2\pi i} \int_C \frac{dz}{(a^2 - z^2) z^n} = \frac{1}{2\pi i} \int_0^{2\pi} \frac{ie^{i\theta} \, d\theta}{(a^2 - e^{2i\theta}) \cdot e^{in\theta}}$$

$$= \frac{1}{2\pi a^2} \int_0^{2\pi} e^{-i(n-1)\theta} \left[1 - \frac{e^{2i\theta}}{a^2} \right]^{-1} d\theta$$

$$= \frac{1}{2\pi a^2} \int_0^{2\pi} e^{-i(n-1)\theta} \left[1 + \frac{e^{2i\theta}}{a^2} + \frac{e^{4i\theta}}{a^4} \right.$$

$$\left. + ... + \frac{e^{\{2i(n-1)\theta\}/2}}{a^{n-1}} + ... + ... \right] d\theta$$

$$= \frac{1}{2\pi a^2} \int_0^{2\pi} \frac{1}{a^{n-1}} \, d\theta, \text{ if } n \text{ is odd.}$$

$$= \frac{1}{2\pi a^2} \cdot \frac{2\pi}{a^{n-1}} = \frac{1}{a^{n+1}} \ (n \text{ odd})$$

All other integrals vanish being of the type $\int_0^{2\pi} e^{ip\theta} \, d\theta = 0, \ p \neq 0.$

$$\therefore \qquad a_n = \frac{1}{a^{n+1}}, \text{ when } n \text{ is odd.}$$

$$= 0, \text{ when } n \text{ is even because the integrals shall vanish.}$$

$$\therefore \qquad f(z) = \sum_{n=0}^{\infty} a_n z^n \quad (n \text{ odd})$$

$$= \sum_{n=0}^{\infty} \frac{1}{a^{n+1}} z^n = \sum_{n=0}^{\infty} \frac{1}{a} \cdot \left(\frac{z}{a} \right)^n$$

$$= \frac{1}{a} \left[\frac{z}{a} + \frac{z^3}{a^3} + \frac{z^5}{a^5} + ... \right], \text{ as } n \text{ is odd.}$$

$$= \frac{z}{a^2} \left[1 + \frac{z^2}{a^2} + \frac{z^4}{a^4} + ... \right] = \frac{z}{a^2} \left[1 - \frac{z^2}{a^2} \right]^{-1}$$

$$= \frac{z}{a^2} \cdot \frac{a^2}{a^2 - z^2} = \frac{z}{a^2 - z^2}.$$

3. *The function* $f(z)$ *is analytic when* $|z| < R$ *and has Taylor's expansion* $\sum\limits_{n=0}^{\infty} a_n z^n$. *Show that if*

$$r < R, \quad \frac{1}{2\pi} \int\limits_0^{2\pi} |f(re^{i\theta})|^2 \, d\theta = \sum\limits_{n=0}^{\infty} |a_n|^2 \, r^{2n}.$$

Hence prove that if $|f(z)| \le M$ *when* $|z| < R$

$$\sum\limits_{n=0}^{\infty} |a_n|^2 \, r^{2n} < M^2.$$ (*Magadh 2004*)

Solution. We are given that $f(z)$ is analytic within the circle $|z| = r \; (r < R)$, therefore $f(z)$ can be expanded in Taylor's series within the circle $|z| = r$, so that

$$f(z) = \sum\limits_{n=0}^{\infty} a_n z^n = \sum\limits_{n=0}^{\infty} a_n r^n e^{in\theta} \qquad\qquad [\because \; z = re^{i\theta}]$$

$$\therefore \qquad \overline{f(z)} = \sum\limits_{m=0}^{\infty} \bar{a}_m r^m e^{-im\theta}$$

$$\therefore \qquad |f(z)|^2 = f(z)\,\overline{f(z)}$$

$$= \left(\sum\limits_{n=0}^{\infty} a_n r^n e^{in\theta} \right)\left(\sum\limits_{m=0}^{\infty} \bar{a}_m r^m e^{-im\theta} \right)$$

$$\therefore \quad \int\limits_0^{2\pi} |f(z)|^2 \, d\theta = \sum\limits_{n=0}^{\infty} \sum\limits_{m=0}^{\infty} a_n \bar{a}_m r^{m+n} e^{i(n-m)\theta} \, d\theta$$

As shown earlier $\int\limits_0^{2\pi} e^{ip\theta} \, d\theta = 0$ if $p \ne 0$

$$= 2\pi \text{ if } p = 0, \text{ i.e., } n = m.$$

$$\therefore \quad \int\limits_0^{2\pi} f(z)|^2 \, d\theta = \sum\limits_{n=0}^{\infty} a_n \cdot \bar{a}_n r^{2n} \cdot 2\pi, \text{ when } n = m.$$

or $\quad \dfrac{1}{2\pi} \int\limits_0^{2\pi} |f(re^{i\theta})|^2 \, d\theta = \sum\limits_{n=0}^{\infty} |a_n|^2 \, r^{2n}$ ...(1)

Second Part. From result (1), we know that

$$\sum\limits_{n=0}^{\infty} |a_n|^2 \, r^{2n} = \frac{1}{2\pi} \int\limits_0^{2\pi} |f(z)|^2 \, d\theta$$

$$\le \frac{1}{2\pi} \int\limits_0^{2\pi} |f(z)|^2 \, d\theta, \text{ as } |f(z)| \le M.$$

$$= \frac{M^2}{2\pi} [\theta]_0^{2\pi} = M^2$$

$$\therefore \quad \sum_{n=0}^{\infty} |a_n|^2 r^{2n} \le M^2.$$

4. *If the function $f(z)$ is analytic and one-valued in $|z - a| < R$ prove that for $0 < r < R$*

$$f'(a) = \frac{1}{\pi r} \int_0^{2\pi} P(\theta) e^{-i\theta} d\theta$$

where $P(\theta)$ is the real part of $f(a + re^{i\theta})$.

Also prove that

$$\frac{f^n(a)}{n!} = \frac{1}{\pi r^n} \int_0^{2\pi} P(\theta) e^{-in\theta} d\theta. \qquad \text{(Sagar 2004)}$$

Solution. We are given that $f(z)$ is analytic in $|z - a| < R$ and as such it must be analytic within $|z - a| = r$ where $r < R$. Hence $f(z)$ can be expanded in Taylor's series within the circle $|z - a| = r$.

$$\therefore \qquad f(z) = \sum_{m=0}^{\infty} a_m (z - a)^m$$

$$= \sum_{m=0}^{\infty} a_m r^m e^{im\theta} \qquad [\because \quad z - a = re^{i\theta}]$$

$$\therefore \qquad \overline{f(z)} = \sum_{m=0}^{\infty} \bar{a}_m r^m e^{-im\theta}.$$

Let us now consider the integral

$$\int_C \frac{\overline{f(z)}}{(z - a)^{n+1}} dz = I \text{ (say)}$$

where C is the circle $|z - a| = r$ or $z = a + re^{i\theta}$.

$$\therefore \qquad I = \int_0^{2\pi} \sum_{m=0}^{\infty} \bar{a}_m \cdot r^m e^{-im\theta} \frac{re^{i\theta} i \, d\theta}{r^{n+1} e^{i(n+1)\theta}}$$

$$= \sum_{m=0}^{\infty} \bar{a}_m r^{m-n} i \int_0^{2\pi} e^{-i(m+n)\theta} d\theta = 0 \ \forall \ n$$

or

$$\int_C \frac{\overline{f(z)}}{(z - a)^{n+1}} dz = 0.$$

Also

$$\frac{1}{2\pi i} \int_C \frac{f(z)}{(z - a)^{n+1}} dz = \frac{f^n(a)}{n!}.$$

Adding the above two results, we get

$$\frac{1}{2\pi i} \int_C \frac{f(z) + \overline{f(z)}}{(z - a)^{n+1}} dz = \frac{f^n(a)}{n!}.$$

But $f(z) + \overline{f(z)} = 2$. Real part of $f(z) = 2\mathrm{Re} \, f(a + re^{i\theta}) = 2P(\theta)$, (given).

$$\therefore \qquad \frac{f^n(a)}{n!} = \frac{1}{2\pi i} \int_0^{2\pi} \frac{2 \cdot P(\theta)}{r^{n+1} e^{i(n+1)\theta}} \cdot r e^{i\theta} \cdot i \, d\theta$$

or

$$\frac{f^n(a)}{n!} = \frac{1}{\pi r^n} \int_0^{2\pi} P(\theta) e^{-in\theta} \, d\theta.$$

This proves the second part and putting $n = 1$ we get the first part.

5. *Prove that the function*

$$\sin\left[c\left(z + \frac{1}{z}\right)\right]$$

can be expanded in a series of the type

$$\sum_{n=1}^{\infty} a_n z^n + \sum_{n=1}^{\infty} b_n z^{-n},$$

in which the coefficients of both z^n and z^{-n} are

$$\frac{1}{2\pi} \int_0^{2\pi} \sin(2c \cos \theta) \cos n\theta \, d\theta.$$

(Garhwal 2000, 2003)

Solution. The function

$$f(z) = \sin\left[c\left(z + \frac{1}{z}\right)\right]$$

is analytic except at $z = 0$, therefore $f(z)$ is analytic in the annulus $r \le z \le R$ where r is small and R is large.

Hence by Laurent's Theorem

$$f(z) = \sin\left[c\left(z + \frac{1}{z}\right)\right] = \sum_{n=1}^{\infty} a_n z^n + \sum_{n=1}^{\infty} b_n z^{-n}$$

where

$$a_n = \frac{1}{2\pi i} \int_C \sin[c(z + z^{-1})] \frac{dz}{z^{n+1}}$$

and

$$b_n = \frac{1}{2\pi i} \int_C \sin[c(z + z^{-1})] z^{n-1} \, dz.$$

Now c being any circle centred at origin, we choose it to be of radius unity so that $|z| = 1$ or $z = e^{i\theta}$, $z^{-1} = e^{-i\theta}$, $z + z^{-1} = 2 \cos \theta$.

$$\therefore \qquad a_n = \frac{1}{2\pi i} \int_0^{2\pi} \sin(c \cdot 2 \cos \theta) \frac{i e^{i\theta} \, d\theta}{e^{i(n+1)\theta}}$$

$$= \frac{1}{2\pi} \int_0^{2\pi} e^{-in\theta} \sin(2c \cos \theta) \, d\theta$$

$$= \frac{1}{2\pi} \int_0^{2\pi} \sin(2c \cos \theta)(\cos n\theta - i \sin n\theta) \, d\theta$$

or
$$a_n = \frac{1}{2\pi} \int_0^{2\pi} \sin (2c \cos \theta) \cos n\theta \, d\theta + 0 \qquad \qquad ...(1)$$

$$\left[\because \int_0^{2\pi} F(\theta) \, d\theta = 0 \text{ if } F(2\pi - \theta) = -F(\theta) \right]$$

Hence a_n has the value as given.

From the values of a_n and b_n it is easy to observe that if we replace n by $-n$ in the value of a_n, we get the value of b_n.

$$\therefore \qquad b_n = a_{-n} = \frac{1}{2\pi} \int_0^{2\pi} \sin (2c \cos \theta) \cos (-n\theta) \, d\theta$$

$$= \frac{1}{2\pi} \int_0^{2\pi} \sin (2c \cos \theta) \cos n\theta \, d\theta = a_n.$$

6. *Prove that*
$$\cosh (z + 1/z) = a_0 + \sum_{n=1}^{\infty} a_n (z^n + 1/z^n)$$

where
$$a_n = \frac{1}{2\pi} \int_0^{2\pi} \cos n\theta \cosh (2 \cos \theta) \, d\theta.$$

(Kanpur 2004; Garhwal 2004; Gorakhpur 2003; Meerut 2005; Himachal 2004)

Solution. The given function $f(z) = \cosh (z + z^{-1})$ is analytic everywhere in the finite part of the z-plane except at $z = 0$. Therefore $f(z)$ is analytic in the annulus $r \le |z| \le R$ where r is small and R is large. Hence $f(z)$ can be expanded by Laurent's series.

$$\therefore \qquad f(z) = \cosh \left(z + \frac{1}{z} \right) = \sum_{n=0}^{\infty} a_n z^n + \sum_{n=1}^{\infty} b_n z^{-n} \qquad ...(1)$$

where
$$a_n = \frac{1}{2\pi i} \int_C \cosh \left(z + \frac{1}{z} \right) \frac{dz}{z^{n+1}}$$

and
$$b_n = \frac{1}{2\pi i} \int_C \cosh \left(z + \frac{1}{z} \right) z^{n-1} \, dz.$$

Now C being any circle centred at origin, we choose it to be of radius unity so that $|z| = 1$ or $z = e^{i\theta}$, $\frac{1}{z} = e^{-i\theta}$, $z + \frac{1}{z} = 2 \cos \theta$.

$$\therefore \qquad a_n = \frac{1}{2\pi i} \int_0^{2\pi} \cosh (2 \cos \theta) \frac{e^{i\theta} \cdot i \, d\theta}{e^{i(n+1)\theta}}$$

$$= \frac{1}{2\pi} \int_0^{2\pi} \cosh (2 \cos \theta) e^{-in\theta} \, d\theta$$

$$= \frac{1}{2\pi} \int_0^{2\pi} \cosh(2\cos\theta)(\cos n\theta - i\sin n\theta)\, d\theta$$

or
$$a_n = \frac{1}{2\pi} \int_0^{2\pi} \cosh(2\cos\theta)\cos n\theta\, d\theta \qquad \ldots(2)$$

$$\left[\because \int_0^{2\pi} F(\theta)\, d\theta = 0 \text{ if } F(2\pi - \theta) = -F(\theta). \right]$$

which is true for $F(\theta) = \cosh(2\cos\theta)\sin n\theta$.

Hence a_n has the value as given.

From the values of a_n and b_n it is easy to observe that if we replace n by $-n$ in the value of a_n, we get the value of b_n.

$$\therefore \qquad b_n = a_{-n} = \frac{1}{2\pi} \int_0^{2\pi} \cosh(2\cos\theta)\cos(-n\theta)\, d\theta$$

$$= \frac{1}{2\pi} \int_0^{2\pi} \cosh(2\cos\theta)\cos n\theta\, d\theta = a_n$$

$$\therefore \qquad \cosh(z + 1/z) = \sum_{n=0}^{\infty} a_n z^n + \sum_{n=1}^{\infty} a_n z^{-n}$$

$$= a_0 + \sum_{n=1}^{\infty} a_n(z^n + z^{-n})$$

where a_n has the value as given in (2).

7. *Prove that*

$$\exp\left\{ \frac{1}{2} c(z - z^{-1}) \right\} = \sum_{n=-\infty}^{\infty} a_n z^n, \text{ when } z \neq 0,$$

where

$$a_n = \frac{1}{2\pi} \int_0^{2\pi} \cos(n\theta - c\sin\theta)\, d\theta.$$

(Meerut 2000, 2002, 2004; Rohilkhand, 1993, 95; Lucknow, 1992, 94; Gorakhpur, 2004)

Solution. Now 0 is the only finite singular point *i.e.*, a point where the function is not analytic of the function

$$\exp\left[\frac{1}{2} c(z - z^{-1}) \right]$$

so that we can expand it as a Laurent's series valid for every value of $z \neq 0$, *i.e.*, for $|z| > 0$.

Thus we have, for $|z| \neq 0$,

$$\exp\left\{ \frac{1}{2} c(z - z^{-1}) \right\} = \sum_{n=-\infty}^{\infty} a_n z^n,$$

when $a_n = \dfrac{1}{2\pi i} \displaystyle\int_C \dfrac{f(z)}{z^{n+1}}\, dz$, where C is any circle with its centre at the origin.

Taking C as the circle with radius unity, we have

$$a_n = \frac{1}{2\pi i} \int_C \frac{e^{c(z+z^{-1})/2}}{z^{n+1}} \, dz.$$

Putting $z = e^{i\theta}$, we obtain

$$a_n = \frac{1}{2\pi i} \int_0^{2\pi} \frac{e^{c(e^{i\theta} - e^{-i\theta})/2}}{e^{i(n+1)\theta}} \, ie^{i\theta} \, d\theta$$

$$= \frac{1}{2\pi} \int_0^{2\pi} e^{ic \sin \theta} \, e^{-in\theta} \, d\theta$$

$$= \frac{1}{2\pi} \int_0^{2\pi} \cos (c \sin \theta - n\theta) \, d\theta + \frac{1}{2\pi} \int_0^{2\pi} \sin (c \sin \theta - n\theta) \, d\theta.$$

Taking $\theta = 2\pi - \varphi$, we have

$$\int_0^{2\pi} \sin (c \sin \theta - n\theta) \, d\theta = - \int_{2\pi}^0 \sin [- c \sin \varphi - 2n\pi + n\varphi] \, d\varphi$$

$$= - \int_0^{2\pi} \sin (c \sin \theta - n\theta) \, d\theta$$

$$\int_0^{2\pi} \sin (c \sin \theta - n\theta) \, d\theta = 0.$$

$\Rightarrow$

Hence the result.

8. *Prove that near $z = 1$, the function*

$$log (1 + z^2)$$

may be expanded in a series of the form

$$log \, 2 + \sum_{n=1}^{\infty} a_n (z - 1)^n,$$

and find the value of a_n; the principal value of the logarithms being taken.

Obtain also the radius of convergence of the series.

Solution. The zeros of $1 + z^2$, i.e., $\pm i$ are the two branch points of

$$f(z) = log (1 + z^2).$$

Thus in the circular domain with its centre at 1 and radius equal to the distance $\sqrt{2}$ of 1 from i or $- i$, the function

$$log (1 + z^2)$$

can be thought of as single valued and analytic; particular branch being defined by assigning a value to the function for any z in the domain. The particular branch referred to in the question is given as the principal value, *i.e.*, the one which is assigned the real value log 2 for $z = 1$.

Thus for

$$|z - 1| < \sqrt{2},$$

we have

$$\log (1 + z^2) f(z) = f(1) + (z - 1) f'(1) + \ldots + \frac{(z - 1)^n}{n!} f^n(1) + \ldots$$

Now
$$f(z) = \log (1 + z^2)$$

$$\Rightarrow \qquad f'(z) = \frac{1}{1 + z^2} = \frac{1}{z - i} + \frac{1}{z + i}$$

$$\Rightarrow \qquad f^n(z) = (-1)^{n-1} (n - 1)! \left[\frac{1}{(z - i)^n} + \frac{1}{(z + i)^n} \right]$$

$$\Rightarrow \qquad f^n(1) = (-1)^{n-1} (n - 1)! \left[\frac{1}{(1 - i)^n} + \frac{1}{(1 + i)^n} \right]$$

Again, we have

$$(1 - i)^{-n} + (1 + i)^{-n} = (\sqrt{2})^{-n} \left[\frac{1}{\sqrt{2}} - \frac{i}{\sqrt{2}} \right]^{-n} + (\sqrt{2})^{-n} \left[\frac{1}{\sqrt{2}} + \frac{i}{\sqrt{2}} \right]^{-n}$$

$$= (\sqrt{2})^{-n} \left(\cos \frac{\pi}{4} - i \sin \frac{\pi}{4} \right)^{-n} + (\sqrt{2})^{-n} \left(\cos \frac{\pi}{4} + i \sin \frac{\pi}{4} \right)^{-n}$$

$$= 2 (\sqrt{2})^{-n} \cos \frac{n\pi}{4}.$$

Thus

$$f^n(1) = 2 (-1)^{n-2} (n - 1)! (\sqrt{2})^{-n} \cos \frac{n\pi}{4}.$$

Hence

$$\log (1 + z^2) = \log 2 + \sum_{n=1}^{\infty} a_n (z - 1)^n,$$

where
$$a_n = \frac{2 (-1)^{n-1}}{n} (\sqrt{2})^{-n} \cos \frac{n\pi}{4}.$$

The radius of convergence of the series is $\sqrt{2}$.

9. *Expand*

$$\frac{1}{z (z^2 - 3z + 2)}$$

for

(i) $0 < |z| < 1$, (ii) $1 < |z| < 2$, (iii) $|z| > 2$.

Solution. We have

$$f(z) = \frac{1}{z (z^2 - 3z + 2)} = \frac{1}{z (z - 1) (z - 2)}$$

$$= \frac{1}{2z} - \frac{1}{z - 1} + \frac{1}{2 (z - 2)} \qquad \ldots(1)$$

For $|z| < 1$, we have

$$\frac{1}{z-1} = -(1-z)^{-1}$$

$$= -(1 + z + z^2 + \dots + \dots) \qquad \dots(2)$$

For $\qquad |z| > 1$, we have

$$\frac{1}{z-1} = \frac{1}{z\left(1 - \frac{1}{z}\right)} = \frac{1}{z}\left(1 - \frac{1}{z}\right)^{-1}$$

$$= \frac{1}{z}\left(1 + \frac{1}{z} + \frac{1}{z^2} + \dots\right) \qquad \dots(3)$$

For $|z| < 2$, we have

$$\frac{1}{z-2} = -\frac{1}{2\left(1 - \frac{z}{2}\right)} = -\frac{1}{2}\left(1 - \frac{z}{2}\right)^{-1}$$

$$= -\frac{1}{2}\left(1 + \frac{z}{2} + \frac{z^2}{2^2} + \dots\right) \qquad \dots(4)$$

For $|z| > 2$, we have

$$\frac{1}{z-2} = \frac{1}{z\left(1 - \frac{2}{z}\right)} = \frac{1}{z}\left(1 - \frac{2}{z}\right)^{-1}$$

$$= -\frac{1}{z}\left(1 + \frac{2}{z} + \frac{2^2}{z^2} + \dots\right) \qquad \dots(5)$$

Thus we have the following:

For $0 < |z| < 1$, from (1), (2) and (4)

$$f(z) = \frac{1}{2z} + (1 + z + z^2 + z^3 + \dots) - \frac{1}{4}\left(1 + \frac{z}{2} + \frac{z^2}{2^2} + \dots\right)$$

$$= \frac{1}{2z} + \frac{3}{4} + \left(1 - \frac{1}{4\cdot2}\right)z + \left(1 - \frac{1}{4\cdot2}\right)z^2 + .$$

For $1 < |z| < 2$, from (1), (3) and (4),

$$f(z) = \frac{1}{2z} - \frac{1}{z}\left(1 + \frac{1}{z} + \frac{1}{z^2} + \dots\right) - \frac{1}{4}\left(1 + \frac{z}{2} + \frac{z^2}{2^2} + \dots\right)$$

$$= \left(-\frac{1}{2z} - \frac{1}{z^2} - \frac{1}{z^3} - \dots\right) - \frac{1}{4}\left(1 + \frac{z}{2} + \frac{z^2}{2^2} + \dots\right).$$

For $|z| > 2$, from (1), (3) and (5),

$$f(z) = \frac{1}{2z} - \frac{1}{z}\left(1 + \frac{1}{z} + \frac{1}{z^2} + \dots\right) + \frac{1}{2z}\left(1 + \frac{2}{z} + \frac{2^2}{z^2} + \dots\right)$$

$$= \left(-1 + \frac{1}{2}\cdot 2^2\right)\frac{1}{z^3} + \left(-1 + \frac{1}{2}\cdot 2^3\right)\frac{1}{z^4} + ...$$

$$= (-1 + 2)\frac{1}{z^3} + (-1 + 2^2)\frac{1}{z^4} + (-1 + 2^3)\frac{1}{z^5} + ...$$

10. *In the annulus defined by* $|a| < |z| < |b|$ *expand*

$$\left[\frac{bz}{(z-a)(b-z)}\right]^{1/2}$$

by Laurent's Theorem and prove that it is equal to

$$s_0 + s_n\left(\frac{a^n}{z^n} + \frac{z^n}{b^n}\right)$$

where

$$s_n = \sum_{l=0}^{\infty} \frac{1\cdot 3\cdot 5 \,.....\, (2l-1)}{2^{2l+n}\cdot l\,!}\cdot\frac{1\cdot 3\cdot 5 \,.....\, (2l+2n-1)}{(l+n)\,!}\cdot\left(\frac{a}{b}\right)^l.$$

Solution. Let us express $f(z)$ in a manner so that the binomial expansion is valid for the annulus $|a| < |z| < |b|$, *i.e.*,

$$\left|\frac{a}{z}\right| < 1, \quad \left|\frac{z}{b}\right| < 1.$$

$$f(z) = \left[\frac{bz}{(z-a)(b-z)}\right]^{1/2} = \left[\frac{1}{(1 - a/z)(1 - z/b)}\right]^{1/2}$$

$$\Rightarrow \qquad f(z) = \left(1 - \frac{a}{z}\right)^{-1/2}\left(1 - \frac{z}{b}\right)^{-1/2} \qquad\qquad ...(1)$$

Also $f(z)$ is analytic everywhere except at $z = a$, $z = b$ and hence it can be expanded in a Laurent's series in the given annulus.

$$\therefore \qquad f(z) = \sum_{n=0}^{\infty} a_n z^n + \sum_{n=1}^{\infty} b_n z^{-n} \qquad\qquad ...(2)$$

where

$$a_n = \frac{1}{2\pi i}\int_C \frac{f(z)}{z^{n+1}}\,dz \quad \text{and} \quad b_n = \frac{1}{2\pi i}\int_C z^{n-1} f(z)\,dz \qquad ...(3)$$

Also we know that

$$(1 - x)^{-1/2} = 1 + \frac{1}{2}x + \frac{1\cdot 3}{2\cdot 2}\cdot\frac{x^2}{2\,!} + \frac{1\cdot 3\cdot 5}{2\cdot 2\cdot 2}\cdot\frac{x^3}{3\,!} + ... x < 1$$

$$= \sum_{n=0}^{\infty} \frac{1\cdot 3\cdot 5 \,.....\, (2n-1)}{2^n\cdot n!}\, x^n$$

$$\therefore \qquad f(z) = \sum_{l=0}^{\infty} \frac{1\cdot 3\cdot 5 \,.....\, (2l-1)}{2^l l\,!}\left(\frac{a}{z}\right)^l \cdot \sum_{m=0}^{\infty} \frac{1\cdot 3\cdot 5 \,.....\, (2m-1)}{2^m\cdot m\,!}\left(\frac{z}{b}\right)^m \qquad ...(4)$$

Also equation to C is $|z| = R$ *i.e.*, $z = Re^{i\theta}$, $dz = Re^{i\theta}\cdot i\,d\theta$.

$$\therefore \quad a_n = \frac{1}{2\pi i} \int_C \frac{f(z)}{z^{n+1}} \, dz = \frac{1}{2\pi i} \int_0^{2\pi} \frac{f(z) \, \text{R} e^{i\theta} i \, d\theta}{\text{R}^{n+1} e^{i(n+1)\theta}}$$

$$= \frac{1}{2\pi i} \int_0^{2\pi} \sum_{l=0}^{\infty} \frac{1 \cdot 3 \cdot 5 \dots (2l-1)}{2^l \cdot l!} \cdot \frac{a^l}{\text{R}^l e^{il\theta}}$$

$$\times \sum_{m=0}^{\infty} \frac{1 \cdot 3 \cdot 5 \dots (2m-1)}{2^m \cdot m!} \cdot \frac{\text{R}^m e^{im\theta}}{b^m} \cdot \frac{i \, d\theta}{\text{R}^n e^{in\theta}}$$

$$= \frac{1}{2\pi} \sum_{l=0}^{\infty} \frac{1 \cdot 3 \cdot 5 \dots (2l-1)}{2^l \cdot l!} a^l$$

$$\times \sum_{m=0}^{\infty} \frac{1 \cdot 3 \cdot 5 \dots (2m-1)}{2^m m! b^m} \cdot \int_0^{2\pi} \text{R}^{m-(l+n)} e^{i[m-(l+n)]\theta} \cdot d\theta$$

Now we know that

$$\int_0^{2\pi} e^{ip\theta} \, d\theta = 0 \text{ if } p \neq 0$$

$$= 2\pi \text{ if } p = 0.$$

Here $p = m - (l + n) = 0$ if $m = l + n$ and in that case integral is 2π.

$$\therefore \quad a_n = \frac{1}{2\pi} \sum_{l=0}^{\infty} \frac{1 \cdot 3 \cdot 5 \dots (2l-1)}{2^l \cdot l!} a^l \sum_{m=0}^{\infty} \frac{1 \cdot 3 \cdot 5 \dots (2l+2n-1)}{2^{l+n} (l+n)! \, b^{l+n}} \text{R}^0 \cdot 2\pi$$

or

$$a_n = \sum_{l=0}^{\infty} \frac{1 \cdot 3 \cdot 5 \dots (2l-1)}{2^{2l+n} \cdot l!} \cdot \frac{1 \cdot 3 \cdot 5 \dots (2l+2n-1)}{(l+n)!} \cdot \left(\frac{a}{b}\right)^l \cdot \frac{1}{b^n} = \frac{S_n}{b^n}.$$

Proceeding exactly as above we can show that $b_n = a^n s_n$.

Also when $n = 0$, $a_n = a_0 = \frac{s_0}{b_0} = s_0$.

$$\therefore \quad f(z) = s_0 + \sum_{n=0}^{\infty} \left(\frac{z^n}{b^n} + \frac{a^n}{z^n}\right) s_n.$$

11. *Find the Taylor's and Laurent's series which represent the function*

$$\frac{z^2 - 1}{(z + 2)(z + 3)}$$

(i)   *when* $|z| < 2$ (ii)   *when* $2 < |z| < 3$

(iii) *when* $|z| > 3$.

(Avadh 2005; Agra 2004, Kerala 1999, 2001, Garhwal 2002, 2007, Meerut 2000, 2001)

Solution. We have

$$f(z) = \frac{z^2 - 1}{(z + 2)(z + 3)} = 1 + \frac{3}{z + 2} - \frac{8}{z + 3}$$

Now we find below expansions of $f(z)$ for specified values of z.

(i) When $|z| < 2$.

$$f(z) = 1 + \frac{3}{z + 2} - \frac{8}{z + 3}$$

$$= 1 + \frac{3}{2}\left(1 + \frac{z}{2}\right)^{-1} - \frac{8}{3}\left(1 + \frac{z}{3}\right)^{-1} \quad \text{binomials valid for } |z| < 2$$

$$= 1 + \frac{3}{2}\sum_{n=0}^{\infty} (-1)^n (z/2)^n - \frac{3}{2}\sum_{n=0}^{\infty} (-1)^n (z/3)^n$$

$$= 1 + \sum_{0}^{\infty} (-1)^n \left[\frac{3}{2^{n+1}} - \frac{8}{3^{n+1}}\right] z^n$$

which is a series in positive powers of z. In other words it is an exapansion of $f(z)$ in Taylor's series within a circle $|z| = 2$.

(ii) When $2 < |z| < 3$.

$$f(z) = 1 + \frac{3}{z + 2} - \frac{8}{z + 3}$$

$$= 1 + \frac{3}{z}\left(1 + \frac{2}{z}\right)^{-1} - \frac{8}{3}\left(1 + \frac{z}{3}\right)^{-1}$$

(arranged suitably to make the binomial expansions valid for $2 < |z| < 3$)

$$= 1 + \frac{3}{z}\sum_{n=0}^{\infty} (-1)^n \left(\frac{2}{z}\right)^n - \frac{8}{3}\sum_{n=0}^{\infty} (-1)^n \left(\frac{z}{3}\right)^n$$

Which is a series in the Positive and Negative Powers of z valid for $2 < |z| < 3$. It is therefore the expansion of $f(z)$ as a Laurent's Series with in the annulus $2 < |z| < 3$.

(iii) When $|z| > 3$

$$f(z) = 1 + \frac{3}{z + 2} - \frac{8}{z + 3}$$

$$f(z) = 1 + \frac{3}{z}\left(1 + \frac{2}{z}\right)^{-1} - \frac{8}{z}\left(1 + \frac{3}{z}\right)^{-1}$$

(arranged suitably to make the Binomial expansion valid for $|z| > 3$).

$$f(z) = 1 + \frac{3}{z}\sum_{n=0}^{\infty} (-1)^n \left(\frac{2}{z}\right)^n - \frac{8}{z}\sum_{n=0}^{\infty} (-1)^n \left(\frac{3}{z}\right)^n$$

$$= 1 + \sum_{n=0}^{\infty} (-1)^n [3.2^n - 8.3^n] \frac{1}{z^{n+1}}$$

This is also Laurent's expansion within the annulus $3 < |z| < R$ where R is large.

12. *If a function $f(z)$ is analytic for all finite values of z and as $|z| \to \infty$,*

$$|f(z)| = A(|z|^k)$$

then $f(z)$ is a polynomial of degree $\leq k$.

Solution. Sicne $f(z)$ is analytic in the finite part of plane, therefore by Taylor's series

$$f(z) = \sum_{n=0}^{\infty} a_n z^n, a_n = \frac{f(a)}{n!} \text{ where } |z| < R.$$

Now, if max $|f(z)| = M(r)$ an the circle $|z| = 1, (r < R)$, then by Cauchy's inequality, we have

$$a_n = \left| \frac{f^n(a)}{n!} \right| \leq \frac{M(r)}{r^n} \text{ for all values of } n.$$

$$= \frac{A(|z|^k)}{r^n}, \text{ since } M(r) = |f(z)| = A|z|^k \text{ when } |z| \to 0$$

$$= \frac{Ar^k}{r^n} \text{ (since on the circle } |z| = r)$$

$$= Ar^{k-n} \text{ where } r \text{ is large}$$

So, when $r \to \infty$ the right hand side tends to zero if $n > k$.

i.e., $a_n = 0$ for all values of $n > k$

i.e., all the coefficients a_n for which $n > k$ become zero.

Hence, $f(z)$ is a polynomial of degree n, where $n \leq k$.

13. *Obtain expansions for $\dfrac{(z-2)(z+2)}{(z+1)(z+4)}$ which are valid, for the regions*

(i) $|z| < 1$, *(ii)* $1 < |z| < 4$ *and (iii)* $|z| > 4$.

(*Kumaon 2002; Garhwal 2000, Delhi 2000, 2002, 2003; Kanpur 2004, 2005*)

Solution. Here,

$$f(z) = \frac{(z-2)(z+2)}{(z+1)(z+4)} = 1 - \frac{1}{z+1} - \frac{4}{z+4}. \qquad ...(1)$$

Clearly the function $f(z)$ is not analytic at $z = -1$ and $z = -4$.

(i) **When** $|z| < 1$.

Then $f(z)$ is regular within the region $|z| < 1$, hence by Taylor's expansion we have

$$f(z) = \sum_{n=0}^{\infty} \frac{z^n}{n!} f^n(0), \qquad \text{round the point } z = 0.$$

$$= f(0) + \sum_{n=1}^{\infty} \frac{f^n(0)}{n!} z^n \qquad ...(2)$$

Now, from (1) $f(z) = 1 - \dfrac{1}{z+1} - \dfrac{1}{1 + \dfrac{1}{4}z}$

so that $f^n(z) = (-1)^{n+1} n! \left[\dfrac{1}{(z+1)^{n+1}} + \dfrac{1}{4^n} \cdot \dfrac{1}{\left(1 + \dfrac{1}{4}z\right)^{n+1}} \right]$

$\therefore \qquad \dfrac{f^n(0)}{n!} = (-1)^{n+1} \left[1 + \dfrac{1}{4^n}\right]$

and from (1), $f(0) = 1 - 1 - 1 = -1$.

Hence substituting in (2), we have

$$f(z) = -1 + \sum_{n=1}^{\infty} (-1)^{n+1} (1 + 4^{-n}) z^n$$

(ii) When $1 < |z| < 4$.

Then $f(z)$ is regular in the annulus $|z| = 1$, $|z| = 4$, therefore by Laurent's Series, we have

$$f(z) = \sum_{n=0}^{\infty} a_n z^n + \sum_{n=1}^{\infty} b_n z^{-n}$$

where $a_n = \dfrac{1}{2\pi i} \displaystyle\int_C \dfrac{f(z)\,dz}{z^{n+1}}$ and $b_n = \dfrac{1}{2\pi i} \displaystyle\int_C z^{n-1} f(z)\,dz$

where C is any circle $|z| = r$ where $1 < r < 4$.

$\therefore \qquad a_n = \dfrac{1}{2\pi i} \displaystyle\int_C \dfrac{1}{z^{n+1}} \left[1 - \dfrac{1}{z+1} - \dfrac{4}{z+4} \right] dz$

$\qquad = \dfrac{1}{2\pi i} \displaystyle\int_C \dfrac{1}{z^{n+1}} \Big[1 - \big\{ 1 - z + z^2 + \ldots + (-1)^n z^n$

$\qquad\qquad + (-1)^{n+1} \dfrac{z^{n+1}}{z+1} \big\} - \dfrac{1}{4} \big\{ 1 - \dfrac{z}{4} + \dfrac{z^2}{4^2} - \ldots$

$\qquad\qquad + (-1)^n \dfrac{z^n}{4^n} + \dfrac{(-1)^{n+1}}{4^n} \cdot \dfrac{z^{n+1}}{z+4} \big\} \Big] dz$

$\qquad = \dfrac{(-1)^{n+1}}{2\pi i} \displaystyle\int_C \left[\left(1 + \dfrac{1}{4^n}\right) \dfrac{1}{z} - \dfrac{1}{z+1} - \dfrac{1}{4^n} \dfrac{1}{z+4} \right] dz$

(only the last two terms of each of the two series within the brackets {} survive. since all the integrals of the form

$\displaystyle\int_C \dfrac{dz}{z^m}$ vanish when $(m \neq 1)$

$\qquad = \dfrac{(-1)^{n+1}}{2\pi i} \left[\left(1 + \dfrac{1}{4^n}\right) 2\pi i - \displaystyle\int_C \dfrac{dz}{z+1} - \dfrac{1}{4^n} \displaystyle\int_C \dfrac{dz}{z+4} \right] \qquad \because \displaystyle\int_C \dfrac{dz}{z} = 2\pi i$

or
$$a_0 = \frac{1}{2\pi i} \int_C \frac{1}{z} f(z)\, dz = \frac{1}{2\pi i} \int_C \frac{(z-2)(z+2)}{z(z+1)(z+4)}\, dz$$

$$= \frac{1}{2\pi i} \left[\int_C \frac{dz}{z+1} - \int_C \frac{dz}{z} + \int_C \frac{dz}{z+4} \right].$$

But $\displaystyle\int_C \frac{dz}{z+4} = 0$ [by Cauchy's theorem, because $\dfrac{1}{z+4}$ is analytic within the contour C]

also $\displaystyle\int_C \frac{dz}{z+1} = \int_{C'} \frac{dz}{z+1}$, [by Cauchy's theorem where C' is a small circle with its centre at $z = -1$

and small radius ρ]

$$= \int_0^{2\pi} \frac{\rho e^{i\theta} i\, d\theta}{\rho e^{i\theta}}, \qquad\qquad\qquad \text{[since } |z|+1 = \rho \text{ or } z+1 = \rho e^{i\theta} \text{]}$$

$$= 2\pi i, \qquad\qquad\qquad\qquad\qquad \therefore\ dz = \rho\, i e^{i\theta} d\theta$$

$$\therefore \qquad a_n = \frac{(-1)^{n+1}}{2\pi i}\left[\left(1 + \frac{1}{4^n}\right)2\pi i - 2\pi i\right] = \frac{(-1)^{n+1}}{4^n}$$

and
$$a_0 = \frac{1}{2\pi i}[2\pi i - 2\pi i + 0] = 0$$

And
$$b_n = \frac{1}{2\pi i}\int_C z^{n-1}\left(1 - \frac{1}{z+1} - \frac{4}{z+4}\right)dz$$

$$= \frac{1}{2\pi i}\left[\int_C z^{n-1} dz - \int_C \frac{z^{n-1}}{z+1}\, dz - 4\int_C \frac{z^{n-1}}{z+4}\, dz\right]$$

Now $\displaystyle\int_C z^{n-1} dz = 0$ being of the form $\displaystyle\int \frac{dz}{z^m}, m \neq 1$. also $\displaystyle\int_C \frac{z^{n-1}}{z+4}\, dz = 0$ (by Cauchy's

theorem, because $\dfrac{z^{n-1}}{z+4}$ is analytic within the contour C) and $\displaystyle\int_C \frac{z^{n-1}}{z+1}\, dz = \int_{C'} \frac{z^{n-1}}{z+1}$ [by Cauchy's

theorem where C' is a small circle about $z = -1$)

$$= \int_0^{2\pi} \frac{(-1 + \rho e^{i\theta})^{n-1}}{\rho e^{i\theta}} \cdot \rho e^{i\theta} i\, d\theta \qquad\qquad |z+1| = \rho$$

$$\qquad\qquad\qquad\qquad\qquad\qquad z+1 = \rho e^{i\theta}$$

$$= i(-1)^{n-1}\int_0^{2\pi} (1 - \rho e^{i\theta})^{n-1}.d\theta$$

$$= i(-1)^{n-1} \cdot 2\pi$$

[Expanding by binomial; all the integrals except first one vanish]

$$\therefore \qquad b_n = (-1)^n.$$

Hence
$$f(z) = \sum_{n=1}^{\infty} \frac{(-1)^{n+1}}{4^n} z^n + \sum_{n=1}^{\infty} (-1)^n z^{-n} \qquad\qquad (\because a_0 = 0)$$

(*iii*) **When $|z| > 4$.**

Put $\qquad\qquad r = (1/\xi),$ $\qquad\qquad\qquad\qquad\qquad\qquad\qquad\qquad$ when $|\xi| < \dfrac{1}{4}$,

and the given function transforms into

$$F(\xi) = \frac{(1 - 2\xi)(1 + 2\xi)}{(1 + \xi)(1 + 4\xi)} = -1 + \frac{1}{1 + \xi} + \frac{1}{1 + 4\xi}.$$

This function $F(\xi)$ is analytic within the circle $|\xi| = \dfrac{1}{4}$ and as such can be expanded in a Taylor's sereis.

$$\therefore \qquad F(\xi) = \sum_{n=0}^{\infty} a_n \xi^n = \sum_{n=0}^{\infty} \frac{F^n(0)}{n!} \xi^n$$

$$= F(0) + \sum_{n=1}^{\infty} \frac{F^n(0)}{n!} \xi^n$$

we have $\qquad F(\xi) = -1 + \dfrac{1}{1 + \xi} + \dfrac{1}{1 + 4\xi}$

$$\therefore \qquad \frac{F^n(\xi)}{n!} = (-1)^n \left[\frac{1}{(1 + \xi)^{n+1}} + \frac{4^n}{(1 + 4\xi)^{n+1}} \right]$$

So that $\dfrac{F_n(0)}{n!} = (-1)^n [1 + 4^n]$, and $F(0) = -1 + 1 + 1 = 1$

$$\therefore \qquad F(\xi) = 1 + \sum_{n=1}^{\infty} (-1)^n (1 + 4^n) \xi^n.$$

Replacing ξ by $1/z$ we have the required expansion when

$$|z| > 4 \text{ as } f(z) = 1 + \sum_{n=1}^{\infty} (-1)^n (1 + 4^n) 1/z^n$$

Aliter. Here $\quad f(z) = \dfrac{(z - 2)(z + 2)}{(z + 1)(z + 4)} = 1 - \dfrac{1}{z + 1} - \dfrac{4}{z + 4}$ $\qquad\qquad\qquad$ ...(1)

(*i*) **When $|z| > 1$.**

From (1), we have

$$f(z) = 1 - (1 + z)^{-1} - \left(1 + \frac{z}{4} \right)^{-1}$$

$$= 1 - \sum_{n=0}^{\infty} (-1)^n z^n - \sum_{n=0}^{\infty} (-1)^n \left(\frac{z}{4} \right)^n$$

$$\left[\text{since bonomial expansions of } (1 + z)^{-1} \text{ and } \left(1 + \frac{z}{4} \right)^{-1} \right.$$

$$\left. \text{are valid when } |z| < 1 \, i.e. |z| < 1 \text{ and } \left| \frac{z}{4} \right| > 1 \right]$$

$$= 1 - \left[1 + \sum_{n=1}^{\infty} (-1)^n z^n \right] - \left[1 + \sum_{n=1}^{\infty} (-1)^n 4^{-n} z^n \right]$$

$$= -1 + \sum_{n=1}^{\infty} (-1)^{n+1} (1 + 4^{-n}) z^n$$

(ii) when $1 < |z| < 4$.

Now we shall arrange the partial fractions in (1) so that the binomial expansions involved may be valid in the given region.

Here we write

$$f(z) = 1 - \frac{1}{z} \left(1 + \frac{1}{z} \right)^{-1} - \left(1 + \frac{z}{4} \right)^{-1}$$

$$= 1 - \frac{1}{z} \cdot \sum_{n=0}^{\infty} (-1)^n \left(\frac{1}{z} \right)^n - \sum_{n=0}^{\infty} (-1)^n \left(\frac{z}{4} \right)^n$$

$$\left[\because \text{Binomial expansions are valid when } \left| \frac{1}{z} \right| < 1 \text{ and } \left| \frac{z}{4} \right| < 1 \right]$$

$$= 1 + \sum_{n=0}^{\infty} (-1)^{n+1} \cdot z^{-(n+1)} - \left[1 + \sum_{n=1}^{\infty} \frac{(-1)^n}{4^n} z^n \right]$$

$$= \sum_{n=1}^{\infty} (-1)^n z^{-n} + \sum_{n=1}^{\infty} (-1)^{n+1} \cdot \frac{z^n}{4^n}$$

(iii) When $|z| > 4$.

Arranging the partial fractions in (1), so that the binomial expansions involved may be valid in the given region,

$$f(z) = 1 - \frac{1}{z} \left(1 + \frac{1}{z} \right)^{-1} - \frac{4}{z} \left(1 + \frac{4}{z} \right)^{-1} \qquad \left[\because \left| \frac{1}{z} \right| < 1 \text{ and } \left| \frac{z}{4} \right| < 1 \right]$$

$$= 1 - \frac{1}{z} \sum_{n=0}^{\infty} (-1)^n \left(\frac{1}{z} \right)^n - \frac{4}{z} \sum_{n=0}^{\infty} (-1)^n \left(\frac{4}{z} \right)^n$$

$$= 1 + \sum_{n=0}^{\infty} (-1)^{n+1} \left[\left(\frac{1}{z} \right)^{n+1} + \left(\frac{4}{z} \right)^{n+1} \right]$$

$$= \sum_{n=1}^{\infty} (-1)^n \left[\left(\frac{1}{z} \right)^n + \left(\frac{4}{z} \right)^n \right]$$

$$= 1 + \sum_{n=1}^{\infty} (-1)^n (1 + 4^n) \cdot (1/z^n).$$

14. *Find the function $f(z)$ which is analytic throughout the circle C and its interior, whose centre is at the origin and whose radius is unity and has the value*

$$\frac{a - \cos \theta}{a^2 - 2a \cos \theta + 1} + \frac{i \sin \theta}{a^2 - 2a \cos \theta + 1} , a > 1$$

and θ is the vertorial angle, at points on the circumference of C.

Solution. Suppose $f(z)$ is analytic within and on the circle C given by $|z| = 1$ so that it can expanded at any point z inside it by Maclaurin's series as

$$f(z) = \sum_{n=0}^{\infty} a_n z^n, \qquad \qquad \dots(1)$$

where

$$a_n = \frac{f^{(n)}(0)}{n!} = \frac{1}{n!} \cdot \frac{n!}{2\pi i} \int_C \frac{f(z)\,dz}{(z-0)^{n+1}}$$

or

$$a_n = \frac{1}{2\pi i} \int_C \frac{f(z)\,dz}{z^{n+1}} \qquad \qquad \dots(2)$$

Given

$$f(z) = \frac{a - \cos\theta + i\sin\theta}{a^2 - 2a\cos\theta + 1} = \frac{a - e^{-i\theta}}{a^2 - a(e^{i\theta} + e^{-i\theta}) + 1}$$

$$= \frac{a - z^{-1}}{a^2 - a(z + z^{-1}) + 1}, \quad \text{where } z = e^{i\theta}$$

$$= \frac{(a - z^{-1})}{(a - z)(a - z^{-1})} = \frac{1}{a - z}$$

or

$$f(z) = \frac{1}{a - z} \text{ on } |z| = 1.$$

$\therefore$ By (2),

$$a_n = \frac{1}{2\pi i} \int_C \frac{1}{a-z} \cdot \frac{dz}{z^{n+1}} = \frac{1}{2\pi i a} \int_C \left(1 - \frac{z}{a}\right)^{-1} \frac{dz}{z.z^n}$$

$$= \frac{1}{2\pi i a} \int_0^{2\pi} \left(1 - \frac{e^{i\theta}}{a}\right)^{-1} \cdot \frac{i.e^{i\theta}\,d\theta}{e^{i\theta}\,e^{in\theta}}$$

or

$$a_n = \frac{1}{2\pi a} \int_0^{2\pi} e^{-in\theta} \left[1 + \frac{e^{i\theta}}{a} + \frac{e^{2i\theta}}{a^2} + \dots + \frac{e^{in\theta}}{a^n} + \dots \right]$$

$$a_0 = \frac{1}{2\pi a} \int_0^{2\pi} \left(1 + \frac{e^{i\theta}}{a} + \frac{e^{2i\theta}}{a^2} + \dots\right) d\theta = \frac{1}{2\pi a} \cdot 2\pi \qquad \text{For } \left[e^{im\theta}\right]_0^{2\pi} = 0$$

$$a_1 = \frac{1}{2\pi a} \int_0^{2\pi} e^{-i\theta}\left(1 + \frac{e^{i\theta}}{a} + \frac{e^{i\theta}}{a^2} + \dots\right) d\theta$$

$$= \frac{1}{2\pi a} \int_0^{2\pi} \frac{1}{a}\,d\theta = \frac{(2\pi/a)}{2\pi a} = \frac{1}{2\pi a} \cdot \frac{2\pi}{a}$$

Thus $\Rightarrow a_n = \dfrac{1}{2\pi a} \cdot \dfrac{2\pi}{a^n} = \dfrac{1}{a^{n+1}}$. Now (1) becomes

$$f(z) = \sum_0^{\infty} a_n z^n = \sum_0^{\infty} \frac{z^n}{a^{n+1}} = \frac{1}{a} \sum_0^{\infty} \left(\frac{z}{a}\right)^n = \frac{1}{a}\left[1 - \frac{z}{a}\right]^{-1}$$

or

$$f(z) = \frac{1}{a\left(1 - \dfrac{z}{a}\right)} \quad \text{or} \quad f(z) = \frac{1}{a - z}$$

15. *Using Cauchy integral formula calculate the following integrals:*

(i) $\int\limits_C \dfrac{z\,dz}{(9 - z^2)\,(z + i)}$, *where C is the circle* $|z| = 2$ *described in positive sense.*

(Kerala 2000, 2005)

(ii) $\int\limits_C \dfrac{dz}{z\,(z + \pi i)}$, *where C is* $|z + 3i| = 1$ (*Kanpur 2000*)

(iii) $\int\limits_C \dfrac{\cosh(\pi z)\,dz}{z\,(z^2 + 1)}$, *where C is circle* $|z| = 2.$ (*IAS 1995, 2000, 2005*)

(iv) $\int\limits_C \dfrac{e^{iz}\,dz}{(z - \pi i)}$, *where C is the ellipse* $|z - 2| + |z + 2| = 6$ (*Kanpur 2000*)

(v) $\int\limits_C \dfrac{5z - 2}{z^2 - z}\,dz$ (*Garhwal 2004*)

(vi) $\int\limits_C \dfrac{dz}{z - 2}$, *where C is* $|z| = 3$ (*Kanpur 2003*)

Solution. By Cauchy's integral formula,

$$f(a) = \frac{1}{2\pi i} \int\limits_C \frac{f(z)\,dz}{z - a}$$

or $\int\limits_C \dfrac{f(z)}{z - a}\,dz = 2\pi i\, f(a)$ ...(1)

where $z = a$ is a point inside contour C and $f(z)$ is analytic within and upon C.

(i) Let $I = \int\limits_C \dfrac{z\,dz}{(9 - z^2)(z + i)}$.

Take $f(z) = \dfrac{z}{9 - z^2}$

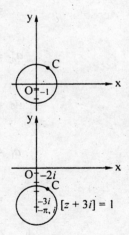

Then $I = \int\limits_C \dfrac{f(z)}{[z - (-i)]} = 2\pi i\, f(-i)$, by (1)

$$= 2\pi i\left[\frac{-i}{9 - (-i)^2}\right] = \frac{2\pi}{9 + 1} = \frac{\pi}{5}$$

Here $f(z)$ is analytic within and upon C and $z = -i$ lies inside C.

(ii) Let $I = \int\limits_C \dfrac{dz}{z\,(z + \pi i)}$

Take $f(z) = \dfrac{1}{z}$ then

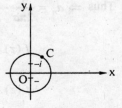

$$I = \int\limits_C \frac{f(z)}{[z - f(-\pi i)]}$$

Fig. 9.22

$$= 2\pi i\, f(-\pi i), \text{ by (I)}$$

$$= 2\pi i\left(\frac{1}{-\pi i}\right) = -2$$

Here $z = -\pi i$ lies inside C and $f(z)$ is analytic within C.

(iii) Let $\qquad I = \int_C \frac{\cosh(\pi z)}{z(z^2+1)}\, dz.$ Take

$$f(z) = \cosh(\pi z) = \cos(i\pi z)$$

Then $\qquad I = \int_C \frac{f(z)}{z(z^2+1)}$

$$I = \int_C \left[\frac{A}{z} + \frac{B}{z-i} + \frac{C}{z+i}\right] f(z)\, dz \qquad \ldots(2)$$

$$\frac{1}{z(z-i)(z+i)} = \frac{A}{z} + \frac{B}{z-i} + \frac{C}{z+i}$$

$$A = \frac{1}{(z-i)(z+i)} = 1 \text{ at } z = 0 \quad B = \frac{1}{z(z+i)} = -\frac{1}{2} \text{ at } z = i$$

$$C = \frac{1}{z(z-i)} = -\frac{1}{2} \text{ at } z = -i$$

Here $z = 0, i, -i$ are ponts inside C.
According to (1), (2) gives

$$I = 2\pi i\,[Af(0) + Bf(i) + Cf(-i)] = 2\pi i\left[f(0) - \frac{1}{2}f(i) - \frac{1}{2}f(-i)\right]$$

$$= 2\pi i\left[\cos(0) - \frac{1}{2}\cos(i^2\pi) - \frac{1}{2}\cos(-i^2\pi)\right] = 2\pi i\left[1 + \frac{1}{2} + \frac{1}{2}\right] = 4\pi i$$

(iv) Let $\qquad I = \int_C \frac{e^{iz}\, dz}{z - \pi i} \qquad \ldots(1)$

C is ellipse $|z-2| + |z+2| = 6$ or

$$[(x-2)^2 + y^2]^{1/2} = 6 - [(x+2)^2 + y^2]^{1/2}$$

Squaring, we get

$$x^2 + y^2 + 4 - 4x = 36 + (x^2 + y^2 + 4 + 4x)$$

$$-12[(x+2)^2 + y^2]^{1/2}$$

or $\qquad 12(x^2 + y^2 + 4 + 4x)^{1/2} = 36 + 8x$

or $\qquad 3(x^2 + y^2 + 4 + 4x)^{1/2} = 9 + 2x$

Again squaring

$$9(x^2 + y^2 + 4 + 4x) = 81 + 4x^2 + 36x$$

or

$$5x^2 + 9y^2 = 45$$

or

$$\frac{x^2}{9} + \frac{y^2}{5} = 1$$

Comparing, $\frac{x^2}{a^2} + \frac{y^2}{b^2} = 1$ we get $a^2 = 9, b^2 = 5, a = 3, b = \sqrt{5} = 2.2$ approx.

Evidently $z = x = 3.34$ lies outside $\hat{C}$. Hence $\dfrac{e^{iz}}{z - \pi i}$ is analytic within and upon C.

$\therefore I = O$, by Cauchy's theorem.

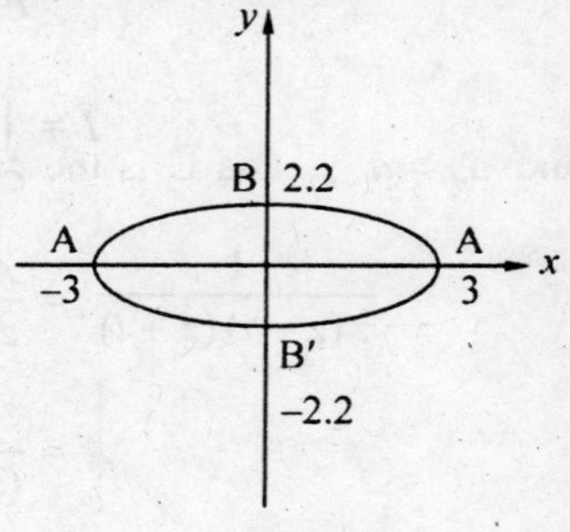

(*v*) Let

$$I = \int_C \frac{dz}{z - 2} = \int_C \frac{f(z)\,dz}{(z - a)}$$

then $a = 2$ lies inside C so that

$$I = 2\pi i\, f(a) = 2\pi i\, f(2) = 2\pi i\,(1) = 2\pi i$$

as

$$f(z) = I \Rightarrow f(z) = 1$$

$$\therefore \quad I = 2\pi i$$

Fig. 9.23

16. (*a*) *Expand* $\dfrac{1}{z}$ *as a Taylor's series about* $z = 1$.

(*Calicut 2003, Calcutta 2000; Kerala 1999*)

(*b*) *Determine Laurent's expansion of the function*

$$f(z) = \frac{\sin z}{\left(z - \dfrac{\pi}{4}\right)^3} \quad \text{in the annulus} \quad 0 < \left|z - \frac{\pi}{4}\right| < 1$$

(*Banglore 2001; Kanpur 1999; Mumbai 2004*)

Solution. (*a*) We have

$$f(z) = \frac{1}{z}$$

differentiate n times w.r.t. z,

$$f^{(n)}z = \frac{(-1)^n n!}{z^{n+1}}$$

or

$$f^{(n)}(1) = \frac{(-1)^n n!}{1^{n+1}} \qquad \text{(by putting } z = 1)$$

If $a_n = \dfrac{f^{(n)}(1)}{n!}$, then $a_n = (-1)^n$. For Taylor's expansion about $z = 1$,

$$f(z) = \sum_{n=0}^{\infty} a_n (z-1)^n = \sum_{n=0}^{\infty} (-1)^n (z-1)^n$$

(b) We have the function $f(z) = \dfrac{\sin z}{\left(z - \dfrac{\pi}{4}\right)^3}$.   ...(1)

For Laurent's expansion about $z = \dfrac{\pi}{4}$

We write $\qquad f(z) = \displaystyle\sum_{n=0}^{\infty} a_n \left(z - \dfrac{\pi}{4}\right)^n + \sum_{n=1}^{\infty} \dfrac{b_n}{\left(z - \dfrac{\pi}{4}\right)^n}$ ...(2)

where $\qquad a_n = \dfrac{1}{2\pi i} \displaystyle\int_C \dfrac{f(z)\,dz}{\left(z - \dfrac{\pi}{4}\right)^{n+1}}$ ...(3)

and $b_n = a_{(-n)}$ and C is the circle $\left|z - \dfrac{\pi}{4}\right| = 1$

or $\qquad z - \dfrac{\pi}{4} = e^{i\theta} \Rightarrow dz = ie^{i\theta}d\theta$

$$f(z) = \dfrac{\sin\left(\dfrac{\pi}{4} + e^{i\theta}\right)}{e^{i3\theta}} \text{ by (1)}$$

Putting these in (3),

$$a_n = \dfrac{1}{2\pi i} \int_C \dfrac{\sin\left(\dfrac{\pi}{4} + \cos\theta + i\sin\theta\right) ie^{i\theta}d\theta}{e^{i3\theta}\,(e^{i\theta})^{n-1}}$$

$$= \dfrac{1}{2\pi} \int_C \sin\left(\dfrac{\pi}{4} + \cos\theta + i\sin\theta\right) e^{-i\theta(n+3)}d\theta$$

$$= \dfrac{1}{2\pi} \int_C [\sin\phi.\cosh(\sin\theta) + i\cos\phi \cdot \sinh(\sin\theta)]$$

$$[\cos m\theta - i\sin m\theta]\,d\theta$$

where $m = n + 3, \phi = \dfrac{\pi}{4} + \cos\theta$

or $\qquad a_n = \dfrac{1}{2\pi} \displaystyle\int_C^{2\pi} \begin{bmatrix} \sin\phi.\cosh\sin\theta\cos(m\theta) + \\ \cos\phi.\sinh(\sin\theta)\sin(m\theta) \end{bmatrix} d\theta$

where $\qquad I_1 = \dfrac{1}{2\pi} \displaystyle\int_0^{2\pi} F(\theta)\,d\theta$

and $\quad F(\theta) = \sin\phi.\sin(m\theta).\cosh(\sin\theta) - \cos\theta.\cos(m\theta).\sinh(\sin\theta)$

In can be proved that $F(2x - \theta) = -F(\theta)$

$\therefore \qquad I_1 = \dfrac{1}{2\pi} \displaystyle\int_0^{2\pi} F(\theta)\,d\theta = 0$

Consequently $\quad a_n = \dfrac{1}{2\pi} \displaystyle\int\limits_0^{2\pi} \begin{bmatrix} \sin\phi \cdot \cosh(\sin\theta)\cos(n\theta) \\ + \cos\phi\sinh(\sin\theta)\sin(n\theta) \end{bmatrix} d\theta$ ...(4)

when $\phi = \pi/4 + \cos\theta, m = n + 3 \Rightarrow b_n = a_{(-n)}$

17. *For the function*

$$f(z) = \frac{2z^3 + 1}{z^2 + z},$$

find

(a) *A Taylor's series valid in the neighbourhood of the point i.*

(b) *A Laurent's series valid within the annulus of which centre is origin.*

(*Ravishankar 2000; Kanpur 2005*)

Solution. (a) $\quad f(z) = \dfrac{2z^3 + 1}{z^2 + z} = 2(z-1) + \dfrac{1}{z+1} + \dfrac{1}{z}$

or $\qquad f(z) = f_1(z) + f_2(z) + f_3(z)$, (say) ...(1)

We have to determine Taylor's expansion in the neighbourhood of $z = i$.

$\therefore \qquad f_1(z) = 2(z-1) = \displaystyle\sum_{n=0}^{\infty} a_n (z-1)^n,$

where $\qquad a_n = \dfrac{f_1^n(i)}{n!}$

$$f_1(z) = 2(z-1), f_1'(z) = 2, f_1''(z) = 0.$$

In general $f_1^n(z) = 0$ for $n \geq 2$.

$\therefore a_n = 0$ for $n \geq 2$ and $a_1 = \dfrac{f_1'(i)}{1!} = 2.$

Also $\qquad a_0 = \dfrac{f_1(i)}{0!} = 2(i-1)$

$\therefore \qquad f_1(z) = a_0 + a_1(z-1) = 2(i-1) + 2(z-1)$ ...(2)

$$f_2(z) = \frac{1}{z+1} = \sum_{n=0}^{\infty} a_n (z-i)^n$$

where $\qquad a_n = \dfrac{f_2^n(i)}{n!}$

$$f_2^n(z) = \frac{(-1)^n \, n!}{(z+1)^{n+1}}$$

$\therefore \qquad \dfrac{f_2^n(i)}{n!} = \dfrac{1}{n!} \cdot \dfrac{(-1)^n \, n!}{(i+1)^{n+1}} = \dfrac{(-1)^n}{(i+1)^{n+1}}$

$\therefore \qquad f_2(z) = \displaystyle\sum_{n=0}^{\infty} \dfrac{(-1)^n}{(i+1)^{n+1}} (z-i)^n$ ...(3)

$$f_3(z) = \frac{1}{z} = \sum_{n=0}^{\infty} a_n (z-i)^n$$

where

$$a_n = \frac{f_3^n(i)}{n!}$$

$$f_3^n(z) = \frac{(-1)^n \cdot n!}{z^{n+1}}$$

$$\therefore \quad \frac{f_3^n(i)}{n!} = \frac{1}{n!} \cdot \frac{(-1)^n \, n!}{i^{n+1}} = \frac{(-1)^n}{i^{n+1}}$$

$$\therefore \quad f_3(z) = \sum_{n=0}^{\infty} \frac{(-1)^n}{i^{n+1}} (z-i)^n \qquad\qquad \text{...(4)}$$

Hence from (1) by the help of (2), (3) and (4), we have

$$f(z) = 2(i-1) + 2(z-i) + \sum_{n=0}^{\infty} (-1)^n (z-i)^n \cdot \left[\frac{1}{(1+i)^{n+1}} + \frac{1}{i^{n+1}} \right].$$

This is the required Taylor's series for $f(z)$ in the neighbourhood of point i.

(b) From $f(z)$ it is clear that its singularities are at $z = 0$ and $z = 1$ and as such $f(z)$ is analytic in the region $0 < |z| < 1$. Therefore, it can be expanded in Laurent's series.

$$f(z) = 2(z-1) + \frac{1}{z} + (1+z)^{-1}$$

$$= 2(z-1) + \frac{1}{z} + \sum_{n=0}^{\infty} (-1)^n z^n.$$

The terms corresponding to $n = 0$ and $n = 1$ are 1 and $-z$ respectively.

$$\therefore \quad f(z) = 2(z-1) + \frac{1}{z} + 1 - z + \sum_{n=2}^{\infty} (-1)^n z^n \quad \therefore$$

$$= -1 + z + \frac{1}{z} + \sum_{n=2}^{\infty} (-1)^n z^n.$$

This is the required Laurent's expansion.

EXERCISES

1. Find the expansions of

$$\frac{1}{(z^2+1)(z^2+2)}$$

in powers of z when

(a) $|z| < 1$,   (b) $1 < |z| < \sqrt{2}$,   (c) $|z| > \sqrt{2}$.

$$\left[\textbf{Ans.} \ (a) \ \sum_{n=0}^{\infty} (-1)^n \left(1 - \frac{1}{2^{n+1}} \right) z^{2n} \right.$$

$$(b) \ \sum_{n=0}^{\infty} (-1)^{n+1} \frac{z^{2n}}{2^{n+1}} + \sum_{n=0}^{\infty} (-1)^n \frac{1}{z^{2n+2}}$$

$$\left. (c) \ \sum_{n=0}^{\infty} \frac{(-1)^n (1 - 2^n)}{z^{2n+2}} \right]$$

2. Find the Laurent's expansion of
$(z^2 - z - 2)^{-1}$ in the domain defined by
$$1 < |z| < 2.$$

$$\left[\text{Ans.} - \frac{1}{3} \sum_{n=0}^{\infty} \frac{z^n}{2^{n+1}} + \frac{1}{3} \sum_{n-0}^{\infty} \frac{(-1)^{n+1}}{z^{n+1}} \right]$$

3. Find expansions of $1/(z^2 + 3)$ valid for
   (i) $|z - 1| < 2$,   (ii) $|z + 1| > 2$.
   and hence show that if

$$a_n = (-1)^n 2^{-n} \sin \frac{(n+1)\pi}{3} \text{ and } b_n = 2^n \sin \frac{(n+2)\pi}{3},$$

   then

$$\sum_{n=0}^{\infty} a_n (z-1)^n + \sum_{n=1}^{\infty} b_n (z+1)^{-n} = 0$$

   where z lies in the crescent formed by the circles of radius 2 with centres at $z = \pm 1$ to the right of the imaginary axis.

4. For each of the following functions, find the radius of convergence of its power series expansion in the neighbourhood of $z = 0$.

   (a) $\dfrac{1}{e^x + 1}$,   (b) $\dfrac{\cos z}{\pi^2 - 4z^2}$,   (c) $\sqrt{1 + 2z + 3z^2}$

   taking in the last case the branch which reduces to -1 when $z = 0$. Also compute first three coefficients of the expansion in each case.

$$\left[\text{Ans. } (a) \ \pi, \ \frac{1}{2} - \frac{1}{4}z + \frac{1}{48}z^3 \right.$$
$$(b) \ \frac{\pi}{2}, \ \frac{1}{\pi^2} + \frac{1}{\pi^2}\left(\frac{4}{\pi^2} - \frac{1}{2}\right)z^2 + \frac{1}{\pi^2}\left(\frac{16}{\pi^4} - \frac{2}{\pi^2} + \frac{1}{24}\right)z^4$$
$$\left. (c) \ \frac{1}{\sqrt{3}}, \ -1 - z - z^2 \right]$$

5. Compute the first five coefficients of the power series expansion about the origin of the following functions:

   (a) $\log (1 + e^z)$,   (b) $\sqrt{\cos z}$,

   taking the branches whose values for $z = 0$ are $\log 2$ and 1 respectively.
   Determine also the domains of convergence of the series.

$$\left[\text{Ans. } (a) \ \log 2 + \frac{z}{2} + \frac{z^2}{8} - \frac{z^4}{192}, \ |z| < \pi \ (b) \ 1 - \frac{z^2}{4} - \frac{z^4}{96}, \ \frac{1}{2}\pi \right]$$

6. Expand the following functions as power series $\Sigma a_n (z - a)^n$; a being given in each case:
   (a) $\log (2 + iz), a = i$, (b) $(\sin z)^{1/2}, a = \pi/2$, (c) $\log \cos z, a = \pi$.

$$\left[\text{Ans. } (a) \ i(z - i) + \frac{(z-i)^2}{2} + ... + \frac{(i)^n (-1)^{n-1}}{4} (z-i)^n + ...; \right.$$
   taking the principal branch.

(b) $1 - \dfrac{\left(z - \dfrac{1}{2}\pi\right)^2}{4} - \dfrac{\left(z - \dfrac{1}{2}\pi\right)^4}{96} - \dots\dots;$

taking the branch whose value for $z = \dfrac{1}{2}\pi$ is $+ 1$.

(c) $i\pi - \dfrac{(z - \pi)^2}{2} - \dfrac{(z - \pi)^4}{12} - \dots\dots;$

taking the principal branch of the function.]

7. Prove that, if $0 < c < 1$ and $c < |z| < c^{-1}$, then

$$\left\{\frac{(1 - cz)(z - c)}{z}\right\}^{1/2} = \pm \frac{1}{\pi} \sum_{n = -\infty}^{\infty} z^n \int_0^\pi \cos n\theta \sqrt{1 - 2c\cos\theta + c^2}\; d\theta.$$

8. Prove that for $|z| < \dfrac{1}{2}\pi$,

$$\frac{\sin z}{4z^2 - \pi^2} = \sum_{n=0}^\infty a_{2n+1} z^{2n+1},$$

where

$$a_{2n+1} = \frac{(-1)^{n+1}}{\pi^2}\left[-\frac{1}{(2n+1)!} - \frac{4}{2(n-1)!\,\pi^2} + \dots\dots + \frac{(-4)^n}{\pi^{2n}}\right]$$

and that for $|z| > \dfrac{1}{2}\pi$,

$$\frac{\sin z}{4z^2 - \pi^2} = \sum_{n=-\infty}^\infty b_{2n+1} z^{2n+1},$$

where

$$b_{2n+2} = \begin{cases} a_{2n+1} + \dfrac{2^{2n+1}}{\pi^{2n+3}} & \text{for } n \geq 0 \\[3mm] \dfrac{2^{2n-1}}{\pi^{2n+2}} & \text{for } n < 0. \end{cases}$$

9. Prove taht

$$f'''(a) = \frac{3!}{2\pi i}\int_C \frac{f(z)\,dz}{(z-a)^4}$$

where C is a centour contained in $z = a$.   *(Nagpur 2001, 2005; Banglore 2005 (BE))*

10. Find the Taylor's or Laurent's series which represents the function

$$\frac{1}{(1 + z^2)(z + 2)}$$

(i) when $|z| < 1$, (ii) when $1 < |z| < 2$, (iii) when $|z| > 2$.

(Avadh 2003; Rohilkhand, 1996; Kumaon, 1991)

$$\left[\text{Ans. } (i) \frac{1}{10} \sum_{n=0}^{\infty} (-1)^n \left(\frac{z}{2}\right)^n + \frac{2-z}{5} \sum_{n=0}^{\infty} (-1)^n z^n \right.$$

$$(ii) \frac{1}{10} \sum_{n=0}^{\infty} (-1)^n \left(\frac{z}{2}\right)^n + \frac{2-z}{5z^2} \sum_{n=0}^{\infty} (-1)^n \left(\frac{1}{z^2}\right)^n$$

$$\left. (iii) \frac{1}{5} \cdot \frac{1}{z} \sum_{n=0}^{\infty} (-1)^n \left(\frac{2}{z}\right)^n - \frac{1}{5} \left(\frac{1}{z} - \frac{2}{z^2}\right) \sum_{n=0}^{\infty} (-1)^n \frac{1}{z^{2n}} \right]$$

11. Expand in the series the function

$$f(z) = \frac{1}{z^2 - 3z + 2}$$

in the regions

$(i) \ |z| < 1, \ (ii) \ 1 < |z| < 2, \ (iii) \ |z| > 2.$

(Kanpur 2003, 2005)

$$\left[\text{Ans. } (i) \ f(z) = \sum_{n=0}^{\infty} z^n - \frac{1}{2} \sum_{n=0}^{\infty} \left(\frac{z}{2}\right)^n \right.$$

$$(ii) \ f(z) = -\sum_{n=0}^{\infty} \left(\frac{z^n}{2^{n+1}}\right) - \sum_{n=0}^{\infty} \frac{1}{z^{n+1}}$$

$$\left. (iii) \ f(z) = \sum_{n=0}^{\infty} (2^n - 1) \frac{1}{z^{n+1}} \right]$$

12. Expand $f(z) = \sin z$, about $z = \pi/4$ in Taylor's series and determine region of convergence.

$$\left[\text{Ans. } \frac{1}{\sqrt{2}} \left\{ 1 + \left(z - \frac{\pi}{4}\right) - \frac{1}{2!}\left(z - \frac{\pi}{4}\right)^2 - \frac{1}{3!}\left(z - \frac{\pi}{4}\right)^3 - \dots \right\}, \right.$$

$$\left. |z| < \infty. \right]$$

13. Expand $f(z) = \dfrac{1}{(z+1)(z+3)}$ in a Laurent's series valid for

(a) $1 < |z| < 3,$ (b) $|z| > 3,$

(c) $0 < |z+1| < 2,$ (d) $|z| < 1.$

(Avadh 2004; Garhwal 2007)

$$\left[\text{Ans. } (a) \ \dots - \frac{1}{2z^4} + \frac{1}{2z^3} - \frac{1}{2z^2} + \frac{1}{2z} - \frac{1}{6} + \frac{z}{18} - \frac{z^2}{54} \right.$$

$$\left. + \frac{z^3}{162} - \frac{z^4}{1536} \right]$$

(b) $\dfrac{1}{z^2} - \dfrac{4}{z^3} + \dfrac{13}{z^4} - \dfrac{40}{z^5} + \ldots\ldots$

(c) $\dfrac{1}{2(z+1)} - \dfrac{1}{4} + \dfrac{1}{8}(z+1) - \dfrac{1}{16}(z+1)^2 + \ldots\ldots$

(d) $\dfrac{1}{3} - \dfrac{4}{9}z + \dfrac{13}{27}z^2 - \dfrac{40}{81}z^3 + \ldots\ldots\bigg]$

14. Show that if $c > 0$, then

$$e^{z + (c^3/2z^2)} = \sum_{n=-\infty}^{\infty} a_n z^n$$

where

$$a_n = \frac{e^{-c/2}}{2\pi c^n} \int_0^{2\pi} e^{c(\cos\theta + \cos^2\theta)} \cos[c\sin\theta(1 - \cos\theta) - n\theta]\, d\theta.$$

(Agra 2004, Gorakhpur, 2001)

15. The series

$$\varphi_1(z) = \sum_{n=-\infty}^{\infty} b_n z^n, \quad \varphi_2(z) = \sum_{n=-\infty}^{\infty} (b_n - 1) z^n$$

are convergent in the rings

$$\lambda_1 < |z| < 1, \ 1 < |z| < \lambda_2$$

respectively.

Prove that the series

$$\sum_{n=-\infty}^{-1} b_n z^n + \sum_{n=0}^{\infty} (b_n - 1) z^n$$

is convergent for $\lambda_1 < |z| < \lambda_2$ and that its sum is either

$$\varphi_1(z) + (1 - z)^{-1} \text{ or } \varphi_2(z) + (1 - z)^{-1}$$

where these functions are defined.

16. The function $f(z)$ is regular in the circle

$$|z| \leq R + \delta,$$

when $\delta > 0$, and the upper bound of $|f(z)|$ on the circle $|z| = R$ is M. The Taylor's expansion of $f(z)$ is $\Sigma a_n z^n$.

Prove that

$$\frac{1}{2\pi}\int_0^{2\pi} |f(Re^{i\theta})|^2\, d\theta = \sum_{n=0}^{\infty} |a_n|^2 R^{2n}$$

and deduce that $|f^n(0)| \leq n!\, MR^{-n}$, the sign of equality occurring if and only if

$$f(z) = Me^{i\alpha}z^n R^{-n},$$

when α is a real constant.

17. A single valued function f has the properties that $f'(z)$ exists for every z for which

$0 < |z| < 1$, and that $\displaystyle\lim_{z \to 0} z\, f(z) = 0$.

Prove that $\lim f(z)$ exists as $z \to 0$.

Prove further that, if

$g(z) = f(z)$ for $0 < |z| < 1$ and $g(0) = \lim f(z)$, as $z \to 0$ then $g'(0)$ exists.

18. Show that, if the function $f(z)$ of z is analytic at every point inside and on the circle $|z| = R$, then there exists a real number $R' > R$ such that $f(z)$ is regular inside and on $|z| = R'$.

19. Prove that if

(i) $f(z)$ is regular in the half-plane $R(z) > 0$,

(ii) $|f(z)| \le 1$, when $R(z) > 0$, and

(iii) $f(1) = 0$, then

$$|f(z)| \le \left| \frac{z-1}{z+1} \right|, \text{ when } R(z) > 0.$$

[Make use of the transformation $w = (z-1)/(z+1)$ and the Schwarz's lemma.]

20. A function $f(z)$ is analytic in the semi-plane $I(z) > 0$ and continuous on the boundary $I(z) = 0$; also $f(z) \to 0$ uniformly as $z \to \infty$; show that

$$f(z) = \frac{1}{\pi} \lim_{R \to \infty} \int_{-R}^{+R} f(\xi) \frac{y}{(\xi - x)^2 + y^2} d\xi,$$

where $z = x + iy$ is any point such that $y > 0$.

[By Cauchy's integral formula

$$f(z) = \frac{1}{2\pi i} \int_{-R}^{+R} \frac{f(\xi)}{\xi - z} d\xi + \frac{1}{2\pi i} \int_{C} \frac{f(\xi)}{\xi - z} d\xi,$$

where C denotes the positively oriented circle $|z| = R$, $I(z) > 0$.

Also

$$0 = \frac{1}{2\pi i} \int_{-R}^{+R} \frac{f(\xi)}{\xi - z} d\xi + \frac{1}{2\pi i} \int_{C} \frac{f(\xi)}{\xi - z} d\xi$$

Now subtract and let R tend to infinity.]

21. A function $f(z)$ is analytic for $|z| < R$; $f(0) \ne 0$ and $r_1, r_2, \ldots, r_n, \ldots$, are the moduli of the zeros of $f(z)$ in the circular domain $|z| < R$ arranged as a monotonically increasing sequence. Show that if

$$r_n \le r \le r_{n+1},$$

then

$$\log \frac{r_n \, |f(0)|}{r_1 r_2 \ldots r_n} = \frac{1}{2\pi} \int_0^{2\pi} \log |f(re^{i\theta})| \, d\theta.$$

Here a zero of order p is counted p times.

[This is known as **Jenson's theorem** and its interest lies in the fact that it connects the modulus of the function with the moduli of the zeros.]

OBJECTIVE QUESTIONS

For each of the following questions, four alternatives are given for the answer. Only one of them is correct. Choose the correct alternative.

1. If $f(z)$ be analytic in a simply-connected domain D and if C be any closed continuous rectifiable curve in D, then

(a) $\displaystyle\int_C f(z)\, dz = 0$

(b) $\displaystyle\int_C f(z)\, dz \neq 0$

(c) $\displaystyle\int_C f(z)\, dz = 2\pi i$

(d) $\displaystyle\int_C f(z)\, dz = \pi i.$

2. Every analytic function in a simply-connected domain
(a) possesses a definite integral
(b) possesses an indefinite integral
(c) does not possess an indefinite integral
(d) None of these.

3. If $f(z)$ is analytic and uniformly bounded in every domain, then
(a) $f(z)$ is zero
(b) $f(z)$ is constant
(c) $f(z)$ is discontinuous
(d) None of these.

4. If $f(z)$ is an analytic function of z and if $f'(z)$ is continuous at each point within and on a closed contour C, then

(a) $\displaystyle\int_C f(z)\, dz = 2\pi i$

(b) $\displaystyle\int_C f(z)\, dz = \pi i$

(c) $\displaystyle\int_C f(z)\, dz = 0$

(d) $\displaystyle\int_C f(z)\, dz \neq 0.$

5. The indefinite integral

$$f(z) = \int_{z_0}^{z} f(z)\, dz$$

of $f(z)$ is

(a) an analytic of its lower limit z_0

(b) an analytic of its upper limit z

(c) analytic of its both limits z and z_0

(d) None of these.

6. If $f(z)$ is analytic within and on a closed contour C and a is any point within C, then $f(z)$ is equal to

(a) $\dfrac{1}{2\pi i}\displaystyle\int \dfrac{f(z)}{(z-a)^n}\, dz$

(b) $\dfrac{1}{2\pi i}\displaystyle\int \dfrac{f(z)}{(z-a)^2}\, dz$

(c) $\dfrac{1}{2\pi i}\displaystyle\int \dfrac{f(z)}{(z-a)}\, dz$

(d) None of these.

7. If a function $f(z)$ is analytic in a region D, then its derivative at any point $z = a$ of D is also analytic in D, and is given by (C is any closed contour D surrounding the point $z = a$)

(a) $\dfrac{1}{2\pi i}\displaystyle\int_C \dfrac{f(z)}{(z-a)}\, dz$

(b) $\dfrac{1}{2\pi i}\displaystyle\int_C \dfrac{f(z)}{(z-a)^2}\, dz$

(c) $\dfrac{3!}{2\pi i}\displaystyle\int_C \dfrac{f(z)}{(z-a)^3}\, dz$

(d) None of these.

8. Let $f(z)$ be a continuous function in a simply-connected domain D and C be any rectifiable closed curve in D, then necessary and sufficient condition for $f(z)$ to be analytic in D is

   (a) $\int_C f(z)\,dz = 2\pi i$

   (b) $\int_C f(z)\,dz = -2\pi i$

   (c) $\int_C f(z)\,dz = 0$

   (d) $\int_C f(z)\,dz \neq 0$.

9. If $f(z)$ be analytic within and on a simple closed contour C, then point giving the maximum of $|f(z)|$ can be

   (a) within C

   (b) outside C

   (c) on the boundary C and not within it

   (d) on the boundary and within C.

10. If C is the circle $|z - a| = r$, then

$$\int_C \frac{dz}{(z-a)^n} = 2\pi i,$$

   when

   (a) $n \neq 1$

   (b) $n = 0$

   (c) $n = 1$

   (d) None of these.

11. If $f(z)$ is an analytic function on a domain D and if the circular region $|z - a| \leq r$ is contained in D, then $f(a)$ is equal to

   (a) $\dfrac{1}{2\pi i} \int_C f(z)\,dz$

   (b) $\dfrac{1}{2\pi} \int_0^{2\pi} f(re^{i\theta})\,d\theta$

   (c) $\dfrac{1}{2\pi} \int_0^{2\pi} f(a + re^{i\theta})\,d\theta$

   (d) $\int_0^{2\pi} f(a + re^{i\theta})\,d\theta$.

ANSWERS

1. (a)   2. (b)   3. (b)   4. (c)   5. (b)   6. (c)   7. (b)   8. (c)   9. (c)
10. (c)   11. (c)

SINGULAR POINTS

10.1. Introduction. This chapter is devoted to a consideration of functions which are analytic at all points in a bounded domain except at a finite number. Such exceptional points are known as *singular points*. In this context, the first problem will naturally consist in classifying singular points in terms of the behaviour of the function in their neighbourhood.

The important notion of *Residue* of a function at a point will also be introduced in this chapter. The evaluation of certain types of real definite integrals which constitutes one of the most important applications of the *Calculus of Residues* will be treated in the next chapter and application to the *Theory of Equations* will be considered in the present chapter.

10.2. The zeros of an analytic function. (*Garhwal 2002*)

A zero of an analytic function $f(z)$ is a value of z such that $f(z) = 0$.

If $f(z)$ is analytic in a domain D and a is any point in D then by Taylor's Theorem $f(z)$ can be expanded about $z = a$, i.e.,

$$f(z) = \sum_{n=0}^{\infty} a_n (z - a)^n,$$

where

$$a_n = \frac{f^n(a)}{n!}.$$

If $a_0 = a_1 = a_2 = \dots = a_{m-1} = 0$ but $a_m \neq 0$,

i.e., $f(a) = f'(a) = f''(a) = \dots = f^{m-1}(a) = 0$ but $f^m(a) \neq 0$,

then we say that $f(z)$ has a *zero of order m at $z = a$*.

In this case

$$f(z) = a_m (z - a)^m + a_{m+1} (z - a)^{m+1} + \dots$$
$$= (z - a)^m [a_m + a_{m+1} (z - a) + \dots]$$

or $\qquad f(z) = (z - a)^m \phi(z)$ (say)

where $\phi(z)$ is analytic and non-zero at and in the neighbourhood of $z = a$.

It is clear that $\phi(a) = a_m$, i.e., $\phi(z) = a_m$ at $z = a$.

In case $f(z)$ has a zero of order one at $z = a$ then $f(z)$ is said to have a **simple zero** at $z = a$.

10.2.1. Zeros are Isolated.

Theorem. *Let $f(z)$ be analytic in a domain D. Then unless $f(z)$ is identically zero, there exists a neighbourhood of each point in D throughout which function has no zero, except possibly at the point itself. In other words, the zeros of an analytic function are isolated.*

(*Calicut 2004; Kanpur 2002, 2003; Garhwal 2002, 2004; Gorakhpur, 2000, 2004*)

Let $z = a$ be a zero of order m of the function $f(z)$ which is analytic at a and its neighbourhood, then

$$f(z) = (z - a)^m \sum_{n=0}^{\infty} a_{m+n} (z - a)^n$$

$$= (z - a)^m \, \phi(z) \qquad \qquad ...(1)$$

where

$$\phi(z) = \sum_{n=0}^{\infty} a_{m+n} (z - a)^n$$

$$= a_m + a_{m+1} (z - a) + ...$$

and

$$\phi(a) = a_m \neq 0.$$

Clearly $\phi(z)$ is analytic at $z = a$ from which it follows that $\phi(z)$ is continuous at $z = a$ and since $\phi(a) \neq 0$, there exists a neighbourhood of a, for no point z of which $\phi(z)$ is zero.

Also $(z - a)^m \neq 0$ for values of $z \neq a$. So, there is no other point in the neighbourhood of $z = 0$ at which $f(z)$ is zero. Hence the zero $z = a$ is isolated. The same is true for every zero of $f(z)$, hence all the zeros of $f(z)$ are isolated.

10.3. Singularities of an Analytic Function.

(Garhwal 2002, 2003, 2005)

10.3.1. Isolated singular points. A point where a given function is not analytic is called a singular point of the function. Considering the set of singular points of a function, we may see that a singular point will be an isolated point of the set, if the function is analytic at each point in some deleted neighbourhood of the point. Clearly a limiting point of the set, of singular points is itself a singular point so that the set of singular points is closed. We shall, in the following, consider isolated singular points only.

10.4. Local study at an isolated singular point. We now proceed to examine the various possibilities for the behaviour of a function near an isolated singular point. Laurent's series expansion about the point will be found useful for the purpose.

Suppose that $z = a$ is an isolated singular point of a function $f(z)$ and that $f(z)$ is analytic in the domain

$$0 < |z - a| < r,$$

where r is a positive number.

Then we have the Laurent's series

$$f(z) = \sum_{n=-\infty}^{\infty} a_n (z - a)^n$$

where

$$a_n = \frac{1}{2\pi i} \int_C \frac{f(z)}{(z - a)^{n+1}} \, dz,$$

C, being the circle

$$|z - a| = \rho < r.$$

The part

$$a_{-1} (z - a)^{-1} + a_{-2} (z - a)^{-2} + ... + a_{-n} (z - a)^{-n} + ...$$

of the Laurent's series consisting of the sum of negative powers of $(z - a)$ is called the *principal part* of $f(z)$ at $z = a$.

Relatively to the principal part, we have three possibilities inasmuch as the same may consist of:

(a) *no term*;

(b) **a finite** *number of terms with non-zero coefficients*;

(c) **an infinite** *number of terms with non-zero coefficients*.

These three cases will now be considered one by one.

10.4.1. Removable Singularity.   (*Meerut 2002*)

In case (a) when the principal part consists of no terms, we have, for $0 < |z - a| < r$,

$$f(z) = a_0 + a_1 (z - a) + ... + a_n (z - a)^n + ...\qquad ...(1)$$

The radius of convergence of the power series on the right-hand side of (1) must at least be r.

The sum function $\phi(z)$ of this power series differs from $f(z)$ only for $z = a$ so that we have

$$\phi(z) = \begin{cases} f(z), & \text{for } 0 < |z - a| < r \\ a_0, & \text{for } z = a. \end{cases}$$

Also, $\phi(z)$, being the sum function of a power series is analytic at $z = a$.

In this case, we say that the singularity of $f(z)$ at $z = a$ is removable, inasmuch as by just suitably modifying or defining the value of the function at the single point $z = a$, the singularity can disappear.

The following theorem due to Riemann gives a criterion for removable singularity.

Riemann's Theorem. *If $z = a$ is an isolated singularity of a function $f(z)$ and the function $f(z)$ is bounded in some neighbourhood of a; then there exists one and only one complex number ξ such that the function which is defined as equal to $f(z)$ in some deleted neighbourhood of a and equal to ξ at a, is analytic at a.*

Let

$$|f(z)| < k \text{ for } 0 < |z - a| < r.$$

Let C_ρ be any circle with its centre at a and radius ρ.

The coefficients a_n in the Laurent's series of $f(z)$ about $z = a$ are given by

$$a_n = \frac{1}{2\pi i} \int_{C_\rho} \frac{f(z)}{(z - a)^{n+1}} \, dz,$$

where the radius ρ of the circle can be taken as small as we like. The coefficients are thus independent of ρ.

Now, we have

$$|a_n| \le \frac{1}{2\pi} \frac{k}{\rho^{n+1}} \cdot 2\pi\rho = \frac{k}{\rho^n},$$

so that if n be a negative integer, then

$$a_n \to 0 \text{ as } \rho \to 0.$$

Thus we see that the principal part of $f(z)$ consists of no non-zero coefficient and accordingly $f(z)$ has a removable singularity at $z = 0$.

If then

$$f(z) = a_0 + a_1 (z - a) + ... + a_n (z - a)^n + ...$$

we see that the required value ξ is given by

$$\xi = a_0 = \frac{1}{2\pi i} \int_{C_\rho} \frac{f(z)}{z - a} \, dz.$$

Note 1. In case $f(z)$ has a removable singularity at a point $z = a$, it will always be understood that the value of $f(z)$ for $z = a$ has been suitably modified so as to render the function analytic at a.

Note 2. It is useful to notice that if $\psi(z)$ denotes the principal part at any isolated singularity $z = a$ of a function $f(z)$, then the function

$$f(z) - \psi(z)$$

has a removable singularity at $z = a$ and, under the supposition made in the Note 1 above, we say that the function $f(z) - \psi(z)$, is analytic at $z = a$.

Note 3. The property referred to above in Riemann's theorem does not hold for real functions of a real variable. Thus for example

$$f(x) = \sin(1/x), \; x \ne 0$$

possesses a derivative for every non-zero value of x and is bounded in every neighbourhood of zero, but for no value assigned to $f(x)$ for $x = 0$ does $f(x)$ become derivable for $x = 0$. In fact $f(x)$ does not even possess removable discontinuity for $x = 0$ inasmuch as $\lim f(x)$ does not exist when $x \to 0$.

10.4.2. Poles.   (*Kanpur 2003*)

We now suppose that there exist only a *finite* number of non-zero coefficients, say n, of negative powers of $(z - a)$.

Let the principal part of $f(z)$ for $z = a$ be given by

$$\phi(z) = a_{-1}(z-a)^{-1} + a_{-2}(z-a)^{-2} + \ldots + a_{-m}(z-a)^{-m}$$
$$= (z-a)^{-m}[a_{-m} + a_{-m+1}(z-a) + \ldots + a_{1}(z-a)^{m-1}]$$

where $a_{-m} \ne 0$.

Also we write

$$\psi(z) = a_0 + a_1(z-a) + a_2(z-a)^2 + \ldots$$

Thus for $0 < |z - a| < r$, we have

$$f(z) = \psi(z) + (z-a)^{-m}[a_{-m} + a_{-m+1}(z-a) + \ldots + a_{-1}(z-a)^{m-1}]$$
$$= (z-a)^{-m}[a_{-m} + a_{-m+1}(z-a)$$
$$+ \ldots + a_{-1}(z-a)^{m-1} + \psi(z)(z-a)^m]$$
$$= (z-a)^{-m} F(z), \text{ (say),}$$

where $F(z)$ is analytic in $|z - a| < r$

and $F(a) = a_{-m} \ne 0$.

We have thus proved that in case the principal part of $f(z)$ consists of a finite number of non-zero terms only and the last non-zero coefficient is that of $(z - a)^{-m}$, then $f(z)$ can, in the domain, $0 < |z - a| < r$, be expressed as

$$f(z) = (z-a)^{-m} F(z), \qquad\qquad \ldots(1)$$

where $F(z)$ is analytic at $z = a$ and $F(a) \ne 0$.

In this case we say that $z = a$ is a **pole of order m** of the function $f(z)$. From (1), we have

$$\frac{1}{f(z)} = (z-a)^m \frac{1}{F(z)} = (z-a)^m G(z), \text{ for } 0 < |$$

where $G(z)$ is analytic at $z - a$ and $\ne 0$ thereat. Clearly $1/f(z)$ has a removable singularity at $z = a$, and if we define $1/f(z)$ to be equal to 0 for $z = a$, we see that *if $f(z)$ has a pole of order m for $z = a$, then $1/f(z)$ has a zero of order m. Thus a pole of a function is a zero of the same* *order of the reciprocal of the function.* The converse is also true *i.e.*, a zero of any order of a function is a pole of the same order of the reciprocal of the function.

Also we may easily see that if $z = a$ is a pole of $f(z)$, then

$$\lim_{z \to a} f(z) = \infty. \qquad \qquad ...(2)$$

The property (2) characterises a pole and gives the behaviour in the neighbourhood of a pole.

10.4.3. Essential Singularity.

(Ravishankar 2002)

A point $z = a$ is called an essential singularity if the Laurent's expansion about $z = a$ consists of an infinite number of terms with negative powers of $(z - a)$. We may also notice that we have an essential singularity at an isolated singular point if the singularity is neither removable nor a pole.

The behaviour of a function in the neighbourhood of an essential singularity is very complicated. In this connection, we shall prove the following result due to Weierstrass :

If $z = a$ is an essential singularity of a function, then for any arbitrary number η, arbitrary $\varepsilon > 0$ and arbitrary $\rho > 0$, there exists a point z such that $0 < |z - a| < \rho$ for which
$$|f(z) - \eta| < \varepsilon.$$

This result means that in every arbitrary neighbourhood of an essential singularity, there exists a point for which the value of the function is arbitrarily near any arbitrarily assigned number.

Suppose now that the result is *not* true. This means that there exists a number η and a deleted neighbourhood $0 < |z - a| < r$ for every point z of which
$$|f(z) - \eta| > \varepsilon,$$

where ε is a given positive number.

Thus for $0 < |z - a| < r$, we have

$$\left| \frac{1}{f(z) - \eta} \right| < \frac{1}{\varepsilon}.$$

Applying Riemann's theorem [Case (a), § ???], we see that the function
$$1 / [f(z) - \eta]$$

has a removable singularity at $z = a$.

Suppose that in the neighbourhood of $z = a$, we have

$$\frac{1}{f(z) - \eta} = c_0 + c_1(z - a) + c_2(z - a)^2 + ...$$

Now if $c_0 \neq 0$ and if we define $f(z)$ for $z = a$, by the equality

$$\frac{1}{f(z) - \eta} = c_0, \quad i.e., \quad f(a) = \eta + \frac{1}{c_0},$$

we see that $1 / [f(z) - \eta]$ becomes analytic and non-zero for $z = a$. From this we deduce that $f(z)$ is itself analytic at $z = a$. Thus we arrive at a contradiction.

Again, we suppose that

$$c_0 = c_1 = ... = c_{m-1} = 0, \quad c_m \neq 0.$$

In this case $z = a$ is a zero of order m of $1 / [f(z) - \eta]$ and accordingly a pole of order m of $[f(z) - \eta]$ and also therefore a pole of $f(z)$. Thus we again arrive at a contradiction.

Hence we have the theorem as stated.

Note 1. It easily follows from above that $f(z)$ can be made to approach any specified limit by an appropriate approach to an essential singularity.

Note 2. From the preceding it is clear that as $z \to a$

(a) $\lim f(z)$ exists finitely if $z = a$ is a removable singularity;

(b) $\lim f(z) = \infty$ if $z = a$ is a pole;

(c) $\lim f(z)$ does not exist if $z = a$ is an essential singularity.

Example. *$z = 0$ is an essential singularity of $e^{1/z}$*; in fact, we have for every $z \neq 0$,

$$e^{1/z} = 1 + \frac{1}{z} + \frac{1}{2!\,z^2} + \frac{1}{3!\,z^3} + \ldots$$

$$= 1 + z^{-1} + \frac{z^{-2}}{2!} + \frac{z^{-3}}{3!} + \ldots$$

Ex. If a is an essential singularity of $f(z)$ and η is any given number, prove that there exists a sequence $\{a_n\}$ of numbers tending to a such that,

$$\lim_{n \to \infty} f(a_n) = \eta.$$

10.5. Behaviour at infinity. We shall at this stage find it convenient to consider the point at infinity and to state what we may mean by saying that a function $f(z)$ is analytic at infinity or that infinity is a singularity of $f(z)$. Of course the consideration of the nature of a function at infinity can arise only when the function is defined in some neighbourhood

$$|z| > k$$

of infinity. We suppose that a function

$$w = f(z)$$

is defined in some neighbourhood of infinity.

We introduce the transformation

$$z = 1/Z$$

and consider the function

$$w = f(1/Z) = \varphi(Z), \text{ (say)}$$

in a neighbourhood of $Z = 0$. Surely $\phi(Z)$ is not defined for $Z = 0$.

We now say that *$f(z)$ is analytic at infinity if the corresponding function $\phi(Z)$ has a removable singularity at $Z = 0$. Further $f(z)$ is said to have a pole of order m or an essential singularity at infinity, according as $\phi(Z)$ has a pole of order m or an essential singularity at $Z = 0$.*

10.5.1. Taylor's expansion and Laurent's expansion about infinity.

Suppose first that $f(z)$ is analytic at infinity. Then since the corresponding function $\phi(Z)$ has a removable singularity at $Z = 0$, we must have, for some deleted neighbourhood of $Z = 0$,

$$\phi(Z) = a_0 + a_1 Z + a_2 Z^2 + a_3 Z^3 + \ldots$$

$$\Rightarrow \qquad f(z) = a_0 + \frac{a_1}{z} + \frac{a_2}{z^2} + \frac{a_3}{z^3} + \ldots$$

which is the Taylor's expansion about $z = \infty$ so that the Taylor's expansion about ∞ consists only of non-positive integral powers of z, if the function is analytic at ∞.

Suppose now that $f(z)$ is singular at infinity. We have, in this case, for some deleted neighbourhood of $Z = 0$, the Laurent's expansion

$$\phi(Z) = a_0 + a_1 Z + a_2 Z^2 + \ldots + a_{-1} Z^{-1} + a_{-2} Z^2 + \ldots$$

This corresponds to the Laurent's expansion

$$f(z) = a_0 + a_1 z^{-1} + a_2 z^{-2} + \ldots + a_{-1} z + a_{-2} z^2 + \ldots$$

about $z = \infty$; the principal part at infinity, viz.,

$$a_{-1} z + a_{-2} z^{-2} + \ldots$$

consisting of a finite or an infinite number of terms with positive integral powers of z according as infinity is a pole or an essential singularity of $f(z)$.

10.6. Entire and Meromorphic Functions. We shall now introduce the two important concepts of *entire* and *meromorphic functions*.

1. Entire functions. Def. *A function which is analytic in the entire complex plane is called an Entire or an Integral function.*

Thus on the extended complex plane, an entire function can have a singularity at infinity only.

Some examples of entire functions are e^z, sin z, cos z, sinh z, cosh z.

2. Meromorphic functions. Def. *A function whose only singularities in the entire complex plane are poles is called a Meromorphic function.*

Thus on the extended complex plane, a meromorphic function can have an essential singularity at infinity only.

Some examples of meromorphic functions are the functions tan z, cot z, sec z, cosec z, tanh$z$, coth z, sech z, cosech z.

In the following, we prove two theorems which characterise polynomials and rational functions as entire and meromorphic functions respectively. This will be done in terms of the nature of singularities at infinity.

Firstly we restate Liouville's theorem which has already been stated and proved in § 9.14.

Liouville's Theorem. *A function having no singularity anywhere in the extended complex plane is a constant.*   (Ravishankar 2000)

The equivalence of the two statements is a simple consequence of the fact that the condition of uniform boundedness of $f(z)$ follows from that of analyticity at infinity.

10.6.1. Characterisation of polynomials as entire functions. Consider a polynomial

$$f(z) = a_0 + a_1 z + \ldots + a_n z^n, \ (a_n \neq 0) \qquad \ldots(1)$$

of order n.

Replacing z by $1 / Z$, we see that the corresponding function $\phi(Z)$ is given by

$$\phi(Z) = f(Z^{-1}) = a_0 + a_1 Z^{-1} + \ldots + a_n Z^{-n}.$$

This shows that *a polynomial of order n has a pole of order n at infinity*. We shall now prove the converse.

Theorem I. *An entire function $f(z)$ whose singularity at infinity is at the most, a pole is necessarily a polynomial.*

Let the Taylor's expansion of $f(z)$ about $z = 0$ be given by

$$f(z) = a_0 + a_1 z + \ldots + a_n z^n + \ldots \qquad \ldots(1)$$

Since $f(z)$ is analytic at every finite point, the equality holds for every value of z and, in particular, for a neighbourhood

$$|z| > k$$

of infinity; k being a positive number.

Replacing z by $1 / Z$, we obtain

$$\phi(z) = f\left(\frac{1}{Z}\right) = a_0 + \frac{a_1}{Z} + \frac{a_2}{Z^2} + ... + \frac{a_n}{Z^n} + ...$$

$$= a_0 + a_1 Z^{-1} + a_2 Z^{-2} + ... + a_n Z^{-n} + ... \qquad ...(2)$$

As given, $f(z)$ has a pole at infinity. Thus $\phi(Z)$ has a pole at $Z = 0$ and according to series (2) can have only a finite number of non-zero coefficients. Suppose that $a_n = 0$ for $n > m$ and $a_m \neq 0$.

Then, we have

$$\phi(Z) = a_0 + a_1 Z^{-1} + ... + a_m Z^{-m},$$

and accordingly

$$f(z) = a_0 + a_1 z + ... + a_m z^m.$$

Thus $f(z)$ is a polynomial of order m. Here, m is the order of the pole at infinity of the given function $f(z)$.

Theorem II. *A polynomial of degree n has no singularities in the finite part of the plane but has a pole of order n at infinity.* (Agra 2001)

Let $f(z) = a_0 + a_1 z + a_2 z^2 + ... + a_n z^n$, $(a_n \neq 0)$

be a polynomial of degree n.

$$\therefore \qquad f\left(\frac{1}{z}\right) = a_0 + \frac{a_1}{z} + \frac{a_2}{z^2} + ... + \frac{a_n}{z^n}.$$

This shows that $f(1/z)$ has a pole of order n at $z = 0$ so that $f(z)$ has a pole of order n at $z = \infty$.

Also it is clear that $f(z)$ has no singularities in the finite part of the plane.

Theorem III. *The order of a zero of a polynomial equals the order of its first non-vanishing derivative.*

Supose $z = a$ is zero of order m of a polynomial $P(z)$.

Then $\qquad P(z) = (z - a)^m Q(z),\ Q(a) \neq 0.$

Differentiating both sides successively m times, we get

$$P'(z) = m(z - a)^{m-1} Q(z) + (z - a)^m Q'(z)$$

$$P''(z) = m(m - 1)(z - a)^{m-2} Q(z) + 2m(z - a)^{m-1} Q'(z) + (z - a)^m Q''(z)$$

---- ---- ---- ---- ---- ----

---- ---- ---- ---- ---- ----

$$P^m(z) = m! Q(z) +{}^m C_1 m!(z - a) Q'(z) + ... + (z - a)^m Q^m(z).$$

Putting $z = a$ in above relations, we get

$$P(a) = P'(a) = P''(a) = ---- = P^{m-1}(a) = 0 \text{ and } P^m(a) = m! Q(a) \neq 0.$$

Hence the order of a zero of a polynomial equals the order of its non-vanishing derivative.

Theorem IV. *(Luca's Theorem). If all the zeros of a polynomial lie in a half plane, then all the zeros of derivative also lie in the same half plane.* (Kerala 2001)

Let $P_n(z)$ be a polynomial of degree n and $z_1, z_2, ... , z_r$ all the zeros of $P_n(z)$.

Then

$$P_n(z) = a_n(z - z_1)(z - z_2)...(z - z_n) \qquad ...(1)$$

all the z_k are not necessarily distinct.

Taking log of both sides of (1) and differentiating, we get

$$\frac{P_n'(z)}{P_n(z)} = \frac{1}{z - z_1} + \frac{1}{z - z_2} + \dots + \frac{1}{z - z_n} \quad \dots(2)$$

Let H be the half plane defined as the part of the complex plane consisting of all the points z with

$$I\left(\frac{z - a}{b}\right) < 0$$

Since all the zeros of $P_n(z)$ lie in the same half plane, therefore

$$I\left(\frac{z_k - a}{b}\right) < 0 \quad \dots(3)$$

where $k = 1, 2, \dots, n$.

If α is any zero of $P_n'(z)$, then we have to show that α also lies in the same half plane H. We shall prove the result by contradiction.

Suppose $\quad I\left(\frac{\alpha - a}{b}\right) > 0 \quad \dots(4)$

Now $\quad I\left(\frac{\alpha - z_k}{b}\right) = I\left[\frac{(\alpha - a) - (z_k - a)}{b}\right]$

$$= I\left(\frac{\alpha - a}{b}\right) - I\left(\frac{z_k - a}{b}\right) > 0 \quad \dots(5)$$

from (3) and (4).

For any complex number z, we have

$$I(z) = -I(z^{-1})|z|^2$$

∴ From (5)

$$-I\left(\frac{b}{\alpha - z_k}\right)\left|\frac{b}{\alpha - z_k}\right|^2 > 0$$

or $\quad I\left(\frac{b}{\alpha - z_k}\right) < 0 \quad \dots(6)$

Putting $z = \alpha$ in (2) and multiplying both sides by b, we get

$$\frac{b\,P_n'(\alpha)}{P_n(\alpha)} = \sum_{k=1}^{n} \frac{b}{\alpha - z_k}$$

∴ $\quad I\left[\frac{b\,P_n'(\alpha)}{P_n(\alpha)}\right] = \sum_{k=1}^{n} I\left(\frac{b}{\alpha - z_k}\right) < 0 \quad$ from (6)

Thus $P_n'(\alpha) \neq 0$ which contradicts the fact that α is a zero of $P_n'(\alpha)$. Hence all the zeros of $P_n'(\alpha)$ must lie in H.

Theorem V. *If a function $f(z)$ is analytic for all finite values of z and as $|z| \to \infty$,*

$$|f(z)| = A(|z|^k)$$

then $f(z)$ is a polynomial of degree $\le k$.

Given that $f(z)$ is analytic in the finite part of the plane so that by Taylor's expansion

$$f(z) = \sum_{n=0}^{\infty} a_n z^n \text{ for } |z| < R.$$

Now let max. $|f(z)| = M(r)$ on the circle $|z| = r$ where $r < R$.

Then by Cauchy's inequality, we have

$$|a_n| \le \frac{M(r)}{r^n} \forall n.$$

$$= \frac{A(|z|^k)}{r^n} \text{ as } M(r) = |f(z)|$$

$$= A(|z|^k) \text{ when } z \to \infty.$$

$$= \frac{Ar^k}{r^n} = \frac{A}{r^{n-k}} \to 0 \text{ as } r \to \infty \text{ since } n > k.$$

$$\therefore \qquad a_n = 0 \ \forall \ n > k.$$

$$\therefore \qquad f(z) = a_0 + a_1 z + a_2 z^2 + \ldots + a_k z^k,$$

i.e., $f(z)$ is a polynomial of degree k.

10.6.2. Characterisation of Rational functions as Meromorphic functions. Consider any rational function

$$R(z) = \frac{a_0 + a_1 z + \ldots + a_n z^n}{b_0 + b_1 z + \ldots + b_m z^m}, \ \ a_n \ne 0, \ b_m \ne 0.$$

The only singularities of $R(z)$ are the zeros of the denominator which are finite in number and possibly also infinity. Infinity will be a singular point and necessarily a pole if $n > m$.

In fact, replacing z by $1/Z$, we obtain

$$\phi(Z) = R\left(\frac{1}{Z}\right) = \frac{1}{Z^{n-m}} \frac{a_n + a_{n-1}Z + \ldots + a_0 Z^n}{b_m + b_{m-1}Z + \ldots + b_0 Z^m}$$

$$= Z^{m-n} \psi(Z), \text{ (say)}.$$

Here $\psi(Z)$ is analytic and non-zero at $Z = 0$. In fact

$$\psi(0) = a_n / b_m \ne 0.$$

Thus we see that $Z = 0$ is a pole [of $\varphi(Z)$ and accordingly $z = \infty$ is a pole of $f(z)$ if and only if $n > m$]. Thus we see that the only singularities of a rational function in the extended complex plane can be poles. We now prove the converse.

Every function which has only poles as singularities in the extended complex plane is a rational function.   *(Kanpur 2007; IPS 2003)*

This means that *a meromorphic function $f(z)$ whose singularity at infinity is, at the most, a pole is necessarily a rational function.*

Suppose that $f(z)$ is a function with poles only as singularities in the extended complex plane. Such a function can have only finite number of poles. For otherwise, the infinite set of poles would have a limiting point which would be a non-isolated singular point and as such at least not a pole.

Let $a_1, a_2, \ldots, a_r$

be the r poles of $f(z)$ in the complex plane and let

$$\psi_1(z) = \frac{a_{11}}{(z-a_1)} + \frac{a_{12}}{(z-a_1)^2} + \dots + \frac{a_{1m_1}}{(z-a_1)^{m_1}}$$

....

....

$$\psi_r(z) = \frac{a_{r1}}{(z-a_r)} + \frac{a_{r2}}{(z-a_r)^2} + \dots + \frac{a_{rm_r}}{(z-a_r)^{m_r}}$$

be the principal parts of $f(z)$ at these poles.

Also let

$$\psi(z) = a_0 + a_1 z + \dots + a_k z^k$$

be the principal part of $f(z)$ at infinity.

Then the function

$$f(z) - [\psi_1(z) + \dots + \psi_r(z) + \psi(z)]$$

is analytic at all points in the extended complex plane and as such, by Liouville's theorem, it is constant, say b.

Thus we have

$$f(z) = \psi_1(z) + \dots + \psi_r(z) + \psi(z) + b.$$

The forms of $\psi_r(z)$, ..., $\psi(z)$, $\psi(z)$ show that $f(z)$ is a rational function.

Note. The above denominator also establishes the fact of existence of partial fractions of a rational function.

10.7. Some Theorems on Poles and Singularities.

Theorem I. *If $f(z)$ has a pole at $z = a$ then $|f(z)| \to \infty$ as $z \to a$.* (M.S. Univ. 2007)

Let $z = a$ be a pole of order m. Then by Laurent's theorem

$$f(z) = \sum_{n=0}^{\infty} a_n (z-a)^n + \sum_{n=1}^{\infty} b_n (z-a)^{-n}$$

$$= \sum_{n=0}^{\infty} a_n (z-a)^n + \frac{b_1}{(z-a)} + \frac{b_2}{(z-a)^2} + \dots + \frac{b_m}{(z-a)^m}$$

$$= \sum_{n=0}^{\infty} a_n (z-a)^n + \frac{1}{(z-a)^m} [b_m + b_{m-1}(z-a)$$

$$+ \dots + b_2 (z-a)^{m-2} + b_1 (z-a)^{m-1}] \qquad \dots(1)$$

The expression within brackets on the R.H.S. tends to b_m as $z \to a$ and consequently R.H.S. tends to infinity.

$\therefore \qquad |f(z)| \to \infty$ as $z \to a$.

Theorem II. *If an analytic function $f(z)$ has a pole of order m at $z = a$, then $1/f(z)$ has a zero of order m at $z = a$ and conversely.*

$$f(z)(z-a)^m = \sum_{n=0}^{\infty} a_n (z-a)^{m+n} + b_m$$

$$+ b_{m-1}(z-a) + b_2 (z-a)^{m-2} + b_1 (z-a)^{m-1}$$

or $\qquad f(z)(z-a)^m = \phi(z)$, (say) $\qquad \dots(1)$

where $\phi(z)$ is analytic and $\phi(a) \neq 0$.

From (1), we have

$$\frac{1}{f(z)} = \frac{(z-a)^m}{\phi(z)} \qquad \qquad ...(2)$$

Let $z \to a$ in (2) and we know that $\phi(a) \neq 0$, we get

$$\frac{1}{f(z)} = 0 \text{ as } z \to a.$$

This relation shows that $1/f(z)$ has a zero of order m at $z = a$.

Conversely, $1/f(z)$ has a zero of order m and as such it can be written as

$$\frac{1}{f(z)} = (z-a)^m \psi(z)$$

where $\psi(z)$ is analytic and $\psi(a) \neq 0$.

$$\therefore \quad (z-a)^m f(z) = \frac{1}{\psi(z)} = \phi(z), \text{ (say)} \qquad ...(3)$$

Since $\psi(z)$ is analytic, therefore, $\phi(z)$ is also analytic. Also as $\psi(a) \neq 0$, therefore, $\phi(a)$ is also not zero.

The form (3) shows that $f(z)$ has a pole of order m at $z = a$.

Poles are isolated. Let $z = a$ be a pole of order m for the analytic function $f(z)$ and hence by the theorem $1/f(z)$ is analytic and has a zero of order m at $z \to a$. But since zeros are isolated (§ 10.2.1) and hence poles are also isolated.

Theorem III. *Let $f(z)$ be an analytic function in a simply connected region D. Let a_1, a_2, ..., a_n be a sequence of zeros having a as its limit point; a being the interior point of D. Then either $f(z)$ vanishes identically or else has an isolated essential singularity.*

Let $f(z)$ be an analytic function in a simply connected domain D, therefore, it is continuous in D. Let a_1, a_2, a_3, ... be an infinite set of zeros of $f(z)$ which must have at least one limit point say a which may or may not be a point of the set.

If a is a point of the set then it is a zero of $f(z)$ and since it is also limit point of the set of zeros, it should have in its neighbourhood cluster of zeros. But we know that zeros are isolated *i.e.*, zeros of a function must not have any other zero around it. Therefore a cannot be a zero of $f(z)$ unless the function is identically zero in the domain D.

In case the function does not vanish identically in D, then a is not a zero of $f(z)$ while being surrounded by many zeros. Thus a is a singularity which is not a pole as $f(z)$ does not tend to infinity in the neighbourhood of a. Hence a is an essential singularity. But the singularity is isolated because in the neighbourhood of a the function $f(z)$ is analytic tending to zero everywhere in the neighbourhood. Thus a is an isolated essential singularity.

Theorem IV. (Identity Theorem). *If $f(z)$ and $g(z)$ are analytic functions in a domain D and if $f(z) = g(z)$ on a subset of D which has a limit point in D, then $f(z) = g(z)$ in whole of D.*

Let $F(z) = f(z) - g(z)$, then $F(z)$ is an analytic function in D. Since $f(z) = g(z)$ on a subset of D, then $F(z)$ vanishes at all points of D. If α is the limit point of this subset then $F(z)$ vanishes at infinite number of points in the small neighbourhood of α. But the limit point α is in D, therefore $F(z)$ is continuous at α and hence $F(\alpha) = 0$. Since the zeros of $f(z)$ are isolated, hence α cannot be a zero of $F(z)$ unless $F(z)$ vanishes identically in D. Hence $F(z)$ vanishes identically in D *i.e.*, $f(z) = g(z)$ in whole of D

Limit Point of Poles.

Theorem V. *The limit point of the poles of a function $f(z)$ is a non-isolated essential singularity.*

Let $z_1, z_2, z_3, \ldots..$ be an infinite set of poles of $f(z)$ having a limit point. Suppose α be this limit point, then $f(z)$ becomes unbounded at an infinite number of points in the small neighbourhood of $z = \alpha$, and hence $f(z)$ cannot be analytic at $z = \alpha$, *i.e.*, $z = \alpha$ is a singularity of $f(z)$.

The limit point $z = \alpha$ cannot be a pole, since it can have an infinite number of poles in the small neighbourhood around itself while the poles are isolated.

Also this limit point $z = \alpha$ cannot be a zero of $f(z)$ because the function $f(z)$ is not analytic in its neighbourhood. Thus we conclude that α is an essential singularity of $f(z)$. Also this singularity is not isolated as there are poles in its neighbourhood. Therefore $z = \alpha$ is a non-isolated essential singularity of $f(z)$.

Hence the limit point of poles is a non-isolated essential singularity.

Theorem VI. *Let $f(z)$ have a pole of order m at $z = a$, then the function $\phi(z)$ defined by $\phi(z) = (z - a)^m f(z)$ has a removable singularity at a and that $\phi(a) \neq 0$, also show that the residue at z_o is given by $\dfrac{\phi^{m-1}(z_0)}{(m-1)!}$.*

Since $f(z)$ has a pole of order m at $z = a$, it can be expanded in Laurent's series in the annulus $0 < |z - a| < R$, in the form

$$f(z) = \sum_{n=0}^{\infty} a_n (z - a)^n + \left[\frac{b_1}{z - a} + \frac{b_2}{(z - a)^2} + \ldots + \frac{b_m}{(z - a)^m} \right]$$

where $b_m \neq 0$.

Now
$$\phi(z) = (z - a)^m f(z)$$

$$= (z - a)^m \left[\sum_{n=0}^{\infty} a_n (z - a)^n + \frac{b_1}{z - a} + \frac{b_2}{(z - a)^2} + \ldots + \frac{b_m}{(z - a)^m} \right]$$

$$= \sum_{n=0}^{\infty} a_n (z - a)^{n+m} + b_1 (z - a)^{m-1} +$$

$$b_2 (z - a)^{m-2} + \ldots + b_m \quad \ldots(i)$$

(1) define a function $\phi(z)$ in the neighbourhood of $z = a$ except at $z = 0$.

If we define $\phi(z)$ at $z = a$ by $\phi(a) = b_m$ then $\phi(a) \neq 0$.

Thus the expansion of $\phi(z)$ given by (i) is valid at the point a and in its neighbourhood. Also the series given by (1) is a convergent power series.

Thus $\phi(z)$ is analytic function if $\phi(a) = b_m \neq 0$.

Hence $\phi(z)$ has a removable singularity at $z = a$ and thus $\phi(a) \neq 0$.

Since $\phi(z)$ has become analytic at z_0 therefore (1) represents a Taylor's series for $\phi(z)$.

Hence coefficient of $(z - z_0)^{m-1} = \dfrac{\phi^{m-1}(z_0)}{(m-1)!}$ but from (1) coefficient of $(z - z_0)^{m-1} = b_1$, which is the residue at z_0.

Hence the residue at $z_0 = \dfrac{\phi^{m-1}(z_0)}{(m-1)!}$.

Limit Point of Zeros

Theorem VII. *The limit point of the zero of a function* $f(z)$ *is a non-isolated essential singularity.*

Let $z_1, z_2, z_3 \ldots$ be an infinite set of zeros of $f(z)$, which necessarily must have at least one limit point. Suppose z_0 is their limit point which may or may not be a point of the set.

If z_0 is a point of the set, it must itself be a zero of $f(z)$, and in addition, by virtue of being the limit point, should have in its neighbourhood of a cluster of zeros, which goes against the proved fact that the zero of a function must not have any other zero around at (zeros are isolated). Hence z_0 cannot be a zero of $f(z)$ unless the function is identically zero in the domain D.

If the function $f(z)$ does not vanish identically in D, then z_0 is not a zero of $f(z)$, while being surrounded by many zeros. This shows that z_0 is a singularity. The singularity is not a pole since $f(z)$ does not tend to infinity in the neighbourhood of z_0 (as a matter of fact it tends to zero). Therefore z_0 is an essential singularity. But the singularity is not isolated since in the neighbourhood of z_0 the function $f(z)$ is analytic (tending to zero everywhere in the neighbourhood). Hence z_0 is an isolated essential singularity.

Theorem VIII. *Let* $f(z)$ *be function such that for some positive integer m, a value* $\phi(a)$ *exists and* $\phi(a) \neq 0$ *such that the function* $\phi(z) = (z-a)^m f(z)$ *is analytic at a, then f has a pole of order m at a.*   (*Meerut 2005*)

Since the function $\phi(z)$ is analytic at $z = a$, it can be expressed in Taylor's series about the point $z = a$.

$$\therefore \qquad \phi(z) = \sum_{n-0}^{\infty} a_n (z-a)^n \qquad \text{where } a_n = \frac{\phi^n(a)}{n!}$$

$$(z-a)^m f(z) = a_0 + a_1(z-a) + a_2(z-a)^2 + \ldots + a_{m-1}(z-a)^{m-1}$$

$$+ \sum_{n=m}^{\infty} a_n (z-a)^n$$

$$f(z) = \left[\frac{a_0}{(z-a)^m} + \frac{a_1}{(z-a)^{m-1}} + \ldots + \frac{a_{m-1}}{(z-a)} \right] + \sum_{n=m}^{\infty} a_n (z-a)^{n-m}.$$

Now, $a_0 = \phi(0) \neq 0$.

Since the expansion of $f(z)$ about $z = a$, there are finite number of negative powers of

$(z-a)$ and the coefficeint of highest negative power, *i.e.*, of $\dfrac{1}{(z-a)^m}$ is zero, hence $f(z)$ has a pole of order m at $z = a$.

Removable Singularity.

Theorem IX. (Riemann Theorem). *If* $z = a$ *is an isolated singularity of* $f(z)$ *and if* $|f(z)|$ *is bounded on some deleted neighbourhood of a, then a is a removable singularity.*

Let $|f(z)|$ be bounded on some deleted neighbourhood N (a) of a, then

$$|f(z)| \leq M$$

where M is the maximum value of $f(z)$ on a circle C bounded by $|z - a| = r$.

The radius r is chosen so small that C lies entirely within N (a). By Laurent's expansion

$$f(z) = \sum_{n=0}^{\infty} a_n (z-a)^n + \sum_{n=1}^{\infty} b_n (z-a)^{-n} \qquad ...(1)$$

where
$$b_n = \frac{1}{2\pi i} \int_C (z-a)^{n-1} f(z)\, dz.$$

$$\therefore \quad |b_n| \le \frac{M}{2\pi i} \int_C |z-a|^{n-1} |dz|$$

$$= \frac{Mr^{n-1}}{2\pi} \cdot 2\pi r = Mr^n$$

or
$$|b_n| \le Mr^n \to 0 \text{ as } r \to 0.$$

$$\therefore \quad b_n = 0 \;\forall\; n.$$

Thus we conclude that principal part of Laurent's expansion for $f(z)$ contains no term. Hence by definition, we conclude that $z = a$ is a removable singularity.

The behaviour of a function near an essential singularity.

Theorem X. (Weierstrass Theorem). *In every neighbourhood of an essential singularity, there exists a point (and therefore an infinite number of such points) at which the function differs as little as we please from any previously assigned number.*

Or

If $z = a$ is an essential singularity of a function, then for any arbitrary number l, arbitrary $\varepsilon > 0$ and arbitrary $\rho > 0$, there exists a point z such that for $0 < |z - a| < \rho$, we have $|f(z) - l| < \varepsilon$. (*Kanpur 2000*)

We shall prove the theorem by contradiction method, *i.e.*, we assume that the theorem is not true. Then there exists a number l and the deleted neighbourhood $0 < |z - a| < \rho$ for every point of which and for arbitrary $\varepsilon > 0$,

$$|f(z) - l| > \varepsilon.$$

i.e. for every z satisfying $0 < |z - a| < \rho$ and for arbitrary $\varepsilon > 0$, we have

$$\left| \frac{1}{f(z) - l} \right| < 1/\varepsilon \qquad ...(1)$$

i.e. the function

$$|\phi(z)| = \left| \frac{1}{f(z) - l} \right|$$

is bounded in the deleted neighbourhood $0 < |z - a| < \rho$ of essential singularity at $z = a$, then by theorem III, $\phi(z)$ has a removable singularity at $z = a$. Thus the Laurent's expansion of $\phi(z)$ in $0 < |z - a| < \rho$ will contain no negative power of $(z - a)$, *i.e.*, in this deleted neighbourhood we can write

$$\phi(z) = \frac{1}{f(z) - l} = \sum_{n=0}^{\infty} a_n (z-a)^n$$

$$= a_0 + a_1 (z-a) + a_2 (z-a)^2 + \ldots \qquad ...(2)$$

Now if $a_0 \ne 0$, then from (2), we have

$$\phi(a) = \frac{1}{f(z) - l} = a_0 \quad \therefore \quad f(z) = l + \frac{1}{a_0}.$$

Thus $\phi(z)$ is analytic and non-zero at $z = a$, from which it follows that $f(z)$ is analytic at $z = a$, which is a contradiction as $z = a$ is an essential singularity.

Again if we take

$$a_0 = 0 = a_1 = a_2 = ... = a_{m-1} \text{ and } a_m \neq 0$$

then from (2), we have

$$\phi(z) = \frac{1}{f(z) - l} = a_m (z-a)^m + a_{m+1} (z-a)^{m+1} + ...$$

$$= (z-a)^m \sum_{n=0}^{\infty} a_{m+n} (z-a)^n.$$

From which it follows that $z = a$ is a zero of order m of

$$\phi(z) = \frac{1}{f(z) - l}$$

and thus

$$f(z) - l = \frac{1}{\phi(z)}$$

has a pole of order m at $z = a$. But l is a constant number, therefore we conclude that $f(z)$ has a pole of order m at $z = a$, which is again a contradiction as $z = a$ is an essential singularity.

Thus our supposition that the theorem is not true is false. Hence the theorem is true.

EXAMPLES

1. *Prove that the function e^z has an isolated essential singularity at $z = \infty$.*

(Gorakhpur 2003, 2004)

Solution. The behaviour of the function $f(z) = e^z$ at $z = \infty$ is the same as the behaviour of the function $f(1/\xi) = e^{1/\xi}$ at $\xi = 0$.

Now

$$\lim_{\xi \to 0} f(1/\xi) = \lim_{\xi \to 0} e^{1/\xi}$$

$$= \lim_{\xi \to 0} \left[1 + \frac{1}{\xi} + \frac{1}{2! \, \xi^2} + ... \right].$$

This limit does not exist. We may also say that the principal part of $f(1/\xi)$ contains an infinite number of terms in $-$ve powers of t. Hence $\xi = 0$ is an isolated essential singularity of $e^{1/\xi}$ or $z = \infty$ is an isolated essential singularity of e^z.

2. *Find the singularities of the function*

$$\frac{e^{c/(z-a)}}{e^{z/a} - 1}$$

indicating the character of each singularity.

(Garhwal 2007, Meerut 2003)

Solution. $$f(z) = \frac{e^{c/(z-a)}}{e^{z/a} - 1}.$$

Equating to zero the denominator of $f(z)$, we get

$$e^{z/a} = 1 = e^{2n\pi i}$$

or $$z = 2n\pi i a \quad (n = 0, \pm 1, \pm 2, ...)$$ ...(1)

The numerator does not vanish for any of these values of z and as such they are the singularities of $f(z)$ and each of the point given by (1) is a pole of order one.

Again
$$e^{z/a} - 1 = e^{1 + (z-a)/a} - 1$$
$$= e \cdot e^{(z-a)/a} - 1$$
$$= e\left[1 + \left(\frac{z-a}{a}\right) + \frac{1}{2!}\left(\frac{z-a}{a}\right)^2 + \ldots\right] - 1$$

$\therefore$
$$f(z) = \frac{1 + \left(\dfrac{c}{z-a}\right) + \dfrac{1}{2!}\left(\dfrac{c}{z-a}\right)^2 + \ldots}{e\left[1 + \left(\dfrac{z-a}{a}\right) + \dfrac{1}{2!}\left(\dfrac{z-a}{a}\right)^2 + \ldots\right] - 1}$$

$$= \frac{\text{Nr.}}{-\left[1 - e\left\{1 + \left(\dfrac{z-a}{a}\right) + \dfrac{1}{2!}\left(\dfrac{z-a}{a}\right)^2 + \ldots\right\}\right]}$$

$$= -\text{Nr.}\left[1 - e\left\{1 + \left(\frac{z-a}{a}\right) + \frac{1}{2!}\left(\frac{z-a}{a}\right)^2 + \ldots\right\}\right]^{-1}$$

$$= -\text{Nr.}\left[1 + e\left\{1 + \left(\frac{z-a}{a}\right) + \frac{1}{2!}\left(\frac{z-a}{a}\right)^2 + \ldots\right\} + e^2\left(1 + \frac{z-a}{a} + \ldots\right)^2 + \ldots\right]$$

On putting for numerator we observe that the expansion contains both +ve and –ve powers of $z - a$ and as such it represents Laurent's expansion of the given function. Besides this there are infinite number of terms which have –ve powers of $z - a$ i.e., the principal part of $f(z)$ contains infinite number of terms. Therefore $z = 0$ is an isolated essential singularity of $f(z)$.

3. *What kind of singularities the following functions have*:

(i) $f(z) = \dfrac{1}{\sin z - \cos z}$ at $z = \pi/4$

(Agra 2000, 2005; Meerut 2002 03; Kanpur 2003)

(ii) $f(z) = \dfrac{\cot \pi z}{(z-a)^2}$ at $z = 0$ and $z = \infty$

(Garhwal 2000)

(iii) $f(z) = \dfrac{1 - e^z}{1 + e^z}$ at $z = \infty$

(iv) $f(z) = z \operatorname{cosec} z$ at $z = \infty$?							(*Meerut* 2002)

Solution. (*i*) Poles of $f(z)$ are given by putting its denominator equal to zero.

$\therefore \quad \sin z - \cos z = 0 \quad \Rightarrow \quad \tan z = 1 = \tan \pi/4$

$\therefore \quad z = n\pi + \pi/4 \ (n = 0, 1, 2, \ldots).$

Clearly $z = \pi/4$ corresponding to $n = 0$ is a simple pole.

(ii) $f(z) = \dfrac{\cos \pi z}{\sin \pi z \, (z - a)^2}.$

Poles are given by $(\sin \pi z) \, (z - a)^2 = 0.$

$\Rightarrow \qquad\qquad \sin \pi z = 0 \text{ and } (z - a)^2 = 0$

$\Rightarrow \qquad\qquad nz = n\pi \text{ and } z = a \text{ (twice)}$

$\Rightarrow \qquad\qquad z = n \ (n = 0, \pm 1, \pm 2, \ldots).$

Clearly $z = \infty$ is the limit point of the poles and hence by definition $z = \infty$ is a non-isolated essential singularity. Also $z = a$ is obviously a pole of order two.

(iii) $f(z) = \dfrac{1 - e^z}{1 + e^z}.$

Poles of $f(z)$ are given by equating to zero the denominator of $f(z)$.

$\therefore \quad 1 + e^z = 0 \quad \Rightarrow \quad e^z = -1 = e^{\pi i}$

$\therefore \quad z = 2n\pi i + \pi i = (2n + 1) \, \pi i \ (n = 0, \pm 1, \pm 2, \ldots).$

Clearly $z = \infty$ is a limit point of the above sequence of poles and hence by definition $z = \infty$ is a non-isolated essential singularity.

(iv) $f(z) = \dfrac{z}{\sin z}.$

Poles are given by $\sin z = 0.$

$\therefore \quad z = n\pi \ (n = 0, \pm 1, \pm 2, \ldots).$

Limit point of the above sequence of poles is given by $z = \infty$ which therefore is a non-isolated essential singularity.

4. What kind of singularity have the following functions:

(i) $\sin \dfrac{1}{1 - z}$ at $z = 1$ (*Meerut 2003, Garhwal 2006*)

(ii) $\tan (1/z)$ at $z = 0$ (*Agra 2001, Kanpur 2004*)

(iii) $\dfrac{1}{\cos (1/z)}$ at $z = 0$

(iv) $\operatorname{cosec} \dfrac{1}{z}$ at $z = 0$

Solution.

(i) $\qquad\qquad f(z) = \sin \dfrac{1}{1 - z}$

zeros of $f(z)$ are given by $\sin \dfrac{1}{1 - z} = 0$, *i.e.*, $\dfrac{1}{1 - z} = n\pi$

or $\qquad\qquad z = 1 - \dfrac{1}{n\pi}$ $\qquad\qquad\qquad\qquad\qquad$ ($n = 0, \pm 1, \pm 2, \ldots$)

Obviously, $z = 1$ is the limit point of these zeros.

Hence $z = 1$ is an isolated essential singularity.

(ii) $\qquad f(z) = \tan \dfrac{1}{z} = \dfrac{\sin 1/z}{\cos 1/z}$

Poles of $f(z)$ are given by

$$\cos 1/z = 0 \quad \text{or} \quad \frac{1}{z} = 2n\pi + \frac{\pi}{2}$$

or $\qquad\qquad z = \dfrac{1}{\left(2n + \dfrac{1}{2}\right)\pi}$ $\qquad\qquad\qquad [n = 0, \pm 1, \pm 2, ...]$

Obviously, $z = 0$ is the limit point of these poles.

Hence $z = 0$ is non-isolated essential singularity.

(iii) $\qquad f(z) = \dfrac{1}{\cos 1/z}$

Poles are given by $\cos 1/z = 0$

or $\qquad\qquad z = \dfrac{1}{\left(2n + \dfrac{1}{2}\right)\pi}$ $\qquad\qquad\qquad [n = 0, \pm 1, \pm 2, ...]$

Obviously, $z = 0$ is the limit point of the sequence of these poles.

Hence $z = 0$ is a non-isolated essential singularity.

(iv) $\qquad f(z) = \mathrm{cosec} \dfrac{1}{z} = \dfrac{1}{\sin 1/z}$

Poles of $f(z)$ are given by putting the denominator equal to zero, i.e., by

$$\sin 1/z = 0 \qquad \text{or} \qquad 1/z = n\pi$$

or $\qquad\qquad z = 1/n\pi$ $\qquad\qquad\qquad\qquad (n = 0 \pm 1, \pm 2, ...)$

Obviously, $z = 0$ is a non-isolated essential singularity.

5. *Show that the function e^{-1/z^2} has no singularities.*

Solution. We have

$$f(z) = e^{-1/z^2}$$

Zeros of $f(z)$ are given by $e^{-1/z^2} = 0$ or $z^2 = 0$

$\therefore \ z = 0$ is a zero of order two.

So, there is no limit points of zeros, hence there is no singularity. Again, poles of $f(z)$ are given by putting the denominator equal to zero, i.e.,

by $\qquad\qquad e^{1/z^2} = 0$

which is not possible for any value of z real or complex. Therefore no poles.

Hence no singularity any where.

6. *Find zeros and poles of* $\left(\dfrac{z+1}{z^2+1}\right)^2$

Solution. Let $f(z) = \dfrac{(z+1)^2}{(z^-+1)^2}$

The zero of $f(z)$ is obtained by putting the numerater as zero, *i.e.,*

$$(z+1)^2 = 0 \qquad \text{or} \qquad z = -1, -1 \qquad \text{or} \qquad z = -1 \text{ is zero of order 2.}$$

The poles of $f(z)$ are given by $(z^2+1)^2 = 0$ or $(z+i)^2 (z-i)^2 = 0$

or $\qquad\qquad\qquad\qquad z = -i, -i, i, i,$

or $\qquad\qquad\qquad\qquad z = -i$ and $z = i$ both are poles of order 2.

10.8. Residue at an isolated singularity. Let $z = a$ be an isolated singularity of $f(z)$ so that $f(z)$ is analytic in a domain

$$0 < |z - a| < r$$

for some $r > 0$.

Thus the integral

$$\frac{1}{2\pi i} \int_C f(z)\, dz$$

is called the *Residue* of $f(z)$ at $z = a$; C being any positively oriented circle with its centre at a and radius $\rho < r$.

Clearly the residue is independent of the circle C and we may as well use any Jordan curve in the domain $0 < |z - a| < r$ with the point a in its interior.

We may see *that the residue of $f(z)$ or a finite isolated singular point $z = a$ is the coefficient of $(z - a)^{-1}$ in the Laurent's expansion of $f(z)$ around $z = a$.*

In fact, the coefficient a_n in the Laurent's expansion

$$f(z) = \sum_{n=-\infty}^{\infty} a_n (z - a)^n$$

is given by

$$a_n = \frac{1}{2\pi i} \int_C \frac{f(z)}{(z-a)^{n+1}}\, dz \quad \Rightarrow \quad a_{-1} = \frac{1}{2\pi i} \int_C f(z)\, dz.$$

Hence the result.

10.8.1. Residue at infinity. If infinity is an isolated singular point we define residue at infinity as being equal to the integral

$$\frac{1}{2\pi i} \int_C f(z)\, dz$$

where C is any *negatively* oriented circle

$$|z| = r.$$

Of course, r must be so chosen that no singular point other than possibly infinity belongs to the domain $|z| > r$.

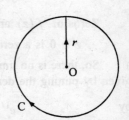

Fig. 10.1

We may also see that C has been taken as negatively oriented for the same is to be so described that the neighbourhood of infinity lies to the left of it.

It is important to notice that the residue of $f(z)$ at infinity cannot be taken as equal to that of the corresponding function $\varphi(Z) = f(1/Z)$ at zero.

In fact, by our definition, residue at infinity is

$$\frac{1}{2\pi i}\int_C f(z)\,dz = \frac{1}{2\pi i}\int_{C_0} f\left(\frac{1}{Z}\right)\left(-\frac{1}{Z^2}\right)dZ$$

$$= -\frac{1}{2\pi i}\int_{C_0}\frac{\varphi(Z)}{Z^2}\,dZ = \frac{1}{2\pi i}\int_{C_0}\varphi(Z)\,dZ.$$

Here C_0 is a circle described about the origin in the positive sense.

We may also remember that, in general, *residue at a point is not invariant for transformations*.

Note. It is easy to see that the residue at any non-infinite point is zero if the function is analytic at the point but this may not be the case for the infinite point. In fact, residue at infinity

$$= -\frac{1}{2\pi i}\int_C f(z)\,dz = -a_1,$$

where a_1 is the coefficient of z^{-1} in the Laurent's expansion of $f(z)$ in the neighbourhood of infinity.

As an illustration we may see that the residue at infinity of $1/z$ is -1, even though the function is analytic there.

10.9. Computation of Residues. As the computation of residues constitutes an important step in the application of the subject of residues, we shall now see how the residue at a point can be computed. Laurent's expansion about a point is the important tool for the determination of the residue at the point.

Now suppose that any given function is of the form

$$\frac{\varphi(z)}{\psi(z)}$$

and that $z = a$ is a zero of any order m of $\psi(z)$ but not a zero of $\varphi(z)$. Then a is a pole of order m of the function.

Firstly we consider the case of a *simple pole* in which case $m = 1$. We then have

$$\psi(z) = (z - a)f(z),$$

where $f(a) \neq 0$.

Thus

$$\frac{\varphi(z)}{\psi(z)} = \frac{1}{z-a}\frac{\varphi(z)}{f(z)}, \qquad\qquad\qquad [f(a) \neq 0]$$

$$= \frac{1}{z-a}F(z),\ \text{(say)} \qquad\qquad\qquad \left[F(z) = \frac{\varphi(z)}{f(z)}\right]$$

Hence $F(z)$ is analytic at a and $F(a) \neq 0$.

By Taylor's theorem, we have, in a neighbourhood of a,

$$F(z) = F(a) + (z - a)F'(a) + \ldots..$$

so that we have the Laurent series

$$\frac{\varphi(z)}{\psi(z)} = \frac{F(a)}{(z-a)} + F'(a) + \frac{(z-a)}{2!}F''(a) + \ldots..$$

Thus

$$\text{Res.}\ (a) = F(a) = \frac{\varphi(a)}{f(a)}.$$

We shall now state this result in a form involving $\varphi(z)$ and $\psi(z)$ only as follows:

The residue of

$$\frac{\varphi(z)}{\psi(z)}$$

at $z = a$ which is a zero of order one of $\psi(z)$ but not a zero of $\varphi(z)$ is

$$\lim_{z \to a} \frac{(z-a)\,\varphi(z)}{\psi(z)} \quad or \quad \frac{\varphi(a)}{\psi'(a)}.$$

Since

$$\frac{(z-a)\,\varphi(z)}{\psi(z)} = \frac{(z-a)\,\varphi(z)}{(z-a)\,f(z)} = F(z), \text{ when } z \neq a.$$

$$\therefore \lim_{z \to a} \frac{(z-a)\,\varphi(z)}{\psi(z)} = \lim_{z \to a} F(z) = F(a) = \text{Res.}(a).$$

Also

$$\psi'(z) = f(z) + (z-a)\,f'(z)$$

so that

$$\psi'(a) = f(a)$$

and

$$\frac{\varphi(a)}{\psi'(a)} = \frac{\varphi(a)}{f(a)} = F(a) = \text{Res.}(a).$$

Now suppose that a is a pole of any order m whatsoever. We have then for a neighbourhood of a,

$$\psi(z) = (z-a)^m f(z),$$

where $f(a) \neq 0$.

Now

$$\frac{\varphi(z)}{\psi(z)} = \frac{1}{(z-a)^m} \cdot \frac{\psi(z)}{f(z)} = \frac{1}{(z-a)^m} F(z), \text{ (say)} \qquad \ldots(1)$$

where $F(a) \neq 0$.

By Taylor's theorem, we have, in some neighbourhood of a,

$$F(z) = F(a) + (z-a)\,F'(a) + \ldots\ldots + (z-a)^{m-1} \frac{F^{m-1}(a)}{(m-1)!}$$

$$+ (z-a)^m \frac{F^m(a)}{m!} + \ldots\ldots \qquad \ldots(2)$$

From (1) and (2), we see that the residue at a of $\varphi(z)/\psi(z)$ is

$$= \frac{F^{m-1}(a)}{(m-1)!}.$$

To find $F^{m-1}(a)$, we proceed as follows:

We have

$$F(z) = \frac{\varphi(z)}{f(z)} = \frac{(z-a)^m \varphi(z)}{(z-a)^m f(z)} = \frac{(z-a)^m \varphi(z)}{\psi(z)}$$

$$\Rightarrow \qquad F(z)\,\psi(z) = (z-a)^m \varphi(z) \qquad \ldots(3)$$

We now substitute the power series expressions for $\phi(z)$ and $\psi(z)$ and the Taylor's power series expression (2) for F (z) in (3). As the multiplication of absolutely convergent series is admissible, we shall, on multiplying and equating the coefficients of a sufficient number of different powers of $(z - a)$ obtain $F^{m-1}(a)$ and hence the residue $F^{m-1}(a) / (m - 1)!$ at a.

EXAMPLES

1. *Find the residues for the following functions at the given points:*

(a) $(z^4 + 1) z^{-1} (z^2 - 1)^{-1}$ *for $z = 0$.*

(b) $\cot z$ *for $z = 0$.*

(c) $(1 + z)^{-1} (1 + z^2)^{-1} e^{iz}$ *for $z = i$.*

Solution. In each of the three cases, the pole is simple.

(a) Res. $(0) = \lim_{z \to 0} \left[z \cdot \dfrac{z^4 + 1}{z(z^2 - 1)} \right] = -1$.

(b) Res. $(0) = \lim_{z \to 0} \left(z \cdot \dfrac{\cos z}{\sin z} \right) = 1$.

(c) Res. $(i) = \lim_{z \to i} \left[(z - i) \cdot \dfrac{e^{iz}}{(1 + z)(z + i)(z - i)} \right] = -\dfrac{i + 1}{4e}$.

2. *Find the residue at i of the function*

$$\frac{1}{(z^2 + 1)^2 \log(2 + iz)}.$$

Solution. Writing

$$f(z) = \log(2 + iz),$$

we see that

$$f(i) = \log 1.$$

Also

$$f'(i) = i \neq 0.$$

Thus considering the principal branch of $\log(2 + iz)$ for which the value is 0 for $z = i$, we see that i is a zero of first order of $\log(2 + iz)$.

Thus i is a pole of third order of the given function. We write

$$\varphi(z) = \frac{1}{(z^2 + 1)^2 \log(2 + iz)}$$

$$= \frac{1}{(z - i)^3} \cdot \frac{(z - i)}{(z + i)^2 \log(2 + iz)} = \frac{1}{(z - i)^3} F(z), \quad \text{(say)}.$$

Here F $(i) \neq 0$.

The required residue is

$$\frac{1}{2!} F''(i)$$

so that we have to find $F''(i)$.

We have

$$(z + i)^2 \log(2 + iz) F(z) = (z - i). \qquad \text{...(1)}$$

We shall now express each side as a power series in $(z - i)$. We have

$$(z + i)^2 = (z - i + 2i)^2$$

$$= - 4 + 4i (z - i) + (z - i)^2$$

$$\log (2 + iz) = 0 + i (z - i) + \frac{1}{2} (z - i)^2 - \frac{i}{3} (z - i)^3$$

Substituting in (1), we get

$$[- 4 + 4i (z - i) + (z - i)^2] \left[0 + i (z - i) + \frac{1}{2} (z - i)^2 - \frac{1}{3} (z - i)^3 + ... \right]$$

$$\times \left[F (i) + (z - i) F' (i) + \frac{1}{2!} (z - i)^2 F'' (i) + \frac{1}{3!} (z - i)^3 F''' (i) + ... \right]$$

$$= (z - i).$$

Multiplication of absolutely convergent series being admissible, we have, equating the coefficients of $(z - i)$, $(z - i)^2$ and $(z - i)^3$,

$$- 4iF (i) = 1,$$

$$- 6F (i) - 4iF' (i) = 0,$$

$$\frac{13i}{3} F (i) - 6F' (i) - 2iF'' (i) = 0.$$

Solving these, we obtain

$$F (i) = \frac{i}{4}, \quad F' (i) = - \frac{3}{8}, \quad F'' (i) = \frac{7}{12i}.$$

Thus the residue at i is $\frac{1}{2} F'' (i) = \frac{- 7i}{24}$.

3. *The function $f (z)$ has a double pole at $z = 0$ with residue 2, a simple pole at $z = 1$ with residue 2, is analytic at all other finite points of the plane and is bounded as $| z | \to \infty$. Also $f (2) = 5$ and $f (- 1) = 2$. Find $f (z)$.*

Solution. The principal parts of $f (z)$ at $z = 0$ and at $z = 1$ are of the form

$$\frac{2}{z} + \frac{a}{z^2}, \quad \frac{2}{z - 1}$$

respectively.

The function being analytic at all other finite points and bounded as $| z | \to \infty$, we see, by Liouville's theorem that the function

$$f (z) - \left(\frac{2}{z} + \frac{a}{z^2} \right) - \left(\frac{2}{z - 1} \right),$$

which is analytic at every point and bounded as $| z | \to \infty$, must be a constant.
Thus

$$f (z) - \left(\frac{2}{z} + \frac{a}{z^2} \right) - \frac{2}{z - 1} = b$$

$$\Rightarrow \qquad f (z) = \frac{2}{z} + \frac{a}{z^2} + \frac{2}{z - 1} + b.$$

Here a and b are constants. Putting $z = 2$ and $z = - 1$, we get

$$5 = f (2) = \frac{2}{2} + \frac{a}{4} + \frac{2}{1} + b = \frac{a}{4} + b + 3$$

$$2 = f(-1) = -2 + a - 1 + b = a + b - 3.$$

On solving these, we obtain
$$a = 4, \ b = 1.$$

Thus

$$f(z) = \frac{2}{z} + \frac{4}{z^2} + \frac{2}{z-1} + 1.$$

10.10. Residue Theorem. *If $f(z)$ be analytic in a simply connected domain D except at a finite number of singular points*

$$z_1, z_2, ..., z_n$$

and be continuous on the boundary C which is a rectifiable Jordan curve, then

$$\frac{1}{2\pi i} \int_C f(z)\, dz = \sum_{i=1}^{n} \ Res.(z_i).$$

(*Kerala 2001, Garhwal 2001, 2004, 2007; Gorakhpur 2005; Gauhati 2001; GNDU 2004; Rohilkhand 2006*)

We enclose the singular points by positively oriented circles

$$C_1, C_2, ..., C_n$$

such that the circles along with their interiors belong to D and do not overlap. Then $f(z)$ is analytic in the multiply connected domain D′ obtained on removing from D these circles and their interiors. Also the boundary of D′ consists of the curves

$$C, -C_1, -C_2, ..., -C_n,$$

so that we have

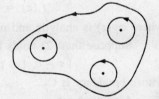

Fig. 10.2

$$\frac{1}{2\pi i} \int_C f(z)\, dz + \frac{1}{2\pi i} \int_{-C_1} f(z)\, dz + ... + \frac{1}{2\pi i} \int_{-C_n} f(z)\, dz = 0$$

$$\Rightarrow \qquad \frac{1}{2\pi i} \int_C f(z)\, dz = \frac{1}{2\pi i} \int_{C_1} f(z)\, dz + ... + \frac{1}{2\pi i} \int_{C_n} f(z)\, dz$$

$$= Res.(z_1) + ... + Res.(z_n) = \sum_{i=1}^{n} \ Res.(z_i).$$

Hence the theorem.

Cor. *If a function is analytic in the whole plane except at a finite number of points z_1, z_2, ..., z_n then the sum of the residues at these points along with that at infinity is zero.*

Let $|z| = \rho$ be a circle C such that no finite singular point is exterior to it. Then we have

$$\frac{1}{2\pi i} \int_C f(z)\, dz = \sum_{i=1}^{n} \ Res.(z_i).$$

Also by definition,

$$\frac{1}{2\pi i} \int_{-C} f(z)\, dz = Res.(\infty).$$

Adding, we obtain

$$\sum_{i=1}^{n} \ Res.(z_i) + Res.(\infty) = 0.$$

10.11. Number of zeros and poles in a domain.

Theorem. *Let $f(z)$ be analytic in a simply connected domain D except at a finite number of points which are poles and let $f(z)$ be continuous on the boundary curve C which is a rectifiable Jordan curve. Finally, let no zero of $f(z)$ lie on C. Then*

$$\frac{1}{2\pi i} \int_C \frac{f'(z)}{f(z)}\, dz = N - P,$$

where N denotes the number of zeros and P the number of poles of $f(z)$ in D; each zero or pole of any order m being counted as m zeros or poles as the case may be.

Clearly the only possible singular points of $f'(z)/f(z)$ in D are the zeros and poles of $f(z)$.

Let α_i be any zero of order m_i and β_j any pole of order n_j of $f(z)$.

Then by the preceding theorem, we have

$$\frac{1}{2\pi i} \int_C \frac{f'(z)}{f(z)}\, dz = \Sigma \operatorname{Res.}(\alpha_i) + \Sigma \operatorname{Res.}(\beta_j) \qquad \ldots(1)$$

where the two summations are separately carried out for all the zeros and the poles.

In the neighbourhood of the zero α_i of order m_i, we have

$$f(z) = (z - \alpha_i)^{m_i}\, \varphi_i(z) \qquad \ldots(2)$$

where $\varphi_i(z)$ is analytic and non-zero at α_i.

Suppose that (2) holds in the neighbourhood

$$|z - \alpha_i| \le \rho_i$$

whose boundary is C_i.

Also we have

$$\frac{f'(z)}{f(z)} = \frac{m_i}{z - \alpha_i} + \frac{\varphi_j(z)}{\varphi_i(z)}.$$

$$\Rightarrow \qquad \frac{1}{2\pi i} \int_C \frac{f'(z)}{f(z)}\, dz - m_i + 0 = m_i \qquad \ldots(3)$$

for

$$\int_{C_i} \frac{1}{z - \alpha_i}\, dz = 2\pi i, \quad \int_{C_i} \frac{\varphi_i'(z)}{\varphi_i(z)}\, dz = 0.$$

Again in the neighbourhood of the pole β_j with order n_j, we have

$$f(z) = (z - \beta_j)^{-n_j}\, \psi_j(z) \qquad \ldots(4)$$

where $\psi_j(z)$ is analytic and non-zero at β_j.

Suppose that (4) holds in the neighbourhood

$$|z - \beta_j| < \rho_j'$$

whose boundary is C_j'.

We have, from (4),

$$\frac{f'(z)}{f(z)} = -\frac{n_j}{z - \beta_j} + \frac{\psi_j'(z)}{\psi_j(z)}.$$

$$\Rightarrow \qquad \frac{1}{2\pi i} \int_{C_j'} \frac{f'(z)}{f(z)}\, dz = -n_j \qquad \ldots(5)$$

Then, from (1), (3) and (5), we obtain

$$\frac{1}{2\pi i} \int_C \frac{f'(z)}{f(z)} dz = \Sigma m_i - \Sigma n_j = N - P.$$

Thus we have proved the theorem.

Cor. From the above theorem, we obtain an elementary result concerning the number of zeros of an analytic function in any simply connected domain.

If $f(z)$ is analytic in a simply connected domain D bounded by a rectifiable Jordan curve C, is continuous on C and has no zero on C, then the number of zeros of $f(z)$ in the interior of C is

$$\frac{1}{2\pi} \Delta c \ arg \ f(z),$$

where $\Delta c \ arg \ f(z)$ denotes the change in $arg \ f(z)$ as z moves along C in the positive sense.

As $f(z)$ has no singular point in the interior of C, we have

$$\frac{1}{2\pi i} \int_C \frac{f'(z)}{f(z)} dz = N,$$

where N denotes the number of zeros of $f(z)$ in the interior of C.

Introducing the substitution

$$w = \log f(z),$$

we obtain,

$$N = \frac{1}{2\pi i} \int_C \frac{f'(z)}{f(z)} dz = \frac{1}{2\pi i} \int_{C_1} dw,$$

where C_1 denotes the closed curve described by w as z describes C.

Since

$$w = \log |f(z)| + i \ arg \ f(z),$$

and C_1 is a closed curve and $\log |f(z)|$ is single valued, we see that

$$\int_{C_1} dw = i \ \Delta c \ arg \ f(z).$$

$$\therefore \qquad N = \frac{1}{2\pi} \Delta c \ arg \ f(z).$$

Cor. Condition for a function to be simple.

Let $w = f(z)$ be analytic in a simply connected domain D and continuous on the boundary C which is a rectifiable Jordan curve. If $f(z)$ takes no value more than once on C, then $f(z)$ also takes no value more than once in D.

In brief the theorem states that if $f(z)$ is simple on C, then it is also simple in D. We shall now prove the result.

Let C' be the image of C by $w = f(z)$.

As $f(z)$ is single valued and C is closed, it follows that C' is also closed. Also since $f(z)$ takes no value more than once on C, therefore, C' is a simple curve. Thus C' is a Jordan curve.

Let D' denotes the interior domain of the Jordan curve C'.

Let z_0 be any point of D and let $w_0 = f(z_0)$. Then

$$\frac{1}{2\pi} \Delta c \ arg \ \{f(z) - f(z_0)\} \qquad \qquad ...(1)$$

is equal to the number of values $z \in D$ for which $f(z)$ takes the value $f(z_0)$. Since $f(z)$ takes the value $f(z_0)$ at least once, viz., for $z = z_0$; we see that (1) is necessarily a positive integer ≥ 1.

Also

$$\frac{1}{2\pi} \Delta c \text{ arg } \{f(z) - f(z_0)\} = \frac{1}{2\pi} \Delta c' \text{ arg } (w - w_0) \qquad ...(2)$$

Now the right hand side of (2) is $+1$, -1 or 0. It cannot, however, be -1 or 0 for the left hand side is ≥ 1.

Thus we see that

$$\frac{1}{2\pi} \Delta c \text{ arg } \{f(z) - f(z_0)\} = 1,$$

so that $f(z)$ is simple in D.

10.11.1. Argument Principle. Let a function $f(z)$ be analytic within and on a closed contour C, having N zeros inside C but no zero on C. Then

$$N = \frac{1}{2\pi} \Delta c \text{ arg } f(z)$$

where $\Delta c \text{ arg } f(z)$ denotes the variation in the value of $\text{arg } f(z)$ as z moves round the closed contour C (a zero of order n must be counted n times).

By § 10.11, we know that

$$N - P = \frac{1}{2\pi i} \int_C \frac{f'(z)}{f(z)} \, dz$$

Put $f(z) = Re^{i\theta}$ $\therefore$ $R = |f(z)|$ and $\theta = \text{arg } f(z)$.

$$\therefore \qquad f'(z) \, dz = df(z) = d(Re^{i\theta})$$
$$= e^{i\theta} (dR + iRd\theta)$$
$$= \frac{f(z)}{R} (dR + iRd\theta)$$

$$\therefore \qquad N - P = \frac{1}{2\pi i} \int_C \frac{f'(z)}{f(z)} \, dz$$

$$= \frac{1}{2\pi i} \int_C \left(\frac{dR}{R} + id\theta \right)$$

$$N - P = \frac{1}{2\pi i} \int_C \frac{dR}{R} + \frac{1}{2\pi} \int_C d\theta \qquad ...(1)$$

Now

$$\int_C \frac{dR}{R} = [\log R] \, C = 0.$$

Because $\log R$ returns to its original value as z moves once round C

$$\int_C d\theta = [\theta] \, C = \Delta c \text{ arg } f(z).$$

Because we know that $\text{arg } f(z)$ does not return to its original value as z moves round C and hence $\Delta c \text{ arg } f(z)$ is not necessarily zero.

$$\therefore \qquad N - P = 0 + \frac{1}{2\pi} \Delta c \text{ arg } f(z).$$

In other words, the excess of the number of zeros over the number of poles of a meromorphic function is equal to $(1 / 2\pi)$ times the increase in arg $f(z)$.

In particular if the function $f(z)$ has no poles then putting P = 0, we have

$$N = \frac{1}{2\pi} \Delta c \text{ arg } f(z).$$

This is known as the **Argument Principle.**

10.12. Rouche's Theorem. We now state and prove a theorem due to E. Rouche (1832 – 1910).

Theorem. *If two functions $f(z)$ and $g(z)$ are analytic in a domain D bounded by a rectifiable Jordan curve C and are continuous on C and $|g(z)| < |f(z)|$ for every point $z \in C$, then the two functions $f(z)$ and $f(z) + g(z)$ have the same number of zeros in D.*

Since   *(Rohilkhand 2002, 2004, MS Univ. 2007)*

$$|g(z)| < |f(z)| \; \forall \; z \in C$$

we may see that neither $f(z)$ nor $f(z) + g(z)$ has any zero on C.

Let m denotes the lower bound of the difference

$$|f(z)| - |g(z)|,$$

when $z \in C$. As $|f(z)| - |g(z)|$ is continuous, the lower bound m is attained.

Also because this difference is positive for every $z \in C$, we see that m is positive.

Let λ be any number in the interval

$$0 \le \lambda \le 1.$$

Then we have

$$|f(z) + \lambda g(z)| \ge m > 0.$$

The integral

$$J(\lambda) = \frac{1}{2\pi i} \int_C \frac{f'(z) + \lambda g'(z)}{f(z) + \lambda g(z)} dz$$

is a continuous function of λ in [0, 1].

Also, J (λ) is necessarily a non-negative integer. Thus J (λ) is a constant so that

$$J(0) = J(1),$$

$\Rightarrow \qquad \dfrac{1}{2\pi i} \int_C \dfrac{f'(z)}{f(z)} dz = \dfrac{1}{2\pi i} \int_C \dfrac{f'(z) + g'(z)}{f(z) + g(z)} dz.$

The result now follows by § 10.10.

Another proof. We have

$$f(z) + g(z) = f(z)\left[1 + \frac{g(z)}{f(z)}\right] = f(z) \varphi(z),$$

where

$$\varphi(z) = 1 + \frac{g(z)}{f(z)} = 1 + \psi(z), \text{ (say).}$$

Then we have

$$\frac{f'(z) + g'(z)}{f(z) + g(z)} = \frac{f'(z) \varphi(z) + f(z) \varphi'(z)}{f(z) \varphi(z)} = \frac{f'(z)}{f(z)} + \frac{\varphi'(z)}{\varphi(z)}.$$

$$\therefore \qquad \frac{1}{2\pi i} \int_C \frac{f'(z) + g'(z)}{f(z) + g(z)} \, dz = \frac{1}{2\pi i} \int_C \frac{f'(z)}{f(z)} \, dz = \frac{1}{2\pi i} \int_C \frac{\varphi'(z)}{\varphi(z)} \, dz.$$

We have

$$|\psi(z)| < M \ \forall \ z \in C,$$

so that the maximum value M of $|\psi(z)|$ on C is less than 1.

Thus for every $z \in C$, we have

$$|\psi(z)| \le M < 1 \Rightarrow |\varphi(z) - 1| \le M < 1,$$

so that the point φ, in the φ-plane, lies inside the circle whose centre is 1, and radius M is < 1.
Thus

$$\Delta c \ \arg \varphi(z) = 0 \Rightarrow \int_C \frac{\varphi'(z)}{\varphi(z)} \, dz = 0.$$

Hence

$$\frac{1}{2\pi i} \int_C \frac{f'(z) + g'(z)}{f(z) + g(z)} \, dz = \frac{1}{2\pi i} \int_C \frac{f'(z)}{f(z)} \, dz.$$

Thus we have proved the theorem.

10.12.1. Another Proof of the Fundamental Theorem of Algebra. As a consequence of Rouche's Theorem we can easily prove that any algebraic equation

$$a_0 z^n + a_1 z^{n-1} + a_2 z^{n-2} + \ldots\ldots + a_{n-1} z + a_n = 0, \ (a_0 \ne 0)$$

of the nth degree has n roots.

We write

$$f(z) = z^n, \quad g(z) = -\frac{1}{a_0}(a_1 z^{n-1} + a_2 z^{n-2} + \ldots\ldots + a_n).$$

Since $g(z)/f(z) \to 0$ as $z \to \infty$, we see that there exists a positive number R such that

$$\left| \frac{g(z)}{f(z)} \right| < 1 \text{ for } |z| > R.$$

Taking the curve C as $|z| = R + 1$, we see that the result follows from Rouche's Theorem.

EXAMPLES

1. *Show that*

$$z^4 + 2z^3 + 3z^2 + 4z + 5 = 0,$$

has no real or purely imaginary roots and that it has one complex root in each quadrant.

Solution. We write

$$f(z) = z^4 + 2z^3 + 3z^2 + 4z + 5.$$

This given equation has obviously no positive real root. Also taking

$$z = -x,$$

we get

$$f(-x^4) = x^4 - 2x^3 + 3x^2 - 4x + 5$$
$$= x^2(x^2 - 2x + 1) + (2x^2 - 4x + 5)$$
$$= x^2(x - 1)^2 + 2\left[(x - 1)^2 + \frac{3}{2}\right].$$

This shows that the given equation has no negative real root also.

Again taking

$$z = iy,$$

we get

$$f(iy) = y^4 - 2iy^3 + 3y^2 + 4iy + 5$$
$$= (y^4 - 3y^2 + 5) + 2i(2y - y^3)$$

which can be zero if and only if the equations

$$\left. \begin{array}{r} y^4 - 3y^2 + 5 = 0 \\ 2y - y^3 = 0 \end{array} \right\}$$

hold good for the same real value of y. These equations being, however, inconsistent, we see that the given equation has no purely imaginary root.

Thus the given equation has no roots on the real or the imaginary axes.

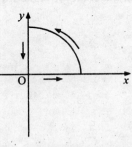

To determine the number of roots in the first quadrant, we examine the change in $\arg f(z)$ while z moves over the closed curve formed of:

(*i*) a segment [0, R] of the real axis,

(*ii*) a circle quadrant

$$z = Re^{iq}$$

where $0 \le \theta \le \pi/2$,

(*iii*) a segment [iR, 0] of the imaginary axis and let R tend to infinity.   Fig. 10.3

While z moves along the positive real axis from 0 to ∞, we see that $f(z)$ remains real and positive and accordingly no change in $\arg f(z)$ occurs.

Along

$$z = Re^{i\theta},$$

we have

$$f(Re^{i\theta}) = z^4 \left(1 + \frac{2}{z} + \frac{3}{z^2} + \frac{4}{z^3} + \frac{5}{z^4} \right)$$

$$= R^4 e^{4i\theta} [1 + \varphi(z)],$$

where $\varphi(z)$ tend to 0 uniformly as $z \to \infty$.

This shows that while z moves along the circle quadrant, the change in $\arg f(z)$ is

$$4 \cdot \frac{\pi}{2} = 2\pi.$$

To find the change in $\arg f(z)$ while z moves along the imaginary axis, we write

$$z = it,$$
$$f(v) = u + iv,$$

and obtain

$$u = t^4 - 3t^4 + 5, \quad v = 2(2t - t^2).$$

We must now discuss how the point (u, v) moves in (u, v) plane as t varies from ∞ to 0. We have

$$\lim_{t \to \infty} \frac{v}{u} - \lim_{t \to \infty} \frac{2t\,(2-t^2)}{t^4 - 3t^2 + 5} = 0.$$

Also

$$u = t^4 - 3t^2 + 5 = \left(t^2 - \frac{3}{2}\right)^2 + \frac{11}{4} > 0 \ \forall \ t$$

and v is negative for $t^2 > 2$, 0 for $t^2 = 0$ and positive for $t^2 < 2$.

Thus while t varies from ∞ to $\sqrt{2}$, the point (u, v) starting from ∞ where the curve is parallel to u-axis and remaining in the fourth quadrant moves to the point $(3, 0)$ on the u-axis. This shows that there is no change in argument when t varies from ∞ to $\sqrt{2}$.

Again when t varies from $\sqrt{2}$ to 0, the point (u, v) starting from $(3, 0)$ and remaining in the first quadrant moves to the point $(5, 0)$ on the u-axis so that again there is no change in argument.

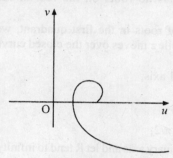

Fig. 10.4

Thus the number of roots in the first quadrant

$$= \frac{1}{2\pi}(0 + 2\pi + 0) = 1.$$

To find the number of roots in the second quadrant, we let z describe the closed curve consisting of the segment $[0, iR]$ of the imaginary axis, the circle quadrant

$$z = Re^{i\theta}, \ \pi/2 \le \theta \le \pi$$

and the segment $[-R, 0]$ of the real axis and let R tend to infinity.

As before, we may easily show that no change in $\arg f(z)$ occurs when z moves along either of the two line segments and the change is 2π when z moves along the circle quadrant. Thus again there is one root in the second quadrant.

Since the coefficients of the given equation are all real, the conjugate imaginary roots will occur in pairs and we shall have one root in each of the third and fourth quadrants also.

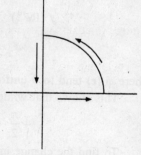

Fig. 10.5

2. *Show that the equation*
$$z^3 + iz + 1 = 0$$

has a root in each of the first, second and fourth quadrants.

Solution. It may be easily seen that the equation has no root on the real or the imaginary axis.

Let z move along the positive real axis from 0 to ∞.

Putting $z = t$, $f(z) = u + iv$, we have
$$u = t^3 + 1, \quad v = t.$$

$\Rightarrow \qquad \lim_{t \to \infty} \frac{v}{u} = 0.$

Thus as the point z moves along the positive real axis *i.e.*, as t varies from 0 to ∞, we see that the point (u, v), while remaining in the first quadrant, moves from $(1, 0)$ to ∞ where the curve is parallel to u-axis. Hence there is no change in the argument while t moves along the real axis.

The change in $\arg f(z)$ is $3\pi/2$ as z moves along
$$z = Re^{i\theta}, \quad 0 \le \theta \le \pi/2$$
and $R \to \infty$.

For the imaginary axis, we put
$$z = it,$$
where t varies from ∞ to 0. This gives
$$u = 1 - t, \quad v = -t^2.$$

$\Rightarrow \qquad \lim_{t \to \infty} \frac{v}{u} = \infty.$

For $t > 1$, the point remains in the third quadrant and for $0 < t < 1$ in the fourth.

Thus we may see that as t varies from ∞ to 0, the point (u, v) starting from ∞ in the third quadrant where the curve is parallel to v-axis moves to $(0, -1)$ and thence remaining in the fourth quadrant to $(1, 0)$. Accordingly the change in $\arg f(z)$ as z moves along the imaginary axis $\pi / 2$.

Thus we have

$$\frac{1}{2\pi} \left(0 + \frac{3\pi}{2} + \frac{\pi}{2} \right) = 1,$$

root in the first quadrant.

We now let z describe a curve around the second quadrant.

The changes in $\arg f(z)$ as z moves from 0 to ∞ along the positive imaginary axis and along the circle quadrant
$$z = Re^{i\theta}, \quad \pi/2 \le \theta \le \pi$$
are $-\pi/2$ and $3\pi/2$ respectively.

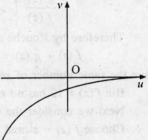

Fig. 10.6

Again putting $z = -t$, we have
$$u = 1 - t^3, \quad v = -t.$$

$\Rightarrow \qquad \lim_{t \to \infty} \frac{v}{u} = 0.$

As t changes from ∞ to 1, the point (u, v), starting from ∞ in the third quadrant where the direction of the curve is parallel to u-axis, and remaining in the third quadrant moves over to $(0, -1)$. As t changes from 1 to 0, the point starting from $(0, 1)$ and remaining in the fourth quadrant moves to $(1, 0)$. Thus the change in argument is π as z moves along the negative real axis from ∞ to 0.

Thus we have

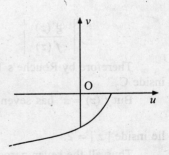

Fig. 10.7

$$\frac{1}{2\pi}\left(-\frac{\pi}{2}+\frac{3\pi}{2}+\pi\right)=1,$$

root in the second quadrant.

We may similarly show that there is a root in the fourth quadrant.

3. *Prove that all the roots of $z^7 - 5z^3 + 12 = 0$ lie between the circles $|z| = 1$ and $|z| = 2$.*

Solution. Let us denote by C_1 and C_2 the circles $|z| = 1$ and $|z| = 2$.

We are to prove that all the zeros lie between these two circles and as such we must first establish that no zeros lie within the smaller circle $|z| = 1$, i.e., C_1.

Choose $f(z) = 12$ and $g(z) = z^7 - 5z^3$.

Clearly both $f(z)$ and $g(z)$ are analytic within and on C_1.

On C_1, we have

$$\frac{|g(z)|}{|f(z)|} = \frac{|z^7 - 5z^3|}{12}$$

$$\leq \frac{|z|^7 + 5|z|^3}{12} = \frac{1+5}{12} \text{ as } |z| = 1 \text{ on } C_1$$

$$= \frac{1}{2}.$$

$$\therefore \quad \left|\frac{g(z)}{f(z)}\right| < 1 \text{ on } C_1.$$

Therefore by Rouche's Theorem both

$$f(z) + g(z) = z^7 - 5z^3 + 12 \text{ and } f(z) = 12$$

have the same number of zeros inside C_1.

But $f(z) = 12$ has no zero and hence $f(z) + g(z) = z^7 - 5z^3 + 12 = 0$ has no zero inside C_1.

Next we consider the circle $|z| = 2$ and we shall prove that all the zeros lie within C_2.

Choose $f(z) = z^7$ and $g(z) = -5z^3 + 12$.

Both $f(z)$ and $g(z)$ are analytic within and on C_2.

On C_2, we have

$$\frac{|g(z)|}{|f(z)|} = \frac{|12 - 5z^3|}{|z^7|} < \frac{12 + 5|z|^3}{|z|^7} = \frac{12 + 5 \cdot 8}{2^7} \text{ on } C_2, \text{ i.e., } |z| = 2$$

$$= \frac{52}{128} < 1.$$

$$\therefore \quad \left|\frac{g(z)}{f(z)}\right| < 1 \text{ on } C_2.$$

Therefore by Rouche's Theorem $f(z) + g(z) = z^7 - 5z^3 + 12$ has the same number of zeros inside C_2.

But $f(z) = z^7$ has seven zeros inside C_2 and hence all the seven zeros of

$$f(z) + g(z) = z^7 - 5z^3 + 12,$$

lie inside $|z| = 2$.

Thus all the seven zeros of the equation $z^7 - 5z^3 + 12$ lie inside C_2 but outside C_1 so that they lie within the circles C_1 and C_2, i.e., $|z| = 1$ and $|z| = 2$.

4. *If a > e then prove by the help of Rouche's Theorem that the equation $e^z = az^n$ has n roots inside the circle $|z| = 1$.*

Solution. Let C be the circle $|z| = 1$ so that $z = e^{i\theta}$.

Choose $f(z) = az^n$ and $g(z) = -e^z$. Both these functions are analytic within and on C.

$$\frac{|g(z)|}{|f(z)|} = \frac{|-e^z|}{|az^n|} = \frac{|-1||e^z|}{|a||z^n|}$$

$$= \frac{|e^z|}{a|z|^n} \text{ as } a \text{ is a positive real number.}$$

$$= \frac{\left|1 + z + \dfrac{z^2}{2!} + \dfrac{z^3}{3!} + \dots\right|}{a|z|^n}$$

$$\leq \frac{1 + |z| + \dfrac{1}{2!}|z|^2 + \dfrac{1}{3!}|z|^3 + \dots}{a|z|^n}$$

$$= \frac{1 + 1 + \dfrac{1}{2!} + \dfrac{1}{3!} + \dots}{a} \text{ as } |z| = 1 \text{ on C.}$$

$$= \frac{e}{a} < 1 \text{ as } a > e.$$

Hence by Rouche's Theorem $f(z) + g(z) = az^n - e^z$ have the same number of zeros as $f(z) = az^n$. Clearly az^n has n zeros all located at $z = 0$, *i.e.*, inside $|z| = 1$ and hence $az^n - e^z$ has all the n zeros inside $|z| = 1$.

5. *Suppose that the function $f(z)$ is analytic at z_0, f is not a constant, $f(z_0) = w_0$ and that $f(z_0) - w_0$ has a zero of order n at z_0. Show that if $\varepsilon > 0$ is sufficiently small then there exists a $\delta > 0$ such that for all 'a' for which $|a - w_0| < \delta$ the equation $f(z) = a$ has exactly n roots in the disc $|z - z_0| < \varepsilon$.*

Solution. Let C be the boundary of the disc $|z - z_0| \leq \varepsilon$ and as $f(z)$ is analytic at z_0 it is analytic in the neighbourhood of z_0. Hence $f(z)$ is analytic within and on C.

Therefore, $f(z) - w_0$ is analytic within and on C and as it has a zero at z_0 it will not have any zero on C as zeros are isolated.

Let min. $|f(z) - w_0| = m$ which by minimum modulus principle is reached on C and not within C.

$\therefore$ $\qquad m < |f(z) - w_0|$ for all z within C.

Now choose $\delta < m$ such that $|w_0 - a| < \delta$ for all permissible values of b.

$\therefore$ $\qquad |w_0 - a| < \delta < m < |f(z) - w_0|$ for z within C

or $\qquad |w_0 - a| < |f(z) - w_0|$ for z within C $\qquad\qquad$ ...(1)

Thus we have two functions $w_0 - a$ and $f(z) - w_0$ which are analytic within and on a closed curve C such that they satisfy the condition (1). Hence by Rouche's Theorem $f(z) - w_0$ and $\{f(z) - w_0\} + (w_0 - a) = f(z) - a$ have the same number of zeros inside C all situated at z_0. Therefore, $f(z) - a$ must have n zeros inside C.

This amounts to saying that the equation $f(z) - a = 0$ has n roots in the disc $|z - z_0| < \varepsilon$.

EXERCISES

1.Examine the nature of singularities of the following functions and determine also the residues at the singularities:

(a) $\dfrac{pz^2 + qz + r}{(z-a)(z-b)}$ (b) $z^{-1}(1-z^2)^{-1}$

(c) tan z (d)   cot z

(e) $(z^4 + z^2)/\sin \pi z$ (f) $(z-\pi)^{-2}\sin z$

(g) tanh z (h) $(z-2)\,z^{-2}\,[\sin(z-1)]^{-1}$

(i) $(z^4 + z^2)/\sinh \pi z$ (j) $z/(1+z^4)$

(k) $z/(\sin z - \tan z)$ at $z = 0$ (l) $\operatorname{cosec}^2 z \log(1-z)$ at $z = 0$

(m) $e^{\tan z}/(z^2 + 1)$ (n) $z \operatorname{cosec}^3(z-a)$ at $z = a$.

[**Ans.** (a) The point a is a pole of first order with residue
$$(pa^2 + qa + r)(a-b)$$
if $pa^2 + qa + r \neq 0$ and $a \neq b$. It is a regular point if $pa^2 + qa + r = 0$ and $a \neq b$. It is a pole of order 2 with residue $2pa + q$ if $pa^2 + qa + r \neq 0$ and $a = b$. We have similar results for the point b.

(b) The points $0, 1, -1$ are three poles of first order with residues $1, -\dfrac{1}{2}, -\dfrac{1}{2}$ respectively.

(c) Each point $(2n+1)\,\pi/2$ is a pole of order one with residue -1; n being any integer.

(d) Each point $n\pi$ is a pole of order one with residue 1; n being any integer.

(e) Each point n is a pole of order one with residue
$$(-1)^n (n^2 + n^4)/\pi;$$
$n \neq 0$ being any integer.

(f) π is a pole of order one with residue -1.

(g) Each point $i(2n+1)\,\pi/2$ is a pole of order one with residue 1.

(h) 'O' is a pole of order two with residue
$$(2\cos 1 - \sin 1)/\sin^2 1.$$
Each point, $1 + n\pi$, is a pole of order one with residue
$$(-1)^n (n\pi - 1)/(n\pi + 1)^2;$$
n being any integer.

(i) Each point in, is a pole of order one with residue
$$(-1)^n/(n^4 - n^2)/\pi;$$
$n \neq 0$ being any integer.

(j) Res. $\left(\cos\dfrac{\pi}{4} \pm i\sin\dfrac{\pi}{4}\right) = \dfrac{\mp i}{4};$

Res. $\left(\cos\dfrac{3\pi}{4} \pm i\sin\dfrac{3\pi}{4}\right) = \dfrac{\pm i}{4};$

each pole being simple.

(k) Res. (0) = 0 and 0, is a pole of second order.

(l) Res. (0) = -1 and 0, is a simple pole.

(m) Res. $(i) = \dfrac{1}{2}[\sin(\tanh 1) - i \cos(\tanh 1)]$;

Res. $(-i) = \dfrac{1}{2}[\sin(\tanh 1) + i \cos(\tanh 1)]$.

Both i and $-i$ are simple poles.

The points $n\pi + \dfrac{1}{2}\pi$ are essential singularities; n being any integer.

(n) Res. $(a) = a/2;\ a \neq 0$ is a pole of order 3.]

2. Functions $\varphi(z)$ and $\psi(z)$ are analytic at $z = a$. Also $z = a$ is a once repeated zero of $\psi(z)$ and $\varphi(a) \neq 0$. Show that the residue of the functions
$$\varphi(z)/\psi(z)$$
at $z - a$ is $\{6\varphi'(a)\psi''(a) - 2\varphi(a)\psi'''(a)\}/3\{\psi''(a)\}^2$.

3. Show that
$$\text{Res.}_{f(-z)}(-\alpha) = -\text{Res.}_{f(z)}(\alpha),$$
$$\text{Res.}_{f(iz)}(-i\alpha) = -i\,\text{Res.}_{f(z)}(\alpha),$$
where $\text{Res.}_{f(z)}(\alpha)$ denotes the residue of $f(z)$ at α and similarly for others.

4. What kind of singularity have the following functions:

(i) $\dfrac{1}{1-e^z}$ at $z = 2\pi i$

(ii) $(z^2+4)/e^z$ at $z = \infty$

(iii) $\cos z - \sin z$ at $z = \infty$ (*Meerut 2003, Garhwal 2006*)

(iv) $\sin\dfrac{1}{z}$ at $z = 0$ (*Garhwal 2006*)

(v) $\cot z$ at $z = \infty$

(v) $\sec 1/z$ at $z = 0$.

Ans. (i) simple pole. (ii) isolated essential singularity
(iii) isolated essential singularity (iv) isolated essential singularity
(v) non-isolated essential singularity (vi) non-isolated essential singularity.

5. Find the poles of the function
$$e^{\alpha z}(\cosh z + \cos \beta)^{-1};\ 0 < \alpha < 1,\ 0 < \beta < \pi$$
and the residues at these points.
What is the residue at infinity?

$$\left[\begin{array}{l}\textbf{Ans.} \text{Res.}[-i(2n\pi+\pi-\beta)] = \dfrac{ie^{-\alpha i(2n\pi+\pi-\beta)}}{\sin\beta} \\[2mm] \text{Res.}[-i(2n\pi+\pi+\beta)] = \dfrac{ie^{-\alpha i(2n\pi+\pi+\beta)}}{\sin\beta}.\end{array}\right]$$

6. Find the singular points of the following functions and determine their nature:

(a) $[(z+1)(z^2+1)^{-1}]^2$

(b) $\tan z^{-1}$

(c) $\log(1+z)$

[**Ans.** (a) $\pm\, i$ are two poles of order two.

(b) 0, is an essential singularity and $2\,/\,(2n+1)\,\pi$ are simple poles; n being any integer.

(c) -1, is a branch point; ∞ is an essential singularity.]

7. Determine the zeros and examine the nature of the singularities of the function:

(a) tanh z (b) $(z-2)\,z^{-2}\sin(z-1)^{-1}$

Find also the residues at the singularities.

[**Ans.** (a) $in\pi$ are the zeros and $(2n+1)\,i\pi\,/\,2$ are simple poles. Also 1 is the residue at each pole.

(b) 2 and $1+(n\pi)^{-1}$ are the zeros, 0 is a pole of order two and 1 is an essential singularity. Also $-\sin 1 + 2\cos 1$ is the residue at 0.]

8. Show that the residue at $z=0$ of the function $f(z)=z^{-7}\cot\pi z\coth\pi z$ is $-19\pi^{6}/567\times 25$.

9. Prove that if $f(z)$ has an essential singularity at $z=a$ then $1/f(z)$ has also an essential singularity at the same point.

10. Classify the singularities (including those at infinity) of

(a) $(z-1)^{-1}e^{z-1}$,   (b) $(1-\cos z)^{-1}$,

(c) $z^{2}(\cosh z-\cos z)^{-1}$.

Also find the residues at these singularities in whose neighbourhood a Laurent's expansion exists.

Ans. (a) 1 is a simple pole with residue e and, 0, is an essential singularity.

(b) $2n\pi$ is a pole of order two with residue 0; n being any integer; ∞ is an essential singularity.

(c)   Res. $\dfrac{2n\pi}{1+i}=\dfrac{-2in^{2}\pi^{2}}{\left(\sinh\dfrac{2n\pi}{1+i}+\sin\dfrac{2n\pi}{1+i}\right)}$.

Res. $\dfrac{2n\pi}{1-i}=\dfrac{2in^{2}\pi^{2}}{\left(\sinh\dfrac{2n\pi}{1-i}+\sin\dfrac{2n\pi}{1-i}\right)}$]

11. Find all the zeros and poles, with their orders, and the essential singularities, of
$$(z^{2}-1)^{-2}\sin z^{-1}.$$

[**Ans.** Res. (1) $=-\dfrac{1}{4}(\sin 1+\cos 1)=$ Res. (-1). The points $\pm\,1$ are poles of order two.

Zero is the essential singularity.

$\therefore n\pi$ is a zero of order one where n is any integer.]

12. Show that the residue at $z=ai$ of
$$\frac{e^{imz}}{z\,(z^{2}+a^{2})} \text{ is } \frac{e^{-ma}(ma+2)}{4a^{4}}.$$

13. Find the residue of the function z^{-3} cosec z cosech z at the origin.

$$\left[\text{Ans. } -\frac{1}{60} \right]$$

14. State with reasons, which of the following are integral functions:
$$z^{3/4}, z^3, e^{-z}, e^{1/2}, (1-z)^{-1}, (1+z)(1+z^2)^{-1}, (e^z-1)z^{-1}.$$

Under what conditions is the reciprocal of an integral function also an integral function?
[**Ans.** z^3, e^{-z}, $(e^z-1)/z$ are integral functions and others are non-integral.
Reciprocal of an integral function is integral if and only if it has no zero.]

15. The analytic function $f(z)$ is an even function whose only singularities are double poles at
$$z = 1, -1, \infty.$$

Determine this function, given that
(*i*)   the residue at 1 is -1;
(*ii*) the first non-zero coefficient in the Taylor's expansion about the origin is the coefficient of z^4; and that
(*iii*) $f(z)/z^2 \to 4$ as $|z| \to \infty$.

$$\left[\text{Ans. } -\frac{1}{(z-1)} + \frac{1}{(z+1)} - \frac{1}{(z-1)^2} - \frac{1}{(z+1)^2} + 4z^2 \right]$$

16. The function $f(z)$ is analytic for all z. If
$$\lim_{z \to \infty} [z^{-r} f(z)] = 0,$$

where $r > 0$ is an integer, show that $f(z)$ is a polynomial of degree less than r.

17. If
$$f(z) = \frac{e^{i\pi z} - 1 + 2z^2}{z(z^2-1)},$$

for every value of z other than 0 and ± 1, show that $f(0), f(1)$ and $f(-1)$ can be so defined as to make $f(z)$ regular at $0, \pm 1$.

$$\left[\text{Ans. } f(0) = i\pi, \ f(1) = \frac{1}{2}(4-i\pi), \ f(-1) = -\frac{1}{2}(4+i\pi). \right]$$

18. Find the value of the integral
$$\int \frac{2z+3}{z(z^2+1)(z+1)^2} dz$$

(*i*)   around the circle $|x + iy| = 3$,

(*ii*) along the whole of the line $x + y = -\frac{1}{2}$ in the direction which makes x increase.

[The integral along the line is $2\pi i$ multiplied by the sum of the residues at $0, i$.]

$$\left[\text{Ans. } (i) \ 0 \quad (ii) \ \frac{1}{2}(10i-3)\pi \right]$$

19. From the integral

$$\int_C \frac{dz}{z+2}$$

where C denotes the circle $|z| = 1$, deduce that

$$\int_0^\pi \frac{1 + 2\cos\theta}{5 + 4\cos\theta} d\theta = 0.$$

20. By considering

$$\int_C \left\{ 2 \pm \left(t + \frac{1}{t} \right) \right\} f(t) \frac{dt}{t}$$

where C is the circle $|t| = 1$ within and on which $f(t)$ is regular, prove that

$$\int_0^{2\pi} f(e^{i\theta}) \cos^2 \left(\frac{1}{2}\theta \right) d\theta = \pi \left\{ f(0) + \frac{1}{2} f'(0) \right\},$$

$$\int_0^{2\pi} f(e^{i\theta}) \sin^2 \left(\frac{1}{2}\theta \right) d\theta = \pi \left\{ f(0) - \frac{1}{2} f'(0) \right\}.$$

Deduce that, if also $R f(t) \geq 0'$ in $|t| \leq 1$, then $|R f'(0)| \leq 2$.

[Put $t = e^{i\theta}$ and find residues at $t = 0$ and employ the *residue* theorem.]

21. Find the value of

$$\int_C \frac{(12z - 7)}{(z - 1)^2 (2z + 3)} dz,$$

where C is

(*i*)   the circle $|z| = 2$,   (*ii*)   the circle $|z + i| = \sqrt{3}$.

[**Ans.** (*i*) 0 (*ii*) $4\pi i$]

22. By integrating the reciprocal of

$$(z - a)^{n+1} (az - 1)^{n+1},$$

round the circle $|z| = 1$, prove that, if $|a| < 1$, and n is a positive integer,

$$\int_0^{2\pi} \frac{\cos n\theta}{(a^2 - 2a\cos\theta + 1)^{n+1}} d\theta = \frac{2\pi (2n)! a^n}{(n!) (1 - a^2)^{2n+1}}.$$

23. Find the value of

$$\int_C \frac{dz}{z^2 (z - a)^n},$$

where n is a positive integer, C is a simple closed curve surrounding the origin, and a is a point

(*i*)   inside C,   (*ii*)   outside C.

[**Ans.** (*i*) 0 (*ii*) $2 (-1)^n n\pi i / a^{n+1}$]

24. The function $f(z)$ has a simple pole at $z = a$ with residue b and $C(\delta)$ denotes the circular arc $z = a + \delta e^{i\theta}$ where $\alpha \leq \theta \leq \beta$. Prove that

$$\lim_{\delta \to 0} \int_{C'\delta_1} f(z) dz = i (\beta - \alpha) b.$$

25. Evaluate

$$\int_C \frac{\sin z}{(1 + z^2)^2} \, dz,$$

where C is the circle $| z - i | = r$, distinguishing between the cases $r > 2$ and $r < 2$.

[**Ans.**The integral is $i\pi$ (sinh 1 – cosh 1) if $r > 2$ and $\frac{1}{2} i\pi$ (sinh 1 – cosh 1) if $r < 2$.]

26. If a function $f(z)$ has simple zeros at the points $z = a_m$, $(m = 1, 2, ..., r)$ and simple poles at the points $z = b_n$, $(n = 1, 2, ..., s)$, and $\varphi(z)$ is analytic within and on a simple closed curve C enclosing all the points a_m and b_n prove that

$$\frac{1}{2\pi i} \int_C \frac{f'(z)}{f(z)} \varphi(z) \, dz = \sum_{m=1}^{r} \varphi(a_m) - \sum_{n=1}^{s} \varphi(b_n).$$

27. If $f(z)$ and $g(z)$ are integral functions, show that

$$\frac{1}{2\pi i} \int_{|\xi|=1} \left[\frac{f(\xi)}{\xi - z} + \frac{z \, g(1/\xi)}{z\xi - \xi^2} \right] d\xi$$

represents $f(z)$ in $| z | < 1$ and $g(1/z)$ in $| z | > 1$.

28. Show that the equation

$$z^4 + z + 1 = 0$$

has one root in *each* quadrant.

29. Show that the polynomial

$$z^5 + z^3 + 2z + 3$$

has just one zero in *the first* quadrant of the plane.

30. Show that the equation

$$z^4 + 4(1 + i) z + 1 = 0$$

has one root *in each* quadrant.

31. Show that the equation

$$z^{10} + z^2 + 1 = 0$$

has two roots which are purely imaginary and in addition two complex roots in each quadrant. Show also that one of the complex roots in the first quadrant lies in the sector

$$\frac{\pi}{10} < \arg z < \frac{\pi}{8}.$$

32. Show that the roots of the equation

$$16z^5 - z + 8 = 0$$

all lie in the annulus between

$$| z | = \frac{1}{2} \text{ and } | z | = 1.$$

33. Show that the roots of the equation

$$z^5 - 12z^2 + 14 = 0$$

lie between the circles

$$| z | = 1 \text{ and } | z | = \frac{5}{2}.$$

34. Show that two of the roots of the equation
$$z^5 - z + 16 = 0$$

have their real parts positive and that three have their real parts negative. Show also that all the five roots lie between the circles
$$|z| = 1 \text{ and } |z| = 2.$$

35. Show that the polynomial
$$z^5 - 10z^3 + 5z^2 - 3z - 1$$

has just two zeros in the annulus
$$1 < |z| < 4\frac{1}{2}$$

and just three zeros in the right half-plane.

36. Prove that, if n is a positive integer, the polynomial
$$z^{2n} + 6z + 10$$

has no real zeros. Find the number of zeros which lie in each quadrant of the complex plane

(*i*)   when n is even,   (*ii*)   when n is odd.

Prove also that, whatever be the value of the positive integer n, all the zeros lie within the circle $|z| = 8$.

[**Ans.** $n/2$ in each quadrant if n is even; $(n-1)/2$ in each of first and fourth and $(n+1)/2$ in each of second and fourth, if n is odd.]

37. Prove that
$$z^8 + 3z^3 + 7z + 5 = 0$$

have two zeros in the first quadrant.

38. Prove that in the half-plane $R(z) < 0$, $e^z - z^{4n} - 2$

has exactly $2n$ zeros, all simple, if n is a positive integer.

[Consider line integral along C, which consists of a semi-circle and its bounding diameter, the latter along the imaginary axis.]

39. Show that
$$e^z - \frac{1}{2}z - 1$$

has just one zero in $R(z) < 0$ and that it is real.

40. Prove that there is exactly one complex number z such that $e^z = z$ and $0 < I(z) < \pi$.

41. Prove that there is exactly one number z such that
$$0 < R(z) < \frac{1}{2}\pi, \ I(z) > 0 \text{ and } z \cos z = 1.$$

42. Show that the equation
$$e^{z-1} = z^n$$

where n is an integer greater than unity, has $(n-1)$ roots in the interior of the unit circle.

43. Prove that there are exactly two complex numbers z such that
$$\log z = z,$$
where the logarithm has its principal value, *i.e.*, $-\pi < I(\log z) \leq \pi$.

44. Show that the equation

$$e^{-z} = z - (1 + i)$$

has precisely one root in the first quadrant.

45. Prove that the equation

$$z^n = b \cos \alpha z,$$

where α is real, has n roots within the circle $|z| = 1$, if $|b| < \operatorname{sech} \alpha$.

If b is real and $b < \operatorname{sech} \alpha$ where $0 < \alpha < 3$, show that for $n = 2$, the equation has one real positive root and one real negative root within $|z| = 1$ and for $n = 3$ it has one real root and two complex roots within $|z| = 1$.

46. Prove that $\tan z$ cannot be equal to z unless z is real.

OBJECTIVE QUESTIONS

For each of the following questions, four alternatives are given for the answer. Only one of them is correct. Choose the correct alternative.

1. A point at which a function $f(z)$ ceases to be analytic is called
  (*a*) zero   (*b*)   singularity
  (*c*) pole   (*d*)   limit point.

2. If in the principal part of $f(z)$, there are infinite number of terms, then $z = a$ is
  (*a*) removable singularity   (*b*)   essential singularity
  (*c*) pole   (*d*)   None of these.

3. If $f(z)$ has a pole at $z = a$, then as $z \to a$
  (*a*) $|f(z)| \to 0$ (*b*) $|f(z)| \to a$
  (*c*) $|f(z)| \to \infty$ (*d*) $|f(z)| \to -\infty$.

4. The limit point of the poles of a function $f(z)$ is
  (*a*) a pole   (*c*)   a non-isolated singularity
  (*b*) an isolated singularity   (*d*)   a non-isolated essential singularity.

5. Let a be an isolated singularity of $f(z)$ and if $|f(z)|$ is bounded on some neighbourhood of a, then a is
  (*a*) removable singularity   (*b*)   essential singularity
  (*c*) isolated singularity   (*d*)   non-isolated singularity.

6. Polynomial of degree n has a pole of order n at
  (*a*) zero   (*b*)   infinity
  (*c*) curve C   (*d*)   anywhere.

7. A function, whose only singularities in the entire complex plane are poles, is called
  (*a*) analytic function   (*b*)   homomorphic function
  (*c*) meromorphic function   (*d*)   regular function.

8. Function e^z has at $z = \infty$,
  (*a*) an isolated singularity   (*b*)   a pole
  (*c*) an infinite point   (*d*)   an isolated essential singularity.

9. Kind of singularity of the function $\dfrac{1}{\sin z - \cos z}$ at $z = \pi/4$ is

(a) simple pole
(b) double pole
(c) singularity
(d) None of these.

10. At $z = 0$, $\tan (1/z)$ has
(a) a simple pole
(b) an isolated singularity
(c) a non-isolated essential singularity
(d) a double pole.

11. At $z = \infty$, $z \csc z$ has
(a) a non-isolated essential singularity
(b) an essential singularity
(c) a removable singularity
(d) a pole.

12. Residue of $f(z)$ at a simple pole $z = a$ is
(a) $\lim\limits_{z \to a} z\, f(z)$
(b) $\lim\limits_{z \to a} (z - a)\, f(z)$
(c) $\lim\limits_{z \to a} \dfrac{f(z)}{(z - a)}$
(d) $\lim\limits_{z \to a} \dfrac{(z - a)}{f(z)}$.

13. Residue of $\dfrac{z^2 - 2z}{(z + 1)^2 (z^2 + 4)}$ at double pole as $z = -1$ is

(a) $\dfrac{4}{5}$
(b) $-\dfrac{4}{5}$
(c) $-\dfrac{14}{25}$
(d) $\dfrac{14}{25}$.

14. Residue of $f(z) = \dfrac{z^3}{(z - 1)^4 (z - 2)(z - 3)}$ at $z = 3$ is
(a) $\dfrac{101}{16}$
(b) -8
(c) $\dfrac{27}{16}$
(d) 0.

15. Residue of $f(z)$ at $z = \infty$ is

(a) $\dfrac{1}{2\pi i} \displaystyle\int_C f(z)\, dz$
(b) $-\dfrac{1}{2\pi i} \displaystyle\int_C f(z)\, dz$
(c) $2\pi i \displaystyle\int_C f(z)\, dz$
(d) $-2\pi i \displaystyle\int_C f(z)\, dz$.

16. Residue of $\dfrac{z^3}{z^2 - 1}$ at $z = \infty$ is
(a) 1
(b) -1
(c) 0
(d) ∞.

17. If $f(z)$ is analytic within and on a closed contour C, except at a finite number of poles inside C and ΣR^+ is the sum of residues of $f(z)$ at all points within C then $\displaystyle\int_C f(z)\, dz$ is equal to

(a) $2\pi\, \Sigma R^+$
(b) $2\pi i\, \Sigma R^+$
(c) $\dfrac{1}{2\pi}\, \Sigma R^+$
(d) $\dfrac{1}{2\pi i}\, \Sigma R^+$.

ANSWERS

1. (b)　　2. (b)　　3. (c)　　4. (d)　　5. (a)　　6. (b)　　7. (c)　　8. (d)　　9. (a)
10. (c)　　11. (a)　　12. (b)　　13. (c)　　14. (c)　　15. (b)　　16. (a)　　17. (a)

CALCULUS OF RESIDUES

EVALUATION OF REAL DEFINITE INTEGRALS

11.1. Introduction. This chapter will be devoted to the technique of evaluating certain types of real definite integrals with the help of the notions of complex integration and of residue at a point. In each given case, the choice of a suitable curve along which integration to be effected will play an important part. This curve is usually known as a contour and integration along the same as *Contour Integration*.

11.2. *Evaluation of the integral.*

$$\int_0^{2\pi} f(\cos \theta \sin \theta)\, d\theta,$$

where $f(\cos \theta, \sin \theta)$ is a real rational function of $\sin \theta$, $\cos \theta$.

We employ the transformation

$$z = e^{i\theta}.$$

We then have

$$\cos \theta = \frac{1}{2}\left(z + \frac{1}{z}\right), \quad \sin \theta = \frac{1}{2i}\left(z - \frac{1}{z}\right),$$

$$dz = ie^{i\theta}\, d\theta \quad \Rightarrow \quad d\theta = \frac{dz}{iz}.$$

Thus

$$\int_0^{2\pi} f(\cos \theta, \sin \theta)\, d\theta = \int_C f\left[\frac{1}{2}\left(z + \frac{1}{z}\right), \frac{1}{2i}\left(z - \frac{1}{z}\right)\right]\frac{dz}{iz}$$

where C, is the positively oriented unit circle so that the given integral appears as equal to the integral of a rational function of z taken along the circle $|z| = 1$. This latter integral can be evaluated by means of the residue theorem so that the integral

$$= 2\pi i \, \Sigma_i \text{ Res. } (z_i),$$

where z_i is any pole in the interior of the circle $|z| = 1$.

11.2.1. Important Theorems.

Theorem I. If $\lim_{z \to a} (z - a) f(z) = A$ and if C is the arc $\theta_1 \leq \theta \leq \theta_2$ of the circle $|z - a| = r$ then

$$\lim_{r \to 0} \int_C f(z)\, dz = iA(\theta_2 - \theta_1). \qquad \text{(Garhwal 2007; Meerut 2005)}$$

Since $\lim\limits_{z \to 0} (z - a) f(z) = A$, therefore for a given ε we can find δ depending upon ε such that

$$| (z - a) f(z) - A | < \varepsilon \text{ for } | z - a | < \delta.$$

But $| z - a | = r$ and hence if we choose $r < \delta$, then

$$| (z - a) f(z) - A | < \varepsilon \text{ on the arc } C.$$

$$\therefore \qquad (z - a) f(z) = A + \eta \text{ where } | \eta | < \varepsilon$$

or

$$f(z) = \frac{A + \eta}{z - a}.$$

$$\therefore \qquad \int_C f(z) \, dz = \int_C \frac{A + \eta}{z - a} \, dz$$

$$= \int_{\theta_1}^{\theta_2} \frac{A + \eta}{re^{i\theta}} \cdot re^{i\theta} \cdot i \, d\theta.$$

$$(A + \eta) \, i \int_{\theta_1}^{\theta_2} d\theta = (\theta_2 - \theta_1) \, iA + (\theta_2 - \theta_1) \, i\eta.$$

$$\therefore \quad \left| \int_C f(z) \, dz - iA \, (\theta_2 - \theta_1) \right|$$

$$= | (\theta_2 - \theta_1) \, i\eta | = (\theta_2 - \theta_1) | \eta |$$

$$< (\theta_2 - \theta_1) \, \varepsilon.$$

Taking limit when $\varepsilon \to 0$ and consequently $r \to 0$, we have

$$\lim\limits_{r \to 0} \int_C f(z) \, dz = iA \, (\theta_2 - \theta_1).$$

Note. $\lim\limits_{z \to a} (z - a) f(z) = \text{Res.} (z = a)$ for a simple pole.

Theorem II. *If C is an arc $\theta_1 \leq \theta \leq \theta_2$ of the circle $| z | = R$ and if $\lim\limits_{R \to \infty} z f(z) = A$, then*

$$\lim\limits_{R \to \infty} \int_C f(z) \, dz = iA \, (\theta_2 - \theta_1). \qquad \qquad \text{(Merrut 2000)}$$

Since $\lim\limits_{R \to \infty} z f(z) = A$, we can choose R so large that

$$| z f(z) - A | < \varepsilon \text{ on the arc } C$$

or

$$z f(z) = A + \eta \text{ where } | \eta | < \varepsilon.$$

$$\therefore \qquad \int_C f(z) \, dz = \int_C \frac{A + \eta}{z} \, dz. \qquad \qquad [\text{Put } z = Re^{i\theta}]$$

$$\therefore \qquad \int_C f(z) \, dz = \int_{\theta_1}^{\theta_2} \frac{(A + \eta)}{Re^{i\theta}} \cdot Re^{i\theta} \cdot i \, d\theta = (A + \eta) \, i \int_{\theta_1}^{\theta_2} d\theta$$

$$= (A + \eta) \, i \, (\theta_2 - \theta_1).$$

$$\therefore \qquad \left| \int_C f(z)\, dz - iA\,(\theta_2 - \theta_1) \right| = |(\theta_2 - \theta_1)\, i\eta|$$

$$= (\theta_2 - \theta_1)\,|\eta|$$

$$< (\theta_2 - \theta_1)\,\varepsilon.$$

Taking limit when $\varepsilon \to 0$ and consequently $R \to \infty$, we get

$$\int_C f(z)\, dz = iA\,(\theta_2 - \theta_1).$$

In particular if $\lim\limits_{R \to \infty} z\, f(z) = 0$, then from above, we have

$$\lim_{R \to \infty} \int_C f(z)\, dz = 0.$$

Note. $\lim\limits_{z \to \infty} [-z\, f(z)] = \text{Res.}\,(z = \infty).$

EXAMPLES

1. *Evaluate*

$$\int_0^{2\pi} e^{-\cos\theta} \cos(n\theta + \sin\theta)\, d\theta,$$

when n is a positive integer. $\hspace{4cm}$ *(Gorakhpur 2005)*

Solution. Consider the integral

$$I = \int_0^{2\pi} e^{-\cos\theta}\,[\cos(n\theta + \sin\theta) - i\sin(n\theta + \sin\theta)]\, d\theta$$

$$= \int_0^{2\pi} e^{-\cos\theta} \cdot e^{-i(n\theta + \sin\theta)}\, d\theta$$

$$= \int_0^{2\pi} e^{-(\cos\theta + i\sin\theta)} \cdot e^{-in\theta}\, d\theta$$

$$= \int_0^{2\pi} e^{-e^{i\theta}} \cdot e^{-in\theta}\, d\theta$$

$$= \int_C \left(e^{-z} \cdot \frac{1}{z^n}\right) \frac{dz}{iz} \qquad \left[\text{Writing } e^{i\theta} = z,\ d\theta = \frac{dz}{iz}\right]$$

where C denotes the unit circle $|z| = 1$.

$$= \frac{1}{i} \int_C \frac{e^{-z}}{z^{n+1}}\, dz = \int_C f(z)\, dz, \text{ where } f(z) = \frac{e^{-z}}{iz^{n+1}}$$

$$= 2\pi i\, \Sigma R^+ \qquad\qquad \text{[By Cauchy's residue theorem]}$$

Obviously the only pole of $f(z)$ within the contour C is $z = 0$ of order $n + 1$.

At $z = 0$, the residue $= \dfrac{1}{n!} \left[\dfrac{d^n}{dz^n}\left(\dfrac{e^{-z}}{i}\right)\right]_{z=0} = \dfrac{(-1)^n}{i\,(n)!} = \Sigma R^+.$

$$\therefore \qquad I = 2\pi i \times \frac{(-1)^n}{i\,(n)!} = \frac{2\pi}{n!}\,(-1)^n,$$

i.e., $\int_0^{2\pi} [e^{-\cos\theta} [\cos(n\theta + \sin\theta) - i\sin(n\theta + \sin\theta)] \, d\theta = \dfrac{2\pi}{n!} (-1)^n.$

Equating real parts, we have

$$\int_0^{2\pi} e^{-\cos\theta} \cos(n\theta + \sin\theta) \, d\theta = \dfrac{2\pi}{n!}(-1)^n.$$

2. *Prove that* $\displaystyle\int_0^{2\pi} \dfrac{d\theta}{a + b\cos\theta} = \dfrac{2\pi}{\sqrt{a^2 - b^2}}$, $a > b > 0.$

(*Garhwal 2000; GNDU 2001; Calicut 2004; Meerut 2001*)

Solution. Putting $e^{i\theta} = z$, so that $d\theta = \dfrac{dz}{iz}$, we have

$$I = \int_0^{2\pi} \dfrac{d\theta}{a + b\cos\theta} = \int_0^{2\pi} \dfrac{d\theta}{a + \dfrac{b}{2}(e^{i\theta} + e^{-i\theta})} = \dfrac{dz/iz}{a + \dfrac{b}{2}\left(z + \dfrac{1}{z}\right)}$$

where C is the unit circle $|z| = 1$

$$= \dfrac{2}{ib} \int_C \dfrac{dz}{z^2 + \dfrac{2a}{b}z + 1} = \int_C f(z) \, dz,$$

where $$f(z) = \dfrac{2}{ib\left(z^2 + \dfrac{2a}{b}z + 1\right)}$$ ..(1)

$$= 2\pi i \, \Sigma R^+ \qquad \text{[By Cauchy's residue theorem]}$$

where ΣR^+ = sum of residues of $f(z)$ at the poles within C.

The poles of $f(z)$ are given by

$$z^2 + \dfrac{2a}{b}z + 1 = 0 \qquad\qquad ...(2)$$

or $$z = \dfrac{-\dfrac{2a}{b} \pm \sqrt{\left(\dfrac{4a^2}{b^2} - 4\right)}}{2} = \dfrac{-a \pm \sqrt{a^2 - b^2}}{b}$$

or $$z = \dfrac{-a + \sqrt{a^2 - b^2}}{b} = \alpha, \text{ (say)}$$

and $$z = \dfrac{-a - \sqrt{a^2 - b^2}}{b} = \beta, \text{ (say)}.$$

Both the poles are simple poles.

$\because$ α, β are roots of (2) $\therefore$ $\alpha\beta = 1$ or $|\alpha\beta| = 1$

or $$|\alpha| \cdot |\beta| = 1.$$

But since $a > b > 0$, $|\beta| = \left| a + \dfrac{\sqrt{a^2 - b^2}}{b} \right| > 1$,

i.e., $\qquad z = \alpha = \dfrac{-a + \sqrt{a^2 - b^2}}{b}$

is the only pole (simple) of $f(z)$ within C.

∴ Residue at simple pole $z = \alpha$ is

$$= \lim_{z \to \alpha} (z - \alpha) f(z) = \lim_{z \to \alpha} (z - \alpha) \frac{2}{ib (z - \alpha)(z - \beta)}$$

∵ α, β are roots of (2)

$$= \frac{2}{ib (\alpha - \beta)} = \frac{2}{ib \cdot \dfrac{2}{b} \sqrt{a^2 - b^2}} = \frac{1}{i \sqrt{a^2 - b^2}} = \Sigma R^+$$

∴ From (1), we have

$$I = \int_0^{2\pi} \frac{d\theta}{a + b \cos \theta} = 2\pi i \cdot \frac{1}{i \sqrt{a^2 - b^2}} = \frac{2\pi}{\sqrt{a^2 - b^2}}.$$

3. *Prove that* $\displaystyle\int_0^{2\pi} \frac{\sin^2 \theta}{a + b \cos \theta}\, d\theta = \frac{2\pi}{b^2} \{a - \sqrt{(a^2 - b^2)}\}$ *if* $a > b > 0$.

(Kanpur 2000; IAS 2004)

Solution. If we write $z = e^{i\theta}$; then

$$\cos \theta = \frac{1}{2}\left(z + \frac{1}{z} \right), \sin \theta = \frac{1}{2i}\left(z - \frac{1}{z} \right)$$

$$d\theta = \frac{dz}{iz}, \text{ then}$$

$$I = \int_0^{2\pi} \frac{\sin^2 \theta\, d\theta}{a + b \cos \theta}$$

$$= \frac{i}{2b} \int_C \frac{(z^2 - 1)^2\, dz}{z^2 \left(z^2 + \dfrac{2a}{b} z + 1 \right)}$$

where C denotes the unit circle $|z| = 1$.

$$= \frac{i}{2b} \int_C \frac{(z^2 - 1)^2\, dz}{z^2 (z - \alpha)(z - \beta)}$$

$$= \int_C f(z)\, dz, \text{ where } f(z) = \frac{(z^2 - 1)^2}{z^2 \left(z^2 + \dfrac{2a}{b} z + 1 \right)}$$

C is unit circle, the poles of $f(z)$ are given by

$$z^2 \left(z^2 + \frac{2a}{b} z + 1 \right) = 0$$

Then

$$\alpha = \frac{-a + \sqrt{(a^2 - b^2)}}{b}, \beta = \frac{-a - \sqrt{(a^2 - b^2)}}{b}$$

and $z = 0$ is a double pole.

Obviously, $|\beta| > 1$, so β lies outside C and since $|\alpha||\beta| = 1$, hence $|\alpha| < 1$. So, α lies inside C.

Then inside the contour C there is a simple pole $z = \alpha$ and a pole $z = 0$ of order two.

Residue at the simple pole $z = \alpha$

$$= \lim_{z \to \alpha} (z - \alpha) f(z)$$

$$= \lim_{z \to \alpha} (z - \alpha) \cdot \frac{i}{2b} \frac{(z^2 - 1)^2}{z^2 (z - \alpha)(z - \beta)}$$

$$= \frac{i}{2b} \frac{(\alpha^2 - 1)^2}{\alpha^2 (\alpha - \beta)} = \frac{i}{2b} \frac{\left(\alpha - \dfrac{1}{\alpha}\right)^2}{\alpha - \beta}$$

$$= \frac{i}{2b} \frac{(\alpha - \beta)^2}{\alpha - \beta} \qquad\qquad \left(\text{because } \alpha\beta = 1, \text{ so } \frac{1}{\alpha} = \beta\right)$$

And residue at the double pole $z = 0$ is the coefficient of $\dfrac{1}{z}$ in

$$\frac{i}{2b} \frac{(z^2 - 1)^2}{z^2 \left(z^2 + \dfrac{2a}{b} z + 1\right)}, \qquad\qquad \text{where } z \text{ is small.}$$

Now.

$$\frac{i}{2b} \frac{(z^2 - 1)^2}{z^2 \left(z^2 + \dfrac{2a}{b} z + 1\right)}$$

$$= \frac{i}{2b} \left(i - \frac{1}{z^4}\right)^2 \left[i + \frac{2a}{b} \cdot \frac{1}{z} + \frac{1}{z^2}\right]^{-1}$$

The coeff. of $\dfrac{1}{z}$ easily seen to be

$$\frac{i}{2b} \left[-\frac{2a}{b}\right] = \frac{-ia}{b^2}$$

Hence by Cauchy's Residue Theorem

$$I = 2\pi i \times (\text{Sum of the residues at the poles within } C)$$

$$= 2\pi i \times \left[\frac{i \sqrt{(a^2 - b^2)}}{b^2} - \frac{ia}{b^2}\right]$$

$$= \frac{2\pi}{b^2} \{a - \sqrt{(a^2 - b^2)}\}.$$

4. *Evaluate:* $\displaystyle\int_0^{2\pi} \frac{\cos 2\theta}{5 + 4\cos\theta}\,d\theta$ (*Ravishankar 2000, Gurukul 2000*)

Solution. Let $\displaystyle I \equiv \int_0^{2\pi} \frac{\cos 2\theta\, d\theta}{5 + 4\cos\theta}$

$$= \frac{1}{2}\int_0^{2\pi} \frac{e^{2i\theta} + e^{-2i\theta}}{5 + 2(e^{i\theta} + e^{-i\theta})}\,d\theta,$$ write $z = e^{i\theta}, d\theta = \dfrac{dz}{iz}$

$$= \frac{1}{2}\int_C \frac{\left(z^2 + \dfrac{1}{z^2}\right)}{5 + 2\left(z + \dfrac{1}{z}\right)} \cdot \frac{dz}{iz}$$

$$= \frac{1}{2i}\int_C \frac{(z^4 + 1)}{z^2(2z^2 + 5z + 2)}\,dz$$

$$= \frac{1}{2i}\int_C \frac{z^4 + 1}{z^2(2z + 1)(z + 2)}\,dz$$

where C denotes the unit circle $|z| = 1$, the pole of $f(z)$ is

$$z^2(2z + 1)(z + 2) = 0$$

$\Rightarrow$ $z = 0, z = -\dfrac{1}{2}, z = -2.$

The poles within the contour C are a simple pole at $z = -\dfrac{1}{2}$, and a pole of order two at $z = 0$.

Now, Residue at $z = -\dfrac{1}{2}$ is

$$\lim_{z\to -\frac{1}{2}}\left(z + \frac{1}{2}\right)\frac{1}{2i}\frac{z^4 + 1}{z^2(2z + 1)(z + 2)}$$

$$= \frac{1}{2}\cdot\frac{1}{2i}\frac{\left(-\dfrac{1}{2}\right)^4 + 1}{\left(-\dfrac{1}{2}\right)^2\left(-\dfrac{1}{2} + 2\right)}$$

$$= \frac{1}{4i}\frac{\dfrac{1}{16} + 1}{\dfrac{1}{2}\cdot\dfrac{3}{2}} = \frac{17}{24i}$$

And residue at $z = 0$ is the coefficient of $\dfrac{1}{z}$ in

$$\frac{1}{2i}\frac{z^4 + 1}{z^2(2z + 1)(z + 2)}, \text{ where } z \text{ is small.}$$

Now, $\dfrac{1}{2i}\dfrac{z^4+1}{z^2(2z+1)(z+2)}$

$$= \frac{1}{4i}\left(1+\frac{1}{z^4}\right)\left(1+\frac{1}{2z}\right)^{-1}\left(1+\frac{2}{z}\right)^{-1}$$

$$= \frac{1}{4i}\left(1+\frac{1}{z^4}\right)\left(1-\frac{1}{2z}+...\right)\left(1-\frac{2}{z}+...\right)$$

the coefficient of $\dfrac{1}{z}$ is easily seen to be $\dfrac{1}{4i}\left(\dfrac{-5}{2}\right)$, i.e., $\dfrac{-5}{8i}$

Hence by Cauchy's residue theorem,

$$I = 2\pi i \times \sum R$$

$$= 2\pi i \times \left\{\frac{17}{24i}+\left(\frac{-5}{8i}\right)\right\} = \frac{\pi}{6}.$$

5. *Use method of contour integration to prove that*

$$\int_0^{2\pi}\frac{d\theta}{1+a^2-2a\cos\theta} = \frac{2\pi}{1-a^2},\ 0\le a<1.$$

(Garhwal 2006)

Solution. Let

$$I = \int_0^{2\pi}\frac{d\theta}{1+a^2-a(e^{i\theta}+e^{-i\theta})}$$

$$= \oint_C \frac{1}{1+a^2-a\left(z+\dfrac{1}{z}\right)}\frac{dz}{iz}$$

$$\left[\text{Writing } e^{i\theta}=z,\text{ so that } d\theta=\frac{dz}{iz}\right]$$

where C is the unit circle $|z|=1$

$$= \frac{1}{i}\oint_C\frac{dz}{(1+a^2)z-az^2-a}$$

$$= -\frac{1}{ia}\oint_C\frac{dz}{(z-a)\left(z-\dfrac{1}{a}\right)}$$

$$= \oint_C f(z)\,dz$$

where

$$f(z) = -\frac{1}{ia(z-a)\left(z-\dfrac{1}{a}\right)}$$

$$= 2\pi i\,\Sigma R^+ \qquad\qquad\qquad ...(1)$$

By Cauchy's residue theorem where ΣR^+ = sum of residues of $f(z)$ within C.

Clearly poles of $f(z)$ are $z = a$, $z = \dfrac{1}{a}$ both simple poles.

As $0 < a < 1$, therefore only $z = a$ lies inside C.

Residues at the simple pole $z = a$ is

$$= \lim_{z \to a} (z - a) f(z)$$

$$= \lim_{z \to 0} (z - a) \left[-\frac{1}{ia \, (z - a) \left(z - \dfrac{1}{a} \right)} \right]$$

$$= -\frac{1}{ia \left(a - \dfrac{1}{a} \right)} = \frac{1}{i \, (1 - a^2)} = \Sigma R^+ \qquad (\because \ a < 1)$$

Hence from (1), we have

$$I = 2\pi i \cdot \frac{1}{i \, (1 - a^2)} = \frac{2\pi}{1 - a^2}.$$

6. *Evaluate*

$$\int_0^\pi \frac{a}{a^2 + \sin^2 \theta} \, d\theta.$$

(Meerut 2006, Kanpur 2004, Garhwal 2001, 2002, 2003; Rohilkhand 2006)

Solution. Let

$$I = \int_0^\pi \frac{a}{a^2 + \sin^2 \theta} \, d\theta = \int_0^\pi \frac{2a}{2a^2 + 1 - \cos 2\theta} \, d\theta$$

$$= \int_0^{2\pi} \frac{a \, d\phi}{2a^2 + 1 - \cos \phi}$$

[Putting $2\theta = \phi$, so that $2d\theta = d\phi$]

$$= \int_0^{2\pi} \frac{2a \, d\phi}{2 \, (2a^2 + 1) - (e^{i\phi} + e^{-i\phi})}$$

$$= \int_C \frac{2a}{2 \, (2a^2 + 1) - \left(z + \dfrac{1}{z} \right)} \cdot \frac{dz}{iz},$$

$$\left[\text{Writing } e^{i\phi} = z, \text{ so that } d\phi = \frac{dz}{iz} \right]$$

where C is the unit circle $|z| = 1$

$$= \int_C \frac{2ai}{z^2 - 2 \, (2a^2 + 1) \, (z + 1)} \, dz$$

$$= \int_C f(z) \, dz$$

where
$$f(z) = \frac{2ai}{z^2 - 2(2a^2 + 1)z + 1}$$
$$= 2\pi i \, \Sigma R^+ \qquad\qquad ...(1)$$

By Cauchy's residue theorem where ΣR^+ = sum of residues at poles within C.
The poles of $f(z)$ are given by $z^2 - 2(2a^2 + 1)z + 1 = 0$.

$\therefore$
$$z = (1 + 2a^2) + 2a\sqrt{1 + a^2} = \alpha, \ \text{(say)}$$

and
$$z = (1 + 2a^2) - 2a\sqrt{1 + a^2} = \beta, \ \text{(say)}.$$

Both are simple poles.
Here $\alpha\beta = 1$ or $|\alpha\beta| = 1$ or $|\alpha||\beta| = 1$ and $|\alpha| > 1$

$\therefore$
$$|\beta| < 1$$

$\therefore$ the pole $z = \beta$ of $f(z)$ lies within C, which is a simple pole.

$\therefore$ Residue at simple pole $z = \beta$

$$= \lim_{z \to \beta} (z - \beta) f(z) = \lim_{z \to \beta} (z - \beta) \frac{2ai}{(z - \alpha)(z - \beta)} = \frac{2ai}{\beta - \alpha}$$

$$= -\frac{i}{2\sqrt{1 + a^2}} = \Sigma R^+$$

$\therefore$ From (1), we have

$$I = \int_0^\pi \frac{a}{a^2 + \sin^2\theta} \, d\theta = 2\pi i \cdot \left[\frac{-i}{2\sqrt{1 + a^2}} \right] = \frac{\pi}{\sqrt{1 + a^2}}.$$

7. Evaluate

$$\int_0^{2\pi} \frac{d\theta}{(a + b\cos\theta)^2}, \ (a > 0, \ b > 0; \ a > b).$$

(Kanpur 2000; Meerut 2005; Gauhati 2002)

Solution. Making the substitution $z = e^{i\theta}$, we see that the given integral

$$= \int_C \frac{dz}{iz\left[a + \dfrac{b}{2}\left(z + \dfrac{1}{z}\right)\right]^2} = -\int_C \frac{4iz \, dz}{(bz^2 + 2az + b)} \qquad ...(1)$$

C, being the positively oriented unit circle $|z| = 1$.

The zeros of the denominator, *viz.*, the roots of
$$bz^2 + 2az + b = 0,$$
are the only singular points of the integrand in (1).

These singular points are

$$\frac{-a \pm \sqrt{a^2 - b^2}}{b}.$$

They are both real. Also their product is 1. Thus, we see that of the two singular points, one lies within and the other outside the unit circle. Clearly then

$$\alpha = [-a + \sqrt{(a^2 - b^2)}]/b$$

lies within and

$$\beta = [-a - \sqrt{(a^2 - b^2)}]/b$$

lies without the unit circle. We thus require the residue at $z = \alpha$.

Now we have

$$\frac{-4iz}{(bz^2 + 2az + b)^2} = \frac{-4iz}{b^2 (z - \alpha)^2 (z - \beta)^2}$$

$$= \frac{4iz}{b^2 (z - \beta)^2} \cdot \frac{1}{(z - \alpha)^2} = \phi(z) \cdot \frac{1}{(z - \alpha)^2}, \text{ (say)}.$$

Thus

$$\text{Res.}(\alpha) = \phi'(\alpha)$$

$$= -\frac{4i}{b^2} \left[\frac{(z - \beta^2) - 2z(z - \beta)}{(z - \beta)^4} \right]_{z = \alpha}$$

$$= -\frac{4i}{b^2} \frac{-\alpha - \beta}{(\alpha - \beta)^3} = -\frac{ai}{(a^2 - b^2)^{3/2}}.$$

Thus, we see that the given integral

$$= 2\pi i \,(\text{Res. }\alpha) = 2a\pi / (a^2 - b^2)^{3/2}.$$

8. *Prove that*

$$\int_0^{2\pi} \frac{\cos^2 3\theta \, d\theta}{1 - 2p \cos 2\theta + p^2} = \pi \frac{1 - p + p^2}{1 - p}, \ 0 < p < 1.$$

(Kerala 2000)

Solution. Let $\quad I = \displaystyle\int_0^{2\pi} \frac{\cos^2 3\theta \, d\theta}{1 - 2p \cos 2\theta + p^2}$

$$= \frac{1}{2} \int_0^{2\pi} \frac{1 + \cos 6\theta}{1 - 2p \cos 2\theta + p^2} \, d\theta$$

$$= \frac{1}{2} \text{ real part of } \int_0^{2\pi} \frac{1 + e^{6i\theta}}{1 - p(e^{ei\theta} + e^{-2i\theta}) + p^2} \, d\theta$$

$$= \frac{1}{2} \text{ real part of } \int_C \frac{1 + z^6}{1 - p\left(z^2 + \dfrac{1}{z^2}\right) + p^2} \frac{dz}{iz}$$

where C denotes the unit circle $|z| = 1$

$$= \frac{1}{2} \text{ real part of } \frac{1}{i} \int_C \frac{z(1 + z^6)}{(1 - pz^2)(z^2 - p)} \, dz$$

$$= \frac{1}{2} \text{ real part of } \int_C f(z) \, dz, \text{ where}$$

$$f(z) = \frac{z(1+z^6)}{i(1-pz^2)(z^2-p)}$$

Poles of $f(z)$ are given by

$$(1-pz^2)(z^2-p) = 0$$

Thus $z = \pm\sqrt{p}$ and $z = \pm\dfrac{1}{\sqrt{p}}$ are the simple poles.

The only poles which lies within C are $z = \pm\sqrt{p}$, as $p < 1$.

Residue at $z = \sqrt{p}$ is

$$\lim_{z \to \sqrt{p}} (z - \sqrt{p}) \cdot \frac{z(1+z^6)}{i(1-pz^2)(z^2-p)} = \frac{1}{2i}\frac{1+p^3}{1-p^2}$$

and residue at $z = -\sqrt{p}$ is

$$\lim_{z \to -\sqrt{p}} (z + \sqrt{p}) \cdot \frac{z(1+z^6)}{(1-pz^2)(z^2-p)} = \frac{1}{2i} \cdot \frac{1+p^3}{1-p^2}$$

so the sum of the residues

$$= \frac{1+p^3}{1-p^2} \times \frac{1}{i}.$$

Hence by Cauchy's residue theorem we have

$$\int_C f(z)\,dz = 2\pi i \times \text{ sum of residues within the contour}$$

$$= 2\pi i \times \frac{1+p^3}{1-p^2} \times \frac{1}{i}$$

$$\therefore \quad I = \frac{1}{2} \text{ real part of } \int_C f(z)\,dz$$

$$= \frac{1}{2} \text{ real part of } 2\pi \cdot \frac{1+p^3}{1-p^2}$$

$$= \pi \cdot \frac{1+p^3}{1-p^2} = \pi \cdot \frac{1-p+p^2}{1-p}.$$

9. *Use the method of contour integration to prove that*

$$\int_0^{2\pi} \frac{(1+2\cos\theta)^n \cos n\theta}{3+2\cos\theta}\,d\theta = \frac{2\pi}{\sqrt{5}}(3-\sqrt{5})^n.$$

Solution.

$$I = \int_0^{2\pi} \frac{(1+2\cos\theta)^n \cos n\theta\, d\theta}{3+2\cos\theta}$$

$$= \text{real part of } \int_0^{2\pi} \frac{(1+e^{i\theta}+e^{-i\theta})^n\, e^{in\theta} d\theta}{3+e^{i\theta}+e^{-i\theta}}$$

$$= \text{real part of } \int_C \frac{\left(1 + z + \frac{1}{z}\right)^n z^n}{3 + z + \frac{1}{z}} \frac{dz}{iz} \text{ writing } e^{i\theta} = z, d\theta = \frac{dz}{iz}$$

$$= \text{real part of } \frac{1}{i} \int_C \frac{(1 + z + z^2)^n}{(1 + 3z + z^2)} dz$$

where the contour C is the unit circle $|z| = 1$.

$$= \text{real part of } \frac{1}{i} \int_C f(z) \, dz, \text{ where}$$

$$f(z) = \frac{(1 + z + z^2)^n}{1 + 3z + z^2}$$

Poles of $f(z)$ are given by $1 + 3z + z^2 = 0$, *i.e.*, by

$$z = \frac{-3 \pm \sqrt{5}}{2}.$$

Let $\qquad \alpha = \frac{-3 + \sqrt{5}}{2}$ and $\beta = \frac{-3 - \sqrt{5}}{2}$

The only pole which lies within C is $\alpha = \frac{-3 + \sqrt{5}}{2}$ and β lies outside C.

The residue at α is

$$\lim_{z \to \alpha} (z - \alpha) \cdot \frac{(1 + z + z^2)^n}{(z - \alpha)(z - \beta)}$$

$$= \frac{(1 + \alpha + \alpha^2)^n}{\alpha - \beta} = \frac{(3 - \sqrt{5})^n}{\sqrt{5}}$$

Hence, by Cauchy's residue theorem, we have

$$\int_C f(z) = 2\pi i \times \frac{(3 - \sqrt{5})^n}{\sqrt{5}}$$

Hence, $\qquad I = \text{real part of } \frac{1}{i} \int_C f(z) \, dz$

$$= \text{real part of } \frac{1}{i} 2\pi i \frac{(3 - \sqrt{5})^n}{\sqrt{5}}$$

$$= \frac{2\pi}{\sqrt{5}} (3 - \sqrt{5})^n$$

10. *Show that if m is real and $-1 < a < 1$*

(i) $\displaystyle \int_0^{2\pi} \frac{e^{m \cos \theta} [\cos (m \sin \theta) - a \sin (m \sin \theta + \theta)] d\theta}{1 + a^2 - 2a \sin \theta} = 2\pi \cos ma$

(ii) $\displaystyle\int_0^{2\pi} \frac{e^{m\cos\theta}[\sin(m\sin\theta) + a\cos(m\sin\theta + \theta)]\,d\theta}{1 + a^2 - 2a\sin\theta} = 2\pi\sin ma.$

Solution. (i) Let $\quad I_1 = \displaystyle\int_0^{2\pi} \frac{e^{m\cos\theta}}{1 + a^2 - 2a\sin\theta} e^{im\sin\theta}\,d\theta$

and $\qquad\qquad I_2 = \displaystyle\int_0^{2\pi} \frac{e^{m\cos\theta}}{1 + a^2 - 2a\sin\theta} e^{i(m\sin\theta + \theta)}\,d\theta$

Then, $\qquad\qquad I_1 = \displaystyle\int_0^{2\pi} \frac{e^{m(\cos\theta + i\sin\theta)}}{1 + a^2 - 2a\sin\theta}\,d\theta$

$\qquad\qquad\qquad = \displaystyle\int_0^{2\pi} \frac{e^{me^{i\theta}}}{1 + a^2 - 2a\sin\theta}\,d\theta$

$\qquad\qquad\qquad = \displaystyle\int_C \frac{e^{mz}}{1 + a^2 - \dfrac{a}{i}\left(z - \dfrac{1}{z}\right)}\,\frac{dz}{iz}$

$\qquad\qquad\qquad = -\frac{1}{a}\displaystyle\int_C \frac{e^{mz}\,dz}{(z - ia)(z - i/a)}$

$\qquad\qquad\qquad = -\frac{1}{a}\displaystyle\int_C f_1(z)\,dz \quad\text{(say)}$

where C is the unit circle $|z| = 1$

Similarly, we have

$\qquad\qquad I_2 = \frac{-1}{a}\displaystyle\int \frac{ze^{mz}}{(z - ia)(z - i/a)}\,dz$

$\qquad\qquad\quad = -\frac{1}{a}\displaystyle\int_C f_2(z)\,dz$

where C is the unit circle $|z| = 1$

$z = ia$ and $z = \dfrac{i}{a}$ are the simple poles of $f_1(z)$ and $f_2(z)$

Since $-1 < a < 1, z = \dfrac{i}{a}$ lies outside the circle C. Thus only $z = ia$ lies inside the circle.

Residue of $f_1(z)$ at $z = ia$ is

$\qquad\qquad\qquad \lim_{z \to ia}(z - ia)\,f_1(z)$

$\qquad\qquad = \lim_{z \to ia}(z - ia)\frac{e^{mz}}{(z - ia)(z - i/a)} = \frac{ae^{ima}}{i(a^2 - 1)}$

Residue of $f_2(z)$ at $z = ai$ is

$\qquad\qquad\qquad \lim_{z \to ia}(z - ia)\,f_2(z)$

$$= \lim_{z \to ia} (z - ia) \frac{z \, e^{mz}}{(z - ia)(z - i/a)}$$

$$= \frac{ia \, e^{ima}}{(ai - i/a)} = \frac{a^2 e^{ima}}{(a^2 - 1)}$$

By Cauchy's residue theorem,

$$I_1 = 2\pi i \left[-\frac{1}{a} \frac{a \, e^{ima}}{i \, (a^2 - 1)} \right]$$

$$= \frac{2\pi}{1 - a^2} e^{ima}$$

and

$$I_2 = 2\pi i \left[-\frac{1}{a} \cdot \frac{a^2 e^{ima}}{i \, (a^2 - 1)} \right]$$

$$= \frac{2a\pi i}{1 - a^2} e^{ima}$$

$$\int_0^{2\pi} \frac{e^{m \cos \theta} e^{im \sin \theta}}{1 + a^2 - 2a \sin \theta} \, d\theta = \frac{2\pi}{1 - a^2} e^{ima} \qquad \qquad ...(1)$$

and

$$\int_0^{2\pi} \frac{e^{m \cos \theta} e^{i \, (m \sin \theta + \theta)}}{1 + a^2 - 2a \sin \theta} \, d\theta = \frac{2a\pi i}{1 - a^2} e^{ima} \qquad \qquad ...(2)$$

Equating real parts on both sides of (1), we get

$$\int_0^{2\pi} \frac{e^{m \cos \theta} \cos (m \sin \theta)}{1 + a^2 - 2a \sin \theta} \, d\theta = \frac{2\pi}{1 - a^2} \cos am \qquad \qquad ...(3)$$

Again equating imaginary parts on both sides of (2), we get

$$\int_0^{2\pi} \frac{e^{m \cos \theta} \sin (m \sin \theta + \theta)}{1 + a^2 - 2a \sin \theta} \, d\theta = \frac{2a\pi}{1 - a^2} \cos am$$

Multiplying (4) by a and subtracting from (3), we get

$$\int_0^{2\pi} e^{m \cos \theta} \frac{\cos (m \sin \theta) - a \sin (m \sin \theta + \theta)}{1 + a^2 - 2a \sin \theta} \, d\theta = 2\pi \cos am.$$

(*ii*) In similar way, find the equations (1) and (2) as in part (*i*). Then equating the **imaginary** parts in (1) and real parts in (2), we get

$$\int_0^{2\pi} \frac{e^{m \cos \theta} \sin (m \sin \theta)}{1 + a^2 - 2a \sin \theta} \, d\theta = \frac{2\pi}{1 - a^2} \sin am \qquad \qquad ...(i)$$

$$\int_0^{2\pi} \frac{e^{m \cos \theta} \cos (m \sin \theta + \theta)}{1 + a^2 - 2a \sin \theta} \, d\theta = -\frac{2a\pi}{1 - a^2} \sin am \qquad \qquad ...(ii)$$

Multiplying both sides of (*ii*) by a and adding to (*i*), we get

$$\int_0^{2\pi} e^{m \sin \theta} \frac{\sin (m \sin \theta) + a \cos (m \sin \theta + \theta)}{1 + a^2 - 2a \sin \theta} \, d\theta = 2\pi \sin am.$$

11. *Evaluate the integral* $\int\limits_0^{2\pi} \cos^{2n}\theta\, d\theta$ *where n is a positive integer.*

Solution. Let

$$I = \int\limits_0^{2\pi} \cos^{2n}\theta\, d\theta$$

$$= \int\limits_0^{2\pi} (\cos^2\theta)^n\, d\theta$$

$$= \frac{1}{2^n} \int\limits_0^{2\pi} (1 + \cos 2\theta)^n\, d\theta$$

Putting $2\theta = t$, so that $d\theta = \frac{1}{2}\, dt$,

$$I = \frac{1}{2^{n+1}} \int\limits_0^{4\pi} (1 + \cos t)^n\, dt$$

$$= \frac{1}{2^n} \int\limits_0^{2\pi} (1 + \cos t)^n\, dt$$

$$= \frac{1}{2^n} \int\limits_C \left\{ 1 + \frac{1}{2}\left(z + \frac{1}{z}\right) \right\}^n \frac{dz}{iz} \qquad \text{putting } z = e^{it}$$

$$= \frac{1}{2^n} \int\limits_C \frac{(z^2 + 2z + 1)^n}{(2z)^n \cdot iz}\, dz$$

$$= \frac{1}{i \cdot 2^{2n}} \int\limits_C \frac{(z+1)^{2n}}{z^{n+1}}\, dz$$

$$= \int\limits_C f(z)\, dz, \text{ where } C \text{ is the unit circle } |z| = 1.$$

The pole of $f(z)$ is $z = 0$ of order $(n + 1)$.

Residue at $z = 0$
$$= \frac{1}{i \cdot 2^{2n}} \frac{d^n}{dz^n} \left[\frac{(z+1)^{2n}}{z^{n+1}} \right]$$

$$= \frac{2n!}{i \cdot 2^{2n}(n!)^2}$$

By Cauchy's residue theorem

$$\int\limits_0^{2\pi} \cos^{2n}\theta\, d\theta = 2\pi i \times \text{ Sum of residues at pole within } C$$

$$= 2\pi i \cdot \frac{2n!}{i \cdot 2^{2n}(n!)^2}$$

$$= \frac{2n!\,\pi}{2^{2n-1}(n!)^2}.$$

12. *Show by calculus of residues that* $\displaystyle\int_0^\pi \tan(\theta + ia)\,d\theta \;=\; i\pi$, *where* $R(a) > 0$.

Solution. Let

$$I = \int_0^\pi \tan(\theta + ia)\,d\theta$$

$$= \int_0^\pi \frac{2\sin(\theta + ia)\cos(\theta - ia)}{2\cos(\theta + ia)\cdot\cos(\theta - ia)}\,d\theta$$

$$= \int_0^\pi \left[\frac{\sin 2\theta + \sin(2ia)}{\cos 2\theta + \cos(2ia)}\right]d\theta$$

$$= \int_0^{2\pi} \frac{\sin t + i\sinh 2a}{\cos t + \cosh 2a}\,dt \qquad\qquad \text{where } 2\theta = t$$

Putting $z = e^{it}$ so that $dz = ie^{it}\,dt,\;\; dt = \dfrac{dz}{iz}$, we get

$$I = \frac{1}{2}\int_C \left[\frac{\dfrac{z - z^{-1}}{2i} + i\sinh 2a}{\dfrac{z + z^{-1}}{2} + \cosh 2a}\right]\frac{dz}{iz}$$

where C denotes the unit circle $|z| = 1$.

$$I = \frac{1}{2}\int_C f(z)\,dz \qquad\qquad\qquad ...(1)$$

where

$$f(z) = \frac{z^2 - 1 - 2z\sinh 2a}{z(z^2 + 2z\cosh 2a + 1)}$$

The poles of the integrand $f(z)$ are $z(z^2 + 2z\cosh 2a + 1) = 0$, *i.e.*, $z = 0$ and

$$z = -\cosh 2a \pm \sqrt{(\cosh^2 a - 1)} \;=\; -\cosh 2a \pm \sinh 2a$$

or $z = 0,\ \alpha,\ \beta$

where $\alpha = -\cosh 2a + \sinh 2a,\ \beta = -\cosh 2a - \sinh 2a$.

Evidently $\alpha\beta = 1, |\alpha| < 1$ so that $|\beta| > 1 \cdot f(z)$ has two simple poles at $z = 0, \alpha$ within C.

Residue at $(z = 0) = \lim_{z \to 0} (z - 0)f(z)$

$$= \lim_{z \to 0} \frac{z^2 - 2z\sinh 2a - 1}{z^2 + 2z\cosh 2a + 1} = -1$$

Res $(z = \alpha) = \lim_{z \to \alpha} (z - \alpha)f(z)$

$$= \lim_{z \to \alpha} \frac{(z - \alpha)(z^2 - 2z\sinh 2a - 1)}{z(z - \alpha)(z - \beta)}$$

$$= \frac{\alpha^2 - 2\alpha\sinh 2a - 1}{\alpha(\alpha - \beta)} = \frac{\alpha - 2\sinh 2a - \beta}{\alpha - \beta}$$

$$= \frac{2\sinh 2a - 2\sinh 2a}{2\sinh 2a} = 0$$

Then by Cauchy's residue theorem

$$\int_C f(z)\,dz = 2\pi i \text{ (sum of residues within } C)$$

$$= 2\pi i(-1) = -2\pi i$$

$$\therefore \int_0^\pi \tan(\theta + ia)\,d\theta = -\frac{1}{2}(-2\pi i) = i\pi.$$

13. *Apply the calculus of residues to evaluate*

(i) $\int_0^{2\pi} \dfrac{\sin n\theta\,d\theta}{1 + 2a\cos\theta + a^2}$ *(Garhwal 2001)*

(ii) $\int_0^{2\pi} \dfrac{\sin n\theta\,d\theta}{1 + 2a\cos\theta + a^2}$ *where* $a^2 < 1$ *and n is a positive integers*

Solution. Let

$$I = \int_0^{2\pi} \frac{\cos n\theta + i\sin n\theta}{1 + 2a\cos\theta + a^2}$$

$$= \int_0^{2\pi} \frac{e^{in\theta}\,d\theta}{1 + 2a\cos\theta + a^2}$$

Then

$$I = \int_0^{2\pi} \frac{(e^{i\theta})^n\,d\theta}{1 + a^2 + ae^{i\theta} + ae^{-i\theta}}$$

Putting $z = e^{i\theta}, \dfrac{dz}{iz} = d\theta$

$$I = \int_C \frac{z^n}{1 + a^2 + a(z + z^{-1})}\,\frac{dz}{iz}$$

$$= \frac{1}{i}\int_C \frac{z^n\,dz}{(1 + a^2)z + az^2 - a}, \text{ where } C \text{ is circle } |z| = 1$$

or

$$I = \frac{1}{ai}\int_C \frac{z^n\,dz}{z^2 + az + \dfrac{z}{a} + 1}$$

$$= \frac{1}{ia}\int_C f(z)\,dz \qquad\qquad\qquad \text{...(1)}$$

where

$$f(z) = \frac{z^n}{(z + a)\left(z + \dfrac{1}{a}\right)}.$$

The poles of $f(z)$ are $(z + a)\left(z + \dfrac{1}{a}\right) = 0$

i.e., $\quad\quad\quad\quad\quad\quad z = -a, -\dfrac{1}{a}$ are the simple poles .

But $a^2 < 1$.

Hence $z = -a$ lies within C and $z = -\dfrac{1}{a}$ lies outside C.

Residue at $(z = -a) = \lim\limits_{z \to -a} (z + a) f(z)$

$$= \lim\limits_{z \to -a} \frac{z^n}{z + (1/a)} = \frac{(-a)^n}{-a + (1/a)}$$

$$= \frac{(-a)^n a^{n+1}}{1 - a^2} .$$

Then by Cauchy's residue theorem

$$\int\limits_C f(z)\, dz = 2\pi i \quad\quad\quad\quad\quad\quad\quad \text{(Sum of residues within } C)$$

$$= \frac{2\pi i (-1)^n a^{n+1}}{1 - a^2}$$

$\therefore \quad\quad\quad\quad I = \dfrac{1}{ai} \dfrac{2\pi i (-1)^n a^{n+1}}{1 - a^2} = \dfrac{2\pi (-1)^n a^n}{1 - a^2}$

or $\quad\quad\quad\quad \displaystyle\int\limits_0^{2\pi} \frac{(\cos n\theta + i \sin n\theta)\, d\theta}{1 + 2a \cos \theta + a^2} = \frac{2\pi (-1)^n a^n}{1 - a^2}$

Equating real and imaginary parts, we get

$$\int\limits_0^{2\pi} \frac{\cos n\theta\, d\theta}{1 + 2a \cos \theta + a^2} = \frac{2\pi (-1)^n a^n}{1 - a^2}$$

and $\quad\quad\quad\quad \displaystyle\int\limits_0^{2\pi} \frac{\sin n\theta\, d\theta}{1 + 2a \cos \theta + a^2} = 0.$

11.3. *Evaluation of the integral*

$$\int\limits_{-\infty}^{+\infty} f(x)\, dx, \quad\quad\quad\quad\quad\quad\quad\quad\quad ...(1)$$

where $f(z)$ is a real rational function of the real variable x.

It is shown in the theory of real variables that the improper integral (1) would converge, if
(*i*) the degree of the denominator of $f(x)$ exceeds that of the numerator by more than one;
(*ii*) the denominator of $f(x)$ does not become zero for any real value of x.

We suppose that the rational function $f(z)$ does satisfy the two conditions (*i*) and (*ii*).
Before proceeding to indicate the method of evaluating the given integral, we prove a lemma.

Lemma. *If $f(z)$ is such that*

$$z f(z) \to 0 \ \text{uniformly as } z \to \infty, \quad\quad\quad\quad\quad\quad ...(2)$$

then

$$\lim_{R \to \infty} \int_{C_1} f(z) = 0,$$

where, C_1, *is the semi-circle*

$$|z| = R, I(z) > 0.$$

Here it is understood that for sufficiently large values of R, $f(z)$ has no singularity on the semi-circle C_1.

Let $\varepsilon > 0$ be any given number. Then, because of (2), there exists a positive number R_0 such that

$$|z f(z)| < \varepsilon \iff |f(z)| < \varepsilon / |z| \text{ when } |z| \ge R_0 \qquad \text{...(3)}$$

Also for any point z on the semi-circle C_1 with radius R, we have

$$\frac{\varepsilon}{|z|} = \frac{\varepsilon}{|R|} \qquad \text{...(4)}$$

From (3) and (4), we deduce that for any semi-circle C_1 with radius $R \ge R_0$,

$$\left| \int_{C_1} f(z)\, dz \right| < \frac{\varepsilon}{R} \cdot \pi R = \pi \varepsilon.$$

This shows that

$$\lim_{R \to \infty} \int_{C_1} f(z)\, dz = 0.$$

In this connection, it will be useful to notice that if

$$f(z) = \frac{a_0 z^n + a_1 z^{n-1} + \dots + a_n}{b_0 z^m + b_1 z^{m-1} + \dots + b^m},$$

where $a_0 \ne 0$, $b_0 \ne 0$ and $m > (n+1)$, then

$$z f(z) \to 0 \text{ uniformly as } z \to \infty.$$

In fact for any point z on $|z| = R$, we have

$$z f(z)| \le R \frac{|a_0| R^n + |a_1| R^{n-1} + \dots + |a_n|}{|b_0| R^m - |b_1| R^{m-1} - \dots - |b^m|}$$

so that $z f(z) \to 0$ as $R \to \infty$.

We now proceed to the evaluation of the given improper integral (1).

We consider a closed curve, C, consisting of

(*a*) the semi-circle C_1 given by $|z| = R$, $I(z) > 0$;

(*b*) the line segment C_2 of the real axis from $-R$ to $+R$.

Since $f(z)$ has only a finite number of singular points, we can choose R so large that the singular points of $f(z)$ are all contained in the interior of C.

Thus if, α_1, be any pole of $f(z)$, we have

$$2\pi i \, \Sigma \text{Res.} (\alpha_i) = \int_C f(z)\, dz$$

$$= \int_{C_1} f(z)\, dz + \int_{C_2} f(z)\, dz$$

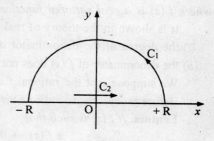

Fig. 11.1

$$= \int_{C_1} f(z)\, dz + \int_{-R}^{+R} f(x)\, dx \qquad \ldots(5)$$

By the lemma above,

$$\lim_{R \to \infty} \int_{C_1} f(z)\, dz = 0.$$

Also

$$\lim_{R \to \infty} \int_{-R}^{+R} f(x)\, dx = P \int_{-\infty}^{+\infty} f(x)\, dx,$$

where P denotes the principal value of the integral following.

As, however, this integral is convergent, we can write

$$P \int_{-\infty}^{+\infty} f(x)\, dx = \int_{-\infty}^{+\infty} f(x)\, dx.$$

Thus proceeding to the limit when $R \to \infty$, we have, from (5),

$$2\pi i\, \Sigma \text{Res.}(\alpha_i) = \int_{-\infty}^{+\infty} f(x)\, dx.$$

EXAMPLES

1. *Show by contour integration that*

$$\int_{0}^{\infty} \frac{dx}{1 + x^2} = \frac{\pi}{2}.$$

(Agra 2000; Gorakhpur 2005)

Solution. Consider the integral

$$\int_{C} f(z)\, dz \text{ where } f(z) = \frac{1}{1 + z^2}.$$

Poles of $f(z)$ are given by

$$1 + z^2 = 0, \ i.e., \ z = \pm i,$$

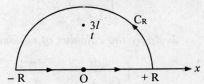

Fig. 11.2

which are simple poles. Since there is no pole on the real axis, therefore we may take the contour C consisting of upper half C_R of a large circle $|z| = R$ and real axis from $-R$ to R.

Hence by Cauchy's residue theorem, we have

$$\int_{C} f(z)\, dz = \int_{-R}^{R} f(x)\, dx + \int_{C_R} f(z)\, dz = 2\pi i\, \Sigma R^+$$

where $\Sigma R^+ = $ sum of residues of $f(z)$ at its poles within C.

or

$$\int_{-R}^{R} \frac{dx}{1 + x^2} + \int_{C_R} \frac{dz}{1 + z^2} = 2\pi i\, \Sigma R^+ \qquad \ldots(1)$$

The pole (simple) $z = i$ lie within the contour C, the residue at this pole

$$= \lim_{z \to i} (z - i)\, f(z) = \lim_{z \to i} (z - i)\, \frac{1}{(1 + z^2)}$$

$$= \lim_{z \to i} \frac{1}{z+i} = \frac{1}{2i}$$

and

$$\left| \int_{C_R} \frac{dz}{1+z^2} \right|$$

$$\leq \int_{C_R} \frac{|dz|}{|1+z^2|} \leq \int_{C_R} \frac{|dz|}{|z|^2 - 1}$$

$$= \int_0^\pi \frac{R}{R^2 - 1} \, d\theta \text{ since } z = Re^{i\theta}, \ |dz| = |iRe^{i\theta} \, d\theta| = R \, d\theta$$

$$= \frac{\pi R}{R^2 - 1} \to 0 \text{ as } R \to \infty.$$

Also we can proceed as follows:

$$\because \quad \lim_{z \to \infty} z \, f(z) = \lim_{z \to \infty} \frac{z}{1+z^2} = \lim_{z \to \infty} \frac{1}{\dfrac{1}{z} + z} = 0$$

$$\therefore \quad \lim_{R \to \infty} \int_{C_R} f(z) \, dz = 0. \qquad\qquad \text{[By Theorem II, § 11.2.1]}$$

Hence when $R \to \infty$, from (1), we have

$$\int_{-\infty}^\infty \frac{dx}{1+x^2} = 2\pi i \cdot \frac{1}{2i} \text{ or } 2 \int_0^\infty \frac{dx}{1+x^2} = \pi$$

$$\therefore \qquad \int_0^\infty \frac{dx}{1+x^2} = \frac{\pi}{2}.$$

2. *Apply the calculus of residues to prove that*

$$\int_{-\infty}^\infty \frac{dx}{(x^2+1)^3} = \frac{3\pi}{8}.$$

(Gauhati 2002; Meerut 2000; Calicut 2004)

Solution. Consider

$$\int_C f(z) \, dz, \text{ where } f(z) = \frac{1}{(z^2+1)^3}.$$

Poles of $f(z)$ are given by

$$(z^2+1)^3 = 0, \text{ i.e., } (z-i)^3 (z+i)^3 = 0, \text{ i.e., } z = \pm i$$

are the poles each of order 3. Since there is no pole on the real axis, therefore, we may take the closed contour C consisting of real axis from $-R$ to R and the upper half C_R of a large semi-circle $|z| = R$.

Hence by Cauchy's residue theorem, we have

$$\int_C f(z) \, dz = \int_{-R}^R f(x) \, dx + \int_{C_R} f(z) \, dz = 2\pi i \, \Sigma R^+$$

where ΣR^+ = sum of residues of $f(z)$ at its poles within C

or
$$\int_{-R}^{R} \frac{dx}{(x^2+1)^3} + \int_{C_R} \frac{dz}{(z^2+1)^3} = 2\pi i \, \Sigma R^+ \qquad \text{...(1)}$$

The only pole which lies within C is $z = i$ of order 3.
We can write

$$f(z) = \frac{1}{(z+i)^3 (z-i)^3} = \frac{\phi(z)}{(z-i)^3}$$

where

$$\phi(z) = \frac{1}{(z+i)^3}.$$

$\therefore$ Residue of $f(z)$ at the pole $z = i$

$$= \frac{1}{2}\left[\frac{d^2}{dz^2} \frac{1}{(z+i)^3}\right]_{z=i} = \frac{3}{16i} = \Sigma R^+$$

and
$$\left|\int_{C_R} \frac{dz}{(z^2+1)^3}\right| \le \int_{C_R} \left|\frac{1}{(z^2+1)^3}\right| |dz|$$

$$\le \int_{C_R} \frac{|dz|}{(|z|^2 - 1)^3}$$

$$= \int_{0}^{\pi} \frac{R}{(R^2-1)^3} \, d\theta \text{ since } z = Re^{i\theta}, |dz| = R \, d\theta$$

$$= \frac{\pi R}{(R^2-1)^3} \text{ which } \to 0 \text{ as } R \to \infty.$$

Hence when $R \to \infty$, relation (1) becomes

$$\int_{-\infty}^{\infty} \frac{dx}{(x^2+1)^3} = 2\pi \cdot \frac{3}{16i} = \frac{3\pi}{8}.$$

3. *Calculate*

$$\int_{0}^{\infty} \frac{x^2}{(x^2+1)^2} \, dx.$$

(Rohilkhand 2006)

Solution. As the integrand is an even function of x, we have

$$\int_{0}^{\infty} \frac{x^2}{(x^2+1)^2} \, dx = \frac{1}{2} \int_{-\infty}^{+\infty} \frac{x^2}{(x^2+1)^2} \, dx.$$

Consider the contour C consisting of the curves C_1, C_2 as shown in the figure on page 424.
We have then

$$\int_{C} \frac{z^2}{(z^2+1)^2} \, dz = \int_{C_1} \frac{z^2}{(z^2+1)^2} \, dz + \int_{C_2} \frac{z^2}{(z^2+1)^2} \, dz$$

$$= I_1 + I_2, \text{ (say)}.$$

Taking $f(z) = z^2 / (z^2 + 1)^2$, we see that the degree 4 of the denominator is greater than $2 + 1 = 3$; 2 being the degree of the numerator.

Thus by the lemma,

$$\lim I_1 = 0 \text{ as } R \to \infty.$$

Also directly for any point of $|z| = R$,

$$\frac{z^2}{(z^2 + 1)^2} \le \frac{R^2}{(R^2 - 1)^2},$$

so that

$$|I_1| = \left| \int_{C_1} \frac{z^2}{(z^2 + 1)^2} \, dz \right| \le \frac{R^2}{(R^2 - 1)^2} \pi R \to 0 \text{ as } R \to \infty.$$

Further

$$I_2 = \int_{-R}^{+R} \frac{x^2}{(x^2 + 1)^2} \, dx \to \int_{-\infty}^{\infty} \frac{x^2}{(x^2 + 1)^2} \, dx.$$

We now calculate the residue at the pole, i, in the interior of C.

We have

$$f(z) = \frac{z^2}{(z^2 + 1)^2} = \frac{z^2}{(z + i)^2} \cdot \frac{1}{(z - i)^2} = \phi(z) \frac{1}{(z - i)^2}, \quad \text{(say)}$$

Then we have

$$\text{Res. } (i) = \phi'(i).$$

Also

$$\phi(z) = \frac{2z(z + i)^2 - 2(z + i) z^2}{(z + i)^4},$$

$$\Rightarrow \quad \phi'(i) = -\frac{i}{4}.$$

Thus, we have

$$\int_{-\infty}^{+\infty} \frac{x^2}{(x^2 + 1)^2} \, dx = 2\pi i \text{ Res. } (i) = 2\pi i \left(-\frac{i}{4} \right) = \frac{\pi}{2}.$$

4. *Prove by contour integration that*

$$\int_0^{\infty} \frac{dx}{(a + bx^2)^n} = \frac{\pi}{2^n b^{1/2}} \cdot \frac{1 \cdot 3 \cdot 5 \,.....\, (2n - 3)}{1 \cdot 2 \cdot 3 \,.....\, (n - 1)} \cdot \frac{1}{a^{(2n - 1)/2}}. \qquad (Agra\ 2001,\ 2005)$$

Solution. Consider the integral

$$\int_C f(z) \, dz \text{ when } f(z) = \frac{1}{(a + bz^2)^n}.$$

Poles of $f(z)$ are given by $(a + bz^2)^n = 0$,

i.e., $\qquad z = \pm i \sqrt{\dfrac{a}{b}}$

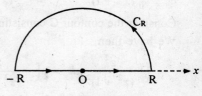

Fig. 11.3

repeated n times. Since there is no pole on the real axis, therefore, we may take the closed contour C consisting of the real axis from $-R$ to R and the upper half C_R of a large circle $|z| = R$.

Hence by Cauchy's residue theorem, we have

$$\int_C f(z)\, dz = 2\pi i \, \Sigma R^+$$

where ΣR^+ = residue of $f(z)$ at all poles within C,

i.e.,

$$\int_{-R}^{R} f(x)\, dx + \int_{C_R} f(z)\, dz = 2\pi i \, \Sigma R^+$$

or

$$\int_{-R}^{R} \frac{dx}{(a + bx^2)^n} + \int_{C_R} \frac{dz}{(a + bz^2)^n} = 2\pi i \, \Sigma R^+ \qquad \qquad ...(1)$$

The only pole within the contour is a pole of order n at

$$z = i\sqrt{\frac{a}{b}}.$$

We can write

$$f(z) = \frac{1}{b^n \left(z + i\sqrt{\dfrac{a}{b}}\right)^n \left(z - i\sqrt{\dfrac{a}{b}}\right)^n}$$

$\therefore$ Residue at pole $z = i\sqrt{\dfrac{a}{b}}$

$$= \frac{1}{b^n\,(n-1)!} \left[\frac{d^{n-1}}{dz^{n-1}} \left\{ \frac{1}{\left[z + \sqrt{\dfrac{a}{b}}\right]^n} \right\} \right]_{z=i} \sqrt{\frac{a}{b}}$$

$$= \frac{(-1)^{n-1}}{(n-1)!} \cdot \frac{1}{b^n} \cdot \frac{n(n+1)(n+2)\dots(2n-2)}{\left(2i\sqrt{\dfrac{a}{b}}\right)^{2n-1}} = \Sigma R^+$$

and

$$\left| \int_{C_R} \frac{dz}{(a + bz^2)^n} \right| \leq \int_{C_R} \frac{|dz|}{|a| |bz^2|^n}$$

$$\leq \int_{C_R} \frac{|dz|}{(b|z|^2 - a)^n}$$

$$= \frac{1}{(bR^2 - a)^n} \int_0^{\pi} R\, d\theta$$

$$= \frac{\pi R}{(bR^2 - a)^n} \to 0 \text{ as } R \to \infty.$$

Hence when $R \to \infty$, relation (1) becomes

$$\int_{-\infty}^{\infty} \frac{dx}{(a + bx^2)^n} = 2\pi i \times \frac{(-1)^{n-1}}{(n-1)!} \cdot \frac{1}{b^n} \cdot \frac{n(n+1)(n+2) \ldots (2n-2)}{\left(2i \sqrt{\dfrac{a}{b}}\right)^{2n-1}}$$

$$= 2\pi i \times \frac{(-1)^{n-1}}{(n-1)!} \cdot \frac{(2n-2)!}{(n-1)!} \cdot \frac{1}{\sqrt{b}\,(2i\sqrt{a})^{2n-1}}$$

$$= \frac{\pi}{2^{n-1}(n-1)!} \cdot \frac{1 \cdot 3 \cdot 5 \ldots (2n-3)}{b^{1/2}\,a^{n-1/2}}$$

or

$$\int_{0}^{\infty} \frac{dx}{(a + bx^2)^n} = \frac{\pi}{2^n b^{1/2}} \cdot \frac{1 \cdot 3 \cdot 5 \ldots (2n-3)}{1 \cdot 2 \cdot 3 \ldots (n-1)} \cdot \frac{1}{a^{(2n-1)/2}}.$$

Particular Case. Taking $a = 1$, $b = 1$ and proceeding as above step by step we can prove that

$$\int_{0}^{\infty} \frac{dx}{(1 + x^2)^n} = \frac{\pi}{2^n} \cdot \frac{1 \cdot 3 \cdot 5 \ldots (2n-3)}{(n-1)!}.$$

5. *Prove that*

$$\int_{-\infty}^{\infty} \frac{x^2 - x + 2}{x^4 + 10x^2 + 9}\, dx = \frac{5\pi}{12}.$$

Solution. Consider the integral

$$\int_{C} f(z)\, dz,$$

where

$$f(z) = \frac{z^2 - z + 2}{z^4 + 10z^2 + 9}.$$

Poles of $f(z)$ are given by $z^4 + 10z^2 + 9 = 0$ or $(z^2 + 1)(z^2 + 9) = 0$ or $z = \pm i, \pm 3i$ are the simple poles. Since there is no pole on the real axis, therefore, we may take the closed contour C, consisting of the upper half C_R of a large circle $|z| = R$ and the real axis from $-R$ to R.

Hence by Cauchy's residue theorem, we have

$$\int_{C} f(z)\, dz = \int_{-R}^{R} f(x)\, dx + \int_{C_R} f(z)\, dz = 2\pi i\, \Sigma R^{+}$$

where ΣR^{+} = sum of residues of $f(z)$ at its poles within C

or

$$\int_{-R}^{R} \frac{x^2 - x + 2}{x^4 + 10x^2 + 9}\, dx + \int_{C_R} \frac{z^2 - z + 2}{z^4 + 10z^2 + 9}\, dz = 2\pi i\, \Sigma R^{+} \qquad \ldots(1)$$

The poles $z = i$ and $z = 3i$ lie within the contour C.

Residue at the simple pole $z = i$ is

$$\lim_{z \to i} (z - i) \frac{z^2 - z + 2}{z^4 + 10z^2 + 9} = \lim_{z \to 3i} \frac{(z - i)(z^2 - z + 2)}{(z - i)(z + z^2)(i + 9)} = \frac{1 - i}{16i}$$

and residue at the simple pole $z = 3i$ is

$$\lim_{z \to 3i} (z - 3i) \frac{(z^2 - z + 2)}{(z^2 + 1)(z - 3i)(z + 3i)} = \frac{7 + 3i}{48i}.$$

$\therefore$ The sum of residues

$$\Sigma R^+ = \frac{1 - i}{16i} + \frac{7 + 3i}{48i} = \frac{5}{24i}.$$

$$\lim_{z \to \infty} z\, f(z) = \lim_{z \to i} \frac{z(z^2 - z + 2)}{z^4 + 10z^2 + 9} = \lim_{z \to \infty} \frac{\left(1 - \dfrac{1}{z} + \dfrac{2}{z^2}\right)}{z\left(1 + \dfrac{10}{z^2} + \dfrac{9}{z^4}\right)} = 0.$$

$\therefore$ By Theorem II, § 11.2.1, $\lim\limits_{R \to \infty} \int_{C_R} f(z) = 0.$

Hence when $R \to \infty$, (1) becomes

$$\int_{-\infty}^{\infty} \frac{x^2 - x + 2}{x^2 + 10x^2 + 9}\, dx = 2\pi i \left(\frac{5}{24i}\right) = \frac{5\pi}{12}.$$

6. Evaluate

$$\int_0^{\infty} \frac{dx}{x^4 + a^4} \quad (a > 0).$$

(UPPCS 2004; Meerut 2002, Garhwal 2007; Ravishankar 2000, 2001;
Gorakhpur 2003, Meerut 2002)

Solution. Consider the integral

$$\int_C f(z)\, dz, \text{ where } f(z) = \frac{1}{z^4 + a^4}.$$

The poles of $f(z)$ are given by
$$z^4 + a^4 = 0$$

i.e., $$z^4 = -a^4 = a^4 e^{\pi i} = a^4 e^{2n\pi i + \pi i}$$

or $$z = a e^{(2n + 1)\,\pi i/4}, \ n = 0, 1, 2, 3.$$

Since there is no pole on the real axis, therefore, we may take the closed contour C consisting of the upper half C_R of a large circle $|z| = R$ and the real axis from $-R$ to R.

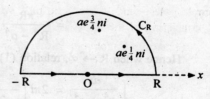

Fig. 11.4

$\therefore$ By Cauchy's residue theorem, we have

$$\int_C f(z)\, dz = \int_{-R}^{R} f(x)\, dx + \int_{C_R} f(z)\, dz = 2\pi i\, \Sigma R^+$$

where ΣR^+ = sum of residues of $f(z)$ at its poles within C

or

$$\int_{-R}^{R} \frac{dx}{x^4 + a^4} + \int_{C_R} \frac{dz}{z^4 + a^4} = 2\pi i\, \Sigma R^+ \qquad \ldots(1)$$

The poles $z = ae^{\pi i/4}$ and $z = ae^{3\pi i/4}$ (for $n = 0$ and 1) are the only two poles which lie within the contour C.

Let α denote any one of these poles. Then

$$\alpha^4 + a^4 = 0 \text{ or } \alpha^4 = -a^4.$$

Residue of $f(z)$ at $z = \alpha$ is

$$\left[\frac{1}{\dfrac{d}{dz}(z^4 + a^4)} \right]_{z=\alpha} = \frac{1}{4\alpha^2} = \frac{\alpha}{4\alpha^4} = \frac{\alpha}{-4a^4}.$$

$\therefore$ Residue at $z = ae^{\pi i/4}$

$$= \frac{-1}{4a^3} e^{\pi i/4}$$

and residue at $ae^{3i\pi/4}$

$$= \frac{e^{3\pi i/4}}{4a^3} = \frac{e^{-\pi i/4}}{4a^3}.$$

$\therefore$ Sum of residues

$$= -\frac{1}{2a^3} \frac{e^{i\pi/4} - e^{-i\pi/4}}{2}$$

$$= -\frac{1}{2a^3} \cdot i \sin\frac{\pi}{4} = -\frac{i}{2\sqrt{2}\, a^3} = \Sigma R^+.$$

Now

$$\left| \int_{C_R} \frac{dz}{z^4 + a^4} \right| \leq \int_{C_R} \frac{|dz|}{|z^4 + a^4|}$$

$$\leq \int_{C_R} \frac{|dz|}{|z|^4 - |a^4|} = \int_0^\pi \frac{R}{R^4 - a^4} d\theta \qquad [\because z = Re^{i\theta}]$$

$$= \frac{\pi R}{R^4 - a^4} \to 0 \text{ as } R \to \infty.$$

Hence when $R \to \infty$, relation (1) becomes

$$\int_{-\infty}^{\infty} \frac{dx}{x^4 + a^4} = 2\pi i \left(-\frac{i}{2\sqrt{2}\, a^3} \right) = \frac{\pi \sqrt{2}}{2a^3}$$

or

$$\int_0^\infty \frac{dx}{R^4 + a^4} = \frac{\pi \sqrt{2}}{4a^3}.$$

7. *Use the method of contour integration to prove that*

$$\int_0^\infty \frac{dx}{(x^2 + b^2)^{n+2}} = \frac{\pi}{(2b)^{2n+1}} \cdot \frac{(2n)!}{(n!)^2}.$$

Solution. Consider the integral

$$\int_C f(z)\,dz$$

where
$$f(z) = \frac{1}{(z^2 + b^2)^{n+1}}$$

taken round the closed contour C consisting of the upper half of a large circle $|z| = R$ and part of the real axis from $-R$ to R.

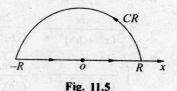

Fig. 11.5

Poles of $f(z)$ are given by
$$(z^2 + b^2)^{n+1} = 0$$

i.e., $z = \pm ib$ are the two poles each of order $(n + 1)$.

The only pole which lies within the contour is $z = ib$ and is of order $(n + 1)$. To find the residue at $z = ib$ put $z = ib + t$ in $f(z)$, then it becomes

$$\frac{1}{[(ib + t)^2 + b^2]^{n+1}}$$

$$= \frac{1}{(2ib)^{n+1} \cdot t^{n+1}} \left[1 + \frac{t}{2ib}\right]^{(n+1)}$$

$$= \frac{1}{(2ib)^{n+1}} \cdot \frac{1}{t^{n+1}} \sum_{n-0}^{\infty} \frac{(-1)^r (n+1)(n+2)(n+3)...(n+n)}{r!}$$

wherein coefficient of $1/t$ is

$$\frac{1}{(2ib)^{n+1}} \cdot \frac{(-1)^n (n+1)(n+2)...(2n)}{n!(2ib)^n}$$

$$= \frac{(2n)!}{i(2b)^{2n+1}(n!)^2}$$

which is therefore the residue at $z = ib$.

Hence by Cauchy's residue therefore we have
$$\int_C f(z)\,dz = 2\pi i \times \text{ sum of the residues within the contour.}$$

i.e.,
$$\int_{-R}^{R} f(x)\,dx + \int_{C_R} f(z)\,dz = 2\pi i \cdot \frac{(2n)!}{i(2b)^{2n+1}} \cdot \frac{1}{(n!)^2}$$

or
$$\int_{-R}^{R} \frac{1}{(x^2 + b^2)^{n+1}}\,dx + \int_{C_R} \frac{1}{(z^2 + b^2)^{n+1}}\,dz = \frac{(2n)!}{(n!)^2} \cdot \frac{2\pi}{(2b)^{2n+1}} \qquad ...(1)$$

Now
$$\left|\int_{C_R} \frac{1}{(z^2 + b^2)^{n+1}}\,dz\right| \leq \int_{C_R} \frac{|dz|}{|z^2 + b^2|^{n+1}}$$

$$\leq \int_{C_R} \frac{|dz|}{(|z|^2 + b^2)^{n+1}}$$

$$= \frac{1}{(R^2 + b^2)^{n+1}} \int_0^{\pi} R\,d\theta$$

since $z = Re^{i\theta}$ which $\to 0$ as $R \to \infty$

$$= \frac{\pi R}{(R^2 + b^2)^{n+1}}$$

Hence by making $R \to \infty$ relation (1) becomes

$$\int_{-\infty}^{\infty} \frac{dx}{(x^2 + b^2)^{n+1}} = \frac{2\pi}{(2b)^{2n+1}} \cdot \frac{(2n)!}{(n!)^2}$$

or

$$\int_{0}^{\infty} \frac{dx}{(x^2 + b^2)^{n+1}} = \frac{\pi}{(2b)^{2n+1}} \cdot \frac{(2n)!}{(n!)^2}$$

8. *Use the method of contour integration to prove that*

$$\int_{-\infty}^{\infty} \frac{dx}{(x^2 + b^2)(x^2 + c^2)^2} = \frac{\pi (b + 2c)}{2bc^3 (b + c)^2} \qquad \text{where } b > 0, c > 0.$$

Solution. Consider the integral $\int_{C} f(z) dz$

where

$$f(z) = \frac{1}{(z^2 + b^2)(z^2 + c^2)^2}$$

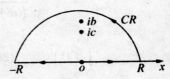

taken round a closed countour C, consisting of the upper half of a large circle $|z| = R$, and the part of the real axis from $-R$ to R.

Fig. 11.6

Poles of $f(z)$ are given by

$$(z^2 + b^2)(z^2 + c^2)^2 = 0$$

i.e., $\qquad z = \pm ib$ are the two simple poles

and $\qquad z = \pm ic$ are the two double poles.

The poles which lie within the contour are a simple pole at $z = ib$ and a double pole at $z = ic$.

Residue at the simple pole $z = ib$ is $\lim_{z \to ib} (z - ib) f(z)$

$$= \lim_{z \to ib} (z - ib) \frac{1}{(z - ib)(z + ib)(z^2 + c^2)^2}$$

$$= \frac{1}{2ib(c^2 - b^2)^2} = -\frac{i}{2b(b^2 - c^2)^2}$$

To find the residue at the double pole $z = ic$ but $z = ic + t$ in $f(z)$, then it becomes

$$= \frac{1}{\{(ic + t)^2 + b^2\} \{(ic + t)^2 + c^2\}^2}$$

$$= \frac{1}{(b^2 - c^2 + 2ict + t^2)(2ict + t^2)^2}$$

$$= \frac{1}{(b^2 - c^2)} \left\{ 1 + \frac{2ict + t^2}{b^2 - c^2} \right\}^{-1} \cdot \frac{1}{-4c^2 t^2} \left\{ 1 - \frac{t}{2ic} \right\}^{-2}$$

$$= \frac{1}{-4c^2 (b^2 - c^2) t^2} \left\{ 1 - \frac{2ict + t^2}{b^2 - c^2} + \ldots \right\} \left\{ 1 - \frac{t}{ic} + \ldots \right\}$$

in which coefficient of $1/t$ is

$$- \frac{1}{4c^2 (b^2 - c^2)} \left\{ \frac{i}{c} - \frac{2ic}{b^2 - c^2} \right\}$$

$$= \frac{(3c^2 - b^2) i}{4c^3 (b^2 - c^2)^2}$$

which is the residue at $z = ic$.

∴ Sum of the residues

$$= - \frac{i}{2b (b^2 - c^2)} + \frac{(3c^2 - b^2) i}{4c^3 (b^2 - c^2)^2}$$

$$= - \frac{i (b + 2c)}{4bc^3 (b + c)^2}.$$

Hence, by Cauchy's residue theorem, we have

$$\int_C f(z) \, dz = 2\pi i \times \text{sum of the residues within the contour.}$$

i.e.,

$$\int_{-R}^{R} \frac{1}{(x^2 + b^2)(x^2 + c^2)^2} \, dx + \int_{C_R} \frac{dz}{(z^2 + b^2)(z^2 + c^2)^2}$$

$$= 2\pi i \times \frac{-i(b - 2c)}{4bc^3 (b + c)^2} \qquad \qquad \ldots(1)$$

Now

$$\left| \int_{C_R} \frac{dz}{(z^2 + b^2)(z^2 + c^2)^2} \right|$$

$$\leq \int_{C_R} \frac{|dz|}{|z^2 + b^2| \, |z^2 + c^2|^2}$$

$$\leq \int_{C_R} \frac{|dz|}{(|z|^2 - b^2)(|z|^2 - c^2)^2}$$

$$= \frac{1}{(R^2 - b^2)(R^2 - c^2)^2} = \int_0^R R \, d\theta, \text{ since } z = \text{Re}^{i\theta}$$

$$= \frac{\pi R}{(R^2 - b^2)(R^2 - c^2)^2} \text{ which} \to 0 \text{ as } R \to \infty$$

Hence by making $R \to \infty$, relation (1) becomes

$$\int_{-\infty}^{\infty} \frac{dx}{(x^2 + b^2)(x^2 + c^2)^2} = \frac{\pi (b + 2c)}{2bc^3 (b + c)^2}$$

9. *Use the method of contour integration to prove that*

$$\int_{-\infty}^{\infty} \frac{x^2 \, dx}{(x^2 + a^2)^3} = \frac{\pi}{8a^3}$$

Solution. See the contour of the last example.

Consider the integral $\int_C f(z) \, dz$ where $f(z) = \dfrac{z^2}{(z^2 + a^2)^3}$ taken round the closed contour C consisting of the upper half of a large circle $|z| = R$ and the real axis from $-R$ to R. Poles of $f(z)$ are given by $(z^2 + a^2)^3 = 0$, *i.e.*, $z = \pm ai$ both of which are of order 3. The only pole which lies within the contour is $z = ia$ and is of order 3. To find the residue at $z = ia$, put $z = ia + t$ in $f(z)$ then it becomes

$$\frac{(ia + t)^2}{\{(ia + t)^2 + a^2\}^3} = \frac{-a^2 + 2iat + t^2}{(2iat + t^2)^3}$$

$$= \frac{-a^2 + 2iat + t^2}{(2iat + t^2)^3}$$

$$= \frac{-a^2 + 2iat + t^2}{-8ia^3 t^3} \left[1 + \frac{t}{2ia} \right]^{-3}$$

$$= \frac{-a^2 + 2iat + t^2}{-8ia^3 t^3} \left[1 - \frac{3t}{2ia} - \frac{6t^2}{4a^2} + \dots \right]$$

in which coefficient of $\dfrac{1}{t}$ is

$$\frac{1}{-8ia^3} \left\{ 1 - \frac{3}{2} - 3 \right\} \ i.e., \ \frac{1}{16ia^3}$$

which is therefore residue at $z = ia$.

Hence, by Cauchy's residue theorem, we get

$$\int_C f(z) \, dz = 2\pi i \times \text{sum of the residues within the contour } C.$$

i.e.,

$$\int_{-R}^{R} f(x) \, dx + \int_{C_R} f(z) \, dz = 2\pi i \cdot \frac{1}{16ia^3}$$

$$\int_{-R}^{R} \frac{x^2}{(x^2 + a^2)^3} \, dx + \int_{C_R} \frac{z^2 \, dz}{(z^2 + a^2)^3} = \frac{\pi}{8a^3} \qquad \dots (1)$$

Now

$$\left| \int_{C_R} \frac{z^2}{(z^2 + a^2)^3} \, dz \right| \le \int_C \frac{|z|^2 |dz|}{|z^2 + a^2|^3}$$

$$\le \int_{C_R} \frac{|z|^2 |dz|}{(|z|^2 + a^2)^3}$$

$$= \frac{R^2}{(R^2 + a^2)^3} \int_0^\pi R\,d\theta \qquad\qquad \text{since } z = Re^{i\theta}$$

$$|dz| = |Re^{i\theta} \cdot i\,d\theta|$$

$$= R\,d\theta$$

$$= \frac{\pi R^3}{(R^2 + a^2)^3} \quad \text{which } \to 0 \text{ as } R \to \infty$$

Hence by making $R \to \infty$ relation (1) becomes

$$\int_{-\infty}^{\infty} \frac{x^2\,dx}{(x^2 + a^2)^3} = \frac{\pi}{8a^3}.$$

10. *Prove that*

$$\int_{-\infty}^{\infty} \frac{(x^2 - x + 2)\,dx}{(x^4 + 10x^2 + 9)} = \frac{5\pi}{12} \qquad\qquad (\textit{Meerut 2001})$$

Solution. Consider the integral $\int_C f(z)\,dz$

where
$$f(z) = \frac{z^2 - z + 2}{z^4 + 10z^2 + 9}$$

taken round the closed contour C, consisting of the upper half of a large circle $|z| = R$ and the real axis from $-R$ to R.

Poles of $f(z)$ are given by

$$z^4 + 10z^2 + 9 = 0$$

i.e.,
$$(z^2 + 1)(z^2 + 9) = 0 \quad \text{or} \quad z = \pm i$$

and $z = \pm 3i$, are the simple poles.

Only $z = i$ and $z = 3i$ lie within the contour.

The residue at $z = i$ is

$$= \lim_{z \to i} (z - i)\,f(z)$$

$$= \lim_{z \to i} \frac{(z - i)(z^2 - z + 2)}{(z - i)(z + i)(z^2 + 9)} = \frac{1 - i}{16i}$$

Similarly, the residue at $z = 3i$

$$\lim_{z \to 3i} \frac{(z - 3i)(z^2 - z + 2)}{(z^2 + 1)(z - 3i)(z + 3i)} = \frac{7 + 3i}{48i}$$

Now, sum of residues
$$= \frac{1 - i}{16i} + \frac{7 + 3i}{48i}$$

$$= \frac{5}{24i}$$

By Cauchy's residue theorem, we have

$$\int_C f(z)\, dz = 2\pi i \times \text{sum of the residues within } C$$

i.e.,

$$\int_{-R}^{R} f(x)\, dx + \int_{C_R} f(z)\, dz = 2\pi i \times \text{ sum of residues}$$

i.e.,

$$\int_{-R}^{R} \frac{x^2 - x + 2}{x^4 + 10x + 9}\, dx + \int_{C_R} \frac{z^2 - z + 2}{z^4 + 10z^2 + 9}\, dz = 2\pi i \times \frac{5}{24i}$$

Now

$$\left| \int_{C_R} \frac{z^2 - z + 2}{z^4 + 10z^2 + 9}\, dz \right| \le \int_{C_R} \frac{|z^2 - z + 2|\,|dz|}{|z^4 + 10z^2 + 9|}$$

$$\le \int_{C_R} \frac{|z^2 - z| + 2}{|z^4 + 10z^2|}\, dz$$

$$\le \int_{C_R} \frac{|z^2| + |z - 2|}{|z|^4 - 10|z^2|}\,|dz|$$

$$= \int_{0}^{\pi} \frac{R^2 + R + 2}{R^2 - 10R^2}\, R\, d\theta \text{ since } |dz| = R\, d\theta$$

$$= \frac{R^3 + R^2 + 2R}{R^4 - 10R^2}\, \pi \text{ which} \to 0 \text{ as } R \to \infty$$

Hence making $R \to \infty$, we get

$$\int_{-\infty}^{\infty} \frac{x^2 - x + 2}{x^4 + 10x^2 + 9}\, dx = 2\pi i \times \frac{5}{24i}$$

$$= \frac{5\pi}{12}.$$

11. *Show that, if m and n are positive integers, and m < n.*

$$\int_{0}^{\infty} \frac{x^{2m}}{x^{2n} + 1}\, dx = \frac{\pi}{2n \sin\left\{ \dfrac{(2m + 1)}{2n} \right\} \pi}$$

Solution. Consider $\displaystyle \int_C \frac{z^{2m}}{z^{2n} + 1}\, dz$

$$= \int_C f(z)\, dz, \text{ where C is the closed contour consisting semi circle } \Gamma,$$

$|z| = R$ and line segment of the real axis from $-R$ to R.

By Cauchy's residue theorem, we have

$$\int_C f(z)\, dz = \int_{-R}^{R} f(x)\, dx + \int_{\Gamma} f(z)\, dz$$

$$= 2\pi i \sum R \qquad\qquad\qquad\qquad ...(1)$$

Now, $\quad \lim\limits_{z \to \infty} z \, f(z) = \lim\limits_{z \to \infty} \left(\dfrac{z^{2m+1}}{z^{2n}+1} \right)$

$$= 0 \text{ as } m < n.$$

Hence $\displaystyle\int_{\Gamma} f(z) \, dz \to 0 \text{ as } R \to \infty$ $\qquad$ ...(2)

Taking $R \to \infty$ and using (2), we get from (1),

$$\int_{-\infty}^{\infty} f(x) \, dx = 2\pi i \sum R \qquad \text{...(3)}$$

Now, poles of $f(z)$ are given by $z^{2n}+1 = 0$ or $z^{2n} = e^{(2r+1)\pi i}$ where $r = 0, 1, 2, ..., 2n-1$.

Therefore the poles are given by $z = e^{\pi i/2n}, e^{3\pi i/2n}, ...e^{(2n+1)\pi i/2n}, \quad e^{(2n+1)\pi i/2n},$

$e^{(2n+3)\pi i/2n}, \ ... \ e^{(4n-1)\pi i/2n}.$

But the first n poles from $2n$ poles lie inside the contour C. Denote these poles by $\alpha_1, \alpha_2, \alpha_3, ..., \alpha_n$. Residue at $z = \alpha$

$$= \left[\frac{z^{2m}}{d/dz \, (1 + z^{2n})} \right]_{z=\alpha}$$

$$= \frac{\alpha^{2m}}{2n\alpha^{2n-1}} = \frac{\alpha^{2m+1}}{2n\alpha^{2n}} = -\frac{\alpha^{2m+1}}{2n},$$

since $\alpha^{2n} = -1$.

Sum of the residues

$$= -\frac{1}{2n} \left[\alpha_1^{2m+1} + \alpha_2^{2m+2} + ... + \alpha_n^{2m+n} \right]$$

$$= -\frac{1}{2n} \left[e^{i\theta} + e^{3i\theta} + ... + e^{(2n-1)\theta} \right], \text{ where } \theta = \frac{2m+1}{2n}\pi$$

$$= -\frac{1}{2n} \frac{e^{i\theta}(1 - e^{2ni\theta})}{1 - e^{2i\theta}}$$

$$= -\frac{1}{2n} \frac{e^{i\theta}(1 - e^{2ni\theta})(1 - e^{-2i\alpha})}{(1 - e^{2i\theta})(1 - e^{-2i\theta})}$$

$$= -\frac{1}{2n} \frac{e^{i\theta} - e^{(2n+1)i\theta} - e^{-i\theta} + e^{(2n-1)i\theta}}{2 - 2\cos 2\theta}$$

$$= -\frac{1}{2n} \frac{2i\sin\theta - e^{2ni\theta} \, 2i\sin\theta}{4\sin^2\theta}$$

$$= -\frac{1}{2n} \frac{i\,[1 - \cos 2n\theta - i \sin 2n\theta]}{2 \sin \theta}$$

$$= -\frac{i}{4n \sin \theta} [2 \sin^2 n\theta - 2i \sin n\theta \cos n\theta]$$

$$= -\frac{1}{2n} \frac{\sin n\theta}{\sin \theta} (\cos n\theta + i \sin n\theta)$$

$$= -\frac{i}{2n} \frac{\sin^2 n\theta}{\sin \theta}, \text{ since } \cos n\theta = \cos \frac{2m+1}{2} \pi = 0.$$

$$= -\frac{i}{2n \sin \theta}, \text{ since } (\sin n\theta)^2 = \left(\sin \frac{2m+1}{2} \pi \right)^2 = 1$$

Hence we have from (2)

$$\int_{-\infty}^{\infty} f(x)\,dx \; = \; 2\pi i \left(-\frac{1}{2\pi \sin \theta} \right) = \frac{\pi}{n \sin \theta}$$

$$\therefore \qquad \int_{0}^{\infty} \frac{x^{2m}}{1 + x^{2n}}\,dx \; = \; \frac{\pi}{2n \sin \left(\dfrac{2m+1}{2n} \right) \pi}.$$

11.4. *Evaluation of the integrals of the form*

$$\int_{-\infty}^{+\infty} f(x) \sin mx\, dx, \quad \int_{-\infty}^{+\infty} f(x) \cos mx\, dx \qquad\qquad ...(1)$$

where m > 0 and f (x) is a rational function of x.

It is shown in Real Variables that the improper integrals (1) converge, if

(*i*) the degree of the denominator of $f(x)$ exceeds that of the numerator;

(*ii*) denominator of $f(x)$ does not have a real zero.

We suppose that $f(x)$ does satisfy the conditions (*i*) and (*ii*).

Firstly we consider a lemma due to Jordan.

Jordan's Lemma. *If*

$$f(z) \to 0 \text{ uniformly as } z \to \infty, \qquad\qquad ...(2)$$

then

$$\lim_{R \to \infty} \int_{C_1} e^{imz}\, f(z)\, dz = 0, \; (m > 0)$$

where C_1 denotes the semi-circle

$$|z| = R, I(z) > 0.$$

Here it is understood that $f(z)$ has no singular point on C_1 for sufficiently large values of R.

If $\varepsilon > 0$ be any given positive number, then, by (2), there exists an $R_0 > 0$ such that

$$|f(z)| < \varepsilon \text{ when } |z| = R \geq R_0 \qquad\qquad ...(3)$$

Let, now, C_1 denote any semi-circle with radius $R \geq R_0$.

Making the substitution $z = Re^{i\theta}$, we obtain

$$\int_{C_1} e^{im\theta} f(z) \, dz = \int_0^\pi e^{imR(\cos\theta + i\sin\theta)} f(z) \, iz \, d\theta \qquad \dots(4)$$

Now

$$e^{|imR(\cos\theta + i\sin\theta)|} = e^{-mR\sin\theta}.$$

*Also we know that for $0 \le \theta \le \dfrac{1}{2}\pi$,

$$\frac{\sin\theta}{\theta} \ge \frac{1}{\pi}, \; i.e., \; \sin\theta \ge \frac{2\theta}{\alpha}.$$

Thus for $0 \le \theta \le \dfrac{1}{2}\pi$, we have

$$e^{-mR\sin\theta} \le e^{-2mR\sin\theta/\pi} \qquad \dots(5)$$

From (3), (4) and (5), we obtain, for $R \ge R_0$,

$$\left| \int e^{imz} f(z) \, dz \right| \le \varepsilon \int_0^\pi e^{-mR\sin\theta} R \, d\theta$$

$$= 2\varepsilon R \int_0^{\frac{1}{2}\pi} e^{-mR\sin\theta} R \, d\theta$$

$$\le 2\varepsilon R \int_0^{\frac{1}{2}\pi} e^{-mR\theta/\pi} \, d\theta$$

$$= \frac{2\varepsilon R (1 - e^{-mR})}{2mR/\pi}$$

$$= \frac{\varepsilon\pi}{m}(1 - e^{-mR}) < \frac{\varepsilon\pi}{m}.$$

Thus we have

$$\lim_{R \to \infty} \int_{C_1} e^{imz} f(z) \, dz = 0,$$

so that the lemma has been proved.

In connection with above, we may easily verify that if

$$f(z) = \frac{a_0 z^n + a_1 z^{n-1} + \dots + a_n}{b_0 z^m + b_1 z^{m-1} + \dots + b_m}.$$

where $a_0 \ne 0$, $b_0 \ne 0$, $m > n$, then $f(z) \to 0$ as $|z| = R \to \infty$.

We now consider the evaluation of the given integral.

$$\frac{\sin(\pi/2)}{\pi/2} \le \frac{\sin\theta}{\theta}.$$

---

* It may be shown that $\sin\theta/\theta$ monotonically decreases as θ increases from θ to $\pi/2$ so that

We consider a closed contour C consisting of C_1 and C_2 as in the preceding § 11.2, and choose the same such that the poles of $e^{imz} f(z)$ which are the same as those of $f(z)$ be in the interior of C. Thus if α_i be any pole, we have

$$2\alpha i \, \Sigma \text{Res.} (\alpha_i) = \int_C e^{imz} f(z) \, dz$$

$$= \int_{C_1} e^{imz} f(z) \, dz + \int_{C_2} e^{imz} f(z) \, dz$$

$$= \int_{C_1} e^{imz} f(z) \, dz + \int_{-R}^{+R} e^{imx} f(x) \, dx.$$

By the lemma, we see that when $R \to \infty$,

$$2\pi i \, \Sigma \text{Res.} (\alpha_i) = 0 + P \int_{-\alpha}^{+\alpha} e^{imx} f(x) \, dx$$

$$= \int_{-\alpha}^{+\alpha} e^{imx} f(x) \, dx$$

$$= \int_{-\alpha}^{+\alpha} \cos mx \, f(x) \, dx$$

$$+ i \int_{-\alpha}^{+\alpha} \sin mx \, f(x) \, dx.$$

Equating the real and imaginary parts, we obtain the values of the two given integrals.

EXAMPLES

1. *Use the method of contour integration to prove that*

$$(i) \int_0^\infty \frac{\cos mx}{a^2 + x^2} \, dx = \frac{\pi}{2a} e^{-ma} \qquad\qquad (ii) \int_{-\infty}^\infty \frac{\sin mx}{a^2 + x^2} \, dx = 0.$$

(Gorakhpur, 2001, 2004; Rohilkhand 2005; Meerut 2006; Kerala 2001)

Deduce that $\displaystyle\int_0^\infty \frac{x \sin mx}{x^2 + a^2} \, dx = \frac{\pi}{2} e^{-ma} \ (m \geq 0).$ *(Rohilkhand 2005)*

Solution. Consider the integral

$$\int_C f(z) \, dz, \text{ where } f(z) = \frac{e^{imz}}{a^2 + z^2}.$$

The poles of $f(z)$ are given by $z^2 + a^2 = 0$, *i.e.*, $z = ai$ and $z = -ai$ are the simple poles of $f(z)$. Since there is no pole on the real axis, therefore, we may take the closed contour C consisting of the upper half C_R of the large circle $|z| = R$ and the real axis from $-R$ to R.

∴ By Cauchy's residue theorem, we have

$$\int_C f(z) \, dz = \int_{-R}^R f(x) \, dx + \int_{C_R} f(z) \, dz = 2\pi i \, \Sigma R^+$$

where ΣR^+ = sum of residues of $f(z)$ at its poles within C

or $$\int_{-R}^{R} \frac{e^{imx}}{a^2 + x^2} dx + \int_{C_R} \frac{e^{imz}}{a^2 + z^2} dz = 2\pi i \, \Sigma R^+ \qquad \text{...(1)}$$

The pole $z = ai$ lies within the contour C.

$\therefore$ Residue at the simple pole $z = ai$

$$\lim_{z \to \infty} (z - ai) f(z) = \lim_{z \to \infty} (z - ai) \frac{e^{imz}}{(z - ai)(z + ai)} = \frac{e^{-ma}}{2ai} = \Sigma R^+.$$

Now $\lim\limits_{z \to \infty} \dfrac{1}{a^2 + z^2} = 0.$

$\therefore$ By Jordan's Lemma

$$\lim_{R \to \infty} \int_{C_R} e^{imz} \frac{1}{a^2 + z^2} dz = 0.$$

Hence when $R \to \infty$, (1) becomes

$$\int_{-\infty}^{\infty} \frac{e^{imx}}{a^2 + x^2} dx = 2\pi i \cdot \frac{e^{-ma}}{2ai} = \frac{\pi e^{-ma}}{a}$$

or $$\int_{-\infty}^{\infty} \frac{\cos mx}{a^2 + x^2} dx + i \int_{-\infty}^{\infty} \frac{\sin mx}{a^2 + x^2} dx = \frac{\pi e^{-ma}}{a}.$$

Equating real and imaginary parts, we have

$$\int_{-\infty}^{\infty} \frac{\cos mx}{a^2 + x^2} dx = \frac{\pi e^{-ma}}{a}$$

or $$\int_{0}^{\infty} \frac{\cos mx}{a^2 + x^2} dx = \frac{\pi e^{-ma}}{a}$$

$\therefore$ $$\int_{0}^{\infty} \frac{\cos mx}{a^2 + x^2} dx = \frac{\pi e^{-ma}}{2a} \qquad \text{...(2)}$$

and $$\int_{-\infty}^{\infty} \frac{\sin mx}{a^2 + x^2} dx = 0.$$

Deduction. Differentiating (2) w.r.t. m, we get

$$\int_{0}^{\infty} \frac{-x \sin mx}{a^2 + x^2} dx = \frac{-\pi a e^{-ma}}{2a}$$

or $$\int_{0}^{\infty} \frac{x \sin mx}{a^2 + x^2} dx = \frac{\pi}{2} e^{-ma}.$$

2. *Apply the calculus of residues to evaluate*

$$\int_{-\infty}^{\infty} \frac{\cos x}{(x^2 + a^2)(x^2 + b^2)} \, dx \quad (a > b > 0).$$

(*Ravishankar 2002*)

Solution. Consider the integral

$$\int_C f(z) \, dz \quad \text{where} \quad f(z) = \frac{e^{iz}}{(z^2 + a^2)(z^2 + b^2)}$$

The poles of $f(z)$ are given by $(z^2 + a^2)(z^2 + b^2) = 0$ or $z = \pm ai, \pm bi$ all simple poles. Since there is no pole on the real axis, therefore, we may take the closed contour C consisting of the upper half C_R of the large circle $|z| = R$ and the real axis from $-R$ to R.

∴ By Cauchy's residue theorem, we have

$$\int_C f(z) \, dz = \int_{-R}^{R} f(x) \, dx + \int_{C_R} f(z) \, dz = 2\pi i \, \Sigma R^+$$

where ΣR^+ = sum of residues of $f(z)$ at its poles within C

or

$$\int_{-R}^{R} \frac{e^{ix}}{(x^2 + a^2)(x^2 + b^2)} \, dx + \int_{C_R} \frac{e^{iz}}{(z^2 + a^2)(z^2 + b^2)} \, dz = 2\pi i \, \Sigma R^+ \qquad \text{...(1)}$$

The poles $z = ai$, $z = bi$ are the poles (both simple poles) within C.

Residue at the simple pole $z = ai$

$$= \lim_{z \to ai} (z - ai) \, f(z) = \lim_{z \to ai} (z - ai) \frac{e^{iz}}{(z - ai)(z + ai)(z^2 + b^2)}$$

$$= \frac{e^{-a}}{2ai(b^2 - a^2)}.$$

Similarly residue at the simple pole $z = bi$ is $\dfrac{e^{-b}}{2bi(a^2 - b^2)}$.

∴ The sum of residues $= \Sigma R^+ = \dfrac{1}{2i(a^2 - b^2)} \cdot \left(\dfrac{e^{-b}}{b} - \dfrac{e^{-a}}{a} \right).$

Now

$$\lim_{z \to ai} \frac{1}{(z^2 + a^2)(z^2 + b^2)} = 0.$$

∴ By Jordan's Lemma

$$\lim_{R \to \infty} \int_{C_R} \frac{e^{iz}}{(z^2 + a^2)(z^2 + b^2)} \, dz = 0.$$

Hence when $R \to \infty$, (1) becomes

$$\int_{-\infty}^{\infty} \frac{e^{ix}}{(x^2 + a^2)(x^2 + b^2)} \, dx = 2\pi i \cdot \frac{1}{2i(a^2 - b^2)} \left(\frac{e^{-b}}{b} - \frac{e^{-a}}{a} \right)$$

or

$$\int_{-\infty}^{\infty} \frac{\cos x}{(x^2 + a^2)(x^2 + b^2)} \, dx + i \int_{-\infty}^{\infty} \frac{\sin x}{(x^2 + a^2)(x^2 + b^2)} \, dx$$

$$= \frac{\pi}{(a^2 - b^2)} \left(\frac{e^{-b}}{b} - \frac{e^{-a}}{a} \right).$$

Equating the real parts, we get

$$\int_{-\infty}^{\infty} \frac{\cos x}{(x^2 + a^2)(x^2 + b^2)} \, dx = \frac{\pi}{(a^2 - b^2)} \cdot \left(\frac{e^{-b}}{b} - \frac{e^{-a}}{a} \right).$$

3. *Evaluate :* $\displaystyle \int_{0}^{\infty} \frac{\cos mx}{x^4 + x^2 + 1} \, dx \ \ (m > 0).$

Solution. The integrand $\dfrac{\cos mx}{x^4 + x^2 + 1}$ being an even function of x, we have

$$\int_{0}^{\infty} \frac{\cos mx}{x^4 + x^2 + 1} \, dx = \frac{1}{2} \int_{-\infty}^{+\infty} \frac{\cos mx}{x^4 + x^2 + 1} \, dx.$$

Consider the integral, $\displaystyle \int_{C} \frac{e^{imz}}{z^4 + z^2 + 1} \, dz,$

where C consists of the union of the semi-circle C_1
$$|z| = R, \ I(z) > 0$$
and of the interval $C_2 = [-R, R]$ of the real axis.

Now

$$f(z) = \frac{1}{z^4 + z^2 + 1} \rightarrow 0 \text{ uniformly as } z \rightarrow \infty.$$

This follows from the relation

$$|f(z)| \leq \frac{1}{R^4 - R^2 - 1}$$

which holds good for every point of $|z| = R$.

Hence

$$\int_{C_1} \frac{e^{imz}}{z^4 + z^2 + 1} \, dz \rightarrow 0 \text{ as } R \rightarrow \infty \qquad \qquad \text{...(1)}$$

Also

$$\int_{C_2} \frac{e^{imz}}{z^4 + z^2 + 1} \, dz = \int_{-R}^{+R} \frac{e^{imx}}{x^4 + x^2 + 1} \, dx$$

$$\rightarrow \int_{-\infty}^{+\infty} \frac{e^{imx}}{x^4 + x^2 + 1} \, dx \qquad \qquad \text{...(2)}$$

The poles of the integrand are the values of z for which
$$z^4 + z^2 + 1 = 0 \qquad \qquad \text{...(3)}$$

We are here interested in only those roots of (1) which lie in the upper semi-plane. As the roots of (1) occur in conjugate pairs, only two of them will lie in the upper semi-plane.

To find these in a convenient form, we proceed as follows :

We have

$$(z^4 + z^2 + 1)(1 - z^4) = 1 - z^6.$$

Also the zeros of $1 - z^6$ are

$$\cos\frac{2n\pi}{6} \pm i\sin\frac{2n\pi}{6}, \quad (n = 0, 1, 2, 3),$$

i.e.,

$$\pm 1, \cos\frac{\pi}{3} \pm i\sin\frac{\pi}{3}, \cos\frac{2\pi}{3} \pm i\sin\frac{2\pi}{3}.$$

Thus,

$$\cos\frac{\pi}{3} + i\sin\frac{\pi}{3}, \quad \cos\frac{2\pi}{3} + i\sin\frac{2\pi}{3}$$

are the two required poles in the upper semi-plane. We write

$$\alpha = \cos\frac{\pi}{3} + i\sin\frac{\pi}{3} \quad \Rightarrow \quad \alpha^2 = \cos\frac{2\pi}{3} + i\sin\frac{2\pi}{3} \qquad \text{...(4)}$$

Now

$$\text{Res.}(\alpha) = \left[\frac{e^{miz}}{4z^3 + 2z}\right]_{z=\alpha} = \frac{e^{mi\alpha}}{4\alpha^3 + 2\alpha},$$

$$\text{Res.}(\alpha^2) = \left[\frac{e^{miz}}{4z^3 + 2z}\right]_{z=\alpha^2} = \frac{e^{mi\alpha^2}}{4\alpha^6 + 2\alpha^2}$$

$$= \frac{e^{mi\alpha^2}}{2\alpha^2 + 4} \quad x^6 = 1.$$

Now

$$4\alpha^3 + 2\alpha = 4(-1) + 2\left(\frac{1}{2} + \frac{\sqrt{3}\,i}{3}\right) = \sqrt{3}\,i - 3,$$

$$2\alpha^2 + 4 = 2\left(-\frac{1}{2} + \frac{\sqrt{3}\,i}{3}\right) + 4 = \sqrt{3}\,i + 3.$$

Also

$$e^{mi\alpha} = e^{mi\left(\frac{1}{2} + \frac{\sqrt{3}\,i}{2}\right)} = e^{\frac{-\sqrt{3}\,m}{2}} e^{\frac{im}{2}},$$

$$e^{mi\alpha^2} = e^{mi\left(-\frac{1}{2} + \frac{\sqrt{3}\,i}{2}\right)} = e^{\frac{-\sqrt{3}\,m}{2}} e^{\frac{-im}{2}}.$$

$$\text{Res.}(\alpha) + \text{Res.}(\alpha^2) = e^{\frac{-\sqrt{3}\,m}{2}}\left[\frac{e^{\frac{im}{2}}}{\sqrt{3}\,i - 3} + \frac{e^{\frac{-im}{2}}}{\sqrt{3}\,i + 3}\right]$$

$$= -\frac{i}{6} e^{\frac{-\sqrt{3}\,m}{2}}\left(\sqrt{3}\cos\frac{m}{2} + 3\sin\frac{m}{2}\right) \qquad \text{...(5)}$$

Now we have

$$\int_C \frac{e^{imz}}{z^4 + z^2 + 1} dz = \int_{C_1} \frac{e^{imz}}{z^4 + z^2 + 1} dz + \int_{C_2} \frac{e^{imz}}{z^4 + z^2 + 1} dz \quad ...(6)$$

Here we suppose that R is taken so large that the interior of the contour C contains the two poles α, α^2. Thus we have

$$\int_C \frac{e^{imz}}{z^4 + z^2 + 1} dz = 2\pi i \, [\text{Res.} \, (\alpha) + \text{Res.} \, (\alpha^2)] \quad ...(7)$$

From (3), (4), (5), (6) and (7), we obtain, on proceeding to the limit when R $\rightarrow \infty$.

$$2\pi i \, [\text{Res.} \, (\alpha) + \text{Res.} \, (\alpha^2)] = \int_{-\infty}^{+\infty} \frac{e^{imx}}{x^4 + x^2 + 1} dx$$

$$\Rightarrow \quad \frac{\pi}{3} e^{\frac{-\sqrt{3}\,m}{2}} \left(\sqrt{3} \cos \frac{m}{2} + 3 \sin \frac{m}{2} \right) = \int_{-\infty}^{\infty} \frac{\cos mx}{x^4 + x^2 + 1} dx + i \int_{-\infty}^{\infty} \frac{\sin mx}{x^4 + x^2 + 1} dx.$$

Equating real parts, we obtain

$$\int_{-\infty}^{\infty} \frac{\cos mx}{x^4 + x^2 + 1} dx = \frac{\pi}{3} e^{\frac{-\sqrt{3}\,m}{2}} \left(\sqrt{3} \cos \frac{m}{2} + 3 \sin \frac{m}{2} \right).$$

Of course

$$\int_{-\infty}^{\infty} \frac{\sin mx}{x^4 + x^2 + 1} dx = 0$$

as is also clear from the fact that the integrand is an odd function of x and the interval of integration is symmetric about the origin.

4. *Show by the method of contour integration that*

$$\int_0^{\infty} \frac{\cos mx}{(a^2 + x^2)^2} dx = \frac{\pi}{4a^3} (1 + ma) \, e^{-ma}, \quad (a > 0, \; m > 0).$$

(Kanpur 2001; Garhwal 2002)

Solution. Consider the integral

$$\int_C f(z) \, dz, \text{ where } f(z) = \frac{e^{imz}}{(a^2 + z^2)^2}.$$

Poles of $f(z)$ are given by $(a^2 + z^2)^2 = 0$, *i.e.*, $z = ia$ and $z = -ia$ are the two poles each of order two.

Since there is no pole on the real axis, therefore, we may take the closed contour C consisting of the upper half C_R of a large circle $|z| = R$ and the real axis from $-R$ to R.

$\therefore$ By Cauchy's residue theorem, we have

$$\int_C f(z) \, dz = 2\pi i \, \Sigma R^+$$

where ΣR^+ = sum of residues of $f(z)$ within C

or
$$\int_{-R}^{R} f(x)\, dx + \int_{C_R} f(z)\, dz = 2\pi i \, \Sigma R^+$$

or
$$\int_{-R}^{R} \frac{e^{imx}}{(a^2 + x^2)^2}\, dx + \int_{C_R} \frac{e^{imz}}{(a^2 + z^2)^2}\, dz = 2\pi i \, \Sigma R^+ \qquad \text{...(1)}$$

The only pole which lies within the contour C is at $z = ia$ of order 2.

Since the pole $z = ia$ is of order 2, hence to find the residue at $z = ia$, put $z = ia + t$ in $f(z)$, then it becomes

$$\frac{e^{im(ia + t)}}{[a^2 + (ia + t)^2]^2} = \frac{e^{-ma} \cdot e^{imt}}{(2iat + t^2)^2} = \frac{e^{-ma} \cdot e^{imt}}{-4a^2 t^2} \left[1 + \frac{t}{2ia}\right]^{-2}$$

$$= \frac{e^{-ma}}{-4a^2 t^2} (1 + imt + ...) \left[1 - \frac{2t}{2ia} + ...\right]$$

$\therefore$ Residue to pole $z = ai$ = coefficient of $\dfrac{1}{t}$ in the above expansion

$$= \frac{-ie^{-ma}(1 + ma)}{4a^3} = \Sigma R^+.$$

Now
$$\lim_{z \to \infty} \frac{1}{(a^2 + z^2)^2} = 0.$$

$\therefore$ By Jordan's Lemma (§ 11.4),

$$\lim_{R \to \infty} \int_{C_R} \frac{e^{imz}}{(a^2 + z^2)^2}\, dz = 0.$$

Hence when $R \to \infty$, (1) becomes

$$\int_{-\infty}^{\infty} \frac{e^{imx}}{(a^2 + x^2)^2}\, dx = 2\pi i \cdot \frac{-ie^{-ma}(1 + ma)}{4a^3}.$$

Equating the real parts, we have

$$\int_{-\infty}^{\infty} \frac{\cos mx}{(a^2 + x^2)^2}\, dx = \frac{\pi}{2a^3}(1 + ma)\, e^{-ma}$$

or
$$\int_{0}^{\infty} \frac{\cos mx}{(a^2 + x^2)^2}\, dx = \frac{\pi}{4a^3}(1 + ma)\, e^{-ma}.$$

5. If $a < \alpha < \dfrac{\pi}{2}$, prove that by method of contour integration,

$$\int_{-\infty}^{\infty} \frac{\tan^{-1} x\, dx}{x^2 - 2x \sin \alpha + 1} = \frac{\pi \alpha}{2 \cos \alpha}. \qquad \textit{(Rohilkhand 2001, 2004)}$$

Solution. Let $f(z) = \dfrac{\log(1 - iz)}{z^2 - 2z \sin \alpha + 1}$

Consider the integral $\int\limits_C f(z)\,dz$, where C is closed contour consisting of Γ, **the upper half of large circle** $|z| = R$ and real axis from $-R$ to R.

$$\lim_{|z|\to\infty} z\,f(z) = \lim_{|z|\to\infty} \frac{z\log(1-iz)}{z^2 - 2z\sin\alpha + 1}$$

$$= \left[\lim_{|z|\to\infty} \frac{\log(iz-1)}{(iz-1)} + \frac{\log(-1)}{iz-1}\right].$$

$$\left[\lim_{|z|\to\infty} \frac{iz^2 - z}{z^2 - 2z\sin\alpha + 1}\right]$$

$$= [0 + 0][i] = 0$$

$\therefore$ By Theorem II, 11.2.1.

$$\lim_{R\to\infty} \int\limits_\Gamma f(z)\,dz = i(\pi - 0)(0) = 0 \qquad \qquad ...(1)$$

Poles of $f(z)$ **are given by** $z^2 - 2z\sin\alpha + 1 = 0$

or
$$z = \frac{2\sin\alpha \pm \sqrt{(4\sin^2\alpha - 4)}}{2}$$

$$= \sin\alpha \pm i\cos\alpha$$

But only one simple pole $z = \sin\alpha + i\cos\alpha$ **lies within** C.

Take $\qquad a = \sin\alpha + i\cos\alpha, b = \sin\alpha - i\cos\alpha.$

$$\mathrm{Res}\,(z = a) = \lim_{z\to a} \frac{(z-a)\log(1-iz)}{(z-a)(z-b)}$$

$$= \frac{\log(1-ia)}{a-b}$$

$$= \frac{\log(1+\cos\alpha - i\sin\alpha)}{2i\cos\alpha}$$

By Cauchy's residue theorem

$$\int\limits_C f(z)\,dz = 2\pi i\,\mathrm{Res}\,(z = a)$$

$$\int\limits_\Gamma f(z)\,dz + \int\limits_{-R}^{R} f(x)\,dx = \frac{2\pi i\log(1+\cos\alpha - i\sin\alpha)}{2i\cos\alpha}$$

Making $R \to \infty$ **and noting (1)**

$$\int\limits_{-\infty}^{\infty} \frac{\log(1-ix)\,dx}{x^2 - 2x\sin\alpha + 1} = \frac{\pi}{\cos\alpha}(1+\cos\alpha - i\sin\alpha)$$

Equating imaginary parts from both sides

$$\int\limits_{-\infty}^{\infty} \frac{\tan^{-1}x\,dx}{x^2 - 2x\sin\alpha + 1} = \frac{\pi}{\cos\alpha}\tan^{-1}\left(\frac{\sin\alpha}{1+\cos\alpha}\right)$$

$$\frac{\pi}{\cos\alpha}\tan^{-1}\left(\frac{\tan\alpha}{2}\right) = \frac{\pi\alpha}{2\cos\alpha}.$$

6. *Use the method of contour integration to prove that*

$$\int_{-\infty}^{\infty} \frac{\cos x^2 + \sin x^2 - 1}{x^2} \, dx = 0.$$

Solution. Consider the integral $\int_C f(z)\, dz$

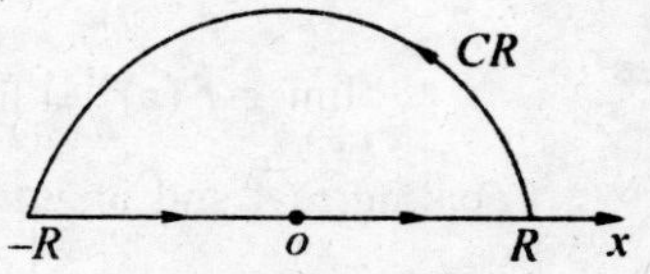

where $$f(z) = \frac{e^{iz^2} - 1}{z^2}$$

Fig. 11.7

taken round the closed contour C consisting of the upper half of a large circle $|z| = R$ and real axis from $-R$ to R.

$$f(z) = \frac{e^{iz^2} - 1}{z^2} = \frac{\left\{1 + iz^2 + \dfrac{i^2 z^4}{2!} + \ldots\right\} - 1}{z^2}$$

$$= i + \frac{i^2 z^2}{2!} + \ldots$$

It is quite obvious that $f(z)$ has no poles within the contour. As a matter of fact it is analytic for all finite values of z.

Hence by Cauchy's residue theorem, we have

$$\int_C f(z) = 2\pi i \times \text{sum of residue within the contour}$$

i.e., $$\int_{-R}^{R} f(x)\, dx + \int_{C_R} f(z)\, dz = 2\pi i \times 0$$

or $$\int_{-R}^{R} \frac{e^{ix^2} - 1}{x^2}\, dx + \int_{C_R} \frac{e^{iz^2} - 1}{z^2}\, dz = 0 \qquad \qquad \ldots(1)$$

Now, $$\left| \int_{C_R} \frac{e^{iz^2} - 1}{z^2}\, dz \right| \le \int_{C_R} \frac{(|e^{iz^2}| + 1)\, |dz|}{|z|^2}$$

$$\le \frac{1}{R^2} \int_0^{\pi} \left(e^{-R^2 \sin 2\theta} + 1 \right) R\, d\theta$$

$$\le \frac{1}{R} 2 \int_0^{\pi/2} \left(e^{-4R^2 \theta / \pi} + 1 \right) d\theta$$

by Jordan's inequality

$$\le \left[\frac{\pi}{R} + \frac{\pi}{2R^3} (1 - e^{-2R}) \right] \text{ which } \to 0 \text{ as } R \to \infty.$$

Hence by making $R \to \infty$, relation (1) becomes.

$$\int_{-\infty}^{\infty} \frac{e^{ix^2} - 1}{x^2}\, dx = 0$$

$$\Rightarrow \qquad \int_{-\infty}^{\infty} \frac{\cos x^2 + i \sin x^2 - 1}{x^2}\, dx = 0$$

Equating real and imaginary parts we have

$$\int_{0}^{\infty} \frac{\cos x^2 - 1}{x^2}\, dx = 0$$

and

$$\int_{0}^{\infty} \frac{\sin x^2}{x^2}\, dx = 0.$$

Adding these we have

$$\int_{0}^{\infty} \frac{\cos x^2 + \sin x^2 - 1}{x^2}\, dx = 0.$$

7. Evaluate by contour integration that

$$\int_{0}^{\infty} \frac{\log(1 + x^2)}{1 + x^2}\, dx = \pi \log 2.$$

(Mithila 2000, 2003, U.P.P.C.S. 1999, 2003; Kanpur 2003)

Solution. Consider the integral

$$\int_{C} f(z)\, dz, \text{ where } f(z) = \frac{\log(z + i)}{z^2 + 1}.$$

Poles of $f(z)$ are given by $z^2 + 1 = 0$ or $z = \pm i$ are simple poles. Since there is no pole on the real axis, therefore, we take the closed contour C consisting of the upper half C_R of the large circle $|z| = R$, and the real axis from $-R$ to R.

Hence by Cauchy's residue theorem, we have

$$\int_{C} f(z)\, dz = 2\pi i\, \Sigma R^{+}$$

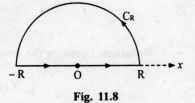

Fig. 11.8

where ΣR^{+} = sum of residues of $f(z)$ at its poles within C

i.e.,

$$\int_{-R}^{R} f(x)\, dx + \int_{C_R} f(z)\, dz = 2\pi i\, \Sigma R^{+}$$

or

$$\int_{-R}^{R} \frac{\log(x + i)}{x^2 + 1}\, dx + \int_{C_R} \frac{\log(z + i)}{z^2 + 1}\, dz = 2\pi i\, \Sigma R^{+} \qquad \text{...(1)}$$

Only pole $z = i$ lies within the contour C, $z = -i$ is the branch point that does not lie within C. The residue at $z = i$

$$= \lim_{z \to i}\, (z - i)\, \frac{\log(z + i)}{(z - i)(z + i)}$$

$$= \frac{\log (2i)}{2i} = \frac{\log 2 + i \frac{1}{2} \pi}{2i}.$$

Now $$\lim_{z \to \infty} \frac{z \log (z + i)}{z^2 + 1} = \lim_{z \to \infty} \frac{z}{z - i} \frac{\log (z + i)}{z + i}.$$

But $$\lim_{z \to \infty} \frac{z}{z - i} = 1 \text{ and } \lim_{z \to \infty} \frac{\log (z + i)}{z + i} = 0.$$

Hence $$\lim_{z \to \infty} \int_{C_R} \frac{\log (z + i)}{z^2 + 1} \, dz = 0.$$

$\therefore$ $$\lim_{R \to \infty} \int_{C_R} \frac{\log (z + i)}{z^2 + 1} = 0.$$

Hence when $R \to \infty$, relation (1) becomes

$$\int_{-\infty}^{\infty} \frac{\log (x + i)}{x^2 + 1} \, dx = \pi \left(\log 2 + \frac{1}{2} i\pi \right).$$

Equating real parts, we have

$$\int_{-\infty}^{\infty} \frac{\frac{1}{2} \log (x^2 + 1)}{x^2 + 1} \, dx = \pi \log 2$$

or $$\int_{0}^{\infty} \frac{\log (1 + x^2)}{1 + x^2} \, dx = \pi \log 2.$$

8. *Using the method of contour integration, evaluate*

$$\int_{-\infty}^{\infty} \frac{e^{-x^2}}{1 + x^2} \, dx.$$

Solution. Consider the integral

$$\int_{C} f(z) \, dz \text{ where } f(z) = \frac{e^{-z^2}}{1 + z^2}.$$

The poles of $f(z)$ are given by $1 + z^2 = 0$ or $z = \pm i$ are two simple poles. Since there is no pole on the real axis, therefore, we may take the closed contour C consisting of the upper half C_R of the circle $| z | = R$ and the part of the real axis from $- R$ to R.

Hence by Cauchy's residue theorem, we have

$$\int_{C} f(z) \, dz = 2\pi i \, \Sigma R^+$$

where ΣR^+ = sum of residues of $f(z)$ at its poles within C

or $$\int_{-R}^{R} f(x) \, dx + \int_{C_R} f(z) \, dz = 2\pi i \, \Sigma R^+$$

or $$\int_{-R}^{R} \frac{e^{-x^2}}{1 + x^2} \, dx + \int_{C_R} \frac{e^{-z^2}}{1 + z^2} \, dz = 2\pi i \, \Sigma R^+ \qquad \text{...(1)}$$

The pole $z = i$ lies within C.

Residue at the simple pole $z = i$ is

$$= \lim_{z \to i} (z - i) f(z) = \lim_{z \to i} (z - i) \frac{e^{-z^2}}{1 + z^2}$$

$$= \lim_{z \to i} (z - i) \frac{e^{-z^2}}{(z - i)(z + i)} = \frac{e}{2i}.$$

Now
$$\left| \int_{C_R} \frac{e^{-z^2}}{1 + z^2} \, dz \right| \leq \int_{C_R} \frac{|e^{-z^2}|}{|1 + z^2|} |dz|$$

$$\leq \int \frac{|e^{-R\cos 2\theta - iR^2 \sin 2\theta}|}{(|z|^2 - 1)} |dz| \qquad \text{since } z = Re^{i\theta} \text{ on } C_R$$

$$= \int_0^{\pi} \frac{e^{-R^2 \cos 2\theta}}{R^2 - 1} R \, d\theta$$

$$= \frac{2R}{R^2 - 1} \int_{-\pi/2}^{\pi/2} e^{-R^2 \cos 2\theta} \, d\theta \qquad \text{[By property of definite integral]}$$

$$= \frac{R}{R^2 - 1} \int_{-\pi/2}^{\pi/2} e^{-R^2 \sin \phi} \, d\phi \qquad \left[\text{Putting } 2\theta = \frac{\pi}{2} - \phi \right]$$

$$= \frac{R}{R^2 - 1} \int_{-\pi/2}^{0} e^{-R^2 \sin \phi} \, d\phi + \frac{R}{R^2 - 1} \int_0^{\pi/2} e^{-R^2 \sin \phi} \, d\phi \qquad \dots(2)$$

Now

$$\frac{R}{R^2 - 1} \int_0^{\pi/2} e^{-R^2 \sin \phi} \, d\phi$$

$$< \frac{R}{R^2 - 1} \int_0^{\pi/2} e^{-2R^2 \phi/\pi} \, d\phi \qquad \text{[By Jordan's inequality]}$$

$$= \frac{R}{R^2 - 1} \cdot \frac{\pi}{2R^2} \left[-e^{-2R^2 \phi/\pi} \right]_0^{\pi/2}$$

$$= \frac{\pi}{2R(R^2 - 1)} \cdot (1 - e^{-R^2}) \text{ which } \to 0 \text{ as } R \to \infty.$$

Since the Jordan's inequality remains unchanged if we write $-\theta$ for θ i.e., $\dfrac{\sin \theta}{\theta} = \dfrac{2}{\pi}$ even if θ is negative.

$\therefore \quad \dfrac{-\sin \theta}{\theta} \leq \dfrac{2}{\pi}$, when θ is positive or negative.

Hence

$$\frac{R}{R^2 - 1} \int_{-\pi/2}^{0} e^{-R^2 \sin\phi} \, d\phi$$

$$< \frac{R}{R^2 - 1} \int_{-\pi/2}^{0} e^{2R^2\phi/\pi} \, d\phi = \frac{R}{R^2 - 1} \cdot \frac{\pi}{2R^2} \left[e^{2R^2\phi/\pi} \right]_{-\pi/2}^{0}$$

$$= \frac{\pi}{2R(R^2 - 1)} (1 - e^{-R^2}) \text{ which} \to 0 \text{ as } R \to \infty.$$

Hence when $R \to \infty$, from (2)

$$\int_{C_R} \frac{e^{-z^2}}{1 + z^2} \, dz \to 0.$$

Hence when $R \to \infty$, (1) becomes

$$\int_{-\infty}^{\infty} \frac{e^{-x^2}}{1 + x^2} \, dx = 2\pi i \cdot \frac{e}{2i} = \pi e.$$

11.5. Case of poles on the real axis. In the preceding cases it has been explicitly assumed that the integrand of the complex integral corresponding to the integrand of the given real definite integral is such that the same has no pole on the real axis. We shall now explain the procedure to be followed when the complex integrand does have a simple pole on the real axis. In this case we have recourse to what is called '*Indenting*' at a point.

Now suppose that a complex function $f(z)$ has a pole of the first order at a point $z = a$ on the real axis.

We draw a semi-circle Γ in the upper semi-plane with its centre at, a, and radius ϵ, which will, later on, be made to tend to zero.

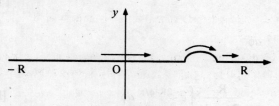

Fig. 11.9

Thus instead of what we denoted by C_2 in the preceding cases, we consider a contour consisting of

(*i*) a segment C_2' of the real axis from $-R$ to $a - \epsilon$;

(*ii*) the semi-circle Γ in the upper semi-plane;

(*iii*) a segment C_2'' of the real axis from $a + \epsilon$ to R.

Consider first the integral

$$\int_{\Gamma} \phi(z) \, dz.$$

As, a, is a pole of the first order of $\phi(z)$, we have, in the neighbourhood of a, an equality of the form

$$\phi(z) = \frac{a_{-1}}{z-a} + a_0 + a_1(z-a) + \dots$$

$$= \frac{a_{-1}}{z-a} + \psi(z),$$

where $\psi(z)$ is analytic at a. As $\psi(z)$ is analytic at a, there exists a positive number k such that in some neighbourhood of a

$$|\psi(z)| \le k.$$

We suppose that ε is taken so small that Γ lies in this neighbourhood.

We have

$$\int_\Gamma \phi(z)\,dz = \int_\Gamma \frac{dz}{z-a} + \int_\Gamma \psi(z)\,dz \qquad \dots(1)$$

Since for points on Γ, we have $z - a = \varepsilon e^{i\theta}$, therefore

$$\int_\Gamma \frac{dz}{z-a} = \int_\pi^0 \frac{\varepsilon i e^{i\theta}}{\varepsilon e^{i\theta}}\,d\theta = -i\pi \qquad \dots(2)$$

Also

$$\left| \int_\Gamma \psi(z)\,dz \right| \le k\varepsilon\pi \qquad \dots(3)$$

From (1), (2) and (3), we obtain

$$\lim_{\varepsilon \to 0} \int_\Gamma \phi(z)\,dz = -i\pi a_{-1} = -(2i\pi)\,\text{Res. }(a) \qquad \dots(4)$$

The negative sign in (4) is explained by the fact that Γ is described negatively.

Also the sum of the integrals along the line segments C_2', C_2'' tend to the limit

$$P\int_{-\infty}^{+\infty} \phi(x)\,dx \text{ when } R \to \infty \text{ and } z \to 0 \qquad \dots(5)$$

We have here written the principal value, for the points $a - \varepsilon$, $a + \varepsilon$ have been taken equivalent from a. In case, however, the improper integral is otherwise known to be convergent, we may delete P.

Thus, we have completed the examination.

EXAMPLES

1. *Evaluate*

$$\int_0^\infty \frac{\sin x}{x}\,dx.$$

[Gorakhpur 2000, 2002, 2004]

Solution. Consider the integral

$$\int_C \frac{e^{iz}}{z}\,dz,$$

where C consists of

(*i*) the semi-circle C_1 given by $|z| = R$, $I(z) > 0$;

(*ii*) the segment C_2, of the real axis from $-R$ to $-\varepsilon$;

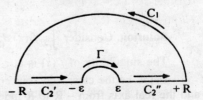

Fig. 11.10

(*iii*) the semi-circle Γ given by $|z| = \varepsilon$, $I(z) > 0$;

(*iv*) the segment C_2'' of the real axis from ε to R.

The orientations are as shown.

The contour has been indented at, 0, for the same is a pole of ε^{iz}/z.

As there is no singular point in the interior of C, we have

$$0 = \frac{1}{2\pi i} \int_{C_1} \frac{e^{iz}}{z}\, dz + \frac{1}{2\pi i} \int_{C_2'} \frac{e^{iz}}{z}\, dz$$

$$+ \frac{1}{2\pi i} \int_{\Gamma} \frac{e^{iz}}{z}\, dz + \frac{1}{2\pi i} \int_{C_2''} \frac{e^{iz}}{z}\, dz \qquad \ldots(1)$$

By Jordan's Lemma or directly,

$$\lim_{R \to \infty} \int_{C_1} \frac{e^{iz}}{z}\, dz = 0.$$

As proved

$$\lim_{\varepsilon \to 0} \int_{\Gamma} \frac{e^{iz}}{z}\, dz = -\frac{1}{2}(2i\pi)\, \text{Res.}(0) = -\frac{1}{2}(2i\pi)(1) = -i\pi.$$

Also

$$\int_{C_2'} \frac{e^{iz}}{z}\, dz = \int_{-R}^{-\varepsilon} \frac{e^{ix}}{x}\, dx + \int_{C_2''} \frac{e^{iz}}{z}\, dz = \int_{\varepsilon}^{R} \frac{e^{ix}}{x}\, dx$$

so that

$$\lim_{\substack{R \to \infty \\ \varepsilon \to 0}} \int_{C_2'} \frac{e^{iz}}{z}\, dz = \int_{-\infty}^{0} \frac{e^{ix}}{x}\, dx,$$

$$\lim_{\substack{R \to \infty \\ \varepsilon \to 0}} \int_{C_2''} \frac{e^{iz}}{z}\, dz = \int_{0}^{\infty} \frac{e^{ix}}{x}\, dx.$$

Thus, we have, from (1), in the limit

$$0 = \frac{1}{2\pi i} \int_{-\infty}^{0} \frac{e^{ix}}{x}\, dx + \frac{1}{2\pi i} \int_{0}^{\infty} \frac{e^{ix}}{x}\, dx - \frac{1}{2}$$

$$\Rightarrow \quad \int_{-\infty}^{\infty} \frac{e^{ix}}{x}\, dx = \pi i \quad \Rightarrow \quad \int_{-\infty}^{\infty} \frac{\sin x}{x}\, dx = \pi.$$

2. *By contour integration prove that*

$$\int_{0}^{\infty} \frac{\sin mx}{x}\, dx = \frac{\pi}{2}.$$

(*UPPCS 2000, 2001*)

Solution. Consider $\int_C f(z)\, dz$, where $f(z) = \dfrac{e^{imz}}{z}$.

The singularity of $f(z)$ is at $z = 0$.

Let C be the closed contour consisting of the upper half C_R of a large semi-circle $|z| = R$ and the real axis from $-R$ to R indenting the path at $z = 0$ by a semi-circle C_r centred at O and of a small radius r. Thus the closed contour C consists of the upper half C_R of the large circle $|z| = R$, real axis from $-R$ to $-r$, semi-circular arc C_r of circle $|z| = r$, where r is very small and again the real axis from r to R.

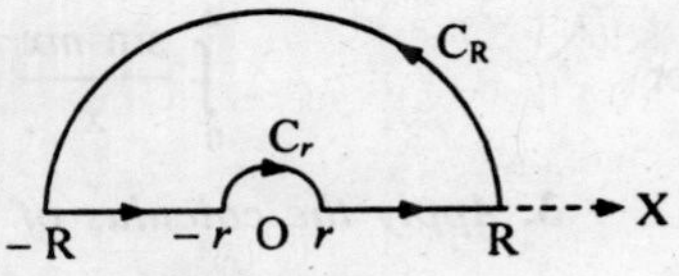

Fig. 11.11

Hence by Cauchy's residue theorem, we have

$$\oint_C f(z)\, dz = 2\pi i\, \Sigma R^+$$

where ΣR^+ = sum of residues of $f(z)$ at its poles within C.

Since there is no pole of $f(z)$ within C, therefore, $\Sigma R^+ = 0$.

i.e.,
$$\int_{-R}^{-r} f(x)\, dx + \int_{C_r} f(z)\, dz + \int_{r}^{R} f(x)\, dx + \int_{C_R} f(z)\, dz = 0$$

$\therefore$ letting $r \to 0$ and $R \to \infty$, we have

$$\int_{-\infty}^{0} f(x)\, dx + \lim_{r \to 0} \int_{C_r} f(z)\, dz + \int_{0}^{\infty} f(x)\, dx + \lim_{R \to 0} \int_{C_R} f(z)\, dz = 0$$

or
$$\int_{-\infty}^{\infty} f(x)\, dx = -\lim_{r \to 0} \int_{C_r} f(z)\, dz - \lim_{R \to 0} \int_{C_R} f(z)\, dz \qquad ...(1)$$

Now
$$\lim_{z \to 0} z\, f(z) = \lim_{z \to 0} (e^{imz}) = 1 = k_1.$$

$$\lim_{r \to 0} \int_{C_r} f(z)\, dz = ik_1\, (\beta - \alpha) = i \cdot 1\, (0 - \pi) = -\pi i.$$

Also
$$\lim_{z \to \infty} \left(\frac{1}{z} \right) = 0.$$

$\therefore$ By Jordan's Lemma, we have

$$\lim_{R \to \infty} \int_{C_R} \frac{e^{imz}}{z}\, dz = \lim_{R \to \infty} \int_{C_R} f(z)\, dz = 0.$$

Hence from (1), we have

$$\int_{-\infty}^{\infty} f(x)\, dx = -(-\pi i)$$

or
$$\int_{-\infty}^{\infty} \frac{e^{imx}}{x}\, dx = \pi i$$

or
$$\int_{-\infty}^{\infty} \frac{\cos mx}{x}\, dx + i \int_{-\infty}^{\infty} \frac{\sin mx}{x}\, dx = \pi i.$$

Equating the imaginary parts, we have

$$\int_{-\infty}^{\infty} \frac{\sin mx}{x}\, dx = \pi$$

or
$$\int_0^\infty \frac{\sin mx}{x}\, dx = \frac{\pi}{2}.$$

3. *Apply the calculus of residues to prove that*

$$\int_0^\infty \frac{\sin \pi x}{x(1-x^2)}\, dx = \pi.$$

(*Garhwal 2004*)

Solution. Consider $\int_C f(z)\, dz$, where $f(z) = \dfrac{e^{i\pi z}}{z(1-z^2)}$.

The poles of $f(z)$ are given by

$$z(1-z^2) = 0 \quad \therefore \quad z = 0,\, -1,\, 1$$

are poles of $f(z)$ which are all simple poles and lie on the real axis.

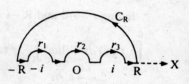

∴ To avoid these poles let C be the contour consisting of the upper half C_R of a large circle $|z| = R$ and real axis from $-R$ to R indented at $z = -1,\, 0$ to 1. Let the small circles with centres at $z = -1$, $z = 0$ and $z = 1$ be denoted by γ_1, γ_2, γ_3 and let their radii be r_1, r_2, r_3 respectively.

Fig. 11.12

Since there is no pole of $f(z)$ within and on C.

∴ By Cauchy's residue theorem, we have

$$\int_C f(z)\, dz = \int_{-R}^{-(1+r_1)} f(x)\, dx + \int_{\gamma_1} f(z)\, dz + \int_{-(1-r_1)}^{-r_2} f(x)\, dx$$

$$+ \int_{\gamma_2} f(z)\, dz + \int_{r_2}^{1-r_3} f(x)\, dx + \int_{\gamma_3} f(z)\, dz + \int_{1+r_3}^{R} f(x)\, dx + \int_{C_R} f(z)\, dz$$

$$= 2\pi i \, \Sigma R^+ = 0.$$

When $r_1,\, r_2,\, r_3 \to 0$ and $R \to \infty$, then we have

$$\int_{-\infty}^{-1} f(x)\, dx + \lim_{r_1 \to 0} \int_{\gamma_1} f(z)\, dz + \int_{-1}^{0} f(x)\, dx + \lim_{r_2 \to 0} \int_{\gamma_2} f(z)\, dz$$

$$+ \int_0^1 f(x)\, dx + \lim_{r_3 \to 0} \int_{\gamma_3} f(z)\, dz + \int_1^\infty f(x)\, dx + \lim_{R \to \infty} \int_{C_R} f(z)\, dz = 0$$

or
$$\int_{-\infty}^{\infty} f(x)\, dx + \lim_{r_1 \to 0} \int_{\gamma_1} f(z)\, dz + \lim_{r_2 \to 0} \int_{\gamma_2} f(z)\, dz$$

$$+ \lim_{r_3 \to 0} \int_{\gamma_3} f(z)\, dz + \lim_{R \to \infty} \int_{C_R} f(z)\, dz = 0 \quad \ldots(1)$$

Now

$$\lim_{z \to -1} [z - (-1)]\, f(z) = \lim_{z \to -1} (z+1) \frac{e^{i\pi z}}{z(1+z)(1-z)}$$

$$= \frac{e^{-i\pi}}{-2} = \frac{1}{2} = k_1.$$

$$\lim_{z \to 0} (z - 0) f(z) = \lim_{z \to 0} z \cdot \frac{e^{i\pi z}}{z (1 - z^2)} = 1 = k_2$$

and

$$\lim_{z \to 1} (z - 1) f(z) = \lim_{z \to 1} (z - 1) \frac{e^{i\pi z}}{z (1 + z)(1 - z)}$$

$$= \frac{e^{i\pi}}{-2} = \frac{1}{2} = k_3.$$

∴ By Theorem I, § 11.2.1, we have

$$\lim_{r_1 \to 0} \int_{\gamma_1} f(z)\, dz = i (\beta - \alpha) k_1 = i (0 - \pi) \frac{1}{2} = -\frac{1}{2} i\pi$$

$$\lim_{r_2 \to 0} \int_{\gamma_2} f(z)\, dz = i (\beta - \alpha) k_2 = i (0 - \pi)\cdot 1 = -i\pi$$

and

$$\lim_{r_3 \to 0} \int_{\gamma_3} f(z)\, dz = i (\beta - \alpha) k_3 = i (0 - \pi) \frac{1}{2} = -\frac{1}{2} i\pi.$$

Also

$$\lim_{z \to \infty} \frac{1}{z (1 - z^2)} = 0.$$

∴ By Jordan's Lemma, we have

$$\lim_{R \to \infty} \int_{C_R} \frac{e^{i\pi z}}{z (1 - z^2)}\, dz = \lim_{R \to \infty} \int_{C_R} f(z)\, dz = 0.$$

Hence from (1), we have

$$\int_{-\infty}^{\infty} f(x)\, dx - \frac{1}{2} i\pi - i\pi - \frac{1}{2} i\pi = \text{or } \int_{-\infty}^{\infty} \frac{e^{i\pi x}}{x (1 - x^2)}\, dx = 2\pi i$$

$$\int_{-\infty}^{\infty} \frac{\sin \pi x}{x (1 - x^2)}\, dx = 2\pi \text{ or } \int_{0}^{\infty} \frac{\sin \pi x}{x (1 - x^2)}\, dx = \pi.$$

4. *By integrating round a suitable contour, prove that*

(i) $\displaystyle\int_{0}^{\infty} \frac{(\log x)^2}{1 + x^2}\, dx = \frac{\pi^2}{8}$ *(Mithila 2003)*

(ii) $\displaystyle\int_{0}^{\infty} \frac{\log x}{1 + x^2}\, dx = 0$ *(Gorakhpur 2001, 2003, 2004; Garhwal 2003)*

Solution. Consider the integral $\displaystyle\int_{C} f(z)\, dz$

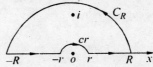

Fig. 11.13

where

$$f(z) = \frac{(\log z)^2}{1 + z^2}$$

taken round the contour C, consisting of the upper half of a large circle $|z| = R$, upper half of a small circle $|z| = R$ and the lines joining their ends.

The singularities of $f(z)$ are given by

$$1 + z^2 = 0, \quad i.e., z = \pm i.$$

Thus the only sinuglarity within the contour is a simple pole at $z = i$ the residue at which is

$$\lim_{z \to i} \left\{ (z - i) \frac{(\log z)^2}{1 + z^2} \right\} = \lim_{z \to i} \left\{ \frac{(\log z)^2}{z + i} \right\}$$

$$= \frac{(\log i)^2}{2i} = \frac{(\log e^{i\pi\ 2})}{2i} = \frac{\left(\dfrac{i\pi}{2} \right)^2}{2i} = -\frac{\pi^2}{8i}$$

Hence by Cauchy's residue theorem, we have

$$\int_C f(z)\, dz = 2\pi i \times \text{ sum of the residues within C}$$

or $$\int_{-R}^{-r} f(x)\, dx + \int_{C_r} f(z)\, dz + \int_r^R f(x)\, dx + \int_{C_R} f(z)\, dz$$

$$= 2\pi i \times \left(\frac{-\pi^2}{8i} \right)$$

Now, we see that

$$\lim_{z \to \infty} z f(z) = \lim_{z \to \infty} \frac{z (\log z)^2}{1 + z^2}$$

$$= \lim_{z \to \infty} \frac{z^3 \left(\dfrac{\log z}{z} \right)^2}{1 + z^2}$$

$$= \lim_{z \to \infty} \frac{\left(\dfrac{\log z}{z} \right)^2}{\dfrac{1}{z^3} + \dfrac{1}{z}} = 0$$

since $$\lim_{z \to \infty} \frac{\log z}{z} = 0.$$

$$\therefore \quad \lim_{R \to 0} \int_{C_R} f(z)\, dz = 0 \text{ by Jordan's lemma.}$$

Also. $$\lim_{z \to 0} z f(z) = \lim_{z \to 0} \frac{z (\log z)^2}{1 + z^2}$$

$$= \lim_{\xi \to 0} \frac{\xi (\log \xi)^2}{1 + \xi^2}, \text{ putting } z = \frac{1}{\xi}$$

$$= 0 \text{ as above.}$$

Hence making $R \to \infty, r \to 0,$ relation (1), becomes

$$\int_{-\infty}^{0} \frac{(\log x)^2}{1 + x^2} dx + \int_{0}^{\infty} \frac{(\log x)^2}{1 + x^2} dx = 2\pi i \left(-\frac{\pi^2}{8i} \right)$$

or

$$\int_{0}^{\infty} \frac{\{\log(-x)\}^2}{1 + x^2} dx + \int_{0}^{\infty} \frac{(\log x)^2}{1 + x^2} dx = -\frac{\pi^3}{4}$$

putting $-x$ for x in first integral.

$$\int_{0}^{\infty} \frac{\{\log(xe^{i\pi})^2\}}{1 + x^2} dx + \int_{0}^{\infty} \frac{(\log x)^2}{1 + x^2} dx = -\frac{\pi^3}{4}, \text{ since } e^{i\pi} = -1$$

or

$$\int_{0}^{\infty} \frac{(\log x + i\pi)^2}{1 + x^2} dx + \int_{0}^{\infty} \frac{(\log x)^2}{3 + 1 + x^2} dx = -\frac{\pi^3}{4}$$

or

$$\int_{0}^{\infty} \frac{2(\log x)^2 - \pi^2 + i \cdot 2\pi \log x}{1 + x^2} dx = -\frac{\pi^2}{4} \qquad \text{...(A)}$$

(*i*) Equating real parts we have

$$2\int_{0}^{\infty} \frac{(\log x)^2}{1 + x^2} dx - \pi^2 \int_{0}^{\infty} \frac{dx}{1 + x^2} dx = -\frac{\pi^3}{4}$$

i.e.,

$$2\int_{0}^{\infty} \frac{(\log x)^2}{1 + x^2} dx - \pi^2 \frac{\pi}{2} = -\frac{\pi^3}{4}$$

or

$$2\int_{0}^{\infty} \frac{(\log x)^2}{1 + x^2} dx = -\frac{\pi^3}{4} + \frac{\pi^3}{2} = \frac{\pi^3}{4}$$

$$\therefore \qquad \int_{0}^{\infty} \frac{(\log x)^2}{1 + x^2} dx = \frac{\pi^3}{8}$$

(*ii*) Equating imaginary parts of (A), we get

$$\int_{0}^{\infty} \frac{2\pi \log x}{1 + x^2} dx = 0$$

or

$$\int_{0}^{\infty} \frac{\log x}{1 + x^2} dx = 0.$$

5. *Use the method of contour integration to prove that*

$$\int_{0}^{\infty} \frac{x - \sin x}{x^3(a^2 + x^2)} dx = \frac{\pi}{2a^4}\left[\frac{1}{2}a^2 - a + 1 - e^{-a} \right], a > 0 \qquad \textit{(Rohilkhand 2003)}$$

Solution. Consider the integral

$$\int_{C} f(z)\, dz, \text{ where } f(z) \doteq \frac{z - i + ie^{iz}}{z^3(z^2 + a^2)}$$

taken round the closed contour C, consisting of the upper half of a large circle $|z| = R$ and the real axis from $-R$ to R indented at the origin and r be the radius of indentation (see figure of Ex. 4).

Poles of $f(z)$ are given by

$$z^3(z^2 + a^2) = 0$$

i.e., $z = 0$, $z = ia$ and $z = -ia$ are the poles.

The only pole which lies inside this contour is $z = ia$.

The residue at $z = ia$, is

$$\lim_{z \to ia} (z - ia) f(z)$$

$$= \lim_{z \to ia} (z - ia) \frac{z - i + ie^{iz}}{z^3(z - ia)(z + ia)}$$

$$= \frac{i}{2a^4}(a - 1 + e^{-a})$$

Hence by Cauchy's residue theorem, we have

$$\int_C f(z)\, dz = 2\pi i \times \text{ sum of residues within the contour}$$

$$\int_{-R}^{r} f(x)\, dx + \int_{C_r} f(z)\, dz + \int_{r}^{R} f(x)\, dx + \int_{C_R} f(z)\, dz$$

$$= 2\pi i \frac{i(a - 1 + e^{-a})}{2a^4} \qquad\qquad\qquad \text{...(1)}$$

Now, $$f(z) = \frac{z - i + ie^{iz}}{z^3(a^2 + z^2)}$$

$$= \frac{z - i + i\left(1 + iz + i^2\dfrac{z^2}{2!} + ...\right)}{z^3(a^2 + z^2)}$$

$$= \frac{-i\dfrac{z^2}{2} + \dfrac{z^3}{6} + ...}{z^3(a^2 + z^2)}$$

So that $$\lim_{z \to 0} zf(z) = \lim_{z \to 0} z\frac{-i\dfrac{z^2}{2} + \dfrac{z^3}{6} + ...}{z^3(a^2 + z^2)}$$

$$= \lim_{z \to 0} \frac{-\dfrac{i}{2} + \dfrac{z}{6}}{a^2 + z^2} = -\frac{i}{2a^2}$$

$$\therefore \qquad \lim_{r \to 0} \int_{C_r} f(z)\, dz = -i(\pi - 0)\left(-\frac{i}{2a^2}\right) = -\frac{\pi}{2a^2}$$

Again write $$f(z) = \frac{z - i + ie^{iz}}{z^3(a^2 + z^2)}$$

$$= \frac{z-i}{z^3(a^2+z^2)} + e^{iz}\frac{i}{z^3(a^2+z^2)}$$

Now, we see that

$$\lim_{z\to\infty} z\frac{z-i}{z^3(a^2+z^2)} = 0,$$

and

$$\lim_{z\to\infty} e^{iz}\frac{i}{z^3(a^2+z^2)} = 0 \text{ by Jordan's Lemma}$$

$$\therefore \qquad \lim_{R\to\infty}\int_{C_R} f(z)\,dz = 0$$

Hence by making $R\to\infty$ and $r\to 0$ relation (1) becomes

$$\int_{-\infty}^{0} f(x)\,dx - \frac{\pi}{2a^2} + \int_{0}^{\infty} f(x)\,dx = 2\pi i\frac{i(a-1+e^{-a})}{2a^4}$$

i.e.,

$$\int_{-\infty}^{\infty} f(x)\,dx = \frac{\pi}{2a^2} - \frac{\pi(a-1+e^{-a})}{a^4}$$

or

$$\int_{-\infty}^{\infty} \frac{x-1+e^{ix}}{x^3(a^2+x^2)}\,dx = \frac{\pi}{2a^2} - \frac{\pi(a-1+e^{-a})}{a^4}$$

$$(\text{put } e^{ix} = \cos x + i\sin x)$$

then equating real parts we have

$$\int_{-\infty}^{\infty} \frac{x-\sin x}{x^3(a^2+x^2)}\,dx = \frac{\pi}{2a^2} - \frac{\pi(a-1+e^{-a})}{a^4}$$

or

$$\int_{0}^{\infty} \frac{x-\sin x}{x^3(a^2+x^2)}\,dx = \frac{\pi}{4a^2} - \frac{\pi(a-1+e^{-a})}{2a^4}$$

$$= \frac{\pi}{2a^4}\left(\frac{1}{2}a^2 - a + 1 - e^{-a}\right)$$

6. *Apply the calculus of residues to prove that*

$$\int_{0}^{\infty} \frac{\sin^2 mx\,dx}{x^2(x^2+a^2)} = \frac{\pi}{4a^3}(e^{-2ma} - 1 + 2ma) \qquad (a>0, m>0)$$

(Meerut 2000, 2004, 2005)

Solution: We have

$$\int_{0}^{\infty} \frac{\sin^2 mx}{x^2(a^2+x^2)}\,dx = \frac{1}{2}\int_{0}^{\infty} \frac{1-\cos 2mx}{x^2(a^2+x^2)}\,dx$$

Consider the integral $\int_{C} f(z)\,dz$,

where

$$f(z) = \frac{1}{2}\frac{1-e^{2imz}}{z^2(a^2+z^2)},$$

taken round a closed contour C consisting of the upper of a large circle $|z| = R$, the real axis from $-R$ to R, indented at $z = 0$, and let r be the radius of indentation. The singularity $z = 0$ is avoided by indentation.

Poles of $f(z)$ are given by $z^2(a^2 + z^2) = 0$ or by $z = 0$ (double point) $z = ia$, $z = -ia$. The only pole within the contour is at $z = ia$, since $a > 0$.

The residue at $z = ia$ is

$$\lim_{z \to ia} (z - ia) f(z)$$

$$= \lim_{z \to ia} (z - ia) \frac{1 - e^{2imz}}{z^2(z - ia)(z + ia)}$$

$$= -\frac{1 - e^{-2am}}{4ia^3} = \frac{e^{-2am} - 1}{4ia^3}$$

Hence by Cauchy's residue theorem, we have

$$\int_C f(z)\,dz = 2\pi i \times \text{sum of the residues within C}$$

i.e.,

$$\int_{-R}^{-r} f(x)\,dx + \int_{C_r} f(z)\,dz + \int_{r}^{R} f(x)\,dx + \int_{C_R} f(z)\,dz$$

$$= 2\pi i \times \frac{e^{-2am} - 1}{4ia^3} \qquad \qquad \text{...(1)}$$

Now,

$$\left| \int_{C_R} f(z)\,dz \right| \le \int_{C_R} |f(z)|\,|dz|$$

$$= \int_{C_R} \left| \frac{1}{2} \cdot \frac{1 - e^{2imz}}{z^2(a^2 + z^2)} \right| |dz|$$

$$\le \int_{C_R} \frac{1 + |e^{2imz}|}{|z|^2(|z|^2 - a^2)} |dz|$$

$$= \frac{1}{R^2(R^2 - a^2)} \int_0^\pi (1 + e^{-2mR\sin\theta}) R\,d\theta$$

$$= \frac{\pi}{R(R^2 - a^2)} + \frac{2}{R(R^2 - a^2)} \int_0^{\pi/2} e^{-4mR\theta/\pi}\,d\theta$$

by Jordan's inequality

$$= \frac{\pi}{R(R^2 - a^2)} + \frac{\pi}{2mR^2(R^2 - a^2)}[1 - e^{-2mR}]$$

both the terms $\to 0$ as $R \to \infty$.

$$\lim_{z \to 0} z f(z) = \lim_{z \to 0} z \frac{(1 - e^{2imz})}{2z^2(a^2 + z^2)}$$

$$= \lim_{z \to 0} \frac{-2imz + 2m^2z^2 + \dots}{2z(a^2 + z^2)} = -\frac{im}{a^2}$$

$\therefore \qquad \lim_{r \to 0} \int_{c_r} f(z)\, dz = -i(\pi - 0)\left(-\dfrac{im}{a^2}\right) = -\dfrac{m\pi}{a^2}.$

Hence making $R \to \infty$ and $r \to 0$ relation (1) becomes

$$\int_{-\infty}^{0} f(x)\, dx + \int_{0}^{\infty} f(x)\, dx - \frac{m\pi}{a^2} = 2\pi i \times \frac{e^{-2ma} - 1}{4ia^3}$$

or

$$\int_{-\infty}^{\infty} f(x)\, dx = \frac{m\pi}{a^2} + \frac{\pi}{2a^3}(e^{-2ma} - 1)$$

or

$$\int_{-\infty}^{\infty} \frac{1}{2} \cdot \frac{1 - e^{-2imx}}{x^2(a^2 + x^2)}\, dx = \frac{\pi}{2a^3}(e^{-2ma} - 1 + 2ma)$$

Equating real parts we have

$$\int_{-\infty}^{\infty} \frac{1}{2} \frac{1 - \cos 2mx}{x^2(a^2 + x^2)}\, dx = \frac{\pi}{2a^3}(e^{-2ma} - 1 + 2ma)$$

i.e.

$$\int_{-\infty}^{\infty} \frac{\sin^2 mx}{x^2(a^2 + x^2)}\, dx = \frac{\pi}{2a^3}\left(e^{-2ma} - 1 + 2ma\right)$$

$$\int_{0}^{\infty} \frac{\sin^2 mx}{x^2(a^2 + x^2)}\, dx = \frac{\pi}{4a^3}(e^{-2ma} - 1 + 2ma).$$

11.6. Evaluation of integrals when the integrand involves multiple valued functions. We shall now consider cases where for the contour integral involves multiple valued functions, such as log z, z^a; a, being any non-integer. In such cases, we have to take care to consider only those contours whose interiors do not contain any branch points and also to specify the particular branches. The procedure will be made clear by the following examples.

EXAMPLES

1. *For what real values of b, the integral*

$$\int_{0}^{\infty} \frac{x^b}{1 + x^2}\, dx$$

is convergent and evaluate it for all these values? (*Meerut 2000, 2005; Garhwal 2007*)

Solution. It can be shown that the given improper real integral converges if and only if $-1 < b < 1$.

Consider the complex integral

$$\int_{C} \frac{z^b}{1 + z^2}\, dz$$

where, C, consists of

(*i*) the semi-circle C_2 given by $|z| = R$, $I(z) > 0$;

(*ii*) the line segment C_3 of the real axis from $-R$ to $-\delta$;

(*iii*) the semi-circle C_4 given by $|z| = \delta$, $I(z) > 0$;

(*iv*) the line segment C_1 of the real axis from δ to R.

The branch point, 0, of z^b is not contained in the interior of C.

Also we shall choose the branch of the function z^b which is real and positive when z is real and positive.

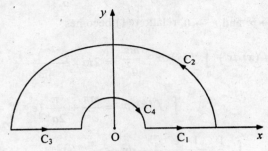

Fig. 11.14

We write

$$z = r (\cos \theta + i \sin \theta).$$

The argument, θ, of z varies from 0 to 0, 0 to π, π to π and π to 0 for the four portions C_1, C_2, C_3, C_4 respectively.

Also we have

$$z^b = E\ (b \log z) = E\ (b \log r + ib\theta)$$
$$= E\ (b \log r) \cdot E\ (ib\theta) = r^b\ E\ (ib\theta).$$

We consider now the integrals along the four parts of the contour one by one.

Integral along C_1. We have $z = r$ where z varies from δ to R.

$$\therefore \quad \int_{C_1} \frac{z^b}{1+z^2}\ dz = \int_\delta^R \frac{r^b}{1+r^2}\ dr.$$

Integral along C_2. We have

$$z = R e^{i\theta}$$

$$\therefore \quad \left| \int_{C_2} \frac{z^b}{1+z^2}\ dz \right| = \left| \int_0^\pi \frac{R^b\ E\ (ib\theta)}{1 + R^2 e^{2i\theta}}\ iR e^{i\theta}\ d\theta \right|$$

$$\leq \left| \frac{R^{b+1}}{R^2 - 1}\ \pi \right| \to 0 \text{ as } R \to \infty \text{ for } b+1 < 2.$$

Integral along C_3. We have

$$z = r (\cos \pi + i \sin \pi)$$

$$\therefore \quad \int_{C_3} \frac{z^b}{1+z^2}\ dz = \int_R^\delta \frac{r^b\ E\ (ib\pi)}{1+r^2}\ (-\ dr)$$

$$= E\ (ib\pi) \int_\delta^R \frac{r^b}{1+r^2}\ dr.$$

Integral along C_4. We have

$$z = \delta (\cos \theta + i \sin \theta),$$

where θ varies from π to 0.

$$\therefore \quad \left| \int_{C_4} \frac{z^b}{1+z^2} \, dz \right| = \left| \int_\pi^0 \frac{\delta^b \, E\,(ib\theta)}{1+\delta^2 e^{2i\theta}} \, \delta i e^{i\theta} \right|$$

$$\leq \frac{\delta^{b+1}}{1-\delta^2} \pi \to 0 \text{ as } \delta \to 0 \text{ for } b+1 > 0.$$

Thus taking limits when $\delta \to 0$ and $R \to \infty$, we obtain

$$\int_0^\infty \frac{r^b}{1+r^2} \, dr + E\,(ib\pi) \int_0^\infty \frac{r^b}{1+r^2} \, dr = 2\pi i \text{ Res.}\,(i),$$

i, is the only pole of the integrand in the interior of the contour C.

We have

$$\text{Res.}\,(i) \;=\; \lim \frac{(z-i)\,z^b}{z^2+1} = \frac{i^b}{2i}$$

$$= r^b \, E\, \frac{\left(ib\,\dfrac{\pi}{2} \right)}{2i} \text{ for } z^b = r^b \, E\,(ib\theta)$$

$$= \frac{1}{2i} \, E\left(ib\,\frac{\pi}{2} \right).$$

$$\therefore \quad \int_0^\infty \frac{r^b}{1+r^2} \, dr + E\,(ib\pi) \int_0^\infty \frac{r^b}{1+r^2} \, dr = \pi E\left(ib\,\frac{\pi}{2} \right).$$

Equating real and imaginary parts, we obtain

$$\int_0^\infty \frac{r^b}{1+r^2} \, dr = \frac{\pi}{2} \sec \frac{b\pi}{2}.$$

2. *Use the method of contour integration to prove that*

$$\int_0^\infty \frac{x^a}{(1+x^2)^2} \, dx = \frac{\pi(1-a)}{4} \cdot \sec\left(\frac{\pi a}{2} \right) \qquad\qquad -1 < a < 3.$$

Solution. Let $f(z) = \dfrac{z^a}{(1+z^2)^2}$

and $\qquad\qquad \displaystyle\int_C f(z)\,dz = I.$

Since $-1 < a < 3$, therefore $z = 0$ is a singularity of $f(z)$. Poles of $f(z)$ are given by $(1+z^2)^2 = 0$, *i.e.*, $z = \pm i$ are two poles each of order 2. Let $\alpha = i$ and $\beta = -i$, then

$$f(z) = \frac{z^a}{(z-\alpha)^2\,(z-\beta)^2}$$

choose the closed contour C consisting of the real axis from $-R$ to R and the upper half of the large circle $|z| = R$ indented at $z = 0$ and let r be the radius of indentation.

The only pole which lies within C is at $z = \alpha$.

The residue at the double pole $z = \alpha$ is

$$\left[\frac{d}{dz} \frac{z^a}{(z-\beta)^2} \right]_{z=\alpha} = \left[\frac{az^{a-1}(z-\beta)^2 - 2z^a(z-\beta)}{(z-\beta)^4} \right]_{z=\alpha}$$

$$= \frac{a\alpha^{a-1}(\alpha-\beta)^2 + 2\alpha^a(\alpha-\beta)}{(\alpha-\beta)^4}$$

$$= \frac{1}{(\alpha-\beta)^2}\left[\left(\frac{a}{\alpha} \right) - \frac{2}{(\alpha-\beta)} \right]\alpha^a$$

$$= \frac{1}{-4}\left[-ia - \frac{2}{2i} \right](i)^a \qquad \text{since } \alpha - \beta = 2i \text{ and } \alpha = i$$

$$= \frac{1}{4i}(1-a)\, e^{ia\pi/2}$$

Hence, by Cauchy's residue theorem, we have

$$\int_C f(z)\, dz \;=\; 2\pi i \times \text{ (sum of residues within } C)$$

or $\displaystyle \int_{-R}^{-r} f(x)\, dx + \int_{c_r} f(z)\, dz + \int_r^R f(x)\, dx + \int_{C_R} f(z)\, dz \;=\; 2\pi i \times \frac{1}{4i}(1-a)\, e^{ia\pi/2}$ ...(1)

Now, $\displaystyle \lim_{z \to \infty} z\, f(z) = \lim_{z \to \infty} z\, \frac{z^a}{(1+z^2)^2}$

$$= \lim_{z \to \infty} \frac{z^{a+1}}{(1+z^2)^2} = 0 \qquad\qquad \text{since } -1 < a < 3$$

$\therefore \qquad \displaystyle \lim_{R \to \infty} \int_{C_R} f(z)\, dz = i(\pi - 0)0$

$$= 0, \text{ integrating anticlockwise.}$$

Also, $\displaystyle \lim_{z \to 0} z\, f(z) = \lim_{z \to 0} z \cdot \frac{z^a}{(1+z^2)^2} = \lim_{z \to 0} \frac{z^{a+1}}{(1+z^2)^2}$ since $a+1$ is positive

$\therefore \qquad \displaystyle \lim_{r \to 0} \int_{c_r} f(z)\, dz = -i(\pi - 0)0 = 0, \text{ integrating clockwise.}$

Hence, making $R \to \infty,\, r \to 0,$ relation (1) becomes

$$\int_{-\infty}^{0} f(x)\, dx + \int_{0}^{\infty} f(x)\, dx = \frac{1}{2}\pi(1-a)\, e^{ia\pi/2}$$

or $\displaystyle \int_{-\infty}^{0} \frac{x^a}{(1+x^2)^2}\, dx + \int_{0}^{\infty} \frac{x^a}{(1+x^2)^2}\, dx = \frac{1}{2}\pi(1-a)\, e^{ia\pi/2}$

But $\displaystyle \int_{-\infty}^{0} \frac{x^a}{(1+x^2)^2}\, dx = \int_{0}^{\infty} \frac{(-x)^a}{(1+x^2)^2}\, dx,$ writing $-x$ for x

$$= \int_0^\infty \frac{(-1)^a \, x^a}{(1+x^2)^2} \, dx$$

$$= e^{ia\pi} \int_0^\infty \frac{x^2}{(1+x^2)^2} \, dx$$

$$(e^{ia\pi} + 1) \int_0^\infty \frac{x^a}{(1+x^2)^2} \, dx = \frac{1}{4} \pi (1-a) e^{ia\pi/2}$$

$$\frac{1}{2}(e^{ia\pi/2} + e^{-ia\pi/2}) \int_0^\infty \frac{x^a}{(1+x^2)^2} \, dx = \frac{1}{4} \pi (1-a)$$

$$\cos\left(\frac{a\pi}{2}\right) \int_0^\infty \frac{x^a}{(1+x^2)^2} \, dx = \frac{1}{4} \pi (1-a)$$

or

$$\int_0^\infty \frac{x^a}{(1+x^2)^2} \, dx = \frac{1}{4} \pi (1-a) \sec\left(\frac{\pi a}{2}\right).$$

3. *Use the method of contour integration to prove that*

$$\int_0^\infty \frac{x^{a-1}}{x^2 - x + 1} \, dx = \frac{2\pi}{\sqrt{3}} \operatorname{cosec}(\pi a) \cos\frac{(2\pi a + \pi)}{6} \qquad 0 < a < 1.$$

Solution. Let $f(z) = \dfrac{z^{a-1}}{z^2 - z + 1}$

Singularities of $f(z)$ are given by $z^{a-1} = 0$ when $a - 1 < 0$ and poles $z^2 - z + 1 = 0$ *i.e.*,
$z = \dfrac{1 \pm i\sqrt{3}}{2}$ are two simple poles.

Let $\qquad\qquad \alpha = \dfrac{1 + i\sqrt{3}}{2}$ and $\beta = \dfrac{1 - i\sqrt{3}}{2}$

or $\qquad\qquad \alpha = e^{i\pi/3}$ and $\beta = e^{-i\pi/3}$

But only α lies within the contour. Residue at the simple pole $z = \alpha$

$$\lim_{z \to \alpha} (z - \alpha) f(z)$$

$$= \lim_{z \to \alpha} (z - \alpha) \frac{z^{a-1}}{(z - \alpha)(z - \beta)} = \frac{(\alpha)^{a-1}}{\alpha - \beta}$$

$$= \frac{(e^{i\pi/3})^{a-1}}{i\sqrt{3}}$$

Also $\qquad \lim_{z \to 0} z f(z) = \lim_{z \to 0} \frac{z^a}{z^2 - z + 1} = 0$, since a is positive

$$\therefore \qquad \lim_{z \to 0} \int_{c_r} f(z)\, dz = i(\pi - 0)0 = 0$$

and

$$\lim_{z \to \infty} z f(z) = \lim_{z \to 0} \frac{z^a}{z^2 - z - 1} = 0, \text{ since } 0 < a < 1$$

$$\therefore \qquad \lim_{R \to \infty} \int_{C_R} f(z)\, dz = i(\pi - 0) \cdot 0 = 0$$

Hence, making $r \to 0, R \to \infty$, we have

$$\int_{-\infty}^{0} f(x)\, dx + \int_{0}^{\infty} f(x)\, dx = 2\pi i \times \frac{1}{i\sqrt{3}} (e^{i\pi/3})^{a-1}$$

or

$$\frac{2\pi}{\sqrt{3}}(e^{i\pi/3})^{a-1} = \int_{-\infty}^{0} \frac{x^{a-1}}{x^2 - x + 1}\, dx + \int_{0}^{\infty} \frac{x^{a-1}}{x^2 - x + 1}\, dx$$

$$= \int_{0}^{\infty} \frac{(-x)^{a-1}}{x^2 + x + 1}\, dx + \int_{0}^{\infty} \frac{x^{a-1}}{x^2 - x + 1}\, dx$$

writing $-x$ for x in the first integral

$$= \int_{0}^{\infty} \frac{(e^{i\pi})^{a-1} x^{a-1}}{x^2 + x + 1}\, dx + \int_{0}^{\infty} \frac{x^{a-1}}{x^2 - x + 1}\, dx$$

$$= -e^{ia\pi} \int_{0}^{\infty} \frac{x^{a-1}}{x^2 + x + 1}\, dx + \int_{0}^{\infty} \frac{x^{a-1}}{x^2 - x + 1}\, dx$$

Equating imaginary parts, we have

$$\sin a\pi \int_{0}^{\infty} \frac{x^{a-1}\, dx}{x^2 - x + 1} = -\frac{2\pi}{\sqrt{3}} \sin \frac{(a-1)\pi}{3}$$

$$= \frac{2\pi}{\sqrt{3}} \cos\left\{\frac{\pi}{2} + \frac{1}{3}(a-1)\pi\right\}$$

$$= \frac{2\pi}{\sqrt{3}} \cos \frac{1}{6}(2a+1)\pi$$

$$\Rightarrow \qquad \int_{0}^{\infty} \frac{x^{a-1}\, dx}{x^2 - x + 1} = \frac{2\pi}{\sqrt{3}} \operatorname{cosec}(\pi a) \cos \frac{(2\pi a + \pi)}{6}.$$

4. *If* $-1 < p < 1$ *and* $-\pi < \lambda < \pi$, *show by contour integration that*

$$\int_{0}^{\infty} \frac{x^{-p}\, dx}{1 + 2x \cos \lambda + x^2} = \frac{\pi \sin p\lambda}{\sin p\pi \sin \lambda}$$

explaining clearly the necessity of combination p *and* λ.

Solution. Consider the integral

$$\int_{c} f(z)\, dz$$

where
$$f(z) = \frac{z^{-p}}{1 + 2z \cos \lambda + z^2}$$

taken round the contour C, consisting of the large circle $|z| = R$, the small circle $|z| = r$, and the lines (cross – cuts) joining the arcs of the two circles along the real axis.

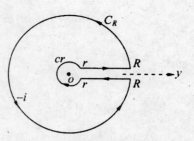

The singularities of $f(z)$ are given by
$$1 + 2z \cos \lambda + z^2 = 0$$

i.e.,
$$(z + e^{i\lambda})(z + e^{-i\lambda}) = 0$$

$\Rightarrow$
$$z = -e^{i\lambda} = e^{i(\pi+\lambda)}$$

and
$$z = -e^{-i\lambda} = e^{i(\pi-\lambda)}.$$

Fig. 11.15

Thus we see that amplitudes of these points are $\pi + \lambda$ and $\pi - \lambda$ and since λ lies between $-\pi$ and π, therefore the two amplitudes lie between 0 and 2π.

So,
$$z = -e^{i\lambda} \text{ and } z = -e^{-i\lambda}$$

are the two simple poles within the contour.

Residue of $f(z)$ and $z = -e^{-i\lambda}$ is
$$\lim_{z \to -e^{-i\lambda}} \frac{(z + e^{i\lambda}) z^{-p}}{(z + e^{i\lambda})(z + e^{-i\lambda})} = \frac{(-1)^{-p} e^{-ip\lambda}}{-2i \sin \lambda}$$
$$= \frac{e^{-p\pi i} e^{-ip\lambda}}{-2i \sin \lambda}$$

Also, Residue at $z = -e^{-i\lambda}$ is
$$\lim_{z \to e^{-i\lambda}} \frac{(z + e^{-i\lambda}) z^{-p}}{(z + e^{i\lambda})(z + e^{-i\lambda})} = \frac{(-1)^{-p} e^{ip\lambda}}{2i \sin \lambda}$$
$$= e^{-p\pi i} \cdot \frac{e^{ip\lambda}}{2i \sin \lambda}$$

$\therefore$ Sum of these two residues
$$= \frac{e^{-p\pi i}}{\sin \lambda} \cdot \frac{e^{ip\lambda} - e^{-ip\lambda}}{2i}$$
$$= e^{-p\pi i} \frac{\sin p\lambda}{\sin \lambda}$$

Hence by Cauchy's Residue theorem we have
$$\int_r^R f(x)\,dx + \int_{C_R} f(z)\,dz + \int_R^r f(xe^{2\pi i})\,d(xe^{2\pi i}) + \int_{c_r} f(z)\,dz$$
$$= 2\pi i \times \text{ sum of residues} \qquad \qquad ...(1)$$

Now,
$$\left| \int_{C_R} f(z)\,dz \right| \leq \int_{C_R} \frac{|z|^{-p}|dz|}{|z + e^{i\lambda}||z + e^{-i\lambda}|}$$

$$\leq \int_{C_R} \frac{|z|^{-p}|dz|}{(|z|-|e^{i\lambda}|)(|z|-|e^{-i\lambda}|)}$$

$$= \int_{C_R} \frac{R^{-p}|dz|}{(R-1)(R-1)}$$

$$= \frac{R^{-p} \cdot 2\pi R}{(R-1)^2} = \frac{2\pi R^{1-p}}{(R-1)^2}$$

which $\rightarrow 0$ as $R \rightarrow \infty$, since $1-p > 0$.

Similarly, $\qquad \left| \int_{c_r} f(z)\,dz \right| \leq \dfrac{2\pi r^{1-p}}{(1-r)^2}$ which $\rightarrow 0$ as $r \rightarrow 0$, since $1-p > 0$.

So the condition $-1 < p < 1$ is necessary.

Hence by making $R \rightarrow \infty$, $r \rightarrow 0$, the relation (1) reduces to

$$\int_0^\infty f(x)\,dx + \int_\infty^0 f(xe^{2\pi i})\,e^{2\pi i}\,dx = 2\pi i \times \text{ sum of residues}$$

i.e., $\displaystyle \int_0^\infty \frac{x^{-p}\,dx}{1+2x\cos\lambda+x^2} + \int_\infty^0 \frac{(xe^{2\pi i})^{-p}\cdot e^{2\pi i}\,dx}{1+2xe^{2\pi i}\cos+(xe^{2\pi i})^2} = 2\pi i \times \frac{e^{-ip\pi}\sin p\lambda}{\sin\lambda}$

i.e., $\displaystyle \int_0^\infty \frac{x^{-p}\,dx}{1+2x\cos\lambda+x^2} - \int_0^\infty \frac{x^{-p}e^{-2p\pi i}\,dx}{1+2x\cos\lambda+x^2} = 2\pi i \times \frac{e^{-ip\lambda}\sin p\lambda}{\sin\lambda}$

$$(1-e^{-2p\pi i}) \times \int_0^\infty \frac{x^{-p}\,dx}{1+2x\cos\lambda+x^2} = 2\pi i \frac{e^{-ip\lambda}\sin p\lambda}{\sin\lambda}$$

i.e., $\displaystyle \int_0^\infty \frac{x^{-p}\,dx}{1+2x\cos\lambda+x^2} = \frac{2\pi i}{e^{p\pi i}-e^{-p\pi i}}\frac{\sin p\lambda}{\sin\lambda}$

$$= \frac{\pi}{\sin p\pi} \cdot \frac{\sin p\lambda}{\sin\lambda}.$$

5. *Prove that*

$$\int_0^\infty \frac{x^{1/6}\,\log x}{(1+x)^2}\,dx = 2\pi - \frac{\pi^3}{\sqrt{3}}.$$

Solution. We shall consider the integral

$$\int \frac{x^{1/6}\,\log z}{(1+z)^2}\,dz \qquad\qquad\qquad ...(1)$$

for a suitable closed contour C.

Before proceeding further, we notice that, 0, is a branch point and, -1, a pole of the integrand in (1).

We take a contour, C, consisting of four oriented parts C_1, C_2, C_3, C_4 as shown in the figure.

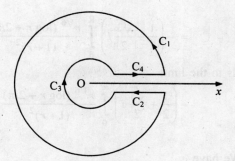

Figure 11.16

Here C_1, C_3 are circles with centres at the origin and radii R, δ respectively and C_2, C_1 are segments of the real axis from R to δ and δ to R respectively.

The branch point, 0, does not belong to the interior of C.

Also the argument, θ, of z varies monotonically from 0 to 2π along C_1, 2π to 2π along C_2, 2π to 0 along C_3 and 0 to 0 along C_4.

Further we shall be considering the branch of

$$\log z = \log |z| + i\theta,$$

for which θ has a value between 0 and 2π.

Integral along C_1. Putting

$$z = Re^{i\theta},$$

we have

$$\left| \int_{C_1} \frac{z^{1/6} \log z}{(1+z)^2} \, dz \right| = \left| \int_0^\pi \frac{R^{1/6} \, e^{i\theta/6} \, (\log R + i\theta) \, iRe^{i\theta}}{(1 + Re^{i\theta})^2} \, d\theta \right|$$

$$\leq \frac{R^{1/6} \sqrt{(\log R)^2 + 4\pi^2}}{(R-1)^2} \, 2\pi$$

which $\to 0$ as $R \to \infty$.

Integral along C_3. Putting

$$z = \delta e^{i\theta},$$

we have

$$\left| \int_{C_3} \frac{z^{1/6} \log z}{(1+z)^2} \, dz \right| = \left| \int_{2\pi}^0 \frac{\delta^{1/6} \, e^{i\theta/6} \, (\log \delta + i\theta) \, i\delta e^{i\theta}}{(1 + \delta e^{i\theta})^2} \, d\theta \right|$$

$$\leq \frac{\delta^{1/6} \sqrt{(\log \delta)^2 + 4\pi^2}}{(1 - \delta)^2} \, 2\pi$$

which $\to 0$ as $\delta \to 0$.

Integral along C_2. We have

$$z = r \, (\cos 2\pi + i \sin 2\pi),$$

where r varies from R to δ.

$$\therefore \quad \int_{C_2} \frac{z^{1/6} \log z}{(1+z)^2} \, dz = \int_R^\delta \frac{r^6 \left(\cos \dfrac{2\pi}{6} + i \sin \dfrac{2\pi}{6} \right) (\log r + 2i\pi)}{(1+r)^2} \, dr$$

$$= -\left(\frac{1}{2} + \frac{\sqrt{3}}{2} i\right) \int_{\delta}^{R} \frac{r^{1/6} (\log r + 2i\pi)}{(1+r)^2} \, dr$$

and this latter integral tends to the limit

$$-\left(\frac{1}{2} + \frac{\sqrt{3}}{2} i\right) \int_{0}^{\infty} \frac{r^{1/6} (\log r + 2i\pi)}{(1+r)^2} \, dr,$$

when $R \to \infty$ and $\delta \to 0$.

Integral along C_4. We have

$$\int_{C_4} \frac{z^{1/6} \log z}{(1+z)^2} \, dz = \int_{\delta}^{R} \frac{r^{1/6} \log r}{(1+r)^2} \, dr,$$

which tends, as $\delta \to 0$, $R \to \infty$, to the limit

$$\int_{0}^{\infty} \frac{r^{1/6} \log r}{(1+r)^2} \, dr.$$

Also we have

$$2\pi i \text{ Res.} (-1) = \int_{C} \frac{z^{1/6} \log z}{(1+z)^2} \, dz$$

$$= \int_{C_1} \frac{z^{1/6} \log z}{(1+z)^2} \, dz + \int_{C_2} \frac{z^{1/6} \log z}{(1+z)^2} \, dz$$

$$+ \int_{C_3} \frac{z^{1/6} \log z}{(1+z)^2} \, dz + \int_{C_4} \frac{z^{1/6} \log z}{(1+z)^2} \, dz.$$

Proceeding to the limit when $R \to \infty$ and $\delta \to 0$, we obtain

$$2\pi i \text{ Res.} (-1) = 0 - \left(\frac{1}{2} + \frac{\sqrt{3}}{2} i\right) \int_{0}^{\infty} \frac{r^{1/6} (\log r + 2i\pi)}{(1+r)^2} \, dr$$

$$+ 0 + \int_{0}^{\infty} \frac{r^{1/6} \log r}{(1+r)^2} \, dr \qquad\qquad ...(1)$$

Now we find Res. (-1). If we write

$$f(z) = z^{1/6} \log z,$$

then we may easily see that the residue at, -1, of

$$z^{1/6} \log z / (1 + z)^2$$

is equal to

$$f'(-1) f'(\cos \pi + i \sin \pi).$$

Also

$$f'(z) = \frac{1}{6} \frac{z^{1/6}}{z} \log z + \frac{z^{1/6}}{z}.$$

$$\therefore \qquad f'(-1) = \frac{1}{6} \frac{\left(\cos \dfrac{\pi}{6} + i \sin \dfrac{\pi}{6}\right)}{-1} (\log 1 + i\pi) + \frac{\left(\cos \dfrac{\pi}{6} + i \sin \dfrac{\pi}{6}\right)}{-1}$$

$$= -\left(\frac{\sqrt{3}}{2} + \frac{i}{2}\right)\left(\frac{i\pi}{6} + 1\right) \qquad\qquad ...(2)$$

Writing

$$I_1 = \int\limits_0^\infty \frac{x^{1/6} \log x}{(1+x)^2} \, dx, \quad I_2 = \int\limits_0^\infty \frac{x^{1/6}}{(1+x)^2} \, dx,$$

we obtain, from (1) and (2)

$$-2\pi i \left(\frac{\sqrt{3}}{2} + \frac{i}{2} \right) \left(\frac{i\pi}{6} + 1 \right) = -\left(\frac{1}{2} + \frac{\sqrt{3}}{2} i \right) (I_1 + 2i\pi I_2) + I_1.$$

Equating real and imaginary parts, we have

$$2\pi \left(\frac{\sqrt{3}\,\pi}{12} + \frac{1}{2} \right) = \frac{1}{2} I_1 + \sqrt{3}\,\pi\, I_2, \quad -2\pi \left(\frac{\sqrt{3}}{2} - \frac{x}{12} \right) = -\frac{\sqrt{3}}{2} I_1 - \pi I_2$$

Solving these for I_1, we obtain

$$I_1 = 2\pi - \frac{\pi^2}{\sqrt{3}}.$$

Also we may see that

$$\int\limits_0^\infty \frac{x^{1/6}}{(1+x)^2} \, dx = I_2 = \frac{\pi}{3}.$$

11.7. Use of rectangular and other contours. We shall now consider integrals wherefore we require rectangular and other types of contours. As an illustration, we shall evaluate three integrals in the following.

EXAMPLES

1. *By integrating*

$$e^{az} \, \mathrm{sech}\, \pi z$$

around the rectangular contour with vertices

$$-R,\ R,\ R+i,\ -R+i$$

and letting B tend to infinity, show that

$$\int\limits_0^\infty \frac{\cosh ax}{\cosh \pi x} \, dx = \frac{1}{2} \sec \frac{a}{2} \, (-\pi < a < \pi).$$ *(U.P.P.C.S., 2004)*

Solution. Integral along C_1 where $z = x$

$$= \int\limits_R^0 \frac{e^{ax}}{-R \cosh \pi x} \, dx = \int\limits_0^R \frac{e^{-ax}}{\cosh \pi x} \, dx.$$

Integral along C_2 where $z = x$

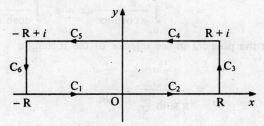

Figure 11.17

$$= \int_0^R \frac{e^{ax}}{\cosh \pi x} \, dx.$$

Integral along C_3 where $z = R + iy$ is, in absolute value,

$$= \left| \int_0^1 \frac{e^{a(R+iy)}}{\cosh \pi (R+iy)} i \, dy \right|$$

$$= \left| i \int_0^1 \frac{2e^{aR} \, e^{aiy}}{e^{\pi R + \pi iy} + e^{-\pi R - \pi y}} \, dy \right|$$

$$\leq \int_0^1 \frac{2e^{aR}}{e^{\pi R} - e^{-\pi R}} \, dy \leq \left| \frac{2e^{aR}}{e^{\pi R} - e^{-\pi R}} \right| \to 0 \text{ as } R \to \infty$$

for $|a| < \pi$.

Integral along C_6 where $z = -R + iy$ is, in absolute value,

$$= \left| \int_0^1 \frac{e^{a(-R+iy)}}{\cosh \pi (-R+iy)} i \, dy \right|$$

$$\leq \frac{e^{-aR}}{e^{\pi R} - e^{-\pi R}} \to 0 \text{ as } R \to \infty$$

for $|a| < \pi$.

Integral along C_4 where $z = x + i$

$$= \int_R^0 \frac{e^{a(x+i)}}{\cosh \pi (x+i)} \, dx$$

$$= -e^{ai} \int_0^R \frac{e^{ax}}{-\cosh \pi x} \, dx = e^{ai} \int_0^R \frac{e^{ax}}{\cosh \pi x} \, dx.$$

Integral along C_5 where $z = x + i$

$$= \int_0^{-R} \frac{e^{a(x+i)}}{\cosh \pi (x+i)} \, dx$$

$$= -e^{ai} \int_0^R \frac{e^{-ax}}{\cosh \pi (-x+i)} \, dx$$

$$= -e^{ai} \int_0^R \frac{e^{-ax}}{-\cosh \pi x} \, dx = e^{ai} \int_0^R \frac{e^{-ax}}{\cosh \pi x} \, dx.$$

Also the residue at the pole $i/2$ in the interior of the rectangle

$$= \frac{e^{\frac{1}{2} ai}}{\pi \sinh \frac{\pi i}{2}} = \frac{e^{\frac{1}{2} ai}}{i\pi}.$$

Considering the integral along the rectangle C and letting R tend to infinity, we obtain

$$\int_0^\infty \frac{e^{ax} + e^{-ax}}{\cosh \pi x} dx + e^{ai} \int_0^\infty \frac{e^{ax} + e^{-ax}}{\cosh \pi x} dx = 2i\pi \frac{e^{\frac{1}{2}ai}}{i\pi}$$

$$\Rightarrow \qquad 2(1 + e^{ai}) \int_0^\infty \frac{\cosh ax}{\cosh \pi x} dx = 2e.$$

Equating imaginary parts, we obtain

$$\int_0^\infty \frac{\cosh ax}{\cosh \pi x} dx = \frac{1}{2} \sec \frac{a}{2}.$$

2. *By integrating e^{-z^2} round the rectangle whose vertices are $0, R, R + ia, ia$, show that*

$$(i) \int_0^\infty e^{-x^2} \cos 2ax \, dx = \frac{e^{-a^2}}{2} \sqrt{\pi}$$

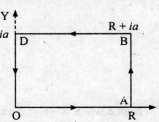

Fig. 11.18

$$and \ (ii) \int_0^\infty e^{-x^2} \sin 2ax \, dx = e^{-a^2} \int_0^a e^{y^2} dy.$$

Solution. Consider the integral

$$\int_C f(z) \, dz, \text{ where } f(z) = e^{-z^2}$$

taken round closed contour C which is the perimeter of the given rectangle OABD.

Since $f(z)$ is analytic within and on the contour C (*i.e.*, there is no singularity within the contour) hence by Cauchy's residue theorem, we have

$$\int_C f(z) \, dz = 0 \text{ or } \int_C e^{-z^2} \, dz = 0$$

or $\displaystyle \int_{OA} e^{-z^2} dz + \int_{AB} e^{-z^2} dz + \int_{BD} e^{-z^2} dz + \int_{DO} e^{-z^2} dz = 0$ ...(1)

Since on OA, $z = x$, $dz = dx$, x varies from 0 to R.

On AB, $z = R + iy$, $dz = i \, dy$, y varies from 0 to a.

On BD, $z = x + ia$, $dz = dx$, x varies from R to 0.

On DO, $z = iy$, $dz = i \, dy$, y varies from a to 0.

Hence the equation (1), becomes

$$\int_0^R e^{-x^2} dx + \int_0^a e^{-(R+iy)^2} \cdot i \, dy + \int_R^0 e^{-(x+ia)^2} dx + \int_a^0 e^{-(iy)^2} \cdot i \, dy = 0 \qquad ...(2)$$

Now, $\displaystyle \left| \int_0^a e^{-(R+iy)^2} \cdot i \, dy \right| \le \int_0^a |e^{-(R+iy)^2}| \, |i \, dy|$

$$= \int_0^a e^{-R^2 + y^2} \, dy$$

$$\le \int_0^a e^{-R^2 + a^2} \, dy \text{ since } y \le a \text{ on AB}$$

$$= e^{-(R^2 - a^2)} \, a \text{ which} \to 0 \text{ as } R \to \infty.$$

Hence when $R \to \infty$, equation (1) becomes

$$\int_0^\infty e^{-x^2} \, dx + \int_0^a e^{-(R+iy)^2} \cdot i \, dy + \int_R^0 e^{-(x+ia)^2} \, dx + \int_a^0 e^{-(iy)^2} \cdot i \, dy = 0 \qquad ...(3)$$

Now, $\left| \int_0^a e^{-(R+iy)^2} \cdot i \, dy \right| \le \int_0^a \left| e^{-(R+iy)^2} \right| \, | \, i \, dy |$

$$= \int_0^a e^{-R^2 + y^2} \, dy$$

$$\le \int_0^a e^{-R^2 + a^2} \, dy \text{ since } y \le a \text{ on AB}$$

$$= e^{-(R^2 - a^2)} \, a \text{ which} \to 0 \text{ as } R \to \infty.$$

Hence when $R \to \infty$, equation (3) becomes

$$\int_0^\infty e^{-(x+ia)^2} \, dx = \int_0^\infty e^{-x^2} \, dx - i \int_0^a e^{y^2} \, dy$$

i.e., $\int_0^\infty e^{(-x^2 + a^2 - 2iax)} \, dx = \dfrac{\sqrt{\pi}}{2} - i \int_0^a e^{y^2} \, dy \text{ since } \int_0^\infty e^{-x^2} \, dx = \dfrac{\sqrt{\pi}}{2}$

and $\int_0^\infty (e^{-x^2 + a^2}) (\cos 2ax - i \sin 2ax) \, dx = \dfrac{\sqrt{\pi}}{2} - i \int_0^a e^{y^2} \, dy.$

Equating real and imaginary parts, we have

$$\int_0^\infty e^{-x^2} \cos 2ax \, dx = \dfrac{e^{-a^2}}{2} \sqrt{\pi}$$

and $\int_0^\infty e^{-x^2} \sin 2ax \, dx = e^{-a^2} \int_0^a e^{y^2} \, dy.$

3. *By integrating the function*

$$\frac{z}{a - e^{-iz}}$$

round the rectangular contour with vertices at the points $\pm \pi, \pm \pi + iR,$
show that

$$\int_0^\pi \frac{x \sin x}{a^2 - 2a \cos x + 1} \, dx = \begin{cases} \dfrac{\pi}{a} \log (1 + a) & \textit{if } 0 < a < 1, \\[2ex] \dfrac{\pi}{a} \log \left(1 + \dfrac{1}{a} \right) & \textit{if } a > 1. \end{cases}$$

(Gorakhpur, 1996)

Solution. The only pole of $z / (a - e^{-iz})$ given by the root of

$$f(z) = a - e^{-iz} = 0,$$

is $i \log a$.

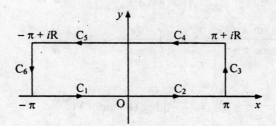

Fig. 11.19

We have

$$\text{Res. } (i \log a) = \left[\frac{2}{f'(z)} \right]_{z = i \log a}$$

$$= \frac{i \log a}{ie^{-i(i \log a)}} = \frac{\log a}{a}.$$

We first suppose that $a > 1$ so that the pole, $i \log a$, lies inside the rectangle as shown in the figure.

Denoting the integrals along C_1, C_2, C_3, C_4, C_5, C_6 by

$$I_1, I_2, I_3, I_4, I_5, I_6$$

respectively, we have the following results:

$$I_1 = \int_\pi^0 \frac{x}{a - e^{-ix}} \, dx = -\int_0^\pi \frac{x}{a - e^{ix}} \, dx.$$

$$I_2 = \int_0^\pi \frac{x}{a - e^{-ix}} \, dx.$$

$$I_3 = \int_0^R \frac{\pi + iy}{a - e^{-i(\pi + iy)}} \, i \, dy = \int_0^R \frac{\pi + iy}{a + e^y} \, i \, dy.$$

$$I_6 = \int_R^0 \frac{-\pi + iy}{a - e^{-i(-\pi + iy)}} \, i \, dy = -\int_0^R \frac{-\pi + iy}{a + e^y} \, i \, dy$$

$$= \int_0^R \frac{\pi - iy}{a + e^y} \, i \, dy.$$

$$I_4 = \int_\pi^0 \frac{x + iR}{a - e^{-i(x + iR)}} \, dx$$

$$= -\int_0^\pi \frac{x + iR}{a - e^{-ix} \, e^R} \, dx \to 0 \text{ as } R \to \infty.$$

$$I_5 = \int_0^{-\pi} \frac{x + iR}{a - e^{-ix} \, e^R} \, dx \to 0 \text{ as } R \to \infty.$$

Thus, we obtain

$$\int_0^\pi x \left[\frac{1}{a - e^{-ix}} - \frac{1}{a - e^{ix}} \right] dx + 2i\pi \int_0^\infty \frac{dy}{a + e^y} = 2\pi i \frac{\log a}{a}.$$

i.e.,

$$\int_0^\pi \frac{-2ix \sin x}{a^2 - 2a \cos x + 1} dx + 2i\pi \int_0^\infty \frac{dy}{a + e^y} = 2\pi i \frac{\log a}{a}.$$

Also

$$\int_0^\infty \frac{dy}{a + e^y} = \int_0^\infty \frac{e^{-y}}{1 + ae^{-y}} dy = -\frac{1}{a} \left[\log (1 + ae^{-y}) \right]_0^\infty$$

$$= \frac{\log (1 + a)}{a}.$$

$$\therefore \quad \int_0^\pi \frac{x \sin x}{a^2 - 2a \cos x + 1} dx = \frac{2i\pi}{-2i} \left[\frac{\log a}{a} - \frac{\log (1 + a)}{a} \right]$$

$$= \frac{\pi}{2} \log \left(\frac{1 + a}{a} \right) = \frac{\pi}{a} \left(1 + \frac{1}{a} \right).$$

If $0 < a < 1$, then the pole lies in the lower semi-plane. We may then take the rectangle with vertices $\pm \pi$, $\pm \pi - iR$ and evaluate the integral as we have done when $a > 1$.

4. *Apply the calculus of residues to prove that*

$$\int_{-\infty}^\infty \frac{e^{ax}}{e^x + 1} dx = \int_0^\infty \frac{t^{a-1}}{1 + t} dt$$

$$= \pi \operatorname{cosec} a\pi, \quad (0 < a < 1) \qquad \qquad (Mithila\ 2001,\ 2005)$$

Solution. Consider $\displaystyle\int_C f(z)\,dz$

where

$$f(z) = \frac{e^{az}}{1 + e^z}$$

taking the contour C as the perimeter of a rectangle whose sides are the lines, real axis, $x = \pm R$ and $y = 2\pi$.

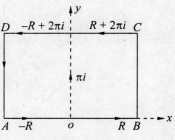

The poles of $f(z)$ are given by $1 + e^z = 0$,

i.e., $e^z = -1 = e^{i(2n+1)\pi}$

i.e., $z = i(2n + 1)\pi$

where $n = 0, \pm 1, \pm 2.$

Out of these poles only the simple pole $z = \pi i$ lies within the contour.

At $z = \pi i$, the residue $\quad = \left[\dfrac{e^{az}}{(d / dz)(1 + e^z)} \right]_{z = \pi i}$

$$= -e^{a\pi i}$$

Hence by Cauchy's residue theorem,

$$\int_C f(z)\,dz = 2\pi i\, \Sigma R^+$$

Fig. 11.20

$$\int_{-R}^{R} f(x)\,dx + \int_{0}^{2\pi} f(R+iy)\,i\,dy + \int_{R}^{-R} f(x+2\pi i)\,dx + \int_{2\pi}^{0} f(-R+iy)\,i\,dy = 2\pi i\,(-e^{a\pi i}) \quad \dots(1)$$

But
$$\left| \int_{0}^{2\pi} f(R+iy)\,i\,dy \right| \le \int_{0}^{2\pi} |f(R+iy)|\,|i\,dy|$$

$$= \int_{0}^{2\pi} \left| \frac{e^{a(R+iy)}}{1+e^{R+iy}} \right| |dy|$$

$$\le \int_{0}^{2\pi} \frac{|e^{a(R+iy)}|}{|e^{R+iy}|-1}\,dy$$

$$\le \int_{0}^{2\pi} \frac{e^{aR}}{e^{R}-1}\,dy$$

$$= \frac{e^{aR}}{e^{R}-1}\,2\pi = \frac{2\pi}{e^{(1-a)R} - e^{-aR}} \to 0 \text{ as } R \to \infty \text{ since } 0 < a < 1.$$

Similarly
$$\left| \int_{2\pi}^{0} f(-R+iy)\,i\,dy \right|$$

$$\le \frac{e^{-aR}}{1-e^{-R}}\,2\pi = \frac{2\pi}{e^{aR} - e^{-(1-a)R}}$$

which $\to 0$ as $R \to \infty$ since $0 < a < 1$.

Hence when $R \to \infty$, relation (1) reduces to

$$\int_{-\infty}^{\infty} f(x)\,dx + \int_{\infty}^{-\infty} f(x+2\pi i)\,dx = -2\pi i\,e^{a\pi i}$$

i.e.,
$$\int_{-\infty}^{\infty} \frac{e^{ax}}{e^{x}+1} - \int_{-\infty}^{\infty} \frac{e^{a(x+2\pi i)}}{e^{x+2\pi i}+1}\,dx = -2\pi i\,e^{a\pi i}$$

or
$$\int_{-\infty}^{\infty} \frac{e^{ax}}{e^{x}+1}\,dx - \int_{-\infty}^{\infty} \frac{e^{2a\pi i}\,e^{ax}}{e^{x}+1}\,dx = -2\pi i\,e^{a\pi i}$$

or
$$(1-e^{2a\pi i}) \int_{-\infty}^{\infty} \frac{e^{ax}}{e^{x}+1}\,dx = -2\pi i\,e^{a\pi i}$$

or
$$\int_{-\infty}^{\infty} \frac{e^{ax}\,dx}{e^{x}+1} = -\frac{2\pi i\,e^{a\pi i}}{1-e^{2a\pi i}}$$

$$= \frac{2i\pi}{e^{a\pi i}-e^{-a\pi i}} = \frac{\pi}{\sin a\pi}$$

Putting $e^{x} = t$, so that $e^{x}\,dx = dt$

or
$$dx = \frac{dt}{t}$$

$$\therefore \quad \int\limits_{-\infty}^{\infty} \frac{e^{ax}\,dx}{e^x + 1} = \int\limits_{0}^{\infty} \frac{t^{a-1}}{1 + t}\,dt$$

Hence,
$$\int\limits_{-\infty}^{\infty} \frac{e^{ax}}{e^x + 1}\,dx = \int\limits_{0}^{\infty} \frac{t^{a-1}}{1 + t}\,dt = \frac{\pi}{\sin a\pi}.$$

5. *By integrating* $\dfrac{e^{ia\,z^2}}{\sin h\,\pi z}$ *round the rectangle with vertices* $\pm R, \pm \dfrac{1}{2}i$, *show that*

$$\int\limits_{0}^{\infty} \frac{\cos(ax^2)\cosh(ax)}{\cosh \pi x}\,dx = \frac{1}{2}\cos\left(\frac{1}{4}a\right)$$

and
$$\int\limits_{0}^{\infty} \frac{\sin(ax^2)\cosh(ax)}{\cosh \pi x}\,dx = \frac{1}{2}\sin\left(\frac{1}{4}a\right), \qquad (0 < a < 1).$$

Solution. Consider the integral $\displaystyle\int\limits_{C} f(z)\,dz$

where
$$f(z) = \frac{e^{ia\,z^2}}{\sinh \pi z}$$

taken round the closed contour C, consisting of the perimeter of the given rectangle.

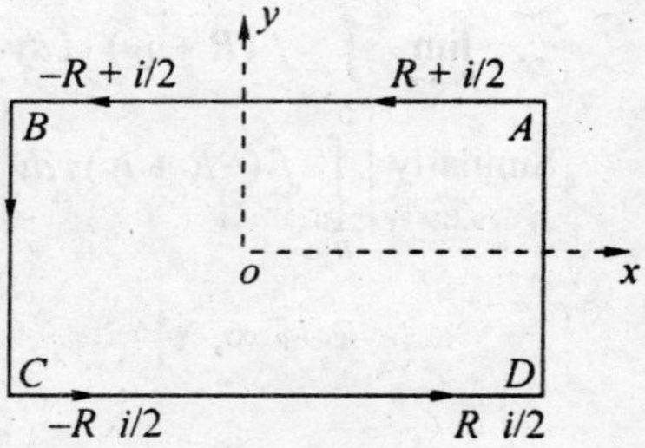

Poles of $f(x)$ are given by $\sinh \pi z = 0$,

i.e., by $e^{\pi z} - e^{-\pi z} = 0$ or $e^{2\pi z} = 1 = e^{2n\pi i}$

or $\qquad z = ni\,(n = 0, \pm 1, \pm 2, \ldots\ldots)$

Fig. 11.21

The only pole which lies within the contour is $z = 0$,

Residue at $z = 0$ is $\left\{\dfrac{e^{iaz}}{\dfrac{d}{dz}(\sinh \pi z)}\right\}_{z=0}$

$$= \left\{\frac{e^{iaz^2}}{\pi \cosh \pi z}\right\}_{z=0} = \frac{1}{\pi}.$$

Hence by Cauchy's residue theorem, we have

$$\int\limits_{C} f(z)\,dz = 2\pi i\, \Sigma R^+$$

or $\displaystyle\int\limits_{AB} f(z)\,dz + \int\limits_{BC} f(z)\,dz + \int\limits_{CD} f(z)\,dz + \int\limits_{DA} f(z)\,dz$

$$= 2\pi i \cdot \frac{1}{\pi}$$

or $\displaystyle\int\limits_{R}^{-R} f\left(x + \frac{i}{2}\right)dx + \int\limits_{1/2}^{-1/2} f(-R + iy)\,i\,dy + \int\limits_{-R}^{R} f\left(x - \frac{i}{2}\right)dx + \int\limits_{-1/2}^{1/2} f(R + iy)\,i\,dy$

$$= 2i \qquad\qquad\qquad \ldots(1)$$

Now, $\left| \int\limits_{-1/2}^{1/2} f(R + iy) \cdot i \, dy \right| \leq \int\limits_{-1/2}^{1/2} \left| \frac{\left| e^{ia(R+iy)^2} \right|}{\left| \dfrac{e^{\pi(R+iy)} - e^{-\pi(R+iy)}}{2} \right|} \right| dy$

$\leq 2 \int\limits_{-1/2}^{1/2} \frac{e^{-2aRy}}{e^{\pi R} - e^{-\pi R}} \, dy$

$= \frac{1}{aR(e^{\pi R} - e^{-\pi R})}(e^{aR} - e^{-aR})$

$= \frac{(1 - e^{-2aR})}{aR \, e^{(\pi-a)R}(1 - e^{-2\pi R})}$ which $\to 0$

as $R \to \infty$. (because $0 < a \leq 1$)

$\therefore \lim\limits_{R \to \infty} \int\limits_{-1/2}^{1/2} f(R + iy) \cdot i \, dy = 0.$

Similarly $\lim\limits_{R \to \infty} \int\limits_{1/2}^{-1/2} f(-R + iy) \cdot i \, dy = 0$

$\therefore$ when $R \to \infty$, (1) becomes

$$\int\limits_{\infty}^{-\infty} f\left(x + \frac{i}{2}\right) dx + \int\limits_{-\infty}^{\infty} f\left(x - \frac{i}{2}\right) dx = 2i$$

or $\displaystyle\int\limits_{\infty}^{-\infty} \frac{e^{ia(x+i/2)^2}}{\frac{1}{2}[e^{\pi(x+i/2)} - e^{-\pi(x+i/2)}]} dx + \int\limits_{-\infty}^{\infty} \frac{e^{ia(x-i/2)^2} dx}{\frac{1}{2}\{e^{\pi(x-i/2)} - e^{-\pi(x-i/2)}\}} = 2i$

or $\displaystyle\int\limits_{\infty}^{-\infty} \frac{2e^{ia(x^2-1/4)}e^{-ax}}{i(e^{\pi x} + e^{-\pi x})} dx + \int\limits_{-\infty}^{\infty} \frac{2 e^{ia(x^2-1/4)} \cdot e^{ax}}{i(-e^{\pi x} - e^{-\pi x})} dx = 2i$

$\because \qquad\qquad e^{i\pi/2} = \cos\frac{\pi}{2} + i \sin\frac{\pi}{2} = i$

and $\qquad\qquad e^{-i\pi/2} = \cos\pi/2 - i\sin\pi/2 = -i$

or $\displaystyle\int\limits_{\infty}^{-\infty} \frac{e^{ia(x^2-1/4)} \cdot e^{-ax}}{i \cosh \pi x} dx - \int\limits_{-\infty}^{\infty} \frac{e^{ia(x^2-1/4)} \cdot e^{ax}}{i \cosh \pi x} dx = 2i$

or $\displaystyle i \int\limits_{-\infty}^{\infty} \frac{e^{ia(x^2-1/4)} \cdot (e^{ax} + e^{-ax})}{\cosh \pi x} dx = 2i$

or $\displaystyle\int\limits_{-\infty}^{\infty} \frac{e^{iax^2} \cdot 2\cos h\,ax}{\cos h\,\pi x} dx = 2e^{ia/4}$

or
$$\int_0^\infty \frac{(\cos ax^2 + i \sin ax^2) \cosh ax}{\cosh \pi x} dx = \frac{1}{2}\left[\cos\left(\frac{a}{4}\right) + i \sin\left(\frac{a}{4}\right)\right]$$

Equating real and imaginary parts, we have

$$\int_0^\infty \frac{\cos(ax^2)\cosh(ax)\,dx}{\cosh \pi x} = \frac{1}{2}\cos(a/4)$$

or
$$\int_0^\infty \frac{\sin(ax^2)\cosh(ax)}{\cosh \pi x} = \frac{1}{2}\sin\left(\frac{a}{4}\right).$$

6. *By contour integration prove that*

$$\int_0^\infty \frac{\cos x}{\sqrt{x}} dx = \sqrt{\left(\frac{\pi}{2}\right)} = \int_0^\infty \frac{\sin x}{\sqrt{x}} dx \qquad (Garhwal\ 2002;\ Lucknow\ 2004)$$

Solution. Consider $\int_C f(z)\,dz$

where
$$f(z) = \frac{e^{iz}}{\sqrt{z}}.$$

The only singularity of $f(z)$ is at $z = 0$.

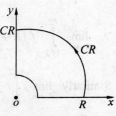

Fig. 11.22

Take the contour C consisting of a positive quadrant of a large circle $|z| = R$, its bounding radii (taken as two axes), indented at $z = 0$, and let r be the radius of indentation at $z = 0$.

Thus, there is no singularity of $f(z)$ inside the given contour.

Hence by Cauchy's residue theorem, we have

$$\int_r^R f(x)\,dx + \int_{C_R} f(z)\,dz + \int_R^r f(iy)\,i\,dy + \int_{c_r} f(z)\,dz = 0 \qquad \text{...(1)}$$

Now
$$\left|\int_{C_R} f(z)\,dz\right| \le \int_{C_R} |f(z)||dz|$$

$$= \int_{C_R} \frac{|e^{iz}||dz|}{|\sqrt{z}|}$$

$$= \int_0^{\pi/2} \frac{e^{-R\sin\theta}}{\sqrt{R}} R\,d\theta, \text{ since } |dz| = R\,d\theta$$

$$\le \frac{R}{\sqrt{R}} \int_0^{\pi/2} e^{-2R\theta/\pi}d\theta \text{ by Jordan's inequality}$$

$$= -\frac{\pi R}{2R\sqrt{R}}[e^{-2R\theta/\pi}]_0^{\pi/2}$$

$$= \frac{\pi}{2\sqrt{R}}(1 - e^{-R}) \text{ which} \to 0 \text{ as } R \to \infty$$

Also,
$$\lim_{z \to 0} z f(z) = \lim_{z \to 0} z\frac{e^{iz}}{\sqrt{z}} = 0$$

$$\therefore \qquad \lim_{r \to 0} \int_{C_r} f(z)\, dz = -i\left(\frac{\pi}{2} - 0\right)0 = 0$$

the negative sign is taken because integral along C_r is in clockwise direction.

Hence making $R \to \infty, r \to 0$, the relation (1) reduces to

$$\int_0^\infty f(x)\, dx + \int_\infty^0 f(iy)\, i\, dy = 0$$

i.e.,
$$\int_0^\infty \frac{e^{ix}}{\sqrt{x}}\, dx + \int_\infty^0 \frac{e^{-y}}{\sqrt{(iy)}}\, i\, dy = 0$$

i.e.,
$$\int_0^\infty \frac{e^{ix}}{\sqrt{x}}\, dx = \int_0^\infty \frac{e^{-y}}{\sqrt{(iy)}}\, i\, dy$$

$$= 2\sqrt{i} \int_0^\infty e^{-t^2}\, dt, \text{ putting } y = t^2$$

$$= 2\sqrt{i}\, \frac{\sqrt{\pi}}{2}, \text{ since } \int_0^\infty e^{-x^2}\, dx = \frac{\sqrt{\pi}}{2}$$

$$= (e^{\pi i/2})^{1/2} \sqrt{\pi} = \sqrt{\pi}\, (e^{\pi i/4})$$

Equating real and imaginary parts we have

$$\int_0^\infty \frac{\cos x}{\sqrt{x}}\, dx = \sqrt{\pi} \cos \frac{\pi}{4}$$

and
$$\int_0^\infty \frac{\sin x}{\sqrt{x}} = \sqrt{\pi} \sin \frac{\pi}{4}$$

or
$$\int_0^\infty \frac{\cos x}{\sqrt{x}}\, dx = \sqrt{\left(\frac{\pi}{2}\right)} = \int_0^\infty \frac{\sin x}{\sqrt{x}}\, dx$$

7. *Evaluate*

$$\int_0^\infty \sin x^2\, dx, \quad \int_0^\infty \cos x^2\, dx.$$

Solution. We take a contour C consisting of three parts C_1, C_2, C_3 where C_2 is given by

$$|z| = R,\ 0 \le \arg z \le \pi/4$$

and consider the integral

$$\int_C e^{-z^2}\, dz.$$

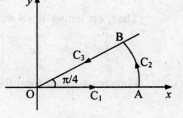

Fig. 11.23

The integrand being analytic we have

$$0 = \int_C e^{-z^2}\, dz = \int_{C_1} e^{-z^2}\, dz + \int_{C_2} e^{-z^2}\, dz + \int_{C_3} e^{-z^2}\, dz.$$

Along C_1, $z = x$ varies from 0 to R so that

$$\int_{C_1} e^{-z^2}\, dz = \int_0^R e^{-x^2}\, dx.$$

Along C_2, $z = R\left(\cos\frac{1}{2}\theta + i\sin\frac{1}{2}\theta\right)$

where θ varies from 0 to $\pi/2$.

$$\therefore \quad \int_{C_2} e^{-z^2}\, dz = \int_0^{\pi/2} e^{-R^2(\cos\theta + i\sin\theta)}\,\frac{i}{2}\,Re^{i\theta/2}\, d\theta$$

$$= \frac{iR}{2}\int_0^{\pi/2} e^{-R^2\cos\theta}\cdot e^{-R^2 i\sin\theta}\cdot e^{i\theta/2}\, d\theta$$

$$\therefore \quad \int_{C_2} |e^{-z^2}\, dz \le \frac{R}{2}\int_0^{\pi/2} e^{-R^2\cos\theta}\, d\theta_e$$

$$= \frac{R}{2}\int_0^{\pi/2} e^{-R^2\sin\theta}\, d\theta$$

$$\le \frac{R}{2}\int_0^{\pi/2} e^{\frac{-2R^2\theta}{\pi}}\, d\theta \qquad \textbf{(By Jordan's Lemma)}$$

$$= \frac{R}{2}\cdot\frac{\pi}{2R^2}(1 - e^{-R^2}) \to 0 \text{ as } R \to \infty.$$

Along C_3, $z = r\left(\cos\frac{\pi}{4} + i\sin\frac{\pi}{4}\right)$

where z varies from R to 0.

$$\therefore \quad \int_{C_3} e^{-z^2}\, dz = \int_R^0 e^{-ir^2}\left(\cos\frac{\pi}{4} + i\sin\frac{\pi}{4}\right) dr.$$

Thus, on letting $R \to \infty$, we obtain

$$\int_0^\infty e^{-x^2}\, dx - \int_0^\infty e^{-ir^2}\left(\cos\frac{\pi}{4} + i\sin\frac{\pi}{4}\right) dr = 0.$$

Further we know from Real Variables,

$$\int_0^\infty e^{-x^2}\, dx = \frac{\sqrt{\pi}}{2}.$$

$$\therefore \quad \left(\cos\frac{\pi}{4} + i\sin\frac{\pi}{4}\right)\int_0^\infty e^{-ir^2}\, dr = \frac{\sqrt{\pi}}{2}$$

$$\Rightarrow \qquad \int_0^\infty e^{-ir^2}\, dr = \frac{\sqrt{\pi}}{2}\left(\cos\frac{\pi}{4} - i\sin\frac{\pi}{4}\right).$$

Equating the real and imaginary parts, we obtain

$$\int_0^\infty \cos r^2 \, dr = \frac{1}{2}\sqrt{\frac{\pi}{2}}, \quad \int_0^\infty \sin r^2 \, dr = \frac{1}{2}\sqrt{\frac{\pi}{2}}.$$

8. *By integrating*

$$\frac{e^{az}}{e^{-2ix}-1}$$

round a suitable contour, prove that

$$\int_0^\infty \frac{\sin ax}{e^{2x}-1}\,dx = \frac{\pi}{4}\coth\left(\frac{\pi a}{2}\right) - \frac{1}{2a}.$$

Solution. Let

$$f(z) = \frac{e^{az}}{e^{-2iz}-1}.$$

Poles of $f(z)$ are given by

$$e^{-2iz}-1 = 0 \text{ or } e^{-2iz} = 1 = e^{2n\pi i}.$$

This $\Rightarrow -2iz = 2n\pi i \Rightarrow z = -n\pi$, where $n = 0, \pm 1, \pm 2, \ldots..$

The two simple poles $z = 0$, $z = \pi$ lie on the x-axis and so we avoid it by indentation.

Consider the integral $\int_C f(z)\,dz$ where C is the perimeter of the rectangle OABC indented at O and A as shown in the figure below. Let r_1 and r_2 be radii of indentation at $z = 0$, $z = \pi$ respectively; $f(z)$ has no singularity within C and so by Cauchy's residue theorem,

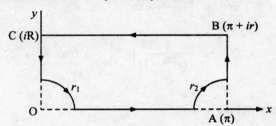

Fig. 11.24

$$\int_C f(z)\,dz = 2\pi i \cdot (\text{Sum of residues within C})$$

or
$$\int_{r_1}^{\pi-r_1} f(x)\,dx + \int_{\gamma_2} f(z)\,dz + \int_{r_2}^{R} f(\pi+iy)\,i\,dy + \int_\pi^b f(x+iR)\,dx$$

$$+ \int_R^{r_1} f(iy)\,i\,dy + \int_{\gamma_1} f(z)\,dz = 0 \qquad \ldots(1)$$

$$\lim_{z \to 0} z\,f(z) = \lim_{z \to 0} \frac{z e^{ax}}{e^{-2iz}-1}, \quad \left[\text{form } \frac{0}{0}\right]$$

$$= \lim_{z \to 0} \frac{e^{az} + z e^{az}}{-2ie^{-2iz}} = \frac{1}{-2i}.$$

∴ By Theorem 6,

$$\lim_{r_1 \to 0} \int_{\gamma_1} f(z)\, dz = -i\left(\frac{\pi}{2} - 0\right)\left(-\frac{1}{2i}\right) = \frac{\pi}{4} \qquad \qquad ...(2)$$

$$\lim_{z \to \pi} (z - \pi) f(z) = \lim_{z \to \pi} \frac{(z - \pi)\, e^{az}}{e^{-2iz} - 1}, \quad \left[\text{form } \frac{0}{0}\right]$$

$$= \frac{e^{az} + a\,(z - \pi)\, e^{az}}{-2ie^{-2iz}}$$

$$= \frac{e^{\pi a}}{-2ie^{-2\pi i}} = \frac{e^{\pi a}}{-2i}.$$

∴ By Theorem 6,

$$\lim_{r_2 \to 0} \int_{\gamma_2} f(z)\, dz = -i\left(\frac{\pi}{2} - 0\right) \frac{e^{\pi a}}{-2i}$$

$$= \frac{\pi}{4} e^{\pi a} \qquad \qquad ...(3)$$

$$\int_\pi^0 f(x + iR)\, dx = \int_\pi^0 \frac{e^{a(x + iR)}}{e^{-2i(x + iR)} - 1}\, dx = -\int_0^\pi \frac{e^{ax} \cdot e^{iaR}}{e^{2R} \cdot e^{-2ix} - 1}\, dx$$

$$\left| \int_\pi^0 f(x + iR)\, dx \right| \leq \int_0^\pi \frac{e^{ax}}{e^{2R} - 1}\, dx$$

$$= \frac{1}{a\,(e^{2R} - 1)} \left[e^{ax} \right]_0^\pi \to 0 \text{ as } R \to \infty.$$

$$\therefore \qquad \lim_{R \to \infty} \int_\pi^0 f(\pi + iR)\, dx = 0. \qquad \qquad ...(4)$$

Making $r_1 \to 0$, $r_2 \to 0$, $R \to \infty$ in (1), we get by virtue of (2), (3) and (4)

$$\int_0^\pi f(x)\, dx + \frac{\pi}{4} e^{\pi a} + \int_0^\infty f(\pi + iy)\, i\, dy + \int_\infty^0 f(iy)\, i\, dy + \frac{\pi}{4} = 0$$

or $$\int_0^\pi f(x)\, dx + \int_0^\infty f(\pi + iy)\, i\, dy - \int_0^\infty f(iy)\, i\, dy = -\frac{\pi}{4}\,(1 + e^{\pi a}) \qquad ...(5)$$

$$\int_0^\pi f(x)\, dx = \int_0^\pi \frac{e^{ax}}{e^{-2ix} - 1}\, dx = \int_0^\pi \frac{e^{ax} e^{ix}}{e^{2ix} - e^{ix}}\, dx = \int_0^\pi \frac{e^{ax} e^{ix}}{(-2i \sin x)}\, dx$$

$$= \frac{i}{2} \int_0^\pi \frac{e^{ax} e^{ix}}{\sin x}\, dx \qquad \qquad ...(6)$$

$$\int_0^\infty f(\pi + iy) i \, dy = \int_0^\infty \frac{e^{a(\pi + iy)}}{e^i - 2i(\pi + iy) - 1} i \, dy = i \int_0^\infty \frac{e^{\pi a} \cdot e^{iya}}{e^{-2i\pi} \cdot e^{2y} - 1} \, dy$$

or

$$\int_0^\infty f(\pi + iy) i \, dy = i e^{\pi a} \int_0^\infty \frac{e^{iax}}{e^{2x} - 1} \, dx \qquad \qquad \text{...(7)}$$

$$\int_0^\infty f(iy) i \, dy = \int_0^\infty \frac{e^{aiy}}{e^{2y} - 1} i \, dy = \int_0^\infty \frac{e^{iax}}{e^{2x} - 1} \, dx \qquad \text{...(8)}$$

Writing (5) with the help of (6), (7) and (8),

$$\frac{i}{2} \int_0^\pi \frac{e^{ax} e^{ix}}{\sin x} \, dx + i e^{\pi a} \int_0^\infty \frac{e^{ixa}}{e^{2x} - 1} \, dx - i \int_0^\infty \frac{e^{iax}}{e^{2x} - 1} \, dx = -\frac{\pi}{4}(1 + e^{\pi a}).$$

Equating real parts,

$$\frac{1}{2} \int_0^\pi \frac{e^{ax}(-\sin x)}{\sin x} \, dx + e^{\pi a} \int_0^\infty \frac{-\sin xa}{e^{2x} - 1} \, dx + \int_0^\infty \frac{\sin ax}{e^{2x} - 1} \, dx = -\frac{\pi}{4}(1 + e^{\pi a})$$

or

$$-\frac{1}{2a} \left[e^{ax} \right]_0^\pi + (1 - e^{\pi a}) \int_0^\infty \frac{\sin ax}{e^{2x} - 1} \, dx = -\frac{\pi}{4}(1 + e^{\pi a})$$

or

$$\frac{1}{2a} + \int_0^\infty \frac{\sin ax}{e^{2x} - 1} \, dx = -\frac{\pi}{4} \left(\frac{1 + e^{\pi a}}{1 - e^{\pi a}} \right) = \frac{\pi}{4} \cdot \frac{e^{\pi a/2} + e^{-\pi a/2}}{e^{\pi a/2} - e^{-\pi a/2}}$$

$$= \frac{\pi}{4} \coth \left(\frac{\pi a}{2} \right)$$

or

$$\int_0^\infty \frac{\sin ax}{e^{2x} - 1} \, dx = \frac{\pi}{4} \coth \left(\frac{\pi a}{2} \right) - \frac{1}{2a}.$$

9. *By integrating*

$$\frac{e^{iaz}}{\sinh z}$$

round a suitably indented rectangle with corners at

$$\pm R, \pm R + \pi i,$$

show that

$$\int_0^\infty \frac{\sin ax}{\sinh x} \, dx = \frac{1}{2} \pi \frac{e^{\pi a} - 1}{e^{\pi a} + 1} = \frac{\pi}{2} \tanh \left(\frac{\pi a}{2} \right)$$

if the imaginary part of 'a' lies between − 1 and 1.

Solution. Consider the integral $\int_C f(z) \, dz$,

where $\qquad f(z) = \dfrac{e^{iaz}}{\sinh z}$

taken round the closed contour C, consisting of the perimeter of the given rectangle, indented at $z = 0$ and $z = i\pi$, where the radii of indentation are r' and r respectively.

Poles of $f(z)$ are given by

$$\sinh z = 0, \ i.e., \ e^z - e^{-z} = 0$$

or
$$e^{2z} = 1 = e^{2n\pi i}$$

or
$$z = n\pi i \ (n = 0, \pm 1, \pm 2, \ .....).$$

None of these poles lie within the contour C.

Hence by Cauchy's residue theorem, we have

$$\oint_C f(z) \, dz = 0$$

$$\left[\int_{AB} + \int_{BP} + \int_{C_r} + \int_{QC} + \int_{CD} + \int_{DR} + \int_{C_r'} + \int_{SA} \right] f(z) \, dz = 0$$

...(1)

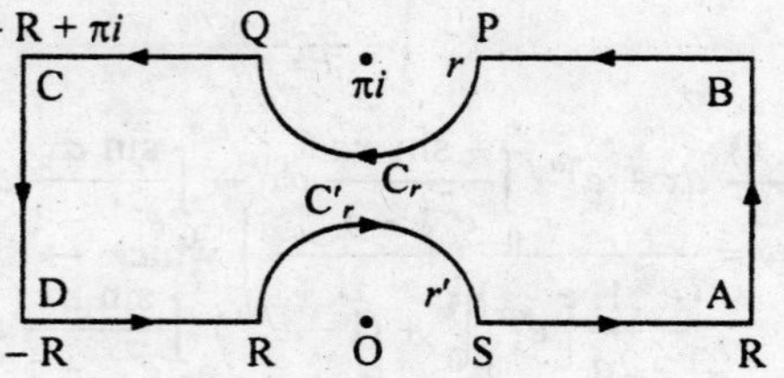

Fig. 11.25

On AB, $z = R + iy$, $dz = i \, dy$;

On CD, $z = -R + iy$, $dz = i \, dy$;

On BP or QC, $z = x + i\pi$, $dz = dx$;

and on DR or SA, $z = x$, $dz = dx$.

∴ From (1), we have

$$\int_0^\pi f(R + iy) \, i \, dy + \int_R^r f(x + i\pi) \, dx + \int_{C_r} f(z) \, dz$$

$$+ \int_{-r}^{-R} f(x + i\pi) \, dx + \int_\pi^0 f(-R + iy) \, i \, dy + \int_{-R}^{r'} f(x) \, dx$$

$$+ \int_{C_r'} f(z) \, dz + \int_{r'}^R f(x) \, dx = 0$$

...(2)

Now

$$\lim_{z \to 0} z \, f(z) = \lim_{z \to 0} \frac{ze^{iax}}{\sinh z} = \lim_{z \to 0} \frac{ze^{iax}}{z + \dfrac{z^3}{3!} + ...}$$

$$= \lim_{z \to 0} \frac{e^{iaz}}{1 + \dfrac{z^2}{3!} + ...} = 1$$

∴
$$\lim_{r' \to 0} \int_{C_r'} f(z) \, dz = i \, (0 - \pi) \cdot 1 = -i\pi$$

$$\lim_{z \to i\pi} (z - i\pi)\, f(z) = \lim_{z \to i\pi} \frac{(z - i\pi)\, e^{iaz}}{\sinh z} \quad \left[\text{form } \frac{0}{0}\right]$$

$$\lim_{z \to i\pi} \frac{e^{iaz} + (z - i\pi)\, iae^{iaz}}{\cosh z} = \frac{e^{-\pi a}}{\cosh i\pi} = \frac{e^{-\pi a}}{\cos i^2 \pi} = -e^{-\pi a}$$

$$\therefore \qquad \lim_{r \to 0} \int_{C_r} f(z)\, dz = -i\,(2\pi - \pi)\,(-e^{-\pi a}) = \pi i e^{-\pi a}$$

−ve sign is taken as integration along C_r is in clockwise direction.

$$\left| \int_0^\pi f(R + iy)\, i\, dy \right| \le \int_0^\pi |f(R + iy)|\, |i\, dy| = \int_0^\pi \left| \frac{e^{ia(R + iy)}}{\sinh(R + iy)} \right| dy$$

$$= \int_0^\pi \frac{|e^{iaR} \cdot e^{-ay}|}{\frac{1}{2}|e^{(R + iy)} - e^{-(R + iy)}|}\, dy \le \int_0^\pi \frac{2e^{-ay}}{|e^{R + iy}| - |e^{-R - iy}|}\, dy$$

$$= \int_0^\pi \frac{2e^{-ay}}{e^R - e^{-R}}\, dy = \frac{2}{(e^R - e^{-R})}\left(\frac{1 - e^{-a\pi}}{a}\right) \text{ which} \to 0 \text{ as } R \to \infty$$

$$\therefore \qquad \lim_{R \to \infty} \int_0^\pi f(R + iy)\, i\, dy = 0.$$

Similarly $\displaystyle \lim_{R \to \infty} \int_\pi^0 f(-R + iy)\, i\, dy = 0.$

Hence when $r \to 0$, $r' \to 0$, $R \to \infty$, from (2), we have

$$\int_\infty^0 f(x + i\pi)\, dx + \pi i e^{-\pi a} + \int_0^{-\infty} f(x + i\pi)\, dx$$

$$+ \int_{-\infty}^0 f(x)\, dx - i\pi + \int_0^\infty f(x)\, dx = 0$$

or $$\int_{-\infty}^\infty f(x)\, dx - \int_{-\infty}^\infty f(x + i\pi)\, dx = \pi i\,(1 - e^{-\pi a})$$

or $$\int_{-\infty}^\infty \frac{e^{iax}}{\sinh x}\, dx + \int_{-\infty}^\infty \frac{e^{iax} e^{-a\pi}}{\sinh x}\, dx = \pi i\,(1 - e^{-\pi a})$$

$$[\because \sinh(x + i\pi) = \sinh x \cos \pi + i \sin \pi \cosh x = -\sinh x]$$

or $$(1 + e^{-a\pi}) \int_{-\infty}^\infty \frac{e^{iax}}{\sinh x}\, dx = \pi i\,(1 - e^{-\pi a})$$

or $$\int_{-\infty}^\infty \frac{\cos ax + i \sin ax}{\sinh x}\, dx = \frac{i\pi\,(1 - e^{-\pi a})}{(1 + e^{-\pi a})}.$$

Equating imaginary parts, we have

$$\int_{-\infty}^\infty \frac{\sinh ax}{\sinh x}\, dx = \frac{\pi\,(1 - e^{-\pi a})}{(1 + e^{-\pi a})}$$

or
$$\int_0^\infty \frac{\sinh ax}{\sinh x}\, dx = \frac{\pi}{2}\cdot\left(\frac{e^{\pi a}-1}{e^{\pi a}+1}\right)$$

$$= \frac{\pi}{2}\cdot\frac{e^{\pi a/2}-e^{-\pi a/2}}{e^{\pi a/2}+e^{-\pi a/2}} = \frac{\pi}{2}\tanh\left(\frac{\pi a}{2}\right).$$

11.8. To find the residue by knowing the integral first. So far we evaluated integral $\int_C f(z)\, dz$ by knowing first the residue of the function $f(z)$ and then using Cauchy's residue theorem. We now illustrate below that residue of $f(z)$ can be found out by integrating $\int_C f(z)\, dz$ first and then using Cauchy's residue theorem. The following example illustrates it.

Example. *If n be an even positive integer, find the residue of*
$\tan^{n-1}(\pi z)$ at $z = 1/2$.

Solution. Let
$$f(z) = \tan^{n-1}(\pi z) = \left(\frac{\sin \pi z}{\cos \pi z}\right)^{n-1}$$

The pole of $f(z)$ are given by
$$\cos \pi z = 0 \text{ or } e^{i\pi z} = -1 = e^{(2m+1)\pi i}$$

or
$$2i\pi z = (2m+1)\pi i$$

$\therefore$
$$z = \frac{1}{2}(2m+1), \quad m = 0, \pm 1, \pm 2, ...$$

When $m = 0$, the pole is $z = 1/2$.

Take the rectangular contour C whose sides are $x = 0$, $x = 1$ and $y = \pm R$; then $z = 1/2$ is the only pole which lies inside the contour.

Hence by Cauchy's residue theorem, we have
$$\int_C f(z)\, dz = 2\pi i \,\Sigma R^+$$

or
$$\int_{AB} f(z)\, dz + \int_{BC} f(z)\, dz + \int_{CD} f(z)\, dz + \int_{DA} f(z)\, dz$$
$$= 2\pi i\left(\text{residue at } z = \frac{1}{2}\right)$$

or
$$\int_0^1 f(x-iR)\, dx + \int_{-R}^R f(1+iy)\, i\, dy + \int_1^0 f(x+iR)\, dx + \int_R^{-R} f(iy)\, i\, dy$$
$$= 2\pi i\left(\text{residue at } z = \frac{1}{2}\right)$$

or
$$\int_0^1 \tan^{-1}\pi(x-iR)\, dx + \int_{-R}^R \tan^{n-1}[\pi(1+iy)]\, i\, dy$$

$$+ \int_1^0 \tan^{n-1}\pi(x+iR)\, dx + \int_R^{-R} \tan^{n-1}(\pi iy)\, i\, dy$$

$$= 2\pi i\left(\text{residue at } z = \frac{1}{2}\right) \quad ...(1)$$

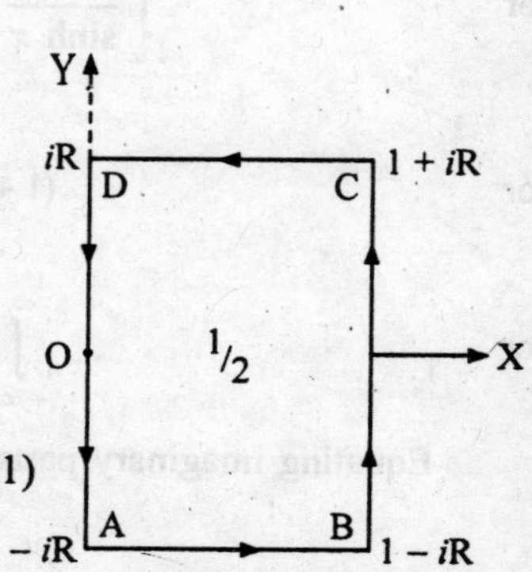

Now

Fig. 11.26

$$\int_0^1 \tan^{n-1} \pi (x - iR) \, dx = \int_0^1 \left[\frac{e^{i\pi(x-iR)} - e^{-i\pi(x-iR)}}{ie^{i\pi(x-iR)} + e^{-i\pi(x-iR)}} \right]^{n-1} dx$$

$$= \left(\frac{1}{i}\right)^{n-1} \int_0^1 \left[\frac{1 - e^{-2\pi ix} e^{-2\pi R}}{1 + e^{-2\pi ix} e^{-2\pi R}} \right]^{n-1} dx$$

$$= \left(\frac{1}{i}\right)^{n-1} \int_0^1 \left(\frac{1}{1}\right) dx \text{ as } R \to \infty$$

$$= \left(\frac{1}{i}\right)^{n-1}$$

Similarly

$$\int_1^0 \tan^{n-1} \pi (x + iR) \, dx = \int_1^0 \left[\frac{e^{i\pi(x+iR)} - e^{-i\pi(x+iR)}}{i\{e^{i\pi(x+iR)} + e^{-i\pi(x+iR)}\}} \right]^{n-1} dx$$

$$= \left(\frac{1}{i}\right)^{n-1} \cdot \int_1^0 \left[\frac{e^{2ix} e^{-2\pi R} - 1}{e^{2ix} e^{-2\pi R} + 1} \right]^{n-1} dx$$

$$= \left(\frac{1}{i}\right)^{n-1} \int_1^0 \left(\frac{-1}{1}\right)^{n-1} dx \text{ as } R \to \infty$$

$$= \left(\frac{1}{i}\right)^{n-1} \cdot (-1)^n.$$

$\therefore$ From (1), we have

$$\left(\frac{1}{i}\right)^{n-1} + \int_{-R}^{R} \tan^{n-1} (i\pi y) \cdot i \, dy + (-1)^n \left(\frac{1}{i}\right)^{n-1} - \int_{-R}^{R} \tan^{n-1} (\pi iy) \, i \, dy$$

$$= 2\pi i \left(\text{residue at } z = \frac{1}{2} \right)$$

or

$$\left(\frac{1}{i}\right)^{n-1} [1 + (-1)^{n-1}] = 2\pi i \left(\text{residue at } z = \frac{1}{2} \right)$$

or

$$\left(\frac{1}{i}\right)^{n-1} 2 = 2\pi i \left(\text{residue at } z = \frac{1}{2} \right) \qquad [\because \ n \text{ is even}]$$

Hence residue at $z = 1/2$ is

$$= \frac{2}{2\pi i} \left(\frac{1}{i}\right)^{n-1} = \frac{1}{\pi} \left(\frac{1}{i}\right)^n = \frac{(-1)^{n/2}}{\pi} \text{ since } n \text{ is even.}$$

11.9. Summation of infinite series. We shall now illustrate by means of an example as to how the calculus of residues can be applied to the determination of the sums of a type of infinite series.

Example. *Prove that the function sec z is bounded in the domain outside the circles*

$$\left| z - \left(n + \frac{1}{2} \pi \right) \right| = \varepsilon; \ n = 0, \pm 1, \pm 2, \ldots..$$

By the method of contour integration, prove that

$$\frac{1}{1^3} + \frac{1}{3^3} + \frac{1}{5^3} + \ldots = \frac{\pi^3}{32}.$$

Solution. The only singularities of sec z are the points

$$\left(n + \frac{1}{2}\right)\pi; \quad n = 0, \pm 1, \pm 2, \ldots$$

and these are simple poles.

We have

$$
\begin{aligned}
|\sec z| &= \frac{2}{|e^{iz} + e^{-iz}|} \\
&= \frac{2}{|e^{i(x+iy)} + e^{-i(x+iy)}|} \\
&\leq \frac{2}{\left||e^{i(x+iy)}| - |e^{-i(x+iy)}|\right|} \\
&= \frac{2}{|e^{-y} - e^{y}|} = \text{cosech}\,|y| \qquad \ldots(1)
\end{aligned}
$$

Also we have

$$\text{cosech}\,|y| < \text{cosech}\,|a|, \text{ if } |y| > |a| \qquad \ldots(2)$$

From (1) and (2), we deduce that

$|\sec z| < \text{cosech}\,|a|$, if I $(z) > |a|$.

Consider now the closed triply connected domain bounded by

$$R(z) = \pm\,\pi, \quad I(z) = \pm\,|a|,$$

$$\left|z - \frac{1}{2}\pi\right| = \varepsilon, \quad \left|z + \frac{1}{2}\pi\right| = \varepsilon.$$

Here, a, is any given real number and ε is any positive number less than $|a|$.

The function sec z is bounded in this domain, as the function is continuous in the same. Thus there exists a number $k > 0$ such that

$$|\sec z| < k$$

for every point z of this domain.

Also as $|\sec z|$ is periodic with period π, we see that

$$|\sec z| < k$$

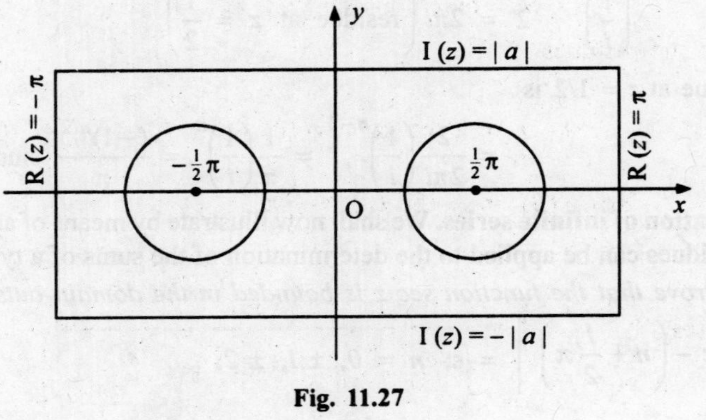

Fig. 11.27

for every point z in the domain bounded by

$$I(z) = \pm |a|,$$

$$\left| z - \left(n + \frac{1}{2} \pi \right) \right| = \varepsilon; \quad n = 0, \pm 1, \pm 2, \dots$$

Thus we see that

$$|\sec z| < \max. (\text{cosech } |a|, k)$$

in the domain outside the circles

$$\left| z - \left(n + \frac{1}{2} \pi \right) \right| = \varepsilon; \quad n = 0, \pm 1, \pm 2, \dots$$

Let C_n denote the contour

$$|z| = \rho_n,$$

where $\rho_n = n$; n being any positive integer.

We now consider

$$f(z) = \frac{\pi \sec \pi z}{z^3},$$

and see that the only singular points of this function are

$$0, \pm \frac{1}{2}, \pm \frac{3}{2}, \dots$$

none of which lies on C_n.

By Cauchy's residue theorem, we have

$$\frac{1}{2\pi i} \int_{C_n} f(z)\, dz = \text{Res.} (0) + \Sigma \text{ Res.} \left(\frac{2m+1}{2} \right) \qquad \dots(3)$$

where the summation extends to all the poles, other than 0, in the interior of C_n.

We have

$$\left| \int_{C_n} f(z)\, dz \right| = \left| \int_{C_n} \frac{\pi \sec \pi z}{z^3}\, dz \right|$$

$$\leq \frac{\pi M}{\rho_n^3} 2\pi \rho_n, \text{ which} \to 0 \text{ as } n \to \infty$$

Here

$$M = \max. (\text{cosech } |a|, k).$$

We now find the residues.

If

$$\varphi(z) = \pi \sec \pi z = \varphi(0) + z\, \varphi'(0) + \frac{z^2}{2!} \varphi''(0) + \dots$$

then

$$\text{Res.}_f (0) = \frac{1}{2!} \varphi''(0) = \frac{1}{2} \pi^3.$$

Also

$$\text{Res.}_f \left(\frac{2m+1}{2} \right) = \frac{\pi}{\left(\dfrac{2m+1}{2} \right)^3 \left[-\pi \sin \left(\pi + \dfrac{2m+1}{2} \right) \right]}$$

$$= - \frac{8(-1)^m}{(2m+1)^3}.$$

Letting n, tending to infinity in (3), we obtain

$$0 = \frac{1}{2} \pi^3 - 8 \left[\frac{2}{1^3} - \frac{2}{3^3} + \frac{2}{5^3} - \ldots \right]$$

$$\Rightarrow \qquad \frac{1}{1^3} - \frac{1}{3^3} + \frac{1}{5^3} - \frac{1}{7^3} + \ldots = \frac{\pi}{32}.$$

11.10. Expansion of a Meromorphic Function.

Theorem. *Mittag - Leffer's Expension Theorem. Let $f(z)$ be a function whose only singularities, except at infinity, are simple poles at $z = a_1$, $z = a_2$, $z = a_3$, ..., $z = a_n$, where*

$$0 < |a_1| < |a_2| < |a_3| < \ldots < |a_n|$$

and let b_1, b_2, b_3, ..., b_n, be respectively the residues of these poles. Let there be a sequence of closed contours, either circles or squares C_1, C_2, C_3, ... such that

(i) *The contour C_n encloses the poles a_1, a_2, a_3, ..., a_n, but no other poles.*

(ii) *The contour C_n must be such that minimum distance R_n of C_n from origin tends to infinity as n tends to infinity.*

(iii) *Length L_n of the contour C_n is $O(R_n)$, i.e.,*

$$L_n = \lambda R_n \text{ when } n \to \infty.$$

(iv) *On C_n, $f(z) = O(R_n)$, or $\dfrac{f(z)}{R_n} = 0$ when $n \to \infty$.*

(v) *$f(z)$ were bounded on the whole system of contours C_n.*

If these conditions are satisfied, then

$$f(z) = f(0) + \sum_{n=1}^{\infty} b_n \left(\frac{1}{z - a_n} + \frac{1}{a_n} \right)$$

for all z except at poles.

Let

$$I = \int_{C_n} \frac{f(\xi)}{\xi(\xi - z)} d\xi \qquad \ldots(1)$$

where z is a point inside C_n. The poles of the integrand are at the values of ξ for which

$$f(\xi) = \infty \text{ and } \xi(\xi - z) = 0.$$

But $f(\xi) = \infty$ at $\xi = a_1, a_2, ..., a_n$.   (By hypothesis)

Hence poles of $\dfrac{f(\xi)}{\xi(\xi - z)}$ inside C_n are $\xi = a_m$ ($m = 1, 2, 3, ..., n$) and $\xi = z$ and at $\xi = 0$.

Residue at $\xi = a_m$ is

$$\lim_{\xi \to a_m} (\xi - a_m) \frac{f(\xi)}{\xi(\xi - z)} = \frac{b_m}{a_m(a_m - z)}$$

[since b_m being residue of $f(\xi)$ at $\xi = a_m$ is
given by $b_m = \lim_{\xi \to a_m} \{(\xi - a_m) f(\xi)\}$]

Also, residue at $\xi = z$ is

$$\lim_{\xi \to z} (\xi - z) \frac{f(\xi)}{\xi (\xi - z)} = \frac{f(z)}{z}$$

and residue at $\xi = 0$ is

$$\lim_{\xi \to 0} \frac{\xi f(\xi)}{\xi (\xi - z)} = \frac{f(0)}{-z}.$$

Hence by Cauchy's residue theorem, we have

$$I = 2\pi i \times \text{sum of residues inside whole system } C_n$$

$$= 2\pi i \left[\left\{ \sum_{m=1}^{n} \frac{b_m}{a_m (a_m - z)} \right\} - \frac{f(0)}{z} + \frac{f(z)}{z} \right] \qquad \text{...(2)}$$

If now we can prove that $I \to 0$ as $n \to \infty$, the theorem is proved.

Now from (1),

$$|I| = \left| \int_{C_n} \frac{f(\xi)}{\xi (\xi - z)} d\xi \right|$$

$$\leq \frac{M_n}{R_n (R_n - |z|)} \int_{C_n} |d\xi|$$

where max. $|f(\xi)| = M_n a_n C_n$

$$= \frac{M_n}{R_n (R_n - |z|)} \cdot L_n$$

$$= \frac{L_n}{R_n (R_n - |z|)} \cdot M_n$$

$$= 0 \qquad \qquad [\text{since as } n \to \infty, R_n \to \infty]$$

Hence relation (2) becomes

$$0 = \lim_{n \to \infty} \left[\sum_{m=1}^{n} \frac{b_m}{a_m (a_m - z)} \right] - \frac{f(0)}{z} + \frac{f(z)}{z}$$

$$\Rightarrow \qquad f(z) = f(0) + \sum_{n=1}^{\infty} b_n \left(\frac{1}{z - a_n} + \frac{1}{a_n} \right).$$

EXAMPLES

1. *Prove that*

$$\cot z = \frac{1}{z} + 2z \sum_{1}^{\infty} \frac{1}{z^2 - n^2 \pi^2}.$$

Solution. Consider the function

$$f(z) = \cot z = \frac{\cos z}{\sin z}.$$

Poles of $f(z)$ are given by $\sin z = 0 \Rightarrow z = m\pi$ ($m = \pm 1, \pm 2, \ldots\ldots$) are the simple poles.

Let the contour C_n be the square ABCD with centre at the origin, the length of each side $(2n + 1) \pi$, so that its vertices are the points

$$\left(n + \frac{1}{2}\right)(\pm 1 \pm i)\,\pi.$$

Hence poles of $f(z)$ inside C_n are $z = m\pi \; (m = \pm 1; \pm 2, \ldots, \pm n)$.

In this sequence of poles there are two poles $z = n\pi$ and $z = -n\pi$ whose absolute value is greatest compared to those of other poles.

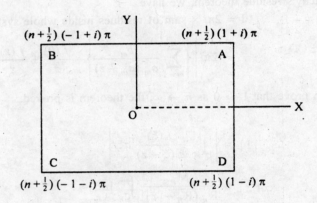

Fig. 11.28

Residue at the poles $z = \pm n\pi$ is

$$\lim_{z \to \pm n\pi}\left[\frac{\cos z}{(d/dz)(\sin z)}\right] = \lim_{z \to \pm n\pi}\left[\frac{\cos z}{\cos z}\right] = 1.$$

Now, the following conditions are satisfied:

(*i*) C_n encloses the poles $z = m\pi \; (m = \pm 1, \pm 2, \ldots, \pm n)$ and no other poles.

(*ii*) The minimum distance R_n of C_n from the origin is $\left(n + \frac{1}{2}\right)\pi$ which tends to infinity as $n \to \infty$.

(*iii*) The length L_n of C_n (the perimeter of the square ABCD) is

$$8n\pi + 4\pi \quad \text{and} \quad R_n = \left(n + \frac{1}{2}\right)\pi;$$

and so $L_n = 8R_n$, *i.e.*, $L_n = O(R_n)$.

(*iv*) $f(z)$ is bounded on C_n, *i.e.*, $f(z)$ is bounded along the perimeter of the square ABCD as shown below:

We have

$$|\cot z| = \left| i\,\frac{e^{iz} + e^{-iz}}{e^{iz} - e^{-iz}} \right|$$

$$= \left| \frac{e^{2iz} + 1}{e^{2iz} - 1} \right| \quad \text{or} \quad \left| \frac{1 + e^{-2iz}}{1 - e^{-2iz}} \right|$$

$$= \left| \frac{e^{2i(x+iy)} + 1}{e^{2i(x+iy)} - 1} \right| \quad \text{or} \quad \left| \frac{1 + e^{-2i(x+iy)}}{1 - e^{-2i(x+iy)}} \right|$$

$$= \left| \frac{1 + e^{-2y + 2ix}}{1 - e^{-2y + 2ix}} \right| \text{ or } \left| \frac{1 + e^{2y - 2ix}}{1 - e^{2y - 2ix}} \right|$$

$$< \frac{1 + e^{-2y}}{1 - e^{-2y}} \text{ or } \frac{1 + e^{2y}}{1 - e^{2y}}$$

to be chosen according as y is positive or negative.

Now, $y = \left(n + \dfrac{1}{2} \right) \pi$ on AB, and $y = -\left(n + \dfrac{1}{2} \right) \pi$ on CD.

$\therefore$ On AB and CD both we have

$$|\cot z| < \frac{1 + e^{-2\left(n + \frac{1}{2}\right)\pi}}{1 - e^{-2\left(n + \frac{1}{2}\right)\pi}}$$

which is finite when n is finite and $\to 1$ as $n \to \infty$, showing that $\cot z$ is bounded on AB and CD. And on AD and BC, y is positive and negative both.

$$\therefore \qquad |\cot z| < \frac{1 + e^{-2y}}{1 - e^{-2y}} \text{ or } \frac{1 + e^{2y}}{1 - e^{2y}}$$

on AD and BC which is finite when y is finite chosen according as y is positive or negative and $\to 1$ as $y \to \infty$ or $-\infty$. As a matter of fact $y = \infty$ when $n = \infty$, showing that $\cot z$ is bounded on AD and BC.

$\therefore$ $\cot z$ is bounded on the contour C_n.

Hence by theorem on expansion of meromorphic functions, we have

$$\cot z = f(0) + \sum_1^\infty b_n \left(\frac{1}{z - a_n} + \frac{1}{a_n} \right)$$

where $b_n = 1$ and $a_n = \pm n\pi$.

$$= [\cot z]_{z=0} + \sum_1^\infty b_n \left(\frac{1}{z - a_n} + \frac{1}{a_n} \right)$$

$$= \left[\frac{1}{z} \cdot \frac{z}{\sin z} \cos z \right]_{z=0} + \sum_1^\infty 1 \cdot \left(\frac{1}{z - n\pi} + \frac{1}{n\pi} \right)$$

$$+ 1 \cdot \left(\frac{1}{z + n\pi} - \frac{1}{n\pi} \right)$$

$$= \frac{1}{z} + \sum_1^\infty \left(\frac{1}{z - n\pi} + \frac{1}{z + n\pi} \right)$$

$$= \frac{1}{z} + \sum_1^\infty \frac{2z}{z - n^2\pi^2}.$$

2. Prove that

$$\frac{1}{e^z - 1} = -\frac{1}{2} + \frac{1}{z} + \sum_{n=1}^\infty \frac{2z}{z^2 + 4n^2\pi^2}.$$

Solution. Let

$$f(z) = \frac{1}{2} \frac{e^z + 1}{e^z - 1}.$$

Poles of $f(z)$ are given by $e^z - 1 = 0$

$$\Rightarrow \qquad e^z = 1 = e^{2m\pi i}$$

$$\therefore \qquad z = 2m\pi i \ (m = 0, \pm 1, \pm 2, \dots).$$

Let the contour C_n be the square ABCD with centre at the origin and length of each side $4\left(n + \frac{1}{2}\right)\pi$, so that its vertices are

$$2\left(n + \frac{1}{2}\right)\pi \, (\pm 1 \pm i).$$

The poles which lie within the contour C_n are

$$z = 2m\pi i \ (m = 0, \pm 1, \pm 2, \pm 3, \dots, \pm n).$$

In this sequence of poles there are two poles $z = 2n\pi i$ and $z = -2n\pi i$ whose absolute value is greatest compared to those of the other poles.

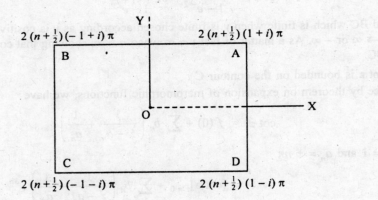

Fig. 11.29

Residue at the pole $z = 2n\pi i$ is

$$\left[\frac{1}{2} \frac{e^z + 1}{\frac{d}{dz}(e^z - 1)}\right]_{z = 2n\pi i} = \frac{1}{2}\left[\frac{e^z + 1}{e^z}\right]_{z = 2n\pi i}$$

$$= \frac{1}{2}\left[1 + e^{-z}\right]_{z = 2n\pi i} = \frac{1}{2}(1 + e^{-2n\pi i})$$

$$= \frac{1}{2}(1 + \cos 2n\pi - i \sin 2n\pi) = 1.$$

Similarly, residue at the pole $z = -2n\pi i$

$$= \frac{1}{2}\left[1 + e^{-z}\right]_{z = -2n\pi i}$$

$$= \frac{1}{2} (1 + e^{2m\pi i}) = 1 \text{ as before.}$$

Now, we see that

(i) The contour C_n encloses the poles $z = 2m\pi i$ ($m = 0, \pm 1, \pm 2, \ldots, \pm n$) and no other poles.

(ii) The minimum distance R_n of C_n from the origin is $2 \left(n + \frac{1}{2} \right) \pi$ which $\to \infty$ as $n \to \infty$.

(iii) The length L_n of C_n is

$$16 \left(n + \frac{1}{2} \right) \pi \text{ and } R_n = 2 \left(n + \frac{1}{2} \right) \pi;$$

so that $L_n = 8R_n$, i.e., $L_n = O(R_n)$.

(iv) $f(z)$ is bounded on the contour C_n as seen below:

We have
$$\left| \frac{1}{2} \frac{e^z + 1}{e^z - 1} \right| = \frac{1}{2} \left| \frac{e^{x+iy} + 1}{e^{x+iy} - 1} \right|$$

$$< \frac{1}{2} \frac{|e^{x+iy}| + 1}{|e^{x-iy}| - 1}$$

$$= \frac{1}{2} \frac{e^x + 1}{e^x - 1} \text{ or } \frac{1}{2} \frac{1 + e^x}{1 - e^{-x}}$$

$$= \frac{1}{2} \frac{1 + e^{-x}}{1 - e^{-x}} \text{ or } \frac{1}{2} \frac{1 + e^x}{1 - e^x}$$

according as x is positive or negative.

We have $x = 2 \left(n + \frac{1}{2} \right) \pi$ on AD, and $x = -2 \left(n + \frac{1}{2} \right) \pi$ on BC.

$\therefore$ On AD and BC both we have

$$\left| \frac{1}{2} \frac{e^z + 1}{e^z - 1} \right| < \frac{1}{2} \frac{1 + e^{-[2(n+1)/2]\pi}}{1 - e^{-[2(n+1)/2]\pi}} \text{ which } \to \frac{1}{2} \text{ as } n \to \infty$$

And on AB and CD both, we have, x positive on the right of the axis of imaginaries, and x negative on the left of it.

$\therefore$ On AB and CD both we have

$$\left| \frac{1}{2} \frac{e^z + 1}{e^z - 1} \right| < \begin{cases} \dfrac{1}{2} \dfrac{1 + e^{-x}}{1 - e^{-x}} & \text{for positive values of } x \\[3mm] \dfrac{1}{2} \dfrac{1 + e^x}{1 - e^x} & \text{for negative values of } x \end{cases}$$

which are finite for finite values of x and tend to $\frac{1}{2}$ as $x \to \infty$ or $-\infty$; as a matter of fact $x \to \infty$ when $n \to \infty$.

Thus, $\dfrac{1}{2} \dfrac{e^z + 1}{e^z - 1}$ is bounded on the contour C_n.

Also, it may be shown that $f(0)$

$$= \left[\frac{1}{2}\left(\frac{e^z + 1}{e^z - 1}\right)\right]_{z=0}$$

$$= \frac{1}{2}\left[\frac{2 + z + \frac{1}{2}z^2 + \ldots}{z + \frac{1}{2}z^2 + \ldots}\right]_{z=0}$$

$$= \left[\frac{1}{2z}\frac{2 + z + \frac{1}{2}z^2 + \ldots}{1 + \frac{1}{2}z + \ldots}\right]_{z=0} = \frac{1}{z}.$$

Hence by theorem on the expansion of meromorphic functions

$$\frac{1}{2}\left(\frac{e^z + 1}{e^z - 1}\right) = f(0) + \sum_{n=1}^{\infty} b_n\left(\frac{1}{z - a_n} + \frac{1}{a_n}\right)$$

where b_n and a_n have usual meanings

$$= \frac{1}{z} + \sum_{n=1}^{\infty}\left[1\cdot\left(\frac{1}{z - 2n\pi i} + \frac{1}{2n\pi i}\right) + 1\cdot\left(\frac{1}{z + 2n\pi i} - \frac{1}{2n\pi i}\right)\right]$$

or

$$\frac{1}{2}\left(1 + \frac{2}{e^z - 1}\right) = \frac{1}{z} + \sum_{n=1}^{\infty}\left[\frac{1}{z - 2n\pi i} - \frac{1}{z + 2n\pi i}\right]$$

$$= \frac{1}{z} + \sum_{n=1}^{\infty}\frac{2z}{z^2 + 4n^2\pi^2}$$

or

$$\frac{1}{e^z - 1} = -\frac{1}{2} + \frac{1}{z}\sum_{n=1}^{\infty}\frac{2z}{z^2 + 4n^2\pi^2}.$$

3. Prove that, if $-\pi < \alpha < \pi$,

$$\frac{\cos \alpha z}{\sin \pi z} = \frac{1}{\pi z} + \frac{2z}{\pi}\sum_{n=1}^{\infty}\frac{(-1)^n \cos n\alpha}{z^2 - n^2}.$$

Solution. Here

$$f(z) = \frac{\cos \alpha z}{\sin \pi z}.$$

Poles of $f(z)$ are given by $\sin \pi z = 0 \Rightarrow \pi z = m\pi \Rightarrow z = m$ $(m = 0, \pm 1, \pm 2, \ldots)$.

Let the contour C_n be the square ABCD with centre at the origin and length of each side equal to $2\left(n + \frac{1}{2}\right)$.

The poles which lie within the contour C_n are

$$z = m \ (m = 0, \pm 1, \pm 2, \ldots, \pm n).$$

In this sequence of poles there are two poles $z = n$ and $z = -n$ whose absolute value is greater than those of the other poles.

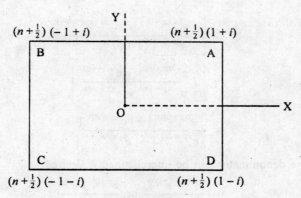

$(n+\frac{1}{2})(-1+i)$ Y $(n+\frac{1}{2})(1+i)$

B   A

O   X

C   D

$(n+\frac{1}{2})(-1-i)$ $(n+\frac{1}{2})(1-i)$

Fig. 11.30

Residue at the pole $z = n$ is

$$\left[\frac{\cos \alpha z}{\dfrac{d}{dz}(\sin \pi z)}\right]_{z=n} = \left[\frac{\cos \alpha z}{\pi \cos \pi z}\right]_{z=n}$$

$$= \frac{\cos \alpha n}{\pi \cos \pi n} = \frac{\cos n\alpha}{\pi (-1)^n}$$

$$= \frac{(-1)^n \cos n\alpha}{\pi}.$$

Also residue at the pole $z = -n$ is

$$\left[\frac{\cos \alpha z}{\dfrac{d}{dz}(\sin \pi z)}\right]_{z=-n} = \frac{(-1)^n \cos n\alpha}{\pi}.$$

Now, we observe that

(i) C_n encloses the poles $z = m$ $(m = 0, \pm 1, \pm 2, \ldots, \pm n)$ and no other poles.

(ii) The minimum distance R_n of C_n from the origin is $\left(n + \dfrac{1}{2}\right)$ which tends to infinity as $n \to \infty$.

(iii) The length L_n of C_n is

$$8\left(n + \frac{1}{2}\right) \text{ and } R_n = \left(n + \frac{1}{2}\right);$$

so that $L_n = 8R_n$, i.e., $L_n = O(R_n)$.

(iv) $f(z)$ is bounded on the contour C_n as shown below :

$$\left|\frac{\cos \alpha z}{\cos \pi z}\right| = \left| i \frac{e^{i\alpha z} + e^{-i\alpha z}}{e^{i\pi z} - e^{-i\pi z}} \right|$$

$$= \left| i \frac{e^{i\alpha (x + iy)} + e^{-i\alpha (x + iy)}}{e^{i\pi (x + iy)} - e^{-i\pi (x + iy)}} \right|$$

$$= \left| i \frac{e^{-\alpha y + i\alpha x} + e^{\alpha y - i\alpha x}}{e^{-\pi y + i\pi x} - e^{\pi y - i\pi x}} \right|$$

$$< \frac{\left| e^{\alpha y - i\alpha x} \right| + \left| e^{\alpha y - i\alpha y} \right|}{\left| e^{\pi y - i\pi x} \right| - \left| e^{-\pi y + i\pi x} \right|}.$$

The terms in the denominator can be interchanged if desired.

$$= \frac{e^{\alpha y} + e^{-\alpha y}}{e^{\pi y} - e^{-\pi y}} \quad \text{or} \quad \frac{e^{-\alpha y} + e^{\alpha y}}{e^{-\pi y} - e^{\pi y}}$$

interchanging terms in the denominator.

$$= \frac{e^{\alpha y} (1 + e^{-2\alpha y})}{e^{-\pi y} (1 - e^{-2\pi y})} \quad \text{or} \quad \frac{e^{-\alpha y} (1 + e^{2\alpha y})}{e^{-\pi y} (1 - e^{2\pi y})}$$

taken according as z is positive or negative

$$< \frac{1 + e^{-2\alpha y}}{1 - e^{-2\pi y}} \quad \text{or} \quad \frac{1 + e^{2\alpha y}}{1 - e^{2\pi y}} \quad \text{since} - \pi < \alpha < \pi$$

taken according as y is positive or negative.

On AB, $y = \left(n + \dfrac{1}{2} \right)$, and on CD, $y = -\left(n + \dfrac{1}{2} \right)$.

∴ On AB and CD both

$$\left| \frac{\cos \alpha z}{\sin \pi z} \right| < \frac{1 - e^{-2\alpha \left(n + \frac{1}{2} \right)}}{1 - e^{-2\pi \left(n + \frac{1}{2} \right)}}$$

which $\to 1$ as $n \to \infty$ and on AD and BC we have y positive above the real axis and negative below it.

∴ On AD and BC we have

$$\left| \frac{\cos \alpha z}{\sin \pi z} \right| < \text{any one of} \ \frac{1 + e^{-2\alpha y}}{1 + e^{-2\pi y}} \quad \text{or} \quad \frac{1 + e^{2\alpha y}}{1 + e^{2\pi y}}$$

according as y is positive or negative, which tend to 1 as $y \to \infty$ or $-\infty$.

∴ By theorem on the expansion of meromorphic functions we have

$$\frac{\cos \alpha z}{\sin \pi z} = f(0) + \sum_{n=1}^{\infty} b_n \left(\frac{1}{z - a_n} + \frac{1}{a_n} \right)$$

$$= \left[\frac{1}{\pi z} \cdot \frac{\pi z}{\sin \pi z} \cos \alpha z \right]_{z=0} + \sum_{n=1}^{\infty} \left[\frac{(-1)^n \cos n\alpha}{\pi} \left(\frac{1}{z - n} + \frac{1}{n} \right) \right.$$

$$\left. + \frac{(-1)^n \cos n\alpha}{\pi} \left(\frac{1}{z + n} - \frac{1}{n} \right) \right]$$

$$= \frac{1}{\pi z} + \sum_{n=1}^{\infty} \frac{(-1)^n \cos n\alpha}{\pi} \left(\frac{1}{z-n} + \frac{1}{z+n} \right)$$

$$= \frac{1}{\pi z} + \frac{2z}{\pi} \sum_{n=1}^{\infty} \frac{(-1)^n \cos n\alpha}{z^2 - n^2}.$$

EXERCISES

1. (*a*) Evaluate

$$\int_{-\pi}^{\pi} \frac{a \cos \theta}{a + \cos \theta} \, d\theta, \ (a > 1)$$

by putting $z = e^{i\theta}$ and using the theory of residues.

$$\left[\textbf{Ans.} \ 2a\pi \left\{ 1 - \frac{a}{\sqrt{a^2 - 1}} \right\} \right]$$

(*b*) Evaluate $\int_0^{\pi} \frac{\sin^4 \theta}{a + b \cos \theta} \, d\theta$

$$\left[\textbf{Ans.} \ \frac{\pi}{b^4} \left[(a^2 - b^2)^{3/2} - a^3 + \frac{3}{2} ab^2 \right] \right]$$ (*Garhwal 2000*)

2. Show that

(*a*) $\int_0^{\pi} \frac{1 + 2 \cos \theta}{5 + 4 \cos \theta} \, d\theta = 0$

(*b*) $\int_0^{\pi} \frac{a}{a^2 + \cos^2 \theta} \, d\theta = \frac{\pi}{\sqrt{1+a^2}}$, where $a > 0$.

(*c*) $\int_0^{2\pi} \frac{d\theta}{2 + \cos \theta} = \frac{2\pi}{\sqrt{3}}$

3. Show that

(*a*) $\int_0^{\pi} \frac{\cos 2\theta}{1 - 2a \cos \theta + a^2} \, d\theta = \frac{\pi a^2}{1 - a^2}$, if $-1 < b < 1$

(*Garhwal 2000, Gorakhpur 2002; Kanpur 2003*)

(*b*) $\int_0^{\pi} \frac{d\theta}{(a + \cos \theta)^2} = \frac{\pi a}{(a^2 - 1)^{3/2}}.$

(*c*) $\int_{-\pi}^{\pi} \frac{a \cos \theta}{a + \cos \theta} \, d\theta = 2\pi a \left\{ 1 - \frac{a}{\sqrt{a^2 - 1}} \right\}$, where $a > 1$

4. Show that

(a) $\int_0^{2\pi} e^{\cos\theta} \cos(n\theta - \sin\theta)\, d\theta = \dfrac{2\pi}{n!}$ *(Garhwal 2005, 2007)*

(b) $\int_0^{2\pi} \dfrac{d\theta}{a + b\sin\theta} = \dfrac{2\pi}{\sqrt{a^2 - b^2}}, \; (a > b).$

(c) $\int_0^{\pi} \dfrac{1 + 2\cos\theta}{5 + 4\cos\theta}\, d\theta = 0.$

5. Show that

(a) $\int_0^{\infty} \dfrac{1}{(1+x^2)^2}\, dx = \dfrac{\pi}{4}$ *(Meerut 2000, 2006)*

(b) $\int_0^{\infty} \dfrac{dx}{(x^2 + b^2)^{n+1}} = \dfrac{\pi}{(2b)^{2n+1}} \dfrac{(2n)!}{(n!)^2}$

(c) $\int_0^{\infty} \dfrac{dx}{1 + x^6} = \dfrac{\pi}{3}$ *(UPPCS 2003, MS. Univ. 2007)*

(d) $\int_0^{\infty} \dfrac{x^6}{(1+x^4)^2}\, dx = \dfrac{3\sqrt{2}\,\pi}{16}$

(e) $\int_0^{\infty} \dfrac{dx}{\sqrt{x\,(1 + 2x\cos\theta + x^2)}} = \dfrac{1}{2}\pi \sec\dfrac{1}{2}\theta; \; -\pi < \theta < \pi$ [Put $x = t^2$]

(f) $\int_0^{\infty} \dfrac{dx}{x^{1/2}\,(1 + x^2)} = \dfrac{\pi}{\sqrt{3}}.$

6. Show that for $a > 0,\, b > 0,\, a \neq b,$

$$\int_{-\infty}^{\infty} \dfrac{dx}{(x^4 + a^4)(x^4 + b^4)} = \dfrac{\pi}{\sqrt{2}} \dfrac{a^2 + ab + b^2}{a^3 b^3 \,(a^3 + a^2 b + ab^2 + b^3)}.$$

Is the formula valid for

$$a = b > 0\,?$$

7. Show by integration round a circular sector of angle π / n, that, if n is an integer greater than 1,

$$\int_0^{\infty} \dfrac{dx}{1 + x^{2n}} = \dfrac{\pi}{2n \sin(\pi / 2n)}.$$

8. Show that

(a) $\int_0^{\infty} \dfrac{\cos x}{a^2 + x^2}\, dx = \dfrac{\pi e^{-a}}{2a}, \; (a > 0)$

(b) $\int_{-\infty}^{\infty} \dfrac{\sin x}{x^2 + 4x + 5}\, dx = -\dfrac{\pi}{e} \sin 2$

(c) $\int_{-\infty}^{\infty} \dfrac{\sin x}{x^2 - 2x + 5} dx = \dfrac{\pi \sin 1}{2e^2}$

(d) $\int_{0}^{\infty} \dfrac{x \sin mx}{x^2 + a^2} dx = \dfrac{\pi}{2e^{am}}$, when $a > 0$

(Gorakhpur, 2002, Kerala 2001)

(e) $\int_{0}^{\infty} \dfrac{\cos x}{(b^2 + x^2)^2} dx = \dfrac{\pi}{4b^3}(1+b)e^{-b}$

(f) $\int_{-\infty}^{\infty} \dfrac{\cos \alpha x - \cos \beta x}{x^2} dx = \pi(\beta - \alpha); \ \alpha > 0, \ \beta > 0$ *(Garhwal 2000)*

(g) $\int_{-\infty}^{\infty} \dfrac{\sin 2(x-a)}{(x-a)(x^2+b^2)} dx = \dfrac{\pi}{b(a^2+b^2)}[b - e^{-2b}(b \cos 2a - a \sin 2a)],$

(a real and $a > 0$)

(h) $\int_{-\infty}^{\infty} \dfrac{\sin 2(x-a)\sin(x-b)}{(x-a)(x-b)} dx = \dfrac{\pi \sin(a-b)}{(a-b)}; \ (a, b \ \text{real})$

(i) $\int_{0}^{\infty} \dfrac{-\cos x}{x^2} dx = \dfrac{\pi}{2}$

(j) $\int_{-\infty}^{\infty} \dfrac{\sin x}{(x^2 - x + 1)^2} dx = \dfrac{2\pi(\sqrt{3}+2)}{3\sqrt{3}} e^{-\frac{\sqrt{3}}{2}} \sin \dfrac{1}{2}.$

9. If m and a are real and positive, find the residue at each of the poles of the function
$$z e^{imz} / (z^4 + a^4).$$
By integrating round a suitable contour, show that
$$\int_{0}^{\infty} \dfrac{x \sin mx}{x^4 + a^4} dx = \dfrac{\pi}{4b^2} e^{-mb} \sin mb,$$
where $b = a/\sqrt{2}$.

10. By integrating
$$z e^{iz} / (z^2 + a^2)$$
around a suitable contour, prove that
$$\int_{0}^{\infty} \dfrac{x \sin x}{x^2 + a^2} dx = \dfrac{\pi}{2e^a}, \quad \text{where } a > 0. \qquad \textit{(Gorakhpur 2000)}$$

11. Prove that if $m > 0$, $a > 0$,

(a) $\int_{0}^{\pi} \dfrac{\sin mx \, dx}{x(x^2 + a^2)} = \dfrac{\pi}{2a^2}(1 - e^{-am})$ *(Meerut 2001; 2004; 2005)*

(b) $\int\limits_0^\infty \dfrac{\sin mx}{x\,(x^2+a^2)^2}\,dx = \dfrac{\pi}{2a^4} - \dfrac{\pi e^{-ma}}{4a^3}\left(m + \dfrac{2}{a}\right).$

12. Calculate

$$\int\limits_0^\infty \dfrac{x^3 \sin x}{(x^2+a^2)\,(x^2+b^2)}\,dx,\ (a > 0,\, b > 0)$$

and deduce the value of

$$\int\limits_0^\infty \dfrac{x^3 \sin x}{(x^2+a^2)^2}\,dx.$$

(*Himachal 2004*)

$$\left[\textbf{Ans.}\ \dfrac{\pi}{2\,(a^2-b^2)}\,(a^2 e^{-a} b^2 e^{-b});\ \dfrac{(2-a)\,\pi e^{-a}}{4}\right]$$

13. Calculate

$$\int\limits_0^\infty \dfrac{\cos mx}{x^4+x^2+1}\,dx,\ (m > 0).$$

$$\left[\textbf{Ans.}\ \dfrac{\pi}{\sqrt{3}}\,\sin\dfrac{1}{2}\left(m + \dfrac{\pi}{3}\right) e^{-\frac{1}{2}m\sqrt{3}}\right]$$

14. Show that if $a > 0,\, m > 0,\, -1 < \lambda < 2,$

$$\int\limits_0^\infty \dfrac{x^\lambda \cos\left(mx - \dfrac{1}{2}\,\pi\lambda\right)}{x^2+a^2}\,dx = \dfrac{1}{2}\,\pi a\lambda^{-1} e^{-ma}.$$

15. Show by integration round an infinite semi-circle and its diameter that

$$\int\limits_0^\infty \dfrac{\sqrt{x}}{x^2+x+1}\,dx = \dfrac{\pi}{\sqrt{3}},\ \int\limits_0^\infty \dfrac{\sqrt{x}}{x^2-x+1}\,dx = \dfrac{\pi^2}{2\sqrt{2}}.$$

16. Show that

$$\int\limits_0^\infty \dfrac{\sqrt{x}\,\log x}{1+x^2}\,dx = \dfrac{1}{4}\,\pi^2\,\sqrt{2}.$$

17. By integrating

$$ze^{az}\,(1+e^{2z})^{-1}\ \text{where}\ 0 < a < 2,$$

round a rectangle with vertices at

$$z = \pm\, R,\ z = \pm\, R + \pi i,$$

or otherwise, prove that

$$\int\limits_0^\infty \dfrac{t^{a-1}\,\log t}{1+t^2}\,dt = -\dfrac{\pi^2 \cos\left(\dfrac{1}{2}\,a\pi\right)}{4\sin^2\left(\dfrac{1}{2}\,a\pi\right)}.$$

18. By integrating

$$z^a / (z^2 + z + 1); \; -1 < a < 1$$

along a suitably indented semi-circular contour, find the value of

$$\int_0^\infty x^a \, (x^2 + x + 1)^{-1} \, dx.$$

$$\left[\textbf{Ans.} \; \frac{2\pi \sin(2a\pi/3)}{\sqrt{3} \sin a\pi} \right]$$

19. By integrating

$$e^{i\pi z^2} / \sin z$$

around a suitable rectangular contour, prove that

$$\int_0^\infty \cos t^2 \, dt = \int_0^\infty \sin t^2 \, dt = \frac{1}{2}\sqrt{\frac{\pi}{2}}.$$

20. Use the method of contour integration to prove that

$$\int_0^\infty \frac{\log x}{(1 + x^2)^2} \, dx = -\frac{\pi}{4}.$$

21. Prove, by contour integration, that *(Garhwal 2002 Meerut 2004)*

$$\int_0^\infty \frac{x^{a-1}}{1 - x} \, dx = \pi \cot a\pi \quad \text{and} \quad \int_0^\infty \frac{x^{a-1}}{1 + x} \, dx = \pi \operatorname{cosec} a\pi. \qquad (0 < a < 1)$$

(Kanpur 2004, UPPCS 2003, Meerut 2006)

22. Integrate $e^{iz} / (z + a)$

along the boundary of the square defined by

$$x = 0, \; x = R, \; y = 0, \; y = R$$

and prove that if $a > 0$

$$\int_0^\infty \frac{\cos x}{x + a} \, dx = \int_0^\infty \frac{xe^{-ax}}{1 + x^2} \, dx, \quad \int_0^\infty \frac{\sin x}{x + a} \, dx = \int_0^\infty \frac{e^{-ax}}{1 + x^2} \, dx.$$

23. Integrate

$$e^{iz^2} / z$$

along the contour C consisting of the quadrant of the circle $|z| = R$

in the first quadrant and intercepts on the two axes, and show that

$$\int_0^\infty \frac{\sin x^2}{x} \, dx = \frac{\pi}{4}.$$

(Gorakhpur 2002)

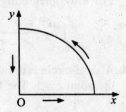

Fig. 11.31.

24. By integrating e^{iz^2} round the rectangle whose vertices are

$$0, \; R, \; R + ia, \; ia$$

prove that

$$\int_0^\infty e^{-x^2} \cos 2ax \, dx = \frac{\sqrt{\pi}}{2} e^{-a^2}.$$

$$\left[\text{You may assume that } \int_0^\infty e^{-x^2} \, dx = \frac{\sqrt{\pi}}{2} \right]$$

Also deduce the value of

$$\frac{1}{\sqrt{2\pi}} \int_{-\infty}^\infty e^{itx} e^{-\frac{1}{2}x^2} \, dx.$$

25. By contour integration obtain, for suitably restricted real values of a and λ, the value of

$$\int_0^\infty \frac{x^a}{(x^2 + 2x \cos \lambda + 1)^2} \, dx.$$

Also show that

$$\int_0^\infty \frac{x^a}{x^2 + 2x \cos \lambda + 1} \, dx = \frac{\pi \sin a\lambda}{\sin ax \sin \lambda}$$

for $-1 < a < 1, -\pi < \lambda < \pi$.

26. By integrating $(1 - e^{2iz})$ round a suitable contour, prove that

$$\int_0^{\pi/2} \log \sin x \, dx = -\frac{1}{2} \pi \log 2.$$

27. A contour C formed by indenting at 0 and $2\pi i$ the rectangle whose vertices are
$$R, R + 2\pi i, -R + 2\pi i, -R.$$
Prove by integrating $e^{az} / (e^z - 1)$ round this contour, or otherwise, that if $0 < \alpha < 1$,

$$\int_0^\infty \frac{e^{\alpha x} - e^{(1 - \alpha) x}}{e^x - 1} \, dx = \pi (\cot \pi\alpha).$$

28. A semi-circle is drawn on the line joining the points $z = i, z = -i$ as diameter to pass through the point $z = 1$. The figure is indented at $-i, 0, i$ to form a closed contour C. By integrating
$$(z + z^{-1})^p z^{q-1},$$
around C, or otherwise, prove that, when $q > p > -1$,

$$\int_0^{\pi/2} \cos^p \theta \cos^q \theta \, d\theta = 2^{-p-1} \sin \frac{1}{2} \pi (q - p) \, B\left[(p + 1), \frac{1}{2} (q - p) \right],$$

where

$$B(m, n) = \int_0^1 x^{m-1} (1 - x)^{n-1} \, dx.$$

29. By integrating the function
$$f(z) = e^{iz} \log (-iz) (z^2 + 4)^{-1}$$

where the logarithm has its principal value, along a contour consisting of two segments of the real axis and two semi-circles, or otherwise, prove that

$$\int_0^\infty \frac{2 \cos x \log x + \pi \sin x}{x^2 + 4} \, dx = \frac{1}{2} \pi e^{-2} \log 2$$

30. By integrating a suitable function of the complex variable z round a circular contour cut along the positive real axis, or otherwise, prove that

$$\int_0^\infty \frac{\log x}{(x^2 + x + 1)^2} \, dx = -\frac{\pi}{3\sqrt{3}}$$

31. By integrating

$$e^\alpha e^{-\beta z} (1 + z^2)^{-1}; \quad -1 < \alpha < 2, \ \beta > 0$$

round a suitable contour, show that

$$\int_0^\infty \frac{x^\alpha \cos\left(\beta x - \frac{1}{2} \alpha \pi \right)}{1 + x^2} \, dx = \frac{\pi}{2e^\beta}.$$

32. Show, by integrating

$$z^{-1} e^{-z \sec \alpha},$$

round the boundary of the region $\delta \leq |z| \leq R, \ -\alpha \leq \arg z \leq \alpha$, or otherwise, that, if $0 < \alpha < \pi/2$,

$$\int_0^\infty \frac{e^{-t} \sin (t \tan \alpha)}{t} \, dt = \alpha.$$

33. By integrating the function

$$f(z) = z^{-3} \operatorname{cosec} \pi z \operatorname{cosec} [\pi (\sqrt{2} - 1) z]$$

round a suitable contour, prove that

$$\sum_{n=1}^\infty \frac{\operatorname{cosec} (\pi n \sqrt{2})}{n^3} = -\frac{13\pi^2}{360\sqrt{2}}.$$

[Integrate round the square with corners at $(m + 1/2)(\pm 1 \pm i)$ and let m tend to ∞.]

34. By integrating the function

$$e^{-\pi a z^2} / (e^{2\pi i z} - 1)$$

in two ways around the rectangle with vertices

$$\pm (m + 1/2) \pm i,$$

or otherwise, prove that

$$\sum_{n=-\infty}^\infty e^{-\pi a n^2} = \frac{1}{\sqrt{a}} \sum_{n=-\infty}^\infty e^{-\pi n^2 / a}.$$

35. Show that the residue of the function

$$f(z) = z^{-7} \cot \pi z \coth \pi z$$

at $z = 0$ is $-19\pi^6 / (567 \times 25)$.

By integrating this function round a suitable sequence of contours, or otherwise, show that

$$\sum_{n=1}^{\infty} \frac{\coth \pi n}{n^7} = \frac{19\pi^7}{56700}$$

36. The simple closed curve C in the z-plane encloses the points $m, m + 1, ..., n + 1$ where m and n are integers but no other integral points, and the function $f(z)$ is regular within and on C except perhaps for a finite number of poles within C, none of which is at an integral point. Prove that

$$\sum_{r=m}^{\infty} f(r) = \frac{1}{2i} \int_C f(z) \cot \pi z \, dz - S,$$

where S denotes the sum of the residues of $\pi f(z) \cot \pi z$ at the poles of $f(z)$ within C.

37. Find the residue of the function

$$z^{-3} \operatorname{cosec} z \operatorname{cosech} z$$

at the origin. Also prove that

$$\sum_{n=1}^{\infty} (-1)^{n-1} n^{-3} \operatorname{cosech} n\pi = \frac{\pi^3}{360}.$$

38. Prove that

(a) $\operatorname{cosec} z = \dfrac{1}{z} + 2z \displaystyle\sum_{n=1}^{\infty} \dfrac{(-1)^{n-1}}{n^2 \pi^2 - z^2}.$

(b) $\sec z = 4\pi \displaystyle\sum_{n=1}^{\infty} \dfrac{(-1)^n (2n+1)}{(2n+1)^2 \pi^2 - 4z^2}.$

39. Prove that, if $-\pi < \alpha < \pi$,

$$\frac{\sin \alpha z}{\sin \pi z} = \frac{2}{\pi} \sum_{n=1}^{\infty} (-1)^n \frac{n \sin n\alpha}{z^2 - n^2}.$$

40. Prove by the method of contour integration

$$\tan z = \sum_{n=1}^{\infty} \frac{2z}{\left(n + \dfrac{1}{2}\right)^2 \pi^2 - z^2}.$$

OBJECTIVE QUESTIONS

For each of the following questions, four alternatives are given for the answer. Only one of them is correct. Choose the correct alternative.

1. To evaluate the integrals of the type $\displaystyle\int_0^{2\pi} \phi(\cos \theta, \sin \theta) \, d\theta$, the contour used is

    (a) Any circle   (b) Unit circle

    (c) Semi-circle   (d) Rectangle.

2. The Jordan's inequality is

(a) $\dfrac{2}{\pi} < \dfrac{\sin \theta}{\theta} < 1$

(b) $2\pi < \sin \theta < 0$

(c) $\dfrac{\pi}{2} < \dfrac{\theta}{\sin \theta} < 1$

(d) None of these.

3. To integrate $\displaystyle\int_0^\infty \dfrac{dx}{1 + x^2}$, we will use a contour

(a) real axis and unit circle $|z| = 1$

(b) real axis and lower half of circle $|z| = R$

(c) real axis and upper half of circle $|z| = R$

(d) circle $|z| = R$.

4. If AB be the arc $\alpha \le \theta \le \beta$ of the circle $|z| = R$ and $\displaystyle\lim_{z \to \infty} z\, f(z) = k$, then

(a) $\displaystyle\lim_{R \to \infty} \int_{AB} f(z)\, dz = i\,(\beta - \alpha)\, k$

(b) $\displaystyle\lim_{R \to 0} \int_{AB} f(z)\, dz = i\,(\beta - \alpha)\, k$

(c) $\displaystyle\lim_{R \to \infty} \int_{AB} f(z)\, dz = (\beta - \alpha)\, k$

(d) $\displaystyle\lim_{R \to 0} \int_{AB} f(z)\, dz = (\beta - \alpha)\, k$.

5. To integrate $\displaystyle\int_{-\infty}^\infty f(x)\, dx$, we should use

(a) circular contour

(b) indented semi-circular contour

(c) rectangular contour

(d) None of these.

ANSWERS

1. (b)   2. (a)   3. (c)   4. (a)   5. (c)

UNIFORM CONVERGENCE
INFINITE PRODUCTS

12.1. Introduction. In this chapter we shall consider the important notion of uniform convergence of a sequence, an infinite series and an infinite product. This notion arises when the members of a sequence, the terms of a series and the factors of a product are functions defined in any closed set. Also it is of importance inasmuch as we can put down sufficient conditions for the validity of the interchange of the order of summation and of the operations of limit, differentiability and integrability in terms of the same while we deal with infinite processes.

12.2. Uniform convergence of a sequence. Suppose that

$$\{u_n(z)\}$$

is a sequence each member of which is a function of z defined in some closed set S. Suppose further that for each $z \in S$, the sequence is convergent. Thus we arrive at a function $\phi(z)$ defined in S such that

$$\phi(z) = \lim_{n \to \infty} u_n(z). \qquad\qquad (z \in S)$$

This means that to each $\varepsilon > 0$, there corresponds a positive integer m such that

$$| u_n(z) - \phi(z) | < \varepsilon \ \forall \, n \ge m \qquad\qquad ...(1)$$

Now, this m would, in addition to depending upon ε, also in general depend upon z and it may not be possible, in any given case, to have a value of m independent of z. Thus it may not be possible to determine m such that (1) holds good for every $z \in S$. In case, however, this is possible, we say that the sequence is uniformly convergent and that it converges uniformly to $\phi(z)$. Thus we have the following definition :

Def. *A sequence* $\{u_n(z)\}$ *of functions defined in a closed set S is said to converge uniformly to a function* $\phi(z)$ *defined in S, if to every given* $\varepsilon > 0$, *there corresponds a positive integer m* **independent** *of z such that*

$$| u_n(z) - \phi(z) | < \varepsilon \ \forall \ n \ge m \text{ and } \forall \ z \in S.$$

The following theorem gives a **general test for the uniform convergence of a sequence.**

Theorem. *A necessary and sufficient condition for the uniform convergence of a sequence*
$$\{u_n(z)\}$$
of functions defined in a closed set S is that to every $\varepsilon > 0$, *there corresponds a positive integer m independent of z such that*

$$| u_{n+p}(z) - u_n(z) | < \varepsilon \ \forall \ n \ge m, p \ge 0, z \in S \qquad\qquad ...(1)$$

The condition is necessary. Suppose that the sequence is uniformly convergent so that it converges uniformly to a function $\phi(z)$.

Let $\varepsilon > 0$ be any given number. Then there exists a positive integer m independent of z such that

$$|u_n(z) - \phi(z)| < \frac{1}{2}\varepsilon \ \forall \ n \geq m, \ \forall \ z \in S \qquad \text{...(2)}$$

Also therefore

$$|u_{n+p}(z) - \phi(z)| < \frac{1}{2}\varepsilon \ \forall \ n \geq m, \ p \geq 0, \ \forall \ z \qquad \text{...(3)}$$

From (2) and (3), we deduce that

$$|u_{n+p}(z) - u_n(z)| < \varepsilon \ \forall \ n \geq m, p \geq 0, \ \forall \ z \in S.$$

Hence the necessity.

The condition is sufficient. By virtue of the given condition, the sequence $\{f_n(z)\}$ is convergent for each $z \in S$.

Let the sequence be convergent to $\phi(z)$. It will now be shown that the convergence is uniform.

Let $\varepsilon > 0$ be any given number. Then there exists a positive integer m such that

$$|u_{n+p}(z) - u_n(z)| < \frac{1}{2}\varepsilon \ \forall \ n \geq m, \ p \geq 0, \ \forall \ z \in S \qquad \text{...(4)}$$

The inequality (4) is equivalent to

$$|u_{n+p}(z)| - \frac{1}{2}\varepsilon < |u_n(z)| < |u_{n+p}(z)| + \frac{1}{2}\varepsilon \qquad \text{...(5)}$$

Keeping n fixed and letting p tend to infinity, we obtain from (5)

$$|\phi(z)| - \frac{1}{2}\varepsilon \leq |u_n(z)| \leq |\phi(z)| + \frac{1}{2}\varepsilon$$

$$\Rightarrow \qquad |u_n(z) - \phi(z)| \leq \frac{1}{2}\varepsilon < \varepsilon \ \forall \ n \geq m, \ \forall \ z \in S.$$

Thus the convergence is uniform.

Uniform convergence of a series. Consider now an infinite series

$$f_1(z) + f_2(z) + \ ..... + f_n(z) + \ .....$$

each term of which is a function of z defined in a closed set S. We set up the sequence $\{S_n(z)\}$ of partial sums where

$$S_n(z) = f_1(z) + \ ..... + f_n(z).$$

Then the series $\Sigma f_n(z)$ is said to be uniformly convergent if the sequence $\{S_n(z)\}$ of partial sums of the series is uniformly convergent.

From the general condition of uniform convergence of a sequence obtained above in § 12.2.1, we deduce the corresponding test for the uniform convergence of a series.

Theorem. *A necessary and sufficient condition for the uniform convergence of a series*

$$f_1(z) + \ ..... + f_n(z) + \ .....$$

of functions defined in a closed set S is that to every given $\varepsilon > 0$, there corresponds a positive integer m such that

$$|f_{n+1}(z) + \ ..... + f_{n+p}(z)| < \varepsilon \ \forall \ n \geq m, p \geq 0, \ \forall \ z \in S.$$

The proof follows immediately on applying the theorem of § 12.2.1, to the sequence $\{S_n(z)\}$.

Sufficient tests for the uniform convergence of a series.

We shall now obtain some sufficient tests for the uniform convergence of a series. The first of these is applicable only to those series which are absolutely convergent.

12.4.1. Weierstrass's M-test for uniform and absolute convergence.

Theorem. *Let* $\Sigma f_n(z)$ *be an infinite series of functions defined in a closed set S and let* $\{M_n\}$ *be a sequence of positive numbers such that*

(i) $|f_n(z)| \le M_n \; \forall \; n \; and \; \forall \; z \in S.$

and (ii) *the series* ΣM_n *is convergent.*

Then the series $\Sigma f_n(z)$ *is uniformly and absolutely convergent.*

Let $\varepsilon > 0$ be any given number. Since, ΣM_n is convergent, there exists a positive integer m such that

$$| M_{n+1} + \ldots + M_{n+p} | < \varepsilon \; \forall \; n \ge m, p \ge 0.$$

Then, with the help of (i), we obtain

$$|f_{n+1}(z) + \ldots + f_{n+p}(z)| \le |f_{n+1}(z)| + \ldots + |f_{n+p}(z)|$$
$$< M_{n+1} + \ldots + M_{n+p} < \varepsilon,$$

$$\Rightarrow \quad |f_{n+1}(z) + \ldots + f_{n+p}(z)| < \varepsilon \; \forall \; n \ge m, p \ge 0, \; \forall \; z \in S.$$

Hence by the general principle of uniform convergence, we see that the series is uniformly convergent, (§ 12.2.1).

Since,

$$\left| |f_{n+1}(z)| + \ldots + |f_{n+p}(z)| \right| < \varepsilon, \; \forall \; n \ge m, p \ge 0,$$

we see that the given series is also absolutely convergent.

Theorem. *Let* $\Sigma f_n(z)$ *be a series and* $\{u_n(z)\}$ *a sequence of functions defined in a closed set S. Let*

(i) *the sequence* $\{S_n(z)\}$ *of partial sums of the series* $\Sigma f_n(z)$ *be uniformly bounded, i.e., let there exist a number* $k > 0$ *such that*

$$| S_n(z) | < k \; \forall \; z \in S,$$

(ii) *the series* $\Sigma \{u_n(z) - u_{n+1}(z)\}$ *be uniformly and absolutely convergent,*

(iii) $u_n(z)$ *tends uniformly to zero in S.*

Then the series $\Sigma u_n(z) f_n(z)$ *is uniformly convergent in S.*

Let $\sigma_n(z)$ denote the sequence of partial sums of the series

$$\Sigma u_n(z) f_n(z).$$

We have

$$\sigma_{n+p}(z) - \sigma_n(z)$$
$$= u_{n+1}(z) f_{n+1}(z) + \ldots + u_{n+p}(z) f_{n+p}(z)$$
$$= u_{n+1}(z) [S_{n+1}(z) - S_n(z)]$$
$$+ \ldots + u_{n+p}(z) [S_{n+p}(z) - S_{n+p-1}(z)]$$
$$= -u_{n+1}(z) S_n(z) + [u_{n+1}(z) - u_{n+2}(z)] S_{n+1}(z)$$
$$+ \ldots + [u_{n+p-1}(z) - u_{n+p}(z)] S_{n+p-1}(z)$$
$$+ u_{n+p}(z) S_{n+p}(z) \qquad \ldots(1)$$

With the help of (i), we have, from (1),

$$| \sigma_{n+p}(z) - \sigma_n(z) | \le k | u_{n+1}(z) | + \ldots + k | u_{n+p}(z) |$$
$$+ k [| u_{n+1}(z) - u_{n+2}(z) |$$
$$+ \ldots + | u_{n+p-1}(z) - u_{n+p}(z) |] \qquad \ldots(2)$$

Now suppose that $\varepsilon > 0$ is any given number.

By virtue of (ii), we see by the general principle of convergence that there exists a positive integer m_1 such that

$$| u_{n+1} (z) - u_{n+2} (z) | + \ ..... \ + | u_{n+p-1} (z) - u_{n+p} (z) | < \varepsilon / 3k \qquad ...(3)$$
$$\forall n \geq m_1, \ p \geq 0, \ \forall \ z \in S.$$

Also by (iii), there exists a positive integer m_2 such that

$$| u_{n+1} (z) | < \varepsilon / 3k, | u_{n+p} (z) | < \varepsilon / 3k \qquad ...(4)$$
$$\forall n \geq m_2, p \geq 0, \ \forall \ z \in S.$$

From (2), (3) and (4), we deduce that

$$| \sigma_{n+p} (z) - \sigma_n (z) | < \varepsilon, \ \forall \ n \geq m = \text{max.} \ (m_1, m_2), p \geq 0, \ \forall \ z \in S.$$

Thus by the general principle of uniform convergence, the series

$$\Sigma \ u_n (z) f_n (z)$$

is uniformly convergent.

Theorem. *Let* $\Sigma f_n (z)$ *be a series and* $\{u_n (z)\}$ *a sequence of functions defined in a closed set S. Let*

(i) the series $\Sigma f_n (z)$ *be uniformly convergent in S, and*

(ii) $\Sigma \ \{u_n (z) - u_{n+1} (z)\}$ *be uniformly and absolutely convergent in S.*

Then

$$\Sigma \ u_n (z) f_n (z)$$

is uniformly convergent in S.

Let $\{S_n (z)\}$, $\{s_n (z)\}$, $\{\sigma_n (z)\}$ denote the sequences of partial sums of the series

$$\Sigma f_n (z), \ \Sigma \ \{u_n (z) - u_{n+1} (z)\}, \ \Sigma \ u_n (z) f_n (z),$$

respectively.

Then we have

$$s_n (z) = u_1 (z) - u_{n+1} (z)$$
$$\Rightarrow \qquad u_{n+1} (z) = u_1 (z) - s_n (z) \qquad ...(1)$$

Since by (ii), $\{s_n (z)\}$ is uniformly convergent, we see, by (1), that the sequence $\{u_n (z)\}$ is also uniformly convergent.

As in the preceding case, we have

$$\sigma_{n+p} (z) - \sigma_n (z) = u_{n+p} (z) \ S_{n+p} (z) - u_{n+1} \ S_n (z)$$
$$+ \ [u_{n+1} (z) - u_{n+2} (z)] \ S_{n+1} (z)$$
$$+ \ ..... \ + \ [u_{n+p-1} (z) - u_{n+p} (z)] \ S_{n+p-1} (z).$$

As the sequences $\{u_n (z)\}$, $\{S_n (z)\}$ are both uniformly convergent, we see that

$$u_{n+p} (z) \ S_{n+p} (z) - u_{n+1} (z) \ S_n (z)$$

uniformly tends to 0 as n tends to infinity so that if $\varepsilon > 0$ be any given number, then there exists a positive integer m_1 such that

$$|u_{n+p} (z) S_{n+p} (z) - u_{n+1} (z) S_n (z)| < \frac{1}{2} \varepsilon \ \forall \ n \geq m, \ \forall \ z \in S \qquad ...(2)$$

Also, by virtue of (ii), there exists a positive integer m_2 such that

$$| u_{n+1} (z) - u_{n+2} (z) | + \ ..... \ + | u_{n+p-1} (z) - u_{n+p} (z) | < \varepsilon / 2k \qquad ...(3)$$

$\forall \ n \geq m_2$, and $\forall \ z \in S$. Here k is a number such that

$$| S_n (z) | < k \ \forall \ n \text{ and } \forall \ z \in S \qquad ...(4)$$

From (1), (2), (3) and (4), we deduce that

$$| \sigma_{n+p}(z) - \sigma_n(z) | < \varepsilon \ \forall \ n \geq \max. (m_1, m_2), p \geq 0, \ \forall \ z \in S \qquad ...(5)$$

Thus $\Sigma \, u_n(z) \, f_n(z)$ is uniformly convergent in S.

12.5. Continuity of the sum function of a uniformly convergent series of continuous function.
It has been seen, that the sum of a *finite* number of continuous functions is continuous. This result, however, may not be true when we consider the sum of an *infinite* series of continuous functions.

As stated and proved below, the uniform convergence of a series is a *sufficient* condition for the continuity of the sum function of an infinite series of continuous functions.

Theorem. *Let $\Sigma f_n(z)$ be a uniformly convergent series of continuous functions defined in a closed set S'. Then the sum function $S(z)$ of the series is continuous in S.*

(Meerut 2000, 2005)

Let z_0 be any point of S. Let $\varepsilon > 0$ be any given number.

The series being uniformly convergent, there exists a positive integer m such that

$$| S(z) - S_n(z) | < \frac{1}{3} \varepsilon \ \forall \ n \geq m, \ \forall \ z \in S \qquad ...(1)$$

In particular, we have, from (1)

$$| S(z) - S_m(z) | < \frac{1}{3} \varepsilon, \ \forall \ z \in S \qquad ...(2)$$

and

$$| S(z_0) - S_m(z_0) | < \frac{1}{3} \varepsilon \qquad ...(3)$$

Further, being the sum of a finite number m of continuous functions, $S_m(z)$ is continuous. There exists, therefore, a positive number δ, such that

$$| S_m(z) - S_m(z_0) | < \frac{1}{3} \varepsilon \ \text{ for } | z - z_0 | \leq \delta, \ z \in S \qquad ...(4)$$

Also, we write

$$| S(z) - S(z_0) | = | S(z) - S_m(z) + S_m(z) - S_m(z_0) + S_m(z_0) - S(z_0) |$$
$$\leq | S(z) - S_m(z) | + | S_m(z) - S_m(z_0) |$$
$$+ | S_m(z_0) - S(z) | \qquad ...(5)$$

From (2), (3), (4) and (5), we obtain

$$| S(z) - S(z_0) | < \varepsilon \ \text{ for } | z - z_0 | \leq \delta, z \in S.$$

Thus $S(z)$ is continuous at z_0 and hence in S.

Note. It is clear from above that we can prove a similar theorem for sequences which may be stated as follows :

If $\{S_n(z)\}$ is a sequence which is uniformly convergent in a closed set S and if each function $S_n(z)$ is continuous in S, then $\lim S_n(z)$
is also continuous in S.

12.6. Integral of the sum function. Integration term by term.

Theorem. *Let $\Sigma f_n(z)$ be a uniformly convergent series of continuous functions in any closed set S and let C be any rectifiable curve in S.*

Then,

$$\int_C [\Sigma \, f_n(z)] \, dz = \Sigma \int_C f_n(z) \, dz,$$

i.e., the integral of the sum is equal to the sum of the integrals.

We write

$$S(z) = S_n(z) + R_n(z).$$

As shown in the preceding section, $S(z)$ is continuous in S. Being the difference of two continuous functions, $R_n(z)$ is also continuous in S.

Hence

$$\int_C S(z)\, dz = \int_C S_n(z)\, dz + \int_C R_n(z)\, dz \qquad \qquad ...(1)$$

Let l be the length of the curve C. If $\varepsilon > 0$, be any given number, then, because of the given uniform convergence, there exists a positive integer m such that

$$|R_n(z)| = |S(z) - S_n(z)| < \varepsilon / l \ \forall \ n \geq m \text{ and } z \in S \qquad ...(2)$$

From (1) and (2), we have

$$\left| \int_C S(z)\, dz - \int_C S_n(z)\, dz \right| = \left| \int_C R_n(z)\, dz \right|$$

$$< l \cdot \frac{\varepsilon}{l} = \varepsilon, \ \forall \ n \geq m.$$

Also $S_n(z)$ being the sum of a finite number of functions, we have

$$\int_C S_n(z)\, dz = \sigma_n,$$

where

$$\sigma_n = \int_C f_1(z)\, dz + ... + \int_C f_n(z)\, dz.$$

Thus we have

$$\left| \int_C S(z)\, dz - \sigma_n \right| < \varepsilon \ \forall \ n \geq m.$$

Hence the result.

Note. We may state and prove an analogous theorem for any sequence $\{S_n(z)\}$.

12.7. Analyticity of the sum function of a series.

Theorem. *Let $\Sigma f_n(z)$ be a series of functions analytic in a domain D. Also let the series*

$$\Sigma f_n(z)$$

be uniformly convergent in every closed set continuous in D.

Then

(i) the sum function $S(z)$ of the series is analytic in D,

(ii) the term by term differentiation is valid, i.e.,

$$S'(z) = \Sigma f_n'(z),$$

(iii) the series

$$\Sigma f_n'(z)$$

of derivatives is uniformly convergent in every closed sub-set of D.

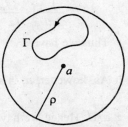

Fig. 12.1

The sum function $S(z)$ of the series is continuous in D by § 12.5.

Let, a, be any point of D and let

$$|z - a| < \rho$$

be any circular neighbourhood of a. Also let Γ be any closed curve in this circular domain.

Since Γ is a closed set, the series

$$\Sigma f_n(z)$$

is uniformly convergent on Γ.

Accordingly term by term integration is valid of Γ and we have

$$\int_\Gamma S(z)\, dz = \int_\Gamma f_1(z)\, dz + \int_\Gamma f_2(z)\, dz + \ldots..$$

As each of $f_n(z)$ is analytic in D and in particular, in the circular domain in question, we have, by Cauchy's theorem,

$$\int_\Gamma f_n(z)\, dz = 0, \ \forall \ n$$

$\Rightarrow$
$$\int_\Gamma S(z)\, dz = 0.$$

Thus by *Morera's theorem*, S (z) is analytic in a circular neighbourhood of a.

As however, a, is *any* point of D, we deduce that S (z) is analytic in D. Hence we have proved (i).

We now come to the proof of (ii).

Let, C, denote any simple closed curve lying in the neighbourhood

$$|z - a| < \rho$$

of, a, and having, a, in its interior.

The series

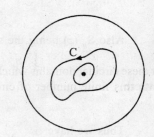

$$\frac{1}{2\pi i} \frac{S(z)}{(z-a)^2} = \frac{1}{2\pi i} \frac{f_1(z)}{(z-a)^2}$$

$$+ \frac{1}{2\pi i} \frac{f_2(z)}{(z-a)^2} + \ldots..$$

is uniformly convergent on the curve C.

Accordingly, we obtain, on term by term integration,   **Fig. 12.2**

$$\frac{1}{2\pi i} \int_C \frac{S(z)}{(z-a)^2}\, dz = \frac{1}{2\pi i} \int_C \frac{f_1(z)}{(z-a)^2}\, dz + \frac{1}{2\pi i} \int_C \frac{f_2(z)}{(z-a)^2}\, dz + \ldots..$$

But

$$\frac{1}{2\pi i} \int_C \frac{S(z)}{(z-a)^2}\, dz = S'(a),$$

$$\frac{1}{2\pi i} \int_C \frac{f_n(z)}{(z-a)^2}\, dz = f_n'(a), \ \forall \ n.$$

Thus we have

$$S'(a) = f_1'(a) + f_2'(a) + \ldots..$$

As, however, a, is any arbitrary point of D, we see that

$$S'(z) = f_1'(z) + f_2'(z) + \ldots..$$

$\forall \ z \in$ D. Hence we have proved (ii).

Finally we proceed to prove that the series

$$\Sigma f_n'(z)$$

is uniformly convergent in every closed sub-set Σ of D.

Let, a, be any point of D and z a point of a closed circular domain with centre, a, and contained in D. Also let, C_1, be any circle which is concentric with the circular domain and which lies in D. Let r_1, be the radius of C_1, and ρ, the distance between C_1 and the frontier of the circular domain.

Since $\Sigma f_n(\xi)$ is uniformly convergent on C_1, there exists a positive integer m such that

$$|R_n(\xi)| = |S(\xi) - S_n(\xi)|$$

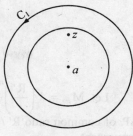

Fig. 12.3

$$= |f_{n+1}(\xi) + f_{n+2}(\xi) + \ldots| < \varepsilon$$
$$\forall \ n \geq m \text{ and } \xi \in C_1.$$

Also

$$R_n(\xi) = S(\xi) - S_n(\xi)$$

is analytic on and in the interior of C_1. Thus we have

$$|R_n'(z)| = \frac{1}{2\pi i} \int_{C_1} \frac{R_n(\xi)}{(\xi - z)^2} \, d\xi$$

$$\leq \frac{1}{2\pi} \frac{\varepsilon}{\rho^2} 2\pi r_1 = \frac{\varepsilon r_1}{\theta^2}; \ \forall \ n \geq m.$$

Thus we see that if $\varepsilon > 0$ is any given number and, a, is any given point of D, then there exists a positive integer N (a, ε) and a circular domain with its centre at a, such that for every point z of this domain, we have

$$|R_n'(z)| < \varepsilon \ \forall \ n \geq N \ (a, \varepsilon).$$

We consider now any closed sub-set Σ of D and cover every point, a of the same with a circular domain in the manner referred to above. Then, by Heine-Borel theorem, there exists a finite number of these circular domains which cover Σ. If then N denote the greatest of the values N (a, ε) associated with this finite number of circular domains, we see that

$$|R_n'(z)| < \varepsilon, \ \forall \ n \geq N, \ \forall \ z \in \Sigma.$$

Hence $\Sigma f_n'(z)$ is uniformly convergent in Σ.

Thus we have proved (*iii*) also.

Note. An analogous theorem for sequences may be stated as follows :

If each member of a sequence $\{S_n(z)\}$ is analytic in a domain D and the sequence is uniformly convergent in every closed sub-domain of D, then

(*i*) $\lim S_n(z)$ is analytic in D,

(*ii*) $[\lim S_n(z)]' = \lim S_n'(z)$, *i.e.*, the limit of the derivative is equal to the derivative of the limit,

(*iii*) the sequence $\{S_n'(z)\}$ is uniformly convergent in every closed sub-domain of D.

We may prove it directly or by a consideration of the infinite series

$$S_1(z) + [S_2(z) - S_1(z)] + \ldots$$

the sequence of whose partial sums is $\{S_n(z)\}$.

12.8. Uniform convergence of power series.   (*Agra 2000*)

Theorem. *A power series is uniformly convergent within its circle of convergence.*

Let $\sum\limits_{n=1}^{\infty} a_n z^n$ be the power series and R its radius of convergence. We have to prove that the series is uniformly convergent for $|z| \leq R'$, where R' is any positive number less than R.

Let z_0 be any number such that $|z_0| = r$ where $R' < r < R$.

Since the series is convergent at z_0, there is a number k, independent of n, such that

$$|a_n z_0^n| < k.$$

Hence for $|z| > R'$,

$$|a_n z^n| = \left| a_n z_0^n \left(\frac{z}{z_0} \right)^n \right|$$

$$= |a_n z_0{}^n| \left| \frac{z}{z_0} \right|^n < k \frac{R'^n}{r^n} \text{ since } |z| > R'$$

$$= k \left(\frac{R'}{r} \right)^n \text{ where } \frac{R'}{r} < 1 \text{ and is independent of } z.$$

Let $M_n = k \left(\dfrac{R'}{r} \right)^n$, we then see that the series M_n is convergent (since its terms form a G.P. of common ratio R'/r which is less than 1). Hence by M-test the series $\Sigma\, a_n z^n$ is uniformly convergent.

We have thus shown that any circle interior to the circle of convergence is a region of uniform convergence.

Theorem. *The circle of convergence itself is not necessarily a region of uniform convergence.*

Consider the series

$$\sum \frac{z^n}{n^2} .$$

Its radius of convergence

$$= \lim_{n \to \infty} |n^2|^{1/n} = \lim_{n \to \infty} |n^{1/n}|^2 = 1$$

as $\lim n^{1/n} = 1$.

∴ On the circle of convergence, we have $|z| = 1$.

Now,

$$\sum \left| \frac{z^n}{n^2} \right| = \sum \frac{|z|^n}{n^2} = 1/n^2$$

as $|z| = 1$ on the circle of convergence.

Again, consider another series $\Sigma\, (z^n/n)$.

Its radius of convergence $= \lim_{n \to \infty} |n|^{1/n}$

$$= \lim_{n \to \infty} |n^{1/n}| = 1.$$

So that on the circle of convergence $|z| = 1$, hence on the circle of convergence we have

$$\sum \left| \frac{z^n}{n} \right| = \sum \frac{|z|^n}{n} = \sum \frac{1}{n} \text{ as } |z| = 1 \text{ on the circle.}$$

Let $M_n = 1/n$, we then see that series $\Sigma\, M_n$ does not converge (p-series with $p = 1$). Hence by M-test the series $\Sigma\, (z^n/n)$ is not uniformly convergent; showing that the power series may not be uniformly convergent on its circle of convergence.

Theorem: *If a power series* $\sum a_n z^n$ *vanishes identically for value of z within its circle of convergence, then all the coefficients in the power series vanish separately, i.e.,* $a_n = 0\, \forall n.$

Suppose $|z| = R$ be the circle of convergence of the power series. Then the series is convergent for $|z| \le r < R$ we shall prove this theorem by contradiction. Suppose if possible there is atleast one non-zero coefficient in the series. Let a_m be the first non-zero coefficient, then

$a_m + a_{m+1}z + a_{m+2}z^2 + \ldots$ vanishes for all values of z except zero and converges absolutely for $|z| \leq r < R$

$$\therefore \quad |a_{m+1} + a_{m+2}z + \ldots| \leq \sum_{n=0}^{\infty} |a_{m+n}| r^{n-1}$$

Therefore if $\phi(z) = a_{m+1}z + a_{m+2}z^2 + \ldots$ we can find a positive number $\delta \leq r$ such that

$$|\phi(z)| \leq \frac{1}{2}|a_m| \; \forall z \leq \delta$$

as
$$|a_m + \phi(z)| \geq |a_m| - |\phi(z)|$$

$$\geq \frac{1}{2}|a_m|$$

$$\therefore \quad |a_m + \phi(z)| \neq 0 \text{ for } z < \delta,$$

which is a contradiction. Hence all the coefficients must vanish seperately.

Hurwitz Theorem: *Let the function $f_n(z)$ be analytic and non-zero in a domain D and let $f_n(z)$ converges to $f(z)$ uniformly on every closed and bounded subset of D, then $f(z)$ is either identically zero or never equal to zero in D.* (*Meerut 2001*)

Let $f(z)$ is not identically zero then we have to show that $f(z)$ is never equal to zero in D.

Let $f(z_0) = 0$ for some $z_0 \in D$. Since zeros of an analytic function are isolated therefore there exists a number $r > 0$ such that $f(z)$ is defined and non-zero for $0 < |z - z_0| \leq r$. In particular, $f(z) \neq 0$ on the circle C, $|z - z_0| = r$.

Let $\qquad \in = \min |f(z)|: z \varepsilon c$

$\Rightarrow \qquad \in \leq |f(z)| \; \forall z \in C$

Since $f_n(z)$ converges to $f(z)$ uniformly on C, therefore for sufficiently large n we have
$$|f_n(z) - f(z)| < \in \; \forall z \in C.$$

Then by Rouche's theorem, the function $f(z)$ and $f_n(z)$ have the same number of zeroes inside C. But $f(z)$ has a zero at $z = z_0$, so $f_n(z)$ must have a zero inside C. But $f_n(z)$ is non-zero in D. Therefore $f(z)$ can number be zero in D.

12.8.1. Continuity of the sum, differentiability and integrability of a power series.

(*i*) *The sum of a power series is continuous in any region which lies entirely inside its circle of convergence.*

This follows from the fact that the power series $\Sigma a_n z^n$ is uniformly convergent within its circle of convergence and each term $a_n z^n$ of the series is continuous in this region.

(*ii*) *A power series can be differentiated term by term in any region which lies entirely inside its circle of convergence, i.e.,*

$$\frac{d}{dz}(\Sigma a_n z^n) = \Sigma \frac{d}{dz}(a_n z^n).$$

This follows from the fact that the power series $\Sigma a_n z^n$ is uniformly convergent within its circle of convergence and each term $a_n z^n$ of the series is analytic in this region.

(*iii*) *A power series can be integrated term by term along a curve which lies entirely in its circle of convergence, i.e.,*

$$\int_C (\Sigma a_n z^n) \, dz = \Sigma \int_C a_n z^n \, dz.$$

This follows from the fact that the power series $\Sigma a_n z^n$ is uniformly convergent within its circle of convergence and each term $a_n z^n$ of the series is continuous in this region.

EXAMPLES

1. *Show that*

$$\sum \frac{1}{n^z}$$

is uniformly convergent in the closed domain $R(z) \geq (1 + \delta)$, *where* δ *is any positive number.*

Solution. We shall consider n^z to have its principal value.

Taking $z = x + iy$, we have

$$n^z = e^{x \log n} = e^{(x + iy) \log n}$$
$$= e^{x \log n}\, e^{iy \log n} = n^x\, e^{iy \log n}$$

$\Rightarrow$ $\left| \dfrac{1}{n^x} \right| = \dfrac{1}{n^x}$, for $|e^{iy \log n}| = 1$.

Let, now, δ be any given positive number and
$$R(z) = x \geq 1 + \delta.$$

We then have

$$n^z \geq n^{1 + \delta} \geq n^{1 + \frac{1}{2}\delta}$$

$\Rightarrow$ $\left| \dfrac{1}{n^z} \right| = \dfrac{1}{n^x} \leq \dfrac{1}{n^{1 + \frac{1}{2}\delta}},$ ...(1)

for every n and every z such that $R(z) \geq (1 + \delta)$.

Since the series

$$\sum \frac{1}{n^{1 + \frac{1}{2}\delta}}$$

is known to be convergent, we deduce, from (1), by the M-test that

$$\sum \frac{1}{n^z}$$

is uniformly convergent in the closed domain
$$R(z) \geq (1 + \delta).\ (\delta > 0)$$

Note : The sum function of the series

$$\sum \frac{1}{n^z}$$

is known as **Riemann's zeta function** and denoted by the symbol $\xi(z)$.

Since, as seen above, $\sum (1/n^z)$ is uniformly convergent in the domain $R(z) \geq 1 + \delta$ for every $\delta > 0$ and $1/n^z$ is analytic in $R(z) > 1$, we see that the zeta function is analytic in the domain $R(z) > 1$.

2. *Show that the function*
$$f(z) = 1^{-z} - 2^{-z} + 3^{-z} - 4^{-z} + \ldots..$$

is analytic in the semi-plane $R(z) > 0$.

Solution. The test obtained in will enable us to settle the question of uniform convergence of the series in the question. We take

$$f_n(z) = (-1)^{n-1},\ u_n(z) = n^{-z}.$$

If $\{S_n(z)\}$ denote the sequence of partial sums of the series $\Sigma f_n(z)$, we have

$$S_n(z) = \begin{cases} 1, & \text{if } n \text{ is even,} \\ 0, & \text{if } n \text{ is odd,} \end{cases}$$

for every z. Thus $\{S_n(z)\}$ is uniformly bounded in every domain.

Also we have

$$|u_n(z) - u_{n+1}(z)| = \left| \frac{1}{n^z} - \frac{1}{(n+1)^z} \right|$$

and

$$\frac{1}{n^z} - \frac{1}{(n+1)^z} = z \int_C t^{-z-j} dt$$

where C denotes the segment of the real axis from n to $n+1$.

Further we may easily see that

$$|t^{-z-1}| \le t^{-\delta-1}, \, R(z) \ge \delta.$$
$$\le n^{-\delta-1}, \text{ if } n \le t \le n+1.$$

Thus we have

$$\left| \frac{1}{n^z} - \frac{1}{(n+1)^z} \right| \le |z| \, n^{-1-\delta}.$$

Now since the series

$$1/n^{1+\delta}, \, (\delta > 0)$$

is convergent, we see that, the series

$$\Sigma \left\{ \frac{1}{n^z} - \frac{1}{(n+1)^z} \right\}$$

is uniformly and absolutely convergent in the closed domain $R(z) \ge \delta$.

Finally, we have

$$|u_n(z)| = \left| \frac{1}{n^z} \right| = \frac{1}{n^x} \le \frac{1}{n^\delta}$$

so that the sequence $\{u_n(z)\}$ tends to zero uniformly in the closed domain $R(z) \ge \delta$.

Thus we see that the given series is uniformly convergent in the closed domain $R(z) \ge \delta$ where δ is any positive number.

Also each term of the series is analytic in the domain $R(z) > 0$.

Hence we deduce that the sum function of the series is analytic in the domain $R(z) > 0$.

3. *Show that series*

$$\sum_{n=0}^{\infty} (-1)^{n-1} \frac{z^{2n-1}}{1-z^{2n-1}}$$

is uniformly convergent in the region $|z| < 1$.

Solution. Write

$$u_n(z) = (-1)^{n-1} \frac{z^{2n-1}}{1-z^{2n-1}}$$

so that

$$|u_n(z)| = \left| (-1)^{n-1} \frac{z^{2n-1}}{1-z^{2n-1}} \right|$$

$$\leq \frac{|(-1)^{n-1}||z|^{2n-1}}{1-|z|^{2n-1}}$$

$$= \frac{r^{2n-1}}{1-r^{2n-1}} \text{ for } |z| = r \ (z < 1).$$

Write $$M_n = \frac{r^{2n-1}}{1-r^{2n-1}}$$

so that $$M_{n+1} = \frac{r^{2n+1}}{1-r^{2n+1}}$$

$$\therefore \quad \lim_{n \to \infty} \frac{M_{n+1}}{M_n} = \lim_{n \to \infty} \left[\frac{r^{2n+1}}{r^{2n-1}} \frac{1-r^{2n-1}}{1-r^{2n+1}} \right] = r^2 < 1, \text{ Since } r < 1$$

$\therefore \Sigma M_n$ is convergent.

Hence by Weierstrass's M-test, the series $\Sigma u_n(z)$, *i.e.*, the series

$$\sum (-1)^{n-1} \frac{z^{2n-1}}{1-z^{2n-1}}$$

is uniformly convergent in the region $|z| < 1$.

   4. *Test for uniform convergence of the series*

$$\sum_{n=1}^{\infty} \frac{1}{n^2 + z^2}$$

in the region $1 < |z| < 2$.

   Solution. Here $$u_n(z) = \frac{1}{n^2 + z^2}$$

so that $$|u_n(z)| = \frac{1}{|n^2 + z^2|} \leq \frac{1}{|n|^2 - |z|^2}$$

$$\leq \frac{1}{n^2 - 4} \text{ for } n \geq 3 \text{ and } 1 < |z| < 2,$$

i.e., the above inequality holds if the first two terms of the given series are removed (this can be done without affecting the convergence of the series).

Thus for $n \geq 3$ and $1 < |z| < 2$, we have

$$|u_n(z)| \leq \frac{1}{n^2 - 4} = \frac{2}{2n^2 - 8} = \frac{2}{n^2 + (n^2 - 8)}$$

$$\leq \frac{2}{n^2} \text{ (for } n \geq 3).$$

Let $M_n = 2/n^2$, we then see that ΣM_n converges (p-series with $p = 2$).

Hence by M-test the given series converges uniformly.

   5. *Show that the series*

$$2 \sin \frac{1}{3z} + 2^2 \sin \frac{1}{3^2 z} + \dots + 2^n \sin \frac{1}{3^n z} + \dots$$

converges absolutely for all values of z except zero, but does not converge uniformly near z = 0.

Solution. Here

$$u_n(z) = 2^n \sin\left(\frac{1}{3^n z}\right)$$

and

$$u_{n-1}(z) = 2^{n-1} \sin\left(\frac{1}{3^{n-1} z}\right)$$

$$\therefore \quad \lim_{n \to \infty} \left| \frac{u_n(z)}{u_{n-1}(z)} \right| = \lim_{n \to \infty} \left| \frac{2^n \sin\dfrac{1}{3^n z}}{2^{n-1} \sin\dfrac{1}{3^{n-1} z}} \right|$$

$$= \lim_{n \to \infty} \frac{2}{3} \left| \frac{\sin\left(\dfrac{1}{3^n z}\right) \bigg/ \dfrac{1}{3^n z}}{\sin\left(\dfrac{1}{3^{n-1} z}\right) \bigg/ \dfrac{1}{3^{n-1} z}} \right|$$

$$= \frac{2}{3} < 1 \text{ for } z \neq 0.$$

∴ The series $\Sigma \mid u_n(z) \mid$ is convergent for all $z \neq 0$.

Hence the series $\Sigma \, u_n(z)$ is absolutely convergent for all values of z except $z = 0$.

To prove that the series does not converge uniformly near $z = 0$ it is sufficient to show that

$$\lim_{z \to 0} |u_n(z)| \text{ does not exist.}$$

Here

$$\lim_{z \to 0} |u_n(z)| = \lim_{z \to 0} \left| 2^n \sin\frac{1}{3^n z} \right|$$

this limit does not exist.

Hence the series $\Sigma \, u_n(z)$ is not uniformly convergent near $z = 0$.

6. *Show that the series*

$$\sum_{n=1}^{\infty} \frac{z^{n-1}}{(1 - z^n)(1 - z^{n+1})} \,]$$

is equal to

$$\frac{1}{(1-z)^2} \text{ when } |z| < 1,$$

and is equal to

$$\frac{1}{z(1-z)^2} \text{ when } |z| > 1.$$

Hence show that the series is non-uniformly convergent near $\mid z \mid > 1$.

Solution. Here

$$u_n(z) = \frac{z^{n-1}}{(1 - z^n)(1 - z^{n+1})}$$

$$= \frac{1}{z(1-z)} \left\{ \frac{1}{(1 - z^n)} - \frac{1}{(1 - z^{n+1})} \right\}.$$

Putting $n = 1, 2, \ldots, n$ and adding column-wise we get the partial sum

$$S_n = \frac{1}{z(1-z)}\left(\frac{1}{1-z} - \frac{1}{1-z^{n+1}}\right).$$

Hence the sum function

$$S(z) = \lim_{n \to \infty} S_n(z)$$

$$\begin{cases} \dfrac{1}{z(1-z)}\left(\dfrac{1}{1-z} - 1\right) = \dfrac{1}{(1-z)^2} & \text{when } |z| < 1, \\[3mm] \dfrac{1}{z(1-z)}\left(\dfrac{1}{1-z} - 0\right) = \dfrac{1}{z(1-z)^2} & \text{when } |z| > 1. \end{cases}$$

The given series is uniformly convergent for $|z| > 1$,

if $|S(z) - S_n(z)| < \varepsilon$

if $\left| \dfrac{1}{z(1-z)^2} - \dfrac{1}{z(1-z)}\left(\dfrac{1}{1-z} - \dfrac{1}{1-z^{n+1}}\right) \right| < \varepsilon$ for $|z| > 1$

or if $\left| \dfrac{1}{z(1-z)(1-z^{n+1})} \right| < \varepsilon$

or if $\dfrac{1}{|z||1-z||1-z^{n+1}|} < \varepsilon$

or if $\dfrac{1}{|z|(|z|-1)(|z|^{n+1}-1)} < \varepsilon$

or if $\dfrac{1}{r(r-1)(r^{n+1}-1)} < \varepsilon$ where $|z| = r > 1$

or if $(n+1) > \dfrac{\log\left[1 + \dfrac{1}{r(r-1)\varepsilon}\right]}{\log r}$ which $\to \infty$ as $r \to 1$

Thus at all the points for which $|z| > 1$, there does not exist a number m such that for all $n \geq m$

$$|S(z) - S_n(z)| < \varepsilon.$$

The same reasoning holds for all the points z for which $|z| < 1$.

Hence the given series is not uniformly convergent near $|z| = 1$.

7. *Test for uniform convergence of the series*

$$\sum \frac{1}{2^n} \tan \frac{z}{2^n}.$$

Solution. Write $a_n = \dfrac{1}{2^n}$ and $u_n(z) = \tan \dfrac{z}{2^n}$ so that the given series can be written as $\Sigma a_n u_n$.

Now, firstly the series $\Sigma a_n = \Sigma(1/2^n)$ is convergent (series in G.P. with common ratio 1/2) for all z and so it has uniformly bounded partial sum. So the condition (*i*) of the test of § 12.4.2 is satisfied.

Secondly,

$$\lim_{n \to \infty} u_n (z) = \lim_{n \to \infty} \tan \frac{z}{2^n} = 0 \text{ for all } z \neq 0.$$

So the condition (*iii*) of the test is satisfied.

Lastly, $2^{n+1} \{u_n (z) - u_{n+1} (z)\}$

$$= 2^{n+1} \left(\tan \frac{z}{2^n} - \tan \frac{z}{2^{n+1}} \right)$$

$$= z \left\{ \left(2 \tan \frac{z}{2^n} \right) \Big/ \left(\frac{z}{2^n} \right) - \left(\tan \frac{z}{2^{n+1}} \right) \Big/ \left(\frac{z}{2^{n+1}} \right) \right\}$$

or

$$\lim_{n \to \infty} 2^{n+1} |u_n (z) - u_{n+1} (z)|$$

$$\leq \lim_{n \to \infty} \left[|z| \left\{ \left| 2 \left(\tan \frac{z}{2^n} \right) \Big/ \frac{z}{2^n} \right| + \left| \left(\tan \frac{z}{2^{n+1}} \right) \Big/ \frac{z}{2^{n+1}} \right| \right\} \right]$$

$$= |z| (2 + 1) = 3 |z|$$

$$= 3r \text{ (finite) where } |z| = r$$

$$\Rightarrow \quad 2^{n+1} |\{u_n (z) - u_{n+1} (z)\}| \leq k$$

where $k = 3r$ is a finite number independent of n.

So that $|u_n (z) - u_{n+1} (z)| \leq \dfrac{k}{2^{n+1}}$.

Let

$$M_n = \frac{k}{2^{n+1}},$$

we then see that the series ΣM_n is convergent (G.P. of common ratio 1/2). Hence by Weierstrass's M-test the series $\Sigma \{u_n (z) - u_{n+1} (z)\}$ is absolutely and uniformly convergent for all finite values of z. So the condition (*ii*) of the test is satisfied.

Hence the given series is uniformly convergent in every bounded closed region.

8. *By differentiating both the series of the identity*

$$\frac{1}{1 - z} = 1 + z + z^2 + z^3 + \ldots, \quad |z| < 1$$

find the sum of the series $\displaystyle\sum_{n=1}^{\infty} nz^n$ *for* $|z| < 1$. *Justify all steps.*

Solution. We have

$$\frac{1}{1 - z} = 1 + z + z^2 + z^3 + \ldots, \quad |z| < 1.$$

It can be easily seen that the series is uniformly convergent and each term is analytic, in the domain $|z| < 1$; therefore the sum function $\dfrac{1}{1 - z}$ is also analytic, hence term by term differentiation is valid.

Thus

$$\frac{d}{dz} \left(\frac{1}{1 - z} \right) = \frac{d}{dz} (1) + \frac{d}{dz} (z) + \frac{d}{dz} (z^2) + \frac{d}{dz} (z^3) + \ldots$$

$$\Rightarrow \qquad \frac{1}{(1-z)^2} = 1 + 2z + 3z^2 + \ldots$$

$$= \frac{1}{z}(z + 2z^2 + 3z^3 + \ldots)$$

$$= \frac{1}{z} \sum_{n=1}^{\infty} nz^n$$

$$\Rightarrow \qquad \sum_{n=1}^{\infty} nz^n = \frac{z}{(1-z)^2}.$$

9. *Show that the series*

$$\sum_{0}^{\infty} ze^{-nz},$$

converges absolutely but not uniformly in the sector

$$|z| \le R \, |arg\, z| \le \delta \text{ where } 0 < \delta < \frac{1}{2}\pi.$$

Also show that the convergence is uniform in

$$0 \ne r \le |z| \le R, \, |arg\, z| \le \delta.$$

Solution. The given series is a G.P. with common ratio e^{-z}.
Taking

$$z = \rho\,(\cos\theta + i\sin\theta),$$

we have $\qquad |ze^{-nz}| = \rho\,|e^{-n\rho\,(\cos\theta + i\sin\theta)}| = \rho e^{-n\rho\cos\theta}.$

Also for $0 < |\theta| < \dfrac{1}{2}\pi$, we have $\rho\cos\theta > 0$ so that

$$e^{-\rho\cos\theta} < 1.$$

Thus we see that the series $\Sigma\,\rho e^{-n\rho\cos\theta}$
of the moduli of the given series is a G.P. with common ratio less than 1. Accordingly we see that the given series is absolutely convergent for

$$0 < |arg\, z| < \frac{1}{2}\pi.$$

Again in the domain defined by $r \le \rho \le R$,
$|arg\, z| \le \delta$, we have

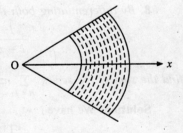

$$|ze^{-nz}| = \rho e^{-n\rho\cos\theta} \le Re^{-nr\cos\delta}$$

and the series $\qquad \Sigma\,Re^{-nr\cos\delta}$ is convergent.

Thus by M-test, the given series is uniformly convergent
in the closed domain

Fig. 12.4

$$r \le \rho \le R, \, |arg\, z| \le \delta.$$

We shall now show that the given series is not uniformly convergent in

$$|z| \le R, \, |arg\, z| \le \delta.$$

Suppose, on the contrary, that the series does converge uniformly in this domain. Then since each term of the series is continuous in this domain, we see that the sum function of the series must also necessarily be continuous in the same domain.

Also we may easily see that the sum function S (z) of the series is given by

$$S(z) = \begin{cases} 0 \text{ if } z = 0 \\ z/(1 - e^{-z}) \text{ if } z \neq 0 \end{cases}$$

so that

$$\lim_{z \to 0} S(z) = \lim_{z \to 0} \frac{z}{1 - e^{-z}} = 1 \neq 0 = S(0).$$

Thus S (z) is not continuous for

$$z = 0$$

which is a point of the domain

$$\mid z \mid \leq R, \mid \arg z \mid \leq \delta.$$

Since we arrive at a contradiction, we see that the convergence cannot be uniform.

10. *A function* $f(z)$ *is analytic when* $\mid z \mid < R$ *and has the Taylor's expansion*

$$\sum_{0}^{\infty} a_n z_n.$$

Show that, if $r < R$,

$$\frac{1}{2\pi} \int_{0}^{2\pi} \mid f(re^{i\theta}) \mid^2 d\theta = \sum_{0}^{\infty} \mid a_n \mid^2 r^{2n}.$$

Deduce Liouville's theorem.

Solution. We have

$$f(z) = \sum_{n=0}^{\infty} a_n z^n, \quad f(\bar{z}) = \sum_{n=0}^{\infty} a_n \bar{z}^n.$$

The two series are absolutely convergent when $\mid z \mid < R$. We can therefore multiply them and arrange the terms in any way we like. We now have

$$f(\bar{z}) f(z) = \sum_{n, m=0}^{\infty} a_n \bar{a}_m z^n \bar{z}^m.$$

We write $z = re^{i\theta}, r < R$,

$$\therefore \quad \mid f(re^{i\theta}) \mid^2 = \sum_{n, m=0}^{\infty} a_n \bar{a}_m r^{n+m} e^{i(n-m)\theta} \qquad \qquad ...(1)$$

The series on the right can easily be shown as uniformly convergent in respect of the variable θ varying from 0 to 2π so that term by term integration is valid.

Also we have

$$\int_{0}^{2\pi} e^{i(n-m)\theta} d\theta = \begin{cases} 2\pi \text{ if } n = m, \\ 0 \text{ if } n \neq m. \end{cases}$$

Thus we have from (1), on term by term integration

$$\int_{0}^{2\pi} \mid f(re^{i\theta}) \mid^2 d\theta = 2\pi \sum_{n=0}^{\infty} \mid a_n \mid^2 r^{2n}.$$

To prove Liouville's theorem, suppose that $f(z)$ is an integral function and

$$\mid f(z) \mid \leq M, \quad \forall \ z.$$

We have, therefore,

$$2\pi \sum_{n=0}^{\infty} |a_n|^2 r^{2n} \leq 2\pi M^2 \ \forall \ r \qquad \qquad ...(2)$$

From (2), we have

$$|a_n|^2 r^{2n} \leq M^2$$

$$\Rightarrow \qquad |a_n| \leq M / r^n \qquad \qquad ...(3)$$

for every r and every n.

Letting r tend to infinity, we obtain, from (3)

$$|a_n| = 0 \ \Rightarrow \ a_n = 0 \ \text{for every} \ n \neq 0.$$

$\therefore f(z)$ is a constant.

12.9. Infinite products. After infinite series, we proceed to consider infinite products. As in the case of infinite series, the notion of the *product* of numbers defined in Chapter 1 is not adequate for dealing with the product of an infinite number of factors and recourse is necessarily to be had to the notion of limit for the purpose.

Consider the infinite product

$$\prod_{n=0}^{\infty} u_n = u_1 u_2 \ldots u_n \ldots$$

(u_n) being any sequence. We set up the sequence $\{P_n\}$ of partial products where

$$P_n = u_1 u_2 \ldots u_n.$$

In the following, we shall always assume that no factor u_n is zero. In fact, if some factor u_m were zero, then we would have

$$P_n = 0 \ \forall \ n \geq m,$$

irrespective of the nature of the other factors and the case would obviously be devoid of interest.

12.9.1. Convergence of infinite products. *An infinite product*

$$\prod_{n=1}^{\infty} u_n$$

is said to be convergent if and only if the sequence $\{P_n\}$ of its partial products converges to a non-zero limit. Also, in the event of convergence, $\lim P_n$ is called the value of the product and is denoted by (Π_n).

The motivation for the exclusion of the case which arises when $\lim P_n$ is zero from the purview of convergence will become clear as we proceed with the development of the subject.

12.9.2. A necessary *condition for the convergence of an infinite product*

$$\Pi u_n$$

is that $$\lim_{n \to \infty} u_n = 1.$$

Let the product converge and let

$$\lim P_n \neq 0.$$

Now $$u_n = \frac{P_n}{P_{n-1}}$$

$$\Rightarrow \qquad \lim u_n = \lim \frac{P_n}{P_{n-1}} = \frac{\lim P_n}{\lim P_{n-1}} = \frac{P}{P} = 1.$$

Note 1. In view of this necessary condition for convergence obtained here, it is usual to write an infinite product in the form

$$\Pi\,(1 + a_n),\ 1 + a_n = u_n,$$

so that the necessary condition for convergence may now be stated as

$$\lim a_n = 0.$$

Note 2. Since for a convergent infinite product $\Pi\,u_n$,

$$\lim u_n \text{ is } 1,$$

we deduce that if u_n is real, then for sufficiently large values of n, *i.e.*, for all values of $n \geq$ some number m, each factor u_n would be positive.

12.10. General principle of convergence for infinite products.

Theorem. *A necessary and sufficient condition for an infinite product*

$$\Pi\,u_n$$

to be convergent is that to every given positive number ε*, there corresponds a positive integer* m *such that*

$$|\,u_{n+1}\,u_{n+2}\,\cdots\cdots u_{n+p} - 1\,| < \varepsilon \ \forall\ n \geq m, p > 0.$$

The condition is necessary.

Let $\lim P_n = P \neq 0$.

There exists, therefore, a positive integer m_1 such that $\forall\ n \geq m_1$,

$$|P_n - P| < \frac{1}{2}|P|.$$

$$\Rightarrow \qquad\qquad |P_n| > \frac{1}{2}|P| \ \forall\ n \geq m_1.$$

If then k_1 be the smallest of the finite set of positive numbers,

$$|P_1|, |P_2|, \cdots\cdots, |P_{m_1} - 1|, \frac{1}{2}|P|,$$

we have $\qquad\qquad |\,P_n\,| > k_1 \ \forall\ n \qquad\qquad\qquad\qquad\qquad \ldots(1)$

Let now $\varepsilon > 0$ be any given number. Then because of the convergence of $\{P_n\}$, there exists a positive integer m such that $\forall\ n \geq m$ and $p \geq 0$,

$$|\,P_{n+p} - P_n\,| < k_1\varepsilon$$

$$\Rightarrow \quad |\,P_n\,|\,|\,u_{n+1}\,\cdots\cdots u_{n+p} - 1\,| < k_1\varepsilon$$

$$\Rightarrow \qquad |\,u_{n+1}\,\cdots\cdots u_{n+p} - 1| < \frac{k_1\varepsilon}{|\,P_n\,|} < \varepsilon \qquad\qquad\qquad \text{[by (1)]}$$

Thus we see that the condition is necessary.

The condition is sufficient. Under the given condition, there exists a positive integer m_2 such that for every $p \geq 0$,

$$\left|\,u_{m_2+1}\,\cdots\cdots u_{m_2+p} - 1\,\right| < \frac{1}{2}$$

$$\Rightarrow \qquad \frac{1}{2} < \left|\,u_{m_2+1}\,\cdots\cdots u_{m_2+p}\,\right| < \frac{3}{2}$$

$$\Rightarrow \qquad \frac{1}{2}|\,P_{m_2}\,| < |\,P_{m_2+p}\,| < \frac{3}{2}|\,P_{m_2}\,| \qquad\qquad\qquad\qquad \ldots(2)$$

Let, now, k_2, k_3 be the smallest and the greatest members respectively of the two finite sets of positive numbers

$$|P_1|, \ldots, |P_{m_2-1}|, \frac{1}{2}|P_{m_2}|,$$

and

$$|P_1|, \ldots, |P_{m_2-1}|, \frac{3}{2}|P_{m_2}|.$$

Thus we have $k_2 < |P_n| < k_3 \ \forall \ n$ ...(3)

If now $\varepsilon > 0$ be a given number, then under the given condition, there exists a positive integer m such that

$$|u_{n+1} \ldots u_{n+p} - 1| < \varepsilon/k_3 \ \forall \ n \geq m, p > 0$$ ...(4)

On multiplying with P_n, we obtain from (4),

$$\left| P_{n+p} - P \right| < \frac{\varepsilon|P_n|}{k_3} < \varepsilon \ \forall \ n \geq m, \ p > 0$$ [using (3)]

Thus we see that the sequence $\{P_n\}$ is convergent.

Also since there exists a positive number k_2 such that

$$|P_n| > k_2,$$

for all n, we see that $\lim P_n$ cannot be zero.

Thus the product is convergent and we have proved that the condition is sufficient.

12.11. Convergence of an infinite product in terms of that of a series. We shall now state and prove a theorem which will express the condition for the convergence of an infinite product in terms of that of a corresponding series.

Theorem. *An infinite product*

$$\Pi \ (1 + a_n)$$

is convergent if and only if the series

$$\Sigma \ log \ (1 + a_n)$$

is convergent, the principal value of the logarithm being taken in each case.

We write

$$P_n = (1 + a_1) (1 + a_2) \ldots (1 + a_n),$$
$$S_n = log \ (1 + a_1) + \ldots + log \ (1 + a_n)$$
$$\therefore \quad e^{S_n} = e^{log \ (1 + a_1) + \ldots + log \ (1 + a_n)}$$
$$= e^{log \ (1 + a_1)} \ e^{log \ (1 + a_2)} \ldots e^{log \ (1 + a_n)}$$
$$= (1 + a_1) (1 + a_2) \ldots (1 + a_n) \ P_n$$ ...(1)

Now suppose that the series is convergent so that

$$S_n \to S$$ ....(2)

Then, exponential function being continuous, we deduce from (1) and (2) that

$$\lim P_n = \lim e^{S_n} = e^{\lim S_n} = e^S \neq 0,$$

so that the product also converges.

Again suppose that the product is convergent. Taking principal values of logarithms, we have

$$log \ P_n = log \ (1 + a_1) + \ldots + log \ (1 + a_n) + 2p_n i\pi$$ ...(3)
$$= S_n + 2p_n i\pi$$ ...(4)

Here $\{P_n\}$ is a well defined sequence of integers. Now we show that for all sufficiently large values of n, p_n is constant. Denoting by α_n and β_n the imaginary parts of $\log (1 + a_n)$ and $\log P_n$ respectively, we obtain from (3),

$$\beta_n = (\alpha_1 + \ldots + a_n) + 2p_n \pi$$
$$\Rightarrow \qquad \beta_{n+1} - \beta_n = \alpha_{n+1} + 2 (p_{n+1} - p_n) \pi,$$
$$\Rightarrow \qquad 2 (p_{n+1} - p_n) \pi = \alpha_{n+1} - (\beta_{n+1} - \beta_n). \qquad \ldots(5)$$

As
$$\lim_{n \to \infty} (1 + a_n) = 1,$$

we have
$$\lim \alpha_n = 0.$$

Also let
$$\lim \beta_n = \beta.$$

Then, from (5), we obtain
$$\lim (p_{n+1} - p_n) = 0.$$

Since, however, p_n is an integer, we deduce that for sufficiently large values of n, p_n remains a constant, say p.

From (4), we have
$$S_n = \log P_n - 2p_n i\pi \to \log P - 2pi\pi.$$

Thus the series is convergent.

Note. Even though the above theorem has reduced the problem of the consideration of the convergence of infinite products to that of series, yet the result is only of theoretical importance. This is so because the consideration of series of the type $\Sigma \log (1 + a_n)$ is, in no way, easier. Anyhow this theorem leads to a sufficient test which often proves convenient in practice. This is given in the following section.

12.12. A sufficient condition for the convergence of infinite products.

Theorem. *The infinite product*
$$\Pi (1 + a_n)$$
will be convergent if the two series
$$\Sigma a_n \text{ and } \Sigma | a_n |^2$$
are both convergent.

With the help of infinite series for $\log (1 + z)$, we may easily see that
$$\frac{\log (1+z) - z}{z^2} \to -\frac{1}{2} \text{ as } z \to 0. \qquad \ldots(1)$$

Also since Σa_n is convergent, therefore,
$$\lim_{n \to \infty} a_n = 0. \qquad \ldots(2)$$

From (1) and (2), we deduce that
$$\lim_{n \to \infty} \frac{\log (1 + a_n) - a_n}{a_n^2} = -\frac{1}{2} \qquad \ldots(3)$$

Writing
$$\frac{\log (1 + a_n) - a_n}{a_n^2} = \theta_n \qquad \ldots(4)$$

we deduce from (3) that $\{\theta_n\}$ is a bounded sequence so that there exists a positive number k such that
$$| \theta_n | < k \ \forall \ n.$$

We re-write (4) as
$$\log(1 + a_n) = a^n + a_n^2 \theta_n \qquad \qquad ...(5)$$

Now since
$$|a_n^2 \theta_n| \le k|a_n|^2,$$
and
$$\Sigma |a_n|^2$$
is convergent, we see that the series
$$\Sigma |a_n^2 \theta_n| \text{ and therefore } \Sigma a_n^2 \theta_n \text{ is convergent.}$$

Also Σa_n is given to be convergent. From (5), we now see that the series
$$\Sigma \log(1 + a_n)$$
is convergent.

Hence the product $\Pi(1 + a_n)$ is convergent.

12.13. Absolute convergence of infinite products. Def. *An infinite product*
$$\Pi(1 + a_n)$$
is said to be absolutely convergent, if the infinite product
$$\Pi(1 + |a_n|)$$
is convergent.

We shall now prove that *every absolutely convergent product is convergent.*

The result would be proved with the help of the general principle of convergence.

Let $\varepsilon > 0$ be any given number.

Since $\Pi(1 + |a_n|)$ is convergent, there exists a positive integer, m, such that
$$|(1 + |a_{n+1}|)(1 + |a_{n+2}|) \dots (1 + |a_{n+p}|)| < \varepsilon \qquad ...(1)$$
$\forall \ n \ge m, p > 0.$

By actual multiplication, we may easily see that
$$|(1 + a_{n+1}), (1 + a_{n+p}) - 1| \le |(1 + |a_{n+1}|) \dots (1 + |a_{n+p}|) - 1| \qquad ...(2)$$
From (1) and (2), we deduce that
$$|(1 + a_{n+1}) \dots (1 + a_{n+p}) - 1| < \varepsilon \ \forall \ n \ge m, p > 0.$$
Thus the product
$$\Pi(1 + a_n)$$
is convergent.

Note 1. The reader may notice that the notion of absolute convergence would be futile, if, in analogy with infinite series, we were to say that $\Pi(1 + a_n)$ is absolutely convergent if $\Pi|(1 + a_n)|$ is convergent. In fact, it may be easily seen that if $\Pi(1 + a_n)$ is convergent, then $\Pi|(1 + a_n)|$ is also convergent. This follows from the inequality
$$|P_n| - |P| \le |P_n - P|.$$

Note 2. The theorem proved above can also be put in another form as follows :

A sufficient condition for the convergence of the product
$$\Pi(1 + a_n)$$
is that the product $\Pi(1 + |a_n|)$ *is convergent.*

This form of sufficient condition points out clearly the importance of studying the behaviour of products of the type
$$\Pi(1 + b_n)$$
wherefor b_n is positive. We obtain an important theorem for products of this type in the following.

12.14. Some Theorems on Infinite Products

Theorem I. *If f_n is real and non-negative, then the series Σf_n and the product $\text{II}\,(1 + f_n)$ converge or diverge together.*

When $f \geq 0$, we have $1 + f \leq e^f$

Thus

$$f_1 + f_2 + \ldots + f_n < (1 + f_1)\,(1 + f_2)\ldots(1 + f_n)$$

$$\leq e^{f_1 + f_2 + \ldots + f_n}$$

or
$$S_n < P_n \leq e^{S_n} \qquad\qquad \ldots(1)$$

Since P_n and S_n are monotonic increasing functions of n, they will have a limit finite or infinite. They can not oscillate.

Hence from (1) it follows that if $S_n \to a$ finite limit, then P_n also does so and if $S_n \to \infty$, P_n also $\to \infty$ and vice versa. That is, the sereis Σf_n and the product $\text{II}\,(1 + f_n)$ converge or diverge together.

Theorem II. *If f_n is real and $-1 < f_n \leq 0$, then the series Σf_n and the product $\text{II}\,(1 + f_n)$ converge or diverge together.*

Let $f_n = -g_n$ so that $0 \leq g_n < 1$ and $P_n = (1 + f_1)(1 + f_2)\ldots(1 + f_n)$

$$S_n = f_1 + f_2 + \ldots + f_n.$$

Since $1 - g \leq e^{-g}$ when $0 \leq g < 1$ we have $0 < (1 - g_1)(1 - g_2)\ldots(1 - g_n)$

$$\leq e^{-(g_1 + g_2 + \ldots + g_n)}$$

or
$$0 < (1 + f_1)(1 + f_2)\ldots(1 + f_n)$$

$$\leq e^{-(f_1 + f_2 + \ldots + f_n)}$$

or
$$0 < P_n \leq e^{(f_1 + f_2 + \ldots + f_n)}$$

Now, if Σf_n diverges it will diverge to $-\infty$ and consequently $P_n \to 0$. Hence the product diverges to zero. Next suppose Σf_n is convergent. Then for a given $\in$ we can find a positive integer m such that

$$0 \leq \sum_{v=m}^{\infty} g_v < \in$$

Also $\quad (1 - g_m)(1 - g_{m+1}) \geq 1 - g_m - g_{m+1}, \ (1 - g_m)(1 - g_{m+1})(1 - g_{m+2})$

$$\geq (1 - g_m - g_{m+1})(1 - g_{m+2})$$

$$\geq 1 - g_m - g_{m+1} - g_{m+2}$$

and therefore, for $n > m$,

$$(1 - g_m)(1 - g_{m+1})\ldots(1 - g_n) > 1 - g_m - g_{m+1}\cdots - g_n > 1 - \in$$

or
$$\frac{P_n}{P_{m-1}} \geq 1 - \in.$$

Since each factor is less than unity, $P_n < P_{m-1}$ and consequently $\dfrac{P_n}{P_{m-1}}$ is monotonic decreasing and hence it must have a positive lower bound. It follows that P_n tends to a finite non-zero limit. In other words. $\text{II}\,(1 - f_n)$ is convergent.

Theorem III. *If the series* Σf_n^2 *is convergent, then the product* $\Pi(1 + f_n)$ *and the series* Σf_n *converge or diverge together.*

Since Σf_n^2 is convergent, we can find such that $\Sigma f_n^2 < \dfrac{1}{4}$

or $|f_n| < \dfrac{1}{2}$ for $n > m$.

For such values of n, we have

$$|\log(1 + f_n) - f_n| = \left| \frac{f_n^2}{2} - \frac{f_n^3}{3} + \frac{f_n^4}{4} - \ldots \right|$$

$$\leq \frac{1}{2} f_n^2 \{1 + |f_n| + |f_n|^2 + \ldots\}$$

$$= \frac{f_n^2}{2(1 + |f_n|)} < f_n^2$$

Hence the series $\Sigma |\log(1 + f_n) - f_n|$ is convergent. It follows that the series $\Sigma\{\log(1 + f_n) - f_n\}$ is convergent, that is, $\log P_n - S_n$ tends to finite limit.

Therefore the series Σf_n and the product $\Pi(1 + f_n)$ converge or diverge together.

12.15. Convergence of infinite products

$$\Pi(1 + b_n), \ \Pi(1 - b_n). \hspace{4cm} (b_n \geq 0)$$

Theorem. *The infinite products*

$$\Pi(1 + b_n), \ \Pi(1 - b_n)$$

converge if and only if the positive term series

$$\Sigma \, b_n$$

converges.

Consider first the case of the infinite product

$$\Pi(1 + b_n).$$

We set up the two sequences

$$P_n = (1 + b_1) \ldots (1 + b_n), \ S_n = b_1 + \ldots + b_n.$$

Since $b_n \geq 0$, the sequences $\{P_n\}$ and $\{S_n\}$ are both monotonically increasing and that

$$P_n \geq 1 \ \forall \ n.$$

We shall now obtain the two necessary inequalities.

We have

$$(1 + b_1)(1 + b_2) = 1 + (b_1 + b_2) + b_1 b_2 \geq 1 + (b_1 + b_2).$$

On multiplying successively with

$$(1 + b_3), (1 + b_4), \ldots, (1 + b_n),$$

we shall obtain

$$(1 + b_1) \ldots (1 + b_n) \geq 1 + (b_1 + \ldots + b_n) \geq (b_1 + \ldots + b_n)$$

$\Rightarrow \hspace{3cm} P_n \geq S_n \hspace{4cm} \ldots(1)$

Again, we know that $\hspace{1cm} e^x \geq 1 + x$ when $x \geq 0$.

Replacing x by $b_1, b_2, \ldots, b_n$ we obtain

$$e^{b_1} \geq 1 + b_1, \ e^{b_2} \geq 1 + b_2, \ldots, e^{b_n} \geq 1 + b_n.$$

From these we obtain,

$$e^{b_1 + \dots + b_n} \geq (1 + b_1) \dots (1 + b_n),$$

$$\Rightarrow \qquad\qquad e^{S_n} \geq P_n \qquad\qquad\qquad \dots(2)$$

From (1) and (2), we deduce that if any one of the two sequences $\{P_n\}$, $\{S_n\}$ is bounded, then the other is also bounded. Also since $P_n \geq 1$ for every n, the sequence $\{P_n\}$ cannot tend to zero.

Thus the infinite product $\Pi (1 + b_n)$ and the infinite series Σb_n are either both convergent or both divergent, if b_n is positive for every n.

We now consider the infinite product

$$\Pi (1 - b_n).$$

We suppose that lim $b_n = 0$, for otherwise the infinite series and the infinite product would both be divergent and thus have identical behaviours. Thus without loss of generality, we suppose that $b_n < 1$.

We write

$$Q_n = (1 - b_1) \dots (1 - b_n)$$

and notice that $\{Q_n\}$ is a monotonically decreasing sequence. Also since $Q_n \geq 0$ for every n, we see that $\{Q_n\}$ is bounded below. Thus the divergence of the product $\Pi (1 - b_n)$ could arise only by the fact of the sequence $\{Q_n\}$ tending to 0.

It will now be shown that $S_n \to \infty$ if and only if $Q_n \to 0$.

We have

$$(1 - b_1) (1 + b_1) = 1 - b_1^2 \leq 1,$$

$$\Rightarrow \qquad\qquad 1 - b_1 \leq \frac{1}{1 + b_1}.$$

Similarly

$$1 - b_2 \leq \frac{1}{1 + b_2}, \ \dots, 1 - b_n \leq \frac{1}{1 + b_n}.$$

Multiplying these, we obtain

$$Q_n \leq \frac{1}{P_n} \leq \frac{1}{S_n}. \qquad\qquad \text{[by (1)]}$$

This shows that if $S_n \to \infty$, then $Q_n \to 0$, *i.e.*, if the series diverges then the product also diverges.

Suppose now that the series Σb_n converges. Then the series $\Sigma 2b_n$ also converges.

There exists a positive integer m such that $\forall \ n \geq m$

$$0 \leq b_n \leq \frac{1}{2}$$

so that we have

$$(1 - b_n) (1 + 2b_n) = 1 + 2b_n \left(\frac{1}{2} - b_n \right) \geq 1$$

$$\Rightarrow \qquad\qquad 1 - b_n \geq \frac{1}{1 + 2b_n} \quad \forall \ n \geq m.$$

Replacing n by m, $m-1$, ..., n and multiplying, we obtain

$$(1-b_m)(1-b_{m+1}).....(1-b_n) \geq \frac{1}{(1+2b_m).....(1+2b_n)}. \qquad \text{...(3)}$$

Since the series $\Sigma\, 2b_n$ converges, the product $\Pi\,(1+2b_n)$ also converges and there exists a positive number k such that

$$\prod_m^n (1+2b_n) \leq k \ \forall \ n \qquad \text{...(4)}$$

From (3) and (4), we obtain

$$\prod_m^n (1-b_n) > 1/k.$$

Hence we see that the infinite product

$$\prod_m^n (1-b_n)$$

converges to a finite non-zero limit.

Thus the product

$$\Pi\,(1-b_n)$$

is convergent.

12.16. Uniform convergence of infinite products.

Def. *An infinite product*

$$\Pi\,\{1+f_n\,(z)\}$$

is said to be uniformly convergent in any closed aggregate, S, if the sequence of partial products is uniformly convergent for S. Of course the limit of the sequence must not be zero for any $z \in S$.

12.16.1. A sufficient condition for the uniform convergence of an infinite product.

Theorem. *The infinite product*

$$\Pi\,\{1+f_n\,(z)\}$$

would be uniformly convergent in S, if the series

$$\Sigma\,|\,f_n\,(z)\,|$$

is uniformly convergent in S.

Since $\Sigma\,|\,f_n\,(z)\,|$ is convergent for every $z \in S$, we see by § 12.13, that the product

$$\Pi\,\{1+|\,f_n\,(z)\,|\}$$

is convergent and accordingly the product

$$\Pi\,\{1+f_n\,(z)\}$$

is absolutely convergent for every $z \in S$.

As $\Sigma\,|\,f_n\,(z)\,|$ is uniformly convergent in S, there exists a positive integer m such that

$$|\,f_m\,(z)\,| + |\,f_{m+1}\,(z)\,| + ... + |\,f_n\,(z)\,| < 1 \ \forall \ n \geq m, \ \forall \ z \in S \qquad \text{...(1)}$$

We write

$$P_n\,(z) = \{1+f_m\,(z)\}\,\{1+f_{m+1}\,(z)\}\,.....\,\{1+f_n\,(z)\},$$

so that $\{P_n\,(z)\}$ denotes the sequence of partial products of the given product $\Pi\,\{1+f_n\,(z)\}$ starting from $\{1+f_m\,(z)\}$. $\qquad (n \geq m)$

Consider now the infinite series

$$P_m\,(z) + \{P_{m+1}\,(z) - P_m\,(z)\} + ... + \{P_n\,(z) - P_{n-1}\,(z)\} + ... \qquad \text{...(2)}$$

which can be re-written as

$$P_m(z) + P_m(z) f_{m+1}(z) + P_{m+1}(z) f_{m+2}(z) + \dots \qquad \dots(3)$$

The sequence of partial sums of the series (2) is

$$\{P_n(z)\}. \qquad (n \geq m)$$

Now we have, $\forall\ n \geq m$ and $\forall\ z \in S$,

$$|P_n| \leq \{1 + |f_m(z)|\}\ \{1 + |f_{m+1}(z)|\} \ \dots \ \{1 + |f_n(z)|\}$$

$$\leq e^{|f_m(z)| + |f_{m+1}(z)| + \dots + |f_n(z)|} \leq e, \text{ by (1)} \qquad \dots(4)$$

Also the series

$$|f_{m+1}(z)| + \dots + |f_n(z)| + \dots \qquad \dots(5)$$

is uniformly convergent in S.

With the help of (4) and (5), we see that the series (3) is uniformly convergent, *i.e.*, the sequence $\{P_n(z)\}$ is uniformly convergent. Hence the given product is uniformly convergent in S.

Cor. If $\{M_n\}$ is a sequence of positive constants such that

(*i*) $|f_n(z)| \leq M_n\ \forall\ z \in S$,

(*ii*) $\Sigma\ M_n$ is a convergent series, then the infinite product

$$\Pi\ \{1 + f(z)\}$$

is uniformly convergent in S.

EXAMPLES

1. *Show that the product*

$$\prod \left(1 + \frac{1}{n^z} \right)$$

converges absolutely if R (z) > 1. Also show that it is uniformly convergent in the closed domain R (z) ≥ 1 + δ where δ is any positive number.

Solution. As shown in Example 1 on page 526, the series

$$\Sigma\ (1 / n^z)$$

is absolutely convergent when R (z) > 1 and accordingly by § 12.12, the product $\prod \left(1 + \dfrac{1}{n^z} \right)$ is absolutely convergent when R (z) ≥ 1 + δ.

Thus by § 12.15.1, the product $\prod \left(1 + \dfrac{1}{n^z} \right)$ is uniformly convergent when R (z) ≥ 1 + δ.

2. *Prove that*

$$\prod_{n=1}^{\infty} \frac{n^z + n^2 + 1}{n^z + n^2 - 1},$$

represents a regular function in the domain R (z) > 2.

Solution. We have

$$\frac{n^z + n^2 + 1}{n^z + n^2 - 1} = 1 + \left(\frac{n^z + n^2 + 1}{n^z + n^2 - 1} - 1 \right) = 1 + \frac{2}{n^z + n^2 - 1}.$$

Consider now any bounded closed domain D contained in R (z) ≥ (2 + δ) where δ is any positive number. For any $z \in$ D, we have

$$\lceil n^z + n^2 - 1 \mid \geq \mid n^z \mid - n^2 - 1$$
$$= \mid n^{x+iy} \mid - n^2 - 1$$
$$= n^x - n^2 - 1$$
$$> n^{2+\frac{1}{2}\delta} - n^2 - 1.$$

$$\Rightarrow \qquad \left| \frac{1}{n^z + n^2 - 1} \right| \leq \frac{1}{n^{2+\frac{1}{2}\delta} - n^2 - 1}$$

$\forall$ n and $\forall$ $z \in$ D.

By comparison with the convergent series

$$\sum \frac{1}{n^{2+\frac{1}{2}\delta}}$$

we may see that the series

$$\sum \frac{1}{n^{2+\frac{1}{2}\delta} - n^2 - 1}$$

is convergent.

Hence by M-test

$$\sum \frac{1}{n^z + n^2 - 1}$$

is uniformly and absolutely convergent in D. Thus

$$\prod \frac{n^z + n^2 + 1}{n^z + n^2 - 1}$$

is uniformly convergent in D and also therefore analytic in D. As δ is any positive number, the product is analytic in the domain R $(z) > 2$.

For no z such that R $(z) > 2$, we can have $n^z + n^2 - 1 = 0$.

3. *The product*

$$\left\{ \left(1 - \frac{z}{1} \right) e^z \right\} \left\{ \left(1 + \frac{z}{1} \right) e^{-z} \right\} \left\{ \left(1 - \frac{z}{2} \right) e^{z/2} \right\} \left\{ \left(1 + \frac{z}{2} \right) e^{-z/2} \right\} \ldots.$$

converges absolutely and uniformly in every bounded closed domain D which does not contain any of the points, $\pm 1, \pm 2, \pm 3, \ldots.$.

Solution. We have

$$\left(1 - \frac{z}{n} \right) e^{z/n} = \left(1 - \frac{z}{n} \right) \left[1 + \frac{z}{n} + \frac{1}{2!} \left(\frac{z}{n} \right)^2 + \ldots \right]$$
$$= 1 - u_n(z),$$

where
$$u_n(z) = \sum_{r=2}^{\infty} \frac{r-1}{r!} \left(\frac{z}{n} \right)^r$$

Now
$$\frac{r-1}{r!} = \frac{1}{(r-2)!} \frac{1}{r} \leq \frac{1}{(r-2)!}.$$

$$\therefore \qquad |u_n(z)| \le \sum_{r=2}^{\infty} \frac{1}{(r-2)} \left(\frac{R}{n}\right)^r , \text{if} \, |z| \le R$$

$$= \left(\frac{R}{n}\right)^2 e^{R/n} \le e^{R^2/n^2} , \text{if} \, R < n.$$

We may similarly see that

$$\left(1 + \frac{z}{n}\right) e^{-z/n} = 1 - v_n(z) \text{ where } |v_n(z)|$$

Also the series $\Sigma \, e^{R^2/n^2}$ is convergent.

Thus we prove that the given product is absolutely and uniformly convergent in every bounded and closed domain not containing any of the points $\pm 1, \pm 2, \dots$.

4. *Show that the product*

$$\prod \left(1 + \frac{z}{n\pi}\right) e^{-z/n\pi}$$

is absolutely convergent.

Solution. Let $\prod \{1 + u_n(z)\}$ denote the given product.
Then

$$\prod \{1 + u_n(z)\} \equiv \prod \left(1 + \frac{z}{n\pi}\right) e^{-z/n\pi}$$

$$\equiv \prod \left(1 + \frac{z}{n\pi}\right) \left(1 - \frac{z}{n\pi} + \frac{1}{2!} \frac{z^2}{n^2\pi^2} - \dots\right)$$

$$\equiv \prod \left(1 - \frac{1}{2} \frac{z^2}{n^2\pi^2} - \frac{1}{3} \frac{z^3}{n^3\pi^3} - \dots\right).$$

So that

$$u_n(z) = -\frac{1}{2} \frac{z^2}{n^2\pi^2} - \frac{1}{3} \frac{z^3}{n^3\pi^3} - \dots$$

Let

$$v_n(z) = \frac{1}{n^2}.$$

Then

$$\lim \left| \frac{u_n(z)}{v_n(z)} \right| = \frac{1}{2\pi^2} |z|^2$$

a finite quantity for all z.

But the series $\Sigma \, (1/n^2)$ is convergent; therefore by comparison test the series $\Sigma \, |u_n(z)|$ is also convergent, *i.e.*, the series is absolutely convergent.

5. *Show that the product*

$$\prod_{n=1}^{\infty} \left\{1 - \left(1 - \frac{1}{n}\right)^{-n} z^{-n}\right\}$$

converges absolutely for all values of z situated outside a circle whose centre is origin and radius unity.

Solution. Let

$$\Pi\,\{1 + u_n\,(z)\} \equiv \prod \left\{ 1 - \left(1 - \frac{1}{n}\right)^{-n} z^{-n} \right\}$$

so that

$$u_n\,(z) = -\left(1 - \frac{1}{n}\right)^{-n} z^{-n}$$

$$\therefore \qquad \lim |\,u_n\,(z)\,|^{1/n} = \lim \left\{ \left(1 - \frac{1}{n}\right)^{-1} |\,z^{-1}\,| \right\}$$

$$= \frac{1}{|\,z\,|} \quad \text{which is less than 1 if } |\,z\,| > 1.$$

Hence the series $\displaystyle\sum_{n=1}^{\infty} |\,u_n\,(z)\,|$ is convergent, *i.e.*, the series $\displaystyle\sum_{n=2}^{\infty} u_n\,(z)$ is absolutely

convergent if $|\,z\,| > 1$. Consequently the product $\displaystyle\prod_{n=2}^{\infty} \{1 + u_n\,(z)\}$ is absolutely convergent if $|\,z$

$|\,> 1$, *i.e.*, if z lies outside the circle $|\,z\,| = 1$.

    6. *Express*

$$\frac{n!\,z!}{(n+z)!}\,(n+1)^z$$

as a product of n factors. If the number of factors is increased indefinitely, show that the product is absolutely convergent except for z = 0, z = 1.

Solution. We can write $\dfrac{n!\,z!}{(n+z)!}\,(n+1)^z$ as

$$= 1 \cdot 2 \cdot 3 \,..... \, n \cdot \frac{z!}{z!\,(z+1)\,(z+2)\,.....\,(z+n)}\,(n+1)^z$$

$$= \frac{1 \cdot 2 \cdot 3 \,..... \, n}{(z+1)\,(z+2)\,.....\,(z+n)} \cdot (n+1)^z$$

$$= \frac{1}{z+1} \cdot \frac{2}{z+2} \cdot \frac{3}{z+3} \,..... \, \frac{n}{z+n} \cdot (n+1)^z$$

$$= \left\{ \frac{1}{z+1} \cdot 2^z \right\} \left\{ \frac{2}{z+2} \cdot \frac{3^z}{2^z} \right\} \left\{ \frac{3}{z+3} \cdot \frac{4^z}{3^z} \right\} \,..... \, \left\{ \frac{n}{z+n} \cdot \frac{(n+1)^z}{n^z} \right\}$$

$$= \prod_{n=1}^{n} \frac{n}{z+n} \cdot \left(\frac{n+1}{n}\right)^z, \quad \text{this is product of } n \text{ factors}$$

$$= \prod \left[\left(1 + \frac{z}{n}\right)^{-1} \left(1 + \frac{1}{n}\right)^z \right]$$

$$= \prod \left[\left(1 - \frac{z}{n} + \frac{z^2}{n^2} - ..... \right) \left\{ 1 + z \cdot \frac{1}{n} + \frac{z\,(z-1)}{2!} \cdot \frac{1}{n^2} + ... \right\} \right]$$

$$= \prod \left[1 + \frac{z(z-1)}{2n^2} + \ldots \right]$$

$$= \prod [1 + u_n(z)] \text{ (say)}$$

when

$$u_n(z) = \frac{z(z-1)}{2n^2} + \ldots$$

$$\therefore \quad \lim_{n \to \infty} \frac{|u_n(z)|}{1/n^2} = \frac{|z||z-1|}{2},$$

a finite and non-zero quantity except for $z = 0$ and $z = 1$.

But the series $\Sigma (1/n^2)$ is convergent; therefore the series $\Sigma |u_n(z)|$ is also convergent; consequently the series $\Sigma u_n(z)$ is absolutely convergent. Hence the product $\prod (1 + u_n)$ is absolutely convergent.

7. *Show that the infinite product*

$$\prod_{n=1}^{\infty} \left[\frac{1 - e^{-a/n}}{\log(1 + a/n)} \right]$$

is convergent $(a > -1)$. *Also show that it is absolutely convergent.*

Solution. Let $\prod (1 + u_n)$ denote the given product.

Then

$$\prod (1 + u_n) \equiv \prod \left\{ \frac{1 - e^{-a/n}}{\log(1 + a/n)} \right\}$$

where

$$\left| \frac{a}{n} \right| < 1 \text{ for all } n.$$

$$\equiv \prod \left[\frac{1 - \left(1 - \dfrac{a}{n} + \dfrac{1}{2!} \dfrac{a^2}{n^2} - \dfrac{1}{3!} \dfrac{a^3}{n^3} + \ldots \right)}{\dfrac{a}{n} - \dfrac{1}{2} \dfrac{a^2}{n^2} + \dfrac{1}{3} \dfrac{a^3}{n^3} - \ldots} \right]$$

$$= \prod \left(1 - \frac{1}{2} \frac{a}{n} + \frac{1}{6} \frac{a^2}{n^2} - \ldots \right) \left(1 - \frac{1}{2} \frac{a}{n} + \frac{1}{3} \frac{a^2}{n^2} - \ldots \right)^{-1}$$

$$= \prod \left(1 - \frac{1}{2} \frac{a}{n} + \frac{1}{6} \frac{a^2}{n^2} - \ldots \right) \left(1 + \frac{1}{2} \frac{a}{n} - \frac{1}{3} \frac{a^2}{n^2} + \frac{1}{4} \frac{a^3}{n^3} - \ldots \right)$$

$$= \prod \left(1 - \frac{1}{6} \frac{a^2}{n^2} + \ldots \right)$$

so that $\quad u_n = -\dfrac{1}{6} \dfrac{a^2}{n^2} + \ldots$

$$\lim \frac{u_n}{1/n^2} = -\frac{1}{6} a^2, \text{ which is a finite quantity.}$$

But $\Sigma (1/n^2)$ is convergent; therefore the series Σu_n is also convergent. It follows that the given product is convergent.

It may also be seen that the given product is absolutely convergent because

$$\lim \frac{|u_n|}{1/n^2} = \frac{1}{6} a^2 \text{ (a finite quantity)}.$$

8. *Show that the product*

$$\prod \left(1 + \frac{1}{n^z} \right)$$

is uniformly convergent in the domain Re. (z) > 1 + δ where δ is any positive number.

Solution. Let

$$\prod \{1 + u_n(z)\} = \prod \left(1 + \frac{1}{n^z} \right)$$

so here $u_n = \dfrac{1}{n^z}$.

$$\therefore \qquad |u_n(z)| = \left| \frac{1}{n^{x+iy}} \right| = \frac{1}{|n^x| |n^{iy}|}$$

$$= \frac{1}{n^x} \text{ since } n^{iy} = 1.$$

$$< \frac{1}{n^{1+\delta}}.$$

But the series $\Sigma (1/n^{1+\delta})$ is convergent (p-series with $p = 1 + \delta > 1$), hence by M-test the series $\Sigma |u_n(z)|$ is uniformly convergent; consequently the product $\prod \{1 + u_n(z)\}$ is uniformly convergent, *i.e.*, the product $\prod \left(1 + \dfrac{1}{n^z} \right)$ is uniformly convergent for Re. $(z) > 1 + \delta$.

12.17. Construction of Meromorphic functions with given poles and corresponding principal parts. Partial Fraction. Decomposition of a meromorphic function. Mittag-Leffler's Theorem.

We have seen that a *rational meromorphic function* is determined to within an added polynomial by the character of its poles. Naturally the question now arises as to how completely is an arbitrary meromorphic function defined by the behaviour of the function at its poles. This question is answered by Mittag-Leffler (1846 – 1927) theorem which we now proceed to consider.

Firstly we see that if $f(z)$ be any given meromorphic function, then the general meromorphic function $\varphi(z)$ having the same poles and the same corresponding principal parts as $f(z)$ is given by

$$\varphi(z) = g(z) + f(z),$$

where $g(z)$ is *any* arbitrary integral function. This follows from the fact that $\psi(z) - f(z)$ has only removable singularities in the entire complex plane and thus, with suitable modification, be thought of as a function with no finite singular point, *i.e.*, an integral function.

Theorem. *Let $f(z)$ be any given meromorphic function with any sequence*

$$z_0, z_1, \ldots, z_n, \ldots$$

of distinct poles tending to infinity such that a given polynomial

$$P_n \left(\frac{1}{z - z_n} \right) in \left(\frac{1}{z - z_n} \right)$$

is the principal part at the pole z_n.

Then there exists a sequence of polynomials
$$Q_n (z),$$
and an integral function g (z) such that

$$f(z) = g(z) + \left[P_1 \left(\frac{1}{z - z_1} \right) - Q_1 (z) \right]$$

$$+ \left[P_2 \left(\frac{1}{z - z_2} \right) - Q_2 (z) \right] + ...$$

$$= g(z) + \sum_{n=1}^{\infty} \left[P_n \left(\frac{1}{z - z_n} \right) - Q_n (z) \right].$$

Since the only limiting point of the sequence $\{z_n\}$ is infinity, we may suppose that the given sequence $\{z_n\}$ is such that

$$| z_0 | \le | z_1 | \le | z_2 | \le | z_3 | \le .....$$

Possibly z_0 and no other point of z_n may be zero but to start with we suppose that
$$z_0 \ne 0.$$

The function

$$P_n \left(\frac{1}{z - z_n} \right),$$

being analytic everywhere except at z_n, is analytic at zero and accordingly possesses a Taylor's expansion of the form

$$P_n \left(\frac{1}{z - z_n} \right) = a_0^{(n)} + a_1^{(n)} z + a_2^{(n)} z^2 + ... + ... \qquad ...(1)$$

with radius of convergence $| z_n |$.

The series is uniformly convergent inside any smaller circle C_n, say

$$| z | \le \frac{1}{2} | z_n |.$$

Consequently inside C_n, the function

$$P_n \left(\frac{1}{z - z_n} \right)$$

can be approximated to uniformly by a polynomial consisting of a finite number of terms on the right of (1) as closely as we like. Thus there exists a polynomial

$$Q_n (z) = a_0^{(n)} + a_1^{(n)} z + a_2^{(n)} z^2 + ... + a_{hn}^{(n)} z^{kn}$$

such that

$$\left[P_n \left(\frac{1}{z - z_n} \right) - Q_n (z) \right] < \frac{1}{2^n},$$

$S\ z \in C_n.$

Consider now the series

$$\sum_{n=0}^{\infty} \left[P_n \left(\frac{1}{z - z_n} \right) - Q_n (z) \right] \qquad ...(2)$$

and let C be *any* circle with its centre at the origin.

Let C_m be a circle containing the given circle C.

The finite part

$$\sum_{n=0}^{m} \left[P_n \left(\frac{1}{z - z_n} \right) - Q_n(z) \right]$$

of (2) is analytic inside C with no singularities except some of the prescribed poles.

The second part

$$\sum_{n=m+1}^{\infty} \left[P_n \left(\frac{1}{z - z_n} \right) - Q_n(z) \right] \qquad \qquad ...(3)$$

is a sum of functions each of which is analytic inside C. Also we have

$$P_n \left(\frac{1}{z - z_1} \right) - Q_n(z) < \frac{1}{2^n}$$

$\forall \; n \geq m$ and $\forall \; z \in C$ and

$$\sum \frac{1}{2^n}$$

is convergent.

Thus by the Weierstrass's M-test, the series (3) is uniformly convergent and by § 12.6, the sum function of the series (3) is analytic in C.

Thus we see that the sum function of the series (2) is analytic everywhere except at the points

$$z_0, z_1, \; ....., \; z_n, \; ......$$

which are poles with assigned corresponding principal parts.

Hence the theorem.

In case $z_0 = 0$, we have merely to add

$$P_0 (1/z),$$

to the series.

Note. The degrees of the polynomials, $Q_n(z)$ may not, in general, be uniformly bounded. If, however, the poles are all simple and such that

$$P_n \left(\frac{1}{z - z_0} \right) = \frac{b_n}{z - z_n},$$

then each polynomial may be chosen of degree m if only the series

$$\sum_{n=1}^{\infty} \frac{|b_n|}{|z_n|^{m+1}}$$

is convergent. This fact is easy to prove.

The case considered here is the most important for applications. A more direct consideration of this case of simple poles is given in the following.

Case of simple poles. We shall now prove two forms of results for the case of simple poles. The first of these is an immediate deduction from the preceding.

1. Let $f(z)$ be a meromorphic function with simple poles

$$z_0, z_1, z_2, \; ....., \; z_n, \; .....$$

where $\qquad\qquad\qquad\qquad 0 < |z_0| \le |z_1| \le |z_2| \le \;.....$

and let $\qquad\qquad\qquad\qquad b_0, \; b_1, \; b_2, \; ....., \; b_n, \; .....$

be the corresponding residues.

We shall now prove that if there exists a *sequence of natural numbers* m_n *such that the series*

$$\sum_{n=1}^{\infty} |b_n| \left| \frac{z}{z_n} \right|^{m_n + 1}$$

is convergent for every z, *then*

$$(z) = g(z) + \sum_{n=1}^{\infty} \left[\frac{b_n}{z - z_n} + \frac{b_n}{z_n} \left\{ 1 + \left(\frac{z}{z_n} \right) + ... + \left(\frac{z}{z_n} \right)^{m_n - 1} \right\} \right]$$

where $g(z)$ *is any integral function.*

We have

$$P_n \left(\frac{1}{z - z_n} \right) = \frac{b_n}{z - z_n}$$

$$= -\frac{b_n}{z_n} \left(1 - \frac{z}{z_n} \right)^{-1}$$

$$= -\frac{b_n}{z_n} \left[1 + \left(\frac{z}{z_n} \right) + \left(\frac{z}{z_n} \right)^2 + ... + \left(\frac{z}{z_n} \right)^{m_n - 1} + ... \right].$$

We take

$$Q_n(z) = -\frac{b_n}{z_n} \left[1 + \left(\frac{z}{z_n} \right) + \left(\frac{z}{z_n} \right)^2 + ... + \left(\frac{z}{z_n} \right)^{m_n - 1} \right]$$

so that

$$P_n \left(\frac{1}{z - z_n} \right) - Q_n(z) = -\frac{b_n}{z_n} \left[\left(\frac{z}{z_n} \right)^{m_n} + \left(\frac{z}{z_n} \right)^{m_n + 1} + ... \right]$$

$$= -\frac{\dfrac{b_n}{z_n} \left(\dfrac{z}{z_n} \right)^{m_n}}{1 - \dfrac{z}{z_n}}.$$

Consider now any circle C with its centre at the origin. There exists a positive integer m such that

$$\frac{|z|}{|z_n|} \le \frac{1}{2}$$

for $n \ge m$ and every z in the interior of C.

Consider now the series

$$\sum_{n=0}^{\infty} \left[P_n \left(\frac{1}{z - z_n} \right) - Q_n(z) \right] \qquad\qquad ...(4)$$

The finite part

$$\sum_{n=0}^{m} \left[P_n \left(\frac{1}{z - z_n} \right) - Q_n (z) \right] \qquad ...(5)$$

of (4) is analytic inside C with no singularities but some of the prescribed poles.

We consider now

$$\sum_{n=m+1}^{\infty} \left[P_n \left(\frac{1}{z - z_n} \right) - Q_n (z) \right] \qquad ...(6)$$

For any terms of (6), we have

$$\left| P_n \left(\frac{1}{z - z_n} \right) - Q_n (z) \right| \leq \left| \frac{b_n}{z_n} \right| 2 \left| \frac{z}{z_n} \right|^{m_n}$$

$$= 2 | b_n | | z |^{-1} \left| \frac{z}{z_n} \right|^{m_n + 1}.$$

It thus follows that the series (6) represents a function which is analytic in the interior of C. Hence the theorem.

II. The poles being isolated, there certainly exists a sequence of closed contours C_n such that

(i) each contains the preceding one in its interior,

(ii) no pole lies on any C_n,

(iii) the distance of C_n from the origin tends to infinity with n.

We shall now prove that if for some such sequence,

$$\lim_{n \to \infty} \int_{C_n} \frac{f(\xi)}{\xi - z} d\xi = 0,$$

then

$$f(z) = \sum_{n=1}^{\infty} \left\{ \sum \frac{b_v^{(n)}}{z - z_v^{(n)}} \right\}$$

where $z_v^{(n)}$ denotes, for different values of v, the poles in doubly connected domain bounded by C_{n+1} and C_n and $b_v^{(n)}$ denotes the residues thereat. Also the sum

$$\sum \frac{b_v^{(n)}}{z - z_v^{(n)}}$$

for a given n, is to be carried over the poles between

$$C_{n-1} \text{ and } C_n.$$

Let, z, be any given point. Let C_n be a contour having z in its interior.

It is easy to see that the residue of

$$f(\xi) / (\xi - z)$$

at z is $f(z)$ and that at any pole z_m of $f(z)$ is

$$- b_m / (z - z_m).$$

Thus we have, by the Residue Theorem,

$$\frac{1}{2\pi i} \int_{C_n} \frac{f(\xi)}{\xi - z} d\xi = f(z) - \sum \frac{b_m}{z - z_m} \qquad ...(1)$$

where the summation on the right is carried over all the poles of $f(z)$ inside C_n.

Letting $n \to \infty$, we obtain from (1)

$$f(z) = \sum_{n=1}^{\infty} \left\{ \sum \frac{b_v^{(n)}}{z - z_v^{(n)}} \right\}.$$

Hence the theorem.

Example. *Show that*

$$\pi \cot \pi z = \frac{1}{z} + \sum_{n=1}^{\infty} \frac{2z}{z^2 - n^2}.$$

Solution. We have

$$\pi \cot \pi z = \pi \frac{\cos \pi z}{\sin \pi z}$$

so that the poles of $\pi \cot \pi z$ are the zeros of $\sin \pi z$ which are

$$0, \pm 1, \pm 2, \dots, \pm n, \dots$$

where n is any positive integer.

Each of these is a simple pole. We may easily show that the residue of $\pi \cot \pi z$ at each of these poles is 1.

For C_n, we shall choose the rectangular path with sides parallel to the two axes and of lengths

$$2n + 1 = 2 \left(n + \frac{1}{2} \right),$$

and lying about the axis. Thus C_n is given by

$$R(z) = \pm \left(n + \frac{1}{2} \right) I(z) = \pm \left(n + \frac{1}{2} \right),$$

and has, as its vertices the points

$$\left(n + \frac{1}{2} \right) - \left(n + \frac{1}{2} \right) i, \quad \left(n + \frac{1}{2} \right) + \left(n + \frac{1}{2} \right) i,$$

$$-\left(n + \frac{1}{2} \right) + \left(n + \frac{1}{2} \right) i, \quad -\left(n + \frac{1}{2} \right) + \left(n + \frac{1}{2} \right) i,$$

which we denote by A, B, C, D, respectively.

Thus C_n contains the poles

$$0, \pm 1, \pm 2, \dots, \pm n.$$

The poles between C_{n-1} and C_n are $\pm n$.

Thus if we prove that

$$\lim_{n \to \infty} \int_{C_n} \frac{f(\xi)}{\xi + z} d\xi = 0,$$

where

$$f(\xi) = \pi \cot \pi \xi \qquad \qquad \dots(1)$$

then

$$\pi \cot \pi z = \frac{1}{z} + \sum_{n=1}^{\infty} \left(\frac{1}{z - n} + \frac{1}{z + n} \right)$$

$$= \frac{1}{z} + \sum_{n=1}^{\infty} \frac{2z}{z^2 - n^2}.$$

We now proceed to prove (1).

We denote the four sides AB, BC, CD, DA of C_n by

$$C_n^{(1)}, C_n^{(2)}, C_n^{(3)}, C_n^{(4)},$$

respectively.

As $\pi \cot (- \pi\xi) = \pi \cot \pi\xi,$

we have

$$\int_{C_n^{(2)}} \frac{\pi \cot \pi\xi}{\xi - z} \, d\xi + \int_{C_n^{(4)}} \frac{\pi \cot \pi\xi}{\xi - z} \, d\xi = \int_{C_n^{(2)}} \pi \cot \pi\xi \, \frac{2z}{\xi^2 - z^2} \, d\xi$$

and

$$\int_{C_n^{(1)}} \frac{\pi \cot \pi\xi}{\xi - z} \, d\xi + \int_{C_n^{(3)}} \frac{\pi \cot \pi\xi}{\xi - z} \, d\xi = \int_{C_n^{(1)}} \pi \cot \pi\xi \, \frac{2z}{\xi^2 - z^2} \, d\xi$$

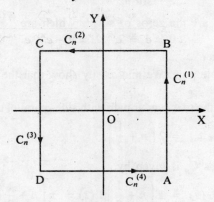

Fig. 12.5

Along $C_n^{(2)}$, we have

$$\xi = x + i \left(n + \frac{1}{2} \right)$$

where x varies from

$$- \left(n + \frac{1}{2} \right) \text{ to } + \left(n + \frac{1}{2} \right).$$

Thus along $C_n^{(2)}$, we have

$$|\pi \cot \pi\xi| = \left| \pi i \, \frac{e^{i\pi\xi} + e^{-i\pi\xi}}{e^{i\pi\xi} - e^{-i\pi\xi}} \right|$$

$$= \left| \pi i \, \frac{e^{2i\pi\xi} + 1}{e^{2i\pi\xi} - 1} \right|$$

$$= \left| \pi i \, \frac{e^{2\pi i [x + i (n + 1/2)]} + 1}{e^{2\pi i [x + i (n - 1/2)]} - 1} \right|$$

$$= \left| \pi i \, \frac{e^{2\pi i x} \, e^{- 2\pi (n + 1/2)} + 1}{e^{2\pi i x} \, e^{- 2\pi (n + 1/2)} - 1} \right|$$

$$\therefore \quad |\pi \cot \pi\xi| \le 2 \frac{e^{-2\pi(n+1/2)}+1}{1-e^{-2\pi(n+1/2)}}.$$

As $e^{-2\pi(n+1/2)} \to 0$ as $n \to \infty$, we see that along $C_n^{(2)}$

$$|\pi \cot \pi\xi| \le 2\pi$$

for sufficiently large values of n.

Also along $C_n^{(1)}$,

$$\pi \cot \pi\xi = \pi i \frac{e^{i\pi\xi} + e^{-i\pi\xi}}{e^{i\pi\xi} - e^{-i\pi\xi}}$$

$$= \pi i \frac{e^{i\pi(n+1/2+iy)} + e^{-i\pi(n+1/2+iy)}}{e^{i\pi(n+1/2+iy)} - e^{-i\pi(n+1/2+iy)}}$$

$$= \pi i \frac{e^{-\pi y} e^{i\pi(n+1/2)} + e^{\pi y} e^{-i\pi(n+1/2)}}{e^{-\pi y} e^{i\pi(n+1/2)} - e^{\pi y} e^{-i\pi(n+1/2)}}$$

$$\therefore \quad |\pi \cot \pi\xi| = \left| \pi \frac{1-e^{-2\pi y}}{1+e^{-2\pi y}} \right| < \pi < 2\pi.$$

Thus $\pi \cot \pi\xi$ is uniformly bounded on C_n.

Also for every point ξ on C_n, we have

$$|\xi \pm z| \ge |\xi| - |z| \ge \left(n + \frac{1}{2} \right) - |z|$$

so that

$$|\xi^2 - z^2| \ge \left[\left(n + \frac{1}{2} \right) - z \right]^2.$$

Thus

$$\left| \int_{C_n} \frac{\pi \cot \pi\xi}{\xi - z} \, d\xi \right| = \int_{C_n^{(1)}} \frac{\pi \cot \pi\xi \cdot 2z}{\xi^2 - z^2} \, d\xi + \int_{C_n^{(2)}} \frac{\pi \cot \pi\xi \cdot 2z}{\xi^2 - z^2} \, d\xi$$

$$\le 2 \cdot \frac{2\pi \cdot 2|z|}{\left[\left(n + \frac{1}{2} \right) - |z| \right]^2} \cdot 4 \left(n + \frac{1}{2} \right) \to 0 \text{ as } n \to \infty.$$

Hence we have the result, *viz.*,

$$\pi \cot \pi z = \frac{1}{z} + \sum_{n=1}^{\infty} \frac{2z}{z^2 - n^2}.$$

12.18. Construction of integral functions with given zeros. Weierstrass's Factorisation Theorem. We know that every polynomial which is only a special case of an integral function can be expressed as a product of factors corresponding to the zeros of the polynomial. We shall now see how the result can be generalised to the case of arbitrary integral functions.

Firstly we shall show that *an integral function with no zeros is expressible in the form*
$$e^{h(z)}$$
where h (z) is an integral function.

Let $f(z)$ be an integral function with no zeros. Then

$$f'(z)/f(z)$$

is itself an integral function. We write

$$\frac{f'(z)}{f(z)} = g(z).$$

Integrating along any rectifiable curve from 0 to z, we have

$$\text{Log } f(z) - \text{Log } f(0) = \int_0^z g(z)\, dz = h(z), \text{ (say)}.$$

$\Rightarrow \qquad\qquad\qquad f(z) = f(0)\, e^{h(z)}.$

Hence the result.

Theorem. *Let $f(z)$ be an integral function with zeros*

$$z_0, z_1, z_2, \ldots, z_n, \ldots$$

of orders

$$b_0, b_1, b_2, \ldots, b_n, \ldots$$

respectively. Then there exists an integral function $h(z)$ with no zeros and a sequence of polynomials $P_n(z)$ such that

$$f(z) = e^{h(z)} \prod_{n=0}^{\infty} \left[\left(1 - \frac{z}{z_n} \right)^{b_n} e^{P_n(z)} \right].$$

It is easy to see that each zero z_n of order b_n of $f(z)$ is a simple pole of

$$f'(z)/f(z)$$

with residue b_n. Thus we can apply Mittag-Leffler's theorem to the meromorphic function $f'(z)/f(z)$.

There exists, therefore, an integral function $g(z)$ and a sequence of polynomials $Q_n(z)$ such that

$$\frac{f'(z)}{f(z)} = g(z) + \sum_{n=1}^{\infty} \left[\frac{b_n}{z - z_n} + Q_n(z) \right].$$

Because of uniform convergence, we have, integrating from 0 to z,

$$\text{Log } f(z) - \text{Log } f(0) = \int_0^z g(z)\, dz + \sum_{n=0}^{\infty} \left[b_n \log\left(1 - \frac{z}{z_n} \right) + P_n(z) \right]$$

$$= h(z) + \sum_{n=0}^{\infty} \left[\log\left(1 - \frac{z}{z_n} \right)^{b_n} + P_n(z) \right], \text{ (say)},$$

where $P_n(z)$ is a polynomial.

Thus we obtain

$$f(z) = e^{h(z)} \sum_{n=1}^{\infty} \left[\left(1 - \frac{z}{z_n} \right)^{b_n} e^{P_n(z)} \right].$$

Hence the theorem.

Example. *Show that*

$$\sin \pi z = \pi z = \sum_{n=1}^{\infty} \left(1 - \frac{z^2}{n^2} \right).$$

Solution. We have

$$\pi \cot \pi z = \frac{1}{z} + \sum_{n=1}^{\infty} \frac{2z}{z^2 - n^2} \qquad \qquad ...(1)$$

In any given domain, the part of the series in (1), obtained on omitting a finite number of the terms in the beginning, is uniformly convergent. Hence we can integrate term by term. Taking the integral along any rectifiable curve from 0 to z, we obtain

$$\left| \log \frac{\sin \pi z}{z} \right|_0^z = \sum_{n=1}^{\infty} \left| \log (z^2 - n^2) \right|_0^z$$

At $z = 0$, $\sin \pi z / z$ has a removable singularity.

Assuming that necessary modification has been made, we obtain

$$\log \frac{\sin \pi z}{\pi z} = \sum_{n=1}^{\infty} \log \left(1 - \frac{z^2}{n^2} \right).$$

Thus we obtain

$$\frac{\sin \pi z}{\pi z_n} = \prod_{n=1}^{\infty} \left(1 - \frac{z^2}{n^2} \right).$$

EXERCISES

1. Discuss the uniform convergence of the following series :

(a) $\displaystyle\sum \frac{(-1)^{n-1}}{n!} \frac{1}{z+n}$ (b) $\displaystyle\sum \frac{1}{z^2 - n^2 \pi^2}$

(c) $\displaystyle\sum \frac{1}{2^n} \tan \frac{z}{2^n}$ (d) $\displaystyle\sum \frac{1}{n^2} \frac{z^n}{1+z^n}$

(e) $\displaystyle\sum \frac{e^{inz}}{n^z}.$

[**Ans.** (a) U.C. in every bounded closed domain.

(b) U.C. in every bounded closed domain not containing the points $\pm n\pi$; n being any positive integer.

(c) U.C. in every bounded closed domain.

(d) U.C. in $|z| \geq 1 + \delta$ as well as $|z| \leq 1 - \delta$, where δ is any positive number.

(e) U.C. in every bounded closed domain contained in

$$I(z) \, n < 0;$$

where δ, η are any positive numbers.]

2. Show that

$$\sum \left(\frac{z^{2n}}{1 - z^{2n}} \right)$$

is uniformly convergent in the closed domain
$$| z | \leq r,$$
where $0 < r < 1$.

3. Show that if $\Sigma\, a_n$ is convergent, then
$$\Sigma\, a_n n^{-z}$$
is convergent when R $(z) > 0$ and uniformly convergent in any bounded closed domain for which R $(z) \geq \delta$ where δ is any positive number.

4. Show that the series
$$\sum_1^\infty \frac{z^n}{1+z^{2n}}, \quad \sum_1^\infty (-1)^{n+1} \frac{z^{2n-1}}{1+z^{2n-1}}$$
represent regular functions in $| z | < 1$.

5. Prove that the series
$$\frac{z}{1+z} + \frac{z^2}{(1+z)(1+z^2)} + \frac{z^4}{(1+z)(1+z^2)(1+z^4)}$$
$$+ ..... + \frac{z^{2n}}{(1+z)(1+z^3).....(1+z^{2n})} + ...$$
converges if $| z | \neq 1$ and that its sum $\phi\,(z)$ is regular when $| z | \neq 1$.
By first verifying that
$$\phi\,(z^2) + z\ = (1+z)\,\phi\,(z),$$
or otherwise, prove that $\phi\,(z) = z$ in a domain D but that the convergence of the series is not uniform in D.

6. Show that near $z = 0$, the series
$$\sum_1^\infty \frac{(-2z)(1+z)^{n-1}}{\{1+(1+z)^{n-1}\}\,\{1+(1+z)^n\}}.$$
Show also that the series is uniformly convergent in any closed domain not containing the circle $| 1 + z | = 1$. Find the function it represents in $| 1 + z | < 1$ and in $| 1 + z | > 1$.
[**Ans.** 1 if $| 1 + z | < 1$, $- 1$ if $| 1 + z | > 1$.]

7. Discuss the convergence of the following products :

(a) $\displaystyle\prod \left\{1 + \frac{(-1)^n}{n^z}\right\}$
(b) $\displaystyle\prod \left\{1 - \frac{e^{inz}}{n^2}\right\}$

(c) $\displaystyle\prod \left\{\frac{2+z^n}{1+z^n}\right\}$
(d) $\displaystyle\prod \left\{\frac{z+z^{2n}}{1+z^{2n}}\right\}$

(e) $\displaystyle\prod \{1 + z^{2n}\}$
(f) $\displaystyle\prod \left\{\cos\left(\frac{z}{n}\right)\right\}$

(g) $\displaystyle\prod \left\{\frac{\sin\,(z/n)}{(z/n)}\right\}$
(h) $\displaystyle\prod \left\{\frac{n\,(n+1)+(1+i)}{n\,(n+1)+(1-i)}\right\}.$

[**Ans.** (a) Absolutely convergent when R $(z) > 1$.

(b) Absolutely convergent for I (z) ≥ 0 and divergent for I (z) > 0.

(c) Convergent for | z | > 1 and divergent otherwise.

(d) Convergent for | z | > 1 and for z = 1 and divergent otherwise.

(e) Convergent for | z | < 1.

(f) Convergent for every z.

(g) Absolutely convergent for every z.

(h) Convergent.]

8. Show that the product

$$\left(1 - \frac{z^2}{1^2}\right)\left(1 - \frac{z^2}{2^2}\right)\left(1 - \frac{z^2}{3^2}\right) \ldots \left(1 - \frac{z^2}{n^2}\right) \ldots$$

converges absolutely and uniformly in every bounded closed domain D which does not contain any of the points ± 1, ± 2, ± 3, ... and that the product

$$\left(1 - \frac{z}{1}\right)\left(1 + \frac{z}{1}\right)\left(1 - \frac{z}{2}\right)\left(1 + \frac{z}{2}\right)\left(1 - \frac{z}{3}\right)\left(1 + \frac{z}{3}\right) + \ldots$$

converges uniformly but not absolutely in Γ.

9. Show that if

$$z_n = \frac{(n + a_1)(n + a_2) \ldots (n + a_e)}{(n + b_1)(n + b_2) \ldots (n + b_e)}$$

then the product Π z_n is convergent, if

$$k = l$$

and

$$\Sigma a_n = \Sigma b_n.$$

10. Find the region of absolute convergence of the infinite product

$$\Pi (1 \pm z_n z^n),$$

when Σ z_n is any absolutely convergent series.　　　　　　　　**[Ans. | z | < 1.]**

11. Prove that

$$\prod_{n=1}^{\infty} \frac{n^z + n^2 + 1}{n^z + n^2 - 1}$$

represents an analytic function f_1 (z) in the domain

$$R (z) > 2$$

and (except at certain pole) an analytic function f_2 (z) in the domain

$$R (z) < 2.$$

Show that both f_1 (z) and f_2 (z) have the same line

$$R (z) = 2$$

as a line of singularities.

12. Prove that, if Σ | u_n |² is convergent, the infinite product

$$\prod_{1}^{\infty} (1 + u_n)$$

is convergent, if, and only if, Σ u_n is convergent.

By taking

$$u_{2n-1} = \frac{1}{\sqrt{n}}, \quad u_{2n} = \frac{1}{\sqrt{n}} + \frac{1}{n}, \quad (n > 1)$$

(or otherwise) show that the convergence of the infinite product $\Pi \, (1 + u_n)$ does not imply the convergence of

$$\Sigma \, u_n, \text{ of } \Sigma \, |u_n|^2 \text{ or of } \Pi \, (1 + 2u_n).$$

13. Show that if

$$a_{2n-1} = \frac{1}{\sqrt{n+1}}, \quad a_{2n} = \frac{1}{\sqrt{n+1}} + \frac{1}{n+1} + \frac{1}{(n+1)(\sqrt{n+1})}$$

the product $\Pi \, (1 + a_n)$ converges though both $\Sigma \, a_n$ and $\Sigma \, a_n$ diverge.

14. Discuss the convergence of

$$\prod_{2}^{\infty} \left\{ \left(1 - \frac{z}{c+n} \right) e^{z/n} \right\},$$

where c is a constant.

[**Ans.** Absolutely convergent for all values of z, if c is a constant other than a negative integer.]

15. Prove that if a sequence $\{f_n \, (z)\}$ of functions analytic in a domain D converges uniformly on the contour C; then it converges uniformly to an analytic function $f(z)$ in any closed domain interior to D and that $\{f_n^{(k)} \, (z)\}$ converges to $f^{(k)} \, (z)$.

16. If $f(z)$ is a meromorphic function with simple poles

$$z_1, z_2, \ldots\ldots, z_n, \ldots\ldots$$

such that $|z_1|$ $< |z_2| < \ldots\ldots$

and corresponding residues

$$b_1, b_2, \ldots\ldots, b_n, \ldots\ldots$$

then $f(z) = f(0) + \sum_{n=1}^{\infty} b_n \left(\frac{1}{z - z_n} + \frac{1}{z_n} \right),$

provided that there exists a sequence of simple closed contours $\{C_n\}$ such that C_n includes the poles

$$z_1, z_2, \ldots\ldots, z_n$$

and no others and such that

$$\lim_{n \to \infty} \int_{C_n} \frac{f(\xi)}{\xi - z} \, d\xi = 0.$$

17. If $f(z)$ is an integral function having simple zeros

$$z_1, z_2, \ldots\ldots, z_n, \ldots\ldots$$

and the function $f'(z) / f(z)$ satisfies the condition of the preceding exercise, then

$$f(z) = f(0) \, e^{z \frac{f'(0)}{f(0)}} \prod_{n=1}^{\infty} \left\{ \left(1 - \frac{z}{n} \right) e^{z/a_n} \right\}.$$

18. Represent the following functions in partial fraction form :

$$\pi \tan \pi z, \ \pi \sec \pi z, \ \pi \operatorname{cosec} \pi z.$$

19. Represent $\pi \cos \pi z$ as an infinite product.

20. Prove the existence of an integral function which assumes arbitrarily preassigned value $\{ f (z_n) \}$ on any sequence $\{z_n\}$ tending to infinity.

21. Obtain a generalisation of the Mittag-Leffler's theorem which has an infinite number of poles but no other singularities in the domain $| z | < 1$.

OBJECTIVE QUESTIONS

For each of the following questions, four alternatives are given for the answer. Only one of them is correct. Choose the correct alternative.

1. A series $\Sigma \, u_n \, (z)$ is said to be absolutely convergent if the series
   (a) $\Sigma \, (u_n)^{1/n}$ is convergent   (b) $\Sigma \, | \, u_n \, (z) \, |$ is convergent
   (c) $\Sigma \, u_n \, (z)$ is not convergent   (d) None of these.

2. If $< S_n \, (z) >$ is a uniformly convergent sequence of functions continuous and bounded in a domain D then the limit function S (z) of the sequence is
   (a) continuous   (b) analytic
   (c) discontinuous   (d) monotonic.

3. A power series is uniformly convergent
   (a) outside its circle of convergence
   (b) on the periphery of circle of convergence
   (c) within its circle of convergence
   (d) in the whole domain.

4. The infinite product $\Pi \, (1 + a_n)$ is absolutely convergent if
   (a) $\Pi \, (1 + | \, a_n \, |)$ is convergent   (b) $\Pi \, (a_n)^2$ is convergent
   (c) $\Pi \, (a_n)$ is convergent   (d) None of these.

5. $\Sigma \, \log \, (1 + a_n)$ is absolutely convergent if
   (a) $\Sigma \, a_n$ is convergent   (b) $\Sigma \, | \, a_n \, |$ is convergent
   (c) $\Sigma \, (1 + | \, a_n \, |)$ is convergent   (d) None of these.

ANSWERS

1. (b)   **2.** (a)   **3.** (c)   **4.** (a)   **5.** (a)

ANALYTIC CONTINUATION

13.1. Introduction. Analytic continuation is a process in which the definition of a domain of an analytic function in which it is originally defined, is extended. This process, obviously, is not possible in case of functions of a real variable and is a special feature of the complex analytic functions.

13.2. Analytic Continuation *(Agra 2001, Rajisthan, 2003)*

Let a function $f_1(z)$ be analytic in the domain D_1. If there exists a function $f_2(z)$ analytic in a domain D_2 such that

(*i*) D_2 has a part D_{12} common with D_1,

(*ii*) $f_1(z) = f_2(z)$ for every z in D_{12},

then the function $f_2(z)$ is known as *analytic continuation of $f_1(z)$ from D_1 into D_2 via D_{12}*. It may equivalently be said that *f_1 is an analytic continuation of f_2 from D_1 to D_2 via D_{12}*.

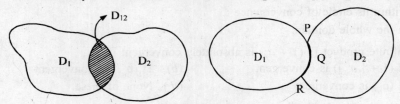

Fig. 13.1

Note. For analytic continuation it is sufficient that D_1 and D_2 have only a small arc in common. For example the arc PQR is common in D_1 and D_2.

Alternately, If $f(z)$ is analytic in a domain D_1 and if $f(z)$ is also analytic in a domain D_2 containing D_1 and if $\phi(z) = f(z) \; \forall \; z \in D_2$ then $\phi(z)$ is said to give the analytic continuation of $f(z)$ in the domain D_2.

For example, let
$$f(z) = \sum_{n=0}^{\infty} z^n, \quad \phi(z) = \frac{1}{1-z}.$$

Clearly, $f(z)$ is analytic at all points within the circle $|z| = 1$ and $\phi(z)$ is analytic at all points except $z = 1$. Also, within $|z| = 1$, $\phi(z) = f(z)$. Hence $\phi(z)$ gives the continuation of $f(z)$ over the rest of the plane.

Again, suppose
$$f(z) = \sum_{n=0}^{\infty} z^n, \quad \phi(z) = \sum_{n=0}^{\infty} \frac{1}{2}\left(\frac{1+z}{2}\right)^n.$$

Obviously, $f(z)$ is convergent inside the circle $|z| = 1$ (say R_1) and has the sum $= \dfrac{1}{1-z}$.

Second function $\phi(z)$ is convergent for

$$\left| \frac{1+z}{2} \right| < 1 \text{ or } |z+1| < 2 \quad (\text{say } R_2).$$

The sum function of

$$\phi(z) = \frac{1}{2} \cdot \frac{1}{1-(1+z)/2} = \frac{1}{1-z}.$$

Clearly, $f(z)$ is analytic inside the circle $|z| = 1$ and $\phi(z)$ is analytic inside the circle $|z+1| = 2$. Also $f(z) = \phi(z)$ in a region common to the interiors of these circles.

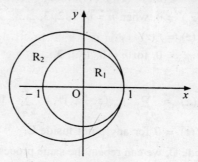

Fig. 13.2

Thus, $\phi(z)$ extends the domain of the analytic function $f(z)$ to a larger domain R_2. Here ϕ is the analytic continuation of f from R_1 into R_2.

An analytic function with domain D is called a *function element* and is denoted by (f, D).

13.3. Complete Analytic Function. Let $f(z)$ is analytic in a domain D. Form all possible analytic continuations of (f, D) and then of $(f_1, D_1), (f_2, D_2), (f_3, D_3), \ldots, (f_n, D_n)$ and so on. At some stage a function $F(z)$ will arrive such that for any v, $F(v)$ denotes the value or values obtained for v by all possible continuations to v, *i.e.*,

$$F(z) = \begin{cases} f_1(z), & \text{if } z \in D_1 \\ f_2(z), & \text{if } z \in D_2 \\ \overline{\hspace{4cm}} \\ \overline{\hspace{4cm}} \\ f_n(z), & \text{if } z \in D_n. \end{cases}$$

Such function $F(z)$ is called *complete analytic function*. In this process of continuation, we may get a closed curve beyond which it is not possible to take analytic continuation. Such closed curve is known as *natural boundary* of the complete analytic function. A point outside the natural boundary is called the *singularity* of complete analytic function.

Theorem. *If $f(z)$ is analytic in a domain D and $f(z) = 0$ at all points on arc AB inside D, then $f(z) = 0$ throughout D.*

(Agra 2003, Rajsthan 2001, 2003)

Let $f(z)$ be analytic within a domain D. Let AB be an arc inside D such that

$$f(z) = 0 \ \forall \ z \text{ on AB} \qquad \qquad \ldots(1)$$

Take an arbitrary point z_0 on the arc AB. Describe a circle C of convergence with its centre at z_0. For any point z inside this circle of convergence, $f(z)$ has Taylor's expansion in the neighbourhood of z, given by

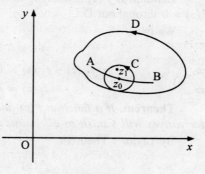

Fig. 13.3

$$f(z) = \sum_{n=0}^{\infty} a_n (z - z_0)^n \qquad \qquad ...(2)$$

where $a_n = \dfrac{f^{(n)}(z_0)}{n!}$.

Since z_0 lies on AB and hence $f(z_0) = 0$, by (1),

This $\Rightarrow$ $\qquad\qquad\qquad f(z) = 0$ at $z = z_0$

$\Rightarrow$ $\qquad\qquad f(z), f'(z), f''(z), ..., f^{(n)}(z) = 0$ at $z = z_0$

$\Rightarrow$ $\qquad\qquad\qquad f^{(n)}(z_0) = 0$, when $n = 0, 1, 2, 3, ...$

Here $\qquad\qquad\qquad f^{(0)}(z) = f(z)$

$\Rightarrow$ $\qquad\qquad\qquad a_n = 0$, for $n = 0, 1, 2, 3, ...$

Then (2) becomes

$$f(z) = \sum_{n=0}^{\infty} a_n (z - z_0)^n = \sum_{n=0}^{\infty} 0 \cdot (z - z_0)^n = 0.$$

$\therefore \qquad\qquad\qquad f(z) = 0$ for any point inside C.

By taking another arc inside D, we can repeat the same process. Thus $f(z) = 0$ throughout R.

Cor. 1. *If $f(z)$ is analytic in a domain D and if $f(z)$ vanishes at any point of C, where C is a part of D, then $f(z) = 0$ throughout D.*

Take an arc AB inside C. Then $f(z) = 0 \ \forall \ z$ on AB. Now prove it as in the main theorem.

Cor. 2. *Show that if two functions $f_1(z)$ and $f_2(z)$ are equal at all points of a line L in a region D in which the arc is holomorphic, the functions are equal at all points of D.*

Let $f_1(z)$ and $f_2(z)$ are holomorphic in a region D. Let C be a part of D such that

$$f_1(z) = f_2(z) \ \forall \ z \in C \qquad\qquad ...(1)$$

To prove that $f_1(z) = f_2(z)$ throughout D, write

$$f(z) = f_1(z) - f_2(z).$$

Now (1)

$\Rightarrow$ $\qquad\qquad\qquad f(z) = 0 \ \forall \ z \in C \qquad\qquad ...(2)$

Take an arc or line AB in C. Then we have

$$f(z) = 0 \ \forall \ z \text{ on AB.}$$

Then by the following Lemma:

Lemma. If $f(z)$ is analytic in a domain D and if $f(z) = 0$ along an arc AB inside D, then $f(z) = 0$ throughout D.

We have

$$f(z) = 0 \ \forall \ z \in D.$$

$\Rightarrow$ $\qquad\qquad f_1(z) - f_2(z) = 0$ throughout D

$\Rightarrow$ $\qquad\qquad\qquad f_1(z) = f_2(z)$ throughout D.

Theorem. *If a function $f(z)$ and all its derivatives vanish at point a, then $f(z)$ and all its derivatives will vanish at all points in the domain of a.*

By Taylor's Theorem

$$f(z) = \sum_{n=0}^{\infty} a_n (z - a)^n$$

where $\dfrac{f^n(a)}{n!} = a_n$ for $n = 0, 1, 2, 3, \ldots$

By assumption, $a_0 = a_1 = a_2 = \ldots = 0$. Hence $f(z), f'(z), f''(z)$ all vanish at all points of the domain.

13.3. Uniqueness of Analytic Continuation.

Theorem. *There cannot be more than one continuation of analytic continuation* $\phi(z)$ *into the same domain.*

(Rohilkhand 2003, 2006)

Suppose $f(z)$ be analytic in a domain D_1 and let $\phi(z)$ and $\psi(z)$ be analytic continuations of the same function $f(z)$ from domain D_1 into the domain D_2 via D_{12} which is common to both D_1 and D_2.

By the definition of analytic continuation

(i) $f(z) = \phi(z) \ \forall \ z \in D_{12}$ and $\phi(z)$ is analytic in D_2,

(ii) $f(z) = \psi(z) \ \forall \ z \in D_{12}$ and $\psi(z)$ is analytic in D_2.

From (i) and (ii),

$$\phi(z) = f(z) = \psi(z) \ \forall \ z \in D_{12}$$

$\Rightarrow \qquad\qquad \phi(z) = \psi(z) \ \forall \ z \in D_{12}$

$\Rightarrow \qquad\qquad (\phi - \psi)(z) = 0 \ \forall \ z \in D_{12}$

ϕ and ψ are analytic in $D_2 \ \Rightarrow \ \phi - \psi$ is analytic in D_2.

Therefore $(\phi - \psi)(z)$ vanishes in D_2 which is a part of D_2. Also the function is analytic in D_2. Hence

$$(\phi - \psi)(z) = 0 \ \forall \ z \in D_2 \qquad\qquad\qquad \text{(by § 13.3.1)}$$

$\Rightarrow \qquad\qquad \phi(z) = \psi(z) \ \forall \ z \in D_2.$

13.4. Analytic continuation by means of power series.

Let the initial function $f_1(z)$ is represented by the Taylor's series

$$f_1(z) = \sum_{n=0}^{\infty} a_n (z - z_1)^n \quad \ldots(1)$$

where $a_n = \dfrac{f_1^{(n)}(z_1)}{n!}$.

This series is convergent inside a circle C_1.

$$|z - z_1| = R_1$$

$$= \lim_{n \to \infty} |a_n|^{1/n}.$$

Draw a curve L from z_1 and perform analytic continuation along this path as follows:

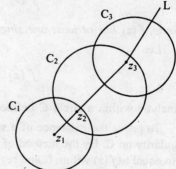

Fig. 13.4

Take a point z_2 on L such that z_2 lies inside C_1. Now, by (1) we can find

$$f_1(z_2), f_1'(z_2), f_1''(z_2), \ldots, f_1^{(n)}(z_2)$$

by repeated differentiation, write

$$f_2(z) = \sum_{n=0}^{\infty} b_n (z - z_2)^n \qquad\qquad \ldots(1)$$

where

$$b_n = \dfrac{f^{(n)}(z_2)}{n!} \qquad\qquad \ldots(2)$$

Power series (2) is convergent inside a circle C_2 defined by

$$|z - z_2| = R_2 = \lim_{n \to \infty} |b_n|^{1/n}.$$

Also, belonging to the common part of C_1 and C_2, we have $f_1(z) = f_2(z) \; \forall \; z$. Hence $f_2(z)$ is an analytic continuation of $f_1(z)$ from C_1 to C_2. Similarly, take a point z_3 lying within C_2. With the help of (2), we can find $f_2^{(n)}(z_3)$.

Write

$$f_3(z) = \sum_{n=0}^{\infty} c_n (z - z_3)^n \qquad \qquad ...(3)$$

where

$$c_n = \frac{f_2^{(n)}(z_3)}{n!}.$$

This power series is convergent inside the circle C_3 defined by

$$|z - z_3| = R_3 = \lim_{n \to \infty} |c_n|^{1/n}$$

$$\Rightarrow \qquad \qquad f_2(z) = f_3(z) \; \forall \; z$$

belonging to the common part of C_2 and C_3.

Now $f_3(z)$ is analytic continuation of $f_1(z)$ from the interior of C_2 to the interior of C_3.

Repeating this process, we get a number of different power series analytic in their respective domains $D_1, D_2, D_3, ...,$ where $D_1, D_2, D_3, ...,$ are respectively interiors of $C_1, C_2, C_3, ...,$ as continuations.

13.4.1. Singularity of power series on its circle of convergence.

If the radius of convergence of the series

$$f(z) = \sum_{n=0}^{\infty} a_n (z - z_0)^n$$

is finite, $f(z)$ has at least one singularity on the circle of convergence.

Let

$$f(z) = \sum_{n=0}^{\infty} a_n (z - z_0)^n$$

is analytic within a circle C defined by $|z - z_0| = R$.

To prove the existence of a singularity on C by contradiction suppose there exists no such singularity on C. By the method of analytic continuation, we can construct an analytic function $f_1(z)$ to equal to $f(z)$ within C and regular in another concentric circle C_1 larger than C. The Taylor's expansion of $f_1(z)$ in powers of $(z - z_0)$ would then converge everywhere within C_1. This is a contradiction because the original series would be having C as its circle of convergence. Hence the result.

13.4.2. *If we continue an analytic function $f(z)$ along two different paths from z_0 to z_1 and obtain two different values of $f(z_1)$, then $f(z)$ must have a singularity somewhere between the two paths.*

(Rohilkhand 2003)

We prove this statement as :

If we continue an analytic function along two different routes from z_0 to z_1 and obtain the same value of $f(z_1)$, then $f(z)$ has no singularity in the closed area included by these two paths.

Construct the following two chains of regions :
$$R_1, R_2, ..., R_n$$
and
$$R_1', R_2', ..., R_m'$$
along the two paths from z_0 to z_1 such that

(i) the two consecutive regions of either chain overlap,

(ii) $z_0 \in R_1$, $z_0 \in R_1'$,

(iii) $z_1 \in R_n$, $z_1 \in R_m'$,

(iv) $f_n(z)$ is analytic in R_n and $g_n(z)$ is analytic in R_m',

(v) $f_k(z) = f_{k-1}(z)$ in the common part of R_k and R_{k-1},

(vi) $g_k(z) = g_{k-1}(z)$ in the common part of R_k' and R_{k-1}',

(vii) $f_1(z) = g_1(z)$ in the common part of R_1 and R_1'.

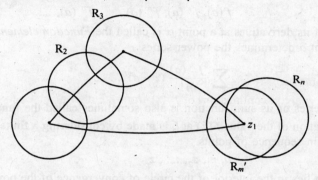

Fig. 13.5

We have to prove that
$$f_n(z_1) = g_m(z_1)$$
provided we can continue the function to every point between the two paths. For this let $a \in R_1 \cap R_1'$, $b \in R_n \cap R_m'$. Now construct a polygonal line PQR from a to b with vertices at point $(p\delta, q\delta)$ to such that

(i) the circles of radii 2δ with these vertices as centres lie entirely within the first chain,

(ii) each such circle contains the centre of the preceding one.

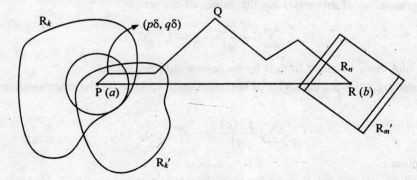

Fig. 13.6

Here δ is supposed to be very small quantity. This chain of the circles can be substituted for the first chain of regions. A similar chain can be substituted for the second chain of regions.

Similarly, we can replace the first path by a succession of new routes of radius 2δ and centre at $(p\delta, q\delta)$ such that each circle of each path intersects the previous path and the circles of the same path on each side of it cannot leave any space uncovered. Radius of every circle is not smaller than 2δ. By uniqueness theorem (§ 13.3.3), we reach the same value of $f(z_1)$ for each root z_1. We pass from one of our original paths to the other in a finite number of steps. As the function is regular at each point between two paths, the process of analytic continuation never comes to an end.

13.5. Determination of a given function analytic in a domain by a function element. It has been seen in § 9.8.1, that if a function $f(z)$ is an analytic in a domain D, then the value $f(\xi)$ at *any* point $\xi \in D$ can be determined in terms of the values of the function and of all its derivatives at any given point a of the domain. This means that as soon as the values of a function which is analytic in a domain are known in a neighbourhood of any one point of the domain, the values at every point of the domain are uniquely fixed.

The set of values

$$f(a), f'(a), f''(a), ..., f^n(a), ...$$

of a function and of its derivatives at a point α is called the *Function element* at a. The function element at any point a determines the power series

$$\sum \frac{f^n(a)}{n!} (z - a)^n.$$

This power series or its sum function is also sometimes called the function element at a.

The determination of the value $f(\xi)$ at ξ is made by considering a finite sequence of power series about a certain sequence of points

$$a, z_1, z_2, ..., z_{p-1}$$

such that each point lies in the interior of the circle of convergence of the power series about the preceding point and ξ belongs to the interior of the circle of convergence of the power series about the last point z_{p-1}.

The power series about any point z_i is

$$\sum \frac{f^n(z_i)}{n!} (z - z_i)^n$$

and the values

$$f(z_i), f'(z_i), f''(z_i), ...$$

for the determination of this series are the values of the series

$$\sum \frac{f^n(z_{i-1})}{n!} (z - z_{i-1})^n$$

about z_{i-1} and those obtained from it by successive differentiation.

The starting point for the series of operation outlined here for the determination of $f(\xi)$ is the series

$$\sum \frac{f^n(a)}{n!} (z - a)^n$$

about the point a.

To sum up, we may say that the function element at any given point, ξ, is obtained in terms of the function element at any point a by means of sequence of function elements about a suitably selected sequence of points.

13.5.1. Extension of a function by a power series with a finite non-zero radius of convergence.
We shall now explain the power series method of extending a function.

Instead of starting with a function $f(z)$ analytic in a domain D we now start with some power series

$$\Sigma a_n (z - a)^n \qquad \qquad ...(1)$$

about any given point a. The only assumption which we make about this power series is that its radius of convergence is non-zero and apart from this, we regard the coefficients a_n of the series as quite arbitrary.

In case the radius of convergence of the series (1) is infinite, the series determines as its sum a function analytic in the whole plane. Such a function is known as an *Integral* or an *Entire* function.

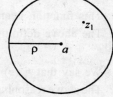

We now suppose that the radius of convergence of (1) is some *finite non-zero* number ρ, so that the sum function is analytic in the circular domain

$$|z - a| < \rho.$$

Fig. 13.7

We denote the sum function by $f(z)$.

Let now z_1 be any point of this domain.

From the series (1) and those obtained on successively differentiating the same, we obtain the values

$$f(z_1), f'(z_1), f''(z_1), ...$$

and set up the Taylor's series

$$\sum \frac{f_\varepsilon(z_1)}{n!} (z - z_1)^n \qquad \qquad ...(2)$$

of $f(z)$ about the point z_1.

By Taylor's Theorem, the radius of convergence of the power series (2) is at least

$$\rho - |z_1 - a|.$$

Also the radius of convergence cannot exceed

$$\rho + |z_1 - a|..$$

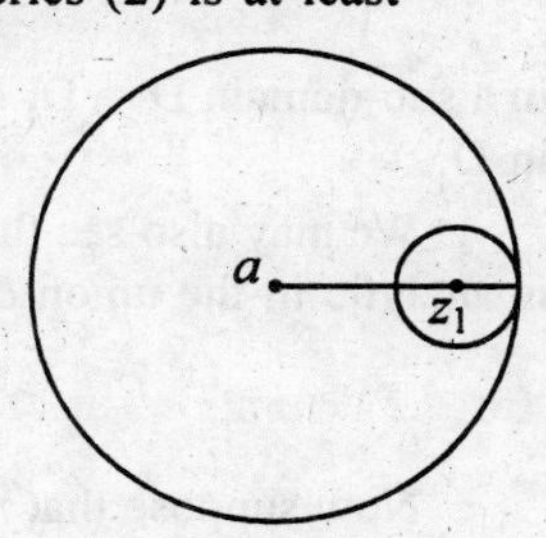

Let, if possible, the radius of convergence of the series (2) be

$$\rho + |z_1 - a| + \delta \ (\delta > 0).$$

It may easily be seen that the domain D given by

$$|z - a| < \rho$$

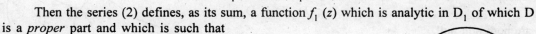
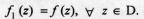

is included in the domain

$$|z - z_1| < \rho + |z_1 - a| + \delta.$$

Fig. 13.8

Then the series (2) defines, as its sum, a function $f_1(z)$ which is analytic in D_1 of which D is a *proper* part and which is such that

$$f_1(z) = f(z), \ \forall \ z \in D.$$

This means that the radius of convergence of the series (1) would exceed ρ. Thus we arrive at a contradiction.

Hence we see that the radius of convergence ρ_1 of the series (2) is such that

$$\rho - |z_1 - a| \le \rho_1 \le \rho + |z_1 - a|.$$

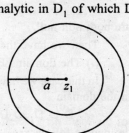

Now in case ρ_1 exceeds, $\rho + |z_1 - a|$, we have a function $f(3)$ defined by the series (2) such that

Fig. 13.9

(*i*) $f_1(z)$ is analytic in a domain D_1;

(*ii*) the intersection $D \cap D_1$ is non-null *i.e.*, D_1 has a part in common with D;

(*iii*) $f(z) = f_1(z)$ if $z \in D \cap D_1$ *i.e.*, for every z of the common part of D and D_1.

Thus in this case, it has been possible to extend the domain of definition of the given function $f(z)$ so that we arrive at a function $F(z)$ given by

$$F(z) = \begin{cases} f(z) & \forall\ z \in D, \\ f_1(z) & \forall\ z \in D_1. \end{cases}$$

This function is analytic in the domain $D \cup D_1$.

The above definition of $F(z)$ is justifiable since we have

$$f(z) = f_1(z)\ \forall\ z \in D \cap D_1.$$

We say that $f_1(z)$ is an *analytic continuation* of $f(z)$.

The above reasoning in respect of z_1 may be applied in respect

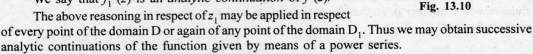

Fig. 13.10

of every point of the domain D or again of any point of the domain D_1. Thus we may obtain successive analytic continuations of the function given by means of a power series.

13.5.2. Analytic continuation of a function. Let there be given a function $f(z)$ analytic in a domain D.

If there exists a function $f_1(z)$ analytic in a domain D_1 such that the intersection $D \cap D_1$ is non-null and such that for every $z \in D \cap D_1$

$$f(z) = f_1(z),$$

we say that $f_1(z)$ is an analytic continuation of $f(z)$ and *vice-versa*.

If $f_1(z)$ and $F_1(z)$ are two analytic continuations in D_1 of the same function $f(z)$ analytic in D_1, then we necessarily have

$$f_1(z) = F_1(z),\ \forall\ z \in D_1.$$

This is so, for the vanishing of

$$f_1(z) = F_1(z)$$

in a sub-domain $D \cap D_1$ of D_1 implies the vanishing of the same in D_1.

We may also see that the function $F(z)$ defined as follows is analytic in the union domain $D \cup D_1$.

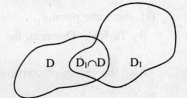

Fig. 13.11

$$F(z) = \begin{cases} f(z) & \forall\ z \in D, \\ f_1(z) & \forall\ z \in D_1. \end{cases}$$

Now suppose that $f_1(z)$ and $f_2(z)$ are two analytic continuations of the same function $f(z)$. We suppose that $f(z), f_1(z), f_2(z)$ are regular in D, D_1, and D_2 to respectively.

By definition, the two intersections

$$D \cap D_1,\ D \cap D_2$$

are both non-null.

Then we have the following possibilities:

(*i*) The domains D_1 and D_2 have no common point.

In this case we have a single valued function $F(z)$ analytic in the domain

$$D \cup D_1 \cup D_2$$

defined as follows:

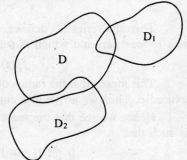

Fig. 13.12

$$F(z) = \begin{cases} f(z) & \forall \ z \in D, \\ f_1(z) & \forall \ z \in D_1, \\ f_2(z) & \forall \ z \in D_2. \end{cases}$$

(ii) The domains D_1 and D_2 have a non-null intersection and furthermore the intersection with D of $D_1 \cap D_2$ is also non-null.

Here, we have

$$f_1(z) = f(z) = f_2(z) \ \forall \ z \in D \cap D_1 \cap D_2$$

so that,

$$f_1(z) = f_2(z) \ \forall \ z \in D_1 \cap D_2.$$

Thus in this case also we arrive at a function $F(z)$ defined and analytic in the domain

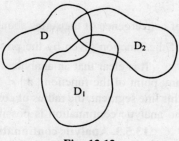

Fig. 13.13

$$D \cup D_1 \cup D_2.$$

(iii) The domains D_1, D_2 have a non-null intersection but the intersection of this intersection with D is null.

In this case we may *not* have

$$f_1(z) = f_2(z)$$

for $z \in D_1 \cap D$ so that in this case, we do not obtain a single valued function defined and analytic in $D \cup D_1 \cup D_2$.

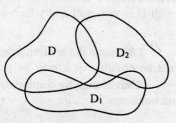

Fig. 13.14

Illustration. Consider the power series

$$1 + z + z^2 + \dots + z^n + \dots \qquad \dots(1)$$

whose domain D of convergence is

$$|z| < 1.$$

The function $f(z)$ defined by this power series is given by

$$f(z) = \frac{1}{1-z} \text{ for } |z| < 1. \qquad \dots(2)$$

Consider the point i of D.

Now

$$f^n(z) = \frac{1}{(1-z)^{n+1}}, \ |z| < 1$$

$\Rightarrow \qquad f^n\left(\frac{1}{2}i\right) = \frac{1}{\left(1-\frac{1}{2}i\right)^{n+1}}.$

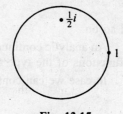

Fig. 13.15

Thus we may write the Taylor's series about $\frac{1}{2}i$. By Taylor's theorem, the radius of convergence of this power series is

$$= \left|\frac{1}{2}i - 1\right| = \frac{\sqrt{5}}{2}.$$

Clearly the domain D_1 given by

$$\left| z - \frac{1}{2} i \right| = \frac{\sqrt{5}}{2}$$

of convergence of the series about $\frac{1}{2} i$ extends beyond D. Thus we obtain an analytic continuation of the function given by the power series (1).

It is clear that an analytical continuation of the given function can be obtained starting with any point of the function $| z | < 1$, not lying on the line segment joining 0, 1. For any point a of this line segment, the radius of convergence of the corresponding power series is $1 - a$, and as such, no analytic continuation is possible with the help of any such point a.

13.5.3. Analytic continuation to a point. Suppose that a function $f(z)$ is analytic in a domain D and ξ is a point not belonging to D. *We then say that $f(z)$ can be analytically continued to ξ,* if there exists a function F(z) which is analytic in a domain D$'$ which contains ξ and whose intersection with D is non-null and which is such that

$$\text{F}(z) = f(z) \ \forall \ z \in \text{D} \cap \text{D}'.$$

Of course the analytic continuation of any given function $f(z)$ to a given point ξ may or may not be possible or it may be possible in more than one way.

Thus if analytic continuation of $f(z)$ to ξ is possible, we shall have at least one finite sequence of functions

$$f_1(z), \ldots, f_m(z) \qquad \qquad \ldots(1)$$

respectively analytic in the domains

$$\text{D}_1, \ldots, \text{D}_m \qquad \qquad \ldots(2)$$

such that

(*i*) $\xi \in \text{D}_m$,

(*ii*) the intersection of every consecutive pair of domains of the sequence (2) is non-null,

(*iii*) for any z belonging to the intersection of any pair of consecutive members of (2), the values of the corresponding functions are equal.

Thus for example

$$f_1(z) = f_2(z) \ \forall \ z \in \text{D}_1 \cap \text{D}_2,$$
$$f_2(z) = f_3(z) \ \forall \ z \in \text{D}_2 \cap \text{D}_3,$$

and so on.

An analytic continuation of $f(z)$ to ξ will not be possible, if there does not exist any sequence of functions of the type referred to above.

In case we can continue $f(z)$ to ξ by two different sequences of functions

$$f_1(z), \ldots, f_m(z)$$
$$g_1(z), \ldots, g_n(z),$$

then, as explained in case (*iii*) above, the value $f_m(\xi)$ may not be equal to $g_n(\xi)$ so that we have at least two different continuations to ξ.

13.5.4. Analytic function in the large or the notion of the complete analytic function. So far we have been concerned with the concept of an *analytic function in a domain* and shall now introduce the concept of an *analytic function in the large* also known as *a complete analytic function.*

Let $f(z)$ be an analytic function defined in some domain D. We now form all possible continuations of $f(z)$ and also all possible continuations of these continuations. Then we arrive at a function F(z) such that for any point ξ, F(ξ) denotes the value or values obtained for ξ by all possible continuations of F (z) to ξ. Then F (z) is called a complete analytic function. In case no analytical continuation of F (z) to ξ is possible, we say that ξ is a *singular point* of the complete analytic function F (z). It is clear that a singular point of a given single valued function $f(z)$ is also a singular point of the corresponding complete analytic function F (z).

It is clear that *there corresponds a complete analytic function to every given function element.*

A closed *curve is called a* **Natural boundary** *of a function if the function cannot be analytically continued to any point of the same.*

13.5.5. Standard method of analytic continuation. Analytic continuation by power series. All sorts of limiting processes, such as employment of infinite series, products, integrals are used for the purposes of analytic continuation. It can, however, be shown that any given analytic continuation, however it might have been effected, can as well be accomplished with the help of power series.

Suppose that a function $f(z)$ analytic in a domain D can be analytically continued to a point to ξ. This means that there exists a domain D_1 containing ξ and a function F (z) analytic in D_1 such that

$$D \cap D_1 \text{ is non-null,}$$

and

$$f(z) = f(z) \ \forall \ z \in D.$$

The power series method explained in § 9.8 and § 13.5.1, can be employed to determine F (ξ) in terms of any function element of $f(z)$.

13.6 Hadamard's Multiplication Theorem

If $f(z) = \displaystyle\sum_{n=0}^{\infty} a_n z^n$ *is convergent for* $|z| < R$ *and* $g(z) = \displaystyle\sum_{n=0}^{\infty} b_n z^n$ *is convergent for* $|z| <$

R' *and if* $f(z)$ *has singularities at* $\alpha_1, \alpha_2, ..., \alpha_n$ *and* $g(z)$ *at* $\beta_1, \beta_2, ..., \beta_n$ *then singularities of*

$F(z)$ *given by* $F(z) = \displaystyle\sum_{n=0}^{\infty} a_n b_n z^n$ *are to found among the points* $\alpha_m \beta_n$.

We shall consider the case in which $f(z)$ has just one singularity say $z = \alpha$ and $g(z)$ has just one singularity at $z = \beta$. The general result will then follow from it.

We have $\qquad f(z) = \displaystyle\sum_{n=0}^{\infty} a_n b_n z^n \qquad\qquad\qquad\qquad$ ...(1)

Firstly we claim that $f(z)$ is regular to sufficiently small values of z and $|z| < RR'$, by hypothesis

$\displaystyle\sum_{n=0}^{\infty} a_n z^n$ is convergent for $|z| < R' \Rightarrow \exists a$ number K_1 independent of n such that $|a_n z^n| < K \ \forall \ n$.

Now, $\qquad\qquad |z| < R \Rightarrow |a_n z^n| = |a_n (R - \epsilon)^n| < K_1$

and similarly, $\qquad |z| < R' \Rightarrow |b_n z^n| = |b_n (R' - \epsilon)^n| < K_2$

Thus, $\qquad\qquad |a_n b_n| < \dfrac{K_1 K_2}{(R - \epsilon)^n (R' - \epsilon)^n}$

$$= \dfrac{K}{(R - \epsilon)^n (R' - \epsilon)^n} \text{ (say), where } K = K_1 K_2$$

If $\epsilon \to 0$, the radius of convergence of the power series $f(z)$ is atleast equal to RR'.

Hadamard's Theorem depends upon the following representation of $f(z)$ as an integral.

$$F(z) = \frac{1}{2\pi i} \int_C F(w) g\left(\frac{z}{w}\right) \frac{dw}{w} \qquad \qquad ...(2)$$

where C is a contour including the origin, on which

$$|w| < R, \quad \left|\frac{z}{w}\right| < R'$$

which may be shown by setting

$$g\left(\frac{z}{w}\right) = \sum_{n=0}^{\infty} b_n \left(\frac{z}{w}\right)^n \text{ in R.H.S. of (2),}$$

so that in view of uniform convergence, term by term integration yields

$$\frac{1}{2\pi i} \int_C f(w) g\left(\frac{z}{w}\right) \frac{dw}{w}$$

$$= \sum_{n=0}^{\infty} \frac{b_n z^n}{2\pi i} \int_C \frac{f(w) \, dw}{w^{n+1}}$$

$$= \sum_{n=0}^{\infty} a_n b_n z^n.$$

Now $|z| < R$ and $\left|\frac{z}{w}\right| < R'$

$\Rightarrow |z| < RR'$ and C may be any circle between

$$|w| = R \text{ and } |w| = \frac{|z|}{R'}$$

In case $f(z)$ has one singularity $z = \alpha$ and $g(z)$ has $|z| = \beta$

i.e., $R = |\alpha|$ and $R' = |\beta|, F(z)$

may be continued analytically beyond the circle $|z| = RR'$ by deforming the contour C. Keeping

C fixed giving z any values such that $\frac{z}{\beta}$ remains inside C, the R.H.S. of (2) is an analytic function

of z for every value of z and continuation of $F(z)$ to all such values follows immediately.

On the other hand if we deform C into another contour C_1 containing $z = 0$ and excluding $z = \alpha$ and set

$$F_1(z) = \frac{1}{2\pi i} \int_{C_1} f(w) g\left(\frac{z}{w}\right) \frac{dw}{w} \qquad \qquad ...(3)$$

then if the point $w = \frac{z}{\beta}$ lies within C and C_1 both, Cauchy's theorem follows

$$F_1(z) = F\left(\frac{z}{\beta}\right).$$

since the integrand in (3) is an analytic function of w, regular between C and C_1. As such (3) provides continuation of $f(z)$ to all values of z such that $\dfrac{z}{\beta}$ lies inside C_1.

Again, the z is restricted for $\dfrac{z}{\beta}$ lying within a contour excluding $z = \alpha$ and we are free to choose such a contour for each z except at $z = \alpha\beta$ so that $F(z)$ is regular except at $z = \alpha\beta$.

Obviously, the proof applies only to the principal branch of $F(z)$, obtained by continuation from the original element without encircling any of the points $\alpha\beta$. The singularity of integrand in (3) being at $\omega = 0$, C_1 cannot have a loop going round α and enclosing the origin again on this side. So C_1 cannot encircle the point α along the path when $\dfrac{z}{\beta} \to 0$ and $z = 0$ may therefore be a singularity of the other branches of $F(z)$. Hence the theorem.

Lambert's Theorem *If* $f(z) = \displaystyle\sum_{n=0}^{\infty} d(n) z^n, (|z| < 1)$, *where $d(n)$ denotes the number of divisors of n, then the unit circle is a natural boundary of this function.*

Consider the double series

$$\sum_{m=1}^{\infty} \sum_{l=1}^{\infty} z^{ml} \qquad \ldots(1)$$

whence $f(z)$ can be obtained by considering the series as a single power series and summing up the rows, *i.e.*,

$$f(z) = \sum_{m=1}^{\infty} (z^m + z^{2m} + z^{3m} + \ldots).$$

by putting $l = 1, 2, 3, \ldots$ and taking $|z| < 1$.

$$= \sum_{m=1}^{\infty} \frac{z^m}{1 - z^m} (|z| < 1) \qquad \ldots(2)$$

The series (1) is absolutely convergent for $|z| < 1$ and thus we can take the transformation

$$z = re^{2\pi pi/q} \qquad \ldots(3)$$

where p, q are positive integers such that $p > 0$, $q < 1$ and p, q are prime to each other.

Now, we claim:

$(1 - r) f(z) \to \infty$ as $r \to 1$.

To prove it, let us assume

$$f(z) = \sum_1 \frac{z^m}{1 - z^m} + \sum_2 \frac{z^m}{1 - z^m} \qquad \ldots(4)$$

where in $\displaystyle\sum_1$, m takes all values

$$\equiv 0 \,(\mathrm{mod}\, q) \text{ and in } \sum_2, \text{ all other values,}$$

Setting $m = tq$ in $\displaystyle\sum_1$, we find

$$z^m = \{r\, e^{2\pi i p/q}\}^{tq}_{\infty} = r^{tq} \text{ as } e^{2\pi i p} = 1$$

$$(1 - r)\sum_1 = (1 - r)\sum_{t=1}^{\infty} \frac{r^{tq}}{1 - r^{tq}}$$

$$= \frac{1-r}{1-r^q} \sum_{t=1}^{\infty} \frac{1-r^q}{1-r^{tq}} r^{tq}$$

$$= \frac{1}{1+r+r^2+\ldots+r^{q-1}} \sum_{t=1}^{\infty} \frac{r^{tq}}{1+r^q+\ldots+r^{(t-1)q}}$$

$$\geq \frac{1}{q} \sum_{t=1}^{\infty} \frac{r^{tq}}{t} = \frac{1}{q} \log \frac{1}{1-r^q} \to \infty \qquad \text{as } r \to 1$$

[since $r \to 1$ and $-\log(1-x^k) = \sum_t \frac{(x^k)^t}{t} = \log \frac{1}{(1-x^k)}$]

Now, if $m \neq 0 \pmod q$, then

$$|1-z^m|^2 = |1-r^m e^{2p\pi im/q}|^2$$

$$= \left|1-r^m\left(\cos\frac{2\pi pm}{q} + i\sin\frac{2\pi pm}{q}\right)\right|^2$$

$$= \left(1-r^m\cos\frac{2\pi pm}{q}\right)^2 + r^{2m}\sin^2\frac{2\pi pm}{q}$$

$$= 1 - 2r^m\cos\frac{2\pi pm}{q} + r^{2m}$$

$$= (1-r^m)^2 + 2r^m\left(1-\cos\frac{2\pi pm}{q}\right)$$

$$\Rightarrow (1-r^m)^2 + 4r^m\sin^2\frac{p\pi m}{q}$$

$$\geq 4r^m\sin^2\frac{p\pi m}{q} \quad as \; (1-r^m)^2 \geq 0$$

$$\geq 4r^m\sin^2\frac{\pi}{q}.$$

Since the inequality does still hold as $\sin^2\frac{p\pi m}{q} \leq 1$ and also $\sin^2\frac{\pi}{q} \leq 1$

$$\therefore \qquad |1-z^m| \geq 2r^{m/2}\sin\frac{\pi}{q} \qquad\qquad\qquad\qquad\qquad \ldots(5)$$

Thus

$$\left|(1-r)\sum_2 \right| = |(1-r)|\left|\sum_2 \frac{z^m}{1-z^m}\right|$$

$$\leq |(1-r)|\sum_2 \frac{|z^m|}{|1-z^m|}$$

$$\leq (1-r)\sum_{m=0}^{\infty} \frac{r^m}{2r^{m/2}\sin\pi/q}, \text{ by (5)}$$

$$\leq \frac{1-r}{2\sin\dfrac{\pi}{q}} \sum_{m-0}^{\infty} r^{m/2}$$

$$\leq \frac{1-r}{2\sin\dfrac{\pi}{q}} \cdot \frac{1}{1-r^{1/2}}, \text{ as } \sum_{m=0}^{\infty} r^{m/2} = \frac{1}{1-r^{1/2}}$$

$$\leq \frac{1+r^{1/2}}{2\sin\pi/q} \leq \frac{1}{\sin\dfrac{\pi}{q}} \text{ as } r \to 1.$$

So that
$$(1-r)f(z) = (1-r) + \sum_1 + \sum_2$$

$$= \frac{1}{q}\log\frac{1}{1-r^q} + \frac{1}{\sin\dfrac{\pi}{q}} \to \infty \text{ as } r \to 1.$$

This follows that $z = e^{2\pi p/q}$ is a singularity of $f(z)$. But the points of such type are dense everywhere round the unit circle $|z| = 1$ and hence an arc, however small, on $f(z)$ is not found to be regular. Thus $f(z)$ cannot be continued across the unit circle so that the unit circle is a natural boundary of the function.

13.6.1. Schwarz's Reflection Principle. *If $f_1(z)$ be analytic in the region R_1 and $f_1(z)$ takes only real values on the part LMN of the real axis then the analytic continuation $f_2(z)$ of $f_1(z)$ into the domain R_2 (considered as the mirror image of R_1 with LMN as mirror) is given by $f_2(z) = f_1(z)$.* (*G.ND.U. Amritsar 2000, 2004; Rohtak 2002; Kanpur 2001, 2004; Kumaon, 2001*)

Let a function $f_1(z)$ be analytic in a region R_1 and that $f_1(z)$ takes only real values on the part LMN of the real axis so that

$$f_1(z) = \overline{f_1(\bar{z})} \text{ on the line LMN} \qquad\qquad ...(1)$$

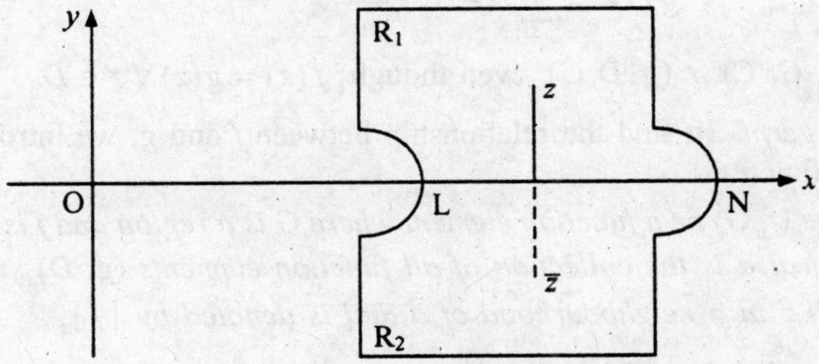

Fig. 13.16

Suppose R_2 be the mirror image of R_1 with LMN as mirror and let

$$f_2(z) = \overline{f_1(\bar{z})} \qquad\qquad ...(2)$$

To establish that $f_2(z)$ is analytic continuation of $f_1(z)$ from R_1 into R_2 via the line LMN, we have to show that (*i*) $f_1(z) = f_2(z)$ on the line LMN,

(*ii*) $f_2(z)$ is analytic in R_2.

To prove the first part, we have on the line LMN, $z = x$, $\bar{z} = x$ so that $z = \bar{z}$.

Now, (1) becomes $f_1(z) = \overline{f_1(z)}$ on the line LMN.

By (2), we get $f_1(z) = f_2(z)$ on the line LMN.

For the second part, let

$$f_1(z) = f_1(x + iy) = u_1(x, y) + iv_1(x\ y) \qquad \qquad ...(3)$$

From (3) $\qquad \qquad f_1(\bar{z}) = f_1(x - iy) = u_1(x, -y) + iv_1(x - y)$

or $\qquad \qquad \overline{f_1(z)} = f_2(z) = u_1(x, -y) - iv_1(x - y) \qquad \qquad ...(4)$

Now $f_2(z)$ is analytic in R_2 if

$$\frac{\partial u_1}{\partial x} = \frac{\partial(-v_1)}{\partial(-y)}, \frac{\partial u_1}{\partial(-y)} = -\frac{\partial(+v_1)}{\partial x}$$

or if $\qquad \qquad \dfrac{\partial u_1}{\partial x} = \dfrac{\partial v_1}{\partial y}, \dfrac{\partial u_1}{\partial y} = -\dfrac{\partial v_1}{\partial x}.$

Thus $f_2(z)$ is analytic in R_2.

13.7. Analytic Continuation along a path.

We know that a function is a triple (f, G, Ω) where G and Ω are sets and f is a *rule* or *set of rules* which assigns to each element of G a unique element of Ω. It follows that the two functions would be same if not only the *rule* or the *set of rules* be the same but the domains and ranges should also coincide. Thus, a change in the domain gives a new function. In fact we have seen that the purpose of analytic continuation is to extend the domain. In the context, let $G = \{z : \operatorname{Re} z > -1\}$ and $f(z) = \log(1 + z)$ for $z \in G$, where log is the principal branch of the logarithm. Let $D = B(0, 1)$ and let

$$g(z) = \sum_{n=0}^{\infty} (-1)^{n-1} \frac{z^n}{n}$$

for $z \in D$. Thus $(f, G, C) \neq (g, D, C)$ even though $f(z) = g(z) \,\forall\, z \in D$.

Concept of a germ. To find the relationship between f and g, we introduce the concept of a *germ* of analytic functions.

Definition: *Let (f, G) be a function element where G is a region and f is an analytic function in G. The germ of f at a is the collection of all function elements (g, D) such that $a \in D$ and $f(z) = g(z)$ for all z in a neighbourhood of a and is denoted by $[f]_a$.*

But $[f]_a$ is a collection of function element and it is not a function element itself. Also, it can easily be verified that $(g, D) \in [f]_a$ if and only if $(f, G) \in [g]_a$.

In terms of germ, the definition of analytic continuation along a path will be as follows:

Let $\gamma : [0, 1] \to C$ be a path and let there be a function element (f_t, D_t) for each t in $[0, 1]$ such that

(*a*) $\gamma(t) \in D_t$;

(*b*) for each t in $[0, 1]$ there is a $\delta > 0$ such that $|s - t| < \delta$ implies $\gamma(s) \in D_t$ and $[f_s]_{\gamma(s)} = [f_t]_{\gamma(t)}$.

Then (f_1, D_1) is said to be the *analytic continuation* of (f_0, D_0) along the path γ or $f_1(D_1)$ is said to be obtained from (f_0, D_0) by analytic continuation along the path γ.

Lemma: *Let $\gamma : [0,1] \to C$ be a path from a to b and let $\{(f_t, D_t) : 0 \le t \le 1\}$ and $\{g_t, B_t\} : 0 \le t \le 1\}$ be analytic continuation along γ such that $[f_0]_a = [g_0]_a$. Then $[f_1]_b = [g_1]_b$.*

To prove this lemma we will show that the set $T = \{t \in [0,1] : [f_t]_{\gamma(t)} = [g_t]_{\gamma(t)}\}$ is both open and closed in $[0, 1]$. Since γ is a path from a to b, hence $\gamma(0) = a$ and $\gamma(1) = b$. By hypothesis, $[f_0]_a = [g_0]_a$; and so $0 \in T$; *i.e.*, T is non-empty. Then it will follow that $T = \{0,1\}$ so that, in particular, $1 \in T$.

To show that T is open, fix t in T and assume that $t \ne 0$ or 1. In fact, if $t = 1$ the proof is complete. If $t = 0$ then the foregoing argument will show that $\{(a, a + \delta) \subset T\}$ for some $\delta > 0$. By the definition of analytic continuation there is a $\delta > 0$ such that for $|s - t| < \delta, \gamma(s) \in D_t \cap B_t$ and

$$[f_s]_{\gamma(s)} = [f_t]_{\gamma(s)}$$

$$[g_s]_{\gamma(s)} = [g_t]_{\gamma(s)}$$

Since $t \in T$, it follows that $f_t(z) = g_t(z) \forall z \in D_t \cap B_t$. Hence $[f_t]_{\gamma(s)} = [g_t]_{\gamma(s)}$ $\forall y(s) \in D_t \cap B_t$. Hence,

$$[f_t]_{\gamma(s)} = [g_t]_{\gamma(s)} \forall \gamma(s) \in D_t \cap B_t$$

So, it follows from (1) that $|s - t| < \delta \Rightarrow [f_s]_{\gamma(s)} = [g_s]_{\gamma(s)}$; *i.e.*, $(t - \delta, t + \delta) \subset T$. This implies that T is open.

Now, to show that T is closed let t be a limit point of T, and again choose $\delta > 0$ so that $\gamma(s) \in D_t \cap S_t$ and (1) is satisfied whenever $|s - t| < \delta$.

Since t is a limit point of T, with $|s - t| < \delta$; so $\gamma(s) \in D_t \cap B_t \cap D_s \cap B_s = G$.

$\Rightarrow$ G is a non-empty open set

$\Rightarrow$ $f_s(z) = g_s(z) \forall z \in G$, by the definition of T.

But according to (1)

$$f_s(z) = f_t(z) \text{ and } g_s(z) = g_t(z) \ \forall z \in G.$$

Which implies that

$$f_t(z) = g_t(z) \forall z \in Z.$$

Since G has a limit point in $D_t \cap B_t$, this equation gives

$$[f_t]_{\gamma(t)} = [g_t]_{\gamma(t)} \Rightarrow t \in T. \text{ Hence } T \text{ is closed.}$$

Definition: *Let $\gamma : [0,1] \to C$ be a path from a to b and $\{(f_t, D_t); 0 \le t \le 1\}$ is an analytic continuation along γ. Then the germ $[f_1]_b$ is the analytic continuation of $[f_0]_1$ along γ.*

Above lemma says that if $\{(g_t, B_t)\}$ for which gthere is a point a in G and a path γ from a to b such that $[g]_b$ is another continuation along γ with $[f_0]_a = [g_0]_a$ then $[f_1]_b = [g_1]_b$. This means that above definition does not depend on the choice of continuation.

Definition: *Let (f, G) is a function element. Thus the complete analytic function obtained from $f(G)$ is the collection of all germs $[g]_b$. for which there is a point in G and a path γ from a to b such that $[g]_b$ is the analytic continuation of $[f]_a$ along γ.*

Definition: Let $D = \{D_0, D_1, ..., D_n\}$ be a collection of open discs. Then D is called a *chain of discs* if $D_{j-1} \cap D_i \neq \phi$ For $1 \leq i \leq n$. If $\{(f_i, D_i); 0 \leq j \leq n\}$ is a collection of function elements such that δ is a chain of discs and $f_{j-1}(z) = f_j(z)$ for in $D_{j-1} \cap D_j, 1 \leq j \leq n$ then $\{(f_j, D_j) : 0 \leq j \leq n\}$ is called on *analytic continuation along a chain of discs*. We say that (f_n, D_n) is obtained by an analytic continuation of (f_0, D_0) along a chain of discs.

13.7.1 Behaviour of the radius of convergence for an analytic continuation along a curve

Let a and b be two points in C and suppose γ and σ are two paths from a to b. Suppose $\{(f_t, D_t)\}$ and $\{g_t, B_t\}$ are analytic continuation along γ and σ respectively. Also let $[f_0]_a = [g_0]_a$. Naturally a question arises. Does it follow thair $[f_1]_b = [g_1]_b$? According to the Lemma §13.7, the answer to this question is affirmative if γ and σ are the same path. However, γ and σ are distinct paths then the answer may be negative.

If (f, D) is a function element and $a \in D$ then f has a power series expansion at $z = a$. Now, we will examine the behaviour of the radius of convergence for an analytic continuation along a curve.

Lemma 1. *Let $\gamma : [0,1] \to C$ be a path and let $\{(f_t, D_t) : 0 \leq t \leq 1\}$ be an analytic continuation along γ. For $0 \leq t \leq 1$ let $R(t)$ be the radius of convergence of the power series expansion of f_t about $z = \gamma(t)$. Then either $R(t) = \infty$ or $R : [0,1] \to (0, \infty)$ is continuous.*

If $R(t) = \infty$ for some value. of, *i.e.*, the radius of circle of convergence is infinite, then it is possible to extend f_t to an entire function. It follows that

$$f_s(z) = f_t(z) \; \forall z \in D_s.$$

Which implies that $R(s) = \infty$ for each $s \in [0,1] \Rightarrow R(s) \equiv \infty$.

So, we suppose that $R(t) < \infty$ for all $t \in [0,1]$. Fix t in $[0,1]$ and let $\tau = \gamma(t)$. Let the power series expansion of f_t about z be

$$f_t(z) = \sum_{n=0}^{\infty} a_n(z - \tau)^n.$$

Now, let $\delta_1 > 0$ be such that

$$|s - t| < \delta_1 \Rightarrow \gamma(s) \in D_1 \cap B(\tau, R(t))$$

and

$$[f_s]_{\gamma(s)} = [f_t]_{\gamma(s)}$$

Let us fix s with $|s - t| < \delta_1$ and let $\sigma = \gamma(s)$.

Now, we can extend f_t to an analytic function in $B(z; R(t))$. Again since f_s agree with f_t on a neighbourhood of σ, f_s can be extended. Consequently, f_s is also analytic in $B(z; R(t)) \cup D_s$. Suppose f_s has the power series expansion about $z = \sigma$ as

$$f_s(z) = \sum_{n=0}^{\infty} b_n(z - \sigma)^n$$

then the radius of convergence $R(s)$ must be greater than the distance from σ to the circle $|z - \tau| = R(t)$; *i.e.*,

$$R(s) \geq d(\sigma, \Gamma) \geq R(t) - |\tau - \sigma|$$

where Γ is the circle defined by

$$\Gamma = \{z : |z - \tau| = R(t)\}.$$

$\Rightarrow$ $\qquad\qquad R(t) - R(s) \leq |\tau - \sigma|$

i.e., $\qquad\qquad R(t) - R(s) \leq |\gamma(t) - \gamma(s)|.$

Similarly, we have

$$R(s) - R(t) \leq |\gamma(t) - \gamma(s)|$$

If follows that

$\max [R(s) - R(t), - (R(s) - R(t))]$

$\qquad \leq |\gamma(t) - \gamma(s)|$

$\Rightarrow \qquad |R(s) - R(t)| \leq |\gamma(t) - \gamma(s)|$ ...(1)

for $|s - t| < \delta_1$. Since γ is continuous, and defined in a compact domain $[0, 1]$; it follows that γ is uniformly continuous. Thus, for a given $\in > 0$, $\exists a \ \delta_1 > 0$ such that $\gamma(s) \in D_t \cap B(\tau)$; $R(t), f_s$ is analytic in $B(\tau; R(t)) \cup D_s$, and

$$|s - t| < \delta_1 \Rightarrow |\gamma(s) - \gamma(t)| < t.$$

So (1) yields that

$$|s - t| < \delta_1 \Rightarrow |R(s) - R(t)| \in.$$

Hence R is uniformly continuous in the neighbourhood $|s - t| < \delta_1$ of t. Therefore, R must be continuous at t.

Lemma 2: *Let $\gamma [0, 1] \to C$ be a path from a to b and let $\{(f_t, D_t) : 0 \leq t \leq 1\}$ be an analytic continuation along γ. There is a number $\in > 0$ such that if $\sigma : [0, 1] \to C$ is any path from a to b with $|\gamma(t) - \sigma(t)| < \in$ for all t and if $\{(g_t, B_t) : 0 \leq t \leq 1\}$ is any continuation along σ with*

$$[g_0]_a = [f_0]_a; \text{ then } [g_1]_b = [f_1]_b.$$

Let the power series expansion of f_t about $z = \gamma(t), 0 \leq t \leq 1$ be

$$f_t(z) = \sum_{n=0}^{\infty} a_n(z - \gamma(t))$$

and let $R(t)$ be its radius of convergence. If $R(t) = \infty$, then any value of $\in$ will serve our purpose. So, suppose $R(t) < \infty \ \forall t \in [0, 1]$.

Now, with the help of lemma 1 above, R is a continuous function and since $R(t) > 0 \forall t \in [0, 1], R$ has a positive minimum value. Let

$$0 < \in < \frac{1}{2} \min . \{R(t) : 0 \leq t \leq 1\}$$ ...(1)

Assume that σ and $\{(g_t, B_t)\}$ are as in the statement of the lemma. Also, assume that D_t is the disc given by

$$D_t = \{z : |z - \gamma(t)| < R(t)\},$$

as it will not affect the conclusion of the lemma.

Since, for $\sigma(t) \in B_t \cap D_t$ and for $t \in [0, 1], |\sigma(t) - \gamma(t)| < \in < R(t)$, it makes sense to ask whether $g_t(z) = f_t(z)$ for all z in $B_t \cap D_t$. Now, let it is true for $t = 1$.

Let t be the set such that

$$T = \{t \in [0,1] : f_t(z) = g_t(z) \text{ for } z \in B_t \cap D_t\};$$

and show that $1 \in T$. For this, we have to show that T is a non-empty open and closed subset of $[0,1]$.

By hypothesis of the lemma, $[f_0]_a = [g_0]_a$; it follows that $f_0(z) = g_0(z)$ for $z \in B_t \cap D_t$ and so $0 \in T$. Thus, $T \ne \phi$. To show that T is open, let us fix $t \in T$ and choose $\delta > 0$ such that

$$|\gamma(s) - \gamma(t)| < \epsilon, [f_s]_{\gamma(s)} = [f_t]_{\gamma(s)}$$

$$|\sigma(s) - \sigma(t)| < \epsilon, [g_s]_{\sigma(s)} = [g_t]_{\sigma(s)} \in B_t \qquad \qquad ...(2)$$

whenever $|s - t| < \delta$.

We now show that $B_s \cap B_t \cap D_s \cap D_t \ne \phi$ for $|s - t| < \delta$. This will be proved by showing that $\sigma(s) \in B_s \cap D_s \cap D_t$. If $|s - t| < \delta$, then $|\sigma(s) - \gamma(s)| < \epsilon < R(s)$

$$\Rightarrow \qquad \qquad \sigma(s) \in D_S.$$

Also, $\qquad |\sigma(s) - \gamma(t)| \le |\sigma(s) - \gamma(s)| + |\gamma(s) - \gamma(t)| < \epsilon + \epsilon$

$$= 2\epsilon < R(t), \qquad \qquad \text{by (1)} \Rightarrow \sigma(s) \in D_t.$$

We already have shown that

$$\sigma(s) \in B_s \cap B_t, \text{ by (2), } \sigma(s) \in B_s \cap D_s \cap D_t.$$

Again, since $t \in T$ it follows that $f_t(z) = g_t(z) \ \forall z \in G$.

Also, from (2), we have $f_s(z) = f_t(z)$ and $g_s(z) = g_t(z) \ \forall z \in G \Rightarrow f_s(z) = g_s(z) \ \forall z \in G$, but since G has a limit point in $B_s \cap D_s$ it must follow that $s \in T$, i.e., $(t - \delta, t + \delta) \in T$.

Hence, T is open. We can easily show that T is closed. This completes the proof of the lemma.

Definition: Unrestricted Analytic continuation. Let (f, D) be a function element and let G be a region which contains D; then (f, D) admits unrestricted *analytic continuation in G with initial point in G if for any path V in G with initial point in D there is an analytic continuation of (f, D) along* γ.

Let us consider $D = \{z : |z - 1| < 1\}$ and f be the principal branch of $\sqrt{z}$ or $\log z$. Then we see that (f, D) admits unrestricted continuation in the punctured plane but not in the whole plane.

Monodromy Theorem. *Let (f, D) be a function element and let G be a region containing D such that (f, D) admits unrestricted continuation in G. Let $a \in D, b \in G$ and let γ_0 and γ_1 be paths in G from a to b. Let $\{(f_t, D_t) : 0 \le t \le 1\}$ and $\{(g_t, D_t) : 0 \le t \le 1\}$ be analytic continuations of (f, D) along γ_0 and γ_1 respectively. If γ_0 and γ_1 are fixed end point homotopic in G then $[f_1]_b = [g_1]_b$.*

Since γ_0 and γ_1 are fixed-end-point homotopic in G, so there is a continuous function $\phi : [0,1] \times [0,1] \to G$ such that

$$\phi(t, 0) = \gamma_0(t) \qquad \qquad \qquad \phi(t, 1) = \gamma_1(t)$$

$$\phi(0, u) = a \qquad \qquad \qquad \phi(1, u) = b$$

for all t and u in $[0, 1]$. Choose $u \in [0, 1]$ and keep it fix. Consider the path γ_u defined by

$$\gamma_u(t) = \phi(t, u), \quad a \le t \le b$$

Again, by hypothesis, there is an analytic continuation $\{(h_t, u', D_t, u) : 0 \le t \le 1\}$ of (f, D) along the path γ_u. Thus, we have $[g_1]_b = [h_1, 1]_b$ and $[f_1]_b = [h_1, 0]_b$. Hence, it will be sufficient to show that $[h_1, 0]_b = [h_1, 1]_b$.

Now, define the set U such that

$$U = \{u \in [0, 1] : [h_1, u]_b = [h_1, 0]\}$$

and we will show that U is a non-empty open and closed subset of $[0, 1]$. Obviously, $a \in U$ and hence $U \ne \phi$. We now show that U is both open and closed. For this, let there exists $\delta \in 0$ and $u \in [0, 1]$, then

$$|u - v| < \delta \Rightarrow [h_1, u]_b = [h_1, v]_b$$

For a fixed u in $[0, 1]$ apply Lemma 2 to find an $\epsilon > 0$ such that if σ is any path from a to b with $|\gamma_n(t) - \sigma(t)| < \epsilon$ for all t and if $\{(k_t, E_t)\}$ is any continuation of (f, D) along σ, then

$$[h_1, u]_b = [k_1]_b.$$

Now, ϕ is a uniformly continuous function, it follows that for any given $\epsilon > 0, \exists \, a \, \delta < 0$ such that

$$|u - v| < \delta \Rightarrow |\gamma_u(t) - \gamma_0(t)|$$
$$= |\phi(t, u) - \phi(t, v)| \in \forall t \qquad \qquad ...(2)$$

Now, equation (1) follows by applying (2).

Suppose $u \in U$ and let $\delta > 0$ be the number given by equation (1). By the definition of U, we have

$$(u - \delta, u + \delta) \subset U.$$

Hence, U is open.

If $u \in U$ and $\delta > 0$ be chosen as in (1), then there exists $au \in U$ such that $|u - v| < \delta$. By (1)

$$[h_1, v]_b = [h_1, 0]_b$$

which implies that $u \in U$. Hence U is closed.

Corollary: *Let (f, D) be a function element which admits unrestricted continuation in the simply connected region G, then there is an analytic function $F : G \to C$ such that $F(z) = f(z)$ for all z in D.*

Suppose $a \in D$ and keep it fix. Let z be any point in G. Let γ be a path in D from a to z and $\{(f_t, D_t) : 0 \le t < 1\}$ be an analytic continuation of (f, D) along γ; then let

$$f(z, \gamma) = f_t(z).$$

Since G is simply connected, we have

$$f(z, \gamma) = f(z, \sigma)$$

for any two paths γ and σ in G from a to z. So if we define $f(z) = f(z, \gamma)$, then $F : C \to C$ is well defined function.

Again, let $z \in G$ and let γ and $\{(f_t, D_t)\}$ be as above. Then it can easily verified that $F(w) = f_t(w)$ for w in a neighbourhood of z. Hence F must be analytic.

13.7.3 The Dilogarithm.

For $|z| < 1$ we define the function

$$f(z) = -\frac{\log(1-z)}{z} = \sum_{n=1}^{\infty} \frac{z^{n-1}}{n}.$$

This function is holomorphic at 0. Let now $z \neq 0$ and let γ be a path in $C - \{0, 1\}$ except for the beginning point at 0. We then have an analytic continuation $f_\gamma(z)$ which depends on γ. Since the continuation of $\log(1-z)$ picks up a constant of integration after integrating around loops around 1, it follows that the analytic continuation of f may have a pole at 0, with residue an integral multiple of $2\pi i$. Instead of integrating along paths starting at 0, we can use a slightly arbitrary device of picking some point, say $1/3$, and defining f by analytic continuation from $1/3$ to z, along paths γ from $\frac{1}{3}$ to z in $C - \{0, 1\}$.

The *dilogarithm* is defined for $|z| < 1$ by the integral and power series.

$$L_2(z) = \int_0^z f(\zeta) \, d_{ce}$$

$$= \sum_{n=1}^{\infty} \frac{z^n}{n^2},$$

and is defined by analytic continuation in general, so we get a function $L_{2,\gamma}(z)$ for each path γ as above. We may write

$$L_{2,\gamma}(z) = -\int_{0,\gamma}^z \log_\gamma(1-\zeta) \frac{d\zeta}{\zeta}$$

Let U be the simply connected set obtained by deleting the set of real numbers ≥ 1 from C. Then for $z \in U$, the function $f_\gamma(z)$ is independent of the path γ in U, and may still be denoted by f. It is analytic.

EXAMPLES

1. *Show that the series*

$$\sum_{n=0}^{\infty} \frac{z^n}{2^{n+1}} \text{ and } \sum_{n=0}^{\infty} \frac{(z-1)^n}{(z-i)^{n-1}}$$

are analytic continuation of each other.   (*Meerut 2004; Agra 2001, 2005*)

The radius of convergence of ϕ the first power series

$$= \lim_{n \to \infty} |2^{n+1}|^{1/n} = \lim_{n \to \infty} |2^{1+i/n}| = 2$$

and its sum is

$$f_1(z) = \frac{\frac{1}{2}}{1 - \frac{1}{2}z} = \frac{1}{2-z}$$

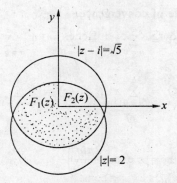

Fig. 13.17

The radius of convergence of the second power series

$$= \lim_{n \to \infty} |(2-i)^{n+1}|^{1/n}$$

$$= \lim_{n \to \infty} |2-i|^{1+1/n} = |2-i| = \sqrt{5}$$

The sum of this series

$$f_2(z) = \frac{\dfrac{1}{2-i}}{1 - \{(z-i)/(2-i)\}} = \frac{1}{2-z}$$

The circle of convergence of first power series has the radius 2 with centre at the origin, and the circle of convergence of the second power series has the radius $\sqrt{5}$ with centre at the point i; hence the two circles intersect.

Thus, we see that both the power series represent the same function $\dfrac{1}{(2-z)}$; and $f_1(z) = f_2(z)$ in the region comman to both the circles. Hence they are analytic continuation of each other.

2. *Show that the series*

$$\sum_{n=0}^{\infty} z^{n!} \to \infty \text{ as } z \to exp\left(\frac{2\pi ip}{q!}\right)$$

along the radius through the point where p is any positive integer less than q!. Deduce that the function represented by the series cannot be continued analytically beyond the unit circle.

Solution.
$$f(z) = \sum_{n=0}^{\infty} z^{n!} = \Sigma u_n(z), \text{ (say)}.$$

Then

$$\lim_{n \to \infty} \frac{u_n}{u_{n+1}} = \lim_{n \to \infty} \frac{z^{n!}}{z^{(n+1)!}} = \lim_{n \to \infty} \frac{1}{z^{n+1}} \to \infty > 1$$

$$\therefore \qquad \lim_{n \to \infty} \frac{u_n}{u_{n+1}} > 1 \text{ if } |z| < 1.$$

This $\Rightarrow \Sigma u_n$ is convergent if $|z| < 1$.

Hence $|z| = 1$ is the circle of convergence.

$$f(z) = \sum_{n=0}^{\infty} z^{n!} = \sum_{n=0}^{q} z^{n!} + \sum_{n=q+1}^{\infty} z^{n!}.$$

Taking

$$f_1(z) = \sum_{n=0}^{q} z^{n!}, \quad f_2(z) = \sum_{n=q+1}^{\infty} z^{n!}$$

we get $f(z) = f_1(z) + f_2(z)$.

Let P be a point at

$$z = r \exp\left(\frac{2\pi i p}{q!}\right)$$

outside the circle of convergence, where p and q are integers and $r > 1$. We now examine the behaviour of $f(z)$ as P tends to move towards the circle of convergence through radius vector.

$$z^{n!} = \left[r \exp\left(\frac{2\pi i p}{q!}\right)\right]^{n!} = r^{n!} \exp\left(\frac{2\pi i p n!}{q!}\right)$$

where $q!$ is a divisor of $n!$ so that q can be selected such that $\dfrac{n!}{q!}$ is an integer. This

$\Rightarrow$
$$z^{n!} = r^{n!} \text{ for } \exp\left(\frac{2\pi i p n!}{q!}\right) = 1.$$

$\Rightarrow$
$$f_1(z) = \sum_{n=0}^{q} r^{n!} \text{ at P}$$

$\Rightarrow$ $f_1(z)$ is a polynomial of degree $q!$ and tends to a unique limit as $r \to 1$.

Also

$$f_2(z) = \sum_{n=q+1}^{\infty} r^{n!} \to \infty \text{ as } r \to 1.$$

Consequently $f = f_1 + f_2 \to \infty$ as $r \to 1$.

Thus the point $z = e^{(2\pi i p)/q!}$ is a singularity of $f(z)$. This point lies on the boundary of the circle of convergence $|z| = 1$. Moreover p is any integer. Therefore the points of the type

$$\exp\left(\frac{2\pi p i}{q!}\right)$$

lie on every arc, however small of the circle $|z| = 1$. Evidently every circle that crosses the circle $|z| = 1$ will contain within its points of this form. Consequently $f(z)$ cannot be continued analytically outside $|z| = 1$. Hence boundary of $|z| = 1$ is a natural boundary.

3. *Show that the circle of convergence of the power series* $\sum_{n=0}^{\infty} z^n$ *is a natural boundary for its sum function.*

                                                                        (Kumaon, 2002)

Solution. Given series is

$$f_1(z) = \sum_{n=0}^{\infty} z^n = 1 + z + z^2 + \dots$$

This series is convergent for $|z| < 1$. Hence the circle of convergence is $|z| = 1$. The sum function is

$$f_2(z) = \frac{1}{1-z}.$$

This function is regular throughout the complex plane except at $z = 1$ and in particular it is regular in the domain defined by $|z| > 1$. Thus $f_1(z) = f_2(z)$ inside the circle $|z| = 1$ and hence $f_2(z)$ is an analytic continuation of $f_1(z)$ from the domain $|z| < 1$ to the domain $|z| > 1$. Hence the sum function represented by the given power series can be continued analytically outside the circle of convergence.

4. *Show that the power series*

$$z - \frac{z^2}{2} + \frac{z^3}{3} - \ldots$$

may be analytically continued to a wider range by means of the series

$$\log 2 - \frac{(1-z)}{2} - \frac{(1-z)^2}{2 \cdot 2^2} - \frac{(1-z)^3}{3 \cdot 2^3} - \ldots$$

Solution. Let

$$f_1(z) = z - \frac{z^2}{2} + \frac{z^3}{3} - \ldots$$

and

$$f_2(z) = \log 2 - \frac{(1-z)}{2} - \frac{(1-z)^2}{2 \cdot 2^2} - \frac{(1-z)^3}{3 \cdot 2^3} - \ldots$$

Now, $f_1(z) = \log(1 + z)$ which is convergent for $|z| < 1$. Thus $f_1(z)$ is analytic inside the circle C_1 defined by $|z| = 1$.

Again,

$$f_2(z) = \log 2 - \left[\left(\frac{1-z}{2} \right) + \left(\frac{1-z}{2} \right)^2 \cdot \frac{1}{2} + \left(\frac{1-z}{2} \right)^3 \cdot \frac{1}{3} + \ldots \right]$$

$$= \log 2 + \log \left[1 - \left(\frac{1-z}{2} \right) \right].$$

This is convergent for $\left| \frac{1-z}{2} \right| < 1$, *i.e.*, $|1-z| < 2$.

Also,

$$f_2(z) = \log \left[2 \left(\frac{1+z}{2} \right) \right] = \log(1+z).$$

Thus $f_2(z)$ is analytic inside the circle C_2 such that $|z - 1| = 2$ and has the sum function $\log(1 + z)$.

Now, we have

(i) $f_1(z)$ is analytic inside the circle C_1,

(ii) $f_2(z)$ is analytic inside the circle C_2,

(iii) $f_1(z) = f_2(z)$ in the area common to both C_1 and C_2.

Hence $f_2(z)$ is an analytic continuation of $f_1(z)$ from the interior of C_1 to the interior of C_2. Moreover C_2 is a larger range in comparison to C_1. Hence the problem.

5. *Show that when b is real, the series*

$$\frac{1}{2} \log(1 + b^2) + i \tan^{-1} b + \frac{z - ib}{1 + ib} - \frac{1}{2} \left(\frac{z + ib}{1 + ib} \right)^2 + \ldots$$

is an analytic continuation of the function defined by the series

$$z - \frac{z^2}{2} + \frac{z^3}{3} - \ldots .$$

Solution. Let

$$f_1(z) = z - \frac{z^2}{2} + \frac{z^3}{3} - \ldots$$

$f_1(z)$ is convergent within a circle C_1, $|z| = 1$ and its sum function is $\log(1 + z)$. Also, $f_1(z)$ has a singularity at $z = -1$.

Let $f_2(z) = \frac{1}{2}\log(1 + b^2) + i\tan^{-1} b + \left(\frac{z - ib}{1 + ib}\right) - \frac{1}{2}\left(\frac{z + ib}{1 + ib}\right)^2 + \ldots$

$$= \log(1 + ib) + \log\left(1 + \frac{z - ib}{z + ib}\right) \qquad \ldots(1)$$

$f_2(z)$ is convergent inside the circle C_2,

$$\left|\frac{z - ib}{1 + ib}\right| = 1 \text{ or } |z - ib| = \sqrt{(1 + b^2)}.$$

From (1),

$$f_2(z) = \log(1 + ib) + \log\left(\frac{1 + z}{1 + ib}\right)$$

$$= \log(1 + z).$$

Thus sum function of $f_1(z)$ and $f_2(z)$ is same and is $\log(1 + z)$.

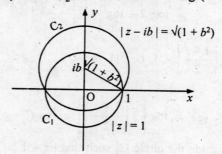

Fig. 13.18

Thus, $f_1(z)$ is analytic inside the circle C_1 $(|z| = 1)$ and $f_2(z)$ is analytic inside the circle C_2 $\{|z - ib| = \sqrt{(1 + b^2)}\}$. Also $f_1(z) = f_2(z) = \log(1 + z)$ in the portion common to C_1 and C_2. Therefore $f_2(z)$ is an analytic continuation of $f_1(z)$ from C_1 to C_2.

6. *The power series*

$$z + \frac{z^2}{2} + \frac{z^3}{3} + \ldots$$

and

$$i\pi - (z - 2) + \frac{1}{2}(z - 2)^2 - \ldots$$

have no common region of convergence. Prove that they are nevertheless analytic continuations of the same function.

Solution. Let

$$f_1(z) = z + \frac{z^2}{2} + \frac{z^3}{3} + \ldots\ldots$$

$$= -\log(1-z).$$

This power series is convergent inside a circle $|z| = 1$ (C_1 say), $z = 1$ is the only singularity.
Let

$$f_2(z) = i\pi - (z-2) + \frac{1}{2}(z-2)^2 - \ldots\ldots$$

$$= i\pi - \left[(z-2) - \frac{1}{2}(z-2)^2 + \ldots\ldots\right]$$

$$= i\pi - \log[1 + (z-2)].$$

This series is convergent within a circle $|z-2| = 1$ (C_2 say).
Also

$$f_2(z) = i\pi - \log(z-1) = i\pi - \log(-1)(1-z)$$

$$= i\pi - [\log e^{i\pi} + \log(1-z)]$$

$$= -\log(1-z).$$

Thus the sum functions of both the series is same, the first one is analytic inside C_1, while the second series is analytic inside C_2. Both the circles only touch each other at $|z| = 1$. Thus there is no region common to the interiors of the two circles. Hence the two series are not analytic continuations of one another.

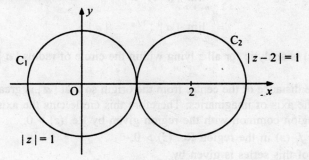

Fig. 13.19

7. *Prove that the function*

$$f_1(z) = \int\limits_0^\infty e^{-zt}\, dt$$

can be continued analytically. Also construct a power series which is an analytic continuation of $f_1(z)$.

Solution.

$$f_1(z) = \int\limits_0^\infty e^{-zt}\, dt = \left[\frac{e^{-zt}}{-z}\right]_{t=0}^\infty$$

$$\therefore f_1\,(z) \to \infty \text{ when Re. }(z) \le 0$$

or $$f_1\,(z) = \frac{1}{z} \text{ when Re. }(z) > 0.$$

Therefore $f_1\,(z)$ is analytic in the region given by Re. $(z) > 0$.

Choose $f_2\,(z) = 1\,/\,z$ which we know is analytic everywhere except at $z = 0$.

Thus $f_2\,(z) = f_1\,(z)\;\forall\;\forall\;z$ for which Re. $(z) > 0$.

Therefore $f_2\,(z)$ is an analytic continuation of $f_1\,(z)$.

Second part. Consider the series given by

$$f_2\,(z) = \sum_{n=0}^{\infty} \frac{(-1)^n}{a^{n+1}}\,(z-a)^n.$$

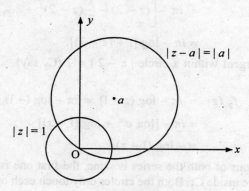

Fig. 13.20

Radius of convergence $$= \lim_{n \to \infty} |(-1)^n\,a^{n+1}|^{1/n}$$

$$= \lim_{n \to \infty} |a|^{1+1/n} = |a|.$$

Therefore $f_2\,(z)$ is analytic for all z lying within the circle of radius $|a|$ centred at the point a.

Now $|a|$ is the distance of the centre from the origin so that $|a|$ is greater than the distance of the centre from the axis of imaginaries. Therefore this circle cuts the axis of imaginaries and as such has some region common with the region given by Re. $(z) > 0$.

Hence $f_2\,(z) = f_1\,(z)$ in the region Re. $(z) > 0$.

Also the sum of this series is given by

$$\frac{1}{a} - \frac{(z-a)}{a^2} + \frac{(z-a)^2}{a^3} - \frac{(z-a)^3}{a^4} + \dots$$

$$= \frac{1}{a}\left[1 - \frac{(z-a)}{a} + \frac{(z-a)^2}{a^2} - \dots\right] \text{ where } |z-a| < |a|$$

$$= \frac{1}{a} \cdot \frac{1}{1 + \dfrac{z-a}{a}} = \frac{1}{z}.$$

The sum is same as that of the given series.

Hence the power series

$$f_2(z) = \sum_{n=0}^{\infty} \frac{(-1)^n}{a^{n+1}} (z-a)^n$$

is an analytic continuation of $f_1(z)$.

8. *If the radius of convergence of a power series*

$$f(z) = \sum_{n=0}^{\infty} a_n z^n$$

is a finite non-zero number, then the complete analytic function F (z) corresponding to f (z) has at least one singularity on the circle of convergence.

Solution. Suppose that r is the radius of the circle of convergence of the given series. Consider any concentric circle

$$|z| = r' < r.$$

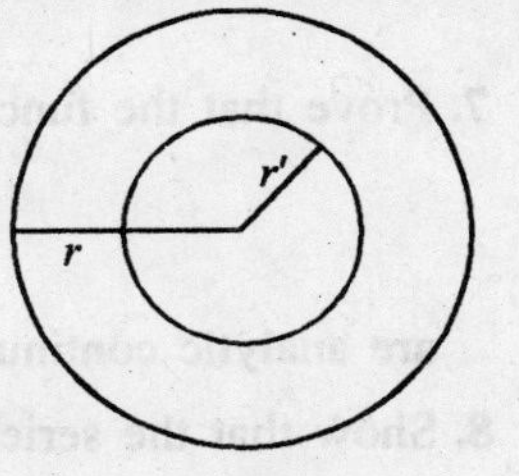

Let ρ be the radius of convergence of the Taylor's series of f (z) for any point z of $|z| = r'$. We have

$$\rho \geq r - r'.$$

Then ρ is a continuous function of z which is any point of the closed set given by $|z| = r'$ [Refer § 13.5.1]. On this account ρ has a least value. Let if possible, this least value of ρ be

$$r - r' + \delta \text{ where } \delta > 0.$$

Fig. 13.21

Then the circles of convergence about points $|z| = r'$ cover every point of the domain

$$|z| < r + \delta,$$

so that we obtain an analytic function F (z) defined in $|z| < r + \delta$ such that F (z) = f (z) when $|z| < r$. This shows that the radius of convergence of the given series is at least $z + \delta$ and we arrive at a contradiction. Thus the least value of ρ is $r - r'$. Let this value be attained for $z = r'e^{i\theta}$ which is a point of $|z| = r'$. Then $re^{i\theta}$ is a singular point, for otherwise, we would have an analytic continuation analytic in a circle with its centre there and as such the radius of convergence of the power series about $r'e^{i\theta}$ would exceed $r - r'$.

Hence the result.

EXERCISE

1. Prove that the function

$$f_1(z) = z - z^2 + z^3 - z^4 + \dots$$

is analytic in the region $|z| < 1$. Also find a function which represents all possible analytic continuations of $f_1(z)$.

2. Show that the series   *(Rohilkhand 2006, Punjab 2005· Rohtak 2000)*

$$1 + z + z^2 + z^4 + z^8 + \dots = 1 + \sum_{n=1}^{\infty} z^{2^n}$$

cannot be continued analytically beyond $|z| = 1$.

3. Show that the power series

$$\sum_{n=0}^{\infty} z^{3^n}$$

cannot be continued analytically beyond the circle $|z| = 1$.

4. Show that the circle of convergence of the power series

$$f(z) = 1 + z + z^2 + z^4 + z^8 + \ldots = 1 + \sum_{n=0}^{\infty} z^{2^n}$$

is a natural boundary.

5. If

$$f(z) = \sum_{n=1}^{\infty} z^{2^n},$$

show that $f(z) = f(z^2) + z$, and deduce from this $|z| = 1$ is a natural boundary of $f(z)$.

6. Discuss analytic continuation of the function

$$f_1(z) = \int_0^{\infty} e^{-zt} \, dt.$$

7. Prove that the functions

$$1 + az + a^2 z^2 + \ldots \quad \text{and} \quad \frac{1}{1-z} - \frac{(1-a)z}{(1-z)^2} + \frac{(1-a)^2 z^2}{(1-z)^3} - \ldots$$

are analytic continuations of each other.

8. Show that the series

$$\sum_{n=0}^{\infty} \frac{z^n}{2^{n+1}} \quad \text{and} \quad \sum_{n=0}^{\infty} \frac{(z-i)^n}{(2-i)^{n+1}}$$

are analytic continuations of each other.

9. Show that the function defined by

$$f_1(z) = \int_0^{\infty} t^3 e^{-zt} \, dt$$

is analytic at all points z for which $R(z) > 0$. Find also a function which is an analytic continuation of $f_1(z)$ into the left hand place $R(z) < 0$, where $R(z)$ means the real part of z.

10. Prove that if for the power series $\Sigma a_n z^n$, the coefficients a_n are all positive and zero and the circle of convergence has unit radius, then the point $z = 1$ is a singularity of the function $f(z) = \Sigma a_n z^n$.

OBJECTIVE QUESTIONS

For each of the following questions, four alternatives are given for the answer. Only one of them is correct. Choose the correct alternative.

1. (f_1, D_1) and (f_2, D_2) are direct analytic continuations of each other if and only if
    (a) $D_1 \cap D_2 = \phi$ and $f_1(z) \neq f_2(z)$ (b) $D_1 \cap D_2 \neq \phi$ and $f_1(z) = f_2(z)$
    (c) $D_1 \cap D_2 \neq \phi$ and $f_1(z) \neq f_2(z)$ (d) $D_1 \cap D_2 = \phi$ and $f_1(z) = f_2(z)$.

2. A closed curve beyond which it is not possible to take analytic continuation is called
    (a) singularity
    (b) open boundary
    (c) natural boundary
    (d) closed boundary.

3. If $f(z)$ is analytic in a domain R and if $f(z)$ vanishes at any point R_0, where R_0 is a part of R then

(a) $f(z) = 0$ throughout R

(b) $f(z) \neq 0$ throughout R

(c) $f(z) \neq 0$ throughout R_0

(d) None of these.

4. If the radius of convergence of the series

$$f(z) = \sum_{n=0}^{\infty} a_n (z - z_0)^n$$

is finite, then $f(z)$ has at least one singularity

(a) on the circle of convergence

(b) inside the circle of convergence

(c) outside the circle of convergence

(d) anywhere.

ANSWERS

1. (b)   **2.** (c)   **3.** (a)   **4.** (a)

ENTIRE FUNCTIONS

14.1. Integral or Entire Functions. *A function $f(z)$ is said to be entire or integral function if it is analytic in every finite region of the z-plane.*

Polynomials are the simplest entire functions, e.g.,

$$P(z) = \sum_{n=0}^{n} a_n z^n = a_0 + a_1 z + a_2 z^2 + \dots + a_n z^n$$

A polynomial $f(z)$ which has zeros at the points $z_1, z_2, \dots, z_n$ can be factorised in the form

$$f(z) = f(0)\left(1 - \frac{z}{z_1}\right)\left(1 - \frac{z}{z_2}\right)\dots\left(1 - \frac{z}{z_n}\right)$$

whereas an integral function which is not a polynomial may have an infinity of zeros.

The exponential function

$$e^z = 1 + z + \frac{z^2}{2!} + \dots \text{ is also an entire function.}$$

Thus, an entire function is expressible as a convergent power series about any point in the plane, having the simplest form as

$$P(z) = \sum_{n=0}^{\infty} a_n z^n$$

Here the radius of convergence can be taken so large that the only singularity of an entire function may be at infinity obviously, three cases will arise:

(*i*) If an entire function has no singularity at infinity then by Liouville's theorem, the function is a constant.

(*ii*) If an entire function has a pole of order n at infinity, then the entire function is a polynomial of degree n, so that polynomials constitute special types of entire functions.

(*iii*) If an entire function has an essential singularity at infinity then the function is an entire transcendental function such as e^z, sin z or cos z.

Theorem. *The most general integral function with no zeros is of the form $e^{\phi(z)}$, where $\phi(z)$ is itself an integral function.*

Let $f(z)$ be an integral function with no zeros so that $f(z)$ never vanishes. Then the function

$$\frac{f'(z)}{f(z)} = g(z)$$

is also an integral function.

We have

$$\int_{z_0}^{z} g(z)\, dz = \int_{z_0}^{z} \frac{f'(z)}{f(z)}\, dz$$

$$= \left[\log f(z)\right]_{z_0}^{z} = \log f(z) - \log f(z_0)$$

or

$$\log f(z) = \log f(z_0) + \int_{z_0}^{z} g(z)\, dz.$$

Take

$$a = f(z_0) \text{ and } g_1(z) = \int_{z_0}^{z} g(z)\, dz.$$

Then

$$\log f(z) = a + g_1(z) = \phi(z), \text{ (say)}$$

$\Rightarrow$

$$f(z) = e^{\phi(z)} \qquad \qquad ...(1)$$

Now, $g(z)$ is an integral function

$\Rightarrow$

$$g_1(z) = \int_{z_0}^{z} g(z)\, dz \text{ is an integral function,}$$

$\Rightarrow$

$$a + g_1(z) = \phi(z) \text{ is an integral function.}$$

Hence $f(z) = e^{\phi(z)}$ is an integral function.

14.2. Factorization of Integral Functions. We know that any polynomial $f(z)$ can be uniquely expressed as product of linear factors, *i.e.*,

$$f(z) = az^p \left(1 - \frac{z}{z_1}\right)\left(1 - \frac{z}{z_2}\right) \ldots \left(1 - \frac{z}{z_n}\right)$$

where a is constant, p is a positive integer or zero, and $z_1, z_2, z_3, \ldots, z_n$ are the zeros of the polynomial.

Conversely, if the zeros of a polynomial are given, then the polynomial can be determined apart from an arbitrary constant multiplier.

An integral function can be factorized under certain circumstances. A simple example is a polynomial whose only singularity is the pole at infinity. In case of integral function, the product,

$$\prod \left(1 - \frac{z}{z_n}\right)$$ may be divergent. Obviously, it is not always possible to factorize an integral function

in the same way as a polynomial.

Weierstrass's Theorem. *If $z_1, z_2, \ldots, z_n$ be any sequence of numbers whose only limiting point is the point at infinity, then it is possible to construct an integral function which vanishes at each of these points z_n.*

$$E[z, m] = (1 - z) \exp\left(z + \frac{z^2}{2} + \ldots + \frac{z^m}{m}\right) \qquad \qquad ...(1)$$

where m is a positive integer or zero is called **Weierstrass primary factor** and construction of integral functions involve these factors which are

$$E(z, 0) = 1 - z, \quad E(z, 1) = (1 - z) \exp(z), \quad E(z, 2) = (1 - z) \exp\left(z + \frac{z^2}{2}\right) \text{ etc.}$$

Clearly each primary factor has one simple zero at $z = 1$.

From (1), we have

$$\log E(z, m) = \log(1 - z) + \left(z + \frac{z^2}{2} + \dots + \frac{z^m}{m} \right)$$

$$= -\sum_{n=1}^{\infty} \frac{z^n}{n} + \sum_{n=1}^{m} \frac{z^n}{n} \quad \text{if } |z| < 1$$

$$= -\sum_{n=m+1}^{\infty} \frac{z^n}{n} = -\sum_{n=1}^{\infty} \frac{z^{m+n}}{m+n}.$$

$$|\log E(z, m)| \le \sum_{n=1}^{\infty} \frac{|z|^{m+n}}{m+n} = z^m \sum_{n=1}^{\infty} \frac{|z|^n}{m+n}$$

$$\le \frac{|z|^{m+1}}{m+1} \sum_{n=0}^{\infty} |z|^n$$

$$= \frac{|z|^{m+1}}{m+1} \cdot \frac{1}{1-|z|} \le \frac{|z|^{m+1}}{1-|z|}$$

or
$$|\log E(z, m)| \le \frac{|z|^{m+1}}{1-|z|} \quad \text{if } |z| < 1.$$

If
$$|z| \le \frac{1}{2}, \text{ then}$$

$$1 - |z| \ge 1 - \frac{1}{2}, \text{ so that } \frac{1}{1-|z|} \le 2.$$

Now the last inequality becomes

$$|\log E(z, m)| \le 2 |z|^{m+1} \quad \text{if } |z| \le \frac{1}{2} \qquad \dots(2)$$

Let the given zeros be $z_1, z_2, \dots, z_n$ arranged in order of non-decreasing modulus, multiple zeros being supposed to be repeated in the set according to their order. Now $r_n = |z_n|$ increases with n so that there exists a sequence $< m_n >$ of positive integers such that the series

$$\sum_{n=1}^{\infty} \left(\frac{R}{r^n} \right)^{m_n+1}$$

is convergent $\forall \ r > 0$.

Now suppose $|z| \le R$ and $|z_n| > 2R$.

Then
$$\left| \frac{z}{z_n} \right| < \frac{R}{2R} \quad \text{or} \quad \left| \frac{z}{z_n} \right| < \frac{1}{2}$$

or
$$\frac{|z|}{r_n} < \frac{1}{2}.$$

For $|z| \le R$

$$\left| \log E\left(\frac{z}{z_n}, m_n \right) \right| \le 2 \left| \frac{z}{z_n} \right|^{m_n+1}$$

$$\leq 2 \left(\frac{R}{r_n} \right)^{m_n + 1} \qquad \qquad \text{[by (2)]}$$

Finally,

$$\left| \log E \left(\frac{z}{z_n}, m_n \right) \right| \leq M_n$$

where

$$M_n = 2 \left(\frac{R}{r_n} \right)^{m_n + 1}$$

Now

$$\Sigma M_n = 2 \sum_{n=1}^{\infty} \left(\frac{R}{r_n} \right)^{m_n + 1}$$

is convergent.

For $\dfrac{R}{r_n} < \dfrac{1}{2}$. Since it is a G.P. with common ratio $< \dfrac{1}{2}$, the series

$$\sum \log E \left(\frac{z}{z_n}, m_n \right)$$

converges uniformly and absolutely when $|z| \leq R$.

Consequently, the infinite product

$$\prod_{n=1}^{\infty} E \left(\frac{z}{z_n}, M_n \right) \qquad \qquad ...(1)$$

converges uniformly and absolutely when $|z| \leq R$, no matter how large R may be.

Hence, the infinite product

$$P(z) = \sum_{n=1}^{\infty} E \left(\frac{z}{z_n}, M_n \right)$$

represents the required integral function.

Weierstrass Factorization Theorem: *An entire function with arbitrary prescribed zeros z_n such that $z_n \to \infty$ as $n \to \infty$, can be expressed as:*

$$f(z) = z^m e^{g(z)} \prod_{n=1}^{\infty} E \left(\frac{z}{z_n}, M_n \right)$$

where the product is taken over all $z_n \neq 0$, the M_n are certain integers and $g(z)$ is an entire function.

(Meerut 2002, 2003)

Refer eqn. (1) § 14.2.1. If, in addition to the points z_n, $z = 0$ is also a zero of order m, then we have to introduce the factor z^m in the product (1) and then the infinite product

$$z^n \prod_{n=1}^{\infty} E \left(\frac{z}{z^n}, M_n \right)$$

defines an entire function whose only zeros are $0, z_1, z_2, ..., z_n, ...$

Finally, if $f(z)$ is an arbitrary entire function with the prescribed zeros, then the quotient

$$\frac{f(z)}{\left[z^m \prod_{n=1}^{\infty} E\left(\frac{z}{z_n}, M_n\right)\right]}$$

$$f(z) = z^m e^{g(z)} \prod_{n=1}^{\infty} E\left(\frac{z}{z_n}, M_n\right)$$

is an entire function without zero and so in view of theorem § 14.1 it must be of the form $e^{g(z)}$ where $g(z)$ is an entire function.

Corollary. *Every function which is meromorphic in the whole complex plane is the quotient of two entire functions.*

Suppose $f(z)$ is meromorphic in the whole complex plane, we can find the entire function $h(z)$ with prescribed zeros which are poles of $f(z)$. It is obvious that the product $f(z) h(z)$ is then an entire function $g(z)$, say. Hence we obtain

$$f(z) = \frac{g(z)}{h(z)}.$$

Picard's Theorem. *An integral function attains every finite value with atmost one possible exception.*

We shall try to prove it by means of an example. Equation $e^z = \lambda$ has an infinite number of roots for any given non-zero value of λ.

If $\lambda = 0$, the equation $e^z = \lambda$ has no real roots at all. Thus, the zero is an exceptional value of the integral function e^z. On the other hand there exist integral functions with no exceptional values. The function $\sin z$ is an example of this.

14.3 Jensen's Inequality. *Let $f(z)$ be an integral function which does not vanish at the origin. Also let $r_1, r_2, r_3, ..., r_n$ be the moduli of zeros $z_1, z_2, ..., z_n$ of $f(z)$, arranged as non-decreasing sequence, multiple zeros being repeated.*

Then

$$R_n \, |f(0)| \le M(R), \, r_1, r_2, ..., r_n \text{ if } r_n < R < r_{n+1}.$$

Consider the function

$$F(z) = f(z) \prod_{m=1}^{n} \left[\frac{R^2 - z \, \bar{z}_m}{R \, (z - z_m)}\right] \qquad ...(1)$$

$f(z)$ is an integral function $\Rightarrow$ F (z) is an integral function.

On the circle $|z| = R$, we have

$$R^2 (z - a)(\bar{z} - \bar{a}) = R^2 [z \, \bar{z} - (a\bar{z} - \bar{a}z) + a\bar{a}]$$

$$= R^2 [R^2 - (a\bar{z} + \bar{a}z) + a\bar{a}]$$

$$= (R^2 - \bar{a}z)(R^2 - a\bar{z})$$

or $$R (z - a) \, R \, (\bar{z} - \bar{a}) = (R^2 - \bar{a}z)(R^2 - \bar{a}z)$$

or $$|R (z - a)|^2 = |R^2 - \bar{a}z|^2$$

or $$\left|\frac{R^2 - \bar{a}z}{R \, (z - a)}\right| = 1.$$

This $\Rightarrow$ $\left| \dfrac{R^2 - z\bar{z}_m}{R(z - z_m)} \right| = 1$ on $|z| = R$.

From this, (1) $\Rightarrow$

$$| F(z) | = | f(z) | \text{ on } | z | = R \qquad \qquad ...(2)$$

By the principle of maximum modulus (§ 9.14)

$$| F(z) | \leq \max_{|z|}. = R^{|F(z)|}$$

$$= \max_{|z|}. = R^{|f(z)|} \qquad \qquad \text{[by (2)]}$$

Taking M (R) to be the maximum modulus of $| f(z) |$ on $| z | = R$, we get

$$| F(z) | \leq M(R).$$

Putting $z = 0$ in (1),

$$\left| f(0) \prod_{m=1}^{n} \frac{R^2}{R(-z_m)} \right| = | F(0) | \leq M(R)$$

or

$$| f(0) | \prod_{m=1}^{n} \frac{R}{|z_m|} \leq M(R)$$

or

$$| f(0) | \frac{R \cdot R \cdot \ ..... \ (n \text{ factors})}{|z_1| \, |z_2| \, ... \, |z_n|} \leq M(R)$$

or

$$\frac{R^n \, | f(0) |}{r_1, r_2, ..., r_n} \leq M(R) \qquad \qquad ...(3)$$

14.3.1. Jensen's Formula. *If $f(z)$ is analytic within and on the circle C such that $|z| = R$, and if $f(z)$ has zeros at the points $a_j \neq 0$, ($j = 1, 2, ..., m$) and poles at $b_j \neq 0$, ($j = 1, 2, ..., n$) inside C, multiple zeros and poles being repeated, then*

$$\frac{1}{2\pi} \int_0^{2\pi} log \, | f(Re^{i\theta}) | \, d\theta = log \, | f(0) |$$

$$+ \sum_{r=1}^{m} log \, \frac{R}{|a_r|} - \sum_{r=1}^{n} log \, \frac{R}{|b_r|}.$$

(Meerut 2003, 2006, Rohtak 2001, 2004, Kurukshetra 2003, 2005, Himachal 2000, 2003, 2004)

Consider the function

$$F(z) = f(z) \prod_{r=1}^{m} \frac{R^2 - z\bar{a}_r}{R(z - a_r)} \cdot \prod_{s=1}^{n} \frac{R(z - b_s)}{(R^2 - z\bar{b}_s)} \qquad \qquad ...(1)$$

Clearly, F (z) is free from singularity. Also F (z) has no zero within and on $| z | = R$. Hence F (z) is analytic within and on the circle C whose equation is $| z | = R$.

By Cauchy's Integral Formula (§ 9.4)

$$log \, F(0) = \frac{1}{2\pi i} \int_C \frac{log \, F(z)}{z - 0} \, dz \qquad \qquad ...(2)$$

On C, $z = Re^{i\theta} \Rightarrow dz = iRe^{i\theta} d\theta$,

$$\frac{dz}{iz} = d\theta.$$

Hence (2) reduces to

$$\log F(0) = \frac{1}{2\pi} \int_0^{2\pi} \log F(Re^{i\theta}) d\theta$$

$\Rightarrow$

$$\log |F(0)| = \frac{1}{2\pi} \int_0^{2\pi} \log |F(Re^{i\theta})| d\theta \qquad ...(3)$$

On the circle C, $|z| = R$ so that $z\bar{z} = |z|^2 = R^2$.

We have

$$R^2 (z - a)(\bar{z} - \bar{a}) = R^2 [z\bar{z} - (\bar{a}z + a\bar{z}) + a\bar{a}]$$

$$= R^2 [R^2 - (\bar{a}z + a\bar{z}) + a\bar{a}]$$

$$= (R^2 - \bar{a}z)(R^2 - a\bar{z})$$

or

$$R(z - a)\overline{R(z - a)} = (R^2 - \bar{a}z)(\overline{R^2 - \bar{a}z})$$

or

$$|R(z - a)|^2 = |R^2 - \bar{a}z|^2$$

or

$$\left| \frac{R^2 - \bar{a}z}{R(z - a)} \right| = 1 \qquad ...(4)$$

Similarly

$$\left| \frac{R^2 - \bar{b}z}{R(z - b)} \right| = 1 \text{ or } \left| \frac{R(z - b)}{R^2 - \bar{b}z} \right| = 1 \qquad ...(5)$$

By (4) and (5), we have

$$\left| \frac{R^2 - z\bar{a}_r}{R(z - a_r)} \right| = 1 = \left| \frac{R(z - b_s)}{R^2 - z\bar{b}_s} \right| \text{ on C} \qquad ...(6)$$

Then (1) $\Rightarrow$

$$|F(z)| = |f(z)| \text{ on } |z| = R$$

or

$$|F(Re^{i\theta})| = |f(Re^{i\theta})| \qquad ...(7)$$

Putting $z = 0$ in (1), we get

$$F(0) = f(0) \prod_{r=n}^{m} \frac{R^2}{(-a_r)} \prod_{s=1}^{n} \frac{R(-b_s)}{R^2}$$

This $\Rightarrow$

$$|F(0)| = |f(0)| \prod_{r=1}^{m} \frac{R}{|a_r|} \prod_{s=1}^{n} \frac{|b_s|}{R}.$$

Taking log of both sides and then using (3), we get

$$\frac{1}{2\pi} \int_0^{2\pi} \log |F(Re^{i\theta})| d\theta = \log |f(0)| + \sum_{r=1}^{m} \log \frac{R}{|a_r|} - \sum_{s=1}^{n} \log \frac{R}{|b_s|}.$$

Using (7),

$$\frac{1}{2\pi} \int_0^{2\pi} \log|f(Re^{i\theta})|\,d\theta = \log|f(0)| + \sum_{r=1}^{m} \log\frac{R}{|a_r|} - \sum_{s=1}^{n} \log\frac{R}{|b_s|}.$$

Deduction. If $f(z)$ has no poles, then

$$\frac{1}{2\pi} \int_0^{2\pi} \log|f(Re^{i\theta})|\,d\theta = \log|f(0)| + \sum_{r=1}^{m} \log\frac{R}{|a_r|}$$

$$= \log|f(0)| \prod_{r=1}^{m} \frac{R}{|a_r|}$$

$$= \log\left[\frac{|f(0)|\cdot R^m}{|a_1\cdot a_2\,\ldots\ldots\,a_m|}\right].$$

This is sometimes called **Jensen's theorem** and due to its special importance we give a separate proof in following § 14.3.3.

Jensen's Theorem. *Let $f(z)$ be analytic for $|f(z)| \le R$. Let $r_1, r_2, \ldots\ldots, r_n$ be the moduli of the zeros of $f(z)$ in $|z| < R$ arranged as a non-decreasing sequence. Then, if $r_n \le r < r_{n+1}$ prove that*

$$\log\frac{r^n|f(0)|}{r_1\cdot r_2\,\ldots\ldots\,r_n} = \frac{1}{2\pi}\int_0^{2\pi} \log|f(re^{i\theta})|\,d\theta.$$

(Meerut 2003, 2004, Kanpur 2002, Nagpur 2001)

Assume the function

$$F(z) = f(z) \prod_{m=1}^{n}\left[\frac{R^2 - z\,\bar{z}_m}{R(z - z_m)}\right] \qquad\qquad ...(1)$$

It is clear that $F(z)$ is free from singularity. Also $F(z)$ has no zeros within and on the circle C, $|z| = R$. Hence $F(z)$ is analytic within and on the circle C.

By Cauchy's Integral Formula (§ 9.4.)

$$\log F(0) = \frac{1}{2\pi i}\int_C \frac{\log F(z)}{z - 0}\,dz$$

On C, $z = Re^{i\theta}$ so that $dz = iRe^{i\theta}\,d\theta$

$$\frac{dz}{iz} = d\theta, \text{ where } r_n \le R < r_{n+1}.$$

$$\therefore \qquad \log F(0) = \frac{1}{2\pi}\int_0^{2\pi} \log F(Re^{i\theta})\,d\theta$$

$$\Rightarrow \qquad \log|F(0)| = \int_0^{2\pi} \log|F(Re^{i\theta})|\,d\theta \qquad\qquad ...(2)$$

On the circle C, $|z| = R$ so that $|z|^2 = z\bar{z} = R^2$. Then

$$R^2(z - a)(\bar{z} - \bar{a}) = R^2[z\bar{z} + (a\bar{z} - \bar{a}z) + a\bar{a}]$$

$$= R^2[R^2 - (a\bar{z} + \bar{a}z) + a\bar{a}]$$

$$= (R^2 - \bar{a}z)(R^2 - a\bar{z})$$

or $\qquad R(z-a)\overline{R(z-a)} = (R^2 - \bar{a}z)(\overline{R^2 - \bar{a}z})$

or $\qquad |R(z-a)|^2 = |R^2 - \bar{a}z|^2$

or $\qquad \left| \dfrac{R - \bar{a}z}{R(z-a)} \right| = 1$

This $\Rightarrow \qquad \left| \dfrac{R^2 - z\bar{z}_m}{R(z - z_m)} \right| = 1.$

Then (1) $\Rightarrow \qquad |F(z)| = |f(z)|$ on C

$\Rightarrow \qquad |F(Re^{i\theta})| = |f(Re^{i\theta})|.$

Then (2) becomes

$$\log|F(0)| = \frac{1}{2\pi} \int_0^{2\pi} \log|f(Re^{i\theta})|\, d\theta \qquad \qquad ...(3)$$

Putting $z = 0$ in (1), we get

$$|F(0)| = \left| f(0) \prod_{m=1}^{n} \frac{R^2}{(-Rz_m)} \right| = |f(0)| \prod_{m=1}^{n} \frac{R}{|z_m|}.$$

Taking log of both sides,

$$\log|F(0)| = \log|f(0)| \cdot \frac{R}{|z_1|} \cdot \frac{R}{|z_2|} \cdots \frac{R}{|z_n|}$$

$$= \log \frac{|f(0)|R^n}{r_1 \cdot r_2 \cdots r_n}.$$

Using (3), we get

$$\frac{1}{2\pi} \int_0^{2\pi} \log|f(Re^{i\theta})|\, d\theta = \log \frac{|f(0)|R^n}{r_1 \cdot r_2 \cdots r_n}.$$

If we take $r_n \leq R < r_{n+1}$ in place of $r_n \leq r < r_{n+1}$ then, we have

$$\log \frac{r^n |f(0)|}{r_1 \cdot r_2 \cdots r_n} = \frac{1}{2\pi} \int_0^{2\pi} \log|f(re^{i\theta})|\, d\theta.$$

14.3.2. Poisson-Jensen Formula

If $f(z)$ be analytic in the closed disc $|z| \leq R$, under the assumption $f(z) \neq 0$ on $|z| = R$ and $z_1, z_2, ..., z_n$ be zeros of $f(z)$ in the open disc $|z| < R$, each repeated as often as its multiplicity and also $z = re^{i\theta}, 0 \leq r \leq R, f(z) \neq 0$, then

$$\log|f(z)| = -\sum_{k=1}^{n} \log \left| \frac{R^2 - \bar{z}_k z}{R(z - z_k)} \right|$$

$$+ \frac{1}{2} \int_0^{2\pi} \frac{(R^2 - r^2)\log|f(Re^{i\phi})|}{R^2 - 2Rr(\theta - \phi) + r^2}\, d\phi \qquad (Meerut\ 2003,\ 2004)$$

Consider
$$F(z) = f(z) \prod_{k=1}^{n} \frac{R^2 - \overline{z_k} z}{R(z - z_k)} \qquad \ldots(1)$$

Evidently $F(z)$ is analytic in any domain in which $f(z)$ is analytic and $F(z) \neq 0$ for $|z| \leq R$, so $F(z)$ is analytic and never zero on an open disc $|z| < \rho$ for some $\rho > R$. Also $|F(z)| = |f(z)|$ on $|z| = R$ by Jenson's formula.

Now, $F(z)$ being analytic and non-zero in $|z| < \rho$, $\log F(z)$ is also analytic in $z| < \rho$ so that its real part in $\log |F(z)|$ is harmonic there. As such applying Poisson formula

$$f(re^{i\theta}) = \frac{1}{2\pi} \int_0^{2\pi} \frac{(R^2 - r^2) f(Re^{i\phi})}{R^2 - 2Rr\cos(\theta - \phi) + r^2} d\phi \qquad 0 < R < \rho$$

for $\log |F(z)|$, we have

$$\log |F(z)| = \frac{1}{2\pi} \int_0^{2\pi} \frac{(R^2 - r^2) \log |F(Re^{i\phi})|}{R^2 - 2Rr\cos(\theta - \phi) + r^2} d\phi \qquad \ldots(1)$$

But $\log |F(Re^{i\phi})| = \log |f(Re^{i\phi})|$ on $|z| = R$.

and
$$\log |F(z)| = \log\left[|f(z)| \prod_{k=1}^{n} \left| \frac{R^2 - \overline{z_k} z}{R(z - z_k)} \right| \right]$$

$$= \log |f(z)| + \sum_{k=1}^{n} \log \left| \frac{R^2 - \overline{z_k} z}{R(z - z_k)} \right|$$

So, (1) gives

$$\log |f(z)| = -\sum_{k=1}^{n} \log \left| \frac{R^2 - \overline{z_k} z}{R(z - z_k)} \right|$$

$$+ \frac{1}{2\pi} \int_0^{2\pi} \frac{(R^2 - r^2) \log f(Re^{i\phi})}{R^2 - 2Rr(\theta - \phi) + r^2} d\phi \qquad \ldots(2)$$

To generalize the above result, take $g(z)$ alos satisfying the above theorem with zeros in $|z| < R$ at $a_1, a_2, ..., a_n$ and $\phi(z) = \dfrac{f(z)}{g(z)}$, then

$$\log |\phi(z)| = \sum_{j=1}^{m} \log \left| \frac{R^2 - \overline{a_j} z}{R(z - a_j)} \right|$$

$$-\sum_{k=1}^{n} \log \left| \frac{R^2 - \overline{z_k} z}{R(z - z_k)} \right| + \frac{1}{2\pi} \int_0^{2\pi} \frac{(R^2 - r^2)|\phi(Re^{i\phi})|}{R^2 - 2Rr\cos(\theta - \phi) + r^2}$$

Corollory 1. *Other Form of Poisson-Jensen Formula*   *(Meerut 2003)*

Let $f(z)$ have zeros at the points $a_1, a_2, ..., a_m$ and poles at $b_1, b_2, ..., b_n$ inside the circle $|z| \leq R$ and be analytic elsewhere inside and on the circle then

$$\log |f(re^{i\theta})| = \frac{1}{2\pi} \int_0^{2\pi} \frac{R^2 - r^2}{R^2 - 2Rr\cos(\theta - \phi) + r^2} \log |f(Re^{i\phi})| d\phi$$

$$-\sum_{\mu=1}^{m} \log \left| \frac{R^2 - \bar{a}_\mu r e^{i\theta}}{R(r e^{i\theta} - a_\mu)} \right|$$

$$+\sum_{\nu=1}^{m} \log \left| \frac{R^2 - \bar{b}_\nu r e^{i\theta}}{R(r e^{i\theta} - a_\nu)} \right|$$

This follows from above generalization.

Corollary 2. Poisson-Kernel

with $z = re^{i\theta}$, we have

$$\frac{Re^{i\phi} + z}{Re^{i\phi} - z} = \frac{Re^{i\phi} + re^{i\theta}}{Re^{i\phi} - re^{i\theta}}$$

$$= \frac{Re^{i\phi} + re^{i\theta}}{Re^{i\phi} - re^{i\theta}} \times \frac{Re^{-i\phi} + re^{-i\theta}}{Re^{-i\phi} - re^{-i\theta}}$$

$$= \frac{R^2 - r^2 + 2iRr\sin(\theta - \phi)}{R^2 - 2Rr\cos(\theta - \phi) + r^2}$$

$$\therefore \qquad \text{Re}\left(\frac{Re^{i\phi} + z}{Re^{i\phi} - z}\right) = \frac{R^2 - r^2}{R^2 - 2Rr\cos(\theta - \phi) + r^2}$$

This real part of $\left(\dfrac{Re^{i\phi} + z}{Re^{i\phi} - z}\right)$ is known as the **Poisson-kernel** of the integral

$$\int_{0}^{2\pi} \frac{(R^2 - r^2) \log|f(Re^{i\phi})|}{R^2 - 2Rr\cos(\theta - \phi) + r^2} d\phi$$

and denoted by $K(Re^{i\phi}, z)$,

In terms of $K(Re^{i\phi}, z)$, we can write

$$\log|f(z)| = -\sum_{k=1}^{n} \log \left| \frac{R^2 - \bar{z}_k z}{R(z - z_k)} \right|$$

$$+\frac{1}{2\pi} \int_{0}^{2\pi} K(Re^{i\phi}, z) \log|f(Re^{i\phi})| \, d\phi.$$

14.4. Growth of an Entire Function

Since a polynomial $P_n(z)$ of degree n has exactly n zeros (multiple zeros counted repeatedly) therefore the rate of growth of $z \to \infty$ of $P_n|z|$ increases with the increase of its degree n. As such the number of zeros and the growth of a polynomial are inter-related.

14.5. Maximum Modulus of an Entire Function

If $f(z)$ be a non-constant entire function and $M(r)$ be defined as $M(r) = $ max. $\{|f(z)| : |z| \le r\}$, then by maximum modulus principle $|f(z)|$ attains in maximum value $M(r)$ on the circle $|z| = r$, such that

$$M(r) = max. \ \{ \, |f(z)| : |z| \leq r \}$$

where $M(r)$ is a steadily increasing function of r for $r < R$.

In case more than one functions are involved, we use the symbol $M(r, f)$ instead of $M(r)$.

By the maximum modulus principle $|f(r_1, e^{i\phi})| < M(r_2)$, when $r_1 < r_2$ and so $M(r_1) < M(r_2)$. Hence $M(r)$ steedily approaches ∞ as $r \to \infty$.

Assuming that $A(r)$ is the upper bound of the real part of $f(z)$ on $|z| = r$, the function $A(r)$ defined to be the maximum of Re $\{ f(z) \}$ is an increasing function of r since.

$$e^{A(r)} = \frac{max}{|z| = r} \ |e^{f(z)}|.$$

14.6. Order of an Integral Function. An integral function $f(z)$ is said to be of *finite order* if there exists a positive number k, independent of r, such that its maximum modulus $M(r)$ on the circle $|z| = r$ satisfies the inequality

$$\log M(r) < r^k$$

for all sufficiently large values of r.

If no such number k exists, then the integral function $f(z)$ is said to be of *infinite order*.

The lower bound of values of k, for which above equation holds, is called the **order** of $f(z)$. Hence if ρ is the order of an integral function $f(z)$,

$\rho = $ inf. $\{\lambda \geq 0 : M(r) \exp(r^{\lambda})$ for sufficiently large $r\}$

$\rho = +\infty$ if $f(z)$ is not of finite order, *i.e.*, if the set on R.H.S. is empty.

14.7. Exponent of convergence of the zeros. The lower bound of positive numbers λ for which the series $\sum_{n} r_n^{-\lambda}$ is convergent, is said to be the *exponent of the convergence of zero* and denoted by ρ_1. Evidently $\rho 1 \leq \rho$, where ρ is the order of $f(z)$.

Note that

$\rho_1 = 0 \Rightarrow$ Existence of finite number of zeros of $f(z)$.

$\rho_1 > 0 \Rightarrow$ Existence of infinite number of zeros of $f(z)$.

14.8. Canonical Product. Let $f(z)$ be an integral function of finite order ρ with an infinite number of zeros $z_1, z_2, z_3, \ldots$, arranged in the order of increasing modulus and ρ_1 be the exponent of the convergence of zeros. We associate an integer p with sequence of zeros such that

$$p = \begin{cases} [\rho_1], & \rho_1 \neq \text{integer} \\ \\ \rho_1 - 1, & \rho_1 \text{ is integer such that } \sum_{n=1}^{\infty} /r_n - \rho_1 \text{ is convergent} \end{cases}$$

Here $[\rho_1]$ denotes greatest integer less than or equal to ρ_1.

Evidently $\rho_1 - 1 \leq p \leq \rho_1 \leq \rho$ in any case.

Then the infinite product

$$G(z) = \prod_{n=1}^{\infty} \left(\frac{z}{z_n}, p \right)$$

converges uniformly and absolutely in any bounded closed domain of the z-plane which does not contain any z_n $(n = 1, 2, 3, \ldots)$.

Also $G(z)$ is an integral function and vanishes if and only if z is a zero of $f(z)$. This product is called *Canonical product* formed with zeros of $f(z)$, the integer p is called *genus* of this product.

Again suppose $f(z)$ is analytic within and on a circle $|z| = R$. Let $M(r)$ denote the maximum value of $|f(z)|$ on $|z| = r < R$. Then $M(r)$ is *steadily increasing function of r, i.e.*,

$$r_1 < r_2 \Rightarrow M(r_1) < M(r_2)$$

where $r_1, r_2 < R$ and $f(z)$ is not constant.

Theorem. *If ρ be the order of an integral function, then*

$$\rho = \lim_{r \to \infty} \frac{sup \ log \ log \ M(r)}{log(r)} \qquad ...(1)$$

where $M(r) = max. \ |f(z)|$ on $|z| = r$.   *(Rohilkhand 2003, 2004)*

Let

$$\rho_1 = \inf. \ \{\lambda \geq 0 : M(r) \leq \exp(r^\lambda) \text{ for sufficiently large } r\}...(2)$$

Then ρ_1 is the order of function $f(z)$. If we prove $\rho_1 = \rho$, the result will be established.
Let $\varepsilon > 0$ be arbitrary. Then from (2)

$$M(r) \leq \exp(r^{\rho_1 + \varepsilon}) = e^{r^{\rho_1 + \varepsilon}}$$

Taking log, we get

$$log \ M(r) \leq r^{\rho_1 + \varepsilon} \cdot log \ e = r^{\rho_1 + \varepsilon}.$$

Again taking log

$$log \ log \ M(r) \leq (\rho_1 + \varepsilon) \ log \ r$$

$$\Rightarrow \qquad \frac{log \ log \ M(r)}{log \ r} \leq \rho_1 + \varepsilon$$

$$\Rightarrow \qquad \lim_{r \to \infty} sup \ \frac{log \ log \ M(r)}{log \ r} \leq \rho_1 + \varepsilon$$

$$\Rightarrow \qquad \rho \leq \rho_1 + \varepsilon$$

Making $\varepsilon \to 0$,

$$\rho \leq \rho_1 \qquad ...(3)$$

Again if $\rho < \infty$ and $\varepsilon > 0$, then from (1)

$$\frac{log \ log \ M(r)}{log \ r} < \rho + \varepsilon \text{ for large } r$$

$$\Rightarrow \qquad log \ log \ M(r) < (\rho + \varepsilon) \ log \ r = log \ r^{\rho + \varepsilon}$$

$$\Rightarrow \qquad log \ log \ M < log \ r^{\rho + \varepsilon}$$

or $$log \ M < r^{\rho + \varepsilon}$$

$$\Rightarrow \qquad M < e^{r^{\rho + \varepsilon}}.$$

It follows that inf. $\{\lambda \geq 0 : M(r) \leq \exp(r^\lambda) \text{ for large } r\} < \rho + \varepsilon$

$$\Rightarrow \qquad \rho_1 < \rho + \varepsilon.$$

Making $\varepsilon \to 0$,

$$\rho_1 \leq \rho \qquad ...(4)$$

By (3) and (4),

$$\rho = \rho_1.$$

Note. If the limit exists whether finite or infinite, then the limit gives order of f. If the limit does not exist, then we obtain its superior to get order of f.

Theorem. *Order of a canonical product is equal to the exponent of convergence of its zeros.*
This theorem can also be read as:

If $f(z)$ is an integral function of finite order ρ, then $n(r) = O(r^{\rho+\varepsilon})$, i.e., $n(r) < r^{\rho+\varepsilon}$, where $n(r)$ is the number of zeros of $f(z)$ in $|z| \leq R$.

Let $f(z)$ be an integral function such that $f(0) \neq 0$. Also suppose that zeros of $f(z)$ in $|z| < r$ are $a_1, a_2, \ldots, a_m$, in non-decreasing order of their moduli, *i.e.,*

$$|a_1| \leq |a_2| \leq |a_3| \leq \ldots \leq |a_m|.$$

This $\Rightarrow$

$$n(t) = 0 \text{ for } 0 \leq t < |a_t|$$
$$n(t) = \mu \text{ for } |a_\mu| \leq t < |a_{\mu+1}|$$
$$n(t) = m \text{ for } |a_m| \leq t < r$$

$\Rightarrow$

$$\sum_{\mu=1}^{m} \log \frac{r}{|a_\mu|} = \int_0^r \frac{n(t)}{t} dt \qquad \ldots(1)$$

By Jensen's formula (§ 14.3.2)

$$\frac{1}{2\pi} \int_0^{2\pi} \log |f(re^{i\theta})| \, d\theta = \log |f(0)| + \sum_{\mu=1}^{m} \log \frac{r}{|a_\mu|}$$

From (1), we get

$$\int_0^r \frac{n(t)}{t} dt = \frac{1}{2\pi} \int_0^{2\pi} \log |f(re^{i\theta})| \, d\theta - \log |f(0)|$$

$$\leq \frac{1}{2\pi} \int_0^{2\pi} \log M(r) \, d\theta - \log |f(0)|$$

[where $M(r) = $ max. $|f(z)|$ on $|z| = r$]

$$< \frac{2\pi}{2\pi} \log M(r) = \log M(r)$$

or

$$\int_0^r \frac{n(t)}{t} dt < \log M(r) \qquad \ldots(2)$$

Since $n(t)$ increases as t increases, hence

$$\int_0^{2r} \frac{n(t)}{t} dt \leq \int_r^{2r} \frac{n(t)}{t} dt$$

$$\geq \int_r^{2r} \frac{n(r)}{t} dt = n(r) \log \frac{2r}{r}$$

i.e.,

$$\int_0^{2r} \frac{n(t)}{t} dt \geq n(r) \log 2 \qquad \ldots(3)$$

By (2), we get

$$\int_0^{2r} \frac{n(t)}{t} dt < \log M(2r).$$

Combining it with (3), we get

$$n(r) \log 2 \le \int_0^{2r} \frac{n(t)}{t} dt < \log M(2r)$$

$\Rightarrow \qquad\qquad n(r) \log 2 < \log M(2r)$

$\Rightarrow \qquad\qquad n(r) < n(r) \log 2 < \log M(2r)$

$\Rightarrow \qquad\qquad n(r) < \log M(2r)$ ...(4)

By definition of order of a function, we have

$$\log M(2r) < (2r)^{\rho+\varepsilon} < 2^{\rho+\varepsilon} \cdot r^{\rho+\varepsilon} < r^{\rho+\varepsilon}$$

or $\qquad\qquad \log M(2r) < r^{\rho+\varepsilon}$ as $\rho, \varepsilon > 0$.

Using this in (4), $n(r) < r^{\rho+\varepsilon}$.

We may express it as :

$$n(r) = O(r^{\rho+\varepsilon}).$$

Theorem. *Let $f(z)$ be an integral function with zeros at $z_1, z_2, \ldots$, arranged in the order of increasing moduli. Let ρ be the order of $f(z)$. Then the series*

$$\sum_{n=1}^{\infty} r_n^{-\lambda}$$

is convergent if $\lambda > \rho$, where $|z_n| = r_n$.

Do yourself. Proof at once follows from § 14.4.

EXAMPLES

1. *If $f(z)$ is an entire function and $f(0) \ne 0$, then show that $f(z) = f(0) P(z) e^{g(z)}$, where $P(z)$ is a product of primary factors.*

Solution. Let $z_1, z_2, \ldots, z_n, z_n \ne 0$ are the zeros of $f(z)$.

We have

$$P(z) = \prod_{n=1}^{\infty} E\left(\frac{z}{z_n}, M_n\right)$$

Then $P(z)$ is the product of primary factors associated with the zero of $f(z)$.

Consider $\phi(z) = \dfrac{f'(z)}{f(z)} - \dfrac{P'(z)}{P(z)}$ ...(1)

then $\phi(z)$ is an entire function because the poles of one term are cancelled by the poles of the other. Integrating (1) along any curve joining 0 to z, we get

$$g(z) = \int_0^z \phi(t)\, dt = \log(z) - \log f(0) - \log P(z)$$ ...(2)

Hence $g(z)$ is an entire function. From (2), we get

$$e^{g(z)} = \frac{f(z)}{f(0) P(z)}$$

or $\qquad\qquad f(z) = f(0) P(z) e^{g(z)}.$

2. *Represent* $\sin \pi z$ *in the form of canonical product.*　　　　　*(Meerut 2002, 2004)*

Zeros of $\sin \pi z$ are at $z = \pm n$, $n = 0, 1, 2, \ldots$ and the genus of the canonical product is 1,

since the series $\sum\limits_{n=1}^{\infty} \dfrac{1}{n}$ diverges and $\sum\limits_{n=1}^{\infty} \dfrac{1}{n^2}$ converges so that $h = 1$ is the least integer such that

$\sum \dfrac{1}{|\pm n|^{h+1}}$ $(h \neq 0)$ converges. Also $z = 0$ is a simple zero. Hence we get a representation of the
form

$$\sin \pi z = z \cdot e^{g(z)} \prod_{n=-\infty}^{\infty} \left(1 - \frac{z}{n}\right) e^{z/n} \qquad \ldots(1)$$

where $\prod'$ is used to indicate that n takes all integral values except 0.

To determine $g(z)$, taking logarithm of either side of (1) and differentiating, we find

$$\pi \cot \pi z = \frac{1}{z} + g'(z) + \sum_{n=1}^{\infty} \left(\frac{1}{z-n} + \frac{1}{n}\right) \qquad \ldots(2)$$

Here term by term differentiation being justified by uniform convergence on any bounded closed set not containing the points $z = n$.

We know that

$$\pi \cot \pi z = \frac{1}{z} + \sum_{n=-\infty}^{\infty} \left(\frac{1}{z-n} + \frac{1}{n}\right)$$

Then, $g'(z) = 0$, whose integration follows that $g(z) = $ constant.

Also, since　　$\lim\limits_{z \to 0} \dfrac{\sin \pi z}{z} = \pi \left\{ \lim\limits_{z \to \infty} \dfrac{\sin \pi z}{\pi z} \right\}$

$$= \pi \text{ as } \lim_{z \to \infty} \frac{\sin \pi z}{\pi z} = 1.$$

We must have $e^{gz} = \pi$ in lieu of (1).

Thus

$$\sin \pi z = \pi z \prod_{n=\infty}^{\infty}{}' \left(1 + \frac{z}{n}\right) e^{z/n} \qquad \ldots(3)$$

Bracketing together the factors corresponding to n and $-n$ we can write

$$\sin \pi z = \pi z \prod_{n=1}^{\infty} \left(1 + \frac{z}{n}\right) e^{z/n} \cdot \left(1 + \frac{z}{n}\right) e^{-z/n}$$

$$= \pi z \prod_{n=1}^{\infty} \left(1 - \frac{z^2}{n^2}\right)$$

from (3), it is evident that $\sin \pi z$ is an entire function of genus 1.

3. *Construct the canonical product associated with the sequence of negative integers.*

Solution. Here the genus of the canonical product being 1, since $h = 1$ is the smallest integer such that

$$\sum_{n=1}^{\infty} \frac{1}{|z_n|^{h+1}} = \sum_{n=1}^{\infty} \frac{1}{|-n|^{h+1}}$$

converges.

As such the canonical product associated witht he sequence $<-n>$ of negative integers is

$$f(z) = \sum_{n=1}^{\infty} \left(1 + \frac{z}{n}\right) e^{-z/n.}$$

Certainly $f(z)$ is an entire function with simple zeros at $z = -1, -2, \ldots.$

4. *If* $|z| < \dfrac{1}{2},$ *then show that*

(i) $|E(z, p) - 1| \leq 2e |z|^{p+1}$

(ii) $|E(z, p)| \leq \exp(2|z|^{p+1})$

(iii) $|E(z, p)| \geq \exp\left(-\dfrac{2}{|z|^{p+1}}\right).$

Solution. (*i*) If $p = 0$, the inequality is trival.

Taking $p \neq 0$, the relation

$$1 - z = e^{\log(1-z)} = e^{-\sum_{n=1}^{\infty} \frac{z^n}{n}} \text{ yields}$$

$$E(z, p) = (1-z) e^{\sum_{n=1}^{p} \frac{z^n}{n}} = e^{-\sum_{n=1}^{\infty} \frac{z^n}{n}} e^{\sum_{n=1}^{p} \frac{z^n}{n}}$$

$$= e^{-\sum_{n=p+1}^{\infty} \frac{z^n}{n}} \qquad\qquad \ldots(1)$$

But for all complex numbers a, we have

$$|e^a - 1| \leq e^{|a|} - 1, \text{ so that from (1), we get}$$

$$|E(z, p) - 1| = \left| -\sum_{n=p+1}^{\infty} \frac{z^n}{n} \right|$$

$$\leq e^{\left| \sum_{n=p+1}^{\infty} \frac{z^n}{n} \right|} - 1 \qquad\qquad \ldots(2)$$

Now,

$$\left| \sum_{n=p+1}^{\infty} \frac{z^n}{n} \right| \leq \sum_{n=p+1}^{\infty} \frac{|z|^n}{n} \leq \sum_{n=p+1}^{\infty} |z|^n$$

$$= |z|^{p+1} \sum_{n=0}^{\infty} |z|^n$$

$$\leq |z|^{p+1} \sum_{n=0}^{\infty} \left(\frac{1}{2}\right)^n \text{ as } |z| < \frac{1}{2}$$

$$\leq |z|^{p+1} \frac{1}{1 - \dfrac{1}{2}} = 2|z|^{p+1} \qquad\qquad \ldots(3)$$

(2) and (3)

$\Rightarrow \qquad\qquad |E(z, p) - 1| \leq e^{2|z|^{p+1}} - 1$

$$\leq 2\,|\,z\,|^{p+1}\,e^{2|z|^{p+1}} \text{ as } e^x - 1 \leq xe^x \text{ for } x \geq 0$$

$$\leq 2\,|\,z\,|^{p+1}\,e^{2|\frac{1}{2}|^{p+1}} \text{ as } |\,z\,| < \frac{1}{2}$$

$$\leq 2\,|\,z\,|^{p+1}\,e^1 = 2e\,|\,z\,|^{p+1}$$

(*ii*) For any two complex numbers a and b we have

$$|\,a\,| - |\,b\,| \leq |\,a - b\,|$$

$\therefore$ from (2), we get

$$|\,E(z,p)\,| - 1 \leq e^{\left|\sum_{n=p+1}^{\infty}\frac{z^n}{n}\right|} - 1$$

$\Rightarrow \qquad |\,E(z,p)\,| \leq e^{\left|\sum_{n=p+1}^{\infty}\frac{z^n}{n}\right|}$

$$\leq e^{\,2|z|^{p+1}} \qquad\qquad \text{by (3)}$$

(*iii*) From (1)

$$E(z,p) = e^{-\sum_{n=p+1}^{\infty}\frac{z^n}{n}} = \frac{1}{e^{\sum_{n=p+1}^{\infty}\frac{z^n}{n}}}$$

$\therefore \qquad |\,E(z,p)\,| = \dfrac{1}{\left|e^{\sum_{n=p+1}^{\infty}\frac{z^n}{n}}\right|}$

$$\geq \frac{1}{e^{\sum_{n=p+1}^{\infty}\frac{(z)^n}{n}}} \geq \frac{1}{e^{\,2|z|^{p+1}}}, \qquad\qquad \text{by (3)}$$

$$= e^{-2\,|z|^{p+1}}$$

5. *Find the order of the following functions:*

(*i*) $\quad P(z) = a_0 + a_1 z + \dots + a_n z^n, a_n \neq 0$

(*ii*) $\quad e^{az}, a \neq 0$ $\qquad\qquad\qquad$ (*iii*) $\quad \cos z$

(*iv*) $\quad \cos \sqrt{z}$ $\qquad\qquad\qquad$ (*v*) $\quad e^{z^\lambda}, \lambda$ being positive integer

(*vi*) $\quad e^{e^r}$.

Solution.

(*i*) It can be easily seen that

$$M(r) = |\,a_n\,|\,r^n \text{ for large } |\,z\,| = r$$

so that $\qquad \dfrac{\log \log M(r)}{\log r} = \lim_{r\to\infty} \dfrac{\log \log (|\,a_n\,|\,r^n)}{\log r}$

$\therefore \qquad \lim_{r\to\infty} \dfrac{\log \log M(r)}{\log r} = \lim_{r\to\infty} \dfrac{\log \log (|\,a_n\,|\,r^n)}{\log r} \qquad \left[\text{form } \dfrac{\infty}{\infty}\right]$

$$= \lim_{r \to \infty} \frac{\dfrac{1}{\log(|a_n| r^n)} \cdot \dfrac{1}{|a_n| r^n} \cdot |a_n| \cdot n r^{n-1}}{1/r}$$

[*By de L Hospital's rule*]

$$= \lim_{r \to \infty} \frac{n}{\log(|a_n| r^n)} = 0$$

$\therefore$ Order of a polynomial is zero.

(*ii*) Here $\qquad M(r) = e^{|a| r}$

$\therefore \qquad \lim_{r \to \infty} \frac{\log \log M(r)}{\log r} = \lim_{r \to \infty} \frac{\log(|a| r)}{\log r} \qquad \left[\text{Form } \dfrac{\infty}{\infty} \right]$

$$= \lim_{r \to \infty} \frac{\dfrac{1}{|a| r} \cdot |a|}{1/r} = 1$$

$\therefore$ order of e^{az} is 1

(*iii*) We have

$$\cos z = 1 - \frac{z^2}{2!} + \frac{z^4}{4!} - \frac{z^6}{6!} + \dots$$

$\therefore \qquad |\cos z| \le 1 + \frac{|z|^2}{2!} + \frac{|z|^4}{4!} + \dots$

$$\le 1 + \frac{r^2}{2!} + \frac{r^4}{4!} + \dots$$

$$= \frac{e^r + e^{-r}}{2} \quad \text{in the disc } |z| \le r.$$

Thus $\qquad |\cos z| \le \dfrac{e^r + e^{-r}}{2}$ if $|z| \le r$

$\therefore \qquad M(r) = \dfrac{e^r + e^{-r}}{2} = e^r \left(\dfrac{1 + e^{-2r}}{2} \right)$

so that $\qquad \log M(r) = r + \log \left(\dfrac{1 + e^{-2r}}{2} \right)$

$$= r \left[1 + \frac{1}{r} \log \left(\frac{1 + e^{-2r}}{2} \right) \right]$$

$\therefore \qquad \lim_{r \to \infty} \dfrac{\log \log M(r)}{\log r} = \dfrac{\lim_{r \to \infty} \log r + \log 1 + \left[\dfrac{1}{r} \left(1 + \dfrac{1}{r} \left(\dfrac{1 + e^{-2r}}{2} \right) \right) \right]}{\log r}$

$$= \lim_{r \to \infty} \left[1 + \frac{\log \left[\dfrac{1}{r} \log \left(\dfrac{1 + e^{-2r}}{2} \right) \right]}{\log r} \right]$$

$= 1$ since the second term tends to 0 as $r \to \infty$.

$\therefore$ order of $\cos z$ is 1.

(iv)
$$M(r) = \left(\frac{e^{\sqrt{r}} + e^{-\sqrt{r}}}{2} \right)$$

Proceeding as in (iii), the order of $\cos \sqrt{z} = \dfrac{1}{2}$.

(v)
$$M(r) = e^{r^{\lambda}}. \text{ Hence}$$

$$\lim_{r \to \infty} \frac{\log \log M(r)}{\log r} = \lim_{r \to \infty} \frac{\lambda \log r}{\log r} = \lambda$$

$\therefore$ order of $e^{z^{\lambda}}$ is λ.

(vi) Similarly, order of $e^{z^{r}}$ is inifinity.

14.8.4. Hadamard's Three Circles Principle. *Suppose $f(z)$ is analytic in the closed ring $r_1 \leq |z| \leq r_2$. Let $r_1 < r_2 < r_3$ and M_i be the maximum value of $|f(z)|$ on the circles $|z| = r_i$ (i = 1, 2, 3). Then*

$$M_2^{\log(r_3/r_1)} \leq M_1^{\log(r_3/r_2)} \cdot M_3^{\log(r_2/r_1)}.$$

(*Kanpur 2004, Meerut 2004, 2005, 2006; Rohilkhand 2006*)

Suppose $F(z) = z^{\alpha} f(z)$, choosing α such that

$$r_1^{\alpha} M_1 = r_3^{\alpha} M_3 \qquad \qquad ...(1)$$

Since $f(z)$ is analytic in the ring $r_1 \leq |z| \leq r_2$, hence $F(z)$ is analytic in the same domain. Evidently

$$|z^{\alpha} f(z)| \leq \max. \ \{r_1^{\alpha} M_1, r_3^{\alpha} M_3\} \qquad \qquad ...(2)$$

Now, if $r_1 < r_2 < r_3$, then from (2)

$$r_2^{\alpha} M_2 \leq \max. \ \{r_1^{\alpha} M_1, r_3^{\alpha} M_3\}$$

or $\qquad \qquad r_2^{\alpha} M_2 \leq r_1^{\alpha} M_1$ or $M_2 \leq (r_2/r_1)^{-\alpha} M_1 \qquad \qquad ...(3)$

By (1),

$$\alpha \log r_1 + \log M_1 = \alpha \log r_3 + \log M_3$$

$\Rightarrow \qquad \qquad -\alpha \log(r_3/r_1) = \log(M_3/M_1) \qquad \qquad ...(4)$

By (3),

$$M_2^{\log(r_3/r_1)} \leq (r_2/r_1)^{-\alpha \log(r_3/r_1)} \cdot M_1^{\log(r_3/r_1)}$$

$$= (r_2/r_1)^{\log(M_3/M_1)} \cdot M_1^{\log(r_3/r_1)} \qquad \qquad \text{[by (4)]}$$

$$= (M_3/M_1)^{\log(r_2/r_1)} \cdot M_1^{\log(r_3/r_1)}$$

$$= M_3^{\log(r_2/r_1)} \cdot M_1^{-\log(r_2/r_1)} \cdot M_1^{\log(r_3/r_1)}$$

$$= M_3^{\log(r_2/r_1)} \cdot M_1^{\log(r_3/r_2)}$$

$\therefore \qquad \qquad M_2^{\log(r_3/r_1)} \leq M_1^{\log(r_3/r_2)} \cdot M_3^{\log(r_2/r_1)}.$

14.9. Convex Function. A real function $f(x)$ is called **convex downwards** or simply **convex** if the curve $y = f(x)$ between x_1 and x_2 always lies below the chord joining the points (x_1, y_1) and (x_2, y_2) where $y_1 = f_1(x_1)$, $y_2 = f_2(x_2)$.

Equation of a chord joining the points (x_1, y_1) and (x_2, y_2) is

$$y - y_1 = \frac{y_2 - y_1}{x_2 - x_1}(x - x_1)$$

or

$$y = \frac{x - x_1}{x_2 - x_1} y_2 + \left(1 - \frac{x - x_1}{x_2 - x_1}\right) y_1$$

or

$$y = \left(\frac{x - x_1}{x_2 - x_1}\right) y_2 + \left(\frac{x_2 - x}{x_2 - x_1}\right) y_1.$$

Hence $y = f(x)$ is convex iff

$$y < \left(\frac{x - x_1}{x_2 - x_1}\right) y_2 + \left(\frac{x_2 - x}{x_2 - x_1}\right) y_1$$

i.e.,

$$f(x) < \frac{x - x_1}{x_2 - x_1} f(x_2) + \frac{x_2 - x}{x_2 - x_1} f(x_1) \text{ where } x_1 < x < x_2$$

The three circles theorem as a convexity theorem. *Let $f(z)$ be analytic in the closed ring $r_1 \leq |z| \leq r_2$. Suppose $r_1 < r_2 < r_3$ and $M(r_i)$ be the maximum value of $|f(z)|$ on the circles $|y| = r_i$, $(i = 1, 2, 3)$. Then*

$$\log M(r_2) \leq \frac{\log r_3 - \log r_2}{\log r_3 - \log r_1} \log M(r_1) + \frac{\log r_2 - \log r_1}{\log r_3 - \log r_1} \log M(r_3).$$

From Hadamard's three circles theorem

$$M(r_2)^{\log (r_3/r_1)} \leq M(r_1)^{\log (r_3/r_2)} \cdot M(r_3)^{\log (r_2/r_1)} \quad\quad\quad …(1)$$

It is clear that $M(r)$ is a convex function of $\log r$. Taking log of (1),

$$\log (r_3/r_1) \cdot \log M(r_2) \leq \log (r_3/r_2) \cdot \log M(r_1) + \log (r_2/r_1) \cdot \log M(r_3)$$

$$\Rightarrow \quad \log M(r_2) \leq \frac{\log (r_3/r_2)}{\log (r_3/r_1)} \log M(r_1) + \frac{\log (r_2/r_1)}{\log (r_3/r_1)} \log M(r_3)$$

$$\Rightarrow \quad \log M(r_2) \leq \frac{\log r_3 - \log r_2}{\log r_3 - \log r_1} \log M(r_1) + \frac{\log r_2 - \log r_1}{\log r_3 - \log r_1} \log M(r_3).$$

14.9.1. Mean Values. *To show that the mean value*

$$I_2(r) = \frac{1}{2\pi} \int_0^{2\pi} |f(re^{i\theta})|^2 \, d\theta$$

increases steadily with r and $\log I_2(r)$ is a complex function of $\log r$.

Let

$$f(z) = \sum_{n=0}^{\infty} a_n z^n.$$

Then

$$I_2(r) = \frac{1}{2\pi} \int_0^{2\pi} |f(re^{i\theta})|^2 \, d\theta$$

$$= \frac{1}{2\pi} \int_0^{2\pi} |\Sigma \, a_n r^n e^{in\theta}|^2 \, d\theta$$

$$= \frac{1}{2\pi} \int_0^{2\pi} \sum_0^\infty |a_n|^2 \, r^{2n} \, d\theta$$

$$= \sum_0^\infty |a_n|^2 \, r^{2n}.$$

Clearly, $I_2 (r)$ is an increasing function of r.

To prove the convexity of $\log I_2 (r)$, let $u = \log r$. Then

$$\frac{d [\log I_2 (r)]}{du} = \frac{1}{I_2 (r)} \frac{d [I_2 (r)]}{du} = \frac{I_2' (r)}{I_2 (r)}.$$

Since $u = \log r \Rightarrow e^u = r$.

We have
$$I_2 (r) = \Sigma |a_n|^2 \, r^{2n}$$
$$= \Sigma |a_n|^2 \, e^{2nu}$$

$$I_2' (r) = \frac{dI_2}{du} = \Sigma |a_n|^2 \, 2ne^{2nu}$$

$$[I_2' (r)]^2 = [\Sigma |a_n|^2 \, 2ne^{2nu}]^2$$
$$\leq (\Sigma |a_n|^2 \, e^{2nu}) (\Sigma |a_n|^2 \, 4n^2e^{2nu})$$
$$= I_2 I_2''$$

or
$$(I_2')^2 \leq I_2 I_2''$$

or
$$I_2 I_2'' - (I_2')^2 \geq 0 \qquad \qquad \dots (1)$$

But
$$\frac{d^2 [\log I_2 (r)]}{du^2} = \frac{d}{du} \left(\frac{I_2'}{I_2} \right) = \frac{I_2 I_2'' - (I_2')^2}{(I_2)^2} \geq 0$$

or
$$\frac{d^2 [\log I_2 (r)]}{du^2} \geq 0 \text{ where } u = \log r.$$

This $\Rightarrow \log I_2 (r)$ is a convex function of $\log r$.

Theorem of Borel and Caratheodory. *Suppose $f (z)$ is analytic for $|z| \leq R$. Also suppose $M (r)$ and $A (r)$ are respectively maxima of $|f (z)|$ and $R \{f (z)\}$ on $|z| = R$ where $0 < r < R$. Then*

$$M (r) \leq \frac{2r}{R - r} A (R) + \left(\frac{R + r}{R - r} \right) |f (0)|.$$

Let $f (z)$ be analytic for $|z| \leq R$ and $0 < r < R$. Again suppose $M (r) = $ max. $|f (z)|$, $A (r) = $ max. $R \{f (z)\}$ on the circle $|z| = r$, where $R \{f (z)\} = $ real part of $f (z)$. Further suppose that $A (r) \geq 0$ so that $|A (r)| = A (r)$.

We have to prove that

$$M (r) \leq \frac{2r}{R - r} A (R) + \left(\frac{R + r}{R - r} \right) |f (0)|.$$

If $f (z)$ were constant, then the result at once follows. Now, suppose that $f (z)$ is not constant.

Let

$$\phi(z) = \frac{f(z)}{2A(R) - f(z)} \qquad \qquad ...(1)$$

Suppose first $f(0) = 0$.

Then

$$\phi(0) = \frac{f(0)}{2A(R) - f(0)} = 0.$$

If $f(z) = u + iv$, then

$$\phi(z) = \frac{u + iv}{2A(R) - (u + iv)} = \frac{u + iv}{[2A(R) - u] - iv}$$

$$\Rightarrow \qquad |\phi(z)|^2 = \frac{u^2 + v^2}{\{2A(R) - u\}^2 + v^2} \le 1.$$

This follows from the fact that

$$- 2A(R) + u \le u \le 2A(R) - u.$$

Now $|\phi(z)| \le 1$ so that max. $|\phi(z)| = 1$ on circle $|z| = R$.

Also $\phi(0) = 0$ and $\phi(z)$ is analytic.

Applying Schwarz's lemma,

$$|\phi(z)| \le 1 \cdot \frac{r}{R} \quad \Rightarrow \quad |\phi(z)| \le \frac{r}{R} \qquad \qquad ...(2)$$

$$|1 + \phi(z)| \ge 1 - |\phi(z)| = 1 - \frac{r}{R} = \frac{R - r}{R}$$

or

$$\frac{1}{|1 + \phi(z)|} \le \frac{R}{R - r}.$$

Comparing this with (2), we get

$$\left| \frac{\phi(z)}{1 + \phi(z)} \right| \le \frac{r}{R} \cdot \frac{r}{R - r}$$

$$\Rightarrow \qquad \left| \frac{\phi(z)}{1 + \phi(z)} \right| \le \frac{r}{R - r}. \qquad \qquad ...(3)$$

Solving (1) for $f(z)$, we get

$$2A(R)\phi(z) = \phi(z)f(z) + f(z)$$

$$\Rightarrow \qquad f(z) = \frac{2A(R)\phi(z)}{1 + \phi(z)}$$

$$\Rightarrow \qquad |f(z)| = 2A(R) \cdot \left| \frac{\phi(z)}{1 + \phi(z)} \right| \le \frac{2A(R) \cdot r}{R - r}$$

$$\Rightarrow \qquad |f(z)| \le \frac{2r}{R - r} A(R).$$

We can say that

$$|f(z)| \leq \frac{2r}{R-r}\left[\max_{|z|=R}. R\{f(z)\}\right] \qquad \ldots(4)$$

Consider the case in which $|f(0)| \neq 0$.

Applying the result (4), we get

$$|f(z) - f(0)| \leq \frac{2r}{R-r}\left[\max_{|z|=R}. R\{f(z) - f(0)\}\right]$$

$$\leq \frac{2z}{R-r}[A(R) + |f(0)|] \qquad [\text{by (1)}]$$

Now

$$|f(z)| - |f(0)| \leq |f(z) + f(0)|$$

$$\leq \frac{2r}{R-r}[A(R) + |f(0)|]$$

$$\Rightarrow \qquad |f(z)| - |f(0)| \leq \frac{2r}{R-r}[A(R) + |f(0)|]$$

$$\Rightarrow \qquad |f(z)| \leq \frac{2r}{R-r}A(R) + \left(1 + \frac{2r}{R-r}\right)|f(0)|$$

$$\Rightarrow \qquad |f(z)| \leq \frac{2r}{R-r}A(R) + \left(\frac{R+r}{R-r}\right)|f(0)|$$

$$\Rightarrow \qquad M(r) \leq \frac{2r}{R-r}A(R) + \left(\frac{R+r}{R-r}\right)|f(0)|.$$

Theorem of Phragman and Lindeloff. *Suppose* $f(z)$ *is analytic and on a simple closed contour C except at one point P of C.*

Let $|f(z)| \leq M$ *on C except at P. Suppose further that there is a function w (z), analytic and not zero in C such that* $|w(z)| \leq 1$ *inside C and such that, given any* $\varepsilon > 0$, *it is possible to obtain a system of curves, arbitrarily close to P and connecting the two sides of C round P, on which*

$$|\{w(z)\} f(z)| \leq M.$$

Then $|f(z)| \leq M$ *at all points inside C.*

Consider the function

$$F(z) = \{w(z)\}^\varepsilon f(z).$$

This function is analytic in C. Let z_0 be any point, then we can, by hypothesis about $w(z)$, find a curve surrounding z_0 on which

$$|F(z)| \leq M.$$

Consequently

$$|F(z_0)| \leq M$$

or

$$\{w(z_0)\}^\varepsilon f(z_0) \leq M$$

Making $\varepsilon \to 0$

$$f(z_0) \leq M.$$

14.10. Exponents of Convergence of Sequence:

If $\{z_n\}$ be a sequence of non-zero complex numbers such that $|z_1| \le |z_2| \le ... \le |z_n| \to \infty$ as $n \to \infty$, then the exponent of convergence σ of the sequence is defined as

$$\sigma = \inf\left\{\alpha > 0 : \sum_{n=1}^{\infty} \frac{1}{|z_n|^\alpha} < \infty\right\}.$$

If this sequence is finite, we define $\sigma = 0$.

Theorem. *The convergence of exponent σ of a sequence $\{z_n\}$ is given by*

$$\sigma = \lim_{n\to\infty} \sup\left\{\frac{\log n}{\log|z_n|}\right\}.$$

Suppose σ is finite, tehn the series $\sum_{n=1}^{\infty} \frac{1}{|z_n|^\alpha}$ converges for every $\alpha < 0$. Since the series

$\sum_{n=1}^{\infty} |z_n|^\alpha$ converges if follows that

$$\lim_{n\to\infty} \sup \frac{n}{|z_n|^\alpha} = 0.$$

therefore for $\in = 1$, there exists $n_0 \in N$ cuch that

$$\left|\frac{n}{|z_n|^\alpha} - 0\right| < 1 \ \forall \ n > n_0$$

$\Rightarrow$ $\log n - \alpha \log|z_n| < 0 \ \forall \ n > n_0$

$\Rightarrow$ $\alpha > \dfrac{\log n}{\log|z_n|} \ \forall \ n > n_0$

$\Rightarrow$ $\alpha \ge \lim_{n\to\infty} \sup \dfrac{\log n}{\log|z_n|}$

$\Rightarrow$ $\alpha \ge \lim_{n\to\infty} \sup \dfrac{\log n}{\log|z_n|}$ ...(1)

Since α is an arbitrary number exceeding σ next. Let α' be an arbitrary number exceeding R.H.S, then there exists $n > N = N(\alpha')$ such that

$$\frac{\log n}{\log|z_n|} < \alpha' \ \forall \ \alpha \in N$$

thus $|z_n|^{-1} < n^{-1/\alpha'} \ \forall n > N.$

It follows from the definition of exponent convergence that $\sigma \le \sigma'$. Hence by definition of α', we have

$$\alpha \le \lim_{n\to\infty} \sup \frac{\log n}{\log|z_n|} \qquad\qquad ...(2)$$

From (1) and (2), we get

$$\sigma = \lim_{n \to \infty} \sup \frac{\log n}{\log |z_n|}$$

Theorem. *If $f(z)$ is an entire function of order ρ and convergence exponent σ, then $\sigma \leq \rho$.*

If ρ is infinite the inequality $\sigma \leq \rho$ is trival. If the number of zeros is finite than $\sigma = 0$ and $\sigma \leq \rho$ holds. So we may suppose that ρ is finite and that there are infinitely many zeros which we arrange as a sequence $\{z_n\}$ such that

$$|z_1| \leq |z_2| \leq |z_3| \leq \dots \leq |z_n| \leq |z_{n+1}| \leq \dots \qquad \dots(1)$$

and $\qquad |z_n| \to \infty$ as $n \to \infty$.

By definition, we have

$$n(|z_n|) \geq n \qquad \dots(2)$$

Strict inequality $n(|z_n|) > n$ will hold if

$$|z_n| = |z_{n+1}| \text{ and } n(|z_n| \leq |a_n|)^{\rho+\epsilon} \qquad \dots(3)$$

if $\epsilon > 0$ and n is sufficiently large.

From (2) and (3), we have

$$|z_n|^{\rho+\epsilon} \geq n. \qquad \dots(4)$$

For n sufficiently large since $|z_n| \to \infty$ we assume that $|z_n| \geq n$ for given $\alpha > \rho$ we may take $\epsilon < \alpha - \rho$ so that $\dfrac{\alpha}{\rho + \epsilon} > 1$.

Then for n sufficiently large we have from (4)

$$|z_n|^{\alpha} \geq n^{\alpha/\rho+\epsilon}$$

$$\Rightarrow \qquad |z_n|^{-\alpha} \leq n^{-\alpha/\rho+\epsilon} \qquad \dots(5)$$

$$\Rightarrow \qquad \sum_{n=1}^{\infty} |z_n|^{-\alpha} \leq \sum_{n=1}^{\infty} n^{-\alpha/\rho+\epsilon} \text{ as } \frac{\alpha}{\rho+\epsilon} > 1$$

the series $\displaystyle\sum_{n=1}^{\infty} n^{-\alpha/\rho+\epsilon}$ is convergent and so $\displaystyle\sum_{n=1}^{\infty} n^{-\alpha/\rho+\epsilon} < \infty$, then by (5)

$$\sum_{n=1}^{\infty} |z_n|^{-\alpha} < \infty \ \forall \ \alpha > \rho \qquad \dots(6)$$

By definition of exponent of convergence we have

$$\inf \left\{ \alpha > 0 : \sum_{n=1}^{\infty} |z_n|^{-\alpha} < \infty \right\}.$$

Since (6) holds for every $\alpha < \rho$ we conclude that

$$\sigma \leq \rho.$$

14.11. An Estimation of Number of Zeros of an Entire Function

14.11. Theorem : *Let $f(z)$ be an entire function of finite order ρ and $n(r)$ be the number of zeros of $f(z)$ in the closed disc $|z| \le r$, not including possible zeros at origin. Then $n(r) = 0 \, (r^{\rho+\epsilon})$, i.e., $n(r) < r^{\rho+\epsilon}$ for large values of r.*

By hypothesis $f(z)$ is an entire function such that $f(0) \ne 0$. Further, suppose that $z_1, z_2, ..., z_n$ are the zeros of $f(z)$ in order of increasing and their moduli in $|z| < r$, such that

$$|z_1| \le |z_2| \le ... \le |z_n|.$$

Thus
$$n(t) = \begin{cases} 0 \text{ for } 0 \le t < |z_1| \\ k \text{ for } |z_k| \le t < |z_{k+1}| \\ n \text{ for } |z_n| \le t < r. \end{cases}$$

This implies that

$$\log \frac{r^n}{|z_1||z_2|...|z_n|}$$

$$= \log \left[\frac{|z_2||z_3|^2}{|z_1||z_2|^2} \cdots \frac{|z_n|^{n-1}}{|z_{n-1}|^{n-1}} \cdot \frac{r^n}{|z_n|^n} \right]$$

$$= \log \left| \frac{z_2}{z_1} \right| + 2\log \left| \frac{z_3}{z_2} \right| + ... + (n-1)\log \left| \frac{z_n}{z_{n-1}} \right| + n\log \left| \frac{r}{z_n} \right|$$

$$= \int_{|z_1|}^{|z_2|} \frac{dt}{t} + \int_{|z_2|}^{|z_3|} \frac{2}{t} dt + ... + \int_{|z_{n-1}|}^{|z_n|} \frac{n-1}{t} dt + \int_{|z_n|}^{r} \frac{n}{t} dt.$$

Since the numerical factor in the numerator of the integral form $|z_k|$ to $|z_{k+1}|$ is just the value of the function $n(t)$ in the interval $|z_k| \le t < |z_{k+1}|$, we therefore have

$$\log \frac{r^n}{|z_1||z_2|...|z_n|} = \int_0^r \frac{n(t)}{t} dt,$$

Since $n(t) = 0$, for $0 \le t < |z_1|$, the lower limit of integration may be set of 0. Thus, we have

$$\sum_{i=1}^n \log \left(\frac{r}{|z_1|} \right) = \int_0^r \frac{n(t)}{t} dt \qquad ...(1)$$

By Jensen's formula, we have

$$\log |f(0)| = -\sum_{i=1}^n \log \left(\frac{r}{|z_i|} \right) + \frac{1}{2\pi} \int_0^{2\pi} \log |f(re^{i\theta})| \, d\theta$$

Applying Jensen's formula to (1), we get

$$\int_0^r \frac{n(t)}{t} dt = \frac{1}{2\pi} \int_0^{2\pi} \log |f(re^{i\theta})| \, d\theta - \log |f(0)|$$

$$\le \frac{1}{2\pi} \int_0^{2\pi} \log M(r) \, d\theta - \log |f(0)|$$

$$< \frac{1}{2\pi} \cdot \log M(r) \cdot 2\pi = \log M(r)$$

or $\qquad \int_0^r \frac{n(t)}{t} dt < \log M(r)$ ...(2)

Since $n(t)$ is an increasing function of t, we again have

$$\int_0^{2r} \frac{n(t)}{t} \geq \int_r^{2r} \frac{n(t)}{t} dt$$

$$\geq \int_r^{2r} \frac{n(r)}{t} dt = n(r) \log \frac{2r}{r}$$

i.e., $\qquad \int_0^{2r} \frac{n(t)}{t} dt \geq n(r) \log 2.$ ...(3)

Hence, by (2) and (3) we obtain

$$n(r) \log 2 \leq \int_0^{2r} \frac{n(t)}{t} dt < \log M(2r)$$

or $\qquad n(r) \log 2 < \log M(2r)$

or $\qquad n(r) < n(r) \log 2 < \log M(2r)$

or $\qquad n(r) < \log M(2r)$ ...(4)

But by the definition of order for given $\epsilon > 0$ there exists r_0 such that for all $r > r_0$,

$$\log M(2r) < (2r)^{\rho+\epsilon} = 2^{\rho+\epsilon} r^{\rho+\epsilon}.$$

Thus, by (4) we get

$$n(r) < Kr^{\rho+\epsilon}, K = \frac{2^{\rho+\epsilon}}{\log 2} > 0$$

for large values of r. Thus

$$n(r) = O(r^{\rho+\epsilon}) \text{ as } r \to \infty.$$

Theorem. *If $p(z)$ be a canonical product of finite order p and $q > 0$ and $\epsilon > 0$, then for all sufficiently large $|z|$*

$$|z - z_i| > |z_i|^{-q} \Rightarrow \log |p(z)| > -|z|^{\rho+\epsilon}$$

Suppose $|z| = r, |z_i| = r_i$. For $|\omega| \leq \frac{1}{2}$, we have

$$|E(\omega p)| \geq \exp(-2|\omega|^{p+1})$$

$$\geq \exp(-2|\omega|^\lambda) \text{ if } \lambda \leq p + 1$$

$\Rightarrow \qquad \log |E(\omega, p)| \geq -2|\omega|^\lambda$

when $\qquad |\omega| \leq \frac{1}{2}$ and $\lambda \leq p + 1$ ...(1)

Also, it can easily be seen that for a sufficiently large $A > 0$ and for all w satisfying $|\omega| \geq \frac{1}{2}$, we have

$$\sum_{k=1}^{p} \frac{|\omega|^k}{k} \leq A|\omega|^p.$$

Further, if $p \leq \lambda \leq p + 1$, then $|2\omega|^p \leq |2\omega|^\lambda$ and consequently

$$|\omega|^p \leq 2^{\lambda-p}|\omega| \leq 2|\omega|^\lambda.$$

Hence

$$\log\left|\exp\left(\sum_{k=1}^{p} \frac{\omega^k}{k}\right)\right|$$

$$= \sum_{k=1}^{p} \frac{|\omega|^k}{k} \leq 2A|\omega|^\lambda \qquad \qquad ...(2)$$

Provided $p \leq \lambda \leq p + 1$ and $|\omega| \geq \frac{1}{2}$.

Now consider a fixed z with $|z| = r > 1$. Then we shall estimate separately the factors by

$$P(z) = \prod_{i=1}^{\infty} E\left(\frac{z}{z_i}, h\right)$$

for which $\left|\frac{z}{z_i}\right| > \frac{1}{2}$, i.e., $r_i < 2r$ and those for which $\left|\frac{z}{z_i}\right| \leq \frac{1}{2}$, i.e., $r_i \geq 2r$, h being genus of $P(z)$.

Thus, we may write

$$|P(z)| = \prod_{r_i < 2r} \left|E\left(\frac{z}{z_i}, h\right)\right| \prod_{r_i \geq 2r} \left|E\left(\frac{z}{z_i}\right)^h\right| \qquad \qquad ...(3)$$

We now estimate $\log|P(z)|$ in (z) by using (2) to write the logarithm of each factor corresponding to $r_i < 2r$ as

$$\log\left|E\left(\frac{z}{z_i}, h\right)\right| = \log\left|\left(1 - \frac{z}{z_i}\right)\exp\left(\sum_{k=1}^{h} \frac{1}{k}\left(\frac{z}{z_i}\right)^k\right)\right|$$

$$= \log\left|1 - \frac{z}{z_i}\right| + \log\left|\exp\sum_{k=1}^{h} \frac{1}{k}\left(\frac{z}{z_i}\right)^k\right|$$

$$\geq \log\left|1 - \frac{z}{z_i}\right| - 2A\left|\frac{z}{z_i}\right|^\lambda \qquad \qquad ...(4)$$

provided $h \leq \lambda \leq h + 1$.

Again by applying (1) to the factor in (3) for which $r_i \geq 2r$, we conclude for each such factor that

$$\log\left|E\left(\frac{z}{z_i}, h\right)\right| \geq -2\left|\frac{z}{z_i}\right|^\lambda \qquad \qquad ...(5)$$

Provided $\lambda \leq h + 1$. Further, the order P of $P(z)$ is also the exponent of convergence of the sequence $\{z_i\}$ if $p < h + 1$, let λ satisfy $p < \lambda < h + 1$ and $p = h + 1$, let $\lambda = h + 1$.

Thus in either case, by the definition of convergence exponent, we get

$$\sum_{i=1}^{\infty} |z_i|^{-\lambda} < \infty \text{ with } h \leq \lambda \leq h + 1$$

Let $\displaystyle\sum_{i=1}^{\infty} |z_i|^{-\lambda} = B$, where B is a finite constant.

Now, using (4) and (5), (3) yields

$$\log |P(z)| \geq \sum_{r_i < 2r} \log\left|1 - \frac{z}{z_i}\right| - 2A |z|^{\lambda} \sum_{r_i < 2r} \frac{1}{|z_i|^{\lambda}}$$

$$-2 |z|^{\lambda} \sum_{r_i \geq 2r} \frac{1}{|z_i|^{\lambda}}$$

$$\geq \sum_{r_i < r} \log\left|1 - \frac{z}{r_i}\right| - 2(A + 1) |z|^{\lambda} \sum_{i=1}^{\infty} \frac{1}{|z_i|^{\lambda}}$$

$$= \sum_{r_i < 2r} \log\left|1 - \frac{z}{z_i}\right| - 2(A + 1) B |z|^{\lambda}$$

Thus, we get

$$\log |P(z)| \geq \sum_{r_i < 2r} \log\left|1 - \frac{z}{z_i}\right| - D |D|^{\lambda} \qquad \text{...(6)}$$

where $$D = 2(A + 1) B.$$

Again, since by our assumption $|z| \geq 1$, we see that (6) must hold for every $\lambda > p$. Further, by our hypothesis

$$\left|\frac{z}{z_i} - 1\right| > |z_i|^{-q-1} \text{ so that}$$

$$=$$

$$\sum_{r_i < 2r} \log\left|1 - \frac{z}{z_i}\right| > \sum_{r_i < 2r} \log |z_i|^{-q-1}$$

$$= \sum_{r_i < 2r} \log r_i^{-q-1} \qquad [\because |z_i| = r_i]$$

$$\geq -(q + 1) \sum_{r_i < 2r} \log (2r) \qquad [\because r_i < 2r]$$

Thus $$\sum_{r_i < 2r} \log\left|1 - \frac{z}{z_i}\right| > -(q + 1)n (2r) \log (2r) \qquad \text{...(7)}$$

where n (2r) has its usual meaning.

We know that

$$n(2r) \geq (2r)^{\rho + \epsilon / 2} \qquad \text{...(8)}$$

for all sufficiently large r.

Using (7) and (8), (6) may be written as

$$\log |\rho(z)| \geq -(q+1)(2r)^{\rho+\epsilon/2} \log (2r) - Dr^\lambda \qquad ...(9)$$

We now suppose $\lambda < \rho + \epsilon$. This is always possible for any prescribed ϵ. Then since r is large, we have

$$-(q+1)(2r)^{\rho+\epsilon/2} \log (2r) \geq -\frac{1}{2} r^{\rho+\epsilon}$$

and

$$-Dr^\lambda \geq -\frac{1}{2} r^{\rho+\epsilon}$$

Substituting these in (9), we get

$$\log |P(z)| \geq -r^{\rho+\epsilon}.$$

Hadmard Factorization Theorem. *If $f(z)$ be an entire function of finite order ρ, then $f(z) = z^m e^{g(z)} P(z)$ where m is the order of zeros of $f(z)$ at $z = 0$, g is a polynomial of degree not exceeding ρ and $p(z)$ is the canonical product associated with the sequence of non-zero of $f(z)$.*   *(Meerut 2002, 2003; Rohilkhand 2003)*

The same proposition has been proved in Weierstrass factorization theorem for entire function $f(z)$ and integral function $g(z)$ (§14.2.2). Since the division of $f(z)$ by cz^m does not affect the hypothesis or conclusion of the theorem, we therefore consider

$$f(z) = e^{g(z)} P(z) \text{ so that } e^{g(z)} = \frac{f(z)}{P(z)}$$

$\therefore$

$$|e^{\{g(z)\}}| = \left| \frac{f(z)}{P(z)} \right|$$

i.e.,

$$e^{\text{Re}\{g(z)\}} = \left| \frac{f(z)}{P(z)} \right|$$

Taking logarithm,

$$\text{Re}\{g(z)\} = \log |f(z)| - \log |P(z)|$$

By the definition of order, we have

$$|f(z)| \leq e^{r^{\rho+\epsilon}} \text{ for sufficiently large } |z| = r \text{ and all } \epsilon > 0, \text{ so that}$$

$$\log |f(z)| \leq r^{\rho+\epsilon}$$

If σ is the convergence exponent of non-zero, of $f(z)$, then

$$\sigma \leq \rho. \qquad \text{[by theorem 14.10.2]}$$

Also σ being the order of the canonical product $P(z)$, it follows that

$$\log |P(z)| > -r^{\sigma+\epsilon} \text{ for large } |z| = r$$

$\Rightarrow$

$$\log |f(z)| - \log |\rho(z)| \leq 2r^{\rho+\epsilon} \text{ and then (1) yields}$$

$$\text{Re}\{g(z)\} \leq 2r^{\rho+\epsilon},$$

where r being large, we conclude that $g(z)$ is a polynomial of degree not exceeding ρ.

EXRCISE

1. Show that a convex function is continuous.

2. If $f(z)$ an entire function, show that $f'(z)$ and $f(z)$ have the same order.

3. Show that

$$\pi z \left(1 + \frac{z}{1}\right)\left(1 + \frac{z}{2}\right)\left(1 + \frac{z}{3}\right)\left(1 - \frac{z}{1}\right)$$

$$\left(1 + \frac{z}{4}\right)\left(1 + \frac{z}{5}\right)\left(1 + \frac{z}{6}\right)\left(1 - \frac{z}{2}\right)\cdots$$

$$= e^{z \log 3} \sin \pi z.$$

4. Find the order of the following Canonical products

(a) $\displaystyle\prod_{n=1}^{\infty} (1 - 2^{-n} z)$ (b) $\displaystyle\prod_{n=1}^{\infty} \left(1 - \frac{z}{n^5 (\log n)^2}\right)$.

[**Ans.** (a) 0, (b) 1/5]

5. Show that the Canonical products $\sin hz$ and $\cos hz$ are given by

(i) $\displaystyle \sin nhz = \prod_{n=1}^{\infty} \left[1 + \frac{z^2}{\pi^2 n^2}\right]$ (ii) $\displaystyle \cos h\, z = \prod_{n=1}^{\infty} \left[1 + \frac{4z^2}{(2n-1)^2 \pi^2}\right]$

6. If g is a polynomial of degrees δ, show that the order of $e^{g(z)}$ is δ.

OBJECTIVE QUESTIONS

For each of the following questions, four alternatives are given for the answer. Only one of them is correct. Choose the correct alternative.

1. If a function $f(z)$ is analytic in the entire complex plane then $f(z)$ is called
   (a) integral function   (b) meromorphic function
   (c) analytic continuation   (d) None of these.

2. Each of Weierstrass's primary factor has
   (a) multiple zero at $z = 1$ (b) simple zero at $z = 1$
   (c) simple zero at $z = 0$ (d) no zero.

3. Let the function $f(z)$ be analytic in $r_1 \leq |z| \leq r_3$ and let $r_1 < r_2 < r_3$. If M_1, M_2, M_3 be the maximum values of $|f(z)|$ on the circles $|z| = r_i$ $(i = 1, 2, 3)$ then
   (a) $M(r)$ is a function of r
   (b) $M(r)$ is a simple function of $\log r$
   (c) $M(r)$ is a convex function of r
   (d) $M(r)$ is a convex function of $\log r$.

4. If $I_2(r)$ be the mean value of $|f(z)|^2$ then $\log I_2(r)$ is
   (a) a convex function of $\log r$ (b) a convex function of r^2
   (c) a convex function of r (d) not a convex function.

ANSWERS

1. (a)   **2.** (b)   **3.** (d)   **4.** (a)

Index